Contents in Brief

Preparation for Focal Points and Connections
See front cover folder for key.

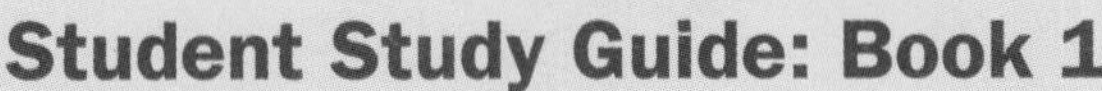

Student Study Guide: Book 1

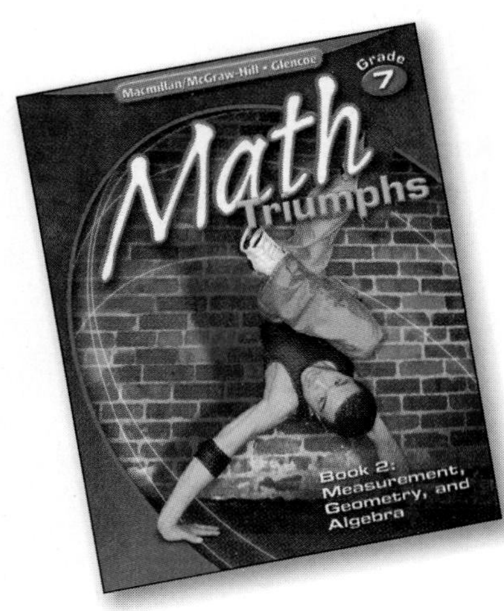

Student Study Guide: Book 2

Student Study Guide: Book 3

Authors and Consultants

AUTHORS

Frances Basich Whitney
Project Director, Mathematics K–12
Santa Cruz County Office of Education
Capitola, California

Kathleen M. Brown
Math Curriculum Staff Developer
Washington Middle School
Long Beach, California

Dixie Dawson
Math Curriculum Leader
Long Beach Unified
Long Beach, California

Philip Gonsalves
Mathematics Coordinator
Alameda County Office of Education
Hayward, California

Robyn Silbey
Math Specialist
Montgomery County Public Schools
Gaithersburg, Maryland

Kathy Vielhaber
Mathematics Consultant
St. Louis, Missouri

CONTRIBUTING AUTHORS

Viken Hovsepian
Professor of Mathematics
Rio Hondo College
Whittier, California

FOLDABLES Study Organizer

Dinah Zike
Educational Consultant,
Dinah-Might Activities, Inc.
San Antonio, Texas

CONSULTANTS

Assessment

Donna M. Kopenski, Ed.D.
Math Coordinator K–5
City Heights Educational Collaborative
San Diego, California

Instructional Planning and Support

Beatrice Luchin
Mathematics Consultant
League City, Texas

ELL Support and Vocabulary

ReLeah Cossett Lent
Author/Educational Consultant
Alford, Florida

Reviewers

Each person below reviewed at least two chapters of the Student Study Guide, providing feedback and suggestions for improving the effectiveness of the mathematics instruction.

Patricia Allanson
Mathematics Teacher
Deltona Middle School
Deltona, Florida

Debra Allred
Sixth Grade Math Teacher
Wiley Middle School
Leander, Texas

April Chauvette
Secondary Mathematics Facilitator
Leander Independent School District
Leander, Texas

Amy L. Chazarreta
Math Teacher
Wayside Middle School
Fort Worth, Texas

Jeff Denney
Seventh Grade Math Teacher, Mathematics Department Chair
Oak Mountain Middle School
Birmingham, Alabama

Franco A. DiPasqua
Director of K-12 Mathematics
West Seneca Central
West Seneca, New York

David E. Ewing
Teacher
Bellview Middle School
Pensacola, Florida

Mark J. Forzley
Eighth Grade Math Teacher
Westmont Junior High School
Westmont, Illinois

Virginia Granstrand Harrell
Education Consultant
Tampa, Florida

Russ Lush
Sixth Grade Math Teacher/Math Dept. Chair
New Augusta - North
Indianapolis, Indiana

Joyce B. McClain
Middle School Math Consultant
Hillsborough County Schools
Tampa, Florida

Suzanne D. Obuchowski
Math Teacher
Proctor School
Topsfield, Massachusetts

Karen L. Reed
Sixth Pre-AP Math
Keller ISD
Keller, Texas

Deborah Todd
Sixth Grade Math Teacher
Francis Bradley Middle School
Huntersville, North Carolina

Susan S. Wesson
Teacher (retired)
Pilot Butte Middle School
Bend, Oregon

Mathematics Teacher Handbook

Table of Contents

Welcome to Math Connects

Concepts • Skills • Problem Solving

The only true vertically aligned PreK–12 Mathematics Curriculum

Math Connects offers three dimensions of vertical alignment.

1 Content Design

Vertical content alignment is a process that ensures you and your students experience an articulated, coherent sequence of content from grade level to grade level. This provides you with the assurance that content is introduced, reinforced, and assessed at appropriate times in the series, eliminating gaps and unnecessary duplication. You are able to target your instruction to student needs because you are not teaching content intended to be covered later or that students have previously mastered.

2 Instructional Design

Our strong vertical alignment in instructional approach from PreKindergarten through Algebra 2 provides a smooth transition for students from elementary to middle school to high school. Our common vocabulary, technology, manipulatives, lesson planning, and Data-Driven Decision Making reduce the confusion students often encounter when transitioning between grade levels without this built-in articulation.

3 Visual Design

The student pages of ***Math Connects*** have a consistent visual design from grade to grade. This aids students' transition from elementary school to middle school and from middle school to Algebra 1. Students are more likely to succeed when they are already familiar with how to navigate student pages.

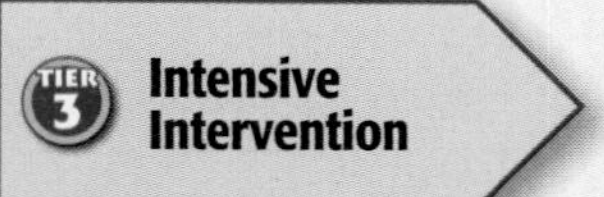

PreK-2 | 3–5

Daily Intervention

Strategic Intervention

5 Keys to Success

❶ Backmapping

According to College Board research, about 80% of students who successfully complete Algebra 1 and Geometry by 10th grade attend and succeed in college. (Changing the Odds: Factors Increasing Access to College, 1990) ***Math Connects*** was conceived and developed by backmapping with the final result in mind–student success in Algebra 1 and beyond.

❷ Balanced, In-Depth Content

Math Connects was developed to specifically target the skills and topics that give students the most difficulty, such as Problem Solving, in each grade span.

Grades K–2	Grades 3–5
1. Problem Solving 2. Money 3. Time 4. Measurement 5. Fractions 6. Computation	1. Problem Solving 2. Fractions 3. Measurement 4. Decimals 5. Time 6. Algebra
Grades 6–8	**Grades 9–12**
1. Fractions 2. Problem Solving 3. Measurement 4. Algebra 5. Computation	1. Problem Solving 2. Fractions 3. Algebra 4. Geometry 5. Computation 6. Probability

– *K–12 Math Market Analysis Survey,* Open Book Publishing, 2006

❸ Ongoing Assessment

Math Connects includes diagnostic, formative, and summative assessment; data-driven instruction; intervention options; and performance tracking, as well as remediation, acceleration, and enrichment tools throughout the program.

❹ Intervention and Differentiated Instruction

A three-tiered Response To Intervention (RTI) is provided.

TIER 1 **Daily Intervention** Reteach masters and Alternative Strategy suggestions address concepts from a different modality or learning style.

TIER 2 **Strategic Intervention** Teachers can use the myriad of intervention tips and ancillary materials, such as the Strategic Intervention Guide (1–5) and Study Guide and Intervention (6–8).

TIER 3 **Intensive Intervention** For students who are two or more years below grade level, ***Math Triumphs*** provides step-by-step instruction, vocabulary support, and data-driven decision making to help students succeed.

❺ Professional Development

Math Connects includes many opportunities for teacher professional development. Additional learning opportunities in various formats–video, online, and on-site instruction–are fully aligned and articulated from Kindergarten through Algebra 2.

6–8 | Pre-Algebra and Algebra 1 | Geometry and Algebra 2

Implementing Intensive Intervention

Data-Driven Intensive Intervention

Ongoing assessment aids the teacher in student placement, progress monitoring, and exit.

Instructional Design	Classroom Implementation
1 Diagnose and Prescribe • Course Placement Test • Online Readiness Quiz • Chapter Preview • Chapter Pretest • Book Pretest	Teacher prepares individual or group intervention plan(s).
2 Teach and Practice • Student Study Guide • Teacher Edition Strategies • Vocabulary Cards • Manipulatives	Teacher modifies instruction based on results of formative assessments.
3 Advance and Exit • Assessment Masters • Chapter Test • Book Test	Test success indicates that a student can progress to another *Math Triumphs* chapter (if needed) or exit the intervention program.

Alignment to NCTM Focal Points

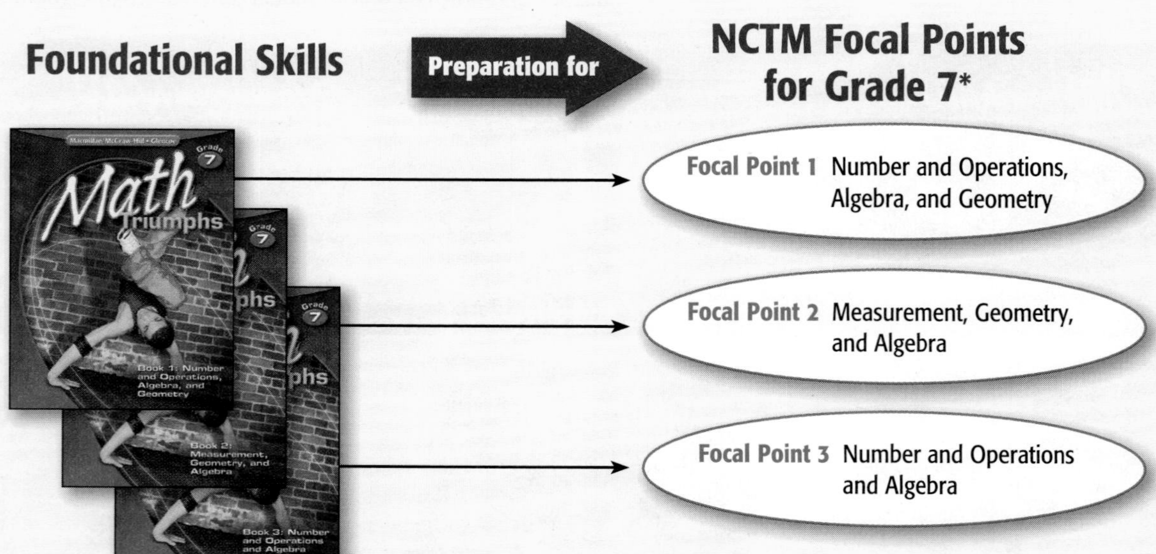

*See front cover folder for key and complete NCTM Focal Points.

Program Organization

Provide Personalized Instruction

Consumable volumes and minimal preparation requirements allow for flexibility and personalized instruction in any setting.

- After school
- Before school
- Tutoring
- Summer school
- Intersession
- Pull-out/Resource room

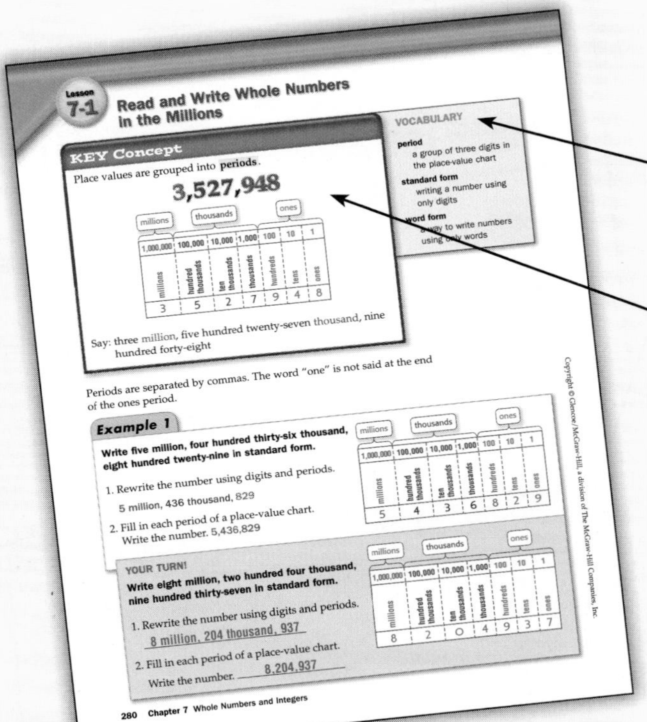

Vocabulary

Vocabulary helps students identify terms presented in the lesson.

Key Concepts

Key Concepts introduce and break mathematics into conceptual steps. Multiple representations demonstrate the skills being presented.

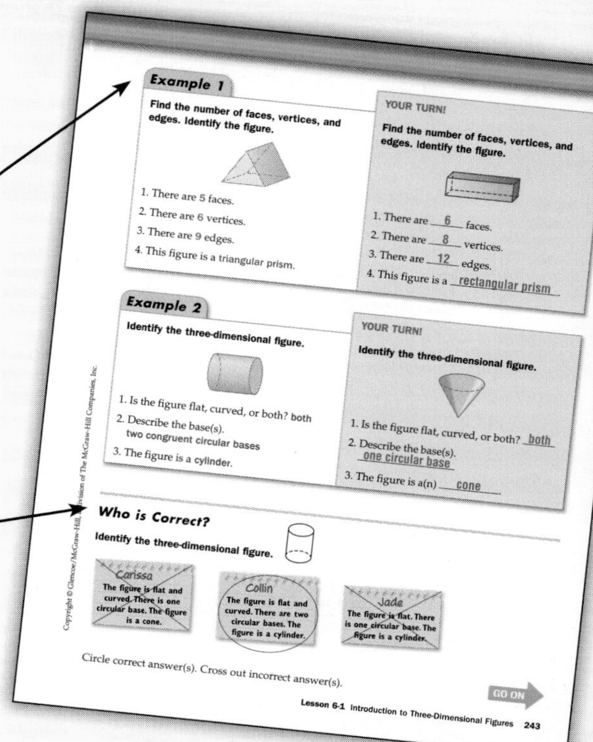

Examples

Fully worked-out **Examples** enable students and parents to see how to solve problems step by step. **Your Turn!** gives students an opportunity to practice skills immediately.

Who is Correct?

Students "grade" sample answers. This formative assessment opportunity generates meaningful classroom discussion and highlights possible misconceptions.

Guided Practice

Guided Practice exercises provide computational practice. They can be used as formative assessment to monitor student progress and guide your instruction.

Step-by-Step Practice guides students to complete a computational problem through a series of conceptual steps. Instructional aids are provided to students in the exercises that follow.

Step-by-Step Problem-Solving Practice walks the student through a four-step problem-solving strategy (Understand, Plan, Solve, Check) that is relevant to the word problem. Aids help the student break down and visualize what the problem is asking and how to solve it.

A **Reflect** question requires the student to think and write about the process of completing a problem.

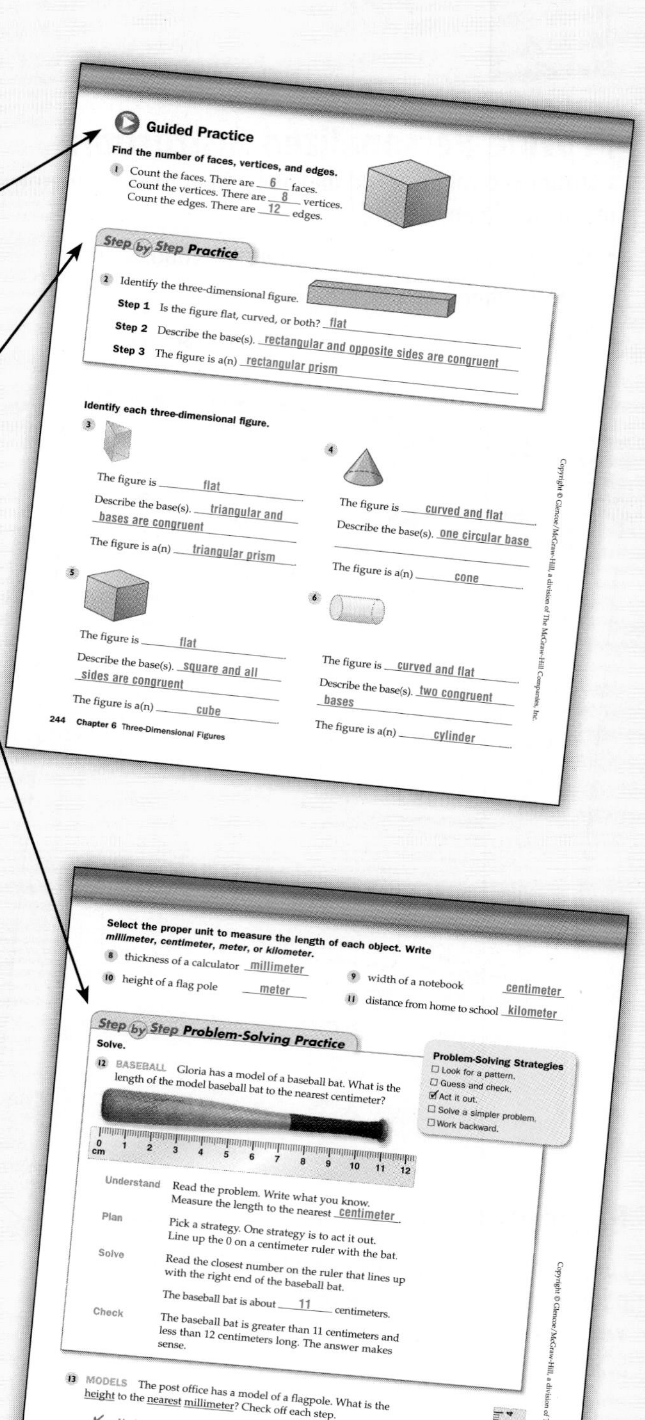

Guided Practice

Find the number of faces, vertices, and edges.

1 Count the faces. There are 6 faces.
Count the vertices. There are 8 vertices.
Count the edges. There are 12 edges.

Step by Step Practice

2 Identify the three-dimensional figure.
Step 1 Is the figure flat, curved, or both? flat
Step 2 Describe the base(s). rectangular and opposite sides are congruent
Step 3 The figure is a(n) rectangular prism

Identify each three-dimensional figure.

3 The figure is flat
Describe the base(s). triangular and bases are congruent
The figure is a(n) triangular prism

4 The figure is curved and flat
Describe the base(s). one circular base
The figure is a(n) cone

5 The figure is flat
Describe the base(s). square and all sides are congruent
The figure is a(n) cube

6 The figure is curved and flat
Describe the base(s). two congruent bases
The figure is a(n) cylinder

244 Chapter 6 Three-Dimensional Figures

Copyright © Glencoe/McGraw-Hill, a division of The McGraw-Hill Companies, Inc.

Select the proper unit to measure the length of each object. Write *millimeter, centimeter, meter,* or *kilometer*.

8 thickness of a calculator millimeter
9 width of a notebook centimeter
10 height of a flag pole meter
11 distance from home to school kilometer

Step by Step Problem-Solving Practice

Solve.

12 BASEBALL Gloria has a model of a baseball bat. What is the length of the model baseball bat to the nearest centimeter?

Problem-Solving Strategies
☐ Look for a pattern.
☐ Guess and check.
☑ Act it out.
☐ Solve a simpler problem.
☐ Work backward.

Understand Read the problem. Write what you know. Measure the length to the nearest centimeter

Plan Pick a strategy. One strategy is to act it out. Line up the 0 on a centimeter ruler with the bat.

Solve Read the closest number on the ruler that lines up with the right end of the baseball bat.
The baseball bat is about 11 centimeters.

Check The baseball bat is greater than 11 centimeters and less than 12 centimeters long. The answer makes sense.

13 MODELS The post office has a model of a flagpole. What is the height to the nearest millimeter? Check off each step.
✔ Understand: I underlined the key words.
✔ Plan: To solve the problem, I will act it out
✔ Solve: The answer is 32 millimeters
✔ Check: I checked my answer by estimating the length in millimeters

146 Chapter 4 Measurement

Copyright © Glencoe/McGraw-Hill, a division of The McGraw-Hill Companies, Inc.

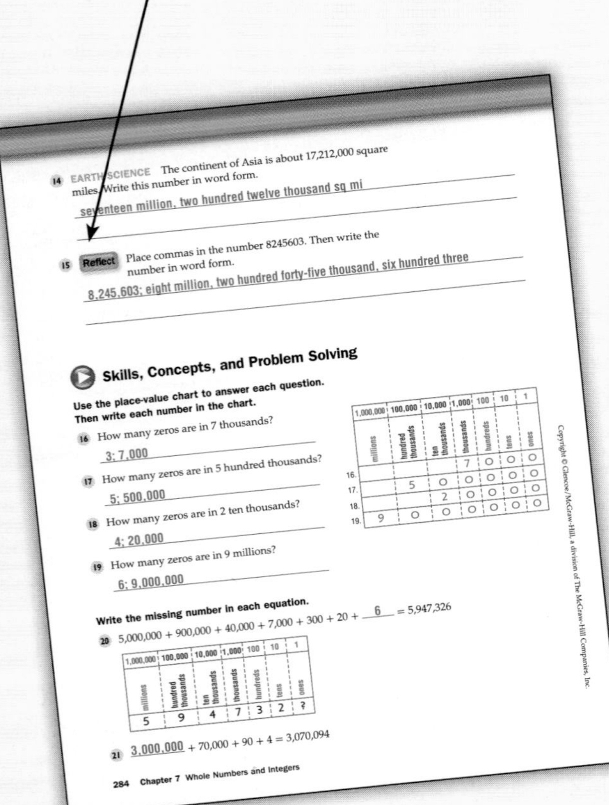

14 EARTH SCIENCE The continent of Asia is about 17,212,000 square miles. Write this number in word form.
seventeen million, two hundred twelve thousand sq mi

15 Reflect Place commas in the number 8245603. Then write the number in word form.
8,245,603; eight million, two hundred forty-five thousand, six hundred three

Skills, Concepts, and Problem Solving

Use the place-value chart to answer each question. Then write each number in the chart.

16 How many zeros are in 7 thousands?
3; 7,000

17 How many zeros are in 5 hundred thousands?
5; 500,000

18 How many zeros are in 2 ten thousands?
4; 20,000

19 How many zeros are in 9 millions?
6; 9,000,000

	1,000,000	100,000	10,000	1,000	100	10	1
	millions	hundred thousands	ten thousands	thousands	hundreds	tens	ones
16.				7	0	0	0
17.		5	0	0	0	0	0
18.			2	0	0	0	0
19.	9	0	0	0	0	0	0

Write the missing number in each equation.

20 5,000,000 + 900,000 + 40,000 + 7,000 + 300 + 20 + 6 = 5,947,326

1,000,000	100,000	10,000	1,000	100	10	1
millions	hundred thousands	ten thousands	thousands	hundreds	tens	ones
5	9	4	7	3	2	?

21 3,000,000 + 70,000 + 90 + 4 = 3,070,094

284 Chapter 7 Whole Numbers and Integers

Copyright © Glencoe/McGraw-Hill, a division of The McGraw-Hill Companies, Inc.

Balance

McGraw-Hill's ***Math Triumphs*** is designed to provide students a balanced approach to mathematics learning by offering them the opportunity to:

- investigate concepts and build their conceptual understanding;
- review, learn, and practice basic computational and procedural skills; and
- apply mathematics to problem solving in real-world situations.

Independent Practice

Skill, Concepts, and Problem Solving provide homework opportunities and independent practice.

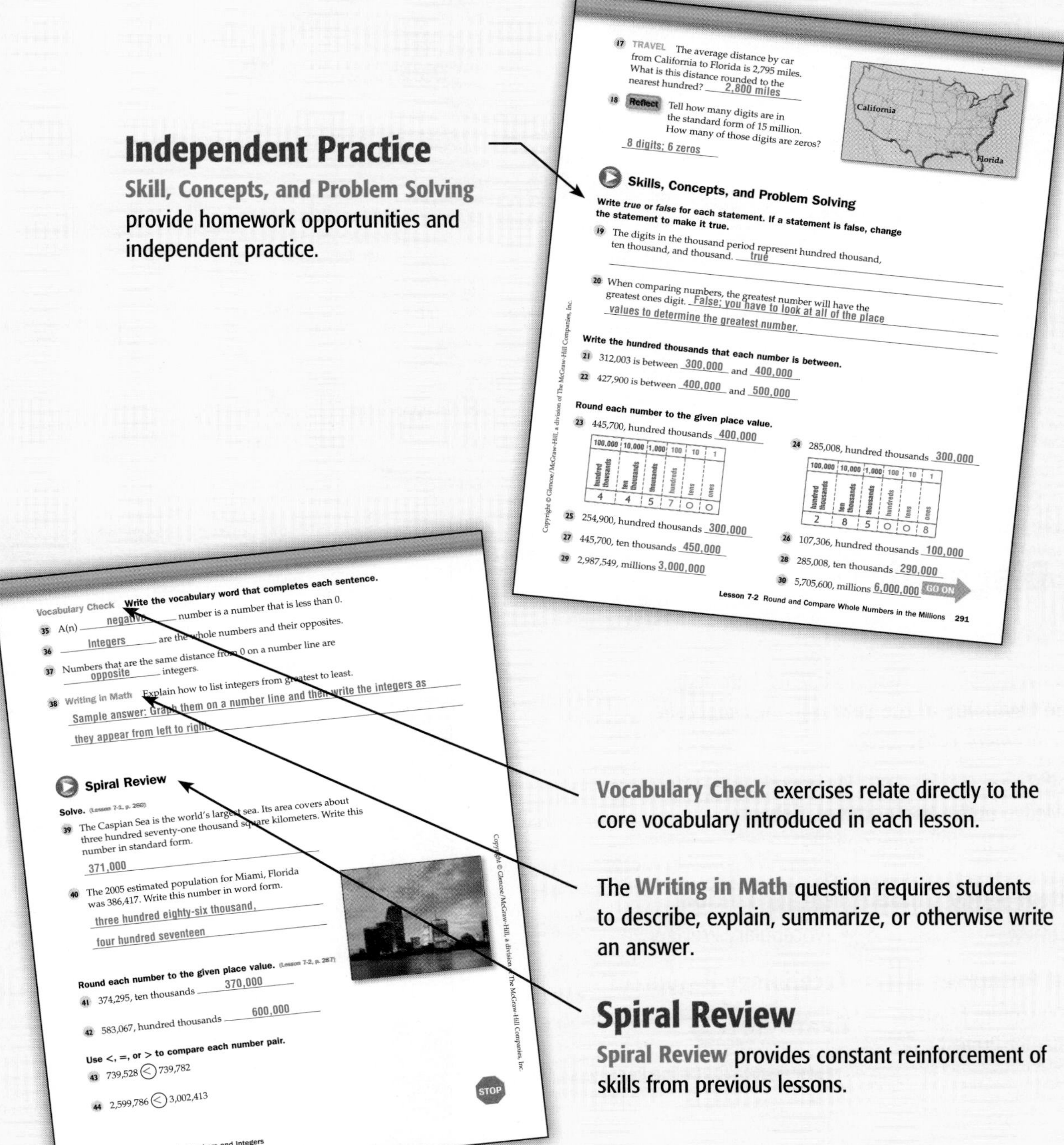

17 TRAVEL The average distance by car from California to Florida is 2,795 miles. What is this distance rounded to the nearest hundred? 2,800 miles

18 Reflect Tell how many digits are in the standard form of 15 million. How many of those digits are zeros? 8 digits; 6 zeros

Skills, Concepts, and Problem Solving

Write *true* or *false* for each statement. If a statement is false, change the statement to make it true.

19 The digits in the thousand period represent hundred thousand, ten thousand, and thousand. true

20 When comparing numbers, the greatest number will have the greatest ones digit. False; you have to look at all of the place values to determine the greatest number.

Write the hundred thousands that each number is between.

21 312,003 is between 300,000 and 400,000

22 427,900 is between 400,000 and 500,000

Round each number to the given place value.

23 445,700, hundred thousands 400,000

100,000	10,000	1,000	100	10	1
hundred thousands	ten thousands	thousands	hundreds	tens	ones
4	4	5	7	0	0

24 285,008, hundred thousands 300,000

100,000	10,000	1,000	100	10	1
hundred thousands	ten thousands	thousands	hundreds	tens	ones
2	8	5	0	0	8

25 254,900, hundred thousands 300,000

26 107,306, hundred thousands 100,000

27 445,700, ten thousands 450,000

28 285,008, ten thousands 290,000

29 2,987,549, millions 3,000,000

30 5,705,600, millions 6,000,000

GO ON

Copyright © Glencoe/McGraw-Hill, a division of The McGraw-Hill Companies, Inc.

Lesson 7-2 Round and Compare Whole Numbers in the Millions 291

Vocabulary Check Write the vocabulary word that completes each sentence.

35 A(n) negative number is a number that is less than 0.

36 Integers are the whole numbers and their opposites.

37 Numbers that are the same distance from 0 on a number line are opposite integers.

38 Writing in Math Explain how to list integers from greatest to least. Sample answer: Graph them on a number line and then write the integers as they appear from left to right.

Spiral Review

Solve. (Lesson 7-1, p. 280)

39 The Caspian Sea is the world's largest sea. Its area covers about three hundred seventy-one thousand square kilometers. Write this number in standard form. 371,000

40 The 2005 estimated population for Miami, Florida was 386,417. Write this number in word form. three hundred eighty-six thousand, four hundred seventeen

Round each number to the given place value. (Lesson 7-2, p. 287)

41 374,295, ten thousands 370,000

42 583,067, hundred thousands 600,000

Use <, =, or > to compare each number pair.

43 739,528 (<) 739,782

44 2,599,786 (<) 3,002,413

STOP

Copyright © Glencoe/McGraw-Hill, a division of The McGraw-Hill Companies, Inc.

300 Chapter 7 Whole Numbers and Integers

Vocabulary Check exercises relate directly to the core vocabulary introduced in each lesson.

The **Writing in Math** question requires students to describe, explain, summarize, or otherwise write an answer.

Spiral Review

Spiral Review provides constant reinforcement of skills from previous lessons.

Comprehensive Assessment System

Data-Driven Decision Making

Math Triumphs offers frequent and meaningful assessment of student progress within the curriculum structure and teacher support materials.

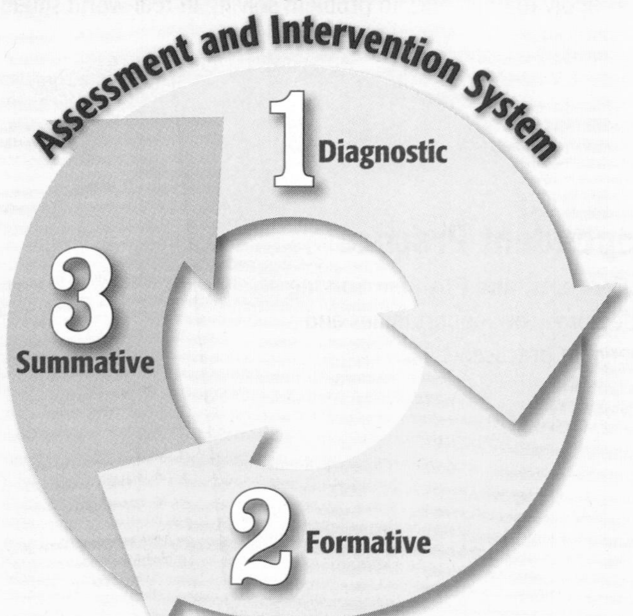

1 Diagnostic

Initial Assessment Assess students' knowledge **at the beginning of the year** with the *Diagnostic and Placement Tests.*

Entry–Level Assessment Assess students' prior knowledge **at the beginning of a chapter** with one of the following options.

Student Study Guide

- Preview

Teacher Edition

- Vocabulary Preview

Print Resources

- Assessment Masters, Chapter Pretest

Technology Resources

ExamView Assessment Suite

Online Readiness Quiz

Advance Tracker

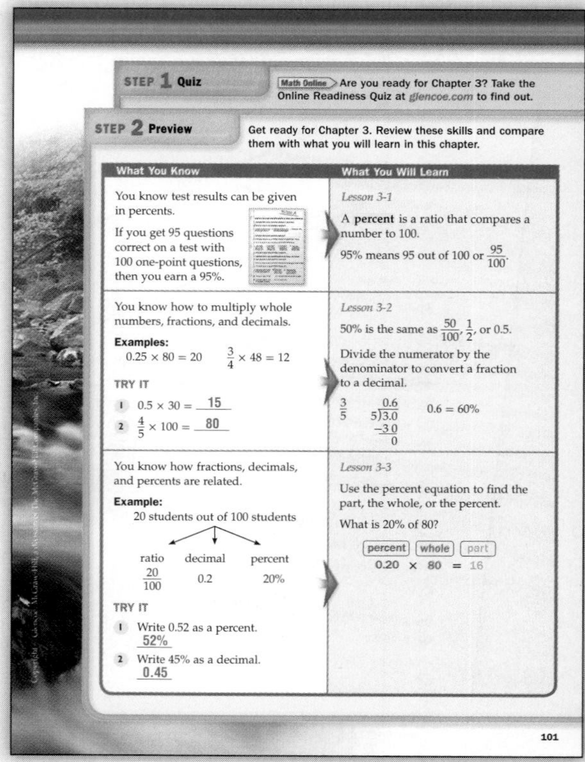

STEP 1 Quiz

Math Online Are you ready for Chapter 3? Take the Online Readiness Quiz at glencoe.com to find out.

STEP 2 Preview

Get ready for Chapter 3. Review these skills and compare them with what you will learn in this chapter.

What You Know	What You Will Learn
You know test results can be given in percents. If you get 95 questions correct on a test with 100 one-point questions, then you earn a 95%.	*Lesson 3-1* A **percent** is a ratio that compares a number to 100. 95% means 95 out of 100 or $\frac{95}{100}$.
You know how to multiply whole numbers, fractions, and decimals. **Examples:** $0.25 \times 80 = 20$ $\frac{3}{4} \times 48 = 12$ **TRY IT** 1 $0.5 \times 30 = \underline{15}$ 2 $\frac{4}{5} \times 100 = \underline{80}$	*Lesson 3-2* 50% is the same as $\frac{50}{100}$, $\frac{1}{2}$, or 0.5. Divide the numerator by the denominator to convert a fraction to a decimal. $\frac{3}{5}$ $5\overline{)3.0}$ = 0.6; -3.0; 0 $0.6 = 60\%$
You know how fractions, decimals, and percents are related. **Example:** 20 students out of 100 students ratio $\frac{20}{100}$ decimal 0.2 percent 20% **TRY IT** 1 Write 0.52 as a percent. <u>52%</u> 2 Write 45% as a decimal. <u>0.45</u>	*Lesson 3-3* Use the percent equation to find the part, the whole, or the percent. What is 20% of 80? percent whole part $0.20 \times 80 = 16$

101

Formative

Progress Monitoring Determine if students are progressing adequately as you teach each lesson. Use the assessments to differentiate lesson instruction and practice.

Student Study Guide
- Progress Check
- Who is Correct?
- Study Guide
- Foldables®

Teacher Edition
- Intervention Strategy
- Are They Getting It?
- Ticket Out the Door
- See It, Do It, Say It, Write It
- Data-Driven Decision Making

Print Resources
- Assessment Masters
- Chapter Resource Masters

Technology Resources

Math Online My Math Zone

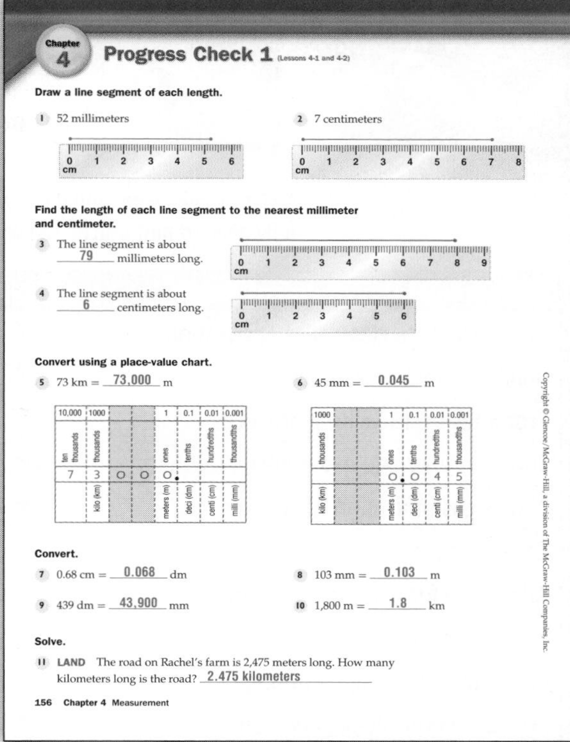

Chapter 4 **Progress Check 1** (Lessons 4-1 and 4-2)

Draw a line segment of each length.

1 52 millimeters

2 7 centimeters

Find the length of each line segment to the nearest millimeter and centimeter.

3 The line segment is about 79 millimeters long.

4 The line segment is about 6 centimeters long.

Convert using a place-value chart.

5 73 km = 73,000 m

10,000	1000			1	0.1	0.01	0.001
ten thousands	thousands			ones	tenths	hundredths	thousandths
7	3	0	0	0.			
	kilo (km)			meters (m)	deci (dm)	centi (cm)	milli (mm)

6 45 mm = 0.045 m

1000			1	0.1	0.01	0.001
thousands			ones	tenths	hundredths	thousandths
			0.	0	4	5
kilo (km)			meters (m)	deci (dm)	centi (cm)	milli (mm)

Convert.

7 0.68 cm = 0.068 dm

8 103 mm = 0.103 m

9 439 dm = 43,900 mm

10 1,800 m = 1.8 km

Solve.

11 LAND The road on Rachel's farm is 2,475 meters long. How many kilometers long is the road? 2.475 kilometers

156 Chapter 4 Measurement

Copyright © Glencoe/McGraw-Hill, a division of The McGraw-Hill Companies, Inc.

Summative

Summative Evaluation Assess student success in learning the concepts in each chapter.

Student Study Guide
- Chapter Test
- Test Practice
- Foldables®

Teacher Edition
- Data-Driven Decision Making

Print Resources
- Assessment Masters
- Chapter Resource Masters

Technology Resources

Math Online

Advance

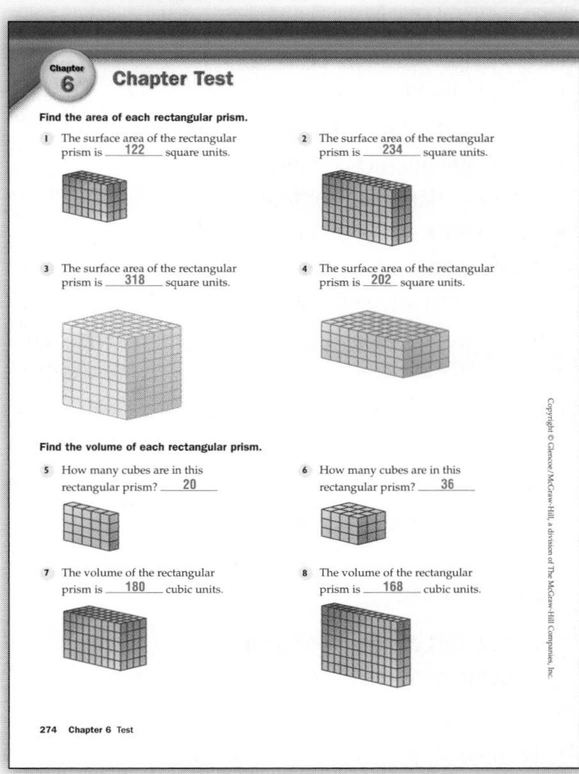

Chapter 6 **Chapter Test**

Find the area of each rectangular prism.

1 The surface area of the rectangular prism is 122 square units.

2 The surface area of the rectangular prism is 234 square units.

3 The surface area of the rectangular prism is 318 square units.

4 The surface area of the rectangular prism is 202 square units.

Find the volume of each rectangular prism.

5 How many cubes are in this rectangular prism? 20

6 How many cubes are in this rectangular prism? 36

7 The volume of the rectangular prism is 180 cubic units.

8 The volume of the rectangular prism is 168 cubic units.

274 Chapter 6 Test

Copyright © Glencoe/McGraw-Hill, a division of The McGraw-Hill Companies, Inc.

PreK-12 Data-Driven Professional Development

McGraw-Hill Professional Development (MHPD) provides a comprehensive plan for mathematics that is fully aligned and articulated with ***Math Connects PreK–8*** and the ***Glencoe Mathematics*** high school series.

Professional Development Needs	Online Courses	DVD Workshops	Video Library	Teach-Use-Succeed	Ready-Access Math
Has immediate classroom application	✔	✔	✔	✔	✔
Builds content knowledge	✔	✔			✔
Promotes best teaching practices		✔	✔		
Supports new and experienced teachers	✔	✔	✔	✔	✔
Allows customization of courses	✔	✔			✔
Can be self-paced	✔	✔		✔	✔
Adaptable for various timeframes	✔	✔	✔	✔	✔
Is grade-level specific			✔	✔	✔
Promotes a learning community	✔	✔			✔
Provides vertically-aligned content	✔	✔	✔		✔
Helps with RTI (Response to Intervention), Tiers 1–3	✔	✔	✔		✔

Use students' mathematics achievement data to help develop a targeted Professional Development Plan.

Accredited Online Courses
(available for purchase)

- Watch video clips of math classrooms.
- Complete interactive exercises.
- Develop electronic portfolios.
- Complete each 3- to 5-hour online module one segment at a time.
- Earn university credit (additional tuition).

DVD Workshops

- Watch video clips of classroom mathematics lessons and commentaries by leading educators.
- Complete lessons and activities.

MHPD Online

- Access this online Professional Development resource for K–12 educators.
- Link to relevant Web sites.
- Download grade-level student resources.

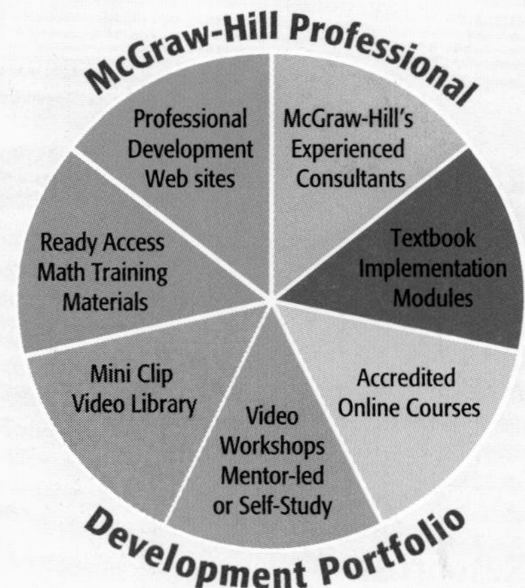

Video Library **Math Online**

- Access hundreds of K–12 video clips.
- See clips that illustrate mathematics content and instructional strategies.
- Watch demonstrations or commentaries.

Teach-Use-Succeed Textbook Implementation Modules

- Watch an experienced teacher demonstrate the *Math Connects* K–8 Student Editions, Teacher Editions, and program ancillaries–Online or DVD.

Ready-Access Math, Personalized Professional Development

- Access training materials for nearly 300 lessons.
- Create a customized sequence of professional development sessions.
- Deliver 45–60 minute after-school professional development sessions.

Contents

Chapter 1 Fractions

Preparation for Focal Points and Connections
See front cover folder for key.

Palm trees in the Florida Keys

Contents

Chapter 2 Ratios, Rates, and Proportional Relationships

Preparation for Focal Points and Connections
See front cover folder for key.

Atlanta, Georgia

Chapter 3 Percents

Preparation for Focal Points and Connections
See front cover folder for key.

Sedona, Arizona

Contents

Chapter 4 Measurement

Preparation for Focal Points and Connections
See front cover folder for key.

Waipio Valley, Hawaii

Chapter 5 Two-Dimensional Figures

Preparation for Focal Points and Connections
See front cover folder for key.

Chicago, Illinois

Contents

Chapter 6 Three-Dimensional Figures

Preparation for Focal Points and Connections
See front cover folder for key.

Bucks County, Pennsylvania

Whole Numbers and Integers

Preparation for Focal Points and Connections
See front cover folder for key.

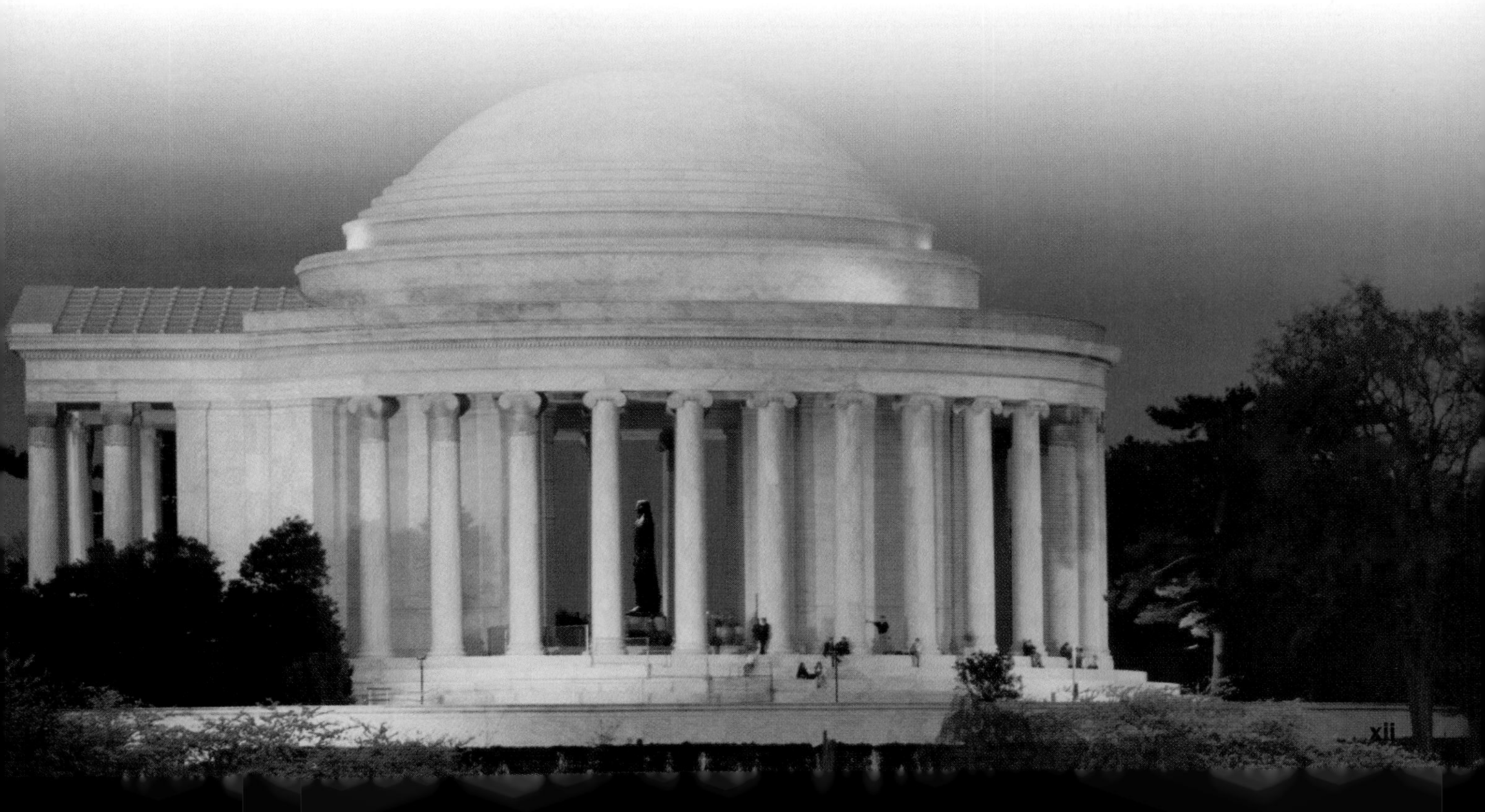

Jefferson Memorial, Washington D.C.

Contents

Chapter 8 Integer Operations

Preparation for Focal Points and Connections
See front cover folder for key.

Woodstock, Vermont

Variables and Expressions

Preparation for Focal Points and Connections
See front cover folder for key.

Saint Augustine, Florida

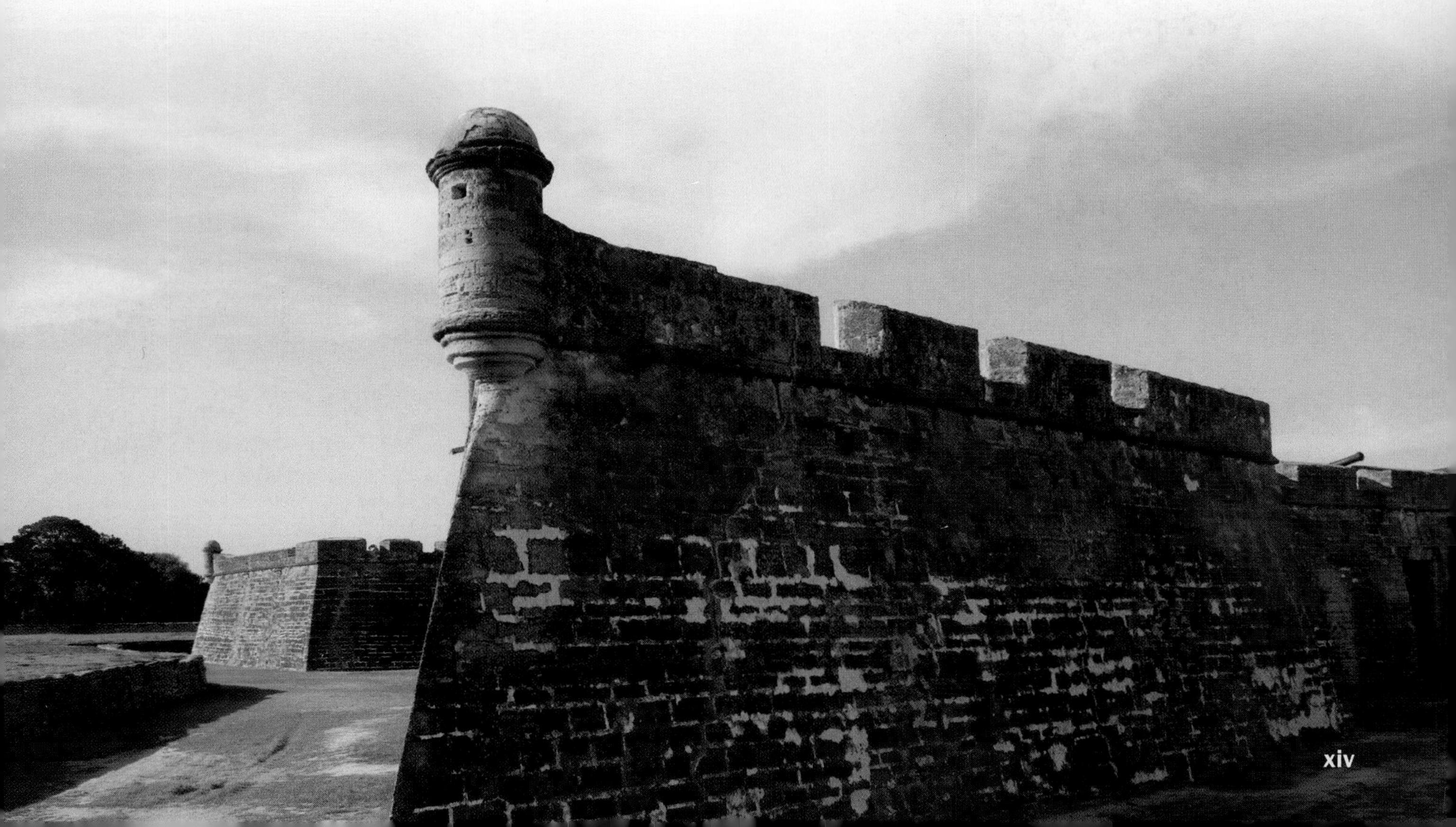

Contents

Chapter 10 Equations

Preparation for Focal Points and Connections
See front cover folder for key.

Grand Teton National Park, Wyoming

BOOK 1

Let's Get Started

Use the Scavenger Hunt below to learn where things are located in each chapter.

1. What is the title of Lesson 2-2? **Ratio Tables**
2. What is the Key Concept of Lesson 1-4? **Compare and Order Fractions**
3. On what page can you find the vocabulary term *circle graph* in Lesson 3-4? **page 125**
4. What are the vocabulary words for Lesson 1-3? **greatest common factor, simplest form**
5. How many Examples are presented in the Chapter 3 Study Guide? **9**
6. What strategy is used in the Step-by-Step Problem-Solving Practice box on page 121? **Solve a simpler problem.**
7. List the fractions that are mentioned in exercise #14 on page 33. $\frac{2}{3}$, $\frac{1}{6}$, **and** $\frac{5}{9}$
8. Describe the art that accompanies exercise #19 on page 107? **The art shows 100 units, where 35 units are shaded.**
9. On what pages will you find the Study Guide for Chapter 2? **pages 91–95**
10. In Chapter 1, find the logo and Internet address that tells you where you can take the Online Readiness Quiz. **It is found on page 3. The URL is glencoe.com.**

SCAVENGER HUNT

BOOK 2

Let's Get Started

Use the Scavenger Hunt below to learn where things are located in each chapter.

1. What is the title of Lesson 5-2? **Triangles**
2. What is the Key Concept of Lesson 4-4? **Unit Conversions: Customary Lengths**
3. On what page can you find the vocabulary term *customary system* in Lesson 4-3? **page 157**
4. What are the vocabulary words for Lesson 6-2? **face, net, surface area, square unit**
5. How many Examples are presented in the Chapter 4 Study Guide? **7**
6. What strategy is used in the Step-by-Step Problem-Solving Practice box on page 245? **Use a diagram.**
7. List the measurements that are mentioned in exercise #13 on page 154. **700 millimeters, and 6 meters**
8. Describe the art that accompanies exercise #6 on page 145? **There is a photo of a gold fish with a ruler beneath it.**
9. On what pages will you find the Test Practice for Chapter 6? **pages 276–277**
10. In Chapter 5, find the logo and Internet address that tells you where you can take the Online Readiness Quiz. **It is found on page 179. The URL is glencoe.com.**

Chapter 1

Chapter Overview

Chapter-at-a-Glance

Lesson	Math Objective	State/Local Standards
1-1 Equivalent Fractions and Equivalent Forms of One (pp. 4-10)	Write equivalent fractions using equivalent forms of one.	
1-2 Greatest Common Factors (pp. 11-17)	Find the greatest common factor of two or more numbers.	
Progress Check (p. 18)		
1-3 Simplify Fractions (pp. 19-26)	Write fractions in simplest form.	
1-4 Compare and Order Fractions (pp. 27-34)	Compare and order fractions and find their approximate locations on a number line.	
Progress Check (p. 35)		

Content-at-a-Glance

The diagram below summarizes and unpacks Chapter 1 content.

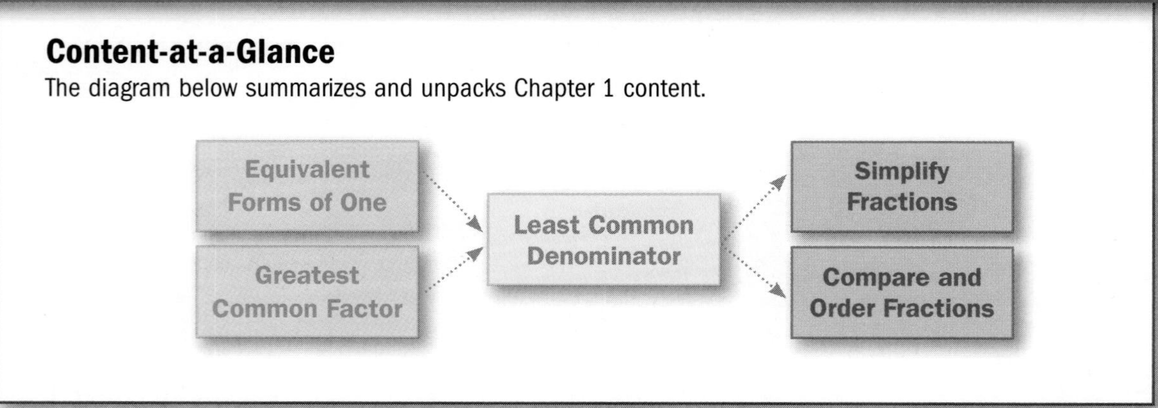

Online Assessment and Reporting
glencoe.com

Chapter Assessment Manager

Diagnostic Diagnose students' readiness.

	Student Study Guide/ Teacher Edition	Assessment Masters	Technology
Course Placement Test		1	ExamView® Assessment Suite
Book 1 Pretest		23	ExamView® Assessment Suite
Chapter 1 Pretest		26	ExamView® Assessment Suite
Quiz/Preview	SSG 3		Math Online glencoe.com StudentWorks™ Plus

Formative Identify students' misconceptions of content knowledge.

	Student Study Guide/ Teacher Edition	Assessment Masters	Technology
Progress Checks	SSG 18, 35		Math Online glencoe.com StudentWorks™ Plus
Vocabulary Review	SSG 36		Math Online glencoe.com
Lesson Assessments			ExamView® Assessment Suite
Are They Getting It?	TE 7, 15, 23, 32		Math Online glencoe.com

Summative Determine student success in learning concepts in the lesson, chapter, or book.

	Student Study Guide/ Teacher Edition	Assessment Masters	Technology
Chapter 1 Test	SSG 40	29	ExamView® Assessment Suite
Test Practice	SSG 42	32	ExamView® Assessment Suite
Alternative Assessment	TE 40	35	
See It, Do It, Say It, Write It	TE 10, 17, 26, 34		
Book 1 Test		59	ExamView® Assessment Suite

Back-mapping and Vertical Alignment **McGraw-Hill's *Math Triumphs*** intervention program was conceived and developed with the final result in mind: student success in grade-level mathematics, including Algebra 1 and beyond. The authors, using the **NCTM Focal Points and Focal Connections** as their guide, developed this brand-new series by backmapping from grade-level and Algebra 1 concepts, and vertically aligning the topics so that they build upon prior skills and concepts and serve as a foundation for future topics.

Chapter Resource Manager

	Lesson 1-1	Lesson 1-2	Lesson 1-3	Lesson 1-4
Concept	Equivalent Fractions and Equivalent Forms of One	Greatest Common Factors	Simplify Fractions	Compare and Order Fractions
Objective	Write equivalent fractions using equivalent forms of one.	Find the greatest common factor of two or more numbers.	Write fractions in simplest form.	Compare and order fractions and find their approximate locations on a number line.
Math Vocabulary	equivalent forms of one equivalent fractions value	composite number greatest common factor (GCF) prime factorization prime number	greatest common factor (GCF) simplest form	common denominators equivalent forms of one least common denominator (LCD) least common multiple (LCM)
Lesson Resources	**Materials** • Index cards **Manipulatives** • Fraction circles • Fraction tiles **Other Resources** CRM Vocabulary and English Language Development CRM Skills Practice CRM Problem-Solving Practice CRM Homework Practice	**Materials** • Colored construction paper **Other Resources** CRM Vocabulary and English Language Development CRM Skills Practice CRM Problem-Solving Practice CRM Homework Practice	**Materials** • Grid paper **Manipulatives** • Fraction circles **Other Resources** CRM Vocabulary and English Language Development CRM Skills Practice CRM Problem-Solving Practice CRM Homework Practice	**Manipulatives** • Fraction circles • Fraction tiles **Other Resources** CRM Vocabulary and English Language Development CRM Skills Practice CRM Problem-Solving Practice CRM Homework Practice
Technology	Math Online glencoe.com StudentWorks™ Plus ExamView® Assessment Suite	Math Online glencoe.com StudentWorks™ Plus ExamView® Assessment Suite	Math Online glencoe.com StudentWorks™ Plus ExamView® Assessment Suite	Math Online glencoe.com StudentWorks™ Plus ExamView® Assessment Suite

Intervention Strategy

Venn Diagrams and the Greatest Common Factor

Visual displays often help students remember concepts more effectively. A Venn diagram will show students the connection between prime factors and the GCF of 2 or 3 numbers.

Step 1: Have students work in pairs. Show students how to find the prime factorization of a number using a tree diagram.

Step 2: Assign each student pair two numbers to find the GCF using a Venn diagram. Demonstrate on the board with 42 and 36. Have students analyze the graph. What are the prime factors of each number? What is the GCF? 6

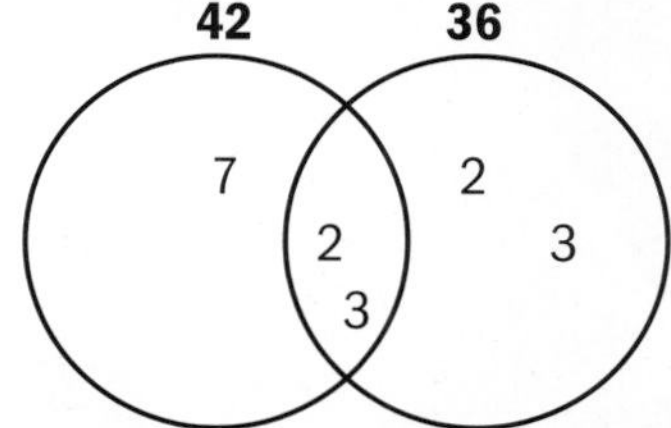

Step 3: Assign each student pair two numbers. Tell them to make a Venn diagram to find the GCF. Students can draw their diagrams on the front board and explain their methods to the class.

Step 4: Assign each student pair three numbers and have them make a Venn diagram to find the GCF. Have students share their work.

Step 5: Write the following problem on the board. Tell students to make a Venn diagram to solve. Again, have students share their work.

There are 84 tulips, 98 dahlias, and 210 daffodils to put in vases. If there are the same numbers of each type of flower in each vase, how many vases will there be? How many of each flower is there? 6 vases of tulips + 7 vases of dahlias + 15 vases of daffodils = 28 vases; 14 of each flower in each vase.

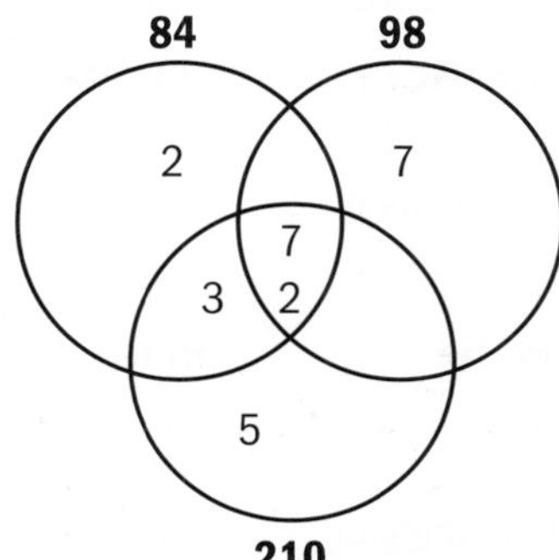

Chapter Notes

Real-World Applications

Baking Brenda is making muffins using a recipe that, in addition to fruit and spices, uses $\frac{1}{2}$ cup of apple sauce, $\frac{3}{4}$ cup of sugar, and $\frac{1}{8}$ cup of milk. She can only find her $\frac{1}{4}$ measuring cup. How can she use this one measuring cup to measure the ingredients listed above?

Intervention Strategy

Fraction of Our Days

1. Ask students to break their days down into at least five activities, which could include, for example, sleeping, school, and getting ready.
2. For each activity, have students write the fraction of the day that is spent on that activity. Reduce each fraction to its lowest terms.
3. Order each activity from the most time to the least time spent on an activity.
4. Have students share their results with the class.

Fractions

You see fractions every day.

During lunch you may eat $\frac{1}{3}$ of your sub sandwich, $\frac{2}{3}$ of your fruit cup, and drink $\frac{1}{2}$ of your milk. To compare these fractions, you need to find equivalent fractions.

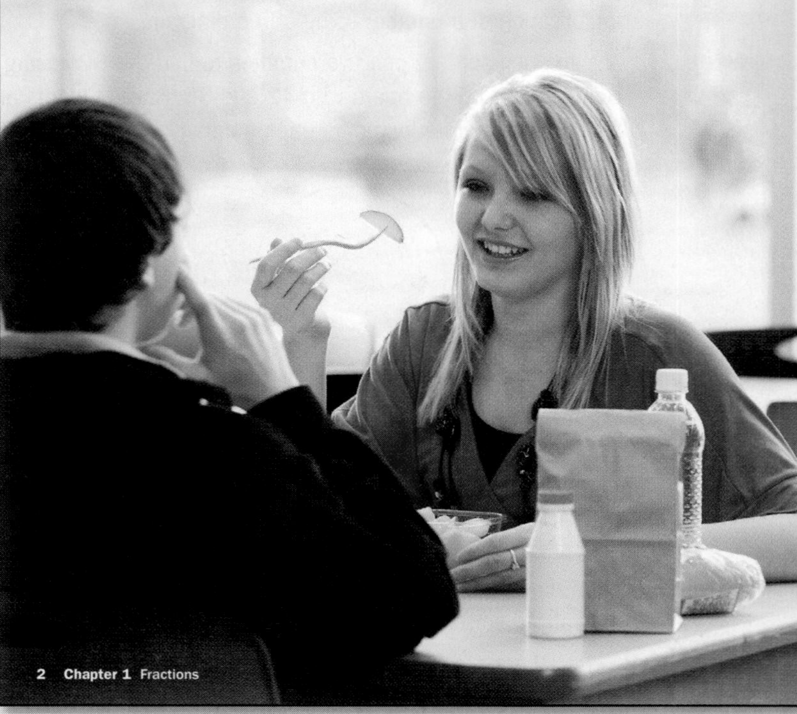

2 **Chapter 1** Fractions

Key Vocabulary

Find interactive definitions in 13 languages in the **eGlossary** at glencoe.com.

English **Español** *Introduce the most important vocabulary terms from Chapter 1.*

composite number **número compuesto**
a number greater than 1 with more than two factors (p. 11)

equivalent forms of one **formas equivalentes de la unidad**
different expressions that represent the same number (p. 4)

equivalent fractions **fracciones equivalentes**
fractions that name the same number (p. 4)
$\frac{3}{4} = \frac{6}{8}$

greatest common factor (GCF) **máximo común divisor (MCD)**
the greatest of the common factors of two or more numbers (p. 11)

least common denominator (LCD) **mínimo común denominador (MCD)**
the least common multiple of the denominators of two or more fractions (p. 27)

prime factorization **factorización prima**
a composite number expressed as a product of prime numbers (p. 11)

prime number **número primo**
a whole number that has exactly two unique factors, 1 and the number itself (p. 11)

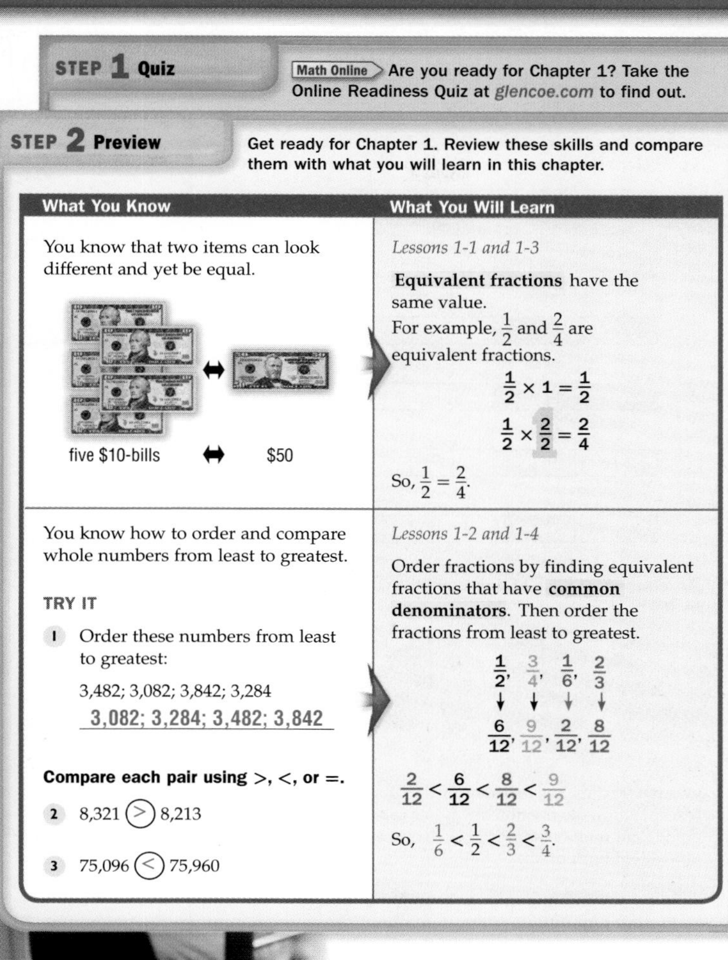

STEP 1 Quiz

Math Online Are you ready for Chapter 1? Take the Online Readiness Quiz at glencoe.com to find out.

STEP 2 Preview

Get ready for Chapter 1. Review these skills and compare them with what you will learn in this chapter.

What You Know	What You Will Learn
You know that two items can look different and yet be equal. five \$10-bills ↔ \$50	*Lessons 1-1 and 1-3* **Equivalent fractions** have the same value. For example, $\frac{1}{2}$ and $\frac{2}{4}$ are equivalent fractions. $\frac{1}{2} \times 1 = \frac{1}{2}$ $\frac{1}{2} \times \frac{2}{2} = \frac{2}{4}$ So, $\frac{1}{2} = \frac{2}{4}$.
You know how to order and compare whole numbers from least to greatest. **TRY IT** 1 Order these numbers from least to greatest: 3,482; 3,082; 3,842; 3,284 3,082; 3,284; 3,482; 3,842 **Compare each pair using >, <, or =.** 2 8,321 (>) 8,213 3 75,096 (<) 75,960	*Lessons 1-2 and 1-4* Order fractions by finding equivalent fractions that have **common denominators**. Then order the fractions from least to greatest. $\frac{1}{2}, \frac{3}{4}, \frac{1}{6}, \frac{2}{3}$ ↓ ↓ ↓ ↓ $\frac{6}{12}, \frac{9}{12}, \frac{2}{12}, \frac{8}{12}$ $\frac{2}{12} < \frac{6}{12} < \frac{8}{12} < \frac{9}{12}$ So, $\frac{1}{6} < \frac{1}{2} < \frac{2}{3} < \frac{3}{4}$.

3

Step 1 Quiz

Pretest/Prescribe Students can take the Online Readiness Quiz or the Diagnostic Pretest in the Assessment Masters.

Step 2 Preview

Use this pre-chapter activity to activate students' prior knowledge, build confidence, and help students preview the lessons.

Dinah Zike's Foldables®

Guide students through the directions on p. A1 in the Chapter Resource Masters to create their own Foldable graphic organizer for use with this chapter.

Home Connections

- Give the fraction of your family that is male and the fraction of your family that is female. Name two equivalent fractions for each.
- Determine what fraction of your week is spent sleeping and what fraction of your week is spent in school. Then write both fractions in simplest form.

Vocabulary Preview

- As students complete the Chapter Preview, have them make a list of important terms throughout the chapter.
- Divide students into pairs. Have each pair choose two to four terms from the list.
- Each student pair will work together to create Vocabulary Boxes, following the model below.

Write the Vocabulary Word	Draw a model, illustration, or example of the word
Definition (in words)	Should not include the term.

Mc Graw Hill Professional Development

Targeted professional development has been articulated throughout **McGraw-Hill's *Math Triumphs*** intervention program. **The McGraw-Hill Professional Development Video Library** provides short videos that support the **NCTM Focal Points and Focal Connections.** For more information, visit glencoe.com.

Model Lessons

Instructional Strategies

Lesson 1-1 Lesson Notes

Lesson Planner

Objective Write equivalent fractions using equivalent forms of one.

Vocabulary **equivalent forms of one**, **equivalent fractions**, **value**

Materials/Manipulatives fraction circles, fraction tiles, index cards

Chapter Resource Masters

- CRM Vocabulary and English Language Development (p. A4)
- CRM Skills Practice (p. A5)
- CRM Problem-Solving Practice (p. A6)
- CRM Homework Practice (p. A7)

1 Introduce

Vocabulary

Access Vocabulary Define *equivalent*. Have students list examples of real-world equivalencies. One possible example is 4 quarts and 1 gallon.

2 Teach

Key Concept

Foundational Skills and Concepts After students have read through the Key Concept box, have them try these exercises.

1. If you simplified $\frac{2}{4}$, $\frac{3}{6}$, $\frac{4}{8}$, and $\frac{5}{10}$, what would be the simplified fraction? $\frac{1}{2}$
2. What do $\frac{2}{2}$, $\frac{3}{3}$, $\frac{7}{7}$, and $\frac{12}{12}$ have in common? They all are equal to one.
3. Explain why a number over the same number in a fraction is equivalent to 1. A fraction is a division problem, and a number divided by the same number is 1.

Lesson 1-1

Equivalent Fractions and Equivalent Forms of One

KEY Concept

Equivalent fractions are fractions that have the same **value**.

1 unit

$\frac{1}{2}$

$\frac{1}{2}$ is equivalent to $\frac{2}{4}$.

$\frac{1}{4}$

$\frac{2}{4}$ is equivalent to $\frac{3}{6}$.

$\frac{1}{6}$

$\frac{3}{6}$ is equivalent to $\frac{4}{8}$.

$\frac{1}{8}$

$\frac{4}{8}$ is equivalent to $\frac{6}{12}$.

$\frac{1}{12}$

So, $\frac{1}{2}=\frac{2}{4}=\frac{3}{6}=\frac{4}{8}=\frac{6}{12}$.

An **equivalent form of one** is any nonzero number divided by itself.

$\frac{2}{2}=1$ $\frac{3}{3}=1$ $\frac{7}{7}=1$ $\frac{12}{12}=1$

When a fraction has the same numerator and denominator (except zero), the fraction always equals 1. To find an equivalent fraction, multiply or divide a fraction by an equivalent form of one.

$$\frac{4}{5}\times 1=\frac{4}{5}\rightarrow\frac{4}{5}\times\frac{2}{2}=\frac{8}{10}$$

So, $\frac{4}{5}=\frac{8}{10}$.

You can name an endless number of fractions that are equivalent to any fraction.

VOCABULARY

equivalent forms of one different expressions that represent the same number

equivalent fractions fractions that name the same number

value the amount of a number

4 **Chapter 1** Fractions

Intervention Strategy — Visual/Kinesthetic Learners

Fraction Circles If students are having difficulty with equivalents of 1, use fraction circles. Have students model fractions, such as $\frac{1}{6}$ and $\frac{4}{6}$. Then have them model $\frac{6}{6}$. How much does $\frac{6}{6}$ represent? one whole

Example 1

Complete the models to name an equivalent fraction.

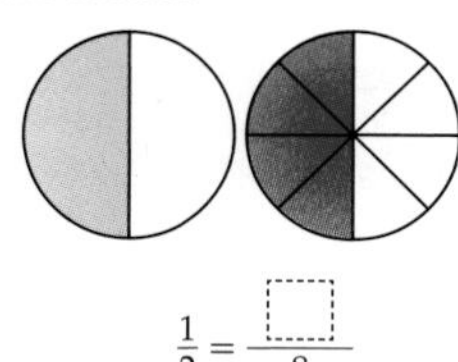

$\frac{1}{2} = \frac{\square}{8}$

1. Multiply the denominator 2 by 4 to get a denominator of 8.
2. Multiply 2 by 4 to get 8. So, multiply the fraction by $\frac{4}{4}$, an equivalent form of one.

$\frac{1}{2} = \frac{1 \times 4}{2 \times 4} = \frac{4}{8}$ So, $\frac{1}{2} = \frac{4}{8}$.

YOUR TURN!

Complete the models to name an equivalent fraction.

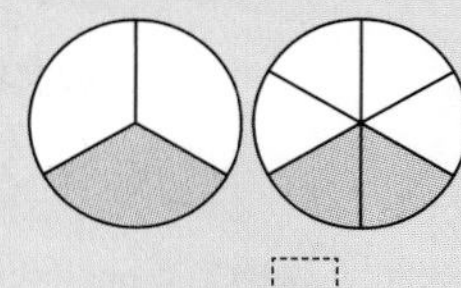

$\frac{1}{3} = \frac{\square}{6}$

1. Multiply the denominator 3 by 2 to get a denominator of 6.
2. Multiply 3 by 2 to get 6. So, multiply the fraction by $\frac{2}{2}$, an equivalent form of one.

$\frac{1}{3} = \frac{1 \times 2}{3 \times 2} = \frac{2}{6}$ So, $\frac{1}{3} = \frac{2}{6}$.

Example 2

Name two fractions equivalent to $\frac{3}{5}$.

1. Multiply the original fraction by an equivalent form of one, such as $\frac{2}{2}$.

$\frac{3}{5} = \frac{3 \times 2}{5 \times 2} = \frac{6}{10}$

2. Multiply the original fraction by another equivalent form of one, such as $\frac{3}{3}$.

$\frac{3}{5} = \frac{3 \times 3}{5 \times 3} = \frac{9}{15}$

So, $\frac{3}{5} = \frac{6}{10}$ and $\frac{3}{5} = \frac{9}{15}$.

YOUR TURN!

Name two fractions equivalent to $\frac{5}{7}$.

1. Multiply the original fraction by an equivalent form of one.

$\frac{5}{7} = \frac{5 \times 2}{7 \times 2} = \frac{10}{14}$

2. Multiply the original fraction by another equivalent form of one.

$\frac{5}{7} = \frac{5 \times 3}{7 \times 3} = \frac{15}{21}$

So, $\frac{5}{7} = \frac{10}{14}$ and $\frac{5}{7} = \frac{15}{21}$.

GO ON

Intervention Strategy Visual/Logical Learners

Build a Fraction Wall Have students work in small groups to create a fraction wall. Have them start by drawing one fraction bar and labeling it "One Whole." Then have them create bars underneath that are divided into halves, thirds, fourths, and so on. This will help them visualize the equivalent forms of one.

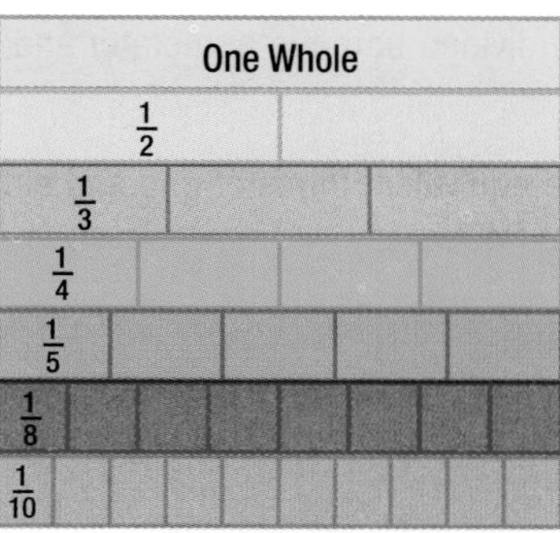

Additional Example 1

Complete the models to name an equivalent fraction.

$\frac{3}{4} = \frac{\square}{16}$

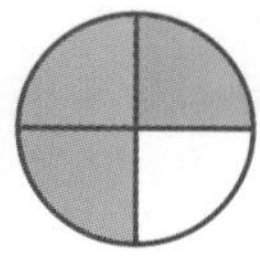

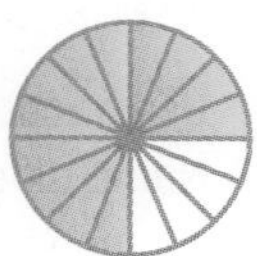

1. Multiply the denominator 4 by 4 to get a denominator of 16.
2. Multiply 4 by 4 to get 16. So, multiply the fraction by $\frac{4}{4}$, an equivalent form of one.

$\frac{3}{4} = \frac{3 \times 4}{4 \times 4} = \frac{12}{16}$

So, $\frac{3}{4} = \frac{12}{16}$.

Additional Example 2

Name two fractions equivalent to $\frac{7}{8}$.

1. Multiply the original fraction by an equivalent form of one.

$\frac{7}{8} = \frac{7 \times 2}{8 \times 2} = \frac{14}{16}$

2. Multiply the original fraction by another equivalent form of one.

$\frac{7}{8} = \frac{7 \times 3}{8 \times 3} = \frac{21}{24}$

So, $\frac{7}{8} = \frac{14}{16}$ and $\frac{7}{8} = \frac{21}{24}$.

3 Practice

Using Manipulatives

Models Use fraction tiles to represent fractions equal to 1. Name different fractions and ask students to point to the model of 1 that can be used with that fraction.

Nonexamples Use the manipulatives to model fractions that are not equivalent forms of one. Have student give examples of non-equivalent fractions.

On-Hand Manipulatives Use notebook paper to show students how to divide a whole into fractional parts. Use several sheets of paper to model several different fractions, such as $\frac{4}{4}, \frac{5}{5}, \frac{10}{10}$, and so on.

Note This!

Choosing the 1 You Need In their notebooks, have students include a sample that illustrates choosing the best way to write 1 as a fraction depending on the other fractions in the problem. Use the denominator of 24 and the given fractions to show how to choose the equivalent form of 1. Students can also include denominators 8 and 12 to make this list complete for all the integral factors of 24.

$\frac{1}{2} \times \frac{12}{12} = \frac{12}{24}$ You need to multiply 2 by 12 to get 24.

$\frac{2}{3} \times \frac{8}{8} = \frac{16}{24}$ You need to multiply 3 by 8 to get 24.

$\frac{3}{4} \times \frac{6}{6} = \frac{18}{24}$ You need to multiply 4 by 6 to get 24.

$\frac{5}{6} \times \frac{4}{4} = \frac{20}{24}$ You need to multiply 6 by 4 to get 24.

Who is Correct?

Write an equivalent fraction for $\frac{9}{12}$.

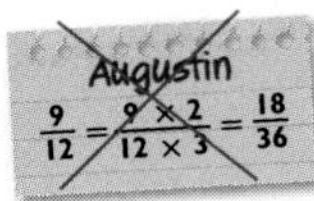

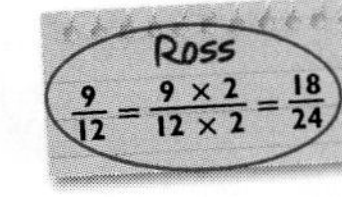

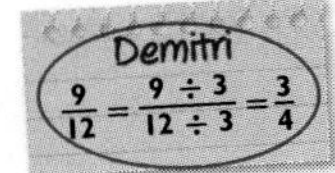

Circle correct answer(s). Cross out incorrect answer(s).

Guided Practice

1 Complete the models to name an equivalent fraction. $\frac{2}{5} = \frac{4}{\boxed{10}}$

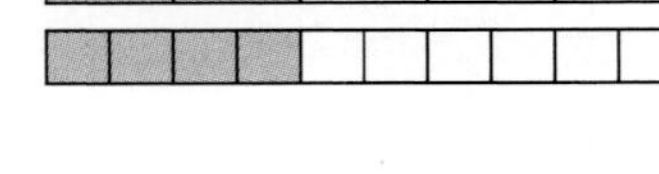

2 Complete the models to name two fractions equivalent to $\frac{6}{8}$. $\frac{3}{4}$ $\frac{12}{16}$

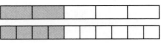

3 This circle shows $\frac{1}{4}$ shaded.

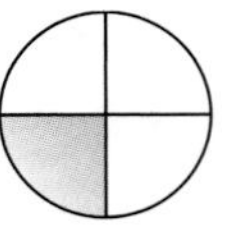

Which fractional part of a circle at the right is equal to $\frac{1}{4}$? Circle Four

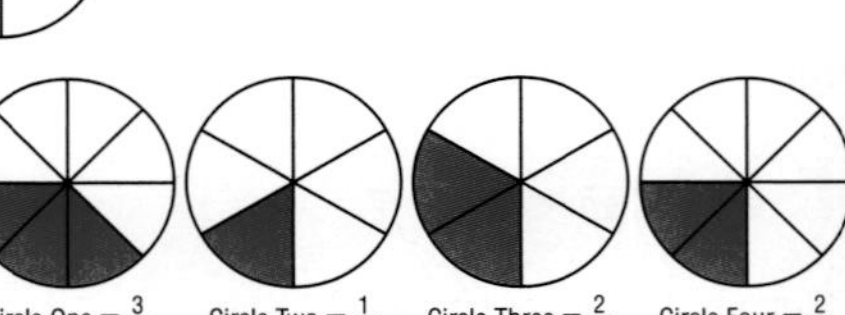

Step by Step Practice

4 Name a fraction equivalent to $\frac{7}{12}$.

Step 1 Choose an equivalent form of one. $\frac{7}{12} = \frac{7 \times \boxed{2}}{12 \times \boxed{2}} = \frac{\boxed{14}}{\boxed{24}}$

Step 2 Multiply the original fraction by the equivalent form of one.

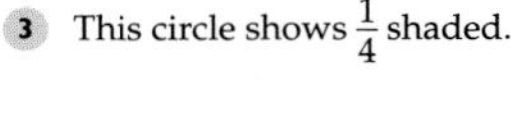

6 **Chapter 1** Fractions

Who *is Correct?*

Diagnostic Teaching

- Augustin is incorrect. He did not multiply by an equivalent form of one.
- Ross is correct. He multiplied both the numerator and the denominator by 2.
- Demitri is correct. He divided both the numerator and the denominator by 3.

Remind students to use equivalent forms of one and either multiply or divide to find equivalent fractions.

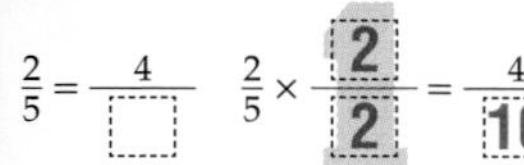

omplete to name an equivalent fraction.

$\frac{2}{5} = \frac{4}{\square}$ $\frac{2}{5} \times \frac{2}{2} = \frac{4}{10}$

6 $\frac{3}{7} = \frac{9}{21}$

$\frac{6}{8} = \frac{30}{40}$

8 $\frac{5}{9} = \frac{20}{36}$

tep by Step Problem-Solving Practice

olve.

MUSIC Ella and Dana listened to an equivalent fraction of songs on each of their own CDs. Dana listened to 4 out of 10 songs on her CD. If Ella's CD has 20 songs, how many songs did she listen to?

Problem-Solving Strategies
- ☑ Draw a diagram.
- ☐ Look for a pattern.
- ☐ Guess and check.
- ☐ Solve a simpler problem.
- ☐ Work backward.

Understand Read the problem. Write what you know.
Dana listened to $\frac{4}{10}$ of the songs on her CD.
Ella listened to an equal amount of songs.

Plan Pick a strategy. One strategy is to draw a diagram.
Draw 10 equal parts. Shade 4 to show $\frac{4}{10}$.

Draw another figure with twice as many parts.
Shade to equal $\frac{4}{10}$.

Solve Count the total parts and the shaded parts of the second figure.

$\frac{4}{10} = \frac{8}{20}$

Ella listened to $\frac{8}{20}$ of the songs on her CD.

Check Does the answer make sense?

GO ON

Common Error *Alert*

Multi-Step Problem If a student is unable to draw a model for Exercise 9, he or she may not understand how equivalent fractions equal the same amount. Begin with fraction circles and show examples of equivalent fractions. Ask: Are the fractions equivalent? Have the student place the equivalent fractions on top of each other. Ask: Are the diagrams exactly the same size? Continue with other equivalent fractions.

Math Coach Notes

Strategies

1. The optimum way for students to learn fraction equivalents is to use multiple concrete models, manipulatives, and pictorial representations. Have students use two different fraction equivalents to represent the same fraction. Drill students repeatedly by asking whether the fractions are equivalent and in the simplest form.

2. Use real-world examples so students will connect fractions outside of math class. Have students name fractions that represent these examples.

Are They Getting It?

Check students' understanding of equivalent fractions by writing these problems on the board. Have students explain the incorrect information in each problem. Tell them to use a fraction circle or another visual aid to show why the answers are correct, or are incorrect.

Name two equivalent fractions.

1. $\frac{3}{5}$ Sample answer: $\frac{6}{15}$; $\frac{9}{45}$ This is incorrect. The fraction was not multiplied by equivalents of one.

2. $\frac{5}{7}$ Sample answer: $\frac{10}{14}$; $\frac{15}{21}$ This is correct.

3. $\frac{2}{3}$ Sample answer: $\frac{4}{6}$; $\frac{6}{9}$ This is correct.

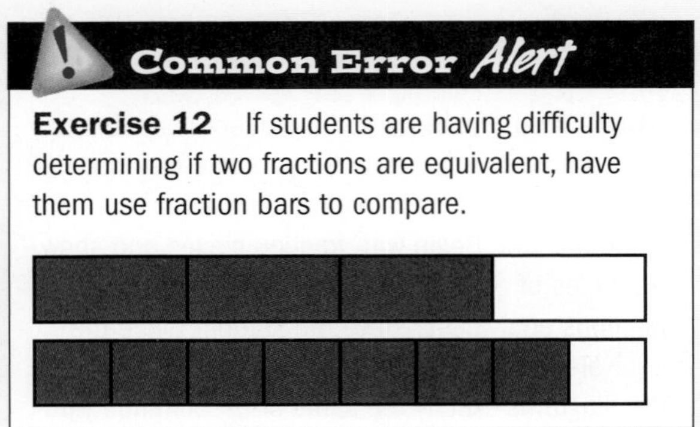

Exercise 12 If students are having difficulty determining if two fractions are equivalent, have them use fraction bars to compare.

Additional Answer

Exercise 12 Answers will vary. Sample answer: In order to compare fractions, the denominators need to be the same. Then compare the numerators. In this case,
$\frac{3}{4} \neq \frac{7}{8}$ because $\frac{3}{4} = \frac{6}{8}$, and $\frac{6}{8} \neq \frac{7}{8}$.

Odd/Even Assignments

Exercises 13–34 are structured so that students practice the same concepts whether they are assigned the odd or even problems.

In-Class Assignment

Have students complete Exercises 14, 16, 18, 23, 31, and 37 to ensure that they understand the concept.

10 BAKING Emil had two pieces of bread the same length. He cut the first piece into 4 equal parts. He cut the second piece into 12 equal parts. How many parts from the second piece of bread equal the same length as 3 parts from the first piece of bread? Check off each step.

✔ Understand: I underlined key words.

✔ Plan: To solve the problem, I will **draw a diagram**

✔ Solve: The answer is **9 parts**

✔ Check: I checked my answer by **multiplying $\frac{3}{4}$ by an equivalent form of one,**

11 NEWSPAPERS Cameron and Luther deliver newspapers everyday after school. On Wednesday, Cameron delivered $\frac{7}{10}$ of the newspapers on his route, and Luther delivered $\frac{4}{5}$ of the newspapers on his route. Did they deliver the same amount of newspapers on Wednesday?

No, Luther delivered more because the equivalent fraction of $\frac{4}{5}$ is $\frac{8}{10}$, and $\frac{8}{10}$ is greater than $\frac{7}{10}$.

12 **Reflect** Han said that $\frac{3}{4}$ is equivalent to $\frac{7}{8}$ because $3 + 4 = 7$ and $4 + 4 = 8$.
Explain what was incorrect in Han's thinking. Be sure to use the terms *numerator* and *denominator* in your explanation.

See TE margin.

Skills, Concepts, and Problem Solving

Complete each model to name an equivalent fraction.

13 $\frac{1}{3} = \frac{2}{6}$

14 $\frac{3}{4} = \frac{9}{12}$

Intervention Strategy — Visual/Kinesthetic/Auditory Learners

Fraction-Bar Kit

1. Hand out templates for students to make fraction bars. Have students cut, fold, and label the bars to twelfths.
2. Write a fraction on the board. Tell students to use their bars to find equivalent fractions. For instance, write $\frac{2}{3}$ on the board. Ask a student to model the fraction. Then have the student place other fraction bars on the model of $\frac{2}{3}$. What other fraction parts fit on the model exactly? Repeat with other fractions.
3. Equivalent fractions can also be visualized using grid paper. Ask students to make a 4 × 7 array. Tell them to shade in 14 of the squares. What is the fraction? Now write $\frac{14}{28} = \frac{\square}{4}$ on the board. Have students fill in the numerator. Repeat with other fractions.

omplete each model to name an equivalent fraction.

5 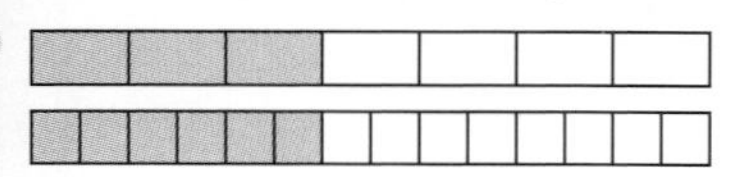

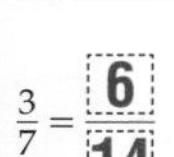

$\frac{3}{7} = \frac{6}{14}$

16 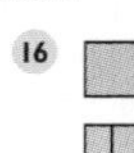

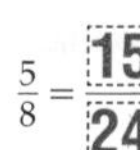

$\frac{5}{8} = \frac{15}{24}$

omplete to name an equivalent fraction.

$\frac{3}{12} = \frac{12}{48}$

18 $\frac{7}{9} = \frac{21}{27}$

$\frac{1}{5} = \frac{2}{10}$

20 $\frac{4}{7} = \frac{8}{14}$

$\frac{5}{6} = \frac{15}{18}$

22 $\frac{3}{8} = \frac{9}{24}$

ame two equivalent fractions for each fraction.

$\frac{1}{2}$ Sample answer: $\frac{2}{4}, \frac{3}{6}$

24 $\frac{2}{3}$ Sample answer: $\frac{4}{6}, \frac{6}{9}$

$\frac{3}{5}$ Sample answer: $\frac{6}{10}, \frac{9}{15}$

26 $\frac{5}{7}$ Sample answer: $\frac{10}{14}, \frac{15}{21}$

$\frac{3}{4}$ Sample answer: $\frac{6}{8}, \frac{9}{12}$

28 $\frac{1}{10}$ Sample answer: $\frac{2}{20}, \frac{3}{30}$

$\frac{3}{11}$ Sample answer: $\frac{6}{22}, \frac{9}{33}$

30 $\frac{2}{9}$ Sample answer: $\frac{4}{18}, \frac{6}{27}$

Math Challenge

Using Division to Make Equivalent Fractions Use division and equivalent forms of 1 to name each fraction as an equivalent fraction with the given denominator.

$\frac{384}{256}$ with a denominator of 2. $\frac{384}{256} \div \frac{128}{128} = \frac{3}{2}$

$\frac{80}{256}$ with a denominator of 16. $\frac{80}{256} \div \frac{16}{16} = \frac{5}{16}$

$\frac{160}{256}$ with a denominator of 8. $\frac{160}{256} \div \frac{32}{32} = \frac{5}{8}$

$\frac{56}{256}$ with a denominator of 32. $\frac{56}{256} \div \frac{8}{8} = \frac{7}{32}$

$\frac{64}{256}$ with a denominator of 4. $\frac{64}{256} \div \frac{64}{64} = \frac{1}{4}$

Math Coach Notes

Study Tip Encourage visual learners to draw pictures of equivalent fractions in their notes. These students may also benefit from making fraction bars or fraction circles and using them at home when they study.

Intervention Strategy

Interpersonal/ Kinesthetic/ Visual Learners

Represent Fractions

1. Have students work in pairs or alone.
2. Each pair should have an ample supply of two-colored counters. Ask students to represent a fraction using the counters. This would be done by placing 3 counters of one color over 4 counters of another color.

3. Tell students to use this model to form equivalent fractions of $\frac{3}{4}$. To do this, they will make another fraction with the same number and color of counters and place it alongside their first model.

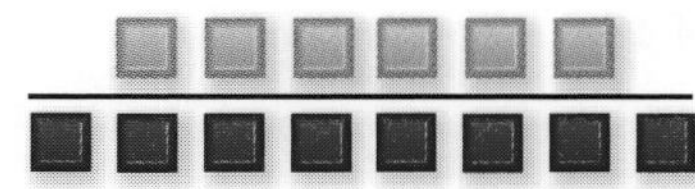

4. Have each pair write down the fractions they make. Discuss the results. Then repeat with other fractions.

4 Assess

See It, Do It, Say It, Write It

Step 1 Have students work in pairs. Write a fraction on the board. Tell students to write an equivalent fraction to represent the fraction on the board. Have students share their work with the class. Repeat several times.

Step 2 Ask students to draw a fraction circle on paper. Give them a fraction to represent. Repeat by having students draw other fractions. Share solutions in a class discussion.

Step 3 Write a fraction on the board. Have students explain how to draw a model to represent an equivalent fraction. Do this several times with different fractions.

Step 4 Have students work alone. Tell them to write what an equivalent fraction is, and tell them to include a picture or a model.

Looking Ahead: Pre-teach

Greatest Common Factor In the next lesson, students will learn about greatest common factors.

Example

Find the greatest common factor of 18 and 24 by using prime factors.

1. List the factors by pairs.

Factors of 18	Factors of 24
(1), 18	(1), 24
(2), 9	(2), 12
(3), (6)	(3), 8
	4, (6)

2. The common factors are 1, 2, 3, and 6.

The greatest common factor of 18 and 24 is 6.

31 DESSERT Delaney and Raquel each ate the same amount of their own cheesecake. Raquel ate $\frac{2}{5}$ of her cheesecake. If Delaney's cheesecake is divided into 10 equal pieces, how much did Delaney eat?

$\frac{2}{5} \times \frac{2}{2} = \frac{4}{10}$; 4 pieces

32 TEST Casey and Felipe completed the same amount of two different assignments in class. Casey's assignment had 14 questions. If Felipe completed $\frac{5}{7}$ of the questions, what fraction of the questions did Casey complete?

$\frac{10}{14}$; $\frac{5}{7} \times \frac{2}{2} = \frac{10}{14}$

33 SCIENCE Uma and Gwen made collages for their science project. They both cut out pictures for their collage. In Gwen's collage, $\frac{4}{6}$ of her pictures were animals. In Uma's collage, $\frac{8}{12}$ of her pictures were animals. Are these fractions equivalent?

yes; $\frac{4}{6} \times \frac{2}{2} = \frac{8}{12}$

34 SANDWICHES Isaac and Hector ate the same amount of their Italian subs. Isaac ate $\frac{2}{3}$ of his Italian sub. If Hector's sub is divided into nine pieces, how much of the sub did he eat?

$\frac{2}{3} \times \frac{3}{3} = \frac{6}{9}$; 6 pieces

Vocabulary Check **Write the vocabulary word that completes each sentence.**

35 Equivalent fractions are fractions that name the same value.

36 A(n) equivalent form of one is any nonzero number divided by itself.

37 **Writing in Math** Write a letter to your teacher describing equivalent forms of one.

Answers will vary. Students should describe that equivalent forms of one are expressions that represent one; example $\frac{2}{2}$, $\frac{4}{4}$, $\frac{5}{5}$.

STO

10 Chapter 1 Fractions

Ticket Out the Door

Equivalent Fractions Hand out a fraction written on an index card to each student. Each student should write four equivalent fractions. Students will hand in their papers as they exit the classroom.

Lesson 1-2

Greatest Common Factors

KEY Concept

The **greatest common factor (GCF)** of two whole numbers is the greatest number that is a factor of both numbers.

Factors of 42	Factors of 54
1 × 42	1 × 54
2 × 21	2 × 27
3 × 14	3 × 18
(6) × 7	(6) × 9

The greatest common number in both lists is 6.
The GCF of 42 and 54 is 6.

Every **composite number** can be written as a product of **prime numbers**. A prime number is a whole number greater than one whose only factors are one and itself. The number 7 has only two factors: 1 and 7. So, 7 is a *prime* number.

The **prime factorization** of a number is the product of its prime factors. One way to find the prime factorization is to use a factor tree.

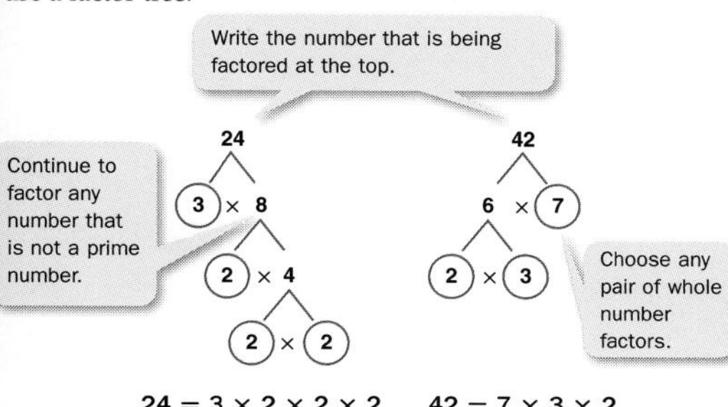

Write the number that is being factored at the top.
Continue to factor any number that is not a prime number.
Choose any pair of whole number factors.
24
3 × 8
2 × 4
2 × 2
42
6 × 7
2 × 3

24 = 3 × 2 × 2 × 2   42 = 7 × 3 × 2

Stop factoring when you have a prime number. The common prime factors are 3 and 2. So, the GCF of 24 and 42 is 3 × 2 or 6.

VOCABULARY

composite number
a number greater than 1 with more than two factors

greatest common factor (GCF)
the greatest of the common factors of two or more numbers; the GCF of 24 and 30 is 6

prime factorization
a composite number expressed as a product of prime numbers

prime number
a whole number that has exactly two unique factors, 1 and the number itself

he numbers 1 and 0 are neither prime nor composite.

GO ON

Intervention Strategy — Linguistic Learners

GCF Remind students of the meaning of *factor.* A factor is a number that is multiplied by another number to get a product. The GCF of a group of numbers cannot be greater than any one of the numbers in the group. Have the partners work together to write and present an example of a GCF.

Lesson Notes

Lesson 1-2

Lesson Planner

Objective Find the greatest common factor of two or more numbers.

Vocabulary **composite number**, **greatest common factor (GCF)**, **prime factorization**, **prime number**

Materials/Manipulatives colored construction paper

Chapter Resource Masters

- CRM Vocabulary and English Language Development (p. A8)
- CRM Skills Practice (p. A9)
- CRM Problem-Solving Practice (p. A10)
- CRM Homework Practice (p. A11)

1 Introduce

Vocabulary

Prime Factorization In this lesson students learn about GCF and prime factorization. Every whole number has a unique prime factorization. Review the difference between *prime numbers* and *composite numbers*. Ensure that students know that regardless of which initial factors are used to find the prime factorization of a number, the final prime factorization will be the same.

2 Teach

Key Concept

Foundational Skills and Concepts After students have read through the Key Concept box, have them try these exercises.

1. Name all the factors of 54.
   1, 2, 3, 6, 9, 18, 27, 54
2. What is the prime factorization of 24? $2^3 \times 3$
3. When making a factor tree, when should you stop factoring? When all the factors are prime numbers.

Additional **Example 1**

Find the GCF of 56 and 98 by listing factor pairs.

1. List the factors by pairs.

Factors of 56	Factors of 98
(1) × 56	(1) × 98
(2) × 28	(2) × 49
4 × (14)	(7) × (14)
(7) × 8	

2. Circle the commons factors.
The common factors are 1, 2, 7, and 14.

3. The GCF of 56 and 98 is 14.

Additional **Example 2**

Find the GCF of 32, 44, and 68 by making a list.

1. List the factors of each number from least to greatest.
32: (1), (2), (4), 8, 16, 32
44: (1), (2), (4), 11, 22, 44
68: (1), (2), (4), 17, 34, 68

2. Circle the common factors.
The common factors are 1, 2, and 4.

3. The GCF of 32, 44, and 68 is 4.

Example 1

Find the GCF of 45 and 63 by listing factor pairs.

1. List the factors by pairs.

Factors of 45	Factors of 63
(1) × 45	(1) × 63
(3) × 15	(3) × 21
5 × (9)	7 × (9)

2. Circle the common factors.
The common factors are 1, 3, and 9.
3. The GCF of 45 and 63 is 9.

YOUR TURN!

Find the GCF of 30 and 42 by listing factor pairs.

1. List the factors by pairs.

Factors of 30	Factors of 42
(1) × 30	(1) × 42
(2) × 15	(2) × 21
(3) × 10	(3) × 14
5 × (6)	(6) × 7

2. Circle the common factors.The common factors are 1, 2, 3, and 6.
3. The GCF of 30 and 42 is 6.

Example 2

Find the GCF of 24, 32, and 40 by making a list.

1. List the factors of each number from least to greatest.
24: (1), (2), 3, (4), 6, (8), 12, 24
32: (1), (2), (4), (8), 16, 32
40: (1), (2), (4), 5, (8), 10, 20, 40
2. Circle the common factors. The common factors are 1, 2, 4, and 8.
3. The GCF of 24, 32, and 40 is 8.

YOUR TURN!

Find the GCF of 18, 36, and 54 by making a list.

1. List the factors of each number from least to greatest.
18: (1), (2), (3), (6), (9), 18
36: (1), (2), (3), 4, (6), (9), 12, 18, 36
54: (1), (2), (3), (6), (9), 18, 27, 54
2. Circle the common factors. The common factors are 1, 2, 3, 6, and 9
3. The GCF of 18, 36, and 54 is 9.

12 **Chapter 1** Fractions

English Learner Strategy

Clarifying Names Verses Meanings The Greatest Common Factor of two numbers can be perplexing to some students. The word *greatest* might imply a number greater than the given numbers. But the word *factor* indicates that the number is used in a multiplication problem to get the given numbers. Students can use this statement to help.

The GCF of two numbers must be ***less than or equal to*** *the given numbers.*

The GCF of 12 and 36 is 12; $12 \leq 36$ and $12 \leq 12$.
The GCF of 32 and 16 is 16; $16 \leq 32$ and $16 \leq 16$.

Example 3

Find the GCF of 30 and 54 by using prime factors.

1. Write the prime factorization.

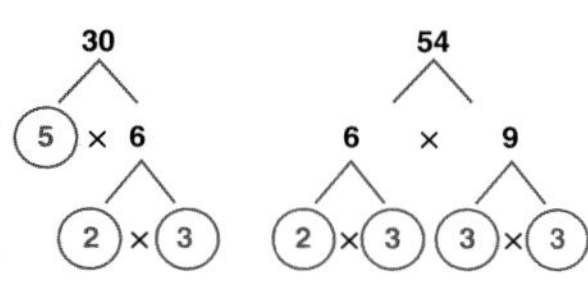

2. The common prime factors are 2 and 3.
   So, the GCF of 30 and 54 is 2 × 3 or 6.

YOUR TURN!

Find the GCF of 35 and 56 by using prime factors.

1. Write the prime factorization.

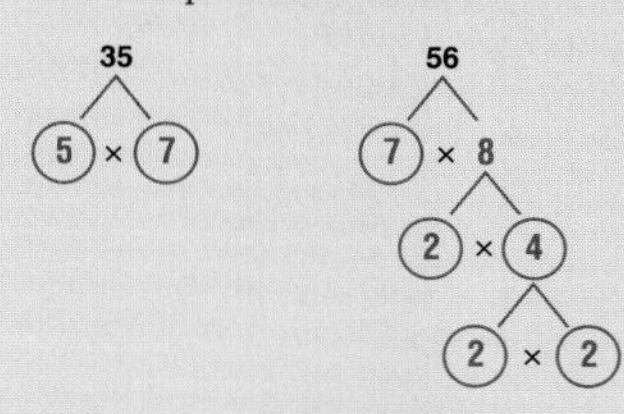

2. The common prime factor is 7.
   So, the GCF of 35 and 56 is 7.

Who is Correct?

Find the GCF of 30 and 45.

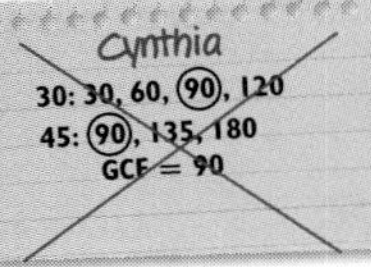

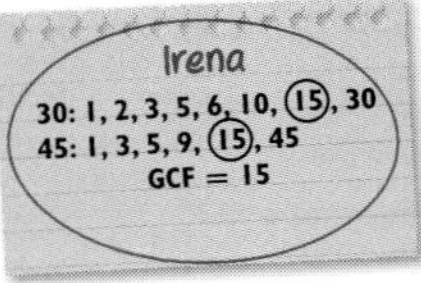

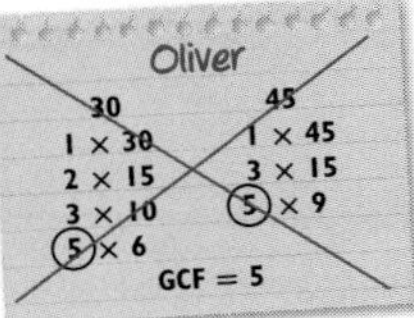

Circle correct answer(s). Cross out incorrect answer(s).

GO ON

Additional Example 3

Find the GCF of 20 and 50 by using prime factors.

1. Write the prime factorization.

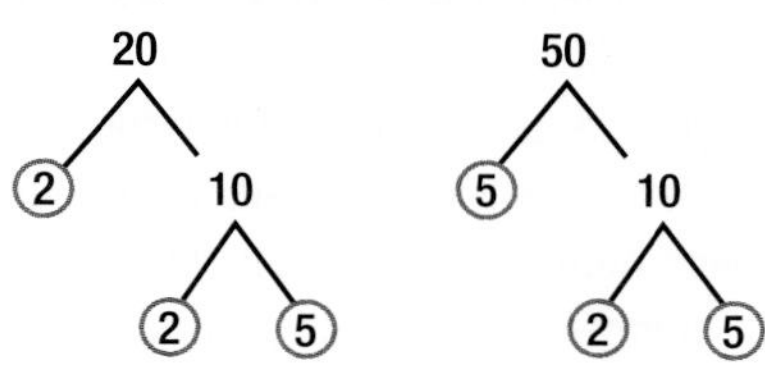

2. The common prime factors are 2 and 5.
   So, the GCF of 20 and 50 is 2 × 5 or 10.

Who is Correct?

Diagnostic Teaching

- Cynthia is incorrect. She found the least common multiple.
- Irena is correct.
- Oliver is incorrect. He found a common factor, but not the **greatest** common factor.

Remind students that the greatest common factor of the numbers is the greatest number in both lists of factors of the numbers.

3 Practice

Using Manipulatives

On-Hand Manipulatives Have students use two different colors of paper. Have them cut the paper into 8 squares. When finding the greatest common factor of a pair of numbers, have them assign a color to each number. They should write each prime factor of the numbers on the corresponding squares of paper. Then make a pile of the factors for each number. Students should compare the two piles and remove a matched pair of squares from both piles. When the squares are removed, stack them on top of each other so that only one is visible, and place them in a separate pile away from the first two piles. Repeat this matching process until no squares in both piles match. Look to the newly created pile and multiply the numbers shown on the top square of each stack. This product is the GCF of the two numbers given.

Note This!

Diagrams Instruct students to draw the diagrams and models in their notes using whatever suits their learning style best. Some students are visual learners, so making a factor tree may be a better model than a list.

Guided Practice

Find the GCF of each set of numbers by listing factor pairs.

1. 12 and 32

12	32
(1) × 12	(1) × 32
(2) × 6	(2) × 16
3 × (4)	(4) × 8

The GCF of 12 and 32 is 4.

2. 18 and 42

18	42
(1) × 18	(1) × 42
(2) × 9	(2) × 21
3 × (6)	3 × 14
	(6) × 7

The GCF of 18 and 42 is 6.

Step by Step Practice

3. Find the GCF of 40 and 64 by using prime factors.

Step 1 Write the prime factorization.

Step 2 The common prime factors are 2, 2, and 2.

So, the GCF of 40 and 64 is 2 × 2 × 2 or 8.

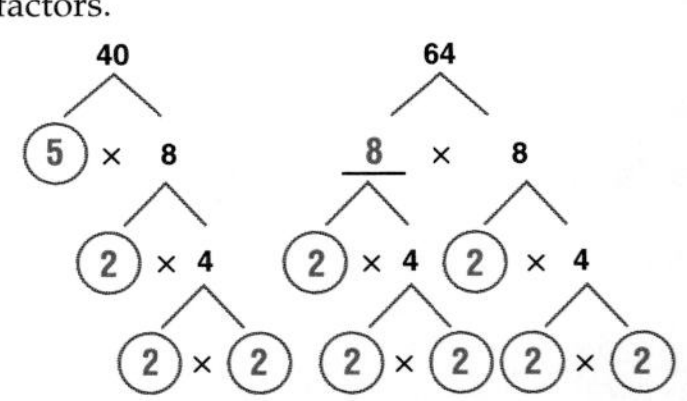

Find the GCF of each set of numbers by making a list.

4. 30 and 54

30: (1), (2), (3), 5, (6), 10, 15, 30

54: (1), (2), (3), (6), 9, 18, 27, 54

The GCF of 30 and 54 is 6.

5. 27 and 36

27: (1), (3), (9), 27

36: (1), 2, (3), 4, 6, (9), 12, 18, 36

The GCF of 27 and 36 is 9.

6. 24, 40, and 56

24: (1), (2), 3, (4), 6, (8), 12, 24

40: (1), (2), (4), 5, (8), 10, 20, 40

56: (1), (2), (4), 7, (8), 14, 28, 56

The GCF of 24, 40, and 56 is 8.

7. 15, 21, and 30

15: (1), (3), 5, 15

21: (1), (3), 7, 21

30: (1), 2, (3), 5, 6, 10, 15, 30

The GCF of 15, 21, and 30 is 3.

Intervention Strategy

Interpersonal/Kinesthetic Learners

Find the GCF Divide students into pairs and give each student a number cube. Both members of the pair roll their number cubes and use the numbers on the two cubes to write a two-digit number. Both students then write the factors of the two-digit number. The pairs roll their number cubes again to get another two-digit number and write the factors of the second two-digit number. Students should find the GCF of their numbers. Students can share their numbers and GCF with the class.

ep by Step Problem-Solving Practice

lve.

Problem-Solving Strategies

- ☐ Look for a pattern.
- ☑ Use logical reasoning.
- ☐ Solve a simpler problem.
- ☐ Work backward.
- ☐ Act it out.

MONEY The list below shows the amount of money that the student council collected on three days. Each student paid the same amount to attend a field trip. What is the most the trip could cost each student? Explain.

Money Collected from Student Council	
Monday	$48
Wednesday	$64
Friday	$56

Understand Read the problem. Write what you know. The club leader collected: **$48, $64, and $56**. Each member paid the **same** amount.

Plan Pick a strategy. One strategy is to use logical reasoning. You need to know the amount each student paid. Logical reasoning tells you that you must find the greatest common factor of the amount of money collected each day.

Solve Write the factors of each amount by making a list. Find the GCF.

48: (1), (2), 3, (4), 6, (8), 12, 16, 24, 48

64: (1), (2), (4), (8), 16, 32, 64

56: (1), (2), (4), 7, (8), 14, 28, 56

The GCF of 48, 64, and 56 is **8**.

Check Did you answer the question? If each student paid **$8**, could the student council collect the amounts listed?

MUSIC Rashelle wants to save different types of music in folders on her computer. There are 32 country songs, 40 rap songs, and 24 rock songs. There should be an equal amount of songs in each folder. Each folder will only have one type of music. What is the greatest number of songs that can be saved in each folder? Check off each step.

✔ Understand: I underlined key words.

✔ Plan: To solve the problem, I will **use logical reasoning**.

✔ Solve: The answer is **8 songs in each folder**.

✔ Check: I checked my answer by **making a list of factor pairs**.

GO ON

Lesson 1-2 Greatest Common Factors 15

Common Error *Alert*

Multi-Step Problem

Exercise 8 If a student is unable to use logical reasoning for Exercise 8, he or she may not understand how to write factors of each amount. Begin by listing factors or making a factor tree and show the diagram of the factors.

Math Coach Notes

Strategies

1. The optimum way for students to learn how to factor is to use multiple concrete models, manipulatives, and pictorial representations. Drill students repeatedly by asking the GCF of numbers.
2. Have students begin the lesson by practicing factoring numbers. Use a factor tree throughout the lesson as a concrete example. Have students write the factors using the factor tree and simplify.
3. Use real-world examples so students will connect to factors outside of math class. Have students name factors that represent these real-world examples.

Are They Getting It?

Check students' understanding of GCF by writing these problems on the board. Have students explain the incorrect information in each problem. Tell them to use a fraction strip or another visual aid to show why the answers are correct or incorrect.

1. The GCF of 24 and 6 is 3. This is incorrect. The GCF is 6.
2. The GCF of 21, 49, and 56 is 7. This is correct.
3. The GCF of 15 and 20 is 10. This is incorrect. 10 is not a factor of 15.

Odd/Even Assignments

Exercises 12–20 are structured so that students practice the same concepts whether they are assigned the odd or even problems.

In-Class Assignment

Have students complete Exercises 12, 18, 20, and 23 to ensure that they understand the concept.

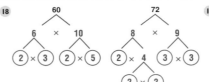

10 MOVIES Cesar wants to arrange his DVDs on shelves. He has 25 animated, 15 action, and 30 comedy movies. He wants only one type of movie on each shelf. Each shelf will have the same number of movies. What is the greatest number of movies he can put on each shelf? **5 movies**

11 **Reflect** Explain how to use prime factorization to find the GCF of two numbers.

Sample answer: The common prime factors of the two numbers are multiplied together to find the GCF.

Skills, Concepts, and Problem Solving

Find the GCF of each set of numbers.

12 28 and 48 **4**

13 56 and 72 **8**

14 28, 49, and 63 **7**

15 36, 48, and 60 **12**

16 25, 40, and 55 **5**

17 21, 30, and 36 **3**

Find the GCF of each set of numbers by using prime factors.

18

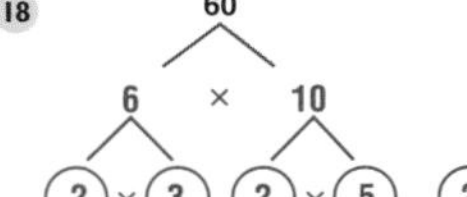

$2 \times 2 \times 3$ or 12

19

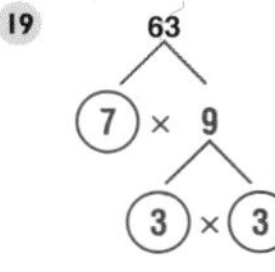

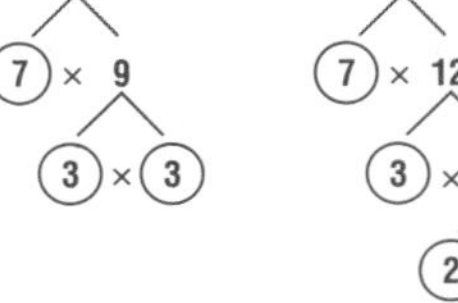

3×7 or 21

Solve.

20 PARTY Mallory is decorating her house with balloons for a party. She wants to arrange the balloons in smaller groups of one color. She has 12 blue balloons, 18 red balloons, and 24 yellow balloons. Each group of balloons should have the same number. What is the greatest number of balloons she can put in each group?

6 ballons

Math Challenge

Starting with the End Challenge students to figure out how to write GCF problems by starting with the answer and working backward to name two numbers that can be given as the problem. Students should write a brief description of the procedures that they used to write the problem.

cabulary Check **Write the vocabulary word that completes each sentence.**

A composite number expressed as a product of prime numbers is called **prime factorization**.

The greatest of the common factors of two or more numbers is called the **greatest common factor**.

Writing in Math Explain the steps in finding the GCF of two numbers.

Sample answer: List the factors of each number. Underline the factors common to both numbers. Circle the greatest common factor to both numbers.

Spiral Review (Lesson 1-1, p. 4)

mplete each model to name an equivalent fraction.

$\frac{4}{10} = \frac{2}{5}$

$\frac{2}{3} = \frac{8}{12}$

me two equivalent fractions for each fraction.

$\frac{1}{4}$ **Sample answer:** $\frac{2}{8}; \frac{3}{12}$

27 $\frac{2}{5}$ **Sample answer:** $\frac{4}{10}; \frac{6}{15}$

$\frac{4}{7}$ **Sample answer:** $\frac{8}{14}; \frac{12}{21}$

29 $\frac{5}{9}$ **Sample answer:** $\frac{10}{18}; \frac{15}{27}$

ve.

SPORTS Edgar and Darius are playing a game where they each get 8 chances to throw a football through a tire. After playing 5 games, they both make $\frac{3}{5}$ of the balls they throw. How many throws does each of them make?

$\frac{3}{5} = \frac{24}{40}$; **24 throws**

Ticket Out the Door

Prime Factors As each student approaches the door to exit, state a composite number between 20 and 100. The student should give you one prime factor of that number. Most answers will be 2, 3, or 5.

See It, Do It, Say It, Write It

1. Write three numbers on the board. Model how to find the factors of each number with a drawing or model. Do this several times with different fractions. Show how to find the GCF.
2. Ask students to draw a factor tree on paper. Give them a few numbers to factor with their factor tree. Repeat with different numbers and students drawing factor trees.
3. Share solutions in a class discussion.
4. Have students work alone. Tell them to write what a GCF is, include a picture or a model.

Looking Ahead: Pre-teach

Simplify Fractions In the next lesson, students will learn how to simplify fractions.

Write $\frac{16}{20}$ in simplest form. Divide by the GCF.

1. List all the factors of the numerator and the denominator.

   The factors of 16 are: 1, 2, 4, 8, 16

   The factors of 20 are: 1, 2, 4, 5, 10, 20
2. The greatest number in both lists is 4.
3. Divide the numerator and the denominator by the GCF.

   $\frac{16}{20} = \frac{16 \div 4}{20 \div 4} = \frac{4}{5}$
4. $\frac{16}{20}$ in simplest form is $\frac{4}{5}$.

Chapter 1

Progress Check 1

Formative Assessment

Use the Progress Check to assess students' mastery of the previous lessons. Have students review the lesson indicated for the problems they answered incorrectly.

Odd/Even Assignments

Exercises are structured so that students practice the same concepts whether they are assigned the odd or even problems.

Common Error Alert

Equivalent Fractions

Exercises 1–4 Students need to understand that in some cases there are two ways to find equivalent fractions. For instance, in some exercises the given fraction can be reduced one or more times for equivalent fractions. In other cases, the given fraction may already be in simplest form, so you have to multiply both the numerator and denominator by an equivalent form of one to find equivalent fractions.

Progress Check 1 (Lessons 1-1 and 1-2)

Name two equivalent fractions.

1. $\frac{1}{2}$ Sample answer: $\frac{2}{4}, \frac{3}{6}$
2. $\frac{5}{7}$ Sample answer: $\frac{10}{14}, \frac{15}{21}$
3. $\frac{3}{4}$ Sample answer: $\frac{6}{8}, \frac{9}{12}$
4. $\frac{2}{3}$ Sample answer: $\frac{4}{6}, \frac{6}{9}$
5. Complete the model to name two fractions equivalent to $\frac{4}{6}$. $\frac{2}{3}, \frac{8}{12}$

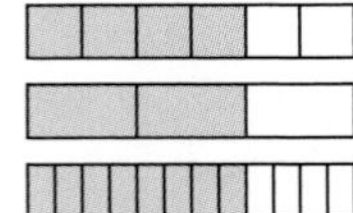

Find the GCF of each set of numbers.

6. 25 and 60 5
7. 18 and 45 9
8. 12, 24, and 60 12
9. 30, 45, and 75 15
10. 8, 20, and 40 4
11. 35, 49, and 84 7

Find the GCF of each set of numbers by using prime factors.

12. 30, 66

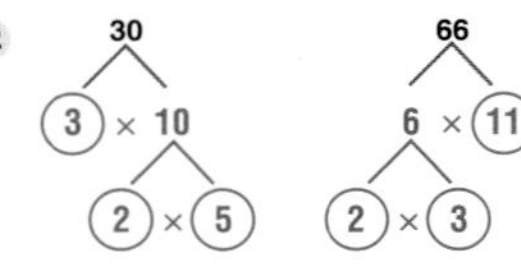

2×3 or 6

13. 27, 63

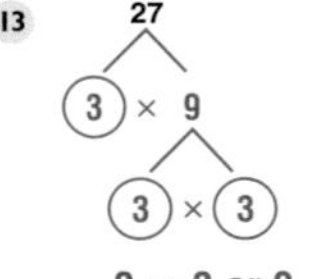

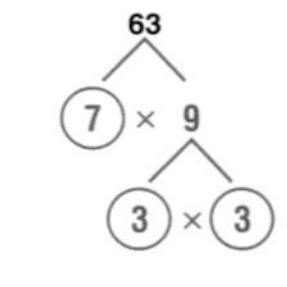

3×3 or 9

Solve.

14. **BANDS** In a marching band, there are 64 woodwinds, 88 brass, and 16 percussion players. When they march in a parade, the director wants the same number of students in each row. What is the greatest number of students in each row?

8 students

STOP

Data-Driven Decision Making

Students missing Exercises . . .	Have trouble with . . .	Should review and practice . . .
1-5	naming two fractions equivalent to a given fraction.	SSG Lesson 1-1, p. 4 CRM Skills Practice, p. A5
6–13	finding greatest common factors.	SSG Lesson 1-2, p. 11 CRM Skills Practice, p. A9
14	solving word problems involving greatest common factor.	CRM Problem-Solving Practice, pp. A6 and A10

Lesson 1-3 Simplify Fractions

KEY Concept

A fraction is in **simplest form** or lowest terms when the numerator and the denominator of the fraction have no common factors other than 1.

To find the simplest form of a fraction, find an equivalent fraction where the numerator and denominator have no common factors.

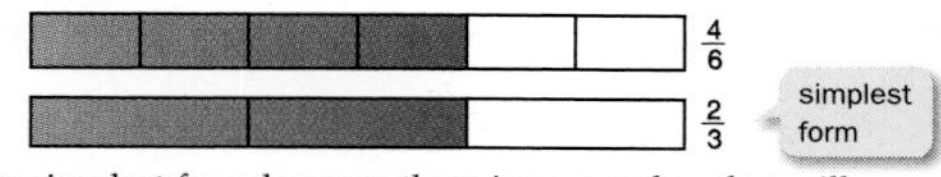

$\frac{2}{3}$ is in simplest form because there is no number that will evenly divide into both the numerator and the denominator.

Any fraction can be written in simplest form by dividing the numerator and denominator by the GCF.

For example, GCF of $\frac{8}{12}$ is 4.

$$\frac{8}{12} = \frac{8 \div 4}{12 \div 4} = \frac{2}{3}$$

So, $\frac{8}{12}$ simplified is $\frac{2}{3}$.

You can also simplify using models and prime factorization.

VOCABULARY

greatest common factor (GCF)
the greatest of the common factors of two or more numbers; the GCF of 24 and 30 is 6

simplest form
the form of a fraction when the GCF of the numerator and the denominator is 1; the fraction $\frac{3}{4}$ is in simplest form because the GCF of 3 and 4 is 1

Example 1

Write $\frac{6}{10}$ in simplest form. Use models.

1. Shade the area of the top bar to represent $\frac{6}{10}$.
2. Shade an area on the bottom bar that is equal to the area of the top bar. Name the equivalent fraction.

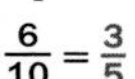

$\frac{6}{10} = \frac{3}{5}$

GO ON

Additional Example 1

Write $\frac{10}{12}$ in simplest form. Use models.

1. Shade the area of the top bar to represent $\frac{10}{12}$.

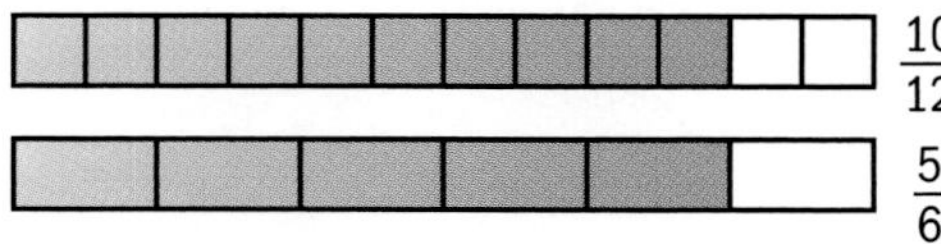

2. Shade an area on the bottom bar that is equal to the area of the top bar. Name the equivalent fraction.

$\frac{10}{12} = \frac{5}{6}$

Lesson Notes

Lesson 1-3

Lesson Planner

Objective Write fractions in simplest form.

Vocabulary **greatest common factor (GCF)**, **simplest form**

Materials/Manipulatives fraction circles, grid paper

Chapter Resource Masters

- CRM Vocabulary and English Language Development (p. A12)
- CRM Skills Practice (p. A13)
- CRM Problem-Solving Practice (p. A14)
- CRM Homework Practice (p. A15)

1 Introduce

Vocabulary

Vocabulary Use Have students state the definition of *simplest form* in their own words. Invite other students to write examples of fractions in simplest form on the board. Use opportunities of incorrect descriptions to clarify the true definition.

2 Teach

Key Concept

Foundational Skills and Concepts After students have read through the Key Concept box, have them try these exercises.

1. How do you know when a fraction is in simplest form? When the numerator and denominator have no common factors other than 1.
2. Can $\frac{8}{12}$ be written in simpler form? Explain. Yes, by dividing the numerator and denominator by 4; $\frac{2}{3}$.

Additional **Example 2**

Write $\frac{18}{45}$ in simplest form. Divide by the GCF.

1. List all the factors of the numerator and denominator.

   Factors of 18: 1, 2, 3, 6, (9), 18

   Factors of 45: 1, 3, 5, (9), 15, 45

2. The greatest common factor in both lists is 9.
3. Divide the numerator and denominator by the GCF.

   $\frac{18}{45} = \frac{18 \div 9}{45 \div 9} = \frac{2}{5}$

4. So, $\frac{18}{45}$ in simplest form is $\frac{2}{5}$.

Common Error *Alert*

Simplify Fractions Students often encounter two major difficulties when simplifying fractions. First, they may have trouble finding a common factor when it is not obvious. Another error is not simplifying a fraction to its lowest terms.

Remind students that a fraction is in simplest form when the numerator and denominator have no factors in common other than 1.

YOUR TURN!

Write $\frac{9}{12}$ in simplest form. Use models.

1. Shade the area of the top bar to represent $\frac{9}{12}$.

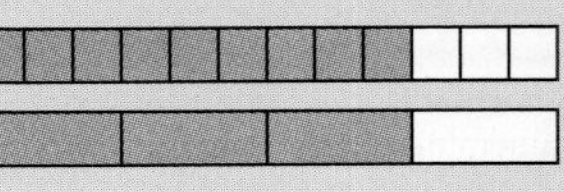

2. Shade an area on the bottom bar that is equal to the area of the top bar. Name the equivalent fraction.

$\frac{9}{12} = \frac{3}{4}$

Example 2

Write $\frac{24}{30}$ in simplest form. Divide by the GCF.

1. List all the factors of the numerator and the denominator.

   Factors of 24: 1, 2, 3, 4, (6), 8, 12, 24

   Factors of 30: 1, 2, 3, 5, (6), 10, 15, 30

2. The greatest common factor in both lists is 6.
3. Divide the numerator and the denominator by the GCF.

   $\frac{24}{30} = \frac{24 \div 6}{30 \div 6} = \frac{4}{5}$

4. So, $\frac{24}{30}$ in simplest form is $\frac{4}{5}$.

YOUR TURN!

Write $\frac{16}{24}$ in simplest form. Divide by the GCF.

1. List all the factors of the numerator and the denominator.

   Factors of 16: 1, 2, 4, (8), 16

   Factors of 24: 1, 2, 3, 4, 6, (8), 12, 24

2. The greatest common factor in both lists is 8.
3. Divide the numerator and denominator by the GCF. $\frac{16}{24} = \frac{16 \div 8}{24 \div 8} = \frac{2}{3}$
4. So, $\frac{16}{24}$ in simplest form is $\frac{2}{3}$.

20 Chapter 1 Fractions

Intervention Strategy Logical/Visual Learners

Greatest Common Factors

Students can use Venn diagrams to find the GCF of two or more numbers. Once the GCF is determined, use it to write fractions in simplified form.

$\frac{6}{32}$ and $\frac{9}{30}$

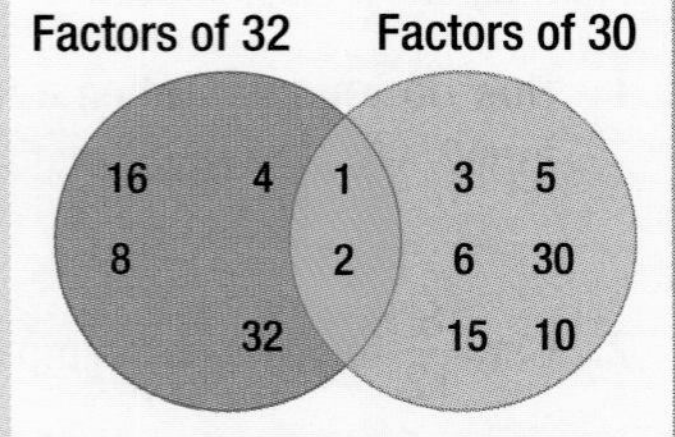

When there are three numbers, use a Venn diagram with three circles.

$\frac{6}{32}, \frac{9}{30},$ and $\frac{12}{16}$

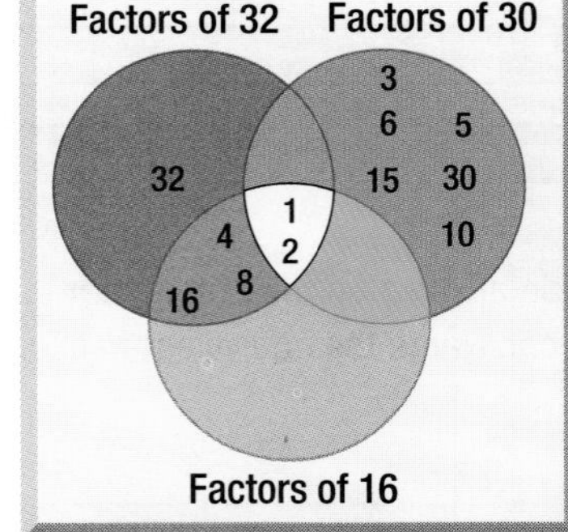

xample 3

Write $\frac{20}{36}$ in simplest form. Use prime factorization.

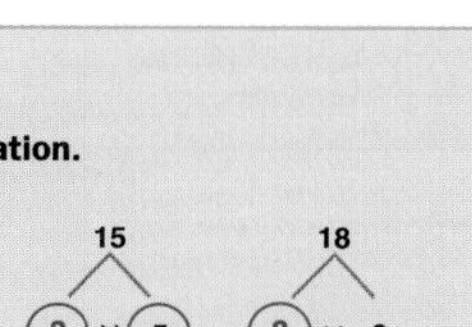
Write the number that is being factored at the top.
Choose any pair of whole number factors of 20 and 36.
Continue to factor each number that is not a prime number.

1. Use a factor tree to write the numerator and the denominator as a product of prime numbers.
2. Replace the numerator and the denominator with their prime factors. Find all equivalent forms of 1.

$\frac{20}{36} = \frac{2 \times 2 \times 5}{2 \times 2 \times 3 \times 3}$

3. Eliminate all equivalent forms of 1.

$\frac{20}{36} = \frac{\not{2} \times \not{2} \times 5}{\not{2} \times \not{2} \times 3 \times 3}$ $\quad \frac{20}{36} = \frac{5}{9}$

YOUR TURN!

Write $\frac{15}{18}$ in simplest form. Use prime factorization.

1. Use a factor tree to write the numerator and the denominator as a product of prime numbers.
2. Replace the numerator and the denominator with their prime factors. Find all equivalent forms of 1.

$\frac{15}{18} = \frac{3 \times 5}{3 \times 3 \times 2}$

3. Eliminate all equivalent forms of 1. $\frac{15}{18} = \frac{\not{3} \times 5}{\not{3} \times 3 \times 2} = \frac{5}{6}$

$\frac{15}{18} = \frac{5}{6}$

GO ON

Additional *Example 3*

Write $\frac{8}{18}$ in simplest form. Use prime factorization.

1. Use a factor tree to write the numerator and the denominator as a product of prime numbers.

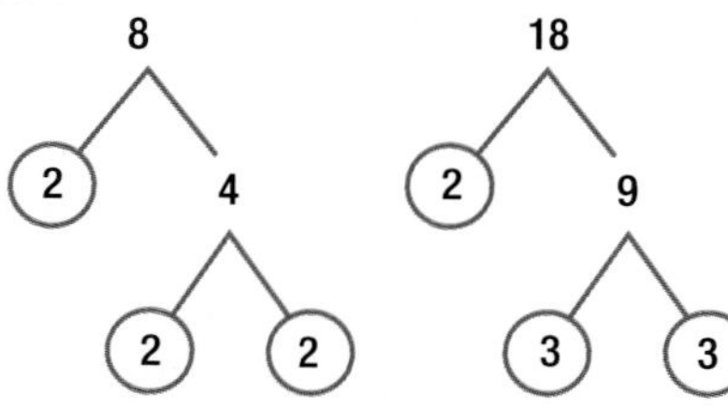

2. Replace the numerator and the denominator with their prime factors. Find all equivalent forms of 1.

$\frac{8}{18} = \frac{2 \times 2 \times 2}{2 \times 3 \times 3}$

4. Eliminate all equivalent forms of 1.

$\frac{8}{18} = \frac{\not{2} \times 2 \times 2}{\not{2} \times 3 \times 3}$

$\frac{8}{18} = \frac{4}{9}$

Intervention Strategy — Logical Learners

Stacking Prime Factorization When finding the prime factors of a number, you can use an alternative format that is more like division. Place the number in the division box and use only prime number divisors. Each quotient becomes the new dividend and divide by a prime number. Continue this process until the quotient is a prime number. Shown is the prime factorization for 324.

```
      3
   3)9
  3)27
  3)81
 2)162
 2)324
```

The prime factorization of 324 = 2 × 2 × 3 × 3 × 3 × 3.

3 Practice

Using Manipulatives

Grid Paper Suggest students use grid paper to model and find equivalent fractions.

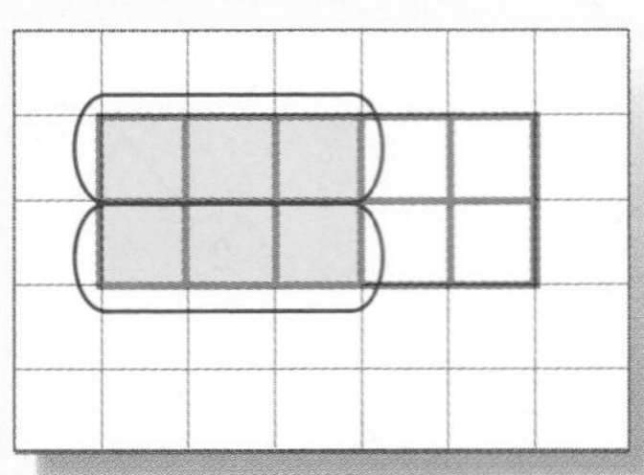

$\frac{6}{10} = \frac{3}{5}$

Fraction Circles Students can use fraction circles to write fractions in their simplest forms.

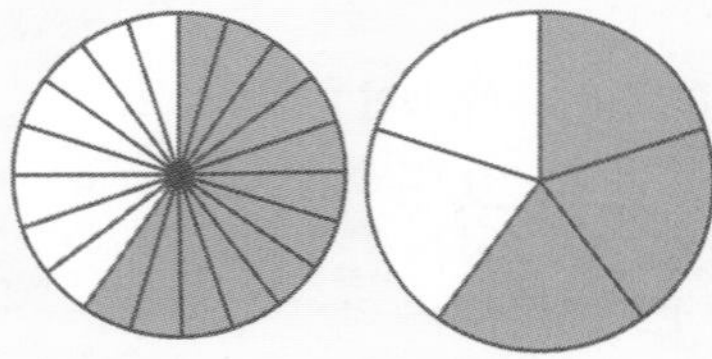

On-Hand Manipulatives Use objects that can be divided into fractional parts, like paper circles or bars, granola bars, pizzas, or pancakes. Students can compare the fractional parts of these real-world items to compare and simplify fractions.

Who is Correct?

Write $\frac{20}{48}$ in simplest form. Use any method.

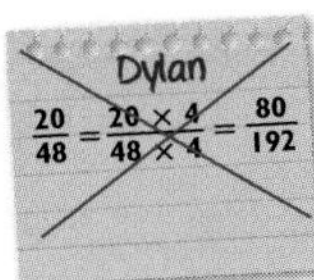

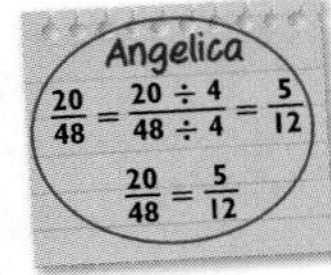

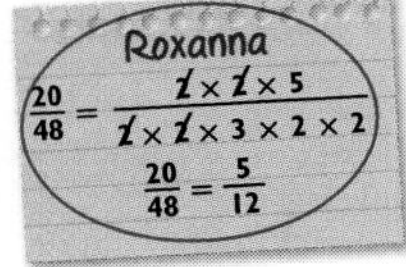

Circle correct answer(s). Cross out incorrect answer(s).

Guided Practice

Write each fraction in simplest form. Use models.

1 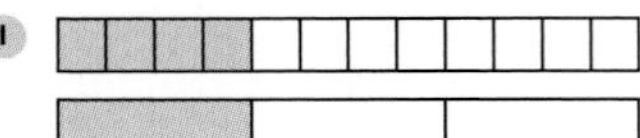

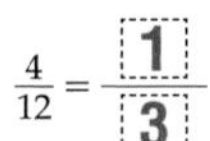

$\frac{4}{12} = \frac{1}{3}$

2 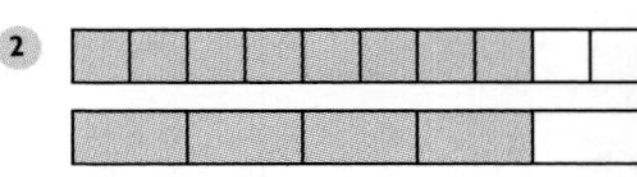

$\frac{8}{10} = \frac{4}{5}$

Write each fraction in simplest form. Divide by the GCF.

3 $\frac{15}{20} = \frac{3}{4}$

Factors of 15: 1, 3, (5), 15

Factors of 20: 1, 2, 4, (5), 10, 20

$\frac{15}{20} = \frac{15 \div 5}{20 \div 5} = \frac{3}{4}$

4 $\frac{12}{30} = \frac{2}{5}$

Factors of 12: 1, 2, 3, 4, (6), 12

Factors of 30: 1, 2, 3, 5, (6), 10, 15, 3

$\frac{12}{30} = \frac{12 \div 6}{30 \div 6} = \frac{2}{5}$

Who *is Correct?*
Diagnostic Teaching

- Dylan is incorrect. He multiplied both the numerator and denominator. This does not simplify the fraction.
- Angelica is correct. She divided the numerator and denominator by 4 to find the simplest form.
- Roxanna is correct. She found the prime factors of the numerator and denominator and eliminated all equivalent forms of 1 to find the simplest form.

Remind students that a fraction is in simplest form when the GCF of the numerator and denominator is 1.

Step by Step Practice

5 Write $\frac{12}{18}$ in simplest form. Use prime factorization.

Step 1 Write the numerator as a product of prime numbers.

Step 2 Write the denominator as a product of prime numbers.

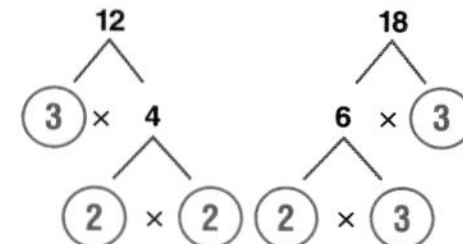

Step 3 Replace the numerator with its prime factors. Replace the denominator with its prime factors. Find and eliminate all equivalent forms of 1.

$$\frac{12}{18} = \frac{\cancel{2} \times \cancel{3} \times 2}{\cancel{2} \times \cancel{3} \times 3} = \frac{2}{3}$$

Step 4 The simplest form of $\frac{12}{18}$ is $\frac{2}{3}$.

Write each fraction in simplest form. Use prime factorization.

6 $\frac{8}{20} = \frac{\cancel{2} \times \cancel{2} \times 2}{\cancel{2} \times \cancel{2} \times 5} = \frac{2}{5}$

7 $\frac{15}{24} = \frac{\cancel{3} \times 5}{2 \times 2 \times 2 \times \cancel{3}} = \frac{5}{8}$

8 $\frac{12}{15}$ $\frac{4}{5}$

9 $\frac{14}{63}$ $\frac{2}{9}$

10 $\frac{35}{60}$ $\frac{7}{12}$

11 $\frac{18}{42}$ $\frac{3}{7}$

12 $\frac{36}{48}$ $\frac{3}{4}$

13 $\frac{28}{36}$ $\frac{7}{9}$

Common Error *Alert*

Factor Tree Students may have difficulty using a factor tree because they are not sure what to do next once they get to a prime number. Tell students that the branches end only at prime numbers. At that point, they are finished with that branch. Suggest they go back and multiply the prime numbers they find to make certain that their product is the original number.

Are They Getting It?

Check students' understanding of simplifying fractions by writing these problems on the board. Ask students to point out wrong answers and explain why they are wrong.

Write each fraction in simplest form.

1. $\frac{9}{39}$ $\quad \frac{9}{39} = \frac{\cancel{3} \times 3}{\cancel{3} \times 13} = \frac{3}{13}$ This is correct.

2. $\frac{12}{20}$ $\quad \frac{12}{20} = \frac{12 \div 2}{20 \div 2} = \frac{6}{10}$ This is incorrect. It is not in simplest form.

3. $\frac{2}{5}$ $\quad \frac{2}{5} = \frac{8}{20}$ This is incorrect. The fraction was already in simplest form.

Common Error *Alert*

Division If students are having trouble dividing by one-digit numbers, then have them model a few basic division facts using counters to refresh their memories.

Also use arrays to help students recall division.

12 divided by 3 rows

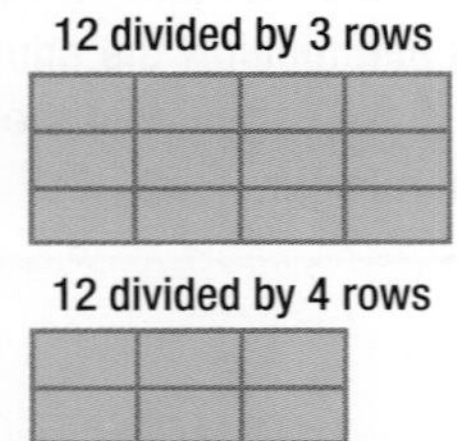

12 divided by 4 rows

Math Coach Notes

Study Tips Give students the ratios:

3 out of 12
6 out of 10
9 out of 15

Have students write each as a fraction and then name a real-world situation where one might use or hear the ratio or fraction.

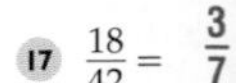

Write each fraction in simplest form. Divide by the GCF.

14 $\frac{14}{21} = \frac{2}{3}$ 15 $\frac{15}{25} = \frac{3}{5}$ 16 $\frac{16}{32} = \frac{1}{2}$ 17 $\frac{18}{42} = \frac{3}{7}$

Step by Step Problem-Solving Practice

Problem-Solving Strategie

- ☐ Look for a pattern.
- ☑ Use logical reasoning.
- ☐ Solve a simpler problem.
- ☐ Work backward.
- ☐ Draw a diagram.

Solve.

18 CARPENTRY A carpenter wants to shingle the roof of a shed. He can choose green or brown shingles of the same size. If he uses green shingles, he will use 32 of the 48 green shingles he has. Write the fraction of the green shingles he will use in simplest form.

Understand Read the problem. Write what you know.

He would use $\frac{32}{48}$ of the green shingles.

Plan Pick a strategy. One strategy is to use logical reasoning.

Simplify the fraction that shows how many green shingles he would use.

Solve Find the GCF of 32 and 48.

Factors of 32: 1, 2, 4, 8, (16), 32

Factors of 48: 1, 2, 4, 6, 8, (16), 24, 48

Divide the numerator and denominator by the GCF.

$$\frac{32}{48} = \frac{32 \div 16}{48 \div 16} = \frac{2}{3}$$

Check Use another method. Use prime factorization. Simplify the fraction.

Does your answer make sense? Did you answer the question?

Intervention Strategy — Interpersonal/Logical/Linguistic Learners

Write the Steps Encourage students to summarize and write the steps for simplifying fractions clearly and concisely in their notes. Have students work in small groups to present concise summaries to the class. Make sure students include the following points.

Simplify a Fraction

Method 1

1. Find a common factor of the numerator and denominator.
2. Divide both the numerator and denominator by the common factor.
3. Repeat this process until there are no more common factors.
4. The fraction is in simplest form when no more common factors exist.

Method 2

1. Find the GCF of the numerator and denominator.
2. Divide the numerator and the denominator by the GCF.

MUSIC Angelo and Joyce are both listening to songs on their own CDs. Angelo listened to $\frac{12}{16}$ of his songs and Joyce listened to $\frac{15}{20}$ of her songs. Angelo says he listened to more songs. Is he correct? Explain. Check off each step.

✔ Understand: I underlined key words.

✔ Plan: To solve the problem, I will use logical reasoning.

✔ Solve: The answer is no, they both listened to the same amount of songs.

✔ Check: I checked my answer by multiplying the simplest form by the GCF.

SPORTS Lisa made 35 out of 50 free throws at basketball practice. What fraction of the free throws did she make? $\frac{35}{50}$

Simplify your answer to its simplest form. $\frac{7}{10}$

What fraction of the free throws did she miss? $\frac{15}{50}$

Simplify your answer to its simplest form. $\frac{3}{10}$

Reflect Explain which method used for simplifying fractions you prefer and why.

Answers will vary. Students should select one of the following: using models, dividing by the GCF, or using prime factorization. Students should explain their answers.

Skills, Concepts, and Problem Solving

Write each fraction in simplest form. Use models.

22 $\frac{6}{8} = \frac{3}{4}$

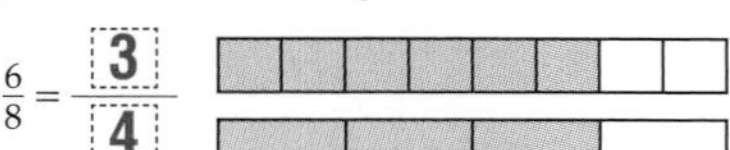

23 $\frac{3}{9} = \frac{1}{3}$

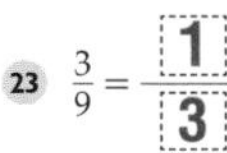

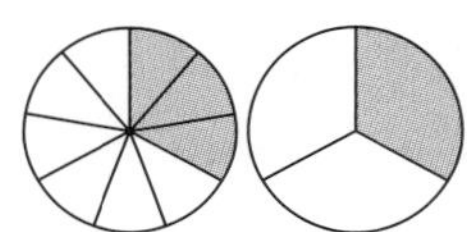

Write each fraction in simplest form. Divide by the GCF.

24 $\frac{14}{16} = \frac{7}{8}$

25 $\frac{10}{16} = \frac{5}{8}$

26 $\frac{7}{28} = \frac{1}{4}$

27 $\frac{27}{36} = \frac{3}{4}$

GO ON

Odd/Even Assignments

Exercises 22–32 are structured so that students practice the same concepts whether they are assigned the odd or even problems.

In-Class Assignment

Have students complete Exercises 23, 27, 30, 32, and 35 to ensure that they understand the concept.

Intervention Strategy

Interpersonal/ Auditory/ Visual Learners

Presentations Give student groups a fraction to simplify. Then assign each group either the method of shading in equivalent fractions, dividing by the GCF, or using prime factorization. Ask student groups to present their methods to the rest of the class. Encourage those sitting to ask questions and interact with the presenters.

Math Challenge

6-digit Numbers Students should choose a partner. Each student writes a 6-digit number on a piece of paper. Partners trade papers and find the prime factorization of the number given to them. When each factorization is complete, trade papers again. Use multiplication to verify that the prime factorization is accurate.

4 Assess

See It, Do It, Say It, Write It

1. Write a fraction on the board. Model how to write it in simplest form. Repeat with other fractions, using different methods.
2. Give each student three fractions. Ask them to use the various methods to simply the fractions. Discuss the results.
3. Have students discuss their results with a partner.
4. Have students work alone. Tell students to write a paragraph about how they would simplify $\frac{21}{28}$. Ask them to include each step as well as the answer.

Looking Ahead: Pre-Teach

Compare and Order Fractions In the next lesson, students will learn how to compare and order fractions.

Order the fractions $\frac{3}{5}, \frac{1}{9}, \frac{9}{10}$ from least to greatest.

1. What is the LCD for these fractions? 90
2. Write the equivalent fractions of each fraction using the LCD. $\frac{54}{90}, \frac{10}{90}, \frac{81}{90}$
3. Write the fractions in order. $\frac{1}{9}, \frac{3}{5}, \frac{9}{10}$

Write each fraction in simplest form. Use prime factorization.

28 $\frac{9}{12} = \frac{3}{4}$ 29 $\frac{36}{40} = \frac{9}{10}$ 30 $\frac{10}{25} = \frac{2}{5}$ 31 $\frac{4}{18} = \frac{2}{9}$

Solve.

32 FOOD Brandon took 36 pieces of pizza to a party. He brought 9 pieces of pizza home. Write the fraction in simplest form of pieces of pizza that were eaten. $\frac{3}{4}$

Brandon took 36 pieces of pizza to a party.

Vocabulary Check **Write the vocabulary word that completes each sentence.**

33 A fraction in simplest form is a fraction in which the numerator and the denominator have no common factor greater than 1.

34 The greatest common factor is the greatest of the common factors of two or more numbers.

35 **Writing in Math** Suppose that you had a fraction that had a symbol in it, such as $\frac{12x}{15x}$. What do you think this fraction is in simplest form? Explain your reasoning.

Answers will vary, but students should realize that an x divided by x is equivalent to one. The correct answer is $\frac{4}{5}$.

Spiral Review

Find the GCF of each set of numbers. (Lesson 1-2, p. 11)

36 30 and 36 6

37 56 and 72 8

38 27, 36, and 81 9

39 16, 52, and 76 4

Solve. (Lesson 1-1, p. 4)

40 HOBBIES Pam had two pieces of cloth the same length for her quilt. She cut the first piece into 8 equal parts. She cut the second piece into 12 equal parts. How many parts from the second piece of cloth equal the same length as 4 parts from the first part of cloth? 6 parts

STOP

26 Chapter 1 Fractions

Ticket Out the Door

Simplified Fractions Students need to write three fractions that can be simplified. Students can trade papers with another student. They should write the fractions in simplified form. When a student approaches the door to exit, have them choose one of the fractions and explain to you how the fraction was simplified. Collect papers as students exit.

Compare and Order Fractions

KEY Concept

Use the terms **greater than (>)**, **less than (<)**, or **equal to (=)** to compare fractions. Here are three ways to compare fractions.

- If the fractions have the **same denominator,** compare the numerators.

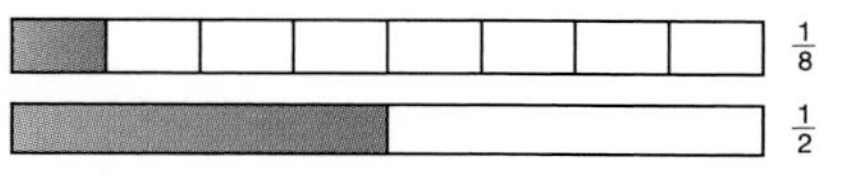

1 out of 4 parts is less than 3 out of 4 parts, so $\frac{1}{4} < \frac{3}{4}$.

- If the fractions have the same numerator, compare the denominators.

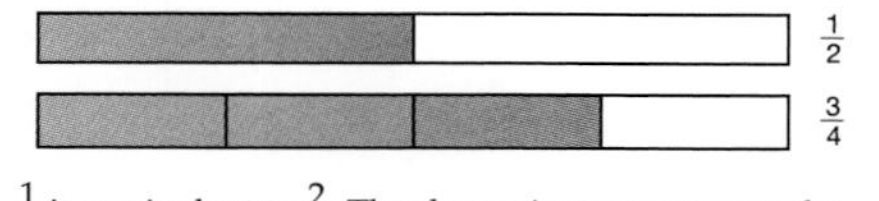

1 out of 8 parts is less than 1 out of 2 parts, so $\frac{1}{8} < \frac{1}{2}$.

- If the fractions have **different numerators and denominators** find the least common denominator (LCD) and compare.

$\frac{1}{2}$ is equivalent to $\frac{2}{4}$. The denominators are now the same, so compare numerators. $\frac{2}{4} < \frac{3}{4}$, so $\frac{1}{2} < \frac{3}{4}$.

- To order fractions, rename fractions using their **least common denominator**. Then compare numerators.

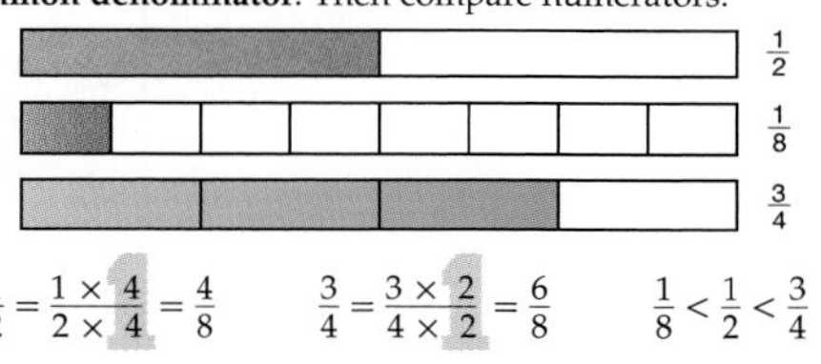

$\frac{1}{2} = \frac{1 \times 4}{2 \times 4} = \frac{4}{8}$ $\quad \frac{3}{4} = \frac{3 \times 2}{4 \times 2} = \frac{6}{8}$ $\quad \frac{1}{8} < \frac{1}{2} < \frac{3}{4}$

VOCABULARY

common denominators
the same denominator (bottom number) used in two or more fractions

equivalent forms of one
different expressions that represent the same number

least common denominator (LCD)
the least common multiple of the denominators of two or more fractions

least common multiple (LCM)
the least whole number greater than 0 that is a common multiple of two or more numbers; the LCM of 2 and 3 is 6

GO ON

Intervention Strategy — Visual/Logical/Kinesthetic Learners

Compare with Models Tell students to draw a model of $\frac{3}{4}$ as a rectangle that is divided into fourths. Ask them to shade 3 parts. Then ask them to make another model to represent $\frac{7}{10}$. Tell them that this rectangle should be the same size as their first rectangle, but divided into tenths. After they shade 7 parts, ask them to compare the models. Which shaded area is larger, that of the $\frac{3}{4}$ or $\frac{7}{10}$ model? Have students draw models to compare other fractions.

Fraction bars and fraction circles can also be used to compare the size of fractions. Remind students that the wholes must be of equal size.

Lesson Notes

Lesson 1-4

Lesson Planner

Objective Compare and order fractions and find their approximate locations on a number line.

Vocabulary **common denominators**, **equivalent forms of one**, **least common denominator (LCD)**, **least common multiple (LCM)**

Materials/Manipulatives fraction circles, fraction tiles

Chapter Resource Masters

- CRM Vocabulary and English Language Development (p. A16)
- CRM Skills Practice (p. A17)
- CRM Problem-Solving Practice (p. A18)
- CRM Homework Practice (p. A19)

1 Introduce

Vocabulary

Apples to Apples Discuss with students what the phrase "Compare apples to apples" means. One example to illustrate this idea is to compare dollars to euros. You can either compare dollars to dollars or euros to euros, but a comparison of dollars to euros does not make any sense. Fractions can be thought of in a similar fashion. To compare fractions, they need to have common denominators.

2 Teach

Key Concept

Foundational Skills and Concepts After students have read through the Key Concept box, have them try these exercises.

1. If the denominators are the same, what do you compare? the numerators
2. What are two ways to compare fractions? Look at models of the fractions, or find equivalent fractions with the same denominators to compare.

Additional **Example 1**

Use $<$, $=$, or $>$ to compare $\frac{3}{4}$ and $\frac{2}{3}$.

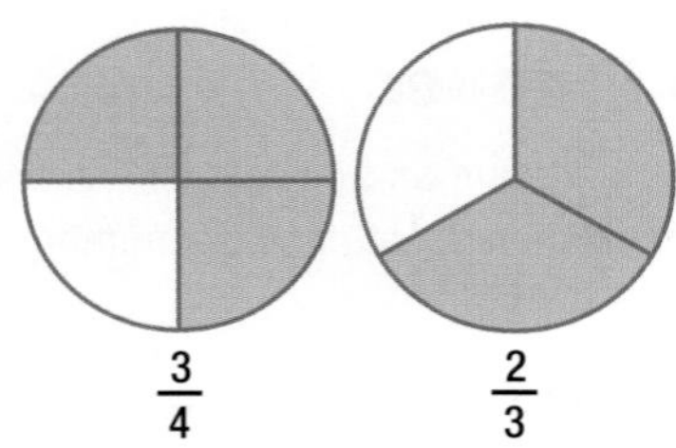

$\frac{3}{4}$ $\frac{2}{3}$

1. The circle on the left has 4 sections. Use it to model $\frac{3}{4}$. Shade 3 sections.
2. The circle on the right has 3 sections. Use it to model $\frac{2}{3}$. Shade 2 sections.
3. Compare the shaded areas. Use $<$, $=$, or $>$ to write a statement.

   $\frac{3}{4} > \frac{2}{3}$

Example 1

Use $<$, $=$, or $>$ to compare $\frac{3}{8}$ and $\frac{2}{3}$.

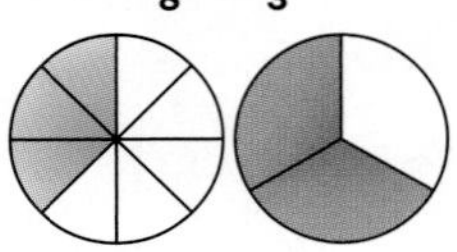

1. The circle on the left has 8 sections. Use it to model $\frac{3}{8}$. Shade 3 sections.
2. The circle on the right has 3 sections. Use it to model $\frac{2}{3}$. Shade 2 sections.
3. Compare the shaded areas. Use $<$, $=$, or $>$ to write a statement.

   $\frac{3}{8} < \frac{2}{3}$

YOUR TURN!

Use $<$, $=$, or $>$ to compare $\frac{2}{3}$ and $\frac{4}{7}$. Shade the models given.

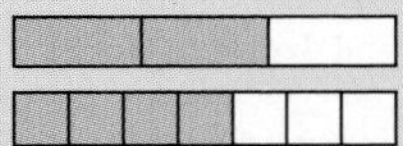

1. The rectangle on the top has 3 sections. Use it to model $\frac{2}{3}$. Shade 2 sections.
2. The rectangle on the bottom has 7 sections. Use it to model $\frac{2}{3}$. Shade 4 sections.
3. Compare the shaded areas. Use $<$, $=$, or $>$ to write a statement.

   $\frac{2}{3} > \frac{4}{7}$

28 Chapter 1 Fractions

Intervention Strategy — Naturalist Learners

Recipes Have students bring a recipe of their favorite dessert to class. Students should list each ingredient measured in cups together and each ingredient measured in teaspoons and tablespoons together. Write each amount in each list so that the amounts can be compared to each other. Write the ingredients measured in cups in order from least to greatest. Write the ingredients measured in spoons from greatest to least. (1 tablespoon = 4 teaspoons)

Example 2

Use <, =, or > to compare $\frac{3}{4}$ and $\frac{5}{6}$.
Rename the fractions using a common denominator.

1. Find the LCM of 4 and 6.

Multiples of 4	Multiples of 6
4 × 1 = 4	6 × 1 = 6
4 × 2 = 8	6 × 2 = 12
4 × 3 = 12	6 × 3 = 18
4 × 4 = 16	6 × 4 = (24)
4 × 5 = 20	
4 × 6 = (24)	

The LCD is 24.

2. Rename each fraction as an equivalent fraction with a denominator of 24.

$\frac{3}{4} = \frac{3 \times 6}{4 \times 6} = \frac{18}{24}$

$\frac{5}{6} = \frac{5 \times 4}{6 \times 4} = \frac{20}{24}$

3. Compare the numerators of the equivalent fractions.
18 < 20

Write a statement using the equivalent fractions.
$\frac{18}{24} < \frac{20}{24}$

4. Replace the equivalent fractions with the original fractions.
$\frac{3}{4} < \frac{5}{6}$

YOUR TURN!

Use <, =, or > to compare $\frac{2}{3}$ and $\frac{5}{9}$.
Rename the fractions using a common denominator.

1. Find the LCM of 3 and 9.

Multiples of 3	Multiples of 9
3 × 1 = 3	9 × 1 = (9)
3 × 2 = 6	9 × 2 = 18
3 × 3 = (9)	9 × 3 = 27

The LCD is 9.

2. Rename each fraction as an equivalent fraction with the same denominators.

$\frac{2}{3} = \frac{2 \times 3}{3 \times 3} = \frac{6}{9}$

$\frac{5}{9} = \frac{5 \times 1}{9 \times 1} = \frac{5}{9}$

3. Compare the numerators of the equivalent fractions.
6 (>) 5

Write a statement using the equivalent fractions.
$\frac{6}{9} > \frac{5}{9}$

4. Replace the equivalent fractions with the original fractions.
$\frac{2}{3} > \frac{5}{9}$

GO ON

Intervention Strategy Logical Learners

Compare Money Amounts Have students think about money. Ask: What fraction of one dollar is a quarter? $\frac{1}{4}$ What fraction of one dollar is a dime? $\frac{1}{10}$ Compare two dimes to one quarter using fractions. $\frac{2}{10} < \frac{1}{4}$ Ask student volunteers to pose other money-related fractions to compare.

Additional *Example 2*

Use <, =, or > to compare $\frac{5}{9}$ and $\frac{4}{7}$.

Rename the fractions using a common denominator.

1. Find the LCM of 9 and 7.

Multiples of 9	Multiples of 7
9 × 1 = 9	7 × 1 = 7
9 × 2 = 18	7 × 2 = 14
9 × 3 = 27	7 × 3 = 21
9 × 4 = 36	7 × 4 = 28
9 × 5 = 45	7 × 5 = 35
9 × 6 = 54	7 × 6 = 42
9 × 7 = (63)	7 × 7 = 49
	7 × 8 = 56
	7 × 9 = (63)

The LCD is 63.

2. Rename each fraction as an equivalent fraction with a denominator of 63.

$\frac{5}{9} = \frac{5 \times 7}{9 \times 7} = \frac{35}{63}$ $\frac{4}{7} = \frac{4 \times 9}{7 \times 9} = \frac{36}{63}$

3. Compare the numerators of the equivalent fractions.
35 < 36
Write a statement using the equivalent fractions.
$\frac{35}{63} < \frac{36}{63}$

4. Replace the equivalent fractions with the original fractions.
$\frac{5}{9} < \frac{4}{7}$

Additional **Example 3**

Order the fractions $\frac{7}{8}$, $\frac{2}{3}$, and $\frac{5}{6}$ from least to greatest.

1. Find the LCM.

Multiples of 8: 8, 16, 24, 32, 40, . . .

Multiples of 3: 3, 6, 9, 12, 15, 18, 21, 24, 27, . . .

Multiples of 6: 6, 12, 18, 24, 30, 36, . . .

The least number in all three lists of multiples is 24. The LCD of the fractions is 24.

2. Write equivalent fractions that have 24 in the denominators.

$$\frac{7}{8} = \frac{7 \times 3}{8 \times 3} = \frac{21}{24}$$

$$\frac{2}{3} = \frac{2 \times 8}{3 \times 8} = \frac{16}{24}$$

$$\frac{5}{6} = \frac{5 \times 4}{6 \times 4} = \frac{20}{24}$$

3. Compare the numerators of the equivalent fractions. $16 < 20 < 21$

4. Order the fractions from least to greatest.

$\frac{16}{24} < \frac{20}{24} < \frac{21}{24}$ means that $\frac{2}{3} < \frac{5}{6} < \frac{7}{8}$.

So, from least to greatest, the fractions are $\frac{2}{3}, \frac{5}{6}, \frac{7}{8}$.

Example 3

Order the fractions $\frac{3}{4}$, $\frac{5}{6}$, and $\frac{7}{9}$ from least to greatest.

1. Find the LCM for 4, 6, and 9.

Multiples of 4: 4, 8, 12, 16, 20, 24, 28, 32, (36), 40, …
Multiples of 6: 6, 12, 18, 24, 30, (36), 42, 48, …
Multiples of 9: 9, 18, 27, (36), 45, …

The least number in all three lists of multiples is 36. The LCD of the fractions is 36.

2. Write equivalent fractions that have 36 as their denominators.

$$\frac{3}{4} = \frac{3 \times 9}{4 \times 9} = \frac{27}{36} \qquad \frac{5}{6} = \frac{5 \times 6}{6 \times 6} = \frac{30}{36} \qquad \frac{7}{9} = \frac{7 \times 4}{9 \times 4} = \frac{28}{36}$$

3. Compare the numerators of the equivalent fractions. $27 < 28 < 30$

4. Order the fractions from least to greatest.

$\frac{27}{36} < \frac{28}{36} < \frac{30}{36}$ means that $\frac{3}{4} < \frac{7}{9} < \frac{5}{6}$.

So, from least to greatest, the fractions are $\frac{3}{4}, \frac{7}{9}, \frac{5}{6}$.

YOUR TURN!

Order the fractions $\frac{4}{5}$, $\frac{1}{8}$, and $\frac{9}{10}$ from least to greatest.

1. Find the LCM for the denominators.

Multiples of 5: 5, 10, 15, 20, 25, 30, 35, 40, 45, ...
Multiples of 8: 8, 16, 24, 32, 40, 48, ...
Multiples of 10: 10, 20, 30, 40, 50, ...

The least number in all three lists of multiples is 40.
The LCD of the fractions is 40.

2. Write equivalent fractions that have 40 in the denominators.

$$\frac{4}{5} = \frac{4 \times 8}{5 \times 8} = \frac{32}{40} \qquad \frac{1}{8} = \frac{1 \times 5}{8 \times 5} = \frac{5}{40} \qquad \frac{9}{10} = \frac{9 \times 4}{10 \times 4} = \frac{36}{40}$$

3. Compare the numerators of the equivalent fractions.

$5 < 32 < 36$

4. Order the fractions from least to greatest.

$\frac{5}{40} < \frac{32}{40} < \frac{36}{40}$ means that $\frac{1}{8} < \frac{4}{5} < \frac{9}{10}$.

English Learner Strategy

Compare to $\frac{1}{2}$ Ordering several fractions can be overwhelming for struggling students. One strategy is to first separate the fractions into two groups: those fractions greater than $\frac{1}{2}$ and those less than $\frac{1}{2}$. This helps students so that they have fewer fractions to compare at a time.

Who is Correct?

Use <, =, or > to compare $\frac{4}{5}$ and $\frac{4}{8}$.

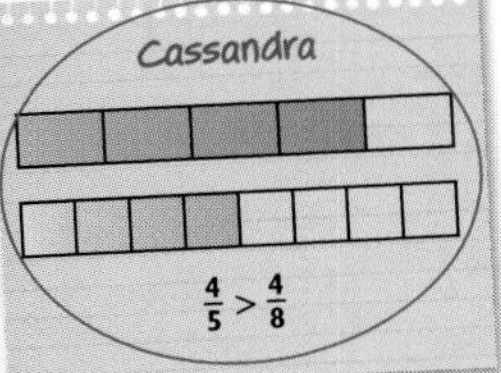

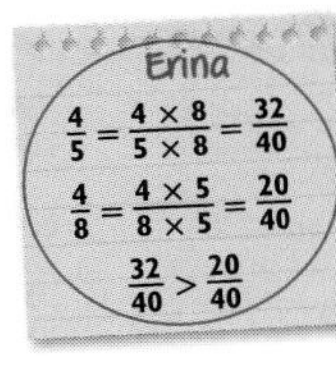

Erina
$\frac{4}{5} = \frac{4 \times 8}{5 \times 8} = \frac{32}{40}$
$\frac{4}{8} = \frac{4 \times 5}{8 \times 5} = \frac{20}{40}$
$\frac{32}{40} > \frac{20}{40}$

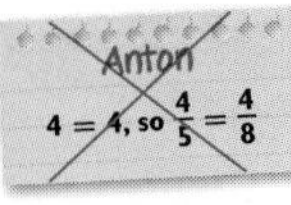

Circle correct answer(s). Cross out incorrect answer(s).

Guided Practice

Use <, =, or > to compare the fractions. Shade the models given.

1 $\frac{5}{8} > \frac{1}{3}$

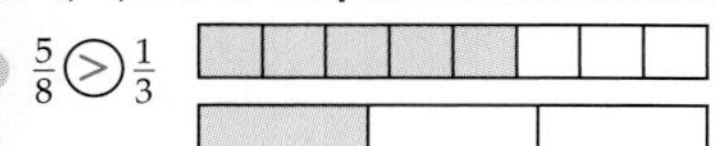

2 $\frac{4}{5} > \frac{3}{10}$

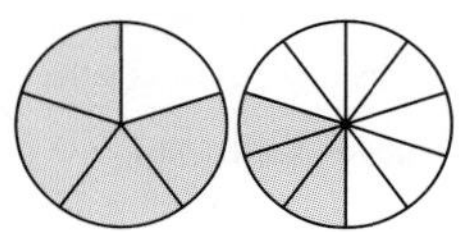

Step by Step Practice

3 Use <, =, or > to compare $\frac{5}{9}$ and $\frac{7}{12}$. Rename the fractions using a common denominator.

Step 1 Find the LCM of 9 and 12. 36

Step 2 Rename each fraction to an equivalent fraction.

$$\frac{5}{9} = \frac{5 \times 4}{9 \times 4} = \frac{20}{36} \qquad \frac{7}{12} = \frac{7 \times 3}{12 \times 3} = \frac{21}{36}$$

Step 3 Compare the numerators. Write a statement using the equivalent fractions. $\frac{20}{36} < \frac{21}{36}$

Step 4 Replace the equivalent fractions with the original fractions. $\frac{5}{9} < \frac{7}{12}$

GO ON

3 Practice

Using Manipulatives

Fraction Tiles Use fraction tiles as a model to compare fractions. Point out that the key part to using fraction tiles is that the tiles are the same lengths. Have students divide each tile into the same number of equal parts as the denominator and shade the numerator. Place the tiles side by side and compare the shaded parts. This will give students a visual model of comparing fractions.

Fraction Circles Have students use fraction circles as they would use fraction tiles.

On-Hand Manipulatives Use objects that can be divided into fractional parts, like paper circles or bars, granola bars, pizzas, or pancakes. Students can compare the fractional parts of these real-world items to compare fractions.

Who *is Correct?*

Diagnostic Teaching

- Cassandra is correct. She used a model to find her answer.
- Erina is correct. She multiplied by equivalent forms of one to get a common denominator.
- Anton is incorrect. He compared only the numerators of the fractions.

Remind students that they can use models or rewrite the fractions with common denominators to compare them.

English Learner Strategy

Make Connections Learning is primarily a process in which we make connections. Help students make more connections and construct meanings. Have students review the lessons in this chapter and the previous chapter and create an outline or graphic organizer that shows how the concepts of each lesson build on one another. Start students out by having them jot the phrase "Parts of a Whole" on a sheet of paper. Then have students review their text and complete the diagram with the other concepts that they have learned. Encourage them to add on to their outlines or organizers as they complete the study of Volume 2. Show students examples of flowcharts, main-idea charts, tables, tree diagrams, and other graphic organizers to get them started.

Order the fractions from least to greatest.

4. $\frac{1}{3}, \frac{5}{9},$ and $\frac{7}{18}$ $\frac{1}{3}, \frac{7}{18}, \frac{5}{9}$

$$\frac{1}{3} = \frac{1 \times 6}{3 \times 6} = \frac{6}{18}$$
$$\frac{5}{9} = \frac{5 \times 2}{9 \times 2} = \frac{10}{18}$$
$$\frac{7}{18} = \frac{7 \times 1}{18 \times 1} = \frac{7}{18}$$

5. $\frac{1}{2}, \frac{3}{4},$ and $\frac{5}{7}$ $\frac{1}{2}, \frac{5}{7}, \frac{3}{4}$

$$\frac{1}{2} = \frac{1 \times 14}{2 \times 14} = \frac{14}{28}$$
$$\frac{3}{4} = \frac{3 \times 7}{4 \times 7} = \frac{21}{28}$$
$$\frac{5}{7} = \frac{5 \times 4}{7 \times 4} = \frac{20}{28}$$

Step by Step Problem-Solving Practice

Problem-Solving Strategies
- ☑ Draw a diagram.
- ☐ Look for a pattern.
- ☐ Guess and check.
- ☐ Act it out.
- ☐ Solve a simpler problem.

Solve.

6. FITNESS Jeff and Ian are twins. They are very close in height. Jeff is 6 feet $\frac{1}{4}$ inch tall, and Ian is 6 feet $\frac{5}{8}$ inch tall. Who is taller?

Understand Read the problem. Write what you know.
Jeff is 6 feet $\frac{1}{4}$ inch tall.
Ian is 6 feet $\frac{5}{8}$ inch tall.

Plan Pick a strategy. One strategy is to draw a diagram.

Compare the two heights. Both heights are 6 feet. Only compare the fractional parts of each boy's height.

Draw a bar divided into 4 equal parts. Draw another bar of equal length. Divide it into 8 equal parts.

Solve Shade $\frac{1}{4}$ and $\frac{5}{8}$. Compare the shaded parts.

6 feet $\frac{1}{4}$ inch $<$ 6 feet $\frac{5}{8}$ inch

So, Ian is taller than Jeff.

Check Does the answer make sense?
Did you answer the question?

Are They Getting It?

Check students' understanding of comparing and ordering fractions by writing these problems on the board. Have students explain the incorrect information in each problem. Tell them to use a fraction tile or another visual aid to show why the answers are correct or incorrect.

Order the fractions from least to greatest.

1. $\frac{1}{2}, \frac{3}{4}, \frac{3}{8}$ $\frac{3}{4}, \frac{1}{2}, \frac{3}{8}$ This is incorrect. The order is from greatest to least.

2. $\frac{2}{3}, \frac{5}{9}, \frac{3}{6}$ $\frac{3}{6}, \frac{5}{9}, \frac{2}{3}$ This is correct.

3. $\frac{4}{15}, \frac{5}{18}, \frac{5}{6}$ $\frac{5}{18}, \frac{4}{15}, \frac{5}{6}$ This is incorrect. The first two fractions should be switched.

7 **WEATHER** In Martinsville, it rained three days in a row. On Tuesday it rained $\frac{1}{6}$ inch, on Wednesday it rained $\frac{7}{8}$ inch, and on Thursday it rained $\frac{5}{12}$ inch. Which day did it rain the most? Check off each step.

✔ Understand: I underlined key words.

✔ Plan: To solve the problem, I will draw a diagram.

✔ Solve: The answer is Wednesday; $\frac{7}{8}$ is the largest fraction.

✔ Check: I checked my answer by finding the LCD and renaming the fractions.

8 **WEATHER** On Friday, it snowed $\frac{5}{6}$ of an inch in Columbus and $\frac{9}{12}$ of an inch in Cleveland. Which city got more snow?

Columbus

9 **Reflect** Tessa said that $\frac{5}{8}$ is greater than $\frac{3}{4}$ because 5 > 3 and 8 > 4. Draw diagrams. Explain if Tessa is correct.

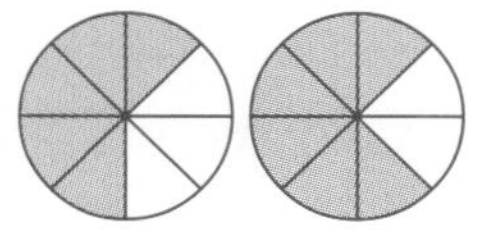

Sample answer: Tessa is incorrect. The equivalent form of $\frac{3}{4}$ is $\frac{6}{8}$, which is greater than $\frac{5}{8}$.

Skills, Concepts, and Problem Solving

Use <, =, or > to compare the fractions. Shade the models given.

10 $\frac{5}{10}$ (=) $\frac{4}{8}$

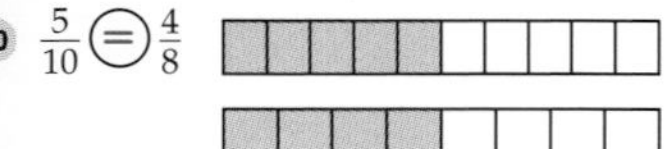

11 $\frac{5}{10}$ (<) $\frac{5}{7}$

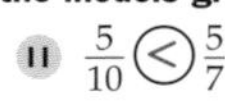

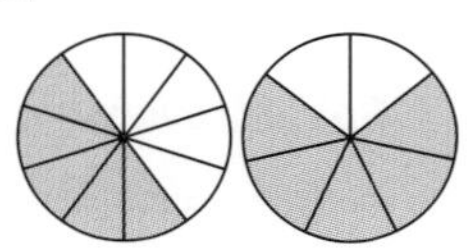

Order the fractions from least to greatest.

12 $\frac{1}{8}$ and $\frac{5}{12}$ $\frac{1}{8}, \frac{5}{12}$

13 $\frac{1}{4}$ and $\frac{5}{6}$ $\frac{1}{4}, \frac{5}{6}$

14 $\frac{2}{3}, \frac{1}{6}$, and $\frac{5}{9}$ $\frac{1}{6}, \frac{5}{9}, \frac{2}{3}$

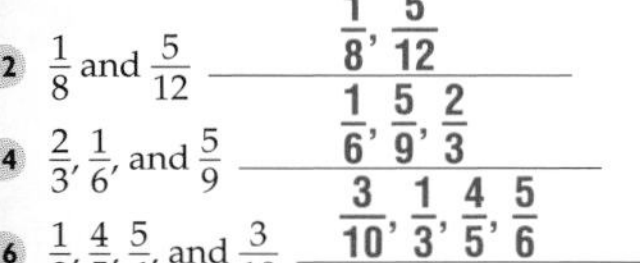

15 $\frac{3}{4}, \frac{2}{5}$, and $\frac{7}{10}$ $\frac{2}{5}, \frac{7}{10}, \frac{3}{4}$

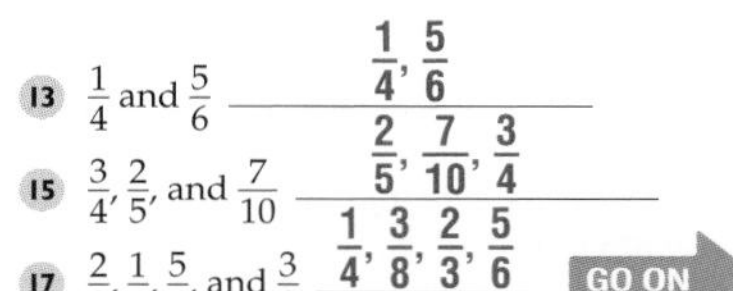

16 $\frac{1}{3}, \frac{4}{5}, \frac{5}{6}$, and $\frac{3}{10}$ $\frac{3}{10}, \frac{1}{3}, \frac{4}{5}, \frac{5}{6}$

17 $\frac{2}{3}, \frac{1}{4}, \frac{5}{6}$, and $\frac{3}{8}$ $\frac{1}{4}, \frac{3}{8}, \frac{2}{3}, \frac{5}{6}$

GO ON

Common Error *Alert*

Exercises 12–17 Remind students to write the original fractions in the answer, not the fractions with the common denominators.

Odd/Even Assignments

Exercises 10–19 are structured so that students practice the same concepts whether they are assigned the odd or even problems.

In-Class Assignment

Have students complete Exercises 11, 12, 15, 18, and 22 to ensure that they understand the concept.

English Learner Strategy

Guiding Questions If students continue to have difficulty renaming fractions to equivalent fractions before comparing them, then ask the following questions.

- How can I find a fraction that is equivalent to $\frac{4}{12}$?
- How do you know if two fractions are equivalent?
- What makes the fractions $\frac{2}{3}$ and $\frac{8}{12}$ equivalent?
- What are two other fractions that are equivalent to $\frac{1}{4}$?

4 Assess

See It, Do It, Say It, Write It

Step 1 Write three fractions on the board. Model how to compare and order each fraction with a drawing or model. Do this several times with different fractions.

Step 2 Give students a few fractions to compare and order. Repeat with students using models. Share solutions in a class discussion.

Step 3 Have students work in pairs. Write three fractions on the board. Tell students to make a model to represent each fraction on the board. Have students share their work with the class. Repeat several times.

Step 4 Have students work alone. Tell them to write how to compare and order fractions and tell them to include a picture or a model.

Solve.

18 BAKING Marlon needs $\frac{3}{4}$ cup of butter to make brownies. He has $\frac{1}{2}$ cup. Does he have enough? Explain.

No. He needs $\frac{3}{4}$ cup of butter. He has $\frac{1}{2}$, which equals $\frac{2}{4}$. He needs $\frac{1}{4}$ cup more butter.

19 VEGETABLES The weights of four vegetables are shown in the table. Order their weights from least to greatest.

tomatoes $\frac{2}{9}$, green beans $\frac{1}{3}$, onions $\frac{1}{2}$, and potatoes $\frac{5}{6}$

Vegetable	Weight (lb)
green beans	$\frac{1}{3}$
onions	$\frac{1}{2}$
potatoes	$\frac{5}{6}$
tomatoes	$\frac{2}{9}$

Vocabulary Check **Write the vocabulary word that completes each sentence.**

20 The least common multiple or LCM is the least whole number greater than 0 that is a common multiple of two or more numbers.

21 A(n) common denominator is the same denominator used in two or more fractions.

22 Writing in Math Explain how to determine if $\frac{2}{3}$ is greater than, less than, or equal to $\frac{3}{5}$.

Sample answer: First you find the LCD which is 15; rename the fractions to $\frac{2}{3} = \frac{10}{15}$ and $\frac{3}{5} = \frac{9}{15}$, compare the numerators. 10 > 9 which means that $\frac{2}{3} > \frac{3}{5}$.

Spiral Review

Write each fraction in simplest form. Divide by the GCF or use prime factorization. (Lesson 1-3, p. 19)

23 $\frac{16}{24} = \frac{2}{3}$

24 $\frac{28}{49} = \frac{4}{7}$

25 BAKERY A bakery puts 64 cinnamon, 48 blueberry, and 32 chocolate chip muffins in a display case. There should be an equal amount of muffins in each row. What is the greatest number of muffins in each row? (Lesson 1-2, p. 11)

16 muffins

STOP

34 Chapter 1 Fractions

Ticket Out the Door

The Greater Fraction As each student approaches the classroom door to leave, say two fractions that have different denominators. The student should tell you which fraction is greater. Encourage complete sentences. For example, $\frac{9}{10}$ is greater than $\frac{2}{3}$.

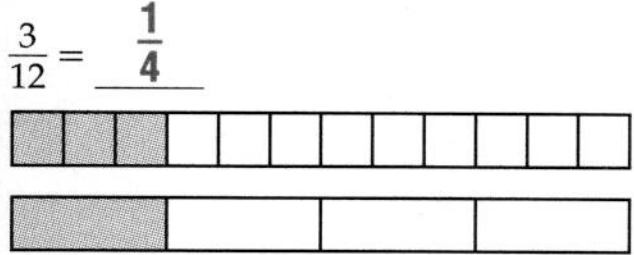

Progress Check 2 (Lessons 1-3 and 1-4)

rite the fraction in simplest form. Use models.

$\frac{3}{12} = \frac{1}{4}$

2 $\frac{4}{14} = \frac{2}{7}$

rite each fraction in simplest form. Divide by the GCF.

$\frac{16}{40} = \frac{16}{40} \div \frac{8}{8} = \frac{2}{5}$

4 $\frac{32}{56} = \frac{32}{56} \div \frac{8}{8} = \frac{4}{7}$

rite each fraction in simplest form. Use prime factorization.

$\frac{18}{27} = \frac{2}{3}$

6 $\frac{25}{30} = \frac{5}{6}$

e TE margin for full answers to Questions 5 and 6.

e <, =, or > to compare the fractions. Rename the fractions using common denominator.

$\frac{2}{9} < \frac{7}{10}$

8 $\frac{3}{4} > \frac{1}{5}$

der the fractions from least to greatest.

$\frac{1}{3}, \frac{1}{4}$, and $\frac{3}{5}$ — $\frac{1}{4}, \frac{1}{3}, \frac{3}{5}$

10 $\frac{1}{2}, \frac{1}{3}$, and $\frac{2}{9}$ — $\frac{2}{9}, \frac{1}{3}, \frac{1}{2}$

$\frac{4}{5}, \frac{7}{20}, \frac{1}{2}$, and $\frac{9}{10}$ — $\frac{7}{20}, \frac{1}{2}, \frac{4}{5}, \frac{9}{10}$

12 $\frac{3}{8}, \frac{1}{4}, \frac{3}{10}$, and $\frac{3}{5}$ — $\frac{1}{4}, \frac{3}{10}, \frac{3}{8}, \frac{3}{5}$

lve.

FUND-RAISER Sondra took 56 muffins to sell at the school fund-raiser. There were 8 muffins left when the fund-raiser was over. Write the fraction of muffins that were sold in simplest form. $\frac{6}{7}$

MUSIC Davis plays the piano and has been practicing for a concert his school is performing. On Tuesday he practiced for $\frac{2}{3}$ hour, on Wednesday he practiced for $\frac{1}{4}$ hour, on Thursday he practiced for $\frac{1}{2}$ hour, and on Friday he practiced for $\frac{5}{6}$ hour. On which day did he practice the most? Friday

Chapter 1 Progress Check 35

Progress Check 2

Chapter 1

Formative Assessment

Use the Progress Check to assess students' mastery of the previous lessons. Have students review the lesson indicated for the problems they answered incorrectly.

Odd/Even Assignments

Exercises are structured so that students practice the same concepts whether they are assigned the odd or even problems.

Common Error *Alert*

Key Abbreviations Students may need to be reminded of what GCF and LCD represent. The GCF is the greatest common *factor* amongst a pair or set of numbers. The LCD is the least common denominator (or multiple) amongst given denominators.

Additional Answer

Exercise 5

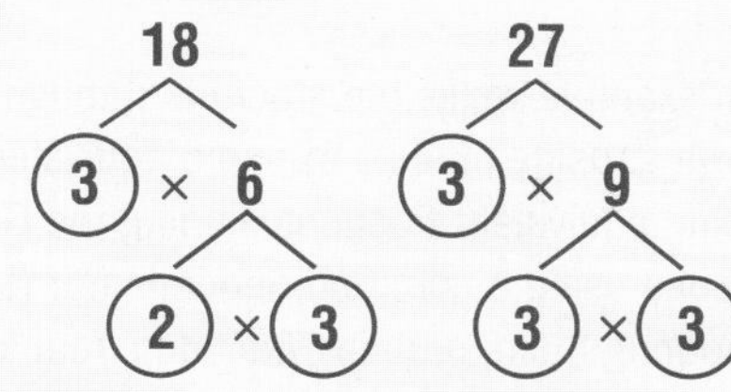

Exercise 6

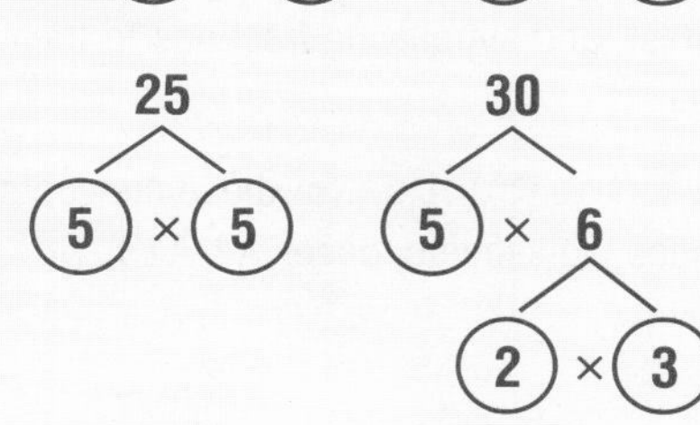

Data-Driven Decision Making

Students missing Exercises . . .	Have trouble with . . .	Should review and practice . . .
1–6	writing fractions in simplest form.	SSG Lesson 1-3, p. 19 CRM Skills Practice, p. A13
7–12	renaming fractions using a common denominator, then using inequality signs to compare or order them.	SSG Lesson 1-4, p. 27 CRM Skills Practice, p. A17
13–14	solving word problems involving fractions.	CRM Problem-Solving Practice, pp. A14 and A18

Chapter 1

Study Guide
Formative Assessment

Vocabulary and Concept Check

If students have difficulty answering Exercises 1–9, remind them that they can use the page references to refresh their memories about the vocabulary terms.

Vocabulary Review Strategies

Vocabulary Flashcards Have students create their own sets of vocabulary flashcards by writing each vocabulary word on one side of index cards or half-sheets of paper. On the other side, they can either write the definition or an example that demonstrates the definition of the term.

The students can study the words by looking at the vocabulary term and stating its definition (flipping the card over to check and see if they got the definition correct), or they can read the side with the definition or study the example and state the corresponding vocabulary term (flipping the card over to see if they got the correct term).

Lesson Review

Each example walks the students through all of the following: using models to name equivalent fractions, naming equivalent fractions, finding the GCF, renaming fractions using a common denominator (LCD) then comparing them, ordering fractions from least to greatest, and simplifying fractions to their most-reduced form.

Find **Extra Practice** for these concepts in the Practice Worksheets, pages A4–A19.

Chapter 1 **Study Guide**

Vocabulary and Concept Check

common denominators, *p. 27*
composite numbers, *p. 11*
equivalent forms of one, *p. 4*
equivalent fractions, *p. 4*
greatest common factor (GCF), *p. 11*
least common denominator (LCD), *p. 27*
least common multiple (LCM), *p. 27*
prime factorization, *p. 11*
prime number, *p. 11*
simplest form, *p. 19*
value, *p. 4*

Write the vocabulary word that completes each sentence.

1. The least common multiple of the denominators (botto numbers) of two or more fractions is the **least common denominator (LCD)**.
2. The **least common multiple (LCM)** is the least common of multiples of two or more numbers.
3. A(n) **prime number** is a who number that has exactly two unique factors, 1 and itsel
4. $\left(\frac{3}{4} = \frac{6}{8}\right)$ is an example of **equivalent fractions**
5. The greatest of the common factors of two or more numbers is known as the **greatest common factor (GCF)**.
6. A fraction is in **simplest form** wher the numerator and the denominator have no common factor other than 1.

Label each diagram below. Write the correct vocabulary term in each blank.

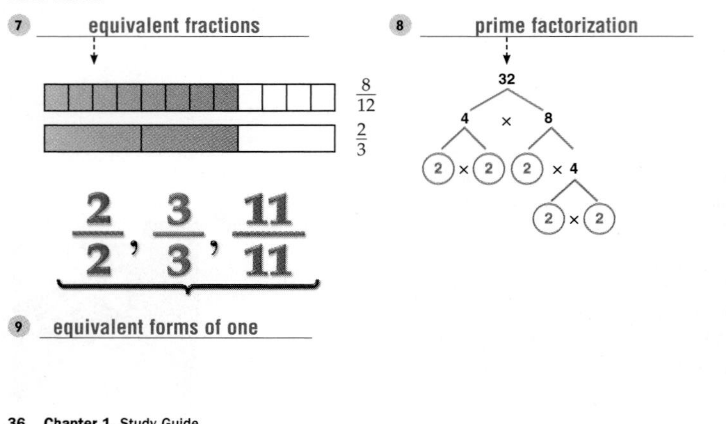

36 **Chapter 1** Study Guide

Classroom Management

Pair and Share Pair a student who has a good grasp of the material with another student who could use some support. Have students take turns explaining the examples to each other. In this case they will both benefit, whether by doing the explaining or having it explained to them in a new way.

.esson Review

-1 Equivalent Fractions and Equivalent Forms of One (pp. 4–10)

omplete each model to name an quivalent fraction.

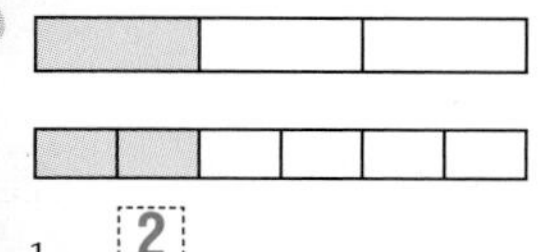

$\frac{1}{3} = \frac{2}{6}$

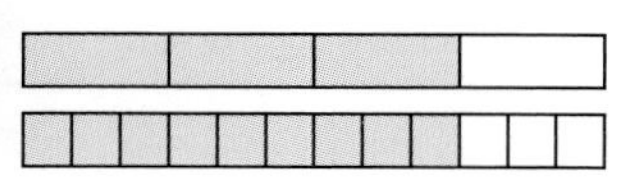

$\frac{3}{4} = \frac{9}{12}$

Example 1

Complete the models to name an equivalent fraction.

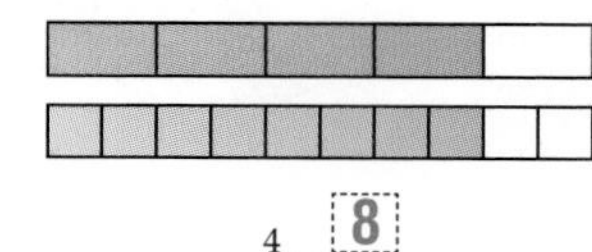

$\frac{4}{5} = \frac{8}{10}$

1. Multiply the denominator 5 by 2 to get the denominator of 10.
2. Multiply 5 by 2 to get 10. So, multiply the fraction by $\frac{2}{2}$, an equivalent form of one.

$\frac{4}{5} = \frac{4 \times 2}{5 \times 2} = \frac{8}{10}$

So, $\frac{4}{5} = \frac{8}{10}$.

-2 Greatest Common Factors (pp. 11–17)

nd the GCF of each set of numbers making a list.

20 and 32 4

35 and 56 7

27, 54, and 72 9

30, 42, and 60 6

Example 2

Find the GCF of 36, 60, and 84 by making a list.

1. List the factors of each number from least to greatest.
   36: (1), (2), (3), (4), 6, 9, (12), 18, 36
   60: (1), (2), (3), (4), 5, 6, 10, (12), 15, 20, 30, 60
   84: (1), (2), (3), (4), 6, 7, (12), 14, 21, 28, 42, 84
2. Circle the common factors.
   The common factors are 1, 2, 3, 4, and 12.
3. The GCF of 36, 60, and 84 is 12.

Chapter 1 Study Guide 37

Intervention Strategy Visual Learners

Use Models For some students, it may be very helpful if you provide them with a set of unshaded fraction circles that are divided into various numbers of sections. Then if students are having trouble making a comparison among fractions, the students could rely on their fraction circles.

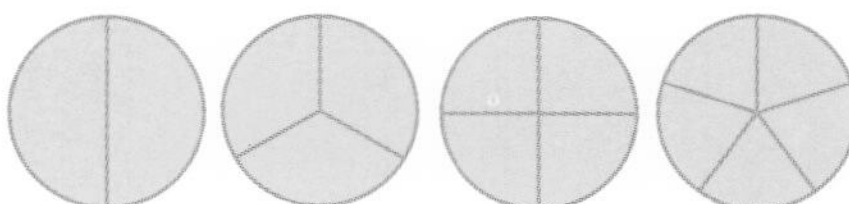

FOLDABLES® Study Organizer Dinah Zike's Foldables®

Review Remind students to complete and refer to their Foldables as they progress through the Chapter 1 Study Guide. Have students share and compare their completed Foldables with a partner. You may also choose to have them use their Foldable as a study aid in preparing for the Chapter Test. (For complete instructions, see Chapter Resource Masters, p. A1.)

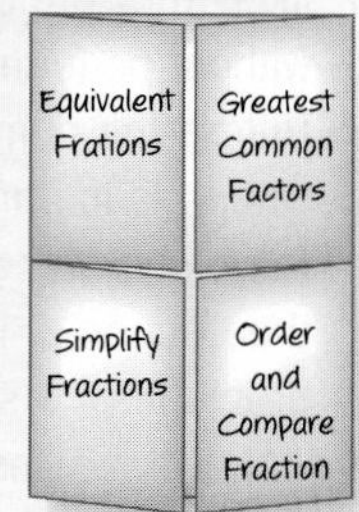

Math Coach Notes

Use Models Have students use models if they are in need of more visualization of equivalent fractions. For some students, actually seeing the same amounts of shading between graphs makes a significant difference from just following an algorithm.

Common Error *Alert*

Exercises 20–25 If students are having difficulty with Exercises 20-25, it is more than likely they are attempting to simplify their fractions without performing all the steps listed in Example 4. Unless the numbers are extremely easy to work with, it is important to list all of the factors of both the numerator and denominator, so as to reduce the fraction to its simplest form. It is a common problem for a student to reduce a fraction but not with the greatest common factor. In other words, they are finding an equivalent fraction, but it is not in simplest form. Stress to students the importance of showing their work.

Find the greatest common factor (GCF) of each set of numbers by using prime factors.

16 16 and 28 __4__

17 20 and 75 __5__

18 48 and 72 __12__

19 45 and 120 __15__

Example 3

Find the greatest common factor (GCF) of 27 and 72 by using prime factors.

1. Write the prime factorization.

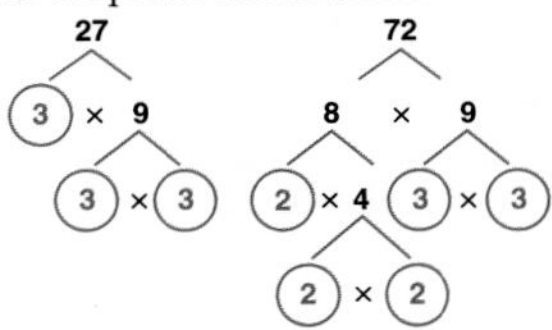

2. The common factors are 3 and 3.
   So, the GCF of 27 and 72 is 3 × 3 or 9.

1-3 Simplify Fractions (pp. 19–26)

Write each fraction in simplest form. Divide by the GCF.

20 $\frac{18}{30} = \frac{3}{5}$

21 $\frac{14}{35} = \frac{2}{5}$

22 $\frac{27}{63} = \frac{3}{7}$

23 $\frac{9}{36} = \frac{1}{4}$

24 $\frac{7}{56} = \frac{1}{8}$

25 $\frac{21}{33} = \frac{7}{11}$

Example 4

Write $\frac{15}{18}$ in simplest form. Divide by the GCF.

1. List all the factors of the numerator and of the denominator.

   Factors of 15: 1, (3), 5, 15

   Factors of 18: 1, 2, (3), 6, 9, 18

2. The greatest number in both lists is 3. The GCF of 15 and 18 is 3.
3. Divide the numerator and denominator by the GCF.

   $$\frac{15}{18} = \frac{15 \div 3}{18 \div 3} = \frac{5}{6}$$

4. So, $\frac{15}{18}$ in simplest form is $\frac{5}{6}$.

38 **Chapter 1** Study Guide

-4 Compare and Order Fractions (pp. 27–34)

se <, =, or > to compare the
actions. Shade the models given.

$\frac{5}{6}$ (>) $\frac{3}{8}$

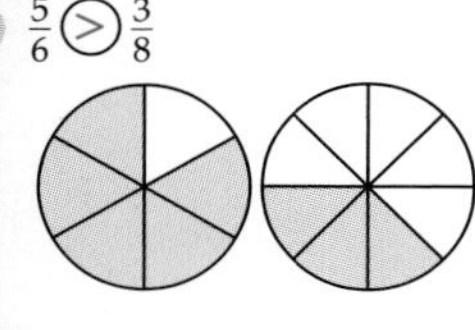

$\frac{2}{3}$ (>) $\frac{4}{9}$

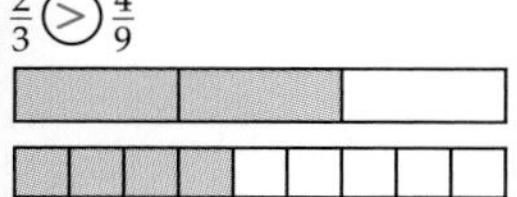

der the fractions from least
greatest.

$\frac{3}{4}, \frac{5}{6}$, and $\frac{11}{12}$

$\frac{3}{4}, \frac{5}{6}, \frac{11}{12}$

$\frac{7}{8}, \frac{3}{4}$, and $\frac{9}{10}$

$\frac{3}{4}, \frac{7}{8}, \frac{9}{10}$

$\frac{1}{6}, \frac{5}{9}$, and $\frac{2}{3}$

$\frac{1}{6}, \frac{5}{9}, \frac{2}{3}$

$\frac{7}{10}, \frac{6}{15}$, and $\frac{3}{5}$

$\frac{6}{15}, \frac{3}{5}, \frac{7}{10}$

Example 5

Use <, =, or > to compare $\frac{3}{4}$ and $\frac{4}{5}$.

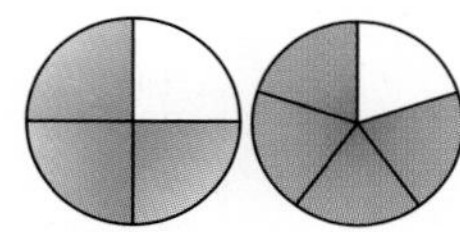

1. The circle on the left has 4 sections.
   Use it to model $\frac{3}{4}$. Shade 3 sections.
2. The circle on the right has 5 sections.
   Use it to model $\frac{4}{5}$. Shade 4 sections.
3. Compare the shaded areas.
   Use <, =, or > to write a statement. $\frac{3}{4}$ (<) $\frac{4}{5}$

Example 6

Order the fractions $\frac{5}{8}, \frac{4}{9}$, and $\frac{7}{12}$ from least to greatest.

1. Find the LCM of 8, 9, and 12.
   Multiples of 8: 8, 16, 24, 32, 40, 48, 56, 64, 72, 80,…
   Multiples of 9: 9, 18, 27, 36, 45, 54, 63, 72, 81,…
   Multiples of 12: 12, 24, 36, 48, 60, 72, 84, …
   The least number in all three lists of multiples is 72.
   The LCD of the fractions is 72.
2. Write equivalent fractions that have 72 as their denominators.
   $$\frac{5}{8} = \frac{5 \times 9}{8 \times 9} = \frac{45}{72} \qquad \frac{4}{9} = \frac{4 \times 8}{9 \times 8} = \frac{32}{72}$$
   $$\frac{7}{12} = \frac{7 \times 6}{12 \times 6} = \frac{42}{72}$$
3. Compare the numerators. $32 < 42 < 45$
4. Order the fractions from least to greatest.
   $\frac{32}{72} < \frac{42}{72} < \frac{45}{72}$ means that $\frac{4}{9} < \frac{7}{12} < \frac{5}{8}$
   So, from least to greatest, the fractions are $\frac{4}{9}, \frac{7}{12}, \frac{5}{8}$.

Common Error *Alert*

Review more than one method for finding GCFs If students are having trouble with finding greatest common factors, be sure that they know there is more than one method for arriving at the correct answer. One way is by listing factors and multiples; the other way is to use the prime factorization technique. Give them examples in addition to the ones in this study guide, if needed.

Ticket Out the Door

Do These Problems Have students answer four problems of the following types: (1) writing equivalent fractions, (2) finding a greatest common factor, (3) simplifying fractions, and (4) comparing and ordering fractions.

Chapter 1 Chapter Test

Chapter Resource Masters

Additional forms of the Chapter 1 Tests are available.

Test Format	Where to Find it
Chapter 1 Test	Math Online glencoe.com
Blackline Masters	Assessment Masters, p. 29

Customize and create multiple versions of your chapter tests and their answer keys. All of these questions from the chapter tests are available on ExamView® Assessment Suite.

Online Assessment and Reporting
glencoe.com

This online assessment tool allows teachers to track student progress with easily accessible comprehensive reports available for every student. Assess students using any internet-ready computer.

Alternative Assessment

Use Portfolios Ask students to write examples of all the different types of problems from this chapter. This should include all of the following: naming equivalent fractions, finding the GCF, comparing fractions, ordering fractions from least to greatest, and simplifying (reducing) fractions to their simplest forms.

Chapter 1 Chapter Test

Name two equivalent fractions.

1. $\frac{2}{8}$ Sample answer: $\frac{4}{16}, \frac{6}{24}$
2. $\frac{4}{9}$ Sample answer: $\frac{8}{18}, \frac{12}{27}$
3. $\frac{5}{7}$ Sample answer: $\frac{10}{14}, \frac{15}{21}$
4. $\frac{3}{4}$ Sample answer: $\frac{6}{8}, \frac{9}{12}$

Complete to name an equivalent fraction.

5. $\frac{4}{12} = \frac{8}{24}$
6. $\frac{8}{9} = \frac{16}{18}$
7. $\frac{2}{5} = \frac{6}{15}$
8. $\frac{6}{7} = \frac{18}{21}$

Find the GCF of each set of numbers.

9. 18, 30, and 42 6
10. 24, 36, and 48 12
11. 27, 45, and 63 9
12. 35, 49, and 70 7

Use <, =, or > to compare the fractions.

13. $\frac{1}{5} < \frac{2}{9}$
14. $\frac{3}{8} < \frac{5}{12}$
15. $\frac{2}{3} > \frac{6}{12}$
16. $\frac{5}{6} > \frac{7}{10}$

Order the fractions from least to greatest.

17. $\frac{4}{9}, \frac{3}{5}$, and $\frac{1}{3}$ $\frac{1}{3}, \frac{4}{9}, \frac{3}{5}$
18. $\frac{2}{3}, \frac{5}{6}$, and $\frac{6}{8}$ $\frac{2}{3}, \frac{6}{8}, \frac{5}{6}$
19. $\frac{2}{3}, \frac{3}{4}, \frac{3}{8}$, and $\frac{5}{12}$ $\frac{3}{8}, \frac{5}{12}, \frac{2}{3}, \frac{3}{4}$
20. $\frac{1}{2}, \frac{4}{5}, \frac{5}{8}$, and $\frac{7}{10}$ $\frac{1}{2}, \frac{5}{8}, \frac{7}{10}, \frac{4}{5}$

40 Chapter 1 Test

English Learner Strategy

Assessment Allow students time to look over the assessment. Have students take a close look at all the words and symbols in the problem directives, as well as all of the terms in the word problems. Be sure students understand what is being asked of them in each problem. If there are some students struggling with terminology, try to offer further explanation of what is being asked.

rite each fraction in simplest form.

$\frac{9}{15} = \frac{3}{5}$

22 $\frac{16}{24} = \frac{2}{3}$

$\frac{28}{49} = \frac{4}{7}$

24 $\frac{27}{30} = \frac{9}{10}$

$\frac{27}{63} = \frac{3}{7}$

26 $\frac{18}{24} = \frac{3}{4}$

$\frac{20}{45} = \frac{4}{9}$

28 $\frac{36}{96} = \frac{3}{8}$

lve.

CONSTRUCTION A carpenter had two pieces of wood the same length. She cut the first piece into 9 equal parts. She cut the second piece into 6 equal parts. How many parts from the second piece of wood equal the same length as 3 parts from the first piece of wood?

$\frac{3}{9} = \frac{1}{3} \times \frac{2}{2} = \frac{2}{6}$; 2 parts

BUSINESS Chris has a paper route. At the end of each week, he must collect the money due from his customers. He was able to collect $75 of the $120 due. What fraction of the total money did he collect? What fraction of the amount due does he still need to collect? Simplify both answers to lowest terms.

$\frac{75}{120} = \frac{5}{8}$; $\frac{45}{120} = \frac{3}{8}$

rrect the mistakes.

Catalina took 36 cupcakes to school for her classroom party. She brought one dozen cupcakes home. She said that only $\frac{1}{3}$ of the cupcakes were eaten. What mistake did Catalina make?

Actually, $\frac{1}{3}$ of the cupcakes were *not* eaten; $\frac{2}{3}$ of the cupcakes were eaten.

Learning from Mistakes

Review Common Questions Review commonly missed questions or topics in small groups or as a class. Ask students to share their methods for answering each question. In some questions, the methods could vary. For example, students can find a GCF by either listing factors or using prime factorization. It may be helpful for students to learn from others' strategies. Try to find out if the mistakes students make are strictly computational or whether they lack adequate understanding of the topic. Some further explanation may be required accordingly.

Data-Driven Decision Making

Students missing Exercises . . .	Have trouble with . . .	Should review and practice . . .
1–8	naming equivalent fractions.	SSG Lesson 1-1, p. 4 CRM Skills Practice, p. A5
9–12	finding the GCF of a set of numbers.	SSG Lesson 1-2, p. 11 CRM Skills Practice, p. A9
13–20	comparing and ordering fractions.	SSG Lesson 1-4, p. 27 CRM Skills Practice, p. A17
21–28	writing a fraction in simplest form.	SSG Lesson 1-3, p. 19 CRM Skills Practice, p. A13
29–31	solving word problems involving fractions.	CRM Problem-Solving Practice, pp. A6, A10, A14, and A18

Test Practice

Diagnose Student Errors

Survey student responses for each item. Class trends may indicate common errors and misconceptions.

1. A miscalculated equivalency
   B considered only the numerator
   (C) correct
   D guess
2. A miscalculated equivalency, $\frac{4}{8} = \frac{1}{2}$
   (B) correct
   C added 3 to numerator and denominator
   D considered only the numerator
3. A compared numerators or denominators and did not make equivalent denominators
   B miscalculated equivalency
   (C) correct
   D misinterpreted concept of comparison
4. A guess
   (B) correct
   C guess
   D not a factor of 28
5. A ordered fractions from greatest to least
   B guess
   (C) correct
   D guess
6. A compared numerators or denominators and did not make equivalent denominators
   (B) correct
   C guess
   D misinterpreted concept of comparison
7. A guess
   B not a factor of 45
   (C) correct
   D guess
8. A miscalculated equivalency
   (B) correct
   C miscalculated equivalency
   D miscalculated equivalency

Test Practice

Choose the best answer and fill in the corresponding circle on the sheet at right.

1 Camila and Ashanti shared an apple pie. The apple pie was cut into 8 equal pieces. If Ashanti ate 3 of the pieces, what fraction of the apple pie did she eat?

A $\frac{1}{2}$ (C) $\frac{3}{8}$
B $\frac{3}{4}$ D $\frac{2}{3}$

2 Which fraction is equal to $\frac{3}{4}$?

A $\frac{4}{8}$ C $\frac{6}{7}$
(B) $\frac{6}{8}$ D $\frac{3}{7}$

3 Which symbol makes the sentence true?

$\frac{7}{12} \square \frac{5}{6}$

A > (C) <
B = D +

4 Which is the GCF of 28 and 48?

A 3 C 5
(B) 4 D 6

5 Order these fractions from least to greatest: $\frac{7}{8}, \frac{1}{2}, \frac{3}{4}$.

A $\frac{7}{8}, \frac{3}{4}, \frac{1}{2}$ (C) $\frac{1}{2}, \frac{3}{4}, \frac{7}{8}$
B $\frac{7}{8}, \frac{1}{2}, \frac{3}{4}$ D $\frac{3}{4}, \frac{7}{8}, \frac{1}{2}$

6 Ethan finished $\frac{4}{6}$ of his homework before dinner. His brother Nathan finished $\frac{6}{8}$ of his homework before dinner. Which math sentence is correct

A $\frac{4}{6} > \frac{6}{8}$ C $\frac{6}{8} < \frac{4}{6}$
(B) $\frac{4}{6} < \frac{6}{8}$ D $\frac{4}{6} = \frac{6}{8}$

7 Which is the GCF of 45 and 72?

A 7 (C) 9
B 8 D 10

8 Write $\frac{8}{10}$ in simplest form.

A $\frac{2}{3}$ C $\frac{2}{5}$
(B) $\frac{4}{5}$ D $\frac{1}{2}$

42 **Chapter 1** Test Practice

9. A miscounted number of parts in model
   (B) correct
   C guess
   D miscounted number of shaded parts in model
10. A miscalculated equivalency
    (B) correct
    C miscalculated equivalency
    D miscalculated equivalency
11. A not greatest common factor
    B not a factor of 36
    C guess
    (D) correct
12. (A) correct
    B compared numerators
    C guess
    D misinterpreted concept of comparison

9 Which fraction does the model represent?

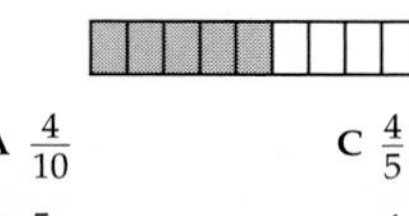

A $\frac{4}{10}$ C $\frac{4}{5}$

(B) $\frac{5}{9}$ D $\frac{4}{9}$

10 Write $\frac{10}{16}$ in simplest form.

A $\frac{2}{4}$ C $\frac{3}{8}$

(B) $\frac{5}{8}$ D $\frac{1}{4}$

11 Olimpia is arranging flowers in her vases. She has 24 carnations and 36 daffodils. Each vase should have the same number of flowers. What is the greatest number of flowers she can put in each vase?

A 6 C 10

B 8 (D) 12

12 Which symbol makes the sentence true?

$\frac{1}{2} \square \frac{1}{12}$

(A) > C <

B = D +

ANSWER SHEET

Directions: Fill in the circle of each correct answer.

1	A	B	**C**	D
2	A	**B**	C	D
3	A	B	**C**	D
4	A	**B**	C	D
5	A	B	**C**	D
6	A	**B**	C	D
7	A	B	**C**	D
8	A	**B**	C	D
9	A	**B**	C	D
10	A	**B**	C	D
11	A	B	C	**D**
12	**A**	B	C	D

Success Strategy

If you do not know the answer to a question, go on to the next question. Come back to the problem, if you have time. You might find another question later in the test that will help you figure out the skipped problem.

Diagnosing Student Errors and Misconceptions

Review When working on the problems, have students show their work on a separate sheet of notebook paper that can be used later as a reference as needed. After the class has completed the Test Practice problems, go over all the correct responses and have the students score their own responses or they can trade and grade papers.

If it is found that the mistakes are not computational and students do not understand the question, further class instruction may be necessary. As another alternative, students could be strategically paired to help each other.

Chapter 2

Chapter Overview

Chapter-at-a-Glance

Lesson	Math Objective	State/Local Standards
2-1 Ratios (pp. 46-52)	Interpret and use ratios.	
2-2 Ratio Tables (pp. 53-59)	Use ratio tables to represent and solve problems involving equivalent ratios.	
Progress Check (p. 60)		
2-3 Probability as a Ratio (pp. 61-68)	Represent probability as a ratio and compute probability.	
2-4 Rates and Unit Costs (pp. 69-75)	Determine unit costs and understand rates.	
Progress Check (p. 76)		
2-5 Proportional Reasoning (pp. 77-82)	Solve proportions.	
2-6 Similar Figures and Proportions (pp. 83-89)	Use proportions to solve problems.	
Progress Check (p. 90)		

Content-at-a-Glance

The diagram below summarizes and unpacks Chapter 2 content.

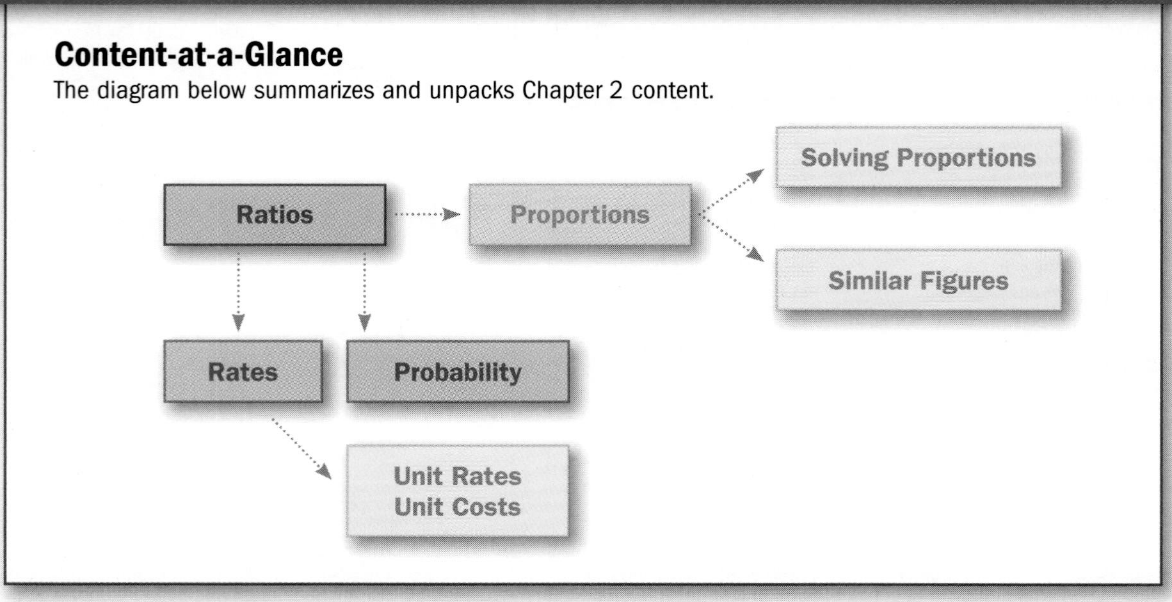

Online Assessment and Reporting
glencoe.com

Chapter Assessment Manager

Diagnostic

Diagnose students' readiness.

	Student Study Guide/ Teacher Edition	Assessment Masters	Technology
Course Placement Test		1	ExamView® Assessment Suite
Book 1 Pretest		23	ExamView® Assessment Suite
Chapter 2 Pretest		37	ExamView® Assessment Suite
Quiz/Preview	SSG 45		Math Online glencoe.com StudentWorks™ Plus

Formative

Identify students' misconceptions of content knowledge.

	Student Study Guide/ Teacher Edition	Assessment Masters	Technology
Progress Checks	SSG 60, 76, 90		Math Online glencoe.com StudentWorks™ Plus
Vocabulary Review	SSG 91		Math Online glencoe.com
Lesson Assessments			ExamView® Assessment Suite
Are They Getting It?	TE 49, 56, 64, 72, 80, 86		Math Online glencoe.com

Summative

Determine student success in learning concepts in the lesson, chapter, or book.

	Student Study Guide/ Teacher Edition	Assessment Masters	Technology
Chapter 2 Test	SSG 96	40	ExamView® Assessment Suite
Test Practice	SSG 98	43	ExamView® Assessment Suite
Alternative Assessment	TE 96	46	
See It, Do It, Say It, Write It	TE 52, 59, 67, 75, 82, 89		
Book 1 Test		59	ExamView® Assessment Suite

Back-mapping and Vertical Alignment **McGraw-Hill's *Math Triumphs*** intervention program was conceived and developed with the final result in mind: student success in grade-level mathematics, including Algebra 1 and beyond. The authors, using the **NCTM Focal Points and Focal Connections** as their guide, developed this brand-new series by backmapping from grade-level and Algebra 1 concepts, and vertically aligning the topics so that they build upon prior skills and concepts and serve as a foundation for future topics.

Chapter Resource Manager

	Lesson 2-1	Lesson 2-2	Lesson 2-3	Lesson 2-4
Concept	Ratios	Ratio Tables	Probability as a Ratio	Rates and Unit Costs
Objective	Interpret and use ratios.	Use ratio tables to represent and solve problems involving equivalent ratios.	Represent probability as a ratio and compute probability.	Determine unit costs and understand rates.
Math Vocabulary	ratio	equivalent forms of one equivalent ratios ratio ratio table	event outcomes probability ratio	rate ratio unit cost unit rate
Lesson Resources	**Materials** • Classroom objects • Grid paper • Index cards **Manipulatives** • Pattern blocks • Connecting cubes • Counters • Tangrams **Other Resources** CRM Vocabulary and English Language Development CRM Skills Practice CRM Problem-Solving Practice CRM Homework Practice	**Materials** • Deck of playing cards • Number cubes **Manipulatives** • Counters **Other Resources** CRM Vocabulary and English Language Development CRM Skills Practice CRM Problem-Solving Practice CRM Homework Practice	**Materials** • Number cubes • Spinners • Color markers • Cardstock **Manipulatives** • Counters **Other Resources** CRM Vocabulary and English Language Development CRM Skills Practice CRM Problem-Solving Practice CRM Homework Practice	**Materials** • Index cards • Poster board **Manipulatives** • Grocery ads, labels, and items **Other Resources** CRM Vocabulary and English Language Development CRM Skills Practice CRM Problem-Solving Practice CRM Homework Practice
Technology	Math Online glencoe.com StudentWorks™ Plus ExamView® Assessment Suite	Math Online glencoe.com StudentWorks™ Plus ExamView® Assessment Suite	Math Online glencoe.com StudentWorks™ Plus ExamView® Assessment Suite	Math Online glencoe.com StudentWorks™ Plus ExamView® Assessment Suite

TE Teacher Edition
DVD

	Lesson 2-5	Lesson 2-6
Concept	Proportional Reasoning	Similar Figures and Proportions
Objective	Solve proportions.	Use proportions to solve problems.
Math Vocabulary	cross multiply proportion ratio	proportion similar figures
Lesson Resources	**Manipulatives** • Algebra tiles **Other Resources** CRM Vocabulary and English Language Development CRM Skills Practice CRM Problem-Solving Practice CRM Homework Practice	**Materials** • Grid paper • Overhead projector • Index cards • Color pens or pencils **Manipulatives** • Geoboards • Colored cubes • Pattern blocks **Other Resources** CRM Vocabulary and English Language Development CRM Skills Practice CRM Problem-Solving Practice CRM Homework Practice
Technology	Math Online glencoe.com StudentWorks™ Plus ExamView® Assessment Suite	Math Online glencoe.com StudentWorks™ Plus ExamView® Assessment Suite

Intervention Strategy

Solving Proportions

Students use a city map with a scale to learn about proportions in a real-life situation.

Step 1: Provide each student pair with a city map with a scale. Have students plan a tour of the city where they will leave school and go to two locations before returning to school.

Step 2: Students will measure the distance from location to location on the map with a ruler. Then they will use the map scale and proportions to calculate the actual distance between each location. Students must use proportions and show their work. Tell students to find the total number of miles of their trip.

For example, if the distance between two locations is 5 inches and the key indicates that an inch equals 2 miles, the student would set up this proportion and solve for x:

$$\frac{1 \text{ in.}}{2 \text{ mi}} = \frac{5 \text{ in.}}{x \text{ mi}}$$

Step 3: Ask student pairs to present their trips to the class. Students can point out and describe the locations they chose, and demonstrate how they found their actual distances.

An extension is to have students calculate how much gasoline they would use in cars that got 17 mpg and 27 mpg. For example, if a trip is 54 miles total, then $\frac{17 \text{ mi}}{1 \text{ gal}} = \frac{54 \text{ mi}}{x \text{ gal}}$ for the vehicle that gets 17 mpg. Students can compare the gallons used for each car.

Chapter 2 Chapter Notes

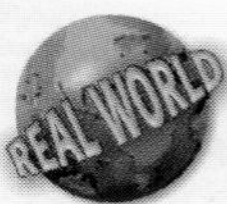

Real-World Applications

Catering Rashid's lasagna recipe serves 8 people. It uses 2 pounds of hamburger, 1 cup of ricotta cheese, 2 eggs, 0.75 pounds of provolone cheese, 16 ounces of spaghetti sauce, and 12 lasagna noodles. He is catering a meal for 96 people. What ratio does he need to use to determine how much of each ingredient he needs?

Intervention Strategy

School Supplies

Step 1 Arrange students into groups of three.

Step 2 Provide students with an office supply catalog. Students should select an item sold in a package of multiple items. Use the price of a package to determine the cost for a single item in the package.

Step 3 Multiply by the number of people in the class to find the cost of buying an item for each student.

Step 4 Write a proportion to find the total cost using the number of students in the class and the number of items in the package with the price of the package. Solve the proportion.

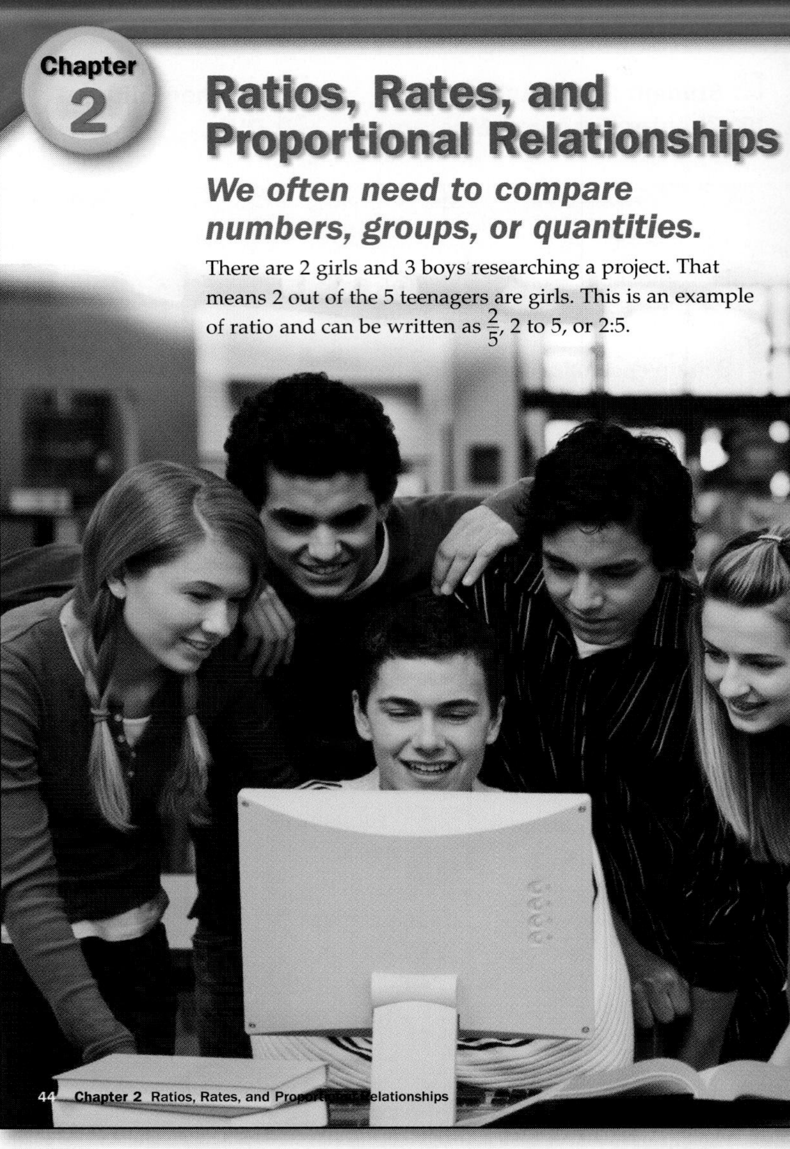

Chapter 2
Ratios, Rates, and Proportional Relationships
We often need to compare numbers, groups, or quantities.
There are 2 girls and 3 boys researching a project. That means 2 out of the 5 teenagers are girls. This is an example of ratio and can be written as $\frac{2}{5}$, 2 to 5, or 2:5.
44 Chapter 2 Ratios, Rates, and Proportional Relationships

Key Vocabulary

Find interactive definitions in 13 languages in the **eGlossary** at glencoe.com.

English **Español** *Introduce the most important vocabulary terms from Chapter 2.*

probability **probabilidad**
the chance that some event will occur (p. 61)

proportion **proporción**
an equation stating that two ratios or rates are equivalent (p. 77)

rate **tasa**
a ratio comparing two quantities with different kinds of units (p. 69)

ratio **razón**
a comparison of two quantities by division (p. 46)

The ratio of 2 to 3 can be stated as 2 out of 3, 2 to 3, 2:3, or $\frac{2}{3}$.

similar figures **figures semejantes**
figures that have the same shape but may have different sizes (p. 83)

unit cost **costo unitario**
the cost of a single item (p. 69)

unit rate **número primo**
a rate that has a denominator of 1 (p. 69)

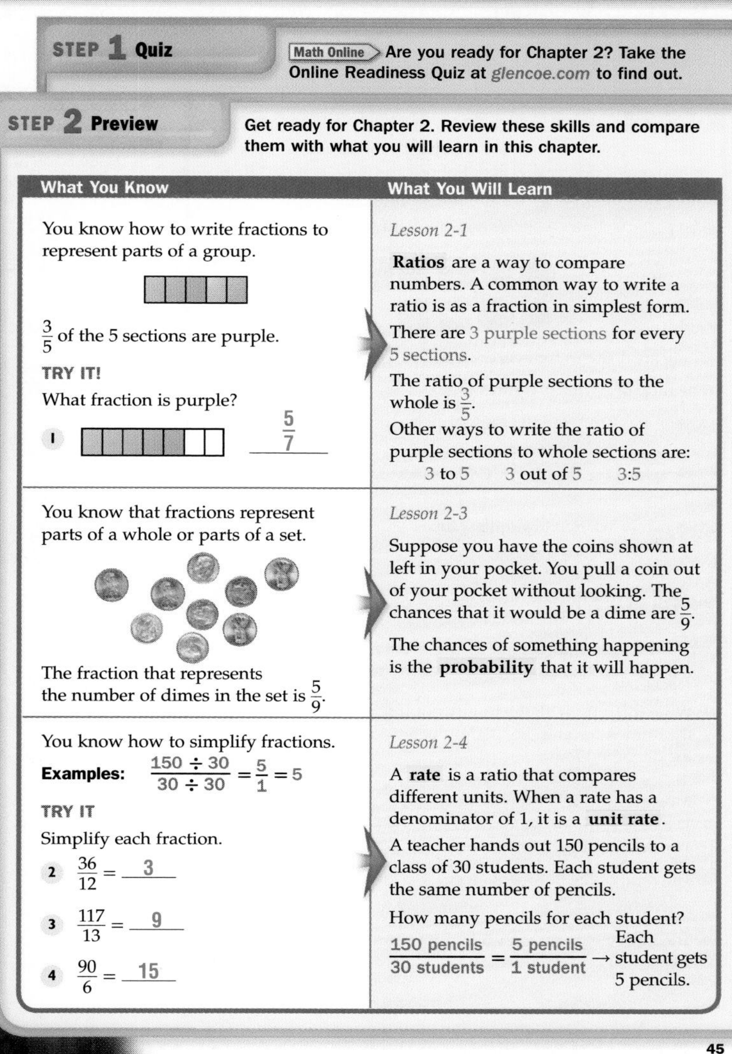

STEP 1 Quiz

Math Online Are you ready for Chapter 2? Take the Online Readiness Quiz at glencoe.com to find out.

STEP 2 Preview

Get ready for Chapter 2. Review these skills and compare them with what you will learn in this chapter.

What You Know	What You Will Learn
You know how to write fractions to represent parts of a group. $\frac{3}{5}$ of the 5 sections are purple. **TRY IT!** What fraction is purple? 1 $\frac{5}{7}$	*Lesson 2-1* **Ratios** are a way to compare numbers. A common way to write a ratio is as a fraction in simplest form. There are 3 purple sections for every 5 sections. The ratio of purple sections to the whole is $\frac{3}{5}$. Other ways to write the ratio of purple sections to whole sections are: 3 to 5 3 out of 5 3:5
You know that fractions represent parts of a whole or parts of a set. The fraction that represents the number of dimes in the set is $\frac{5}{9}$.	*Lesson 2-3* Suppose you have the coins shown at left in your pocket. You pull a coin out of your pocket without looking. The chances that it would be a dime are $\frac{5}{9}$. The chances of something happening is the **probability** that it will happen.
You know how to simplify fractions. **Examples:** $\frac{150 \div 30}{30 \div 30} = \frac{5}{1} = 5$ **TRY IT** Simplify each fraction. 2 $\frac{36}{12} = 3$ 3 $\frac{117}{13} = 9$ 4 $\frac{90}{6} = 15$	*Lesson 2-4* A **rate** is a ratio that compares different units. When a rate has a denominator of 1, it is a **unit rate**. A teacher hands out 150 pencils to a class of 30 students. Each student gets the same number of pencils. How many pencils for each student? $\frac{150 \text{ pencils}}{30 \text{ students}} = \frac{5 \text{ pencils}}{1 \text{ student}} \rightarrow$ Each student gets 5 pencils.

45

Vocabulary Preview

- As students complete the Chapter Preview, have them make a list of important terms throughout the chapter.
- Using graph paper, have students create a word search of at least 10 important terms throughout the chapter, including the key vocabulary terms.
- Instead of giving a list of the terms to search for, have students make a list of the definitions of each term. The seeker will then have to search for the terms described by the definitions.
- Once students are finished with creating their word searches, have them trade with a partner to complete the challenge.

Step 1 Quiz

Pretest/Prescribe Students can take the Online Readiness Quiz or the Diagnostic Pretest in the Assessment Masters.

Step 2 Preview

Use this pre-chapter activity to activate students' prior knowledge, build confidence, and help students preview the lessons.

Dinah Zike's Foldables®

Guide students through the directions on p. A20 in the Chapter Resource Masters to create their own Foldable graphic organizer for use with this chapter.

Home Connections

- Type or write for three minutes to find your keyboarding or handwriting rate. Then have a family member do the same and compare your rates.

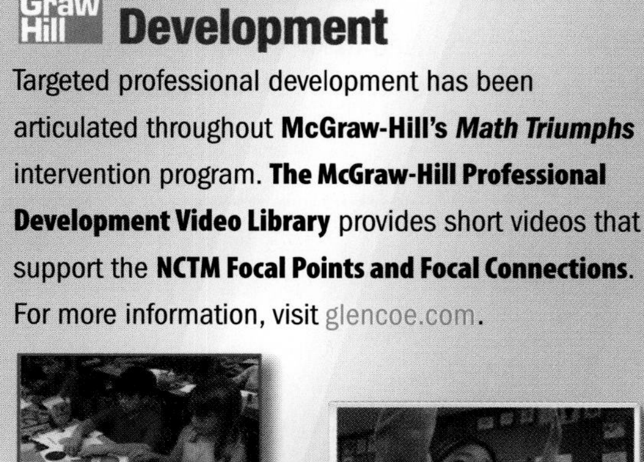

Mc Graw Hill Professional Development

Targeted professional development has been articulated throughout **McGraw-Hill's *Math Triumphs*** intervention program. **The McGraw-Hill Professional Development Video Library** provides short videos that support the **NCTM Focal Points and Focal Connections**. For more information, visit glencoe.com.

Model Lessons

Instructional Strategies

Lesson 2-1

Lesson Notes

Lesson Planner

Objective Interpret and use ratios.

Vocabulary **ratio**

Materials/Manipulatives pattern blocks, connecting cubes, counters, tangrams, grid paper, index cards, classroom objects

Chapter Resource Masters

- CRM Vocabulary and English Language Development (p. A23)
- CRM Skills Practice (p. A24)
- CRM Problem-Solving Practice (p. A25)
- CRM Homework Practice (p. A26)

Vocabulary

Ratios Students need to know that in a ratio of A to B, B is the divisor. Therefore, a ratio is another way to represent division.

Key Concept

Foundational Skills and Concepts After students have read through the Key Concept box, have them try these exercises.

1. What type of operation is a ratio? division
2. What are two other ways to write the ratio "5 to 3"? $\frac{5}{3}$, 5:3

Lesson 2-1

Ratios

KEY Concept

Ratios are a way to compare numbers. A **ratio** is a comparison of two quantities by division. Ratios can compare a part to a part, a part to a whole, or a whole to a part.

The pattern shows 4 circles out of 9 figures.

There are 4 circles for every 9 figures.

The ratio of circles to figures is $\frac{4}{9}$.

Other ways to write the ratio of cicles to figures are:

4 to 9 4 out of 9 4:9

VOCABULARY

ratio
a comparison of two quantities by division; the ratio of 2 to 3 can be stated as 2 out of 3, 2 to 3, 2:3, or $\frac{2}{3}$

Ratios can be written in simplest form.

Example 1

Write the ratio that compares the number of trapezoids to the total number of figures. Explain the meaning of the ratio.

1. Write the ratio with the number of trapezoids in the numerator and the total number of figures in the denominator.
   $\frac{5}{11}$ ← trapezoids / ← total figures
2. The only common factor of 5 and 11 is 1. The ratio is in simplest form.
3. The ratio of the number of trapezoids to the total number of figures is written as $\frac{5}{11}$, 5 to 11, 5 out of 11, or 5:11.
4. The ratio means *for every 5 trapezoids, there are 11 total figures.*

46 Chapter 2 Ratios, Rates, and Proportional Relationships

Additional **Example 1**

Write the ratio that compares the number of circles to the number of trapezoids. Explain the meaning of the ratio.

1. Write the ratio with the number of circles in the numerator and the number of trapezoids in the denominator. $\frac{5 \text{ circles}}{2 \text{ trapezoids}}$
2. The only common factor of 5 and 2 is 1. The ratio is in simplest form.
3. The ratio of the number of circles to the number of trapezoids can be written as: $\frac{5}{2}$, 5 to 2, or 5:2.
4. The ratio means *for every 5 circles there are 2 trapezoids.*

YOUR TURN!

Write the ratio that compares the number of squares to the total number of figures. Explain the meaning of the ratio.

1. Write the ratio.

$\frac{6}{14}$ ← squares / ← total figures

2. The numerator and denominator have a common factor of 2. Write the fraction in simplest form. $\frac{6}{14} = \frac{6 \div 2}{14 \div 2} = \frac{3}{7}$

3. Write the ratio of the number of squares to the total number of figures. $\frac{3}{7}$, 3 to 7, or 3:7

4. What does the ratio mean? For every 3 squares, there are 7 figures.

Example 2

Write the ratio as a fraction in simplest form.

8 blue hats out of 12 total hats

1. Write the ratio with the number of blue hats in the numerator and the total number of hats in the denominator. $\frac{8}{12}$
2. The numerator and denominator have a common factor of 4. Divide each by 4 to write the fraction in simplest form. $\frac{8}{12} = \frac{8 \div 4}{12 \div 4} = \frac{2}{3}$

YOUR TURN!

Write the ratio as a fraction in simplest form.

15 DVDs to 18 CDs

1. Write the ratio. $\frac{15}{18}$
2. The numerator and denominator have a common factor of 3. Write the fraction in simplest form. $\frac{15}{18} = \frac{15 \div 3}{18 \div 3} = \frac{5}{6}$

GO ON

Additional *Example 2*

Write the ratio as a fraction in simplest form.

4 hits out of 12 total at bats

1. Write the ratio with the number of hits in the numerator and the total number of at bats in the denominator. $\frac{4}{12}$
2. The numerator and the denominator have a common factor of 4. Divide each by 4 to write the fraction in simplest form. $\frac{4}{12} = \frac{4 \div 4}{12 \div 4} = \frac{1}{3}$

Intervention Strategy — Visual Learners

Grid Ratios Have students use grid paper to model ratios. For a ratio such as 8:20, students should enclose 20 grid squares with a dark line and then shade 8 of the enclosed grid squares. Have students model the ratios 8:20; 4:12; 2:9; and 5:24. When all students have made their models, have students share their colored grid models with the class and notice how many different ways students showed each ratio.

Additional *Example 3*

Write the ratio of the width to the length in the rectangle as a fraction in simplest form.

45 m

9 m

1. Write the ratio as a fraction with the width over the length. $\frac{9}{45}$

2. The numerator and denominator have a common factor of 9. Divide each by 9 to write the fraction in simplest form.

$$\frac{9}{45} = \frac{9 \div 9}{45 \div 9} = \frac{1}{5}$$

3 Practice

Using Manipulatives

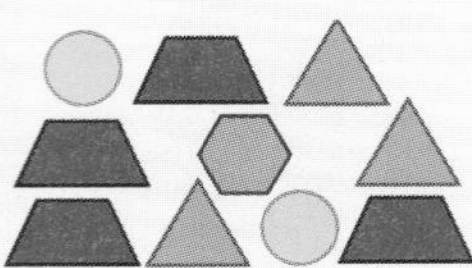

Pattern Blocks Represent Example 2 using pattern blocks to give students a visual representation of the ratio.

Connecting Cubes Connect different-colored cubes to represent ratios.

Two-Color Counters Use two different colors to represent the part and the whole.

Tangrams Compare the different pieces to explore ratios.

On-Hand Manipulatives Use classroom objects to represent the objects in a ratio.

Example 3

Write the ratio of the width to the length of the rectangle as a fraction in simplest form.

20 in.

4 in.

1. Write the ratio as a fraction with the width over the length. $\frac{4}{20}$
2. The numerator and denominator have a common factor of 4. Divide each by 4 to write the fraction in simplest form.

$$\frac{4}{20} = \frac{4 \div 4}{20 \div 4} = \frac{1}{5}$$

YOUR TURN!

Write the ratio of the length to the width of the rectangle as a fraction in simplest form.

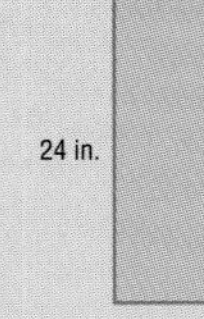

1. Write the ratio. $\frac{9}{24}$
2. The numerator and denominator have a common factor of 3. Write the fraction in simplest form.

$$\frac{9}{24} = \frac{9 \div 3}{24 \div 3} = \frac{3}{8}$$

Who is Correct?

Write the ratio as a fraction in simplest form. **36 pens to 4 pencils**

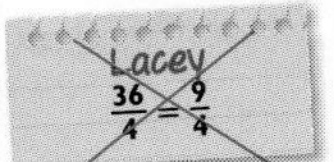

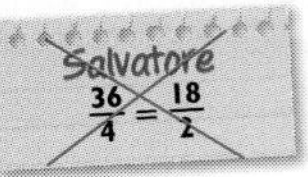

Circle correct answer(s). Cross out incorrect answer(s).

Guided Practice

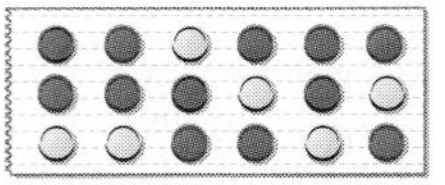

Use the diagram to write each ratio as a fraction in simplest form.

1. The number of purple counters to the number of blue counters is $\frac{1}{2}$.
2. The number of purple counters to the total number of counters is $\frac{1}{6}$.
3. The number of blue counters to the total number of counters is $\frac{1}{3}$.

Who *is Correct?*

Diagnostic Teaching

- Lacey is incorrect. She wrote a ratio of 36 pens to 4 pencils. She did not simplify correctly.
- Salvatore is incorrect. He wrote a ratio of 36 pens to 4 pencils. He did not simplify completely.
- Jaime is correct.

Review the different ways that ratios can be written: $\frac{9}{1}$, 9 to 1, 9:1.

Step by Step Practice

A dog trainer has 10 golden retrievers, 5 German shepherds, 9 Labrador retrievers, and 6 Dalmatians. Write the ratio of each type of dog to the total number of dogs.

Step 1 The total number of dogs is 30. This will be the denominator in the fraction.

Step 2 Write a ratio for the number of golden retrievers to the total number of dogs. $\frac{10}{30}$

What is the common factor of the numerator and denominator? 10

Write the fraction in simplest form. $\frac{10}{30} = \frac{10 \div 10}{30 \div 10} = \frac{1}{3}$

Step 3 Write a ratio for the number of German shepherds to the total number of dogs. $\frac{5}{30}$

What is the common factor of the numerator and denominator? 5

Write the fraction in simplest form. $\frac{5}{30} = \frac{5 \div 5}{30 \div 5} = \frac{1}{6}$

Step 4 Write a ratio for the number of Labrador retrievers to the total number of dogs. $\frac{9}{30}$

What is the common factor of the numerator and denominator? 3

Write the fraction in simplest form. $\frac{9}{30} = \frac{9 \div 3}{30 \div 3} = \frac{3}{10}$

Step 5 Write a ratio for the number of Dalmatians to the total number of dogs. $\frac{6}{30}$

What is the common factor of the numerator and denominator? 6

Write the fraction in simplest form. $\frac{6 \div 6}{30 \div 6} = \frac{1}{5}$

GO ON

Note This!

Simplest Form Often it is necessary to reduce a ratio to simplest form. Have students list the factors of the numerator and denominator on their papers. They should circle the greatest common factor for both the numerator and denominator. Then divide both the numerator and denominator by the greatest common factor to reduce the ratio. Students should do and write these steps in their notebooks as a reminder.

Are They Getting It?

Check students' understanding of ratios by writing these problems on the board. Ask students to point out the wrong answers and explain why they are wrong.

1. This figure shows the ratio $\frac{1}{2}$. This is incorrect. The ratio shown is $\frac{6}{10}$, or $\frac{3}{5}$.

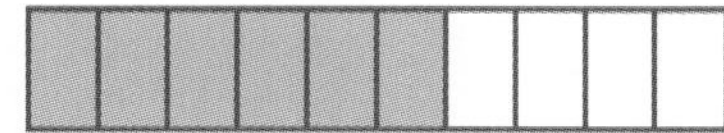

2. The ratio of the length to the width is 14 to 6. This is correct.

14 yd

6 yd

Note This!

Real-World Examples Have students write three ratios in their notebooks. For each ratio, they should relate it to a real-world situation and then draw a model.

Math Coach Notes

Divisibility Rules Review the divisibility tests with students so that they can more easily determine numbers they can use to write fractions in simplest form.

2 - last digit must be 0, 2, 4, 6, 8
3 - sum the digits, the sum must be divisible by 3
4 - the last two digits must be divisible by 4
5 - last digit must be 0, 5
6 - it is divisible by 2 AND divisible by 3
8 - the last three digits must be divisible by 8
9 - sum the digits, the sum must be divisible by 9
10 - last digit must be 0

Write each ratio as a fraction in simplest form.

5. In a garden, there are 9 rows of tomatoes and 15 rows of corn. Write the ratio of rows of tomatoes to rows of corn.

rows of tomatoes → / rows of corn → $\frac{9}{15} = \frac{9 \div 3}{15 \div 3} = \frac{3}{5}$

6. In David's class, 11 students like pepperoni pizza, 4 like mushroom pizza, and 9 like cheese pizza. Write the ratio of students who like cheese pizza to the total number of students. $\frac{3}{8}$

7. There are 7 tulips in a vase. Write the ratio of yellow tulips to the total number of tulips. $\frac{3}{7}$

Step by Step Problem-Solving Practice

Problem-Solving Strategies
- ☐ Look for a pattern.
- ☐ Guess and check.
- ☐ Act it out.
- ☑ Solve a simpler problem.
- ☐ Work backward.

Solve.

8. AGES Clarence is 16 years old, and his sister Takara is 10 years old. In two years, what will be the ratio of Clarence's age to Takara's age?

Understand Read the problem. Write what you know. Clarence is 16 years old. Takara is 10 years old. In 2 years, Clarence will be 18 years old, and Takara will be 12 years old.

Plan Pick a strategy. One strategy is to solve a simpler problem.

Solve First, write the ratio of their ages in two years. $\frac{18}{12}$

To write the ratio in simplest form, divide the numerator and denominator by a common factor. Divide the numerator and denominator by 2. $\frac{18}{12} = \frac{18 \div 2}{12 \div 2} = \frac{9}{6}$

Is there still a common factor? yes
Divide the numerator and denominator by 3. $\frac{9}{6} = \frac{9 \div 3}{6 \div 3} = \frac{3}{2}$

Is there still a common factor? no

Write the ratio in simplest form. $\frac{3}{2}$

Check Does the answer make sense? Look over your solution. Did you answer the question?

Intervention Strategy — Interpersonal Learners

Ratios of A Group Arrange students into groups of 3 to 5 students. Within each group, have students write ratios, in simplest form, for each of the following:

1. boys to girls
2. siblings to no siblings
3. brown hair to blonde hair
4. blue eyes to green eyes
5. glasses to no glasses

As a class, determine which groups have equal ratios.

BASKETBALL In the state finals, the Jefferson Hawks played the Washington Eagles. The Hawks' season record was 12 wins and 6 losses. The Eagles' season record was 16 wins and 2 losses. What was the ratio of wins for the Hawks to wins for the Eagles? Check off each step.

✔ Understand: I underlined key words.

✔ Plan: To solve the problem, I will solve a simpler problem.

✔ Solve: The answer is $\frac{3}{4}$, 3 to 4, or 3:4.

✔ Check: I checked my answer by multiplying the numerator and denominator by the GCF.

In a classroom, there are 27 students and 6 calculators. Write the ratio of students to calculators. $\frac{9}{2}$

Reflect What is a ratio? Explain using examples.

See TE margin.

Skills, Concepts, and Problem Solving

Write each ratio as a fraction in simplest form.

parallelograms and triangles to circles and trapezoids $\frac{1}{3}$

circles and parallelograms to triangles and trapezoids $\frac{7}{5}$

parallelograms to total number of figures $\frac{1}{6}$

Write each ratio as a fraction in simplest form.

Russ had 4 hits out of 12 at bats. $\frac{1}{3}$

The grapes were $6 for 3 pounds. $\frac{\$2}{1}$ or $2 per pound

Laurie swam 9 laps in 72 minutes. $\frac{1}{8}$

There are 14 baseballs to 20 gloves. $\frac{7}{10}$

GO ON

Math Challenge

Model Racing Lay out several blocks of two colors. Call two students to the front to have a seat at a table with the colored blocks. Have students close their eyes. Write a ratio on the board. When you say "Open," those two students should open their eyes and use the blocks to build a model of the ratio in simplest form. The first student to build the correct ratio is the winner and remains at the table to meet another challenger. Repeat the race as many times as it takes for all students to have a chance to build a model.

Additional Answer

Exercise 11 Sample answer: A ratio is a comparison using division. You can compare parts to parts, like the number of blue hats to red hats; and parts to whole, like the number of games won to the number of games played.

Odd/Even Assignments

Exercises 12–23 are structured so that students practice the same concepts whether they are assigned the odd or even problems.

In-Class Assignment

Have students complete Exercises 13, 16, 19, 22, and 26 to ensure that they understand the concept.

4 Assess

See It, Do It, Say It, Write It

Step 1 Give each student pair a ratio written on an index card. Tell them to model the ratio with a model or drawing and then write the ratio in three different forms on the other side of the index card. Discuss the results with the class. Compare different representations of the same ratio.

Step 2 Draw 4 circles on the board and shade 2. Ask: What is the ratio? Model several ratios using both drawings and items from the class. Have students name the ratio. Ask them how to represent other ratios.

Step 3 Tell students to write the definition of *ratio* in their own words. Have them provide two real-life examples of a ratio.

Looking Ahead: Pre-teach

Ratio Tables In the next lesson, students will learn about equivalent ratios and equivalent forms of 1.

Example

5 miles in 60 minutes is the ratio $\frac{5}{60}$.

Divide the numerator and the denominator by 5 to find an equivalent ratio. $\frac{5 \div 5}{60 \div 5} = \frac{1}{12}$

Write two ratios equivalent to the given ratio.

1. $\frac{3}{7}$ $\frac{6}{14}, \frac{9}{21}$
2. $\frac{4}{32}$ $\frac{2}{16}, \frac{1}{8}$
3. $\frac{20}{40}$ $\frac{10}{20}, \frac{5}{10}$

Write the ratio of length to width for each rectangle as a fraction in simplest form.

19 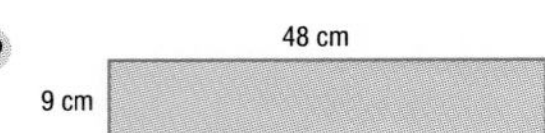

$\frac{16}{3}$

20 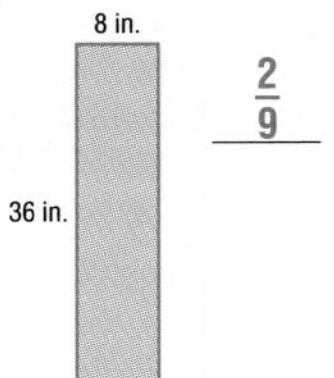

$\frac{2}{9}$

SPORTS The batting average is the ratio of the number of hits to the total number of at bats. Refer to the table to answer Exercises 21–23.

Player	Hits	At Bats
Tracy	12	36
Rex	24	56
Leonardo	27	81
Heidi	20	45
Bob	15	45

21 Which players had the same batting average?
Tracy, Leonardo, and Bob

What is their batting average? $\frac{1}{3}$

22 Did the player with the most hits have the highest batting average? Explain.
No; Leonardo had the most hits, but Heidi had the highest batting average at $\frac{4}{9}$.

23 Explain the meaning of Leonardo's batting average.
Answers will vary. Leonardo got a hit 1 out of every 3 times at bat.

Vocabulary Check **Write the vocabulary word that completes each sentence.**

24 A(n) ratio compares two quantities by division.

25 A(n) rate compares two quantities with different kinds of units.

26 Writing in Math Write the ratio of *2 pens out of a total of 3 pens* four different ways.
$\frac{2}{3}$, 2 out of 3, 2 to 3, 2:3

STOP

52 Chapter 2 Ratios, Rates, and Proportional Relationships

Ticket Out the Door

Pairs of Ratios Have students approach the door in pairs. Give the pair a ratio that can be written in a simpler form. The pair of students should name two equivalent ratios; one from dividing the numerator and denominator and one from multiplying the numerator and denominator. An example is to give the ratio $\frac{5}{15}$ and the students reply with the ratios $\frac{1}{3}$ and $\frac{10}{30}$.

Lesson 2-2

Ratio Tables

KEY Concept

A **ratio table** displays pairs of numbers that have the same ratio.

Suppose you are making punch for a party. For every 3 cans of juice, you will need 5 cups of water. The **ratio** is $\frac{3}{5}$. Multiplying the original ratio by an **equivalent form of one** produces **equivalent ratios**.

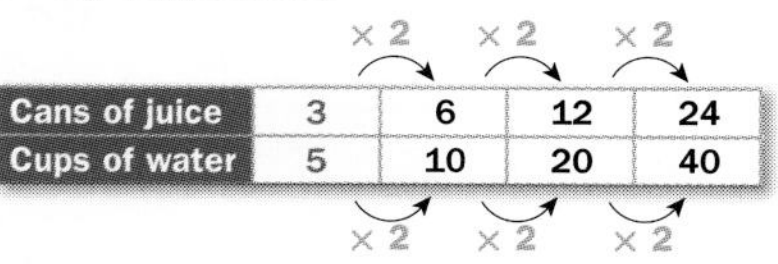

Cans of juice	3	6	12	24
Cups of water	5	10	20	40

So, you would need 6 cans of juice for every 10 cups of water, 12 cans of juice for every 20 cups of water, and so on.

The ratios $\frac{6}{10}$, $\frac{12}{20}$, and $\frac{24}{40}$ are all equivalent since each can be reduced to the ratio of $\frac{3}{5}$.

VOCABULARY

equivalent forms of one
different expressions that represent the same number
Example: $\frac{2}{2}$

equivalent ratios
ratios that have the same value

ratio
a comparison of two quantities by division; the ratio of 2 to 3 can be stated as 2 out of 3, 2 to 3, 2:3, or $\frac{2}{3}$

ratio table
a table with columns filled with pairs of numbers that have the same ratio

Multiplication and division can be used to find values in a ratio table. Use multiplication when changing from a small ratio to a larger ratio. Use division when changing from a larger ratio to a smaller ratio.

Example 1

Carolyn runs 3 miles in 30 minutes. At this rate, how long would it take her to run 24 miles? Use the ratio table given.

1. Identify the original ratio. $\frac{3}{30}$
2. Find equivalent forms of one.

$\frac{3 \times 2}{30 \times 2} = \frac{6}{60}$ $\quad \frac{6 \times 2}{60 \times 2} = \frac{12}{120}$ $\quad \frac{12 \times 2}{120 \times 2} = \frac{24}{240}$

Miles	3	6	12	24
Minutes	30	60	120	240

× 2 × 2 × 2

3. Complete the table.

It would take Carolyn 240 minutes to run 24 miles.

GO ON

Additional Example 1

Enrique read 60 pages in 2 hours. At this rate, how long will it take him to read 480 pages? Use a ratio table.

1. Identify the original ratio. $\frac{2}{60}$
2. Find equivalent forms of one.

$\frac{2 \times 2}{60 \times 2} = \frac{4}{120}$ $\quad \frac{4 \times 2}{120 \times 2} = \frac{8}{240}$ $\quad \frac{8 \times 2}{240 \times 2} = \frac{16}{480}$

3. Complete the table.

× 2 × 2 × 2

Hours	2	4	8	16
Number of Pages	60	120	240	480

× 2 × 2 × 2

It would take Enrique 16 hours to read 480 pages.

Lesson Notes

Lesson 2-2

Lesson Planner

Objective Use ratio tables to represent and solve problems involving equivalent ratios.

Vocabulary **equivalent forms of one**, **equivalent ratios**, **ratio**, **ratio table**

Materials/Manipulatives number cubes, deck of playing cards, dried beans or counters

Chapter Resource Masters

- CRM Vocabulary and English Language Development (p. A27)
- CRM Skills Practice (p. A28)
- CRM Problem-Solving Practice (p. A29)
- CRM Homework Practice (p. A30)

1 Introduce

Vocabulary

Simplest Form Review how to write fractions in simplest form. Distinguish numerator and denominator and relate fractions to ratios. Discuss multiples and how this relates to equivalent forms of one.

2 Teach

Key Concept

Foundational Skills and Concepts After students have read through the Key Concept box, have them try these exercises.

1. Are the ratios $\frac{1}{15}$ and $\frac{12}{30}$ equivalent? No. the ratios do not simplify to the same value.
2. A student earns 1 raffle ticket for every 4 T-shirts he sells. How many raffle tickets will he earn if he sells 12 T-shirts? He will earn 3 raffle tickets.

Additional **Example 2**

Kaylee swam 18 laps in 45 minutes. At this rate, how many laps could she swim in 5 minutes? Use a ratio table.

1. Identify the original ratio. $\frac{45}{18}$

2. Find the equivalent forms of one.

$\frac{45 \div 3 = 15}{18 \div 3 = 6}$ $\frac{15 \div 3 = 5}{6 \div 3 = 2}$

3. Complete the table.

÷ 3 ÷ 3

Minutes	45	15	5
Laps	18	6	2

÷ 3 ÷ 3

Kalyee could swim 2 laps in 5 minutes.

YOUR TURN!

Taquan made 4 batches of muffins in 1 hour. How long does it take him to bake 32 batches of muffins? Use a ratio table.

1. Identify the original ratio. $\frac{4}{1}$
2. Find equivalent forms of one. $\frac{4 \times 2 = 8}{1 \times 2 = 2}$ $\frac{8 \times 2 = 16}{2 \times 2 = 4}$ $\frac{16 \times 2 = 32}{4 \times 2 = 8}$
3. Complete the table.

× 2 × 2 × 2

Batches of muffins	4	8	16	32
Hours	1	2	4	8

× 2 × 2 × 2

It would take Taquan 8 hours to bake 32 batches of muffins.

Example 2

Max bought 24 raffle tickets for $8 at the school fundraiser. At this rate, how much would 3 tickets cost? Use a ratio table.

1. Identify the original ratio. $\frac{24}{8}$
2. Find equivalent forms of one.

$\frac{24 \div 2 = 12}{8 \div 2 = 4}$

$\frac{12 \div 2 = 6}{4 \div 2 = 2}$

$\frac{6 \div 2 = 3}{2 \div 2 = 1}$

3. Complete the table.

÷ 2 ÷ 2 ÷ 2

Number of Tickets	24	12	6	3
Cost($)	8	4	2	1

÷ 2 ÷ 2 ÷ 2

It would cost Max $1 for 3 tickets.

YOUR TURN!

In the first 243 minutes, 27 students voted in the school election. At this rate, how many students voted in the first minute? Use a ratio table.

1. Identify the original ratio. $\frac{243}{27}$
2. Find equivalent forms of one.

$\frac{243 \div 3 = 81}{27 \div 3 = 9}$

$\frac{81 \div 3 = 27}{9 \div 3 = 3}$

$\frac{27 \div 3 = 9}{3 \div 3 = 1}$

3. Complete the table.

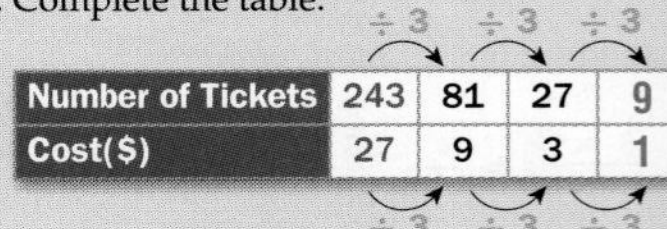

÷ 3 ÷ 3 ÷ 3

Number of Tickets	243	81	27	9
Cost($)	27	9	3	1

÷ 3 ÷ 3 ÷ 3

There were 9 students that voted in the first minute.

Intervention Strategy Kinesthetic Learners

Model Ratios Have students work in pairs. Distribute dried beans or counters to each group. Write the following ratios on the board. Have students use the beans or counters to create a table for each ratio, labeling the relationship between numerators and denominators. Tell students to find five equivalent ratios for each example. Have students practice explaining to their partners how to find the equivalent ratios, and then write the modeled ratio tables on a piece of paper. Ask pairs to share their ratio tables with other classmates. $\frac{2}{3}, \frac{5}{4}, \frac{1}{6}, \frac{3}{7}$

Who is Correct?

st two equivalent ratios of $\frac{9}{2}$.

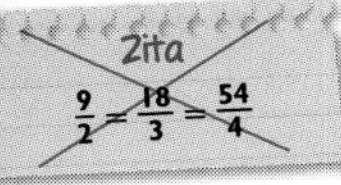

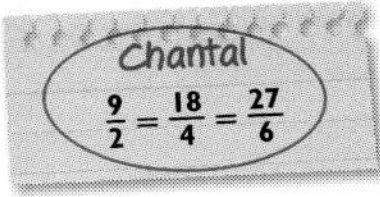

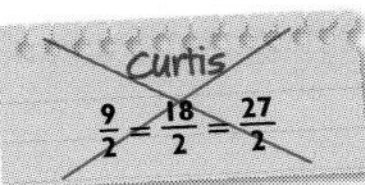

ircle the correct answer(s). Cross out incorrect answer(s).

Guided Practice

omplete each ratio table.

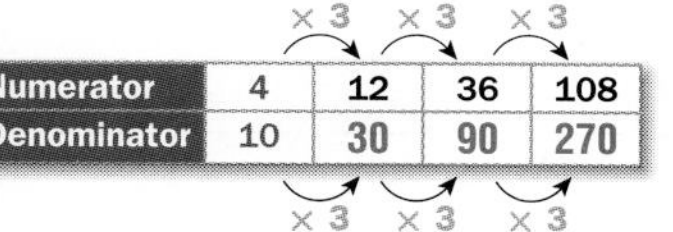

Numerator	4	12	36	108
Denominator	10	30	90	270

2 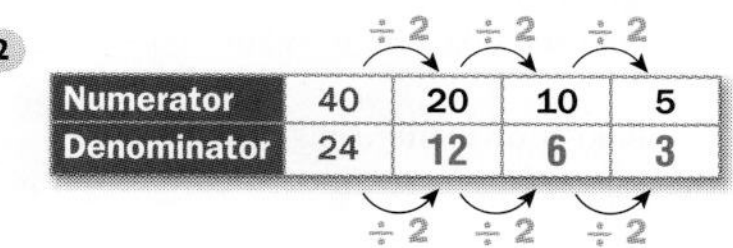

Numerator	40	20	10	5
Denominator	24	12	6	3

Step by Step Practice

Marie's field hockey team is washing cars for a fund-raiser. If they charge $5 for every car they wash, how much will they make if they wash 40 cars? Use the ratio table.

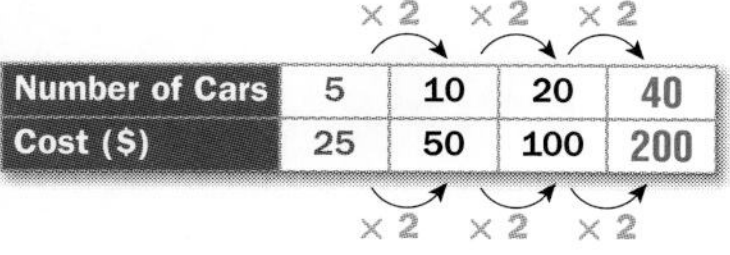

Number of Cars	5	10	20	40
Cost ($)	25	50	100	200

Step 1 The original ratio is $\frac{5}{25}$.

Step 2 Find the equivalent forms of one used to determine the missing values.

$\frac{5 \times 2 = 10}{25 \times 2 = 50}$ $\frac{10 \times 2 = 20}{50 \times 2 = 100}$ $\frac{20 \times 2 = 40}{100 \times 2 = 200}$

Step 3 The missing ratio is $\frac{40}{200}$.

They will make $200 if they wash 40 cars.

GO ON

Lesson 2-2 Ratio Tables 55

3 Practice

Using Manipulatives

Number Cubes Have students roll a number cube for a numerator and again for a denominator to create an original ratio. Students can then find equivalent ratios.

On-Hand Manipulatives Model how to use playing cards to create ratios. Remove the face cards from the deck, or assign a numeric value to each face card. Draw two cards and have one be the numerator and the other be the denominator. Create ratio tables from this original ratio, reducing when possible.

Who *is Correct?*

Diagnostic Teaching

- Zita is incorrect. She increased the denominators incorrectly.
- Chantal is correct. She multiplied correctly.
- Curtis is incorrect. He did not change the denominators.

Math Coach Notes

Common Factors Remind students to look for common factors shared by the numerator and denominator of each ratio. This will help students simplify or find multiples for equivalent ratios.

Use the ratio table to solve each exercise.

4. A recipe for 1 banana cream pie calls for 5 bananas. How many bananas are needed to make 8 banana cream pies?

Find equivalent forms of one. $\frac{1 \times 2}{5 \times 2} = \frac{2}{10}$ $\frac{2 \times 2}{10 \times 2} = \frac{4}{20}$ $\frac{4 \times 2}{20 \times 2} = \frac{8}{40}$

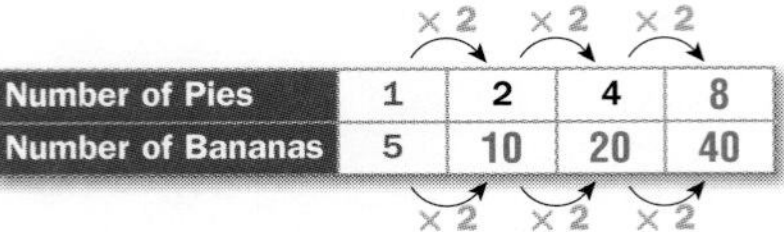

Number of Pies	1	2	4	8
Number of Bananas	5	10	20	40

You would need 40 bananas to make 8 banana cream pies.

5. Armando can swim 36 laps in 54 minutes. At this rate, how long would it take him to swim 4 laps?

Find equivalent forms of one. $\frac{36 \div 3}{54 \div 3} = \frac{12}{18}$ $\frac{12 \div 3}{18 \div 3} = \frac{4}{6}$

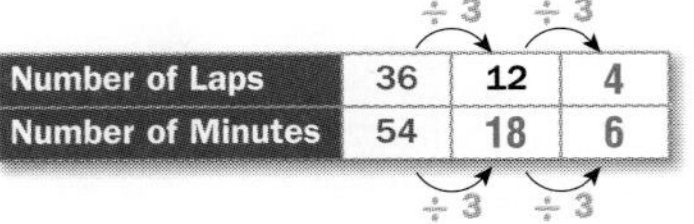

Number of Laps	36	12	4
Number of Minutes	54	18	6

Armando would finish 4 laps in 6 minutes.

6. Marco earns $7 an hour at a grocery store. How much will he earn if he works 27 hours?

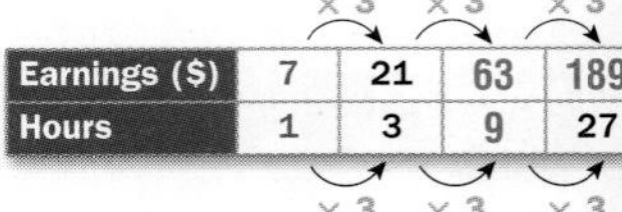

Earnings ($)	7	21	63	189
Hours	1	3	9	27

Marco will earn $189 if he works for 27 hours.

7. A recipe that makes 8 cups of soup calls for 64 ounces of chicken broth. At that rate, how many cups of soup can be made by using 16 ounces of chicken broth?

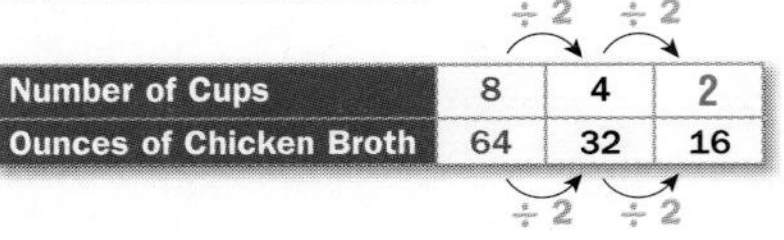

Number of Cups	8	4	2
Ounces of Chicken Broth	64	32	16

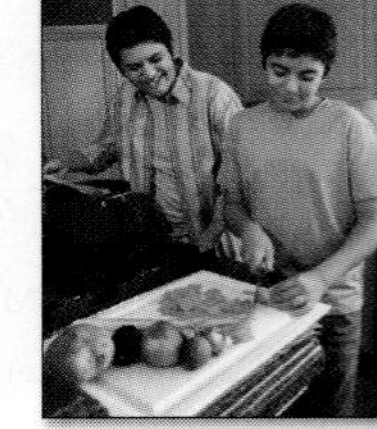

2 cups of soup can be made by using 16 ounces of chicken broth.

Are They Getting It?

Check students' understanding of ratio tables by writing these problems on the board. Ask them to point out incorrect answers and explain their reasoning.

1. At an Internet café, the fee for connection is $5 for 30 minutes. At this rate, it would cost $25 for 120 minutes. This is incorrect. The equivalent ratio is $20 for 120 minutes.
2. Admission to the Hands-On Science Museum is $42 for 6 children. So, the cost for 2 children is $14. This is correct.
3. Javier cycled 120 miles in 6 hours. At this rate, he would cycle 60 miles in 4 hours. This is incorrect. The equivalent ratio is 60 miles in 3 hours.

56 Chapter 2 Ratios, Rates, and Proportional Relationships

Step by Step Problem-Solving Practice

Problem-Solving Strategies
- ☑ Look for a pattern.
- ☐ Guess and check.
- ☐ Act it out.
- ☐ Solve a simpler problem.
- ☐ Work backward.

Solve.

8 CARS Mr. Rivera's car can travel 28 miles per gallon of gas. How many miles can he travel on 8 gallons of gas?

Miles	28	56	?	?
Gallons of Gas	1	2	?	8

Understand Read the problem. Write what you know. The base ratio of miles to gallons of gas is $\frac{28}{1}$.

Plan Pick a strategy. One strategy is to look for a pattern.

Solve Find a pattern to find the equivalent forms of one that determine the equivalent ratios.

$$\frac{28 \times 2}{1 \times 2} = \frac{56}{2} \qquad \frac{56 \times 2}{2 \times 2} = \frac{112}{4} \qquad \frac{112 \times 2}{4 \times 2} = \frac{224}{8}$$

Complete the table.

Miles	28	56	112	224
Gallons of Gas	1	2	4	8

(× 2 between each column, top and bottom)

Mr. Rivera can travel 224 miles on 8 gallons of gas.

Check Work backward. Use division.

9 JUICE Tyree bought a 64-ounce bottle of juice that contains 32 grams of sugar. How many grams of sugar would be in 8 ounces of juice? Use the ratio table given to solve the problem.

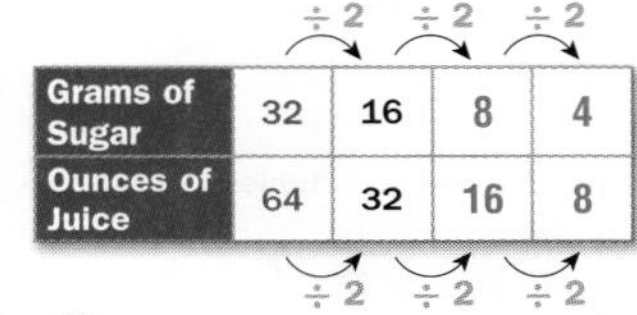

Grams of Sugar	32	16	8	4
Ounces of Juice	64	32	16	8

(÷ 2 between each column, top and bottom)

✔ Understand: I underlined key words.

✔ Plan: To solve the problem, I will look for a pattern.

✔ Solve: The answer is 4 grams of sugar.

✔ Check: I checked my answer by working backward using multiplication.

GO ON

Note This!

Reduced Form Discuss how to check a ratio table by reducing the ratios in each column to their simplest forms. If each ratio simplifies to the same value, they are all equivalent.

Math Coach Notes

Step-by-Step Have students practice evaluating a ratio table and describing what it shows. Tell students to explain what patterns they find between the numbers and how to determine equivalent ratios. Ask them to extend a ratio table from the lesson and explain how they used an equivalent form of one to find the new ratios.

Common Error Alert

Ratio Tables Remind students that to solve the ratio tables, they are to multiply or divide by the same number.

Intervention Strategy — Naturalistic Learners

Noticing Ratios Tell students to work in small groups. Students should use their classroom and school environment to find ratios. Encourage them to consider smaller ratios such as the number of paintbrushes per can in the art room, as well as larger ratios such as the number of certain colored tiles on the floor of one classroom. Have groups brainstorm as many ratio examples as they can, and then write two problems with ratio tables. Tell students to include the completed tables and the answers to their problems. Encourage groups to share their problems with the class and invite their classmates to find the answers.

Odd/Even Assignments

Exercises 11–19 are structured so that students practice the same concepts whether they are assigned the odd or even problems.

In-Class Assignment

Have students complete Exercises 11, 15, 19, and 22 to ensure that they understand the concept.

Common Error Alert

Understanding Ratio Tables Remind students that the relationship between the numbers in each row of the ratio table involves either multiplication or division. Reinforce that the greater ratios are simply multiples of the original ratio, or the ratio in its simplest form.

10  **Reflect** How do you use equivalent forms of one to complete a ratio table?

Sample answer: After finding the original ratio, multiply it by equivalent forms of one.

Skills, Concepts, and Problem Solving

Use the ratio tables to solve each exercise.

11 GROCERIES Cans of green beans are on sale for 3 for $2. How much would 24 cans of green beans cost?

Cans of Green Beans	3	6	12	24
Cost ($)	2	4	8	16

24 cans of green beans would cost $ 16 .

12 FIELD TRIP The field trip to the local museum requires that there is 1 adult for every 6 students. How many adults must go along with 162 students?

Number of Adults	1	3	9	27
Number of Students	6	18	54	162

27 adults must go along with 162 students.

13 PARTY Ellen wants to buy sub sandwiches for her party. The store says 24 subs will be enough for 48 people. How many people will 3 subs feed?

Number of Subs	24	12	6	3
People Served	48	24	12	6

Three sub sandwiches will feed 6 people.

14 KNITTNG Suzanne used 450 yards of yarn to make 9 scarves. At this rate, how many yards of yarn will she need to make 1 scarf?

Yards of Yarn	450	150	50
Number of Scarves	9	3	1

Suzanne will need 50 yards of yarn to make 1 scarf.

Complete the ratio tables.

15

Numerator	1	2	4	8
Denominator	7	14	28	56

16

Numerator	81	27	9	3
Denominator	27	9	3	1

17

Numerator	3	9	27	81
Denominator	5	15	45	135

18

Numerator	64	32	16	8
Denominator	40	20	10	5

58 Chapter 2 Ratios, Rates, and Proportional Relationships

Math Challenge

Complete the ratio table to solve the problem.

Rosie can make 28 necklaces in 16 hours. At this rate, how long would it take her to make 7 necklaces?

Number of Necklaces	28	14	7
Number of Hours	16	8	4

It would take her 4 hours to make 7 necklaces.

Solve.

19 DOGS A 10-pound bag of dog food will feed a large-sized dog for about 1 week. Use a ratio table to determine how long an 80-pound bag of dog food will feed a large-sized dog.

Pounds of Dog Food	10	20	40	80
Number of Weeks	1	2	4	8

An 80-pound bag of dog food will feed a large-sized dog for about 8 weeks.

Vocabulary Check **Write the vocabulary word that completes each sentence.**

20 A(n) ratio table is a table with columns filled with pairs of numbers that have the same ratio.

21 Ratios that have the same value are equivalent ratios.

22 Writing in Math Alicia can fill 32 boxes in 120 minutes. At this rate, how many boxes can she fill in 4 minutes? Explain a strategy that can be used to find the missing value in the ratio table.

Number of Boxes	32	16	8	4
Number of Minutes	120	60	30	15

Sample answer: Complete the ratio table by dividing by an equivalent form of one to find that Alicia can fill 32 boxes in 120 minutes. Since $32 \div 2 = 16$, divide each quantity by 2.

Spiral Review (Lesson 2-1, p. 46)

Write each ratio as a fraction in simplest form.

23 Pamela walked 3 miles in 75 minutes. $\frac{1}{25}$ or 25 minutes per mile

24 There are 27 students to 6 computers. $\frac{9}{2}$ students per computer

Write the ratio of length to width of each rectangle as a fraction in simplest form.

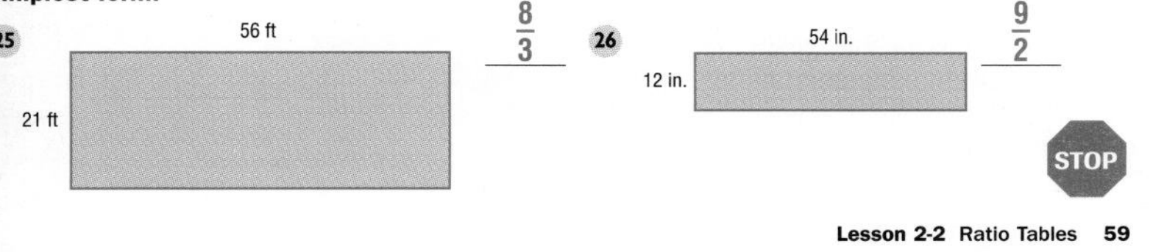

25 $\frac{8}{3}$ 26 $\frac{9}{2}$

STOP

Lesson 2-2 Ratio Tables 59

Ticket Out the Door

Equivalent Ratios Draw the following ratio table on the board. As students approach the classroom door to exit, alternate asking them to name the ratio in simplest form and the number of photos that could fit on 16 pages in a photo album.

Number of Photos	9	18	36	72
Number of Pages	2	4	8	16

See It, Do It, Say It, Write It

Step 1 Draw the following ratio table on the board.

Cups of Punch	5	10	20	40
Ounces of Pineapple Juice	2	4	8	16

Step 2 Tell students to complete the ratio table to find the number of ounces of pineapple juice needed for 5 cups of punch. Then have them find the number of cups of punch that could be made with 16 ounces of pineapple juice.

Step 3 Have students work in pairs. Ask them to discuss what the ratio table shows and explain how they found the equivalent ratios.

Step 4 Have students work alone to write an evaluation of the ratio table on the board. Encourage students to use correct vocabulary terms and clear language in their explanations.

Looking Ahead: Pre-teach

Probability as a Ratio In the next lesson, students will learn about probability ratios.

Example

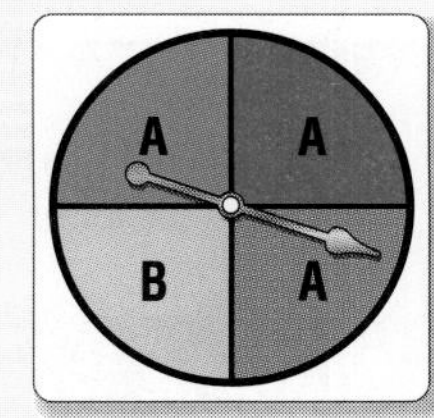

The probability of spinning a B is

$$\frac{\text{number of B sections}}{\text{number of total sections}} = \frac{1}{4}.$$

For one out of every four spins, you can expect to land on the B section.

Exercises.

1. What is the probability of spinning an A? $\frac{3}{4}$

2. If you spun the spinner 40 times, how many times would you expect the spinner to land on A? 30

Chapter 2

Progress Check 1

Formative Assessment

Use the Progress Check to assess students' mastery of the previous lessons. Have students review the lesson indicated for the problems they answered incorrectly.

Odd/Even Assignments

Exercises are structured so that students practice the same concepts whether they are assigned the odd or even problems.

Common Error Alert

Key Words Students may have trouble with terms such as *simplest form.* Remind them that to be in simplest form the numerator and denominator can have no common factors other than 1.

Exercises 1–5 Students may have difficulty reducing fractions to simplest form. They may have to reduce the fractions more than once if they do not come up with the greatest common factor the first time.

Progress Check 1 (Lessons 2-1 and 2-2)

Write the ratio of width to length of each rectangle as a fraction in simplest form.

1 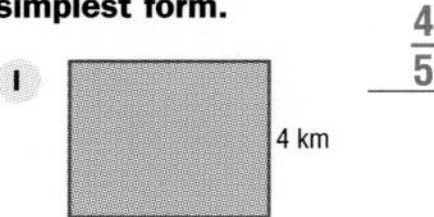

$\frac{4}{5}$

2 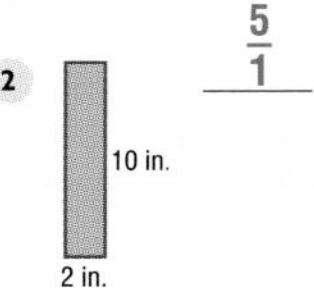

$\frac{5}{1}$

Write each ratio as a fraction in simplest form.

3 18 out of 27 girls had green eyes $\frac{2}{3}$

4 5 long-haired cats out of 12 cats $\frac{5}{12}$

Solve.

5 **SPELLING** Write a fraction in simplest form for the ratio of the number of vowels in *Mathematics* to the total number of letters. $\frac{4}{11}$

Complete each ratio table.

6 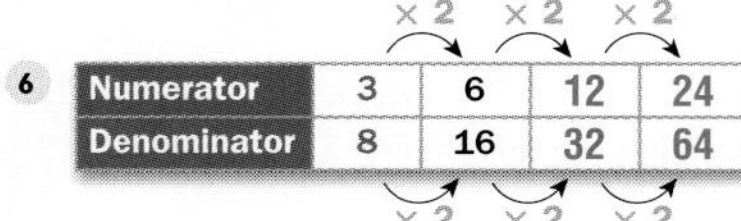

Numerator	3	6	12	24
Denominator	8	16	32	64

(× 2, × 2, × 2)

7 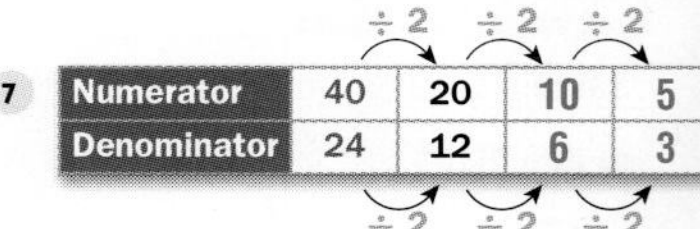

Numerator	40	20	10	5
Denominator	24	12	6	3

(÷ 2, ÷ 2, ÷ 2)

Use the ratio tables to solve each problem.

8 **GROCERIES** Frozen pizzas are on sale for 3 for $7. How much would 12 frozen pizzas cost?

Twelve frozen pizzas would cost $28.

Frozen Pizzas	3	6	12
Cost ($)	7	14	28

9 **CHORES** Mitch washed 64 tables in 32 minutes. At this rate, how many tables could he wash in 8 minutes?

Mitch could wash 16 tables in 8 minutes.

Number of Tables	64	32	16
Time (min)	32	16	8

10 **SOUP** A recipe that makes 2 cups of soup calls for 12 ounces of broth. How many ounces of broth do you need to make 16 cups of soup?

You would need 96 ounces of broth to make 16 cups of soup.

Cups of Soup	2	4	8	16
Ounces of Broth	12	24	48	96

Data-Driven Decision Making

Students missing Exercises . . .	Have trouble with . . .	Should review and practice . . .
1–5	writing ratios as fractions in simplest form.	SSG Lesson 2-1, p. 46 CRM Skills Practice, p. A24
6–7	writing ratios using a ratio table.	SSG Lesson 2-2, p. 53 CRM Skills Practice, p. A28
8–10	solving word problems involving ratios and rates.	CRM Problem-Solving Practice, pp. A25 and A29

Lesson 2-3 Probability as a Ratio

KEY Concept

Probability is a number that measures the chance of an event happening. The probability of an event is a **ratio** that compares the number of favorable outcomes to the number of possible **outcomes**. The probability of an **event** is written as *P*(event).

Suppose you roll a number cube.

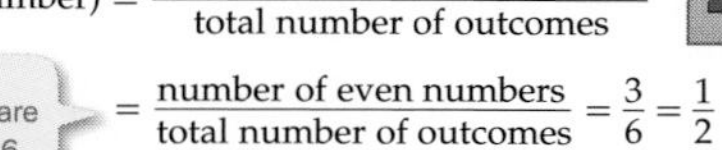

$P(\text{even number}) = \frac{\text{number of favorable outcomes}}{\text{total number of outcomes}}$

The even numbers are 2, 4, and 6. $= \frac{\text{number of even numbers}}{\text{total number of outcomes}} = \frac{3}{6} = \frac{1}{2}$

The ratio of the even numbers to the total numbers is $\frac{3}{6}$ or $\frac{1}{2}$. Notice that the ratio and the probability are the same.

Probability can also be written as a decimal or as a percent.

$\frac{1}{2}$ 0.50 50%

The probability, $\frac{1}{2}$, means that you can expect to roll an even number one out of every two times or 50% of the time.

The probability of an event can be 0, 1, or any number between 0 and 1.

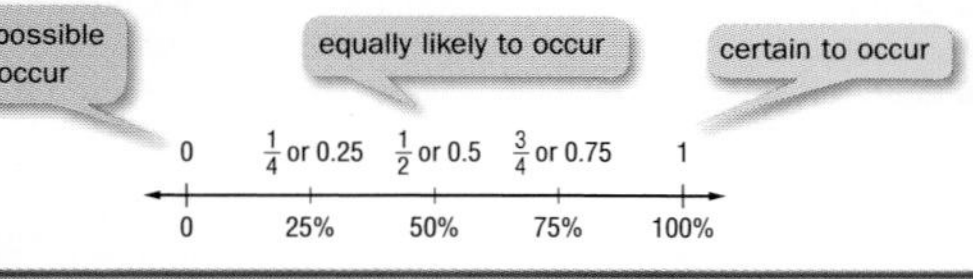

VOCABULARY

event
a set of outcomes

outcomes
the possible results of a probability event; Example: 4 is an outcome when a number cube is rolled.

probability
the chance that some event will occur

ratio
a comparison of two quantities by division; the ratio of 2 to 3 can be stated as 2 out of 3, 2 to 3, 2:3, or $\frac{2}{3}$

Vhen probability equals 0, the event is **impossible.** For example, ıe probability of rolling a 7 on a six-sided number cube is 0.

Vhen probability equals 1, the event is **certain.** For example, the robability of rolling a natural number that is 6 or less is 1.

he probability that one event does **not** occur is equal to – *P*(event does occur).

GO ON

Intervention Strategy

Logical/Kinesthetic Learners

Build a Bag Have students work in small groups. Provide students with a variety of different colored markers and cardstock paper. Students should cut out small circular disks from the card stock and color them so that when they put them into a bag, the probability of selecting a disk of each color matches the probability given below.

$P(\text{red}) = \frac{1}{10}$ $P(\text{blue}) = \frac{1}{2}$ $P(\text{green}) = \frac{3}{20}$ $P(\text{orange}) = 0$ $P(\text{purple}) = \frac{1}{4}$

Write a ratio for each colored disk to the total number of disks. red 2:20; blue 10:20; green 3:20; orange 0:20; purple 5:20

Lesson Notes

Lesson 2-3

Lesson Planner

Objective Represent probability as a ratio and compute probability.

Vocabulary **event**, **outcomes**, **probability**, **ratio**

Materials/Manipulatives number cubes, spinners, counters, color markers, cardstock

Chapter Resource Masters

- CRM Vocabulary and English Language Development (p. A31)
- CRM Skills Practice (p. A32)
- CRM Problem-Solving Practice (p. A33)
- CRM Homework Practice (p. A34)

1 Introduce

Vocabulary

Probability of a Number Cube Hold up a number cube so that all students can see that the cube has the numbers 1 through 6 on the faces. Write the following equations on the board:

$P(3) = \frac{1}{6}$ $P(\text{even}) = \frac{1}{2}$ $P(3 \text{ or } 4) = \frac{1}{3}$ $P(7) = 0$

Discuss the meaning of each probability in terms of a ratio. $P(3) = \frac{1}{6}$ means that in a perfect statistical world, 1 out of every 6 rolls would result in the face with the number 3 landing up. Have students verbalize the meaning of the ratios for the other three probabilities.

2 Teach

Key Concept

Foundational Skills and Concepts After students have read through the Key Concept box, have them try these exercises.

1. How many total outcomes are possible on a six-sided number cube? 6
2. How do you know when an event is *not likely* to occur? The probability is close to 0.

Additional **Example 1**

Use the spinner to find the probability of spinning a prime number. Write the probability as a fraction in simplest form. Explain the probability.

1. Count the number of sections labeled with prime numbers. Write this number in the numerator.
2. Count the total number of sections. Write this number in the denominator.

   $P(\text{prime}) = \frac{4}{8}$ ← The spinner has 4 prime numbers, 2, 3, 5, and 7. / The spinner has 8 sections.

3. The ratio is $\frac{4}{8}$. Rewrite the fraction in simplest form.

   $\frac{4}{8} = \frac{4 \div 4}{8 \div 4} = \frac{1}{2}$

4. The probability of $\frac{1}{2}$ means that 1 out of every 2 spins should land on a prime number.

Example 1

Use the spinner to find the probability of spinning 5. Write the probability as a fraction in simplest form. Explain the probability.

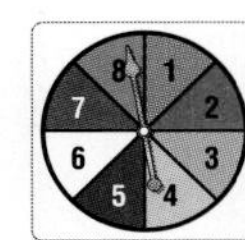

1. Count the number of sections labeled 5. Write this number in the numerator.
2. Count the total number of sections. Write this number in the denominator.

   $P(5) = \frac{1}{8}$ ← The spinner has one 5. ← The spinner has 8 sections.

3. The ratio is $\frac{1}{8}$. It is already in simplest form.
4. The probability of $\frac{1}{8}$ means that 1 out of every 8 spins should be a 5.

YOUR TURN!

Use the spinner in Example 1 to find the probability of spinning an even number. Write the probability as a fraction in simplest form. Explain the probability.

1. What number of sections are labeled with an even number? 4
2. What is the total number of sections? 8
3. $P(\text{even number}) = \frac{4}{8}$
4. The ratio can be simplified.

   $\frac{4 \div 4}{8 \div 4} = \frac{1}{2}$

5. The probability of $\frac{1}{2}$ means that 1 out of every 2 spins should be an even number.

Example 2

A jar of marbles contains 4 blue, 6 red, 5 yellow, and 3 green marbles. What is the probability of choosing a blue marble if you choose a marble without looking?

1. There are 4 blue marbles.
2. There are a total of 18 marbles in the jar.
3. Write the ratio for the $P(\text{blue})$. $\frac{4}{18}$
4. Write the fraction in simplest form.

   $\frac{4 \div 2}{18 \div 2} = \frac{2}{9}$

5. 2 out of every 9 times you take a marble from the jar without looking it will be blue.

YOUR TURN!

A box of figures has 5 squares, 9 triangles, 10 circles, and 6 trapeziods. What is the probability that a triangle is selected if you choose a figure without looking?

1. There are a total of 9 triangles.
2. There are a total of 30 figures in the bag.
3. Write the ratio for $P(\text{triangle}) = \frac{9}{30}$
4. Write the fraction in simplest form. $\frac{3}{10}$
5. 3 out of every 10 times you take a figure from the bag without looking it will be a triangle.

Additional **Example 2**

A package of mints has 6 cinnamon, 6 spearmint, 2 wintergreen, and 1 peppermint flavored mints. What is the probability of choosing a spearmint flavored mint without looking?

1. There are 6 spearmint mints.
2. There are a total of 15 mints in the package.
3. Write the ratio for $P(\text{spearmint})$. $\frac{6}{15}$
4. Write the fraction in simplest form. $\frac{6 \div 3}{15 \div 3} = \frac{2}{5}$
5. 2 out of every 5 times you take a mint from the package without looking it will be spearmint.

Who is Correct?

he ratio of blue tickets to the total number of tickets in a box is $\frac{5}{12}$. What is the probability that when you pick a ticket without ooking it will not be blue?

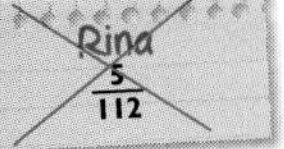

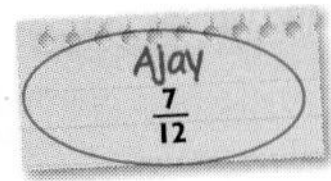

ircle correct answer(s). Cross out incorrect answer(s).

Guided Practice

se the spinner to find each probability. Write the probability as a action in simplest form.

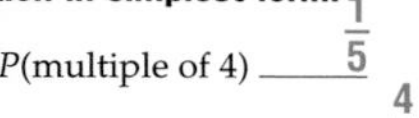
P(multiple of 4) $\frac{1}{5}$

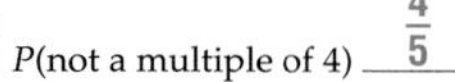
P(not a multiple of 4) $\frac{4}{5}$

Step by Step Practice

ind the probability. Write the probability as a fraction in implest form.

3 In a jar there are 5 pennies, 12 nickels, 6 dimes, and 4 quarters. Find the probability of reaching into the jar without looking and not getting a nickel.

Step 1 Count the number of coins in the jar that are not nickels. 15
This is the numerator in the fraction.

Step 2 Count the total number of coins. 27
This is the denominator in the fraction.

Step 3 Write a ratio for the P(not a nickel). $\frac{15}{27}$

Step 4 Write the ratio in simplest form. $\frac{15}{27} = \frac{5}{9}$

GO ON

Who *is Correct?*

Diagnostic Teaching

- Rina wrote $\frac{5}{12}$. This is incorrect because there are 5 blue tickets. She did not give the probability of *not* choosing a blue ticket.
- Malina wrote $\frac{5}{17}$. This is incorrect because the total number of tickets is 12, not 17.
- Ajay wrote $\frac{7}{12}$. This is correct.
  Since $P(\text{blue}) = \frac{5}{12}$, $P(\text{not blue}) = 1 - \frac{5}{12}$ or $\frac{7}{12}$.

Remind students that to subtract a fraction from 1, rewrite 1 as an equivalent fraction with the same denominator as the subtracted fraction. For example, $1 - \frac{5}{12} = \frac{12}{12} - \frac{5}{12}$.

3 Practice

Using Manipulatives

Spinner Recreate the examples and exercises by allowing students to use a spinner.

Number Cubes Use number cubes to recreate examples or practice probability experiments.

Two-Color Counters Use counters to recreate examples or practice probability experiments.

On-Hand Manipulatives Place classroom objects in a bag to use as a probability problem.

Note This!

Writing as Percents Probabilities are usually expressed as a fraction and the fraction is often not a common fraction. Instruct students to express a probability as a percent in their notebooks when they want to better understand the likelihood of an event. For example, $\frac{4}{15}$ and $\frac{7}{15}$ are not common fractions. If students write $\frac{4}{15} = 26.7\%$ and $\frac{7}{15} = 46.7\%$, they will be able to compare the percents to each other, and to 100%, to have a better understanding of their meanings. A probability of $\frac{4}{15}$ means that a little more than 25% of the time the event will occur. A probability of $\frac{7}{15}$ means that a little less than 50% of the time the event will occur.

Note This!

Probability in Real Life When taking notes on probability as a ratio, tell students to write the definition of *probability* using their own words. Beneath their definition, have students write examples of probability ratios in the real world. Prompt them with examples from the classroom, sports, and so on, if necessary. Using real-world examples that are relevant to students will help them connect with the concepts.

Find each probability. Write the probability as a fraction in simplest form.

4 In a box of bagels, there are 8 blueberry, 10 cinnamon, and 6 onion bagels. What is the probability that without looking you would choose a bagel that is not blueberry?

$P(\text{not blueberry}) = \frac{16}{24} = \frac{16 \div 8}{24 \div 8} = \frac{2}{3}$

5 In a jar, there are 12 red jellybeans, 5 blue jellybeans, 9 green jellybeans, 6 pink jellybeans, and 8 yellow jellybeans. Find the probability of randomly selecting a yellow jellybean.

$P(\text{yellow}) = \frac{1}{5}$

Find each probability using a number cube. Write the probability as a fraction in simplest form.

6 $P(\text{roll a 3})$ $\frac{1}{6}$

7 $P(\text{roll a 1 or a 6})$ $\frac{1}{3}$

8 $P(\text{roll a number less than 3})$ $\frac{1}{3}$

9 $P(\text{roll a number less than 6})$ $\frac{5}{6}$

10 $P(\text{roll an odd number})$ $\frac{1}{2}$

11 $P(\text{roll an 8})$ 0

Find the probability of each event. Write the probability as a fraction in simplest form.

12 You pick a month that begins with the letter *J*. $\frac{1}{4}$

13 You pick the letter A from the letters in FLORIDA. $\frac{1}{7}$

14 You pick a day of the week that ends in the letter *Y*. 1

15 You pick a day of the week that begins with the letter *T*. $\frac{2}{7}$

16 You pick a weekend day from the days of the week. $\frac{2}{7}$

17 You pick one of the letters *A*, *F*, or *G* from the alphabet. $\frac{3}{26}$

Are They Getting It?

Check students' understanding of probability as a ratio by writing these problems on the board. Ask students to point out wrong answers and explain why they are wrong.

1. A probability of 0.8 means that 8 out of 100 times the event will occur. This is not correct. The decimal 0.8 equals $\frac{8}{10}$, which means 8 out of 10 times.
2. A probability of $P(\text{blue}) = \frac{2}{5}$ means that for every five times you draw from a bag, you can expect to get 2 blue items. This is correct.
3. When dealing with probabilities, there are no absolutes. This is not correct. When a probability equals 0, it is absolutely certain that the event will not occur. When a probability equals 1, it is absolutely certain that the event will occur.

tep by Step Problem-Solving Practice

Problem-Solving Strategies
- ☐ Draw a diagram.
- ☐ Look for a pattern.
- ☑ Use logical reasoning.
- ☐ Act it out.
- ☐ Solve a simpler problem.

olve.

3 EYE COLOR The ratio of blue-eyed students to the total number of students in a fifth-grade class is 9 out of 30. What is the probability, if one student is picked by the teacher without looking, that the student will not have blue eyes?

Understand Read the problem. Write what you know. Out of 30 students, 9 have blue eyes.

Plan Pick a strategy. One strategy is to use logical reasoning.

Solve Write the ratio of blue-eyed students to total students. $\frac{9}{30}$

The probability of choosing a student who does not have blue eyes is the same as the difference of the ratio of the entire class and the ratio of blue-eyed students.

$$\frac{30}{30} - \frac{9}{30} = \frac{21}{30} = \frac{7}{10}$$

The probability of choosing a student who does not have blue eyes is $\frac{7}{10}$.

Check Check your answer. The sum of the probability that an event occurs and the probability that the event does not occur is 1. Is the sum of your probabilities equal to one? Explain. Yes; $\frac{9}{30} + \frac{21}{30} = \frac{30}{30}$

MARBLES The probability of choosing a purple cube out of a bag without looking is $\frac{16}{72}$. What is the probability of not picking a purple cube?
Check off each step.

✔ Understand: I underlined key words.

✔ Plan: To solve the problem, I will use logical reasoning.

✔ Solve: The answer is $\frac{7}{9}$.

✔ Check: I checked my answer by finding the sum of the probabilities.

GO ON

Common Error Alert

Denominator of a Ratio When students are representing probability as a ratio, they might have a tendency to use the number of favorable outcomes divided by the number of failures instead of the number of total possible outcomes. Connect with previous lessons on ratios. Remind them that they know how to correctly write a ratio; encourage them to do so and then to think in terms of probability to ensure the answer is correct.

Intervention Strategy — Kinesthetic/Interpersonal/Visual Learners

Probability Experiment Have students work in pairs. Give each pair a six-sided number cube. Have students calculate the probability of rolling a number less than 4, a number greater than or equal to 4, or an odd number. Once they have calculated the probabilities, have them roll the cube 10 times and record the results in a table. How do their actual results compare with the calculated results? Draw a table on the board and combine the classroom results. Are the results close to the calculated probabilities?

Odd/Even Assignments

Exercises 22–36 are structured so that students practice the same concepts whether they are assigned the odd or even problems.

In-Class Assignment

Have students complete Exercises 23, 25, 29, 31, and 39 to ensure that they understand the concept.

Intervention Strategy

Logical/ Naturalist Learners

Money Have students design two experiments that deal with coins. One experiment should use coins so that the chances of each event are equally likely. Another experiment should use coins so that the chances of each event are not equally likely. Students will need to figure out that equally likely experiments will deal with one type of coin or heads/tails situation. Not equally likely experiments will deal with coins of varying sizes.

20 GOLF Trent bought a bucket of balls at the golf range. Twelve balls have red stripes, 6 balls have orange stripes, 10 balls have black stripes, and 16 balls have yellow stripes. What is the probability of choosing a ball with yellow stripes? $\frac{4}{11}$

21 **Reflect** How are probability and ratios the same?
Probability is a special kind of ratio that tells the likelihood of an event.
Probability is always a ratio, but a ratio is not always a probability.

Skills, Concepts, and Problem Solving

Use the spinner to find each probability. Write the probability as a fraction in simplest form.

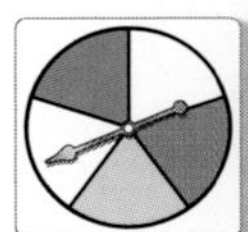

22 P(white) $\frac{2}{5}$ 23 P(not white) $\frac{3}{5}$

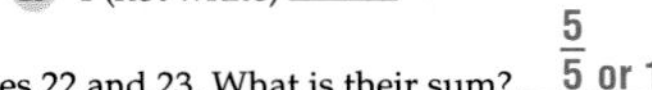

24 Add your answers to Exercises 22 and 23. What is their sum? $\frac{5}{5}$ or 1

Use the rows of figures to find each ratio or probability. Write the ratio or probability as a fraction in simplest form.

25 Write the ratio for the number of squares and pentagons to the total number of figures. $\frac{7}{16}$

26 Write the ratio for the number of triangles to the number of circles. $\frac{1}{2}$

27 What is the probability of choosing a figure without looking and getting a pentagon? $\frac{1}{8}$

28 What is the probability of choosing a figure without looking and getting a figure that is not a circle? $\frac{5}{8}$

Math Challenge

Equally Likely For students to better understand the concept of probability and what it means for each event to have an equal chance of occurring, display the following spinners.

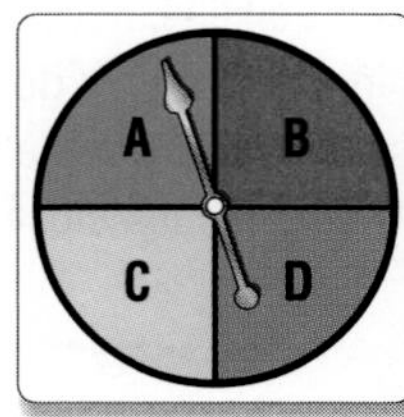

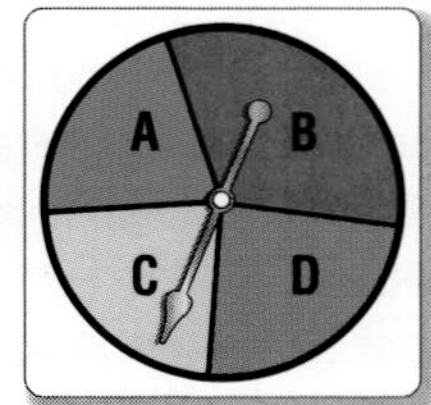

Have a classroom discussion. Discuss why the four outcomes from the spinner on the left each have an equal chance of occurring. Discuss why the four outcomes from the spinner on the right do not have an equal chance of occurring. Ask students to design a spinner where the events A and C have a greater possibility of occurring than events B and D.

nd each probability. Write the probability as a fraction in simplest form.

In a box of DVDs, there are 6 comedies, 4 action-adventure, and 8 animated movies. What is the probability that without looking you would choose a DVD that is not a comedy?

$$P(\text{not a comedy}) = \frac{12}{18} = \frac{12 \div 6}{18 \div 6} = \frac{2}{3}$$

In a bowl of nuts, there are 9 walnuts, 24 peanuts, 10 cashews, and 7 almonds. Find the probability of randomly selecting a cashew.

$$P(\text{cashew}) = \frac{10}{50} = \frac{10 \div 10}{50 \div 10} = \frac{1}{5}$$

7 red hats, 9 green hats, and 4 blue hats; P(blue hat)

$\frac{1}{5}$

14 basketballs, 6 footballs, and 10 baseballs; P(not a football)

$\frac{4}{5}$

10 baseball cards, 7 football cards, and 4 basketball cards;

P(football cards) $\frac{1}{3}$

7 rock songs, 9 country songs, 4 rap songs; P(not a rap song)

$\frac{4}{5}$

BULLETIN BOARD The ratio of red pins to the total number of pins in a plastic container is $\frac{7}{12}$. What is the probability if a pin is chosen without looking that the pin will not be red?

$\frac{5}{12}$

CLOTHES A drawer of shirts contains 3 white T-shirts, 2 blue T-shirts, 6 gray T-shirts, and 5 black T-shirts. What is the probability of choosing a gray T-shirt if you take 1 T-shirt without looking?

$\frac{3}{8}$

GO ON

See It, Do It, Say It, Write It

Step 1 Draw a spinner on the board. The sectors can be colored or numbered. Ask for volunteers to give the probabilities of various outcomes. Include examples such as not landing on red, not landing on a number under 4, and so on.

Step 2 Have students work in pairs. Tell them to write a probability problem using colored counters, marbles, pattern blocks, number cubes, or spinners. Model an example if necessary.

Step 3 Students can present their work for a classroom discussion.

Step 4 Ask students to write a summary of what they learned about probability. Explain that their work should be detailed enough so that a student who was absent that day could learn from their explanation.

Looking Ahead: Pre-Teach

Rates and Unit Costs In the next lesson, students will learn about rates and how to calculate a unit rate.

Example

40 miles in 5 hours is written as the ratio $\frac{40 \text{ miles}}{5 \text{ hours}}$.

To find the unit rate, rewrite the fraction so that the denominator is 1 hour. $\frac{40 \text{ miles} \div 5}{5 \text{ hours} \div 5} = \frac{8 \text{ miles}}{1 \text{ hour}}$

Have students try the exercises below.

Find each unit rate.

1. 20 pages in 5 minutes $\frac{4 \text{ pages}}{1 \text{ minute}}$
2. 750 miles in 2 days $\frac{375 \text{ miles}}{1 \text{ day}}$
3. 15 laps in 20 seconds $\frac{0.75 \text{ lap}}{1 \text{ second}}$

Vocabulary Check **Write the vocabulary word that completes each sentence.**

37 Probability is the chance that some event will occur.

38 A(n) ratio compares two quantities by division.

39 **Writing in Math** Write an example of a situation in which the probability of an event occurring is 0.

Answers will vary. Sample answer: the probability of a number cube landing on 7

Spiral Review

Write each ratio as a fraction in simplest form. (Lesson 2-1, p. 46)

40 Lia made 5 baskets out of 15 shots.

$\frac{1}{3}$

41 There are 16 rulers to 24 students.

$\frac{2}{3}$

42 Gabriela completed 12 problems in 30 minutes.

$\frac{2}{5}$

Solve. (Lesson 2-2, p. 53)

43 HOMEWORK Dion completes 3 word problems in 7 minutes. At this rate, how many word problems will he finish in 56 minutes?

Word Problems	3	6	12	24
Time (min)	7	14	28	56

Dion will finish 24 word problems in 56 minutes.

44 MONEY Ivana volunteers at the community center 9 hours a week. At this rate, how many hours would she volunteer in 27 weeks?

Time (hours)	9	27	81	243
Number of Weeks	1	3	9	27

Ivana would volunteer 243 hours in 27 weeks.

STO

Ticket Out the Door

What is in a Name? As students approach the door to exit the classroom, ask them the probability of randomly selecting a letter from letters that make up their names. For example, when a student named Matthew approaches the door, ask the following question.

What is the probability of randomly selecting a T from the letters of your name? $\frac{2}{7}$

Lesson 2-4

Rates and Unit Costs

KEY Concept

A **rate** is a **ratio** of two measurements having different units.

400 miles in 20 days → $\frac{400 \text{ miles}}{20 \text{ days}}$ — The units *miles* and *days* are different.

When a rate is simplified so that it has a denominator of 1 unit, it is called a **unit rate**.

$\frac{400 \text{ miles} \div 20}{20 \text{ days} \div 20} = \frac{20 \text{ miles}}{1 \text{ day}}$ — The unit rate is $\frac{20 \text{ miles}}{1 \text{ day}}$.

Unit cost is the cost of a single item or unit of measurement.

The cost of a 40-ounce box of cereal is $3.49.

$\frac{3.49}{40} \rightarrow 40\overline{)3.49} \rightarrow$ about $0.08 \rightarrow \frac{8 \text{ cents}}{1 \text{ ounce}}$ — The unit cost is 8 cents per ounce.

VOCABULARY

rate
a ratio comparing two quantities with different kinds of units

ratio
a comparison of two quantities by division; the ratio of 2 to 3 can be stated as 2 out of 3, 2 to 3, 2:3, or $\frac{2}{3}$

unit cost
the cost of a single item

unit rate
a rate that has a denominator of 1

…tes are often written using abbreviations, such as …0 mi/20 days, 80 mi/h, or $0.08/oz.

…xample 1

…Write the rate 45 steps in 15 seconds as a fraction. Find the unit rate.

1. Write the rate as a fraction. $\frac{45 \text{ steps}}{15 \text{ seconds}}$
2. Find an equivalent rate with a denominator of 1. The numerator and denominator have a common factor of 15. Divide each by 15.

$$\frac{45 \text{ steps} \div 15}{15 \text{ seconds} \div 15} = \frac{3 \text{ steps}}{1 \text{ second}}$$

3. Name the unit rate.
3 steps per second or 3 steps/s

YOUR TURN!

Write the rate 150 miles in 2 hours as a fraction. Find the unit rate.

1. Write the rate as a fraction. $\frac{150 \text{ miles}}{2 \text{ hours}}$
2. The numerator and denominator have a common factor of 2.

$$\frac{150 \text{ miles} \div 2}{2 \text{ hours} \div 2} = \frac{75 \text{ miles}}{1 \text{ hour}}$$

3. Name the unit rate.
75 miles per hour or 75 mi/h

GO ON

Additional Example 1

Write the rate 150 beats in 5 minutes as a fraction. Find the unit rate.

1. Write the rate as a fraction. $\frac{150 \text{ beats}}{5 \text{ minutes}}$
2. Find an equivalent rate with a denominator of 1. The numerator and denominator have a common factor of 5. Divide each by 5.

$$\frac{150 \text{ beats} \div 5}{5 \text{ minutes} \div 5} = \frac{30 \text{ beats}}{1 \text{ minute}}$$

3. Name the unit rate.
30 beats per minute or 30 beats/min

Lesson Notes

Lesson 2-4

Lesson Planner

Objective Determine unit costs and understand rates.

Vocabulary **rate**, **ratio**, **unit cost**, **unit rate**

Materials/Manipulatives product labels, index cards, poster board

Chapter Resource Masters

- CRM Vocabulary and English Language Development (p. A35)
- CRM Skills Practice (p. A36)
- CRM Problem-Solving Practice (p. A37)
- CRM Homework Practice (p. A38)

1 Introduce

Vocabulary

Vocabulary Rates Write a *ratio* on the board, such as $\frac{40}{8}$. Then write different units in the numerator and the denominator, such as students and classes, miles and minutes, and dollars and shirts. Compare *ratios* and *rates*. Then ask: If 8 shirts cost $40, how much is 1 shirt? Give other examples of *unit cost* and *unit rate*. Provide nonexamples. If 8 shirts cost $40, how much are 4 shirts? Ask: Is this a *unit cost*? Have students provide other nonexamples.

2 Teach

Key Concept

Foundational Skills and Concepts After students have read through the Key Concept box, have them try these exercises.

1. What is the difference between *unit rate* and *unit cost*? They are both rates with a 1 in their denominators, but unit cost always uses units of money in the numerator.
2. If 10 ounces of cheese costs $2.50, what is the unit cost? $0.25 an ounce

Additional **Example 2**

Find the unit rate for 1,566 people coming to a concert in 3 days. Use the unit rate to find the number of people coming to the concert in 9 days.

1. Write the rate as a fraction. $\frac{1{,}566 \text{ people}}{3 \text{ days}}$
2. Find an equivalent rate with a denominator of 1.
   Divide the numerator and denominator by 3.
   $$\frac{1{,}566 \div 3}{3 \div 3} = \frac{522}{1}$$
3. The unit rate is $\frac{522 \text{ people}}{1 \text{ day}}$.
4. To find how many people will come to the concert in 9 days, multiply the numerator and denominator by 9.
   $$\frac{522 \text{ people} \times 9}{1 \text{ day} \times 9} = \frac{4{,}698 \text{ people}}{9 \text{ days}}$$
5. At this rate, 4,698 people will come to the concert in 9 days.

Additional **Example 3**

Ken bought 4 baseball tickets for $70.00. Find the unit cost to the nearest cent.

1. Write the rate as a fraction. $\frac{\$70.00}{4 \text{ tickets}}$
2. Divide the numerator by the denominator.

```
  17.50
4)70.00
 -4
  30
 -28
   20
  -20
    00
    -0
     0
```

3. The unit cost rounded to the nearest cent is $17.50.

Each ticket costs $17.50.

Example 2

Find the unit rate if you ran 90 kilometers in 6 days. Use the unit rate to find the number of kilometers you ran in 5 days.

1. Write the rate as a fraction.
   $\frac{90 \text{ km}}{6 \text{ days}}$
2. Find an equivalent rate with a denominator of 1.
   Divide the numerator and denominator by 6.
   $\frac{90 \div 6}{6 \div 6} = \frac{15}{1}$
3. The unit rate is 15 km/day.
4. To find how many kilometers you can run at the same rate in 5 days, multiply the numerator and denominator by 5.
   $\frac{15 \text{ km} \times 5}{1 \text{ day} \times 5} = \frac{75 \text{ km}}{5 \text{ days}}$

   At this rate, you can run 75 kilometers in 5 days.

YOUR TURN!

Find the unit rate if you traveled 480 feet in 12 seconds. Use the unit rate to find the number of feet you can travel in 25 seconds.

1. Write the rate as a fraction.
   $\frac{480 \text{ ft}}{12 \text{ s}}$
2. Divide the numerator and denominator by 12.
   $\frac{480 \text{ ft} \div 12}{12 \text{ s} \div 12} = \frac{40 \text{ ft}}{1 \text{ s}}$
3. The unit rate is 40 ft / s.
4. Multiply the numerator and denominator by 25.
   $\frac{40 \text{ ft} \times 25}{1 \text{ s} \times 25} = \frac{1{,}000 \text{ ft}}{25 \text{ s}}$

   At this rate, you can travel 1,000 feet in 25 seconds.

Example 3

Ines downloaded 18 songs for $17.82. Find the unit cost to the nearest cent.

1. Write the rate as a fraction.
   $\frac{\$17.82}{18 \text{ songs}}$
2. Divide the numerator by the denominator.
3. The unit cost rounded to the nearest cent is $0.99.

```
    0.99
18)17.82
  - 162
     162
   - 162
       0
```

Each song costs about $0.99.

YOUR TURN!

Sophie bought 5 pounds of potatoes for $6.45. Find the unit cost to the nearest cent.

1. Write the rate as a fraction.
   $\frac{\$6.45}{5 \text{ pounds}}$
2. Divide the numerator by the denominator.
3. The unit cost rounded to the nearest cent is $1.29.

```
  1.29
5)6.45
 -5
  14
 -10
   45
  -45
    0
```

Each pound costs about $1.29.

70 **Chapter 2** Ratios, Rates, and Proportional Relationships

Intervention Strategy — Linguistic/Visual Learners

Cell-Phone Rates Have students use the newspaper or Internet to research information about cell-phone rate plans. Tell them to determine the unit cost for each plan. For example, one plan could be $40 for 200 minutes, so the unit cost would be $0.20 per minute. Have them complete a table like the one shown using unit rate to determine the cost for 5, 10, 20, 25, 30, and 60 minutes.

Cost ($)	1					
Time (min)	5	10	20	25	30	60

Who is Correct?

Brock bought a bouquet of flowers for 27.99. The bouquet contains 12 flowers. Find the unit cost to the nearest cent.

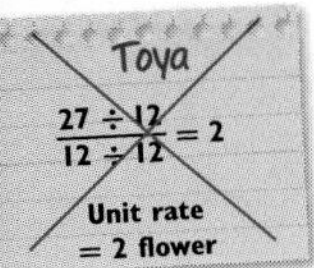

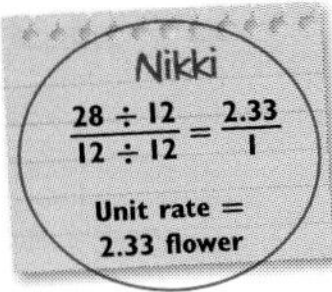

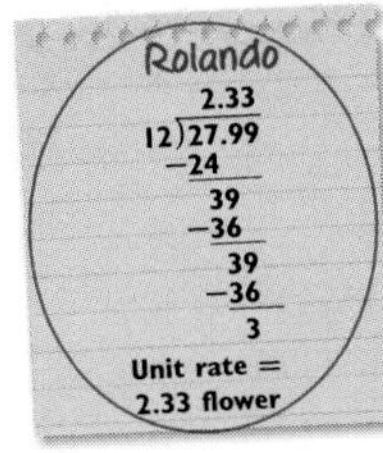

Circle correct answer(s). Cross out incorrect answer(s).

Guided Practice

Write each rate as a fraction. Find each unit rate.

1. 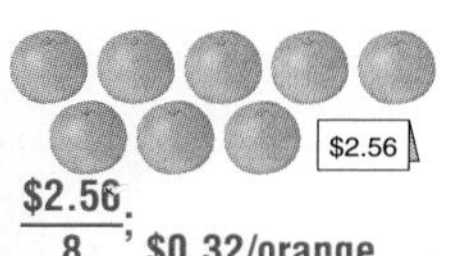

$\frac{\$2.56}{8}$; $0.32/orange

2. 291 words in 3 minutes
$\frac{291}{3}$; 97 words/min

3. 225 miles in 3 hours
$\frac{225}{3}$; 75 mi/hr

4. $23.94 for 6 pounds
$\frac{\$23.94}{6}$; $3.99/pound

Find each unit rate. Use the unit rate to find the unknown amount.

5. 5 pounds for 8 people; □ pounds for 20 people 0.625 lb/person; 12.5
6. 12 hours for 5 classes; □ hours for 4 classes 2.4 hours/class; 9.6
7. 170 feet in 8 seconds; □ feet in 15 seconds 21.25 ft/s; 318.75
8. $9 for 4 magazines; □ dollars for 15 magazines $2.25/magazine; $33.75

Who *is Correct?*

Diagnostic Teaching

- Toya wrote $2. This is incorrect because $27.99 ÷ 12 = $2.33, not $2.00.
- Nikki is correct. She divided by an equivalent of 1, $\frac{12}{12}$.
- Rolando is correct. He used the long division format.

Remind students that a ratio is a comparison by division and the denominator is always 1.

Using Manipulatives

On-Hand Manipulatives Have students note prices on the package and the unit costs of individual items contained in the package.

Math Coach Notes

Strategies

1. Begin this lesson with a hands-on experience to anchor the concepts. Students can read, do sit-ups, blink their eyes, walk as quickly as they can down the hall, bounce a ball, and so on. Students can find the unit rate of each activity; for example, the number of sit-ups they can do in 1 minute.
2. Write the price and amount of some items on index cards, such as *20 lb of cat food for $7.* Give a card to small groups of students. Tell students to create an advertisement on poster board for their item. They should include the unit cost on their poster board.

Common Error *Alert*

Denominators Students may continue to forget what to divide to find the unit cost or unit rate. Tell them to ask themselves, what word is after the "per"? That unit is the denominator, the one to divide *by*. So, to find a heart rate *per* minute, divide the number of heartbeats *by* the number of minutes. To find the cost *per* ounce, divide the total cost *by* the number of ounces. Tell students to multiply once they have an answer to check to see if they have calculated correctly.

Step by Step Practice

9 Use the table to find which box of crackers has the lowest unit cost. Round to the nearest cent.

Box Size	Price	Price per oz
12 oz	$1.29	$0.11
16 oz	$1.99	$0.12
32 oz	$2.49	$0.08

Round to the nearest cent means the nearest hundredth.

Step 1 Find the unit cost of a 12-oz box.

$\frac{1.29}{12} \rightarrow 12\overline{)1.29} \rightarrow$ about $ 0.11 /oz

Step 2 Find the unit cost of a 16-oz box.

$\frac{1.99}{16} \rightarrow 16\overline{)1.99} \rightarrow$ $ 0.12 /oz

Step 3 Find the unit cost of a 32-oz box.

$\frac{2.49}{32} \rightarrow 32\overline{)2.49} \rightarrow$ about $ 0.08 /oz

Step 4 Which box costs the least per ounce?

The 32-oz box costs the least per ounce.

Which product has the lowest unit cost? Round to the nearest cent.

10 a 16-oz box of baking soda for $0.89, or a 32-oz box of baking soda for $1.59

16-oz box: $\frac{0.89}{16} \rightarrow 16\overline{)0.89} \rightarrow$ about $ 0.06 /oz

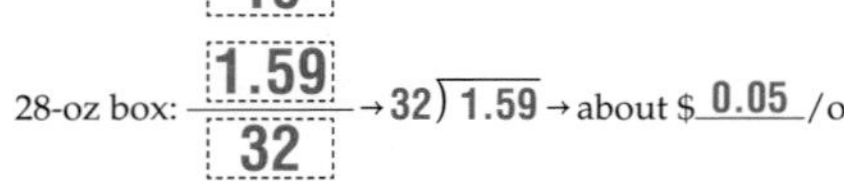

28-oz box: $\frac{1.59}{32} \rightarrow 32\overline{)1.59} \rightarrow$ about $ 0.05 /oz

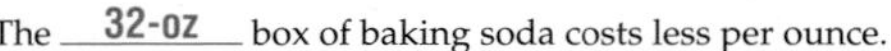

The 32-oz box of baking soda costs less per ounce.

11 50-count vitamins for $5.49, 100-count vitamins for $8.29, or 150-count vitamins for $13.99 100-count package; $0.08

12 a 6-pack of yogurt for $2.49, or a 12-pack of yogurt for $3.99 12-pack; $0.33

13 a 16-oz bag of apples for $2.99, a 32-oz bag of apples for $3.99, or a 48-oz bag of apples for $5.49 48-oz bag; $0.11

72 **Chapter 2** Ratios, Rates, and Proportional Relationships

Are They Getting It?

Check students' understanding of rates and unit costs by writing these problems on the board. Ask students to point out wrong answers and explain why they are wrong.

1. A 3-lb bag of rice for $1.99 has a higher unit cost than a 5-lb bag for $2.99. This is correct.
2. Two students jumped rope. Sue jumped 133 times in 4 minutes, and Lucy jumped 241 times in 7 minutes. Sue had the faster rate. This is not correct. Lucy's rate is faster.
3. A bag of 10 kiwis for $4.49 has a higher unit cost than a bag of 12 kiwis for $5.99. This is not correct. The price per kiwi (unit cost) is $0.45 for the smaller bag, and $0.50 for the larger bag.
4. Jack read 110 pages in 5 hours. LaShawn read 100 pages in 4 hours. Jack is a faster reader. This is not correct. Jack read 22 pages per hour, while LaShawn read 25 pages per hour.

Step by Step Problem-Solving Practice

Solve.

Problem-Solving Strategies
- ☐ Draw a diagram.
- ☐ Look for a pattern.
- ☐ Guess and check.
- ☐ Make a table.
- ☑ Solve a simpler problem.

14 NATURE The American robin can travel 32 miles in a 20-hour flight. The grey-cheeked thrush can travel 33 miles in 6 hours. Which bird flies at a faster rate?

Understand Read the problem. Write what you know.

The American robin can travel __32__ miles in a __20__-hour flight.

The grey-cheeked thrush can travel __33__ miles in a __6__-hour flight.

Plan Pick a strategy. One strategy is to solve a simpler problem. Find each unit rate.

Solve Write each rate as a fraction. Find an equivalent rate with a denominator of 1.

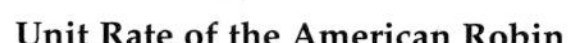

Unit Rate of the American Robin

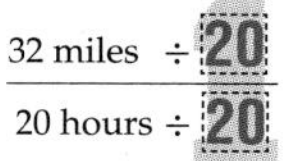

$$\frac{32 \text{ miles} \div 20}{20 \text{ hours} \div 20} = \frac{1.6 \text{ miles}}{1 \text{ hour}}$$

American Robin

Unit Rate of the Grey-Cheeked Thrush

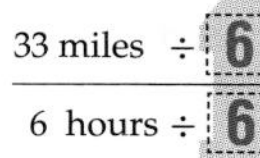
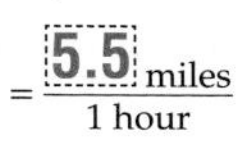
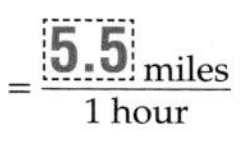

$$\frac{33 \text{ miles} \div 6}{6 \text{ hours} \div 6} = \frac{5.5 \text{ miles}}{1 \text{ hour}}$$

Grey-Cheeked Thrush

Compare the unit rates for each bird.

__1.6__ miles/hour < __5.5__ miles/per hour

The __Grey-Cheeked Thrush__ flies at a faster rate.

Check Does the answer make sense? Did you answer the question?

15 BUSINESS While working at a grocery store for the summer, Alvar earned $1,650 in 10 weeks. Find a unit rate to describe his weekly wages. Check off each step.

__✔__ Understand: I underlined key words.

__✔__ Plan: To solve the problem, I will __solve a simpler problem__.

__✔__ Solve: The answer is __$165 per week__.

__✔__ Check: I checked my answer by __multiplying 165 by 10__.

Intervention Strategy

Kinesthetic/Visual Learners

Unit Costs of Products Have students bring in empty (or full) items from home, such as a soup can, pasta box, or pack of raisins. Tell them to ask their parents the cost of the item and then determine the cost per ounce; or, if it is a multipack, the cost per single piece. Discuss the results. Find the lowest and highest unit costs and draw a number line that includes those and all the other items. Have students come to the board and write their products and its unit costs at the appropriate places on the number line.

English Learner Strategy

Rate Table For a deeper understanding of unit cost and unit rate, use a rate table. The advantages are that students can see step by step how the unit cost or unit rate is found.

Heartbeat	292	146	73
Time (minutes)	4	2	1

Note This!

Include Examples Students might think it is better not to include examples in their notes of a concept that they understand. All too often, students think they know how to do something, only to find when they are home ready to study, they forget. Encourage them to write examples down, even brief ones, of information that is new to them. If the material is something that has been covered in past grades, they will have to use their own judgment.

Additional Answers

Exercise 17 A ratio is a comparison of two quantities by division. A rate is a special ratio that compares different units. A unit rate reduces the rate so the denominator is one. Unit cost refers specifically to the cost (in dollars or cents) of one item.

Odd/Even Assignments

Exercises 18–30 are structured so that students practice the same concepts whether they are assigned the odd or even problems.

In-Class Assignment

Have students complete Exercises 19, 25, 28, 30, and 33 to ensure that they understand the concept.

16 POPULATION The estimated population for Florida in 2007 was 18,300,000 people. Its land area is approximately 65,755 square miles. Find the population per square mile.

278 people/sq mi

17 Reflect Explain the difference between a rate and ratio. What is the difference between unit rate and unit cost?

See TE margin.

Skills, Concepts, and Problem Solving

Write each rate as a fraction. Find each unit rate.

18 12 jumping jacks in 8 seconds
$\frac{12}{8}$ or $\frac{4}{3}$; 1.3 jumping jacks/second

19 9 feet in 12 years
$\frac{9}{12}$ or $\frac{3}{4}$; 0.75 ft/yr

20 $18.06 for 14 pounds of turkey
$\frac{\$18.06}{14}$; $1.29 per lb

21 21 hits out of 40 at bats
$\frac{21}{40}$; 0.53 hits/at bat (batting average

Find each unit rate. Use the unit rate to find the unknown amount.

22 $42 for 15 ounces; □ dollars for 8 ounces $2.80/oz; $22.40

23 50 meters every 8 seconds; □ meters for 20 seconds 6.25 m/s; 125

24 150 feet in 8 seconds; □ feet in 14 seconds 18.75 ft/s; 262.5

25 16 yards in 4 plays; □ yards in 7 plays 4 yd/play; 28

Which product has the lower unit cost? Round to the nearest cent.

26 12 golf balls for $9, or 10 golf balls for $8.50 12 golf balls; $0.75

27 18-oz box of cereal for $3.49, or 24-oz box of cereal for $4.99 18-oz box; $0.19

28 26-oz can of soup for $2.49, or 10-oz can of soup for $1.29 26-oz can; $0.10

29 8-pack of crackers for $2.99, or 16-pack of crackers for $7.59 8-pack; $0.37

74 Chapter 2 Ratios, Rates, and Proportional Relationships

Math Challenge

Go Shopping Give students a pile of grocery ads to review. Tell them to find two similar items from different stores and find the unit cost of the items. They should then cut out pictures of the items and put them on one side of an index card and write the unit cost on the other side. As a class, compare the cards and unit costs. Whoever has the lowest price per unit wins a point.

lve.

LIFE SCIENCE The heart of a rat beats about 840 times in 2 minutes, while the heart of a guinea pig beats about 1,200 times in 4 minutes. The heartbeat of a rabbit is about 1,025 beats in 5 minutes. Which animal's heart beats the most times in one hour? Explain.

The heart of a rat beats about 420 times in a minute; therefore, it beats the most times in one hour.

cabulary Check **Write the vocabulary word that completes each sentence.**

A rate that has a denominator of 1 is called a(n) unit rate.

The cost of a single item or unit is the unit cost.

Writing in Math Which of the following statements are sometimes, always, or never true? Give an example or counterexample to illustrate.

A ratio is a rate. A rate is a ratio.

A rate is always a ratio, but a ratio is only sometimes a rate. A ratio is a rate if the units of the two quantities being compared are different.

Spiral Review

e the diagram shown at the right to write each io as a fraction in simplest form. (Lesson 2-1, p. 46)

The number of red counters to the number of blue counters is $\frac{3}{2}$.

The number of red counters to the total number of counters is $\frac{3}{5}$.

The number of blue counters to the total number of counters is $\frac{2}{5}$.

lve. (Lesson 2-3, p. 61)

MARBLES The probability of choosing a blue marble out of a bag of marbles without looking is $\frac{3}{15}$. What is the probability of not picking a blue marble? $\frac{4}{5}$

Ticket Out the Door

Units Costs Hand each student a label with unit weight or volume from food items. These can be soup-can labels, copies of cracker boxes, milk labels, and so on. Write $1.99 on the board. Tell students to use that cost to find the unit cost based on the units of weight or volume on the label. Students will hand in their work as they exit the classroom.

4 Assess

See It, Do It, Say It, Write It

Step 1 Make a table on the board. Write different costs and sizes for students to use to find the unit costs. Model how to find the first unit cost.

Step 2 Tell students to work in pairs and write their names as many times as they can while you time them for 2 or 3 minutes. When time is up, have them count how many times they wrote their names. Have them work with their partners to find the unit rates.

Step 3 Discuss both unit cost and unit rate. Ask students to provide real-world examples of each.

Step 4 Tell students to write about the differences between unit rate and unit cost. Ask them to provide an example of each.

Looking Ahead: Pre-teach

Proportional Reasoning In the next lesson, students will learn how to use proportional reasoning to solve problems.

Example

Lydia walked 1 mile in 15 minutes. How many miles can she walk in 45 minutes?

$$\frac{1 \text{ mile}}{15 \text{ minutes}} = \frac{x \text{ miles}}{45 \text{ minutes}}$$
$$1 \times 45 = 15 \times x$$
$$45 = 15x$$
$$x = 3$$

Lydia can walk 3 miles in 45 minutes.

Chapter 2 Progress Check 2

Formative Assessment

Use the Progress Check to assess students' mastery of the previous lessons. Have students review the lesson indicated for the problems they answered incorrectly.

Odd/Even Assignments

Exercises are structured so that students practice the same concepts whether they are assigned the odd or even problems.

Common Error *Alert*

Exercises 11–12 Ensure that students realize they have to do three division problems in order to find three different unit costs. Then they can make their comparisons.

Chapter 2 Progress Check 2 (Lessons 2-3 and 2-4)

Find each probability. Write the probability as a fraction in simplest form.

1. 5 apples, 3 pears, 8 oranges, and 4 plums; P(apple) $\frac{1}{4}$
2. 8 yellow chips, 9 green chips, and 10 purple chips; P(not a green chip) $\frac{2}{3}$

Find each probability using a number cube. Write the probability as a fraction in simplest form.

3. P(roll a 2) $\frac{1}{6}$
4. P(roll an odd number) $\frac{1}{2}$
5. P(roll a number less than 5) $\frac{2}{3}$
6. P(roll a number less than 2) $\frac{1}{6}$
7. P(roll a 9) 0
8. P(roll a 1 or 6) $\frac{1}{3}$

Write each rate as a fraction. Find each unit rate.

9. 45 miles in 9 minutes $\frac{45}{9}$; 5 mi/min
10. 3 tons in 75 years $\frac{3}{75}$; 0.04 T/yr

Which product has the lowest unit cost? Round to the nearest cent.

11. 12-oz can for \$1.99, a 16-oz can for \$2.50, or a 32-oz can for \$3.79
32-oz can; \$0.12
12. 9 kiwis for \$1.35, 14 kiwis for \$2.25, or 20 kiwis for \$3.80
9 kiwis; \$0.15

Solve.

13. **GAMES** The probability of choosing an orange marble out of a bag of marbles without looking is $\frac{4}{9}$. What is the probability of not picking an orange marble? $\frac{5}{9}$
14. **SPORTS** Nina swam 200 feet in 44 seconds. What is her unit rate?
4.55 feet per second

76 **Chapter 2** Ratios, Rates, and Proportional Relationships

Data-Driven Decision Making

Students missing Exercises . . .	Have trouble with . . .	Should review and practice . . .
1-2	writing probability as a fraction in simplest form.	SSG Lesson 2-3, p. 61 CRM Skills Practice, p. A32
3-8	finding probability using a number cube and writing probability as a fraction in simplest form.	SSG Lesson 2-3, p. 61 CRM Skills Practice, p. A32
9-10	writing rates as a fraction, then writing the unit rates.	SSG Lesson 2-4, p. 69 CRM Skills Practice, p. A36
11-12	finding the lowest unit cost.	SSG Lesson 2-4, p. 69 CRM Skills Practice, p. A36
13–14	solving word problems involving probability and unit rates.	CRM Problem-Solving Practice, pp. A33 and A37

Lesson 2-5 Proportional Reasoning

KEY Concept

The ratios $\frac{4}{6}$ and $\frac{2}{3}$ are equivalent, or equal.

$\frac{4}{6} = \frac{2}{3}$ — This equation is an example of a **proportion**.

The cross products of a proportion are equal. **Cross multiply** to solve proportions when one value in the proportion is not known.

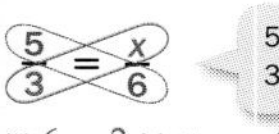

5 × 6 is one cross product. 3x is the other cross product.

$5 \times 6 = 3 \times x$	Cross multiply.
$30 = 3x$	Simplify.
$10 = x$	Divide each side of the equation by 3.

A proportion is a comparison of ratios. It can be written two ways.

$\frac{5}{3} = \frac{x}{6}$ or $5:3 = x:6$ — Both are read "5 is to 3 as x is to 6."

VOCABULARY

cross multiply find the product of the numerator of one fraction and the denominator of the other fraction

proportion an equation stating that two ratios or rates are equivalent

ratio a comparison of two quantities by division

Example 1

Find the value of y.

$\frac{8}{12} = \frac{4}{y}$

1. $8 \times y = 12 \times 4$ Cross multiply.
2. $8y = 48$ Simplify.
3. $\frac{8y}{8} = \frac{48}{8}$ Divide each side of the equation by 8.
   $y = 6$
4. Check. Replace y with 6 and solve.
   $\frac{8}{12} = \frac{4}{6}$
   $48 = 48$

YOUR TURN!

Find the value of c.

$\frac{c}{10} = \frac{6}{5}$

1. $c \times 5 = 10 \times 6$ Cross multiply.
2. $5c = 60$ Simplify.
3. $\frac{5c}{5} = \frac{60}{5}$ Divide each side of the equation by 5.
   $c = 12$
4. Check. Replace c with 12 and solve.
   $\frac{12}{10} = \frac{6}{5}$
   $60 = 60$

GO ON

Lesson 2-5 Proportional Reasoning 77

Additional Example 1

Find the value of b.

$\frac{6}{b} = \frac{3}{4}$

1. $6 \times 4 = 3 \times b$ Cross multiply.
2. $24 = 3b$ Simplify.
3. $\frac{24}{3} = \frac{3b}{3}$ Divide each side of the equation by 3.
   $8 = b$
4. Check. Replace b with 8 and solve.
   $\frac{6}{8} = \frac{3}{4}$
   $24 = 24$ ✓

Lesson Notes

Lesson 2-5

Lesson Planner

Objective Solve proportions.

Vocabulary **cross multiply**, **proportion**, **ratio**

Materials/Manipulatives algebra tiles

Chapter Resource Masters

- CRM Vocabulary and English Language Development (p. A39)
- CRM Skills Practice (p. A40)
- CRM Problem-Solving Practice (p. A41)
- CRM Homework Practice (p. A42)

1 Introduce

Vocabulary

Access Vocabulary Write this proportion on the board. Point out the parts of the proportion.

$$\frac{12 \text{ eggs}}{9 \text{ omelets}} = \frac{8 \text{ eggs}}{6 \text{ omelets}}$$

Emphasize that both numerators represent the number of eggs. Both denominators represent the number of omelets. Also, point out that both fractions can be reduced to the same simplest form, $\frac{4}{3}$. Ask for volunteers to go to the board and identify each *ratio*.

2 Teach

Key Concept

Foundational Skills and Concepts After students have read through the Key Concept box, then have them try this exercise.

The ratios at the top of the box are $\frac{4}{6}$ and $\frac{2}{3}$.

What relationship do you notice between the ratios?

You can simplify $\frac{4}{6}$ to $\frac{2}{3}$. (If you divide the left side by $\frac{2}{2}$, you get the right side.)

Additional ***Example 2***

Jameson can run 1 mile in 6 minutes. How many minutes will it take Jameson to run 5 miles?

1. Set up a proportion. Let x represent the number of minutes it will take Jameson to run 5 miles.

$$\frac{1\text{ mile}}{6\text{ minutes}} = \frac{5\text{ miles}}{x\text{ minutes}}$$

2. $1 \times x = 6 \times 5$ Cross multiply.

3. $1x = 30$ Simplify.

4. $\frac{1x}{1} = \frac{30}{1}$ Divide each side of the equation by 1.

$x = 30$

Jameson can run 5 miles in 30 minutes.

Math Coach Notes

Constant Rate For a constant rate of change, every change in the input variable causes the same change in the output variable. In the Additional Example 2, each mile takes 6 minutes. So if the number of miles increases by 1, the number of minutes increases by 6. Jameson can run 2 miles in 12 minutes, 3 miles in 18 minutes, and so on. A constant rate of change is a linear relationship. The graph of a linear relationship is a straight line.

Cross Multiplication When you cross multiply a proportion and set the products equal to each other, it is the same as multiplying each side of the equation by the inverse, or reciprocal, of the coefficient of the variable term.

Example 2

Nicole rode her bike 15 miles in 2 hours. How many miles can she ride in 8 hours?

1. Set up a proportion. Let m represent the number of miles Nicole can ride in 8 hours.

$$\frac{15\text{ miles}}{2\text{ hours}} = \frac{m\text{ miles}}{8\text{ hours}}$$

2. $15 \times 8 = 2 \times m$ Cross multiply.
3. $120 = 2m$ Simplify.
4. $\frac{120}{2} = \frac{2m}{2}$ Divide each side of the equation by 2.

$m = 60$

Nicole can ride 60 miles in 8 hours.

YOUR TURN!

A farmer claims that 10 cows can be raised on 40 acres of land. How many acres of land would the farmer need to raise 15 cows?

1. Set up a proportion. Let a represent the number of acres of land needed to raise 15 cows.

$$\frac{10\text{ cows}}{40\text{ acres}} = \frac{15\text{ cows}}{a\text{ acres}}$$

2. $10 \times a = 40 \times 15$ Cross multiply.
3. $10a = 600$ Simplify.
4. $\frac{10a}{10} = \frac{600}{10}$ Divide each side of the equation by 10.

$a = 60$

The farmer needs 60 acres of land to raise 15 cows.

Who is Correct?

Find the value of m. $\frac{3}{m} = \frac{4}{12}$

Jason
$3m = 4 \times 12$
$3m = 48$
$m = 16$

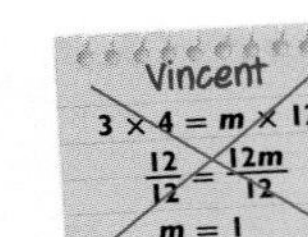

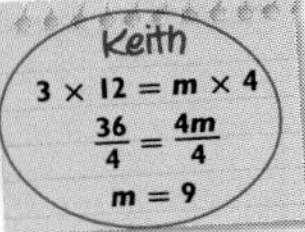

Circle correct answer(s). Cross out incorrect answer(s).

Who ***is Correct?***

Diagnostic Teaching

- Jason is incorrect. He did not cross multiply correctly.
- Vincent is incorrect. He did not cross multiply correctly.
- Keith is correct.

Remind students to cross multiply and set the products equal to each other.

Guided Practice

nd the value of each variable.

1. $\frac{n}{8} = \frac{7}{4}$

$\underline{n} \times \underline{4} = \underline{8} \times \underline{7}$

$\underline{4n} = \underline{56}$

$\frac{4n}{4} = \frac{56}{4}$

$n = \underline{14}$

2. $\frac{6}{3} = \frac{h}{9}$

$\underline{6} \times \underline{9} = \underline{3} \times \underline{h}$

$\underline{54} = \underline{3h}$

$\frac{54}{3} = \frac{3h}{3}$

$h = \underline{18}$

Step by Step Practice

3. Ignacio made a scale model of his bedroom. His bedroom is 10 feet long. What is the width of Ignacio's bedroom?

Width = 12 inches

Length = 8 inches

My Bedroom

Step 1 Set up a proportion. Let w represent the width of Ignacio's bedroom.

model length → $\frac{8 \text{ inches}}{10 \text{ feet}} = \frac{12 \text{ inches}}{W \text{ feet}}$ ← model width

actual length → ← actual width

Step 2 Solve the proportion.

$\underline{8} \times \underline{w} = \underline{10} \times \underline{12}$ Cross multiply.

$\underline{8w} = \underline{120}$ Simplify.

$\frac{8w}{8} = \frac{120}{8}$ Divide each side of the equation by $\underline{8}$.

$w = \underline{15}$

Step 3 Ignacio's bedroom is _15_ feet wide.

4. **CHESS** There are 5 boys to every 2 girls in the chess club. This year there are 20 boys in the chess club. How many girls are in the club? Let g represent the number of girls.

$\frac{5 \text{ boys}}{2 \text{ girls}} = \frac{20 \text{ boys}}{g \text{ girls}}$

There are _8_ girls in the chess club.

GO ON

Lesson 2-5 Proportional Reasoning 79

Intervention Strategy — Kinesthetic Learners

Constant Rate To help students gain a better understanding of constant rate, ask them to choose three different physical activities that they perform. Encourage them to select one activity that is easy for them to do, one that is of average difficulty, and one that is difficult. Have them repeat each activity for three minutes and measure the rates of their performances. Have them analyze the rate of change for their first minute, their second minute, and their third minute for each activity. Most likely, their easy activity will have a constant rate. Their average activity will have a slight change of rate, and their difficult activity will have an increased change of rate.

3 Practice

Using Manipulatives

Algebra Tiles

Use algebra tiles to give students a visual concept of a proportion. Point out that the algebra tiles can help in two ways for students. The first is that they can isolate the variable after cross multiplying, which will give the variable a value. The second is that the algebra tiles can be used to check their answers, which will show the proportion.

$$\frac{3}{3} = \frac{x}{4}$$

$3 \times 4 = 3x$

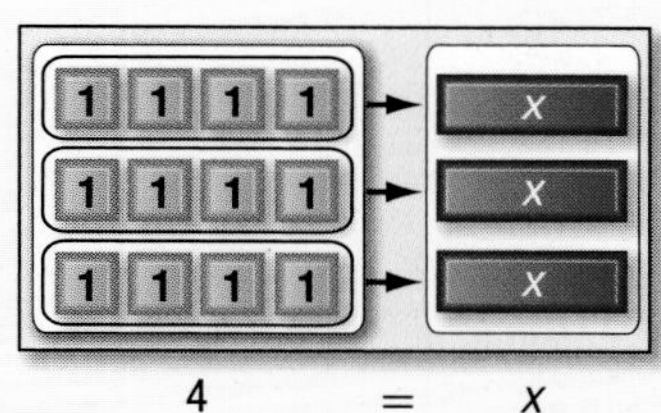

$4 = x$

On-Hand Manipulatives Use classroom objects to represent objects in each question. This will give students a visual concept of a proportion.

Math Coach Notes

Strategies

1. When students are learning about proportions and cross multiplying, review variables and how to solve for them. Make sure students know how to isolate the variable by using properties correctly. Review and model situations with which students may have trouble.
2. Write real-world examples on the board to help students write the proportions.

5 GAMES A game board has 9 blue sections for every 15 red sections. How many blue sections are there if the game board has 45 red sections? Let x represent the number of blue sections.

$$\frac{9 \text{ blue}}{15 \text{ red}} = \frac{x \text{ blue}}{45 \text{ red}}$$

$$9 \times 45 = 15 \times x$$

$$405 = 15x$$

$$\frac{405}{15} = \frac{15x}{15}$$

$$x = 27$$

There are 27 blue sections for a game board with 45 red sections.

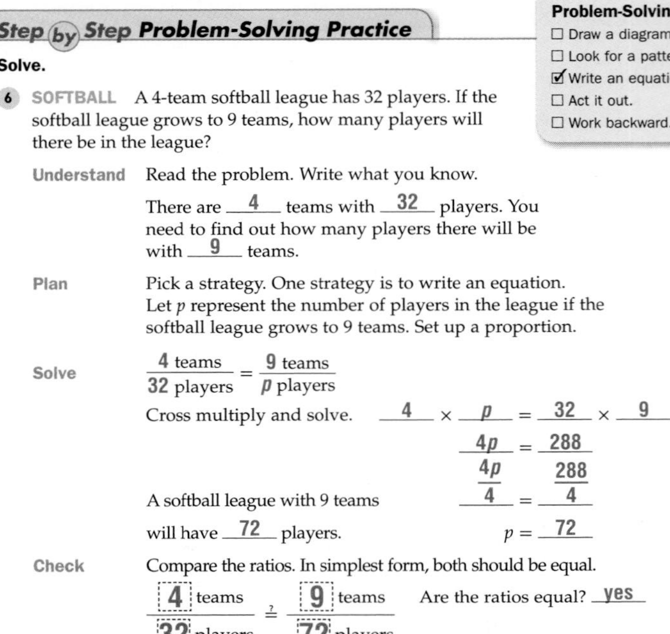

Step by Step Problem-Solving Practice

Solve.

6 SOFTBALL A 4-team softball league has 32 players. If the softball league grows to 9 teams, how many players will there be in the league?

Problem-Solving Strategies
- ☐ Draw a diagram.
- ☐ Look for a pattern.
- ☑ Write an equation.
- ☐ Act it out.
- ☐ Work backward.

Understand Read the problem. Write what you know.
There are 4 teams with 32 players. You need to find out how many players there will be with 9 teams.

Plan Pick a strategy. One strategy is to write an equation. Let p represent the number of players in the league if the softball league grows to 9 teams. Set up a proportion.

Solve $\frac{4 \text{ teams}}{32 \text{ players}} = \frac{9 \text{ teams}}{p \text{ players}}$

Cross multiply and solve. $4 \times p = 32 \times 9$

$$4p = 288$$

$$\frac{4p}{4} = \frac{288}{4}$$

A softball league with 9 teams will have 72 players. $p = 72$

Check Compare the ratios. In simplest form, both should be equal.

$\frac{4 \text{ teams}}{32 \text{ players}} \stackrel{?}{=} \frac{9 \text{ teams}}{72 \text{ players}}$ Are the ratios equal? yes

Intervention Strategy — Logical Learners

Real-World Problem Veronica can decorate 10 cookies in 30 minutes at her uptown bakery. At this rate, how many cookies can she decorate in 6 hours?

$$\frac{60 \text{ minutes}}{1 \text{ hour}} = \frac{x \text{ minutes}}{6 \text{ hours}}$$

$$60 \times 6 = 1x$$

$$360 = 1x$$

$$x = 360 \text{ minutes}$$

$$\frac{10 \text{ cookies}}{30 \text{ minutes}} = \frac{x \text{ cookies}}{360 \text{ minutes}}$$

$$10 \times 360 = 30x$$

$$3{,}600 = 30x$$

$$x = 120 \text{ cookies}$$

Common Error *Alert*

Fractions and Decimals Students mistakenly think that the solution of a proportion cannot be a fraction or a decimal when other numbers in the proportion are whole numbers. You can demonstrate that ratios can include fractions and decimals. Two equivalent ratios can form a proportion. Provide examples of proportions in which both numerators and both denominators are given so that students can verify that the ratios are equivalent. An example is $\frac{2}{5} = \frac{1}{2.5}$.

Are They Getting It?

Check students' understanding of proportions by writing these problems on the board. Ask students to point out wrong answers. Encourage students to use manipulatives or a drawing in their explanations.

1. One pizza can feed 3 people. If there are 24 people in Ms. Heiser's class, how many pizzas does she need to buy?
   Ms. Heiser will buy 8 pizzas for her class of 24 students.
   This is correct.
2. Paula can make 12 cookies in 30 minutes. How many minutes does it take Paula to make 48 cookies?
   It will take Paula 120 minutes to make 48 cookies.
   This is correct.
3. Jorge can mow 2 lawns every 1.5 hours. How many lawns can he mow in 6 hours?
   Jorge can mow 6 lawns in 6 hours.
   This is incorrect. Jorge can mow 8 lawns in 6 hours.

PACKAGING A small package of granola bars has 3 bars with nuts and 5 bars with raisins. Bruno bought a large box of granola bars that has 9 bars with nuts. If the ratio of granola bars with nuts to granola bars with raisins remains the same, how many bars with raisins are in the large box?
Check off each step.

✔ Understand: I underlined key words.

✔ Plan: To solve the problem, I will write a proportion.

✔ Solve: The answer is $\frac{3}{5} = \frac{9}{r}$; $r = 15$; 15 bars with raisins.

✔ Check: I checked my answer by comparing the ratios.

GROCERIES A bag of 5 pounds of potatoes costs \$3. Neil needs 20 pounds of potatoes. How much will it cost Neil to buy 20 pounds of potatoes?

$\frac{5 \text{ pounds}}{\$3} = \frac{20 \text{ pounds}}{\$c}$

It will cost Neil \$12 for 20 pounds of potatoes.

Reflect Is 28 the solution to the proportion below? Use a ratio table to solve the proportion. Explain.

$$\frac{10}{7} = \frac{40}{x}$$

Yes; $10 \times x = 7 \times 40$; $10x = 280$; $x = 28$

Skills, Concepts, and Problem Solving

Find the value of each variable.

$\frac{k}{3} = \frac{12}{6}$ $k =$ 6

11 $\frac{5}{7} = \frac{d}{70}$ $d =$ 50

$\frac{13}{5} = \frac{z}{15}$ $z =$ 39

13 $\frac{2}{j} = \frac{18}{36}$ $j =$ 4

$\frac{12}{14} = \frac{6}{g}$ $g =$ 7

15 $\frac{r}{16} = \frac{8}{4}$ $r =$ 32

Math Challenge

Write About It Review the physical activities that students performed to experience constant rate and change of rate. Assign students to write a few paragraphs to describe how they performed the three activities and what they learned about rates.

Note This!

Word Problems Show students how to use the four-step plan to solve any word problem in their notes. Tell students that as they study, they can see every step to review and see any common mistakes to correct. Make sure that they write their corrections either in the margins or with another color for differentiation.

Math Coach Notes

Means and Extremes Many times people use the following statement to remind them how to use cross multiplication to solve a proportion. *The product of the means equals the product of the extremes.* In the proportion $\frac{a}{b} = \frac{c}{d}$, $a \times d = b \times c$, a and d are the *extremes*. The *means* are b and c.

$$\frac{a}{b} = \frac{c}{d}$$

Odd/Even Assignments

Exercises 10–17 are structured so that students practice the same concepts whether they are assigned the odd or even problems.

In-Class Assignment

Have students complete Exercises 13, 16, 17, and 20 to ensure that they understand the concept.

See It, Do It, Say It, Write It

Step 1 Write multiple proportion word problems on the board.

Step 2 Have students set up a proportion that shows the unknown value as a variable.

Step 3 Arrange the students in pairs and have them explain to each other how they set up the proportion that fits each situation.

Step 4 Have students write in their own words the definitions of each of the vocabulary words and how they set up a proportion in their math journal.

Looking Ahead: Pre-teach

Solve Problems Using Proportions In the next lesson, students will learn how to solve problems using proportions. Proportions can be used to find the side length of a figure that is similar (the same shape) to another figure.

Example

The two figures are similar. What is the value of x?

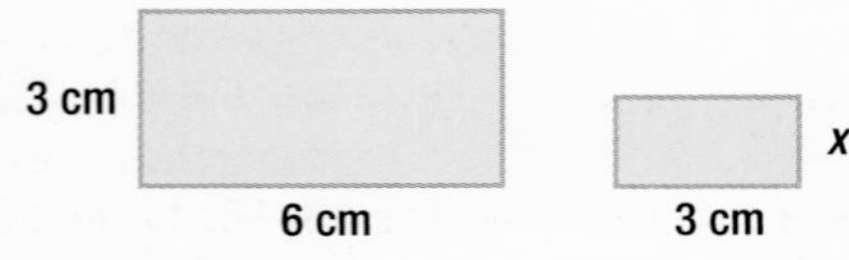

$\frac{6 \text{ cm}}{3 \text{ cm}} = \frac{3 \text{ cm}}{x}$; $x = 1.5$ cm

16 SHOPPING Lora purchased decorations online. The decoration company charges \$2 for shipping on every \$15 spent. If Lora spent \$75, how much will her total be after the shipping charge is added?

Lora's total will be \$85 after the shipping charge is added.

17 There are 7 girls to every 3 boys in student council. There are 28 girls in student council. How many boys are in student council this year?

There are 12 boys in student council this year.

Vocabulary Check **Write the vocabulary word that completes each sentence.**

18 A(n) proportion is an equation stating that two ratios or rates are equivalent.

19 To cross multiply, find the product of the numerator of one fraction and the denominator of the other fraction.

20 Writing in Math Explain how to solve for a variable in a proportion.

Cross multiply to set up an equation. Simplify both sides of the equation. Divide both sides of the equation by the coefficient of the variable.

Spiral Review

Find each unit rate. Use the unit rate to find the unknown amount. (Lesson 2-4, p. 69)

21 \$31.96 for 4 pounds; □ for 9 pounds \$7.99/lb; \$71.91

22 34 yards in 5 plays; □ yards in 12 plays 6.8 yd/play; 81.6

Solve.

23 GAMES The ratio of red marbles to the total number of marbles in a bag is $\frac{6}{11}$. What is the probability that when you pick a marble without looking it will not be red? (Lesson 2-3, p. 61)

$\frac{5}{11}$

82 **Chapter 2** Ratios, Rates, and Proportional Relationships

Ticket Out the Door

Summary Have students write a summary of how to solve a proportion using cross multiplication. Students should hand in their papers as they exit the classroom.

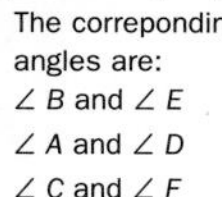

Similar Figures and Proportions

KEY Concept

You can use proportions to solve problems about similar figures. **Similar figures** have the same shape but may have different sizes. The corresponding angles of similar figures are congruent, or the same. The corresponding sides of similar figures are proportional.

The correponding angles are:
$\angle B$ and $\angle E$
$\angle A$ and $\angle D$
$\angle C$ and $\angle F$

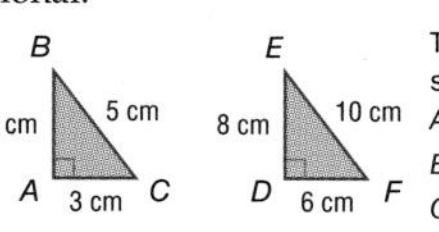

The correponding sides are:
AB and *DE*
BC and *EF*
CA and *FD*

The corresponding angles of triangles *ABC* and *DEF* are congruent. The **ratios** of their corresponding sides are equivalent. $\frac{4}{8} = \frac{5}{10} = \frac{3}{6}$

If two figures are similar, the ratio of the two sides of one of the figures is equal to the ratio of the corresponding two sides of the other figure. In triangles *ABC* and *DEF*, the ratio $\frac{AB}{AC}$, which is $\frac{4}{3}$, is equal to the ratio $\frac{DE}{DF}$, which is $\frac{8}{6}$.

VOCABULARY

proportion
an equation stating that two ratios or rates are equivalent

similar figures
figures that have the same shape but may have different sizes

Example 1

Find the value of *y*. The two rectangles are similar.

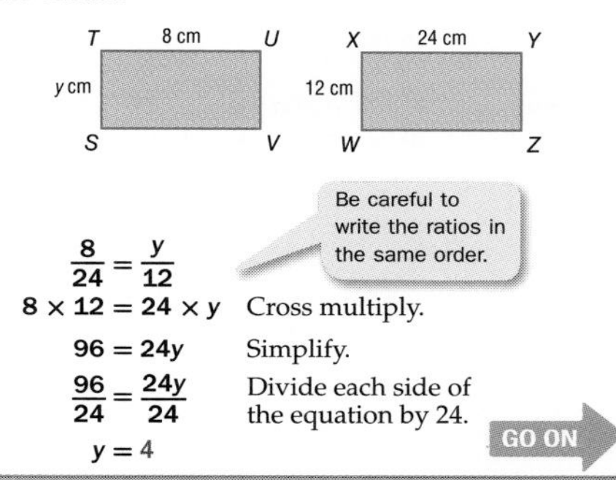

1. The ratio of the corresponding sides *TU* and *XY* is $\frac{8}{24}$.
2. The ratio of the corresponding sides *TS* and *XW* is $\frac{y}{12}$.
3. Since the two rectangles are similar, these two ratios are equal. Write the proportion and solve for *y*.
4. The length of side *TS* is 4 centimeters.

$\frac{8}{24} = \frac{y}{12}$

$8 \times 12 = 24 \times y$ Cross multiply.

$96 = 24y$ Simplify.

$\frac{96}{24} = \frac{24y}{24}$ Divide each side of the equation by 24.

$y = 4$

GO ON

Additional Example 1

Find the value of *y*. The two figures are similar.

1. The ratio of one pair of corresponding sides is $\frac{2}{5}$.
2. The ratio of the other corresponding sides is $\frac{1.5}{y}$.
3. Since the two figures are similar, these two ratios are equal. Write the proportion and solve for *y*.

$\frac{2}{5} = \frac{1.5}{y}$

$2 \times y = 1.5 \times 5$ Cross multiply.

$2y = 7.5$ Simplify.

$\frac{2y}{2} = \frac{7.5}{2}$ Divide each side of the equation by 2.

$y = 3.75$

4. The length of the unknown side is 3.75 inches.

Lesson Notes

Lesson 2-6

Lesson Planner

Objective Use proportions to solve problems.

Vocabulary **proportion**, **similar figures**

Materials/Manipulatives grid paper, geoboards, overhead projector, index cards, color pens or pencils, colored cubes, pattern blocks

Chapter Resource Masters

- CRM Vocabulary and English Language Development (p. A43)
- CRM Skills Practice (p. A44)
- CRM Problem-Solving Practice (p. A45)
- CRM Homework Practice (p. A46)

1 Introduce

Vocabulary

Equations with Fractions A proportion is an equation that shows that two fractions are equal. In the equation, there are two numerators and two denominators. If you know three of the four values, you can solve the proportion to find the fourth value. To solve a proportion, cross multiply to write an equation without fractions.

2 Teach

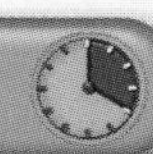

Key Concept

Foundational Skills and Concepts After students have read through the Key Concept box, have them try these exercises.

1. Which angle corresponds to angle A? angle *D*
2. Which side corresponds to $\overline{AC}$? $\overline{DF}$
3. Are the figures below similar? Explain. No, because they are not the same shape.

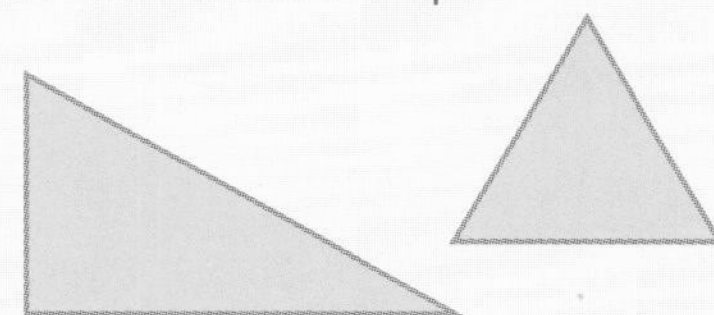

Additional **Example 2**

Edie's toy boat traveled 45 feet in 9 seconds. How long would it take the boat to travel a total of 90 feet?

1. Write a ratio for feet to seconds. $\frac{45 \text{ ft}}{9 \text{ s}}$
2. Set up a proportion to find the time it would take the toy boat to travel 90 feet.
   $\frac{45 \text{ ft}}{9 \text{ s}} = \frac{90 \text{ ft}}{x}$
3. Cross multiply.
   $45x = 90 \times 9$
4. Divide each side of the equation by 45.
   $\frac{45x}{45} = \frac{810}{45}$
   $x = 18$

It will take about 18 seconds for the toy boat to travel 90 feet.

YOUR TURN!

Find the value of *x*. The two figures are similar.

A 5 cm B, 4 cm, D C; E x F, 3 cm, H G

1. The ratio of side *AB* to corresponding side *EF* is $\frac{5}{x}$.
2. The ratio of side *AD* to corresponding side *EH* is $\frac{4}{3}$.
3. Since the two figures are similar, these two ratios are equal. Write the proportion and solve for *x*.

$\frac{5}{x} = \frac{4}{3}$

$5 \times 3 = 4x$

$15 = 4x$

$\frac{15}{4} = \frac{4x}{4}$

The length of side *EF* is 3.75 cm.

$x = 3.75$

Proportions can be used to find unknown measures in similar figures, in percent proportions, and for unit conversions.

Example 2

A battery-powered toy car traveled 28 feet in 4 seconds. How long would it take the car to travel a total of 70 feet?

1. Write a ratio for feet to seconds. $\frac{28 \text{ ft}}{4 \text{ s}}$
2. Set up a proportion to find the time it would take to travel 70 feet. $\frac{28 \text{ ft}}{4 \text{ s}} = \frac{70 \text{ ft}}{t}$
3. Cross multiply. $28t = 4 \times 70$
4. Divide each side of the equation by 28. $\frac{28t}{28} = \frac{280}{28}$

   It will take about 10 seconds for the car to travel 70 feet. $t = 10$

Intervention Strategy

Kinesthetic/Interpersonal Learners

Write Ratio Problems Have students work in pairs. Provide each student with an index card. Prompt each student to write a word problem that can be solved with a proportion on their index card. Have students exchange index cards with their partners and solve each other's problem.

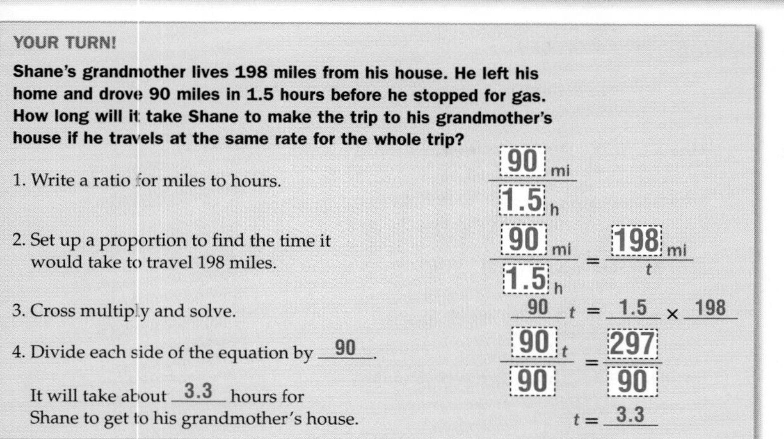
YOUR TURN!

Shane's grandmother lives 198 miles from his house. He left his home and drove 90 miles in 1.5 hours before he stopped for gas. How long will it take Shane to make the trip to his grandmother's house if he travels at the same rate for the whole trip?

1. Write a ratio for miles to hours. $\frac{90 \text{ mi}}{1.5 \text{ h}}$
2. Set up a proportion to find the time it would take to travel 198 miles. $\frac{90 \text{ mi}}{1.5 \text{ h}} = \frac{198 \text{ mi}}{t}$
3. Cross multiply and solve. $90\, t = 1.5 \times 198$
4. Divide each side of the equation by 90. $\frac{90t}{90} = \frac{297}{90}$

It will take about 3.3 hours for Shane to get to his grandmother's house. $t = 3.3$

Who is Correct?

Jerry ran 5 miles in 35 minutes. Use a proportion to find how long it would take him to run 7.5 miles at that rate.

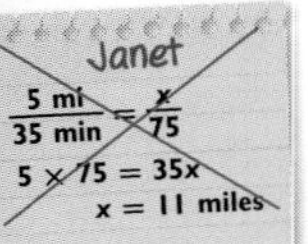

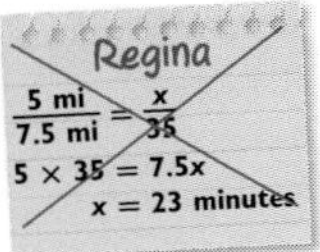

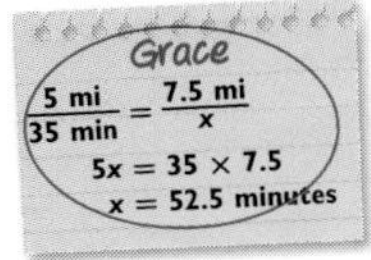

Circle correct answer(s). Cross out incorrect answer(s).

 **Guided Practice**

Find the value of *x* in each pair of similar figures.

1 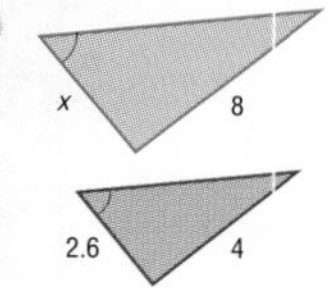

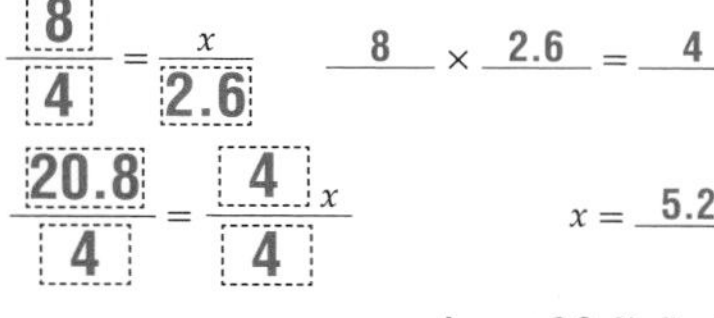

$8 \times 2.6 = 4x$

$x = 5.2$

GO ON

Who *is* Correct?

Diagnostic Teaching

- Janet wrote 11 miles. This is not correct. She used 75 instead of 7.5 in the proportion, and placed it incorrectly within the proportion.
- Regina wrote 23 minutes. This is incorrect. The first ratio should be 5 miles over 35 minutes, not over 7.5 miles.
- Grace wrote 52.5 minutes. This is correct.

Remind students to be sure that their ratios represent a rate described in the problem.

Using Manipulatives

Grid Paper Students can learn about similar figures by drawing the figures on grid paper. The scale will vary depending on the problem.

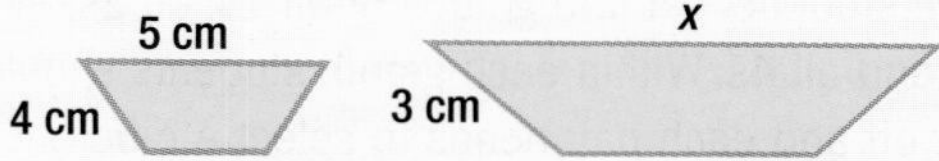

Geoboard Students can experiment with similar figures using a geoboard. Tell them to make a figure with one color band and then make another figure that is similar, therefore proportional, using another color. They can calculate the ratios to verify the figures are similar.

Overhead Projector Draw a triangle on transparency and project onto the board using an overhead projector. The triangle should be scalene. Trace over the triangle and label the triangle *ABC*. Move the projector farther from the board to create a large triangle that is similar to the $\triangle ABC$. Label this triangle *STU*. Use the two triangles to discuss corresponding sides. Then move the projector closer to the board to create a smaller triangle that is similar to both $\triangle ABC$ and $\triangle STU$. Label this triangle *LMN*.

On-Hand Manipulatives Have students draw sketches of similar figures in their notebooks. Give them different colors of pens or pencils to outline the corresponding sides. This will aid them in setting up the correct proportion.

Intervention Strategy — Interpersonal Learners

Writing Problems Have students count off by 4s so that each student is assigned a number 1, 2, 3, or 4. Write the following proportion on the board:

$$\frac{①}{②} = \frac{③}{④}$$

Have students get into groups of all 1s, all 2s, all 3s, and all 4s. Within each group, students should pair off and each pair needs to select a different shape, such as rectangle, trapezoid, triangle, and so on. Each pair needs to write a problem modeled after Example 1 but having the missing element that corresponds with their assigned numbers. When all problems are written, students should trade papers with others that were assigned a different number.

Step by Step Practice

2 Raul traveled 150 miles in 3 hours. How long would it take Raul to travel a total of 325 miles?

Step 1 Write a ratio for miles to hours. $\frac{150 \text{ mi}}{3 \text{ h}}$

Step 2 Set up a proportion to find the time it would take to travel 325 miles. $\frac{150 \text{ mi}}{3 \text{ h}} = \frac{325}{t}$

Step 3 Cross multiply and solve. $150\,t = 3 \times 325$

Step 4 Divide each side of the equation by 150. $\frac{150t}{150} = \frac{975}{150}$

$t = 6.5$

It will take 6.5 hours to travel 325 miles.

Solve.

3 MOWING Levi earns \$35 for mowing 5 lawns. At that rate, how many lawns would he need to mow in order to earn \$140?

$\frac{\$35}{5}$

$$\frac{35}{5} = \frac{140}{L}$$

$$35\,L = 5 \times 140$$

$$\frac{35L}{35} = \frac{700}{35}$$

$$L = 20$$

Levi needs to mow 20 lawns.

4 HIKING On a hike through the mountains, Jody walked 10 kilometers in 3 hours. At this rate, how long would it take Jody to walk 14 kilometers?

$$\frac{10 \text{ km}}{3 \text{ h}} = \frac{14 \text{ km}}{w}$$

It will take Jody 4.2 hours to walk 14 kilometers.

86 Chapter 2 Ratios, Rates, and Proportional Relationships

Are They Getting It?

Check students' understanding of solving problems using proportions by writing these problems on the board. Ask students to point out wrong answers and explain why they are wrong.

1. If the value of x is 10 m, then these figures are similar. This is incorrect. The sides are not proportional.

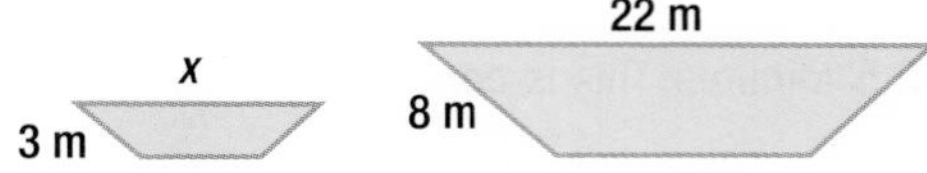

2. Similar figures are the same size and the same shape. This is incorrect. Similar figures are the same shape, but could be different sizes. If they are the same size and shape, then they are called *congruent*.

tep by Step Problem-Solving Practice

Problem-Solving Strategies

- ☑ Use a table.
- ☐ Look for a pattern.
- ☐ Guess and check.
- ☐ Solve a simpler problem.
- ☐ Act it out.

olve.

GEOMETRY Each side of polygon *ABCD* is 3 times as long as the corresponding side of polygon *FGHI*. Find the perimeter of polygon *ABCD*.

Understand Read the problem. Write what you know.

Each side of polygon *ABCD* is 3 times as long as the corresponding side of polygon *FGHI*.

Plan Pick a strategy. One strategy is to make a table showing the corresponding sides.

Solve First, fill in the corresponding sides of polygons *FGHI* and *ABCD*. Then, fill in the measurements of the sides of polygon *FGHI*. All measurements are in inches.

Multiply the length of each side of polygon *FGHI* by 3 to find the lengths of the sides of polygon *ABCD*. Complete the table.

	side	length	side	length	side	length	side	length
FGHI	$\overline{FG}$	3	$\overline{GH}$	2	$\overline{HI}$	5	$\overline{IF}$	3
ABCD	$\overline{AB}$	9	$\overline{BC}$	6	$\overline{CD}$	15	$\overline{DA}$	9

The perimeter is the sum of the lengths of the sides. What is the perimeter of polygon *ABCD*? 39 inches

Check Does the answer make sense? Look over your solution. Did you answer the question?

PROPORTIONS At the same time of day, the height of an object and its shadow are proportional to the height of another object and its shadow. If a 6-feet-high doghouse casts a shadow 5 feet long, how tall is a flagpole that casts a 40-ft shadow? Check off each step.

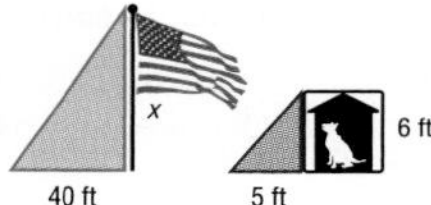

✔ Understand: I underlined key words.

✔ Plan: To solve the problem, I will solve a proportion.

✔ Solve: The answer is 48 feet.

✔ Check: I checked my answer by substituting 48 for *x*.

Common Error *Alert*

Exercise 5 If students have difficulty with Exercise 5, they might not understand how to approach the problem. Tell them to use a ruler and recreate the polygon *ABCD* on paper. Now ask them how they could make a figure that is exactly the same shape, but 3 times as large. Guide students to see that the length of each side of the original polygon would have to be 3 times longer. Ask them how they would arrive at those lengths.

English Learner Strategy

Draw Similar Figures Give students grid paper. Tell them to draw a rectangle that is 2 squares wide and 5 squares in length. What is the ratio of width to length? A figure that is similar will have the same ratio of width to length and will also be the same shape. (See sample answer below.) Use grid paper to make a similar figure. Write the ratio of the width to length. Is it the same as the ratio for the first figure?

7.5 units, 3 units; 5 units, 2 units

Odd/Even Assignments

Exercises 9–17 are structured so that students practice the same concepts whether they are assigned the odd or even problems.

In-Class Assignment

Have students complete Exercises 9, 12, 15, 17, and 20 to ensure that they understand the concept.

7 EVENTS Tierra decided to participate in a walk-a-thon for charity. She walked 18 miles in 252 minutes. How long would it take Tierra to walk 26 miles?

It will take Tierra about 364 minutes to walk 26 miles.

8 Reflect List the types of problems that proportions can be used to solve.

Sample answer: Proportions can be used to find missing lengths in similar figures, indirect measurement, percents, unit costs, and unit rates.

Skills, Concepts, and Problem Solving

Find the value of x in each pair of similar figures.

9 $x =$ 10.2 ft

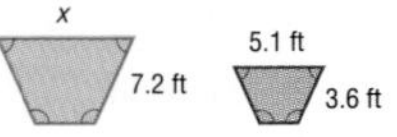

10 $x =$ 12 mm

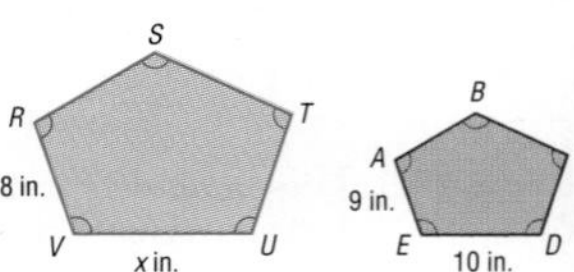

11 $x =$ 11 cm

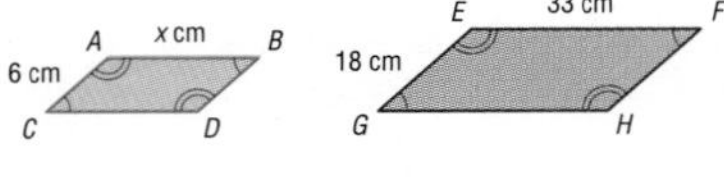

12 $x =$ 20 in.

S
R
T
18 in.
V
x in.
U
B
A
C
9 in.
E
10 in.
D

Use a proportion to solve each problem.

13 A jet can travel at about 225 miles in 30 minutes. At this speed, how long will it take to travel 800 miles?
about 107 minutes or 1 hour and 47 minutes

14 Enola ran 2 miles in 18 minutes. At this rate, how long would it take Enola to run 3 miles?
27 minutes

15 A bird flies 30 miles in 18 minutes. How far would the bird fly if it continued at the same rate for 45 minutes?
75 miles

88 Chapter 2 Ratios, Rates, and Proportional Relationships

Math Challenge

Cubes and Blocks Divide students into pairs. Give each student a colored cube. One student rolls a cube and uses the color to choose a corresponding pattern block. That student will trace and label the pattern block and then draw a similar polygon and label the side measurements. Then students switch roles. The student who draws the most correct polygons, with the correct proportional measures, wins.

Solve.

16 FITNESS Douglas jogged 5 miles on Saturday morning at a rate of 7 miles per hour. How long did he jog? 0.71 hours
He jogged 3 miles on Monday at a rate of 6 miles per hour. Did he jog for a longer amount of time on Saturday or Monday?

He jogged for a longer amount of time on Saturday.

17 SCUBA DIVING A company produces 39 wetsuits every 2 weeks. How long will it take the company to produce 429 wetsuits?
22 weeks

Vocabulary Check **Write the vocabulary word that completes each sentence.**

18 Figures whose shapes are the same but may have different sizes are similar figures.

19 A(n) ratio is a comparison of two numbers by division.

20 Writing in Math Candace says that if two figures are similar, their corresponding sides are equal and their corresponding angles are proportional. Is she correct? Explain.

Sample answer: No, Candace is not correct. If two figures are similar, their corrresponding angles are equal and their corresponding sides are proportional.

Spiral Review

Solve. (Lesson 2-4, p. 69)

21 SHOPPING Mr. Jonas bought a bag of oranges for $12.50. The bag contains 15 oranges. Find the unit cost to the nearest cent.
$0.83

22 One dozen eggs costs $0.99. How much do four dozen eggs cost?
$3.96

Find the value of each variable. (Lesson 2-5, p. 77)

23 $\frac{1}{3} = \frac{9}{z}$ $z =$ 27

24 $\frac{3}{4} = \frac{a}{20}$ $a =$ 15

See It, Do It, Say It, Write It

Step 1 Draw two figures on the board. Label their measures so they are similar. Have students guide you to find the ratios of the corresponding sides to verify. Draw other figures that look similar but are not. Have students calculate and verify. Finally, draw similar figures with side lengths that must be determined.

Step 2 Tell students to work in pairs. Have them measure and draw a triangle of any type. Then tell them to make another triangle that is similar to the first.

Step 3 Students will present their work and explain their methodology.

Step 4 Tell students to write how they know if two figures are similar or not. Ask them to include an example.

Ticket Out the Door

Green Beans, Anyone? Write a proportion to solve the problem: An 8-oz can of green beans contains about 132 green beans. How many green beans would you expect to find in a 6-oz can? Students will hand in their work as they exit the class.

$\frac{8\text{-oz}}{132} = \frac{6\text{-oz}}{g}$; $8g = 792$; 99 green beans

Chapter 2

Progress Check 3

Formative Assessment

Use the Progress Check to assess students' mastery of the previous lessons. Have students review the lesson indicated for the problems they answered incorrectly.

Odd/Even Assignments

Exercises are structured so that students practice the same concepts whether they are assigned the odd or even problems.

Common Error *Alert*

Check Work Make sure students check their work and verify that the rates they calculated make sense in a real-world context.

Exercises 7–10 Students may need a reminder of the definition of *similar* before trying to apply it. Be sure they know *similar* and *congruent* have different meanings.

Chapter 2

Progress Check 3 (Lessons 2-5 and 2-6)

Find the value of each variable.

1. $\frac{a}{4} = \frac{9}{6}$ $a =$ 6
2. $\frac{3}{9} = \frac{z}{15}$ $z =$ 5
3. $\frac{12}{7} = \frac{y}{21}$ $y =$ 36
4. $\frac{8}{4} = \frac{b}{16}$ $b =$ 32
5. $\frac{10}{14} = \frac{5}{x}$ $x =$ 7
6. $\frac{3}{c} = \frac{6}{18}$ $c =$ 9

Find the value of *x* in each pair of similar figures.

7. $x =$ 6 in.

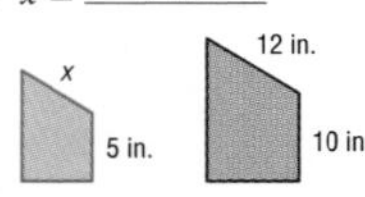

8. $x =$ 16 mm

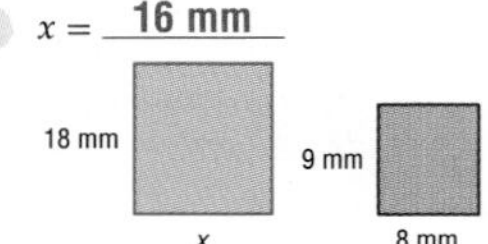

9. $x =$ 10 cm

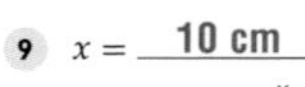

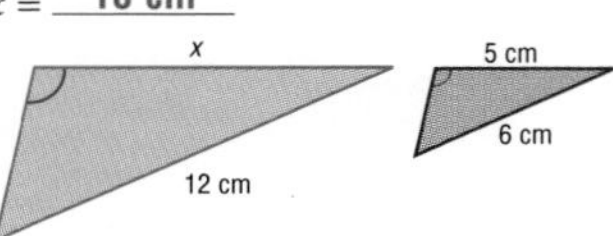

10. $x =$ 4 ft

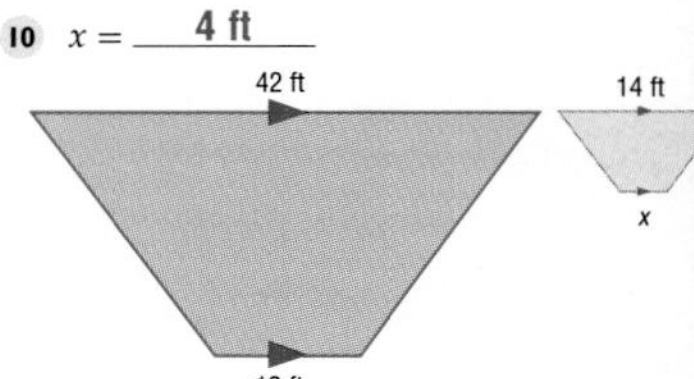

Use a proportion to solve each problem.

11. Ricardo runs 50 meters in 9 seconds. What is his average speed? Round to the nearest tenth.
5.6 meters per second

12. A plane can travel at about 300 miles in 90 minutes. At this speed, how long will it take to travel 1,200 miles?
360 minutes or 6 hours

Solve.

13. **HIKING** Paloma hikes 10 miles in 4 hours. At this rate, how long would it take her to hike 15 miles?
6 hours

14. **GROCERIES** A bag of onions weighing 5 pounds costs $2.99. How much will it cost to buy a 12-pound bag?
$7.18

90 **Chapter 2** Ratios, Rates, and Proportional Relationships

Data-Driven Decision Making

Students missing Exercises . . .	Have trouble with . . .	Should review and practice . . .
1–6	solving proportions.	SSG Lesson 2-5, p. 77 CRM Skills Practice, p. A40
7–10	applications with similar figures.	SSG Lesson 2-6, p. 83 CRM Skills Practice, p. A44
11–12	using proportions to solve situational problems.	SSG Lesson 2-5, p. 77 CRM Skills Practice, p. A40
13–14	solving word problems involving proportions.	CRM Problem-Solving Practice, pp. A41 and A45

Study Guide

Vocabulary and Concept Check

cross multiply, *p. 77*
event, *p. 61*
outcomes, *p. 61*
probability, *p. 61*
proportion, *p. 77*
ratio, *p. 46*
unit rate, *p. 69*

Write the vocabulary word that completes each sentence.

1. Probability is a number between 0 and 1 that measures the likelihood of an event happening.
2. An equation stating that two ratios or rates are equivalent is a(n) proportion.
3. When finding the probability, put the number of possible outcomes in the denominator.
4. A(n) ratio is a comparison of two numbers by division.
5. The probability of a(n) event can be written as a fraction.

Write the correct vocabulary term in each blank.

6. unit cost
$2.73 per gallon

7. unit rate
65 miles per hour

Lesson Review

2-1 Ratios (pp. 46–52)

Write each ratio as a fraction in simplest form.

8. 16 baseball cards to 24 football cards $\frac{2}{3}$
9. 27 bracelets to 15 necklaces $\frac{9}{5}$
10. 14 skateboards to 24 rollerblades $\frac{7}{12}$
11. 36 roses to 16 tulips $\frac{9}{4}$

Example 1

Write the ratio as a fraction in simplest form.
4 white cars out of 20 total cars

1. Write the ratio with the number of white cars in the numerator and the total number of cars in the denominator.
$\frac{4}{20}$
2. The numerator and denominator have a common factor of 4. Divide each by 4 to write the fraction in simplest form.
$\frac{4}{20} = \frac{4 \div 4}{20 \div 4} = \frac{1}{5}$

Study Guide
Formative Assessment

Chapter 2

Vocabulary and Concept Check

If students have difficulty answering Exercises 1–7, remind them that they can use the page references to refresh their memories about the vocabulary terms.

Vocabulary Review Strategies

Vocabulary Flashcards Have students create a flashcard for the vocabulary words. On one side of the card, state the definition, and on the other side, the vocabulary term. The students can study these cards by looking at the vocabulary term and stating its definition (flipping the card over to check and see if they got the definition correct). Students can also read the side with the definition and state its corresponding vocabulary term (flipping the card over to see if they got the correct term).

Lesson Review

The examples walk the students through writing ratios as fractions in simplest form, writing rates as fractions and finding the corresponding unit rates, finding the probability of a given event, and using proportions to solve problems. If the given examples are not sufficient to review the questions, have students design their own example from a particular section of the chapter. When finished, have them share their example and its solution with a partner.

Find **Extra Practice** for these concepts in the Practice Worksheets, pages A23–A46.

Classroom Management

Early Finishers Have students who finish the review problems for each example create additional problems. They should create the problem and include an answer (including a labeled diagram as needed). When complete, have these students exchange their problems and double-check each other's work or share them with the class.

Dinah Zike's Foldables®

Class Review Remind students to complete and refer to their Foldables as they progress through the Chapter 2 Study Guide. Have students share and compare their completed Foldables with a partner. You may also choose to have them use their Foldable as a study aid in preparing for the Chapter Test. (For complete instructions, see Chapter Resource Masters, p. A20.)

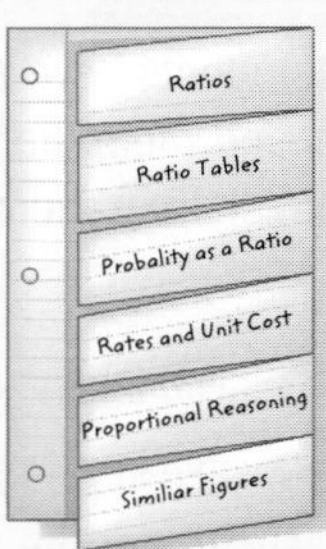

2-2 Ratio Tables (pp. 53–59)

Fill in the blanks and complete the ratio tables.

12

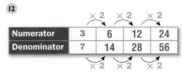

Numerator	3	6	12	24
Denominator	7	14	28	56

(× 2, × 2, × 2)

13

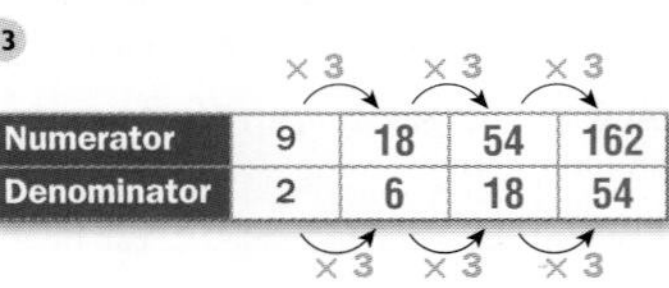

Numerator	9	18	54	162
Denominator	2	6	18	54

(× 3, × 3, × 3)

Fill in the blanks and complete the ratio tables.

14

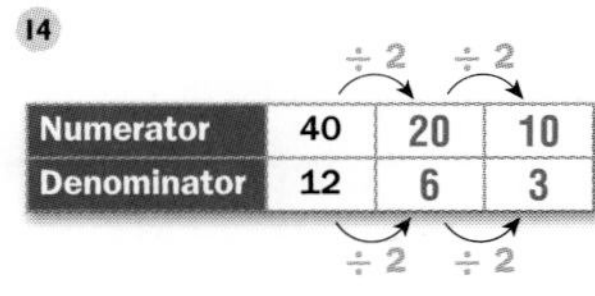

Numerator	40	20	10
Denominator	12	6	3

(÷ 2, ÷ 2)

15

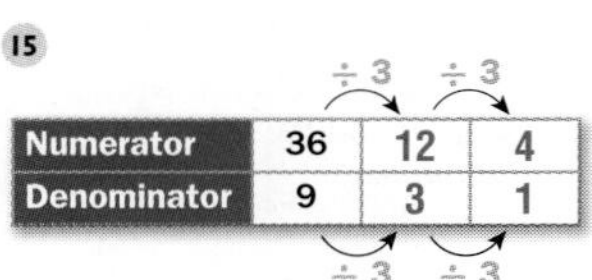

Numerator	36	12	4
Denominator	9	3	1

(÷ 3, ÷ 3)

Example 2

Jesse bought 4 packs of baseball cards for \$10. At this rate, how much would 32 packs of baseball cards cost? Use a ratio table.

1. Identify the original ratio. $\frac{4}{10}$
2. Find equivalent forms of one.

$\frac{4 \times 2 = 8}{10 \times 2 = 20}$ $\frac{8 \times 2 = 16}{20 \times 2 = 40}$ $\frac{16 \times 2 = 32}{40 \times 2 = 80}$

3. Complete the table.

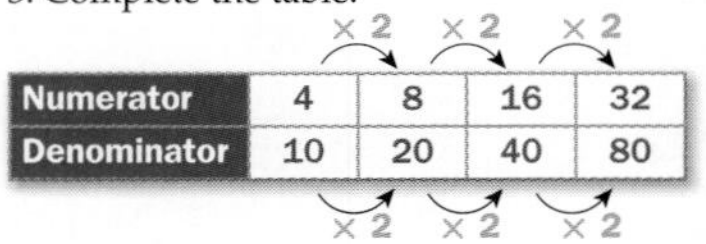

Numerator	4	8	16	32
Denominator	10	20	40	80

(× 2, × 2, × 2)

It would cost Jesse \$80 to buy 32 packs of baseball cards.

Example 3

Omar baked 96 muffins in 8 hours. At this rate, how many muffins did he bake in 2 hours? Use a ratio table.

1. Identify the original ratio. $\frac{96}{8}$
2. Find an equivalent form of one used to determine the missing values.

$\frac{96 \div 2 = 48}{8 \div 2 = 4}$ $\frac{48 \div 2 = 24}{4 \div 2 = 2}$

3. Complete the table.

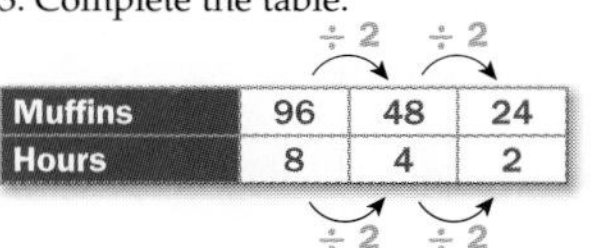

Muffins	96	48	24
Hours	8	4	2

(÷ 2, ÷ 2)

Omar baked 24 muffins in 2 hours.

2-3 Probability as a Ratio (pp. 61–68)

16 Use the spinner in Example 4 to find the probability of spinning a 3 or a 4. Write the probability as a fraction in simplest form. Explain the probability.

$\frac{2}{8} = \frac{1}{4}$

The probability of $\frac{1}{4}$ means that 1 out of every 4 spins should be a 3 or 4.

17 Use the spinner in Example 4 to find the probability of spinning a number less than 7. Explain the probability.

$\frac{6}{8} = \frac{3}{4}$ The probability of $\frac{3}{4}$ means that 3 out of every 4 spins should be less than 7.

Find each probability. Write the probability as a fraction in simplest form.

18 2 red pens, 5 blue pens, and 3 black pens; P(red or black pen)

$\frac{1}{2}$

19 9 DVDs, 6 CDs, and 3 video games; P(not a video game)

$\frac{5}{6}$

Example 4

Use the spinner to find the probability of spinning an even number. Write the probability as a fraction in simplest form. Explain the probability.

1. Count the number of sections labeled with an even number. Write this number in the numerator.

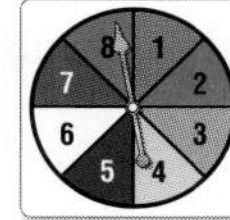

2. Count the total number of sections. Write this number in the denominator.

$P(\text{even number}) = \frac{4}{8}$ — The spinner has four even numbers. / The spinner has 8 numbers.

3. The ratio is $\frac{4}{8}$. The ratio can be simplified.

$\frac{4 \div 4}{8 \div 4} = \frac{1}{2}$

4. The probability of $\frac{1}{2}$ means that 1 out of every 2 spins should be an even number.

Example 5

In a bag there are 6 green chips, 3 yellow chips, 4 blue chips, and 2 red chips. What is the probability of reaching into the bag and choosing a yellow chip without looking?

1. There are 3 yellow chips.
2. There are a total of 15 chips in the bag.
3. Write the ratio for the P(yellow). $\frac{3}{15}$
4. Write the fraction in simplest form.

$\frac{3 \div 3}{15 \div 3} = \frac{1}{5}$

5. 1 out of 5 times you take a chip out of the bag without looking it will be yellow.

Note This!

Create a Checklist Help students create a study checklist. The checklist should include all of the following:

- Notes from class/examples from each lesson
- Vocabulary terms and definitions
- Foldables
- Corrected homework assignments
- Quizzes and Progress Checks
- Chapter 2 Study Guide

Intervention Strategy Kinesthetic Learners

Probability Problems Have students answer some probability questions that require the "hands-on" spinning of a spinner. Example: Spin the spinner 12 times and record your results. Now write the ratio of the number of times you spun a 2 out of the 12 total spins as a fraction in simplest form.

Math Coach Notes

Create a Checklist Give the students a short list of important ideas from the chapter that they need to understand:

- What is the significance of cross products?
- What is a proportion?
- Name some of the ways we used proportions in this chapter.
- What does it mean for two figures to be similar?

2-4 Rates and Unit Costs (pp. 69–75)

Write each rate as a fraction. Find each unit rate.

20 100 miles in 4 hours

$\frac{100}{4}$; 25 mi/h

21 60 gallons in 5 minutes

$\frac{60}{5}$; 12 gal/min

22 24 baskets out of 42

$\frac{24}{42}$; 0.57 baskets/min

23 50 sit-ups in 30 seconds

$\frac{50}{30}$; 1.7 sit-ups/second

Which product has the lower unit cost? Round to the nearest cent.

24 32-oz shampoo bottle for $6, or 8-oz shampoo bottle for $1.75

32-oz bottle; $0.19

25 4-pack of tissues for $3.39, or 16-pack of tissues for $14.75

4 pack; $0.85

26 18-oz box of cereal for $2.99, or 24-oz box of cereal for $4.29

18-oz box; $0.17

27 12-pack of baseball cards for $3.25, or 24-pack of baseball cards for $5.50

24-pack; $0.23;

Example 6

Write the rate 80 beats per 10 seconds as a fraction. Find the unit rate.

1. Write the rate as a fraction.

   $\frac{80 \text{ beats}}{10 \text{ seconds}}$

2. Find an equivalent rate with a denominator of 1. The numerator and denominator have a common factor of 10. Divide each by 10.

   $\frac{80 \text{ beats} \div 10}{10 \text{ seconds} \div 10} = \frac{8 \text{ beats}}{1 \text{ second}}$

3. Name the unit rate.

   8 beats per second or 8 beats/s

Example 7

Ms. Gordon bought a box of pens for $6.75. The box contains 12 pens. Find the unit cost to the nearest cent.

1. Write the rate as a fraction.

   $\frac{\$6.75}{12 \text{ pens}}$

2. Divide the numerator by the denominator.
3. 0.5625 rounded to the nearest cent is $0.56.

   Each pen costs about $0.56.

Intervention Strategy Visual Learners

Color Coding Until the students have a grasp of where to place the measures and their corresponding unit labels within the proportion's fractions, assign a color to each unit type. This should serve as a visual aid to guide the students in their proper placement. For example, students can have quarts in the denominator in the color green and gallons in the numerator in the color orange.

2-5 Proportional Reasoning (pp. 77–82)

ind the value of each variable.

28 $\frac{d}{5} = \frac{12}{60}$

$d =$ 1

29 $\frac{12}{15} = \frac{4}{h}$

$h =$ 5

Example 8

Find the value of t.

$\frac{6}{9} = \frac{t}{3}$

1. $6 \times 3 = 9 \times t$ — Cross multiply.
2. $18 = 9t$ — Simplify.
3. $\frac{18}{9} = \frac{9t}{9}$ — Divide each side of the equation by 9.

   $t = 2$
4. Check. — Replace t with 2 and solve.

   $\frac{6}{9} = \frac{2}{3}$

   $18 = 18$

-6 Similar Figures and Proportions (pp. 83–89)

ind the value of x in each pair of imilar figures.

30 $x =$ 9 ft

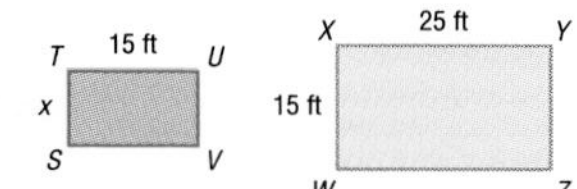

31 $x =$ 20

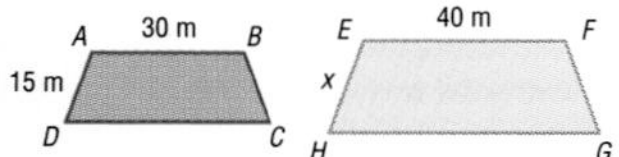

Example 9

Find the value of x. The two figures are similar.

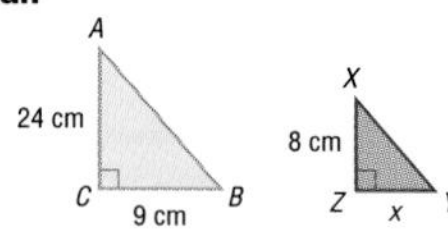

1. The ratio of the corresponding sides AC to XZ is $\frac{24}{8}$.
2. The ratio of the corresponding sides BC and YZ is $\frac{9}{x}$.
3. Since the two figures are similar, these two ratios are equal. Write the proportion and solve for x.

   $\frac{24}{8} = \frac{9}{x}$ — Cross multiply.

   $24x = 8 \times 9$ — Simplify.

   $\frac{24x}{24} = \frac{72}{24}$ — Divide each side of the equation by 24.

   $x = 3$
4. The length of $\overline{YZ}$ is 3 centimeters.

Ticket Out the Door

Proportion Applications Have students write and answer four proportion problems: one involving similar figures, one straightforward unit-conversion problem, one involving a rate, and one involving a cost. Because these directives are not giving a great deal of specifics, tell students to look back through their lessons and try to imitate what they have already written and solved.

Chapter 2 Chapter Test

Chapter Resource Masters

Additional forms of the Chapter 2 Tests are available.

Test Format	Where to Find it
Chapter 2 Test	Math Online glencoe.com
Blackline Masters	Assessment Masters, p. 40

Customize and create multiple versions of your chapter tests and their answer keys. All of these questions from the chapter tests are available on ExamView® Assessment Suite.

Online Assessment and Reporting
glencoe.com

This online assessment tool allows teachers to track student progress with easily accessible comprehensive reports available for every student. Assess students using any internet-ready computer.

Alternative Assessment

Use Portfolios Ask students to write examples of all of the different types of problems from this chapter. These should include: writing a ratio as a fraction in simplest form, finding unit rates, finding unit cost, and writing probabilities as ratios in simplest form, and solving proportions.

Chapter Test

Write the ratio of width to length for each rectangle as a fraction in simplest form.

1 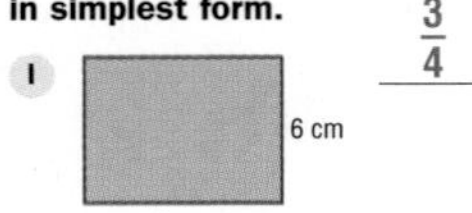

$\frac{3}{4}$

2 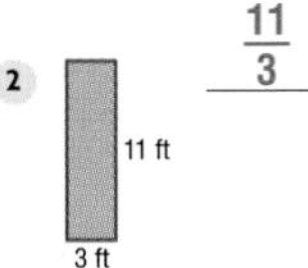

$\frac{11}{3}$

Write each rate as a fraction. Find each unit rate.

3 60 miles in 2 hours $\frac{60}{2}$; 30 mi/h

4 12 pounds in 3 weeks $\frac{12}{3}$; 4 lb/wk

Write each ratio as a fraction in simplest form.

5 7 of the 15 fish in the tank were goldfish $\frac{7}{15}$

6 21 laps in 3 days $\frac{7}{1}$ or 7 laps a day

Which product has the lower unit cost? Round to the nearest cent.

7 8-oz bag of chocolate chips for \$1.99, a 12-oz bag of chocolate chips for \$2.49, or a 16-oz bag of chocolate chips for \$2.99
16-oz bag; \$0.19

8 4 oranges for \$1, 10 oranges for \$2, or 24 oranges for \$6
10 oranges; \$0.20

Use the spinner to find each probability. Write the probability as a fraction in simplest form.

9 $P(\text{odd})$ $\frac{1}{2}$

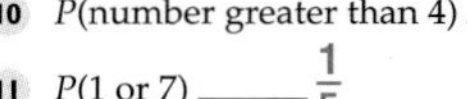

10 $P(\text{number greater than } 4)$ $\frac{3}{5}$

11 $P(1 \text{ or } 7)$ $\frac{1}{5}$

Find the value of each variable.

12 $\frac{f}{17} = \frac{3}{51}$
$f =$ 1

13 $\frac{20}{y} = \frac{5}{9}$
$y =$ 36

96 Chapter 2 Test

English Learner Strategy

Assessment Allow students time to look over the assessment. Have the students take a close look at all the problem directions, as well as any terms in the word problems. Be sure students understand what is being asked of them in each problem. If necessary, provide them with some form of clarification.

se the ratio table to solve the problem.

4 **MONEY** Berta spends $20 on lunch every week. At this rate, how much money will she spend in 8 weeks? **$160**

Money Spent ($)	20	40	80	160
Number of Weeks	1	2	4	8

ind the value of x in each pair of similar figures.

5

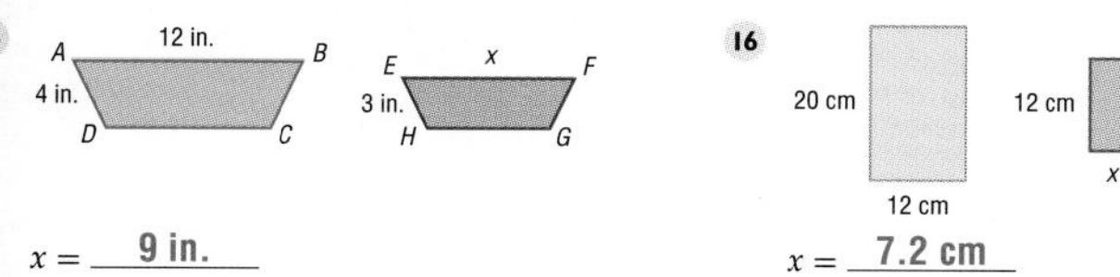

$x =$ **9 in.**

16

20 cm

12 cm

12 cm

x

$x =$ **7.2 cm**

olve.

7 **SPORTS** A group of friends jogged during lunch time. After 60 minutes, they jogged 6 miles. If they kept a steady pace, then how far had they jogged after 45 minutes?

4.5 miles

3 **TRAVEL** Isabel drove her truck 225 miles in 3 hours. What was her unit rate?

75 mi per hour

9 **POPULATION** The population of Scottville grows by approximately 300 citizens every 4 years. By about how many citizens will the population of Scottville grow in 12 years?

approximately 900 citizens

orrect the mistakes.

) **CARDS** When Rob and his sister Jenny were playing a game, Rob shuffled the deck of 52 game cards and asked Jenny to draw one from the deck without looking. He told her that she had a $\frac{2}{25}$ chance of drawing a red card. (There were 4 red cards in the deck of 52 game cards.) Is he correct?

No; her chance of drawing a red card out of the deck of game cards is $\frac{4}{52} = \frac{2}{26} = \frac{1}{13}$.

Learning from Mistakes

Review Review commonly missed questions or topics in small groups or as a class. Ask students to share their methods of answering each question. Try to point out when any errors occur and take corrective measures.

Data-Driven Decision Making

Students missing Exercises . . .	Have trouble with . . .	Should review and practice . . .
1–2, 5–6	writing ratios as fractions in simplest form.	SSG Lesson 2-1, p. 46 CRM Skills Practice, p. A24
3–4, 7–8	writing rates as fractions in simplest form and finding unit cost.	SSG Lesson 2-4, p. 69 CRM Skills Practice, p. A36
9–11	finding probabilities.	SSG Lesson 2-3, p. 61 CRM Skills Practice, p. A32
12–13, 15–16	solving proportions.	SSG Lessons 2-5 and 2-6, pp. 77 and 83 CRM Skills Practice, pp. A40 and A44
14	using a ratio table.	SSG Lesson 2-2, p. 53 CRM Skills Practice, p. A28
17–20	solving word problems involving ratios, rates, and probability.	CRM Problem-Solving Practice, pp. A25, A29, A33, A37, A41, and A45

Chapter 2 Test Practice

Diagnose Student Errors

Survey student responses for each item. Class trends may indicate common errors and misconceptions.

1. A found ratio of mysteries to science fiction novels
   (B) correct
   C found ratio of nonfiction to mysteries
   D guess

2. A this is number of apples for 4 pies
   B chose number of pies, not apples
   C this is number of apples for 8 pies
   (D) correct

3. (A) correct
   B guess
   C divided quantity by cost instead of reverse
   D this is cost of 8-pack

4. A guess
   B calculated cost of 6 CDs
   C miscalculated
   (D) correct

5. (A) correct
   B guess
   C guess
   D guess

6. A found rate per day
   B miscalculated
   (C) correct
   D guess

7. A incorrect marble color considered
   B incorrect marble color considered
   (C) correct
   D miscounted total number of marbles

8. A unit rate not applied to 5 gallons
   B miscalculated
   (C) correct
   D misinterpreted rate

9. A guess
   (B) correct
   C ratio was written in incorrect order
   D number of faces to total objects

Chapter 2 Test Practice

Select the best answer and fill in the corresponding circle on the sheet at right.

1 In Cassie's bookshelf, there are 32 mysteries, 8 nonfiction titles, and 6 science fiction novels. What is the ratio of mysteries to nonfiction books?

A $\frac{16}{3}$, 16:3, or 16 to 3
(B) $\frac{4}{1}$, 4:1, or 4 to 1
C $\frac{1}{4}$, 1:4, or 1 to 4
D $\frac{16}{7}$, 16:7, or 16 to 7

2 To make 2 apple pies you will need 7 apples. How many apples will you need to make 16 apple pies? Use the table given to solve the problem.

Number of Pies	2	4	8	16
Number of Apples	7	14	28	56

A 14
B 16
C 28
(D) 56

3 A store sells an 8-pack of bottled water for $4. What is the cost of one bottle of water?

(A) $0.50
B $1.00
C $2.00
D $4.00

4 Music CDs are on sale this week, 3 for $29.97. How much will 7 CDs cost during this sale?

A $44.96
B $59.94
C $64.93
(D) $69.93

5 Find the value of x in the pair of similar figures.

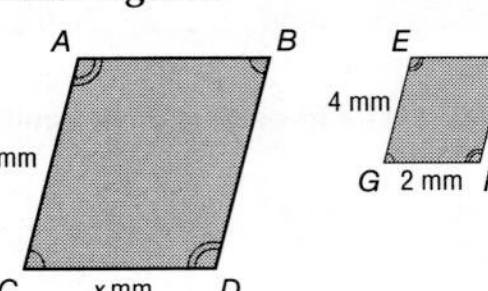

(A) 4
B 5
C 6
D 7

6 Damian is an avid biker. He rides abou[t] 140 miles every 4 days. At this rate, how many miles does he ride in 6 days?

A 35 miles
B 175 miles
(C) 210 miles
D 840 miles

7 A bag contains 5 blue, 6 white, and 3 re[d] marbles. A marble is drawn without looking. What is the probability of drawing a white marble?

A $\frac{5}{14}$
B $\frac{3}{14}$
(C) $\frac{3}{7}$
D $\frac{1}{2}$

10. A found probability of bus travelers
    (B) correct
    C found probability of car travelers
    D found probability of bikers

11. A doubled 13 miles; guess
    B multiplied 15 by 3; guess
    (C) correct
    D multiplied 13 by 15; guess

Federico can travel 270 miles on 9 gallons of gas. At this rate, how many miles can he travel on 5 gallons of gas?

A 30 miles
(C) 150 miles
B 120 miles
D 270 miles

Write a ratio that compares the number of faces to the number of hearts.

A 1 to 1
C 4 to 1
(B) 1 to 4
D 1 to 5

Mykia took a survey of the ways her classmates get to school. The results are shown in the table. Based on her survey, if a student from this class is asked at random, what is the probability that a student walks to school?

Form of Travel	Number of Responses
Bus	10
Car	6
Walk	5
Bike	4

A $\frac{2}{5}$
C $\frac{6}{25}$
(B) $\frac{1}{5}$
D $\frac{4}{25}$

11 A bird flew at 13 miles per hour for 2 hours. Then the bird flew at 15 miles per hour for 3 hours. How far did the bird fly in all?

A 26 miles
(C) 71 miles
B 45 miles
D 195 miles

ANSWER SHEET

Directions: Fill in the circle of each correct answer.

1	A	**B**	C	D
2	A	B	C	**D**
3	**A**	B	C	D
4	A	B	C	**D**
5	**A**	B	C	D
6	A	B	**C**	D
7	A	B	**C**	D
8	A	B	**C**	D
9	A	**B**	C	D
10	A	**B**	C	D
11	A	B	**C**	D

Success Strategy
Align your answers to the correct circles. Make sure you are filling in the correct bubble for each question. Hold your place as you read the questions with your finger, your pen, or a sheet of paper.

Diagnosing Student Errors and Misconceptions

Polls When working on the Test Practice problems, have students show their work on a separate sheet of notebook paper that can be used later as a reference as needed. After the class has completed the Test Practice problems, randomly solicit answers to each question. After each question, take an informal poll of how many students answered the question correctly. If you notice that a significant number of students missed a particular question or questions, then review the method or strategy behind the question with the entire class.

Common Error *Alert*

Eliminate Wrong Answers If students are not able to successfully eliminate wrong answer choices, they may need the corresponding reminder.

Exercise 6 There are two ways to do this. Students can find the unit rate of miles per day and then multiply it by 6. They may also set up a proportion and find the unknown. A likely mistake here may be that students only find the unit rate for miles per day.

Chapter 3

Chapter Overview

Chapter-at-a-Glance

Lesson	Math Objective	State/Local Standards
3-1 Introduction to Percents (pp.102-108)	Identify ratios as percents, decimals, and fractions.	
3-2 Percents, Fractions, and Decimals (pp.109-115)	Use the equivalencies of percents, fractions, and decimals.	
Progress Check (p. 116)		
3-3 Calculate Percents (pp.117-124)	Calculate with percents.	
3-4 Interpret Circle Graphs (pp.125-130)	Apply percentages to make and interpret circle graphs.	
Progress Check (p.131)		

Content-at-a-Glance

The diagram below summarizes and unpacks Chapter 3 content.

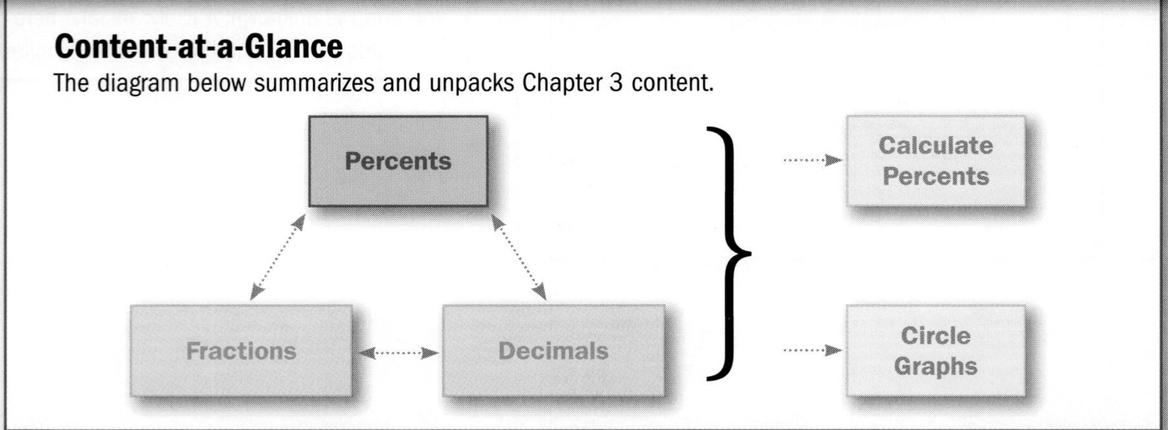

Online Assessment and Reporting
glencoe.com

Chapter Assessment Manager

Diagnostic — Diagnose students' readiness.

	Student Study Guide/ Teacher Edition	Assessment Masters	Technology
Course Placement Test		1	ExamView® Assessment Suite
Book 1 Pretest		23	ExamView® Assessment Suite
Chapter 3 Pretest		48	ExamView® Assessment Suite
Quiz/Preview	SSG 101		Math Online glencoe.com StudentWorks™ Plus

Formative — Identify students' misconceptions of content knowledge.

	Student Study Guide/ Teacher Edition	Assessment Masters	Technology
Progress Checks	SSG 116, 131		Math Online glencoe.com StudentWorks™ Plus
Vocabulary Review	SSG 132		Math Online glencoe.com
Lesson Assessments			ExamView® Assessment Suite
Are They Getting It?	TE 105, 112, 120, 128		Math Online glencoe.com

Summative — Determine student success in learning concepts in the lesson, chapter, or book.

	Student Study Guide/ Teacher Edition	Assessment Masters	Technology
Chapter 3 Test	SSG 136	51	ExamView® Assessment Suite
Test Practice	SSG 138	54	
Alternative Assessment	TE 136	57	ExamView® Assessment Suite
See It, Do It, Say It, Write It	TE 108, 115, 123, 130		
Book 1 Test		59	ExamView® Assessment Suite

Back-mapping and Vertical Alignment **McGraw-Hill's *Math Triumphs*** intervention program was conceived and developed with the final result in mind: student success in grade-level mathematics, including Algebra 1 and beyond. The authors, using the **NCTM Focal Points and Focal Connections** as their guide, developed this brand-new series by backmapping from grade-level and Algebra 1 concepts, and vertically aligning the topics so that they build upon prior skills and concepts and serve as a foundation for future topics.

Chapter Resource Manager

	Lesson 3-1	Lesson 3-2	Lesson 3-3	Lesson 3-4
Concept	Introduction to Percents	Percents, Fractions, and Decimals	Calculate Percents	Interpret Circle Graphs
Objective	Identify ratios as percents, decimals, and fractions.	Use the equivalencies of percents, fractions, and decimals.	Calculate with percents.	Apply percentages to make and interpret circle graphs.
Math Vocabulary	decimal equivalent fractions percent ratio	decimal equivalent fractions percent	percent ratio variable	circle graph sector
Lesson Resources	**Materials** • Money (100 pennies) **Manipulatives** • Base-ten blocks • Grid paper • Fraction circles **Other Resources** CRM Vocabulary and English Language Development CRM Skills Practice CRM Problem-Solving Practice CRM Homework Practice	**Materials** • Money **Manipulatives** • Base-ten blocks • Fraction tiles • Fraction circles • Grid paper **Other Resources** CRM Vocabulary and English Language Development CRM Skills Practice CRM Problem-Solving Practice CRM Homework Practice	**Materials** • Money **Manipulatives** • Counters • Grid paper **Other Resources** CRM Vocabulary and English Language Development CRM Skills Practice CRM Problem-Solving Practice CRM Homework Practice	**Materials** • Protractors **Manipulatives** • Fraction circles **Other Resources** CRM Vocabulary and English Language Development CRM Skills Practice CRM Problem-Solving Practice CRM Homework Practice
Technology	Math Online glencoe.com StudentWorks™ Plus ExamView® Assessment Suite	Math Online glencoe.com StudentWorks™ Plus ExamView® Assessment Suite	Math Online glencoe.com StudentWorks™ Plus ExamView® Assessment Suite	Math Online glencoe.com StudentWorks™ Plus ExamView® Assessment Suite

Intervention Strategy

Real-Word Data Displays

Analyzing circle graphs used in real-world applications will help students understand the usefulness of percents in everyday activities.

Step 1: Have students bring to the classroom circle graphs that they find in newspapers, magazines, other school textbooks, or other public media.

Step 2: Tell students to work in pairs or small groups.

Step 3: Begin by asking students how information can be obtained from their graphs. Guide them to clues such as the title, key, size of the sectors, categories within each sector, and percentages. Write their ideas on the board.

Step 4: Now ask each student group to work together and analyze their graphs. Tell them to create a numbered list with complete sentences of information their graph provides.

Step 5: When they are finished thoroughly analyzing each graph, tell them to summarize the usefulness of the information displayed by the graph and how their lives connect to it. Challenge them to think of any other type of display or table that would present the information as effectively.

Step 6: Have students share their ideas of alternative displays. Ask students why they think their alternative displays would be as or more effective representing the data.

Step 7: Allow each group a few minutes at the end of the class time to present their graphs, summarizing the information it contains, including how the data applies to their lives.

Chapter Notes

Real-World Applications

Chance of Precipitation The local news weather reporter will make a 5- or 7-day forecast of the weather to help you plan your week. He or she will usually include the high and low temperatures, the overall sky appearance (sunny, cloudy, rainy, snowy, partly sunny, and so on), and will also give a percentage. The percentage is a prediction of the chance of precipitation for that day. The higher the percentage, the higher the chance of precipitation. Have students listen to the weather report, then come to class with a model of the percent of precipitation forecast for the day.

Intervention Strategy

Place Percents, Fractions, and Decimals

Step 1 Divide students into small groups. Hand out 12 index cards to each group.

Step 2 Each group should write a different fraction, decimal, or percent on each of the index cards.

Step 3 As the groups write, divide the board into three areas marked as 0%, 50%, and 100%; 0.0, 0.5, and 1.0; or 0, $\frac{1}{2}$, and 1.

Step 4 Each group will take turns taping their index cards into the appropriate spots on the board (in between your benchmarks).

Step 5 After the cards are placed, have the class check their placement for accuracy.

Chapter 3

Percents

We use percents, fractions, and decimals to show values every day.

For example, you might earn a 97% on a test, learn in science class that $\frac{70}{100}$ of Earth's surface is covered with water, or need $0.75 to buy a snack.

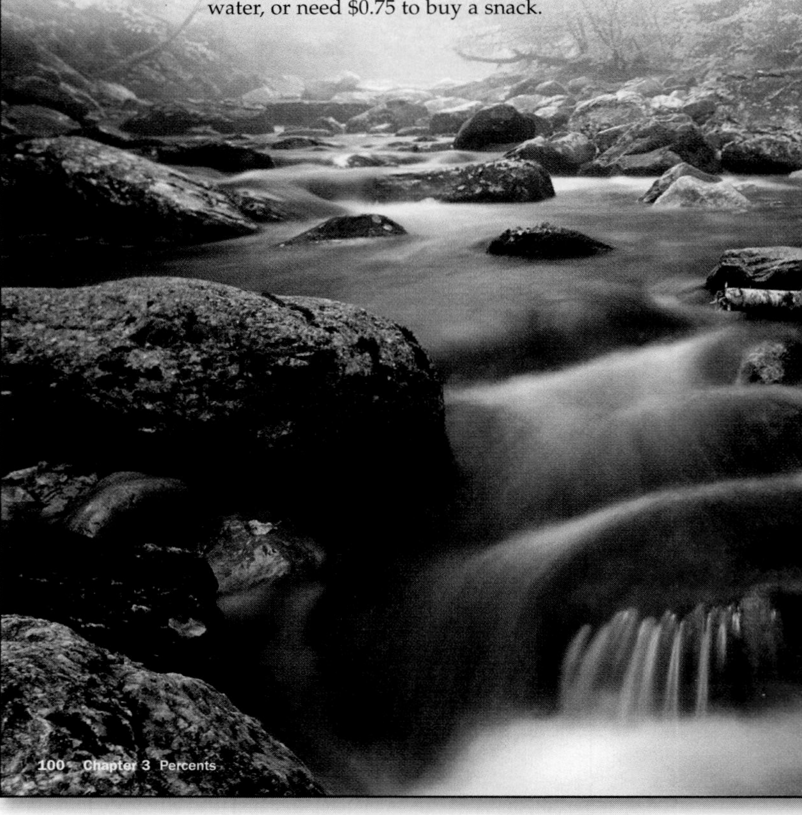

Key Vocabulary

Find interactive definitions in 13 languages in the **eGlossary** at glencoe.com.

English **Español** *Introduce the most important vocabulary terms from Chapter 3.*

circle graph **gráfico circular**

a graph used to compare parts of a whole; the circle represents the whole and is separated into parts of a whole (p. 125)

equivalent fractions **fracciones equivalentes**

fractions that name the same number (p. 102)

$\frac{1}{2} = \frac{5}{10}$

percent **por ciento**

a ratio that compares a number to 100 (p. 102)

80% means 80 out of 100

ratio **razón**

a comparison of two quantities by division (p. 102)

The ratio of 2 to 3 can be stated as 2 out of 3, 2 to 3, 2:3, or $\frac{2}{3}$.

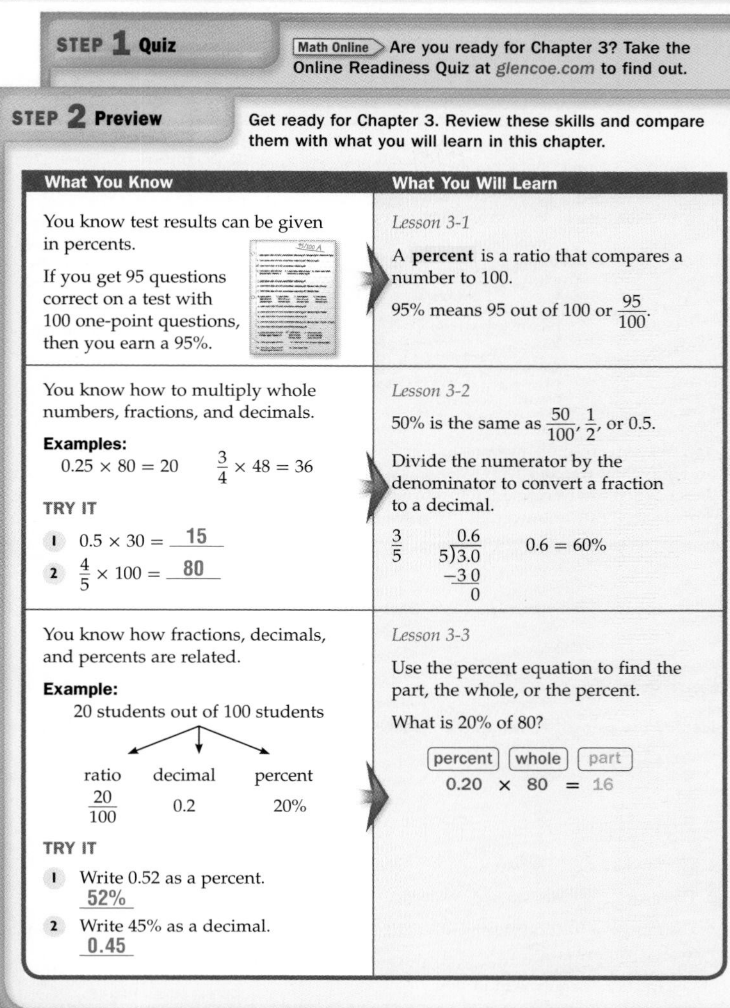

STEP 1 Quiz

Math Online Are you ready for Chapter 3? Take the Online Readiness Quiz at glencoe.com to find out.

STEP 2 Preview

Get ready for Chapter 3. Review these skills and compare them with what you will learn in this chapter.

What You Know	What You Will Learn
You know test results can be given in percents. If you get 95 questions correct on a test with 100 one-point questions, then you earn a 95%.	*Lesson 3-1* A **percent** is a ratio that compares a number to 100. 95% means 95 out of 100 or $\frac{95}{100}$.
You know how to multiply whole numbers, fractions, and decimals. **Examples:** $0.25 \times 80 = 20$ $\frac{3}{4} \times 48 = 36$ **TRY IT** 1 $0.5 \times 30 =$ 15 2 $\frac{4}{5} \times 100 =$ 80	*Lesson 3-2* 50% is the same as $\frac{50}{100}$, $\frac{1}{2}$, or 0.5. Divide the numerator by the denominator to convert a fraction to a decimal. $\frac{3}{5}$ $5\overline{)3.0}$ = 0.6, $-3\,0$, 0 $0.6 = 60\%$
You know how fractions, decimals, and percents are related. **Example:** 20 students out of 100 students ratio $\frac{20}{100}$ decimal 0.2 percent 20% **TRY IT** 1 Write 0.52 as a percent. 52% 2 Write 45% as a decimal. 0.45	*Lesson 3-3* Use the percent equation to find the part, the whole, or the percent. What is 20% of 80? percent × whole = part $0.20 \times 80 = 16$

101

Step 1 Quiz

Pretest/Prescribe Students can take the Online Readiness Quiz or the Diagnostic Pretest in the Assessment Masters.

Step 2 Preview

Use this pre-chapter activity to activate students' prior knowledge, build confidence, and help students preview the lessons.

Dinah Zike's Foldables®

Guide students through the directions on p. A47 in the Chapter Resource Masters to create their own Foldable graphic organizer for use with this chapter.

Home Connections

- Find five assignments or assessments in your math folder. Write the fraction of problems that you have correct and then find the percentage of each.

Vocabulary Preview

- As students complete the Chapter Preview, have them make a three-column table. In the first column, students should write the vocabulary term. In the second column, students should write what they think the word means. Then, as students read the chapter, they will fill in the third column with the true definition of the term.

Vocabulary Term	What I Think It Means	Definition

- Have a class discussion. Did students guess the definitions correctly? What clues did they use?

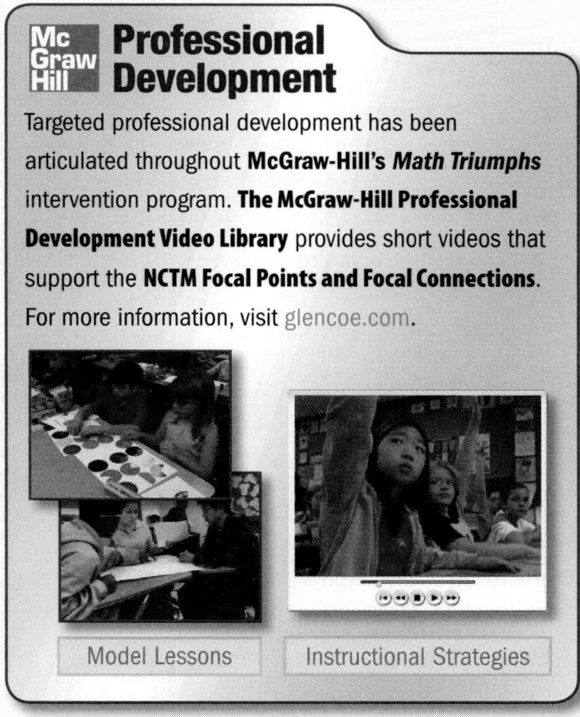

Professional Development

Targeted professional development has been articulated throughout **McGraw-Hill's *Math Triumphs*** intervention program. **The McGraw-Hill Professional Development Video Library** provides short videos that support the **NCTM Focal Points and Focal Connections**. For more information, visit glencoe.com.

Model Lessons

Instructional Strategies

Lesson 3-1

Lesson Notes

Lesson Planner

Objective Identify ratios as percents, decimals, and fractions.

Vocabulary **decimal**, **equivalent fractions**, **percent**, **ratio**

Materials/Manipulatives grid paper, base-ten blocks, fraction circles, 100 pennies

Chapter Resource Masters

- CRM Vocabulary and English Language Development (p. A50)
- CRM Skills Practice (p. A51)
- CRM Problem-Solving Practice (p. A52)
- CRM Homework Practice (p. A53)

Vocabulary

Ratios and Percents Explain that when the denominator of a ratio is 100, then the ratio can be written as a *percent*. For some students it is best to start by defining percents as a fraction with a denominator of 100. In the percent $\frac{x}{100}$, call it x percent and write x%.

Key Concept

Foundational Skills and Concepts After students have read through the Key Concept box, have them try these exercises.

1. Write 73 out of 100 as a percent, a fraction, and a decimal. 73%, $\frac{73}{100}$, and 0.73
2. How is a percent a ratio? It compares a number (the numerator) with 100 (the denominator).

Lesson 3-1

Introduction to Percents

KEY Concept

A **ratio** is a comparison of two numbers by division.
A **percent** is a ratio that compares a number to 100. A percent is written using the percent symbol: %.

Percents can also be written as fractions or decimals.

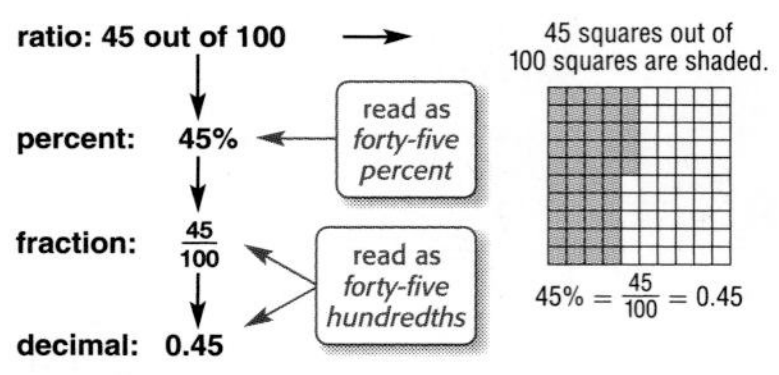

You can convert some fractions to percents by finding an **equivalent fraction** with a denominator of 100.
Any fraction can be converted to a decimal using division.
Any decimal can be converted to a percent.

VOCABULARY

decimal
numbers that have digits in the tenths place and beyond

equivalent fractions
fractions that name the same number

percent
a ratio that compares a number to 100

ratio
a comparison of two quantities by division; the ratio of 2 to 3 can be stated as 2 out of 3, 2 to 3, 2:3, or $\frac{2}{3}$

You can use models to show percents, fractions, and decimals.

Example 1

Identify the percent shown in the model.

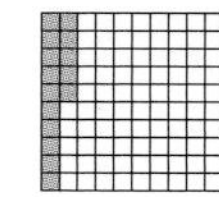

1. The model has 100 squares.
2. There are 15 squares shaded.
3. The ratio as a fraction of shaded squares to total squares is $\frac{15}{100}$.
4. The fraction is equivalent to 15%.

YOUR TURN!

Identify the percent shown in the model.

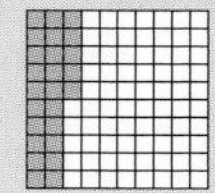

1. The model has __100__ squares.
2. There are __25__ squares shaded.
3. The ratio as a fraction of shaded squares to total squares is $\frac{25}{100}$.
4. The fraction is equivalent to __25%__.

102 Chapter 3 Percents

Additional *Example 1*

Identify the percent shown in the model.

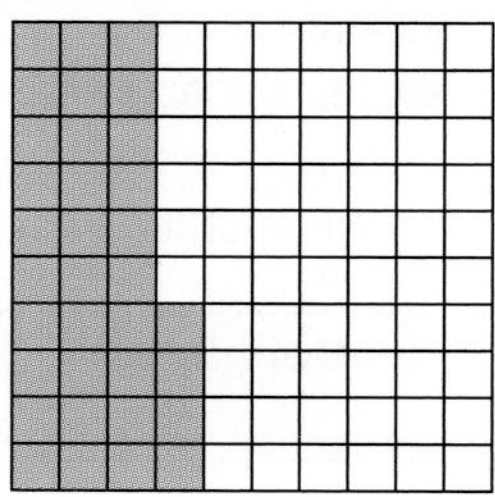

1. The model has 100 squares.
2. There are 34 squares shaded.
3. The ratio as a fraction of shaded squares to total squares is $\frac{34}{100}$.
4. The fraction is equivalent to 34%.

xample 2

By the time a child reaches the age of 16 years, about 39% of his or her life has been spent sleeping. Write this percent as a fraction with 100 in the denominator and as a decimal.

1. To write 39% as a fraction, drop the percent sign. Then write a fraction with 39 in the numerator and 100 in the denominator.

$\frac{39}{100}$

2. To write the fraction as a decimal, divide 39 by 100.

0.39

Remember, to divide by 100, move the decimal point of the dividend two places to the left.

YOUR TURN!

Ruby works as an office manager. Her company recently moved to a new building with 133% more square feet of space. Write this percent as a fraction with 100 in the denominator and as a decimal.

1. Write 133% as a fraction.

$\frac{133}{100}$

2. Write 133% as a decimal.

1.33

ho is Correct?

rite 20% as a decimal.

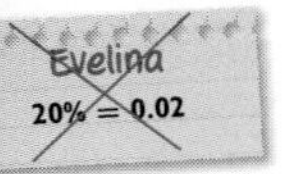

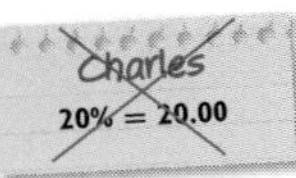

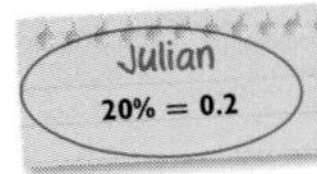

rcle correct answer(s). Cross out incorrect answer(s).

Guided Practice

entify the percent shown in each model.

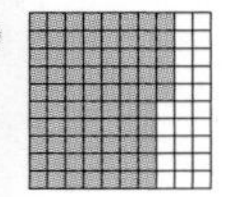

75%

2 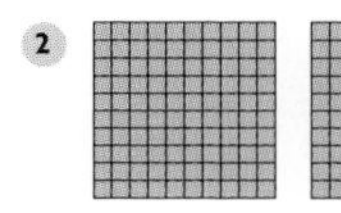

150%

GO ON

Lesson 3-1 Introduction to Percents 103

Additional *Example 2*

In Roy's school, 65% of the students visit the library at least once per week. Write this percent as a fraction with 100 in the denominator and as a decimal.

1. To write 65% as a fraction, drop the percent sign, then write a fraction with 65 in the numerator and 100 in the denominator. $\frac{65}{100}$
2. To write the fraction as a decimal, divide 65 by 100. 0.65

Using Manipulatives

Base-Ten Blocks Represent Example 2 with base-ten blocks.

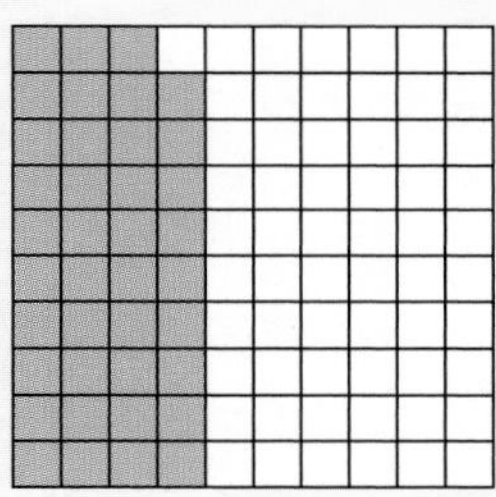

Fraction Circles Students can learn to recognize different percents of a whole using fraction circles.

On-Hand Manipulatives Use money to show percents. Since there are 100 pennies in a dollar, use the dollar as a whole.

Who *is Correct?*

Diagnostic Teaching

- Evelina wrote 0.02. This is incorrect. The decimal was moved too many places.
- Charles wrote 20.00. This is incorrect. He did not move the decimal. He only dropped the percent sign.
- Julian wrote 0.2. This is correct.

Math Coach Notes

Strategies

1. Begin this activity by using grid paper or base-ten blocks. Represent different ratios using 100 as the whole. Connect the lesson to ratios, and then to a special kind of ratio called percents. Have students practice writing ratios as fractions, with the percent symbol, and then as decimals. Talk about equivalency.
2. Spend some time focusing on common percents, such as 50% and 25%. Students can use these as benchmarks for later lessons.

Step by Step Practice

3 Write 40% as a fraction with 100 in the denominator and as a decimal.

Step 1 Write 40% as a fraction.

$\frac{40}{100}$

Step 2 Write 40% as a decimal.

0.40

Write each ratio as a percent. Then write the ratio as a fraction with 100 in the denominator and as a decimal.

4 a student club with 100 students; 56 are girls

percent: $\frac{56}{100}$ = 56 %

fraction: $\frac{56}{100}$

decimal: 0.56

5 a pack of 100 crayons; 52 are broken

percent: $\frac{52}{100}$ = 52 %

fraction: $\frac{52}{100}$

decimal: 0.52

104 **Chapter 3** Percents

English Learner Strategy

Create a Graphic Organizer Have students write 25% and circle it on the center of a sheet of paper. Then tell them to think of other ways to represent 25%. The first choice might be using a base-ten flat. Other representations could be grid paper, a quarter, the fraction $\frac{25}{100}$, the fraction $\frac{1}{4}$, the decimal 0.25, and a drawing of 4 counters with 1 shaded. Students can draw these ideas in a circle around the percent with a ray from the center to the percent. Repeat this with different percents.

'rite each ratio as a percent. Then write the ratio as a fraction with
)0 in the denominator and as a decimal.

100 pets at an animal shelter; 25 are dogs

percent: 25%

fraction: $\frac{25}{100}$

decimal: 0.25

a bookcase with 100 books; 37 are graphic novels

percent: 37%

fraction: $\frac{37}{100}$

decimal: 0.37

'rite each percent as a fraction with 100 in the denominator and
a decimal.

14% $\frac{14}{100}$; 0.14

9 8% $\frac{8}{100}$; 0.08

65% $\frac{65}{100}$; 0.65

11 98% $\frac{98}{100}$; 0.98

72% $\frac{72}{100}$; 0.72

13 43% $\frac{43}{100}$; 0.43

GO ON

Note This!

Prior Knowledge Students who connect with the material are more likely to understand and remember it. Encourage students to list instances in which they have used or encountered percents.

Are They Getting It?

Check students' understanding of percents by writing these problems on the board. Ask students to point out wrong answers and explain why they are wrong.

1. This figure shows 60%. This is incorrect. The figure shows 70%.

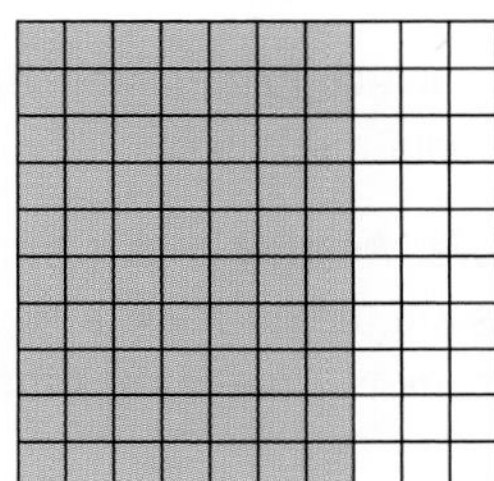

2. 116% written as a decimal is 11.60 This is incorrect. The decimal is 1.16.

3. The model represents 30%. This is correct.

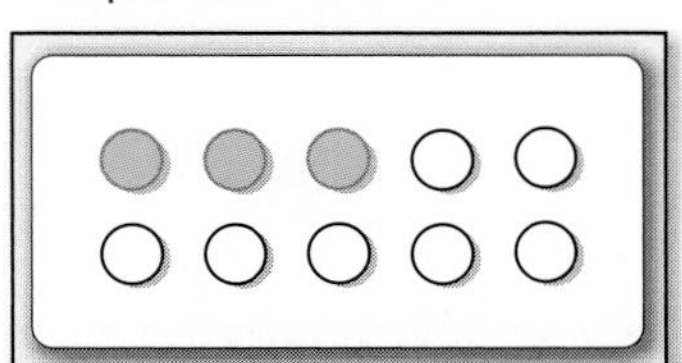

4. 40% written as a fraction is $\frac{4}{100}$. This is incorrect. The correct fraction is $\frac{40}{100}$ or $\frac{2}{5}$.

Intervention Strategy

Linguistic/ Kinesthetic/ Visual Learners

Real-World Examples Have students collect examples of percents from magazines, advertisement circulars, and newspapers. For example, a store advertisement ("40% off coats"), a bank loan ("6.5% introductory rate"), skin care ad ("15% fewer wrinkles"), and so on. Students can create a collage of their percent examples.

Note This!

Practice In application problems, students will need to convert percents into decimals or fractions. Encourage students to write the decimal equivalent of each percent for each exercise. If they do this while in class, they can check their answers before leaving.

Step by Step Problem-Solving Practice

Problem-Solving Strategies
- ☑ Use a table.
- ☐ Look for a pattern.
- ☐ Guess and check.
- ☐ Act it out.
- ☐ Write an equation.

Solve.

14 MUSIC In Kareem's class, 32% of the students like country music, 43% like hip-hop music, and 25% like rock music. Write each percent as a fraction with 100 in the denominator and as a decimal. What type of music did Kareem's class like the most?

Understand Read the problem. Write what you know. In Kareem's class, 32% of the students like country music, 43% like hip-hop music, and 25% like rock music.

Plan Pick a strategy. One strategy is to use a table.

Solve Complete the table to write each percent as a fraction with 100 in the denominator and as a decimal.

Write the fraction as a decimal, divide the percent by 100.

Music	Percent	Fraction	Decimal
Country	32%	$\frac{32}{100}$	0.32
Hip-Hop	43%	$\frac{43}{100}$	0.43
Rock	25%	$\frac{25}{100}$	0.25

Kareem's class liked hip-hop music the most.

Check Add all three fractions. The sum should equal $\frac{100}{100}$.

15 DOGS In 2005, 15% of dogs registered with the American Kennel Club were Labrador retrievers. About 39% were German shepherds. Write each percent as a fraction with 100 in the denominator and as a decimal. Check off each step.

✔ Understand: I underlined key words.

✔ Plan: To solve the problem, I will use a table

✔ Solve: The answer is $\frac{15}{100}$; 0.15 Labrador retrievers, $\frac{39}{100}$; 0.39 German shepherd

✔ Check: I checked my answer by using a 100 square to model each percent

Intervention Strategy

Auditory/Naturalist Learners

Percent Memory Students can play individually or in teams. Make a memory game on the board. Write different representations of the same percent on index cards and tape them facedown to the front board or wall. Number them consecutively. For example, you might write 0.04 and 4%, 0.23 and $\frac{23}{100}$, and so on. Make certain there is a pair of cards of each correct answer. You might want to write a key for the final arrangement on paper.

One index card is turned over. Another card is turned to see if there is a match. If not, both cards are turned back. If there is, pull the cards off and give them to the student. Whoever has the most pairs at the end of the game wins.

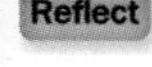 **BASKETBALL** In one basketball season, Alana made 48 out of 100 baskets. In the same season, Tess made 59 out of 100 baskets. Write the ratios as percents.

Alana made 48%; Tess made 59%

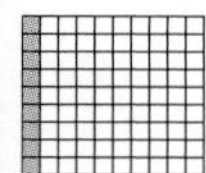 Name the decimal, percent, and fraction shown in the model. Explain your answer.

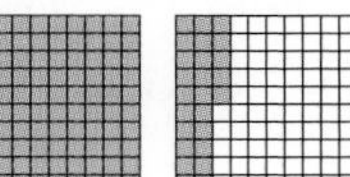

0.1; 10%; $\frac{1}{10}$; 1 of 10 is shaded, which equals $\frac{1}{10}$. Both the decimal and fraction are read as one-tenth. One-tenth equals 10%.

Skills, Concepts, and Problem Solving

entify the percent shown in each model.

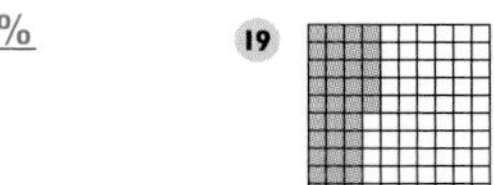 125%

19 35%

rite each ratio as a percent. Then write the ratio as a fraction with)0 in the denominator and as a decimal.

baseball league with 100 players; 60 are girls

percent: 60%

fraction: $\frac{60}{100}$

decimal: 0.60

21 a puzzle with 100 pieces; 12 are blue

percent: 12%

fraction: $\frac{12}{100}$

decimal: 0.12

Math Challenge

Decimals to Fractions Give one student in a student pair a list of decimals. That student will read off the decimals as the other student writes down the decimal and the fraction over 100. Now give the other student a list of percents. The first student will write the decimal for the percents as they are read.

Odd/Even Assignments

Exercises 18–29 are structured so that students practice the same concepts whether they are assigned the odd or even problems.

In-Class Assignment

Have students complete Exercises 18, 20, 23, 28, and 33 to ensure that they understand the concept.

Intervention Strategy — Auditory Learners

Say and Write Recite different numbers. Have students write the number in the form it is read. The number would then be written as a percent, decimal, or fraction. For example, if you say "56%," the student would write 56%. If you say "0.26," the student would write 0.26. Discuss the responses.

Math Coach Notes

Model Percents Use base-ten blocks or grid paper to show 100 units. What is 50%? 50 Then show 50 blocks. What is 50% now? 25 Guide students to see that the same percent, in this case 50%, represents different numbers depending on how many items are in the set.

See It, Do It, Say It, Write It

Step 1 Write 17% on the board. Ask students for help as you write the fraction, then the decimal. Do this with percents that cannot be reduced and then percents, such as 16%, that can be written in simplest form.

Step 2 Have students work in pairs. Give them each a percent or decimal. Tell them to model the number and then write two other equivalents, either fraction and decimal or percent and fraction. Students can present their work to the class.

Step 3 Discuss ratios and percents. Practice writing equivalent fractions by dividing or multiplying by forms of one.

Step 4 Write 0.70, 0.07, $\frac{7}{100}$, 70%, 7%, and $\frac{7}{10}$ on the board. Ask students to match the equivalent numbers. Then tell them to write about the relationship between ratios and percents, and between percents, fractions, and decimals.

Looking Ahead: Pre-teach

Percents, Fractions, and Decimals In the next lesson, students will learn about percents, fractions, and decimals. To convert a fraction to a decimal and a percent, divide the numerator by the denominator.

Example

Write $\frac{1}{4}$ as a percent and as a decimal.

$$\frac{1}{4} = 4\overline{)1.00} = 25\%$$

(quotient 0.25; work: 8, 20)

Have students write each fraction as a percent and decimal.

1. $\frac{1}{5}$ 0.2; 20%
2. $\frac{4}{5}$ 0.8; 80%
3. $\frac{9}{10}$ 0.9; 90%

Write each percent as a fraction with 100 in the denominator and as a decimal.

22 16% $\frac{16}{100}$; 0.16

23 75% $\frac{75}{100}$; 0.75

24 80% $\frac{80}{100}$; 0.8

25 50% $\frac{50}{100}$; 0.5

26 150% $\frac{150}{100}$; 1.5

27 112% $\frac{112}{100}$; 1.12

Solve.

28 EDUCATION In the eighth-grade class of 100 students, 21 students have A's in math. Write the ratio of A students to total students as a percent. Then write the ratio as a fraction with 100 in the denominator and as a decimal.

21%; $\frac{21}{100}$; 0.21

29 FOOD The cafeteria kept track of the food selections of 100 students. The results are shown in the table at the right. Write each percent as a decimal.

Food	Percent of Students
Chicken	14%
Taco	26%
Pasta	20%
Pizza	40%

Chicken = 0.14, Taco = 0.26, Pasta = 0.20,

Pizza = 0.40

Vocabulary Check **Write the vocabulary word that completes each sentence.**

30 A(n) percent is a ratio that compares a number to 100.

31 A(n) ratio is a comparison of two quantities by division.

32 Fractions that name the same number are equivalent fractions.

33 **Writing in Math** To write a percent as a decimal, you can write the percent as a fraction with a denominator of 100. For example, $35\% = \frac{35}{100} = 0.35$. So, 35 divided by 100 is 0.35.

How can you write a decimal as a percent using multiplication?

Since multiplication is the inverse of division, instead of dividing 35 by 100, multiply the quotient, 0.35 by 100 to get the dividend. $0.35 \times 100 = 35\%$

STOP

108 Chapter 3 Percents

Ticket Out the Door

Fraction Circle Draw a fraction circle on the board (see models below). Divide the parts and label them as percents, decimals, or fractions. Make certain the sum is 100%. Tell students to draw three circles on paper. Tell them to rewrite the graphs using just percents, just fractions, and just decimals. Students will turn in their work as they exit the classroom. Students can work in pairs or in small groups, if desired.

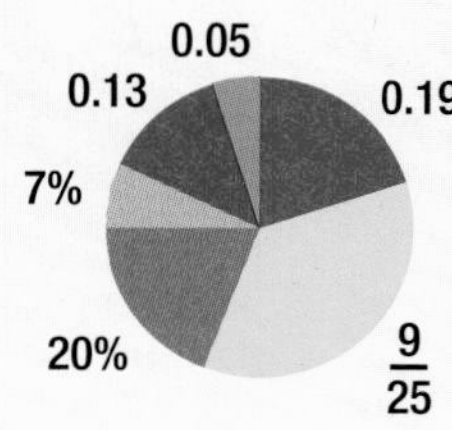

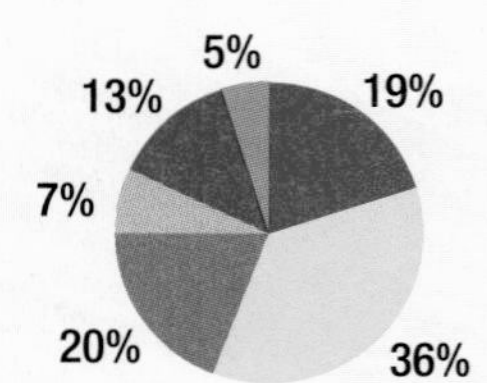

Lesson 3-2

Percents, Fractions, and Decimals

KEY Concept

A fraction in simplest form has a numerator and denominator that do not have a common factor. Recall that to write fractions in simplest form, you have to divide the numerator and denominator by their greatest common factor (GCF).

Half of all percents, when written as a fraction with 100 in the denominator, can be reduced.

An even number and 100 have a common factor of at least 2.

$34\% = \frac{34}{100} = \frac{34 \div 2}{100 \div 2} = \frac{17}{50}$ $50\% = \frac{50}{100} = \frac{50 \div 50}{100 \div 50} = \frac{1}{2}$

When you convert a fraction to a decimal and a percent, divide the numerator by the denominator.

$\frac{4}{5}$ $5\overline{)4.0}$ = 0.8; −40; 0 $0.8 = 80\%$

VOCABULARY

decimal numbers that have digits in the tenths place and beyond

equivalent fractions fractions that name the same number

percent a ratio that compares a number to 100

or percents that are commonly used, you should become familiar with e equivalent decimals and fractions in simplest form.

Example 1

Write 8% as a decimal and as a fraction in simplest form.

1. The % sign means *out of 100*. Write 8% as a fraction using this definition.
   $8\% = \frac{8}{100}$
2. $\frac{8}{100}$ is read as *8 hundredths*.
   Write this as a decimal.
   0.08
3. Simplify the fraction, if possible.
   $\frac{8 \div 4}{100 \div 4} = \frac{2}{25}$

YOUR TURN!

Write 115% as a decimal and as a fraction in simplest form.

1. Write 115% as a fraction.
   $115\% = \frac{115}{100}$ or $1\frac{15}{100}$
2. $1\frac{15}{100}$ is read as *1 and 15 hundredths*.
   Write this as a decimal. 1.15
3. Simplify the fraction, if possible.
   $1\frac{15}{100} = 1\frac{15 \div 5}{100 \div 5} = 1\frac{3}{20}$

GO ON

Lesson 3-2 Percents, Fractions, and Decimals 109

Additional Example 1

Write 6% as a decimal and as a fraction in simplest form.

1. The % sign means *out of 100*. Write 6% as a fraction using this definition.
   $6\% = \frac{6}{100}$
2. $\frac{6}{100}$ is read as *6 hundredths*. Write this as a decimal. 0.06
3. Simplify the fraction, if possible.
   $\frac{6}{100} = \frac{6 \div 2}{100 \div 2} = \frac{3}{50}$

Lesson Notes

Lesson 3-2

Lesson Planner

Objective Use the equivalencies of percents, fractions, and decimals.

Vocabulary **decimal**, **equivalent fractions**, **percent**

Materials/Manipulatives money, base-ten blocks, grid paper, fraction tiles, fraction circles

Chapter Resource Masters

- CRM Vocabulary and English Language Development (p. A54)
- CRM Skills Practice (p. A55)
- CRM Problem-Solving Practice (p. A56)
- CRM Homework Practice (p. A57)

Vocabulary

Vocabulary Usage Remind students that a percent is a ratio of a number to 100. Have students describe a model of each of the following in a different way.

Answers will vary.

10% A dime is 10% of a dollar.

0.18 18 blocks in a base-ten flat is 18 hundredths.

Key Concept

Foundational Skills and Concepts After students have read through the Key Concept box, have them try these exercises.

1. Write 75% as a decimal and a fraction. 0.75, $\frac{3}{4}$
2. Write 60% as a fraction. $\frac{60}{100}$
3. Write $\frac{80}{100}$ in simplest form. $\frac{4}{5}$

Additional **Example 2**

Write $\frac{4}{5}$ as a percent and as a decimal.

1. Identify the denominator. 5
2. What number multiplied by 5 is 100? 20
3. Write a fraction with a denominator of 20 that is equivalent to 1. $\frac{20}{20}$
4. Multiply $\frac{4}{5}$ by $\frac{20}{20}$ to obtain a fraction with a denominator of 100.
   $\frac{4}{5} \times \frac{20}{20} = \frac{4 \times 20}{5 \times 20} = \frac{80}{100}$
5. Write the fraction as a percent and as a decimal.
   $\frac{4}{5} = \frac{80}{100} = 80\%$
   $\frac{4}{5} = \frac{80}{100} = 0.80$

Additional **Example 3**

Write $\frac{1}{5}$ as a decimal and as a percent.

1. Divide to write the fraction as a decimal.
   $\frac{1}{5} = 5\overline{)1.0}$ = 0.2; −1 0; 0
2. Write the decimal as a percent by moving the decimal point two places to the right and adding a % sign.
   $\frac{1}{5} = 0.20 = 20\%$

Example 2

Write $\frac{3}{5}$ as a percent and as a decimal.

1. Identify the denominator. **5**
2. What number multiplied by 5 is 100? **20**
3. Write a fraction with a denominator of 20 that is equivalent to 1. $\frac{20}{20}$
4. Multiply $\frac{3}{5}$ by $\frac{20}{20}$ to obtain a fraction with a denominator of 100.
   $\frac{3}{5} \times \frac{20}{20} = \frac{3 \times 20}{5 \times 20} = \frac{60}{100}$
5. Write the fraction as a percent and as a decimal.
   $\frac{3}{5} = \frac{60}{100} = 60\%$ $\frac{3}{5} = \frac{60}{100} = 0.60$

To write 0.60 as a percent, you can move the decimal point two places to the right and add a % symbol. 0.60 = 60%

YOUR TURN!

Write $\frac{3}{4}$ as a percent and as a decimal.

1. Identify the denominator. 4
2. What number multiplied by 4 is 100? 25
3. Write a fraction with a denominator of 25 that is equivalent to 1. $\frac{25}{25}$
4. Multiply $\frac{3}{4}$ by $\frac{25}{25}$ to obtain a fraction with a denominator of 100.
   $\frac{3}{4} \times \frac{25}{25} = \frac{3 \times 25}{4 \times 25} = \frac{75}{100}$
5. Write the fraction as a percent and as a decimal.
   $\frac{3}{4} = \frac{75}{100} = 75\%$ $\frac{3}{4} = \frac{75}{100} = 0.75$

Example 3

Write $\frac{1}{8}$ as a decimal and as a percent.

1. Divide to write the fraction as a decimal.
   Read $\frac{1}{8}$ as *1 divided by 8.*
   $\frac{1}{8} \rightarrow 8\overline{)1.000}$ = 0.125; − 8; 20; − 16; 40; − 40; 0
2. Write the decimal as a percent by moving the decimal point two places to the right and adding a % sign.
   $\frac{1}{8} = 0.125 = 12.5\%$

YOUR TURN!

Write $\frac{5}{8}$ as a decimal and as a percent.

1. Divide to write the fraction as a decimal.
   Read $\frac{5}{8}$ as *5 divided by 8.*
   $\frac{5}{8} \rightarrow 8\overline{)5.000}$ = 0.625; − 48; 20; − 16; 40; − 40; 0
2. Write the decimal as a percent by moving the decimal point two places to the right and adding a % sign.
   $\frac{5}{8} = 0.625 = 62.5\%$

110 Chapter 3 Percents

English Learner Strategy

Guiding Questions Use base-ten blocks as models and ask the following questions.

- Show 50% of the blocks.
- Use 1 flat. What part is 25%?
- Show 75% of the blocks. Write this as a decimal.
- Use 1 flat. What part is 80%?

Who is Correct?

Write $\frac{1}{16}$ as a decimal.

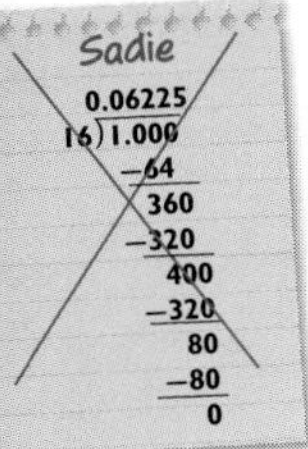

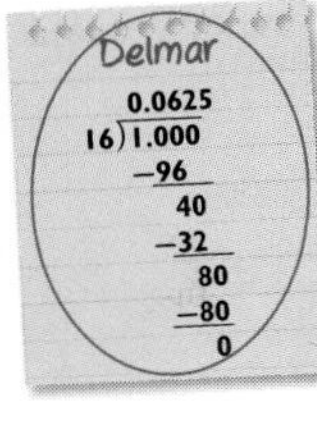

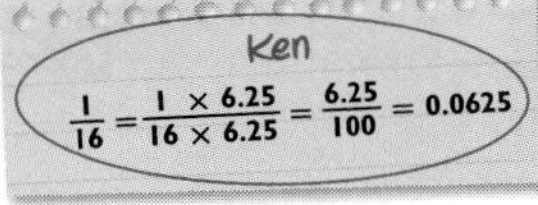

Ken
$\frac{1}{16} = \frac{1 \times 6.25}{16 \times 6.25} = \frac{6.25}{100} = 0.0625$

Circle correct answer(s). Cross out incorrect answer(s).

 **Guided Practice**

Write each percent as a fraction or mixed number in simplest form and as a decimal.

1 $4\% = \frac{4}{100} =$ 0.04

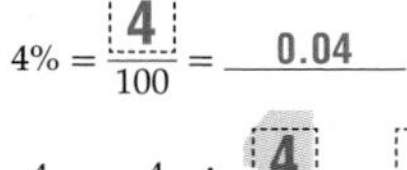

$\frac{4}{100} = \frac{4 \div 4}{100 \div 4} = \frac{1}{25}$

2 $16\% = \frac{16}{100} =$ 0.16

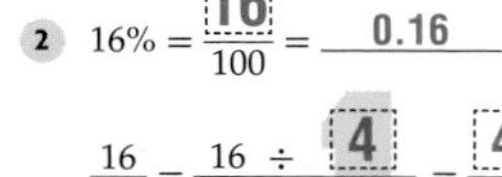

$\frac{16}{100} = \frac{16 \div 4}{100 \div 4} = \frac{4}{25}$

Step by Step Practice

3 Write $\frac{5}{16}$ as a percent and as a decimal.

Step 1 Divide 5 by 16.

Step 2 To write as a percent, move the decimal point two places to the right and add the percent sign.

0.3125 = 31.25%

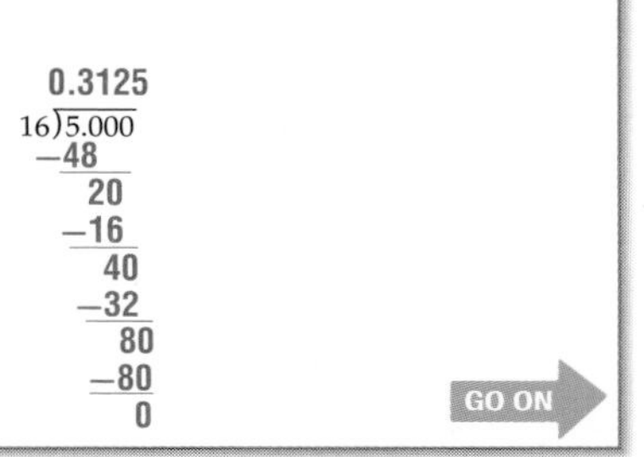

Who *is Correct?*

Diagnostic Teaching

- Sadie divided 1 by 16; however, she made a computational error. Her answer is not correct.
- Delmar divided 1 by 16 to get 0.0625. His answer is correct.
- Ken multiplied the numerator and denominator by an equivalent form of one to get 100 as a denominator. His answer is correct.

Remind students that when they are given a fraction to convert to a decimal and a percent, they need to divide the numerator by the denominator.

Math Coach Notes

Strategies

1. Begin this lesson using fraction strips or circles to represent common percents. Have students practice writing the percents in decimal and fraction form.
2. If students have a difficult time understanding the percents, begin with half. This is a concept most students can understand. Divide half into half, and you have a fourth. Use different models, including number lines and money, to represent these percents.
3. Make certain to connect to the past lesson. Sometimes students learn lessons in isolation; it is important to continually remind students of what they have already learned.

Using Manipulatives

Fraction Tiles Represent Example 3 with fraction tiles. Bars can be cut from paper if a set is not available.

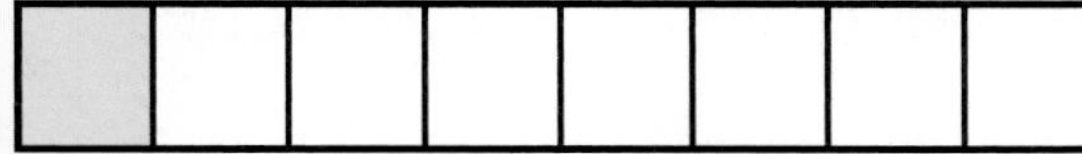

Fraction Circles Students can learn to recognize percents using fraction circles.

On-Hand Manipulatives Use money to show percents. Since there are 100 pennies in a dollar, use the dollar as a whole. Use coins to represent percents as fractions and decimals. For example, a dime represents $\frac{10}{100}$ or 0.1.

Math Coach Notes

Study Tip Have students make flashcards with common fraction, decimal, and percent equivalents. Have them practice with fraction equivalents of the percents, and then with the decimal equivalents. Eventually, mix them all up and randomly have students quiz each other.

Write each fraction as a decimal and as a percent.

4. $\frac{8}{25}$ 0.32; 32%

5. $\frac{2}{25}$ 0.08; 8%

6. $\frac{6}{32}$ 0.1875; 18.75%

7. $\frac{7}{16}$ 0.4375; 43.75%

Step by Step Problem-Solving Practice

Problem-Solving Strategies
- ☐ Use a table.
- ☐ Look for a pattern.
- ☐ Guess and check.
- ☑ Use logical reasoning.
- ☐ Work backward.

Solve.

8. CHEMISTRY During a chemistry experiment, Madela filled four beakers with different amounts of liquid. She must mark each beaker with the percent of liquid with which it was filled. How should she mark the beakers?

Understand Read the problem. Write what you know.
The beakers must be marked with a percent.

Plan Pick a strategy. Two strategies are to look for a pattern and use logical reasoning.

Solve Look at the first beaker. How full is it? completely

How does the second beaker compare to the first one?
It is half full.

How does the third beaker compare with the second one?
It is half as full.

How does the fourth beaker compare with the other three beakers?
It is halfway between the first and second beakers. This means it is 75% full.

Label each beaker with the correct percent, fraction, and decimal.

	1	2	3	4
Percent:	100%	50%	25%	75%
Fraction:	$\frac{1}{1}$	$\frac{1}{2}$	$\frac{1}{4}$	$\frac{3}{4}$
Decimal:	1	0.5	0.25	0.75

Check Is the greatest percent under the beaker with the greatest amount of liquid? Is the least percent under the beaker with the least amount of liquid?

112 Chapter 3 Percents

Are They Getting It?

Check students' understanding of percents, fractions, and decimals by writing these problems on the board. Ask students to point out wrong answers and explain why they are wrong.

1. The decimal form of 75% is 0.75. This is correct.
2. $\frac{14}{100}$ written as a percent is 140%. This is not correct. $\frac{14}{100} = 14\%$
3. 20% written as a fraction is $\frac{1}{5}$. This is correct.
4. To convert a fraction to a decimal, you divide the denominator by the numerator. This is not correct. To convert a fraction to a decimal, you divide the numerator by the denominator.

9 MOVIES The table shows student responses to a survey about the students' favorite types of movies. There were 100 responses. What fraction of students chose action films as their favorite type of movie?

Favorite Types of Movies	% of Students
Animated	50%
Action	25%
Foreign	12.5%
Science Fiction	12.5%

Check off each step.

✔ Understand: I underlined the key words.

✔ Plan: To solve the problem, I will use a table.

✔ Solve: The answer is $\frac{1}{4}$ of the students chose action films.

✔ Check: I checked my answer by working backward.

10 **Reflect** When you change a percent to a decimal, you move the decimal point two place values to the left. Why is it always two places?

Percent means "out of 100." When you divide by 100, the decimal point moves two places to the left.

Skills, Concepts, and Problem Solving

Write each percent as a fraction or mixed number in simplest form and as a decimal.

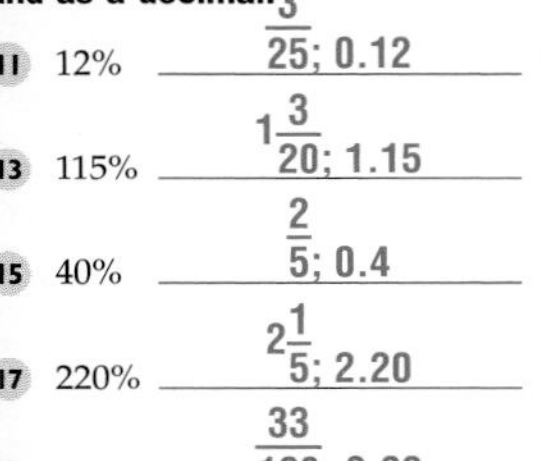

11 12% $\frac{3}{25}$; 0.12

12 6% $\frac{3}{50}$; 0.06

13 115% $1\frac{3}{20}$; 1.15

14 130% $1\frac{3}{10}$; 1.30

15 40% $\frac{2}{5}$; 0.4

16 75% $\frac{3}{4}$; 0.75

17 220% $2\frac{1}{5}$; 2.20

18 3% $\frac{3}{100}$; 0.03

19 33% $\frac{33}{100}$; 0.33

20 125% $1\frac{1}{4}$; 1.25

GO ON

Lesson 3-2 Percents, Fractions, and Decimals 113

Intervention Strategy — Interpersonal/Kinesthetic/Visual Learners

Create Discount Ads Have students pretend that they work for a retail store. They can choose the type of store, such as a grocery, sporting goods, or card store. Instruct students to create an advertisement that incorporates as many percents as possible. For example, they may create an ad that has baseball gloves for 50% off. Students can post their work in the classroom.

Note This!

Represent Numbers During the lesson, have students choose a percent, decimal, or fraction. Tell them to represent the number in all three forms (percent, fraction, and decimal). Then, instruct students to draw a picture that represents the number. For example, 75% could be represented by a circle that is 75% shaded.

Intervention Strategy — Interpersonal Learners

Budgets Have students work in small groups. Give each group $100 in play money to budget on entertainment, food, clothing, savings, and so on. Discuss how they could use fractions and percents to describe their budgets.

Odd/Even Assignments

Exercises 11–37 are structured so that students practice the same concepts whether they are assigned the odd or even problems.

In-Class Assignment

Have students complete Exercises 11, 17, 21, 27, 33, 37, and 40 to ensure that they understand the concept.

Intervention Strategy — Logical Learners

Birthday Percents Have students separate into groups according to the month they were born. Each group can estimate the percent of the class that their group makes.

Common Error *Alert*

Multi-Step Problem If students have difficulty with Exercise 37, have them break the problem into steps.

Step 1 Find the total parts.

Step 2 Write the fractional part made up by peanuts.

Step 3 Convert the fraction to a percent.

Step 4 Then find the fractional part made up by raisins.

Write each fraction as a decimal and as a percent.

21 $\frac{1}{3}$ $0.\overline{3}$; 33.3%

22 $\frac{2}{3}$ $0.\overline{6}$; 66.7%

23 $\frac{3}{2}$ 1.5; 150%

24 $\frac{9}{4}$ 2.25; 225%

25 $\frac{3}{5}$ 0.6; 60%

26 $\frac{5}{8}$ 0.625; 62.5%

27 $\frac{23}{10}$ 2.3; 230%

28 $\frac{5}{6}$ $0.8\overline{3}$; 83.3%

29 $\frac{3}{4}$ 0.75; 75%

30 $\frac{8}{5}$ 1.6; 160%

Write each percent as a fraction and decimal to complete this chart of common percents.

	Percent	Meaning	Fraction	Decimal
31	10%	10 out of 100	$\frac{1}{10}$	0.1
32	20%	20 out of 100	$\frac{1}{5}$	0.2
33	25%	25 out of 100	$\frac{1}{4}$	0.25
34	50%	50 out of 100	$\frac{1}{2}$	0.5
35	75%	75 out of 100	$\frac{3}{4}$	0.75

Solve.

36 PARTY Harrison is making punch for a party that is $\frac{2}{5}$ pineapple juice. What percent of the punch is pineapple juice?

40% is pineapple juice

37 SNACKS Justin is making trail mix. The recipe says 2 parts crunchy cereal, 1 part peanuts, 1 part raisins, and 1 part pretzels. What fraction of the mix is peanuts? What percent of the mix is raisins?

$\frac{1}{5}$ is peanuts; 20% is raisins

Math Challenge

From Memory Ask students to write as many fractions, decimals, and percents as they can. For each number listed, students should write it as a fraction, decimal, and percent. The longer a student's list, the better prepared he or she is. Students who are unable to list many numbers and their equivalencies should plan study time to commit these to memory.

ocabulary Check **Write the vocabulary word that completes each sentence.**

Numbers that have digits in the tenths place and beyond are called decimals.

A percent is a(n) ratio that compares a number to 100.

Writing in Math Explain how to change a fraction to a percent.

Divide the numerator by the denominator to write the fraction as a decimal. Then move the decimal point two place values to the right and add the percent symbol.

Spiral Review

entify the percent shown in each model. (Lesson 3-1, p. 102)

75%

42 20%

43 110%

rite the ratio as a percent. Then write the ratio as a fraction with)0 in the denominator and as a decimal.

a soccer league with 100 players; 34 are in the 7th grade

percent: 34%

fraction: $\frac{34}{100}$

decimal: 0.34

olve.

PIZZA In Ava's class, 11 out of 20 students like pepperoni pizza and 9 out of 20 students like cheese pizza. Write these ratios as percents.

55% like pepperoni pizza; 45% like cheese pizza

STOP

Ticket Out the Door

Percents in the Classroom Have students work in groups of three. Give each group a percent. Ask them to look around the room and find an item in the classroom they can use to model the percent. Tell them they can use models, but they can also use other things, such as the clock, a ruler, a set of books, and so on. Tell them to also write the percent in three forms: fraction, decimal, and words. Have students present their findings. Students can turn their papers in as they exit the classroom.

See It, Do It, Say It, Write It

Step 1 Model 25% for students using a fraction circle. Ask students to tell you what the decimal and fraction are. Repeat this with several different percents and model types.

Step 2 Have students work in pairs. Give them each the meaning of a percent, such as 20 out of 100. Ask them to model the percent with a drawing or manipulative and then to write the percent in three forms.

Step 3 Have students share their work with the rest of the class.

Step 4 Ask students to draw a model of two-thirds, 75%, and $\frac{60}{100}$. Tell them to name each in three forms.

Looking Ahead: Pre-teach

Calculate Percents In the next lesson, students will learn how to calculate percents of a given number, and calculate what percent a number is of another.

Example

What number is 60% of 210? 126

20% of what number is 72? 360

What percent of 88 is 22? 25%

Have students calculate the following percents.

1. What number is 45% of 300? 135
2. 15% of what number is 36? 240
3. What percent of 500 is 100? 20%

Chapter 3 Progress Check 1

Formative Assessment

Use the Progress Check to assess students' mastery of the previous lessons. Have students review the lesson indicated for the problems they answered incorrectly.

Odd/Even Assignments

Exercises are structured so that students practice the same concepts whether they are assigned the odd or even problems.

Common Error Alert

Simplify Completely Often students think their answers are simplified when, in actuality, they may not be completely simplified.

Exercises 3-8 These problems require students to write answers in simplest form. An example in which a student might reduce a fraction, but not to simplest form, would be as follows:

Exercise 3 If the student writes $\frac{25}{100}$; the fraction can be reduced to $\frac{1}{4}$.

Chapter 3 Progress Check 1 (Lessons 3-1 and 3-2)

Identify the percent shown in each model.

1 10%

2 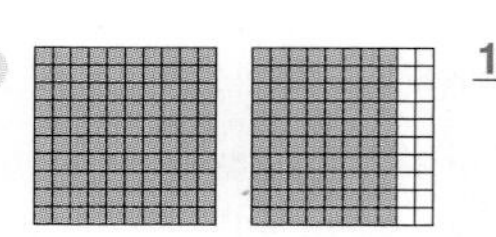 180%

Write each percent as a decimal and as a fraction in simplest form.

3 25% $0.25; \frac{1}{4}$

4 66% $0.66; \frac{33}{50}$

5 150% $1.50; 1\frac{1}{2}$

6 101% $1.01; 1\frac{1}{100}$

A bag of nuts has 8 peanuts, 4 cashews, and 8 walnuts. Write each ratio as a fraction in simplest form, a percent, and a decimal.

7 number of peanuts to total number of nuts $\frac{2}{5}$; 40%; 0.4

8 number of cashews to total number of nuts $\frac{1}{5}$; 20%; 0.2

Write each fraction as a percent and as a decimal.

9 $\frac{1}{4}$ 25%; 0.25

10 $\frac{3}{4}$ 75%; 0.75

11 $\frac{11}{2}$ 550%; 5.5

12 $\frac{6}{4}$ 150%; 1.5

13 $\frac{3}{8}$ 37.5%; 0.375

14 $\frac{7}{8}$ 87.5%; 0.875

Solve.

15 **GIFT BASKETS** Kirby is making fruit baskets as gifts. Each basket contains 3 apples, 2 oranges, 1 banana, 1 grapefruit, and 1 pear. What percent of the fruit is oranges? 25%

16 **EXERCISE** Jodi works out for 40 minutes each morning. She does stretching exercises for 5 minutes, weight training for 15 minutes, and a cardio workout for 20 minutes. What percent of her workout is cardio? 50%

17 **ENTERTAINMENT** In one town, 66% of the residents read the newspaper. Before an election, 87% of the same residents read the paper. Write each percent as a decimal and a fraction in simplest form.
66%, 0.66, $\frac{33}{50}$; 87%, 0.87, $\frac{87}{100}$

116 Chapter 3 Percents

Data-Driven Decision Making

Students missing Exercises . . .	Have trouble with . . .	Should review and practice . . .
1–2	identifying the percent modeled.	SSG Lesson 3-1, p. 102 CRM Skills Practice, p. A51
3–6	writing each percent as a decimal and a fraction in simplest form.	SSG Lesson 3-2, p. 109 CRM Skills Practice, p. A55
7–8	writing each ratio as a fraction in simplest form, a percent, and a decimal.	SSG Lesson 3-2, p. 109 CRM Skills Practice, p. A55
9–14	writing each fraction as a percent and a decimal.	SSG Lesson 3-2, p. 109 CRM Skills Practice, p. A55
15–17	solving word problems involving percents, decimals, and fractions.	CRM Problem-Solving Practice, pp. A52 and A56

Lesson 3-3

Calculate Percents

KEY Concept

Percents can be less than 1% or more than 100%. A percent that is less than 1% is written as a fraction or decimal. A percent more than 100% is expressed with a number greater than 100.

Use the equation below to solve percent problems. Express the percent as a decimal or a fraction before you multiply or divide.

The term *base* can be used in place of the word *whole*.

Percent Equation:	percent	×	whole	=	part
What is 35% of 180?	0.35	×	180	=	n
Ninety percent of what number is 45?	0.90	×	n	=	45
What percent of 300 is 60?	n	×	300	=	60

VOCABULARY

percent
a ratio that compares a number to 100

ratio
a comparison of two numbers by division; the ratio of 2 to 3 can be stated as 2 out of 3, 2 to 3, 2:3, or $\frac{2}{3}$

variable
a symbol, usually a letter, used to represent a number

You can use the percent equation to find the part, the whole, or the percent.

Example 1

15% of what number is 24?

1. Write the percent equation. percent × whole = part
2. Substitute the given numbers and a variable (unknown number) into the equation. Write 15% as a decimal. $0.15 \times n = 24$
3. Solve for the variable. $\frac{0.15n}{0.15} = \frac{24}{0.15}$, $n = 160$
4. Check your answer. $0.15 \times 160 = 24$ ✓

GO ON

Additional Example 1

12% of what number is 36?

1. Write the percent equation. percent × whole = part
2. Substitute the given numbers and a variable (unknown number) into the equation. Write 12% as a decimal.

   $0.12 \times n = 36$
3. Solve for the variable.

   $$0.12n = 36$$
   $$\frac{0.12n}{0.12} = \frac{36}{0.12}$$
   $$n = 300$$
4. Check your answer.

   $0.12 \times 300 = 36$ ✔

Lesson Notes

Lesson 3-3

Lesson Planner

Objective Calculate with percents.

Vocabulary **percent**, **ratio**, **variable**

Materials/Manipulatives counters, grid paper, money

Chapter Resource Masters

- CRM Vocabulary and English Language Development (p. A58)
- CRM Skills Practice (p. A59)
- CRM Problem-Solving Practice (p. A60)
- CRM Homework Practice (p. A61)

1 Introduce

Vocabulary

Access Vocabulary Draw a 10 by 10 grid on the board. Ask for volunteers to go to the board and shade in 25 squares. Ask the students to calculate the *ratio* of shaded squares to the total number of squares. Inform students that the shaded number of squares is the *percent* of squares shaded.

2 Teach

Key Concept

Foundational Skills and Concepts After students have read through the Key Concept box, have them try these exercises.

1. What are the three values used in the percent equation? the percent, the whole, and the part
2. How do you express a percent as a fraction? Place the percent value over 100.

Additional **Example 2**

What is 43% of 260?

1. Write the percent equation.
   percent × whole = part
2. Substitute the known numbers and variable into the equation.
   $0.43 \times 260 = n$
3. Solve for the variable.
   $111.8 = n$
4. Check your answer.
   $0.43 \times 260 = 111.8$ ✔

Note This!

Note Any Patterns As students take notes on calculating percents, encourage them to look for patterns emerging in the notes. Prompt students to add these patterns to their notes.

Math Coach Notes

Strategies When calculating percents, have students review and practice multiplying and dividing by decimals. This will help students calculate the unknown values when using percents.

YOUR TURN!

28% of what number is 182?

1. Write the percent equation. percent × whole = part
2. Substitute the known numbers and variable into the equation. $0.28 \times n = 182$
3. Solve for the variable. $\frac{0.28n}{0.28} = \frac{182}{0.28}$
   $n = 650$
4. Check your answer.
   $0.28 \times 650 = 182$ ✓

Example 2

What is 35% of 1,050?

1. Write the percent equation. percent × whole = part
2. Substitute the known numbers and variable into the equation. $0.35 \times 1{,}050 = n$
3. Solve for the variable. $367.5 = n$
4. Check your answer.
   $0.35 \times 1{,}050 = 367.5$ ✓

YOUR TURN!

What is 12% of 380?

1. Write the percent equation. percent × whole = part
2. Substitute the known numbers and variable into the equation. $0.12 \times 380 = n$
3. Solve for the variable. $45.6 = n$
4. Check your answer.
   $0.12 \times 380 = 45.6$ ✓

118 Chapter 3 Percents

Intervention Strategy — Kinesthetic Learners

Use Models Provide students with 100 tiles or markers. Have them calculate a variety of percents by using the tiles. For example, a student may be asked to find 38% of 100. Students can physically count the markers to determine 38 is 38% of 100.

Example 3

What percent of 500 is 125?

1. Write the percent equation.	percent × whole = part
2. Substitute the given numbers and a variable into the equation.	$n \times 500 = 125$ $\frac{500n}{500} = \frac{125}{500}$
3. Solve for the variable.	$n = 0.25$
4. Change the decimal to a percent by multiplying by 100.	0.25 = 25%
5. Check your answer.	

$0.25 \times 500 = 125$ ✓

YOUR TURN!

What percent of 750 is 600?

1. Write the percent equation.	percent × whole = part
2. Substitute the given numbers and a variable into the equation.	$n \times 750 = 600$
3. Solve for the variable.	$\frac{750n}{750} = \frac{600}{750}$
4. Change the decimal to a percent by multiplying by 100.	$n = 0.80$
5. Check your answer.	0.80 = 80%

$0.80 \times 750 = 600$ ✓

Who is Correct?

What percent of 440 is 132?

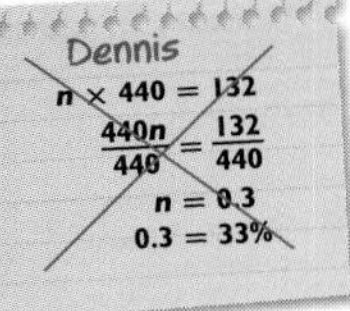

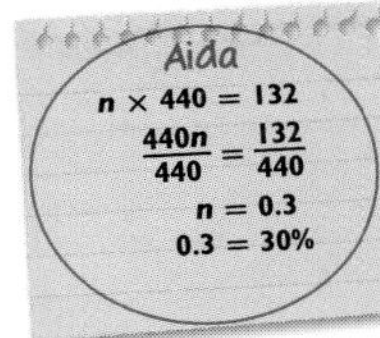

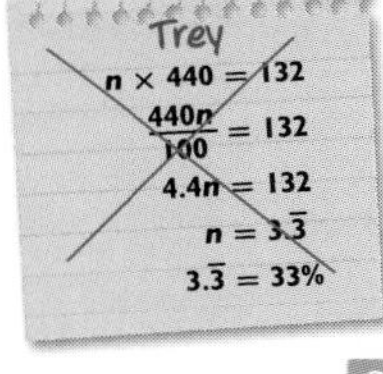

Circle correct answer(s). Cross out incorrect answer(s).

GO ON

Additional Example 3

What percent of 900 is 315?

1. Write the percent equation.
   percent × whole = part
2. Substitute the given numbers and a variable into the equation.
   $n \times 900 = 315$
3. Solve for the variable.
   $900n = 315$
   $\frac{900n}{900} = \frac{315}{900}$
   $n = 0.35$
4. Change the decimal to a percent by multiplying by 100.
   $0.35 \times 100 = 35\%$
5. Check your answer. $0.35 \times 900 = 315$ ✔

Common Error Alert

Percent and 100 When the percent is the unknown, students often forget to multiply the answer by 100. Remind them that 100 is always used in the equation, either at the beginning (when they turn the percent into a decimal by dividing) or at the end (when they turn the decimal into a percent by multiplying). The two circles (%) in the percent sign can remind them of the two zeroes in 100.

Who is Correct?

Diagnostic Teaching

- Dennis is incorrect. He converted from a decimal to a percent incorrectly.
- Aida is correct. She used the *percent* × *whole* = *part* equation.
- Trey is incorrect. He wrote the wrong equation after substituting the correct values.

Remind students that the percent is multiplied by the number that represents the whole.

3 Practice

Using Manipulatives

Grid Paper Demonstrate percentages with 10 by 10 grid paper. Have students shade the percentage value in the grid to show the students the part of a whole.

On-Hand Manipulatives Demonstrate percentages using money. Have students use 100 pennies as the whole and take away the percentage value.

Guided Practice

Remember that to write a percent as a decimal, you divide by 100.

Write each percent as a decimal.

1. 76% 0.76
2. 27.5% 0.275
3. 12.5% 0.125
4. 114% 1.14

Step by Step Practice

Solve using the percent equation. Check your answer.

5. 30% of what number is 66?

Step 1 Write the percent equation.

percent × whole = part

Step 2 Substitute the given numbers and a variable into the equation.

$0.30 \times n = 66$

Step 3 Solve for the variable.

$\frac{0.30n}{0.30} = \frac{66}{0.30}$

$n = 220$

Step 4 Check your answer.

$0.30 \times 220 = 66$

Solve using the percent equation. Check each answer.

6. What is 140% of 60?

percent × whole = part

$1.40 \times 60 = n$

$84 = n$

Check: $1.4 \times 60 = 84$

7. 20% of what number is 55? 275

8. 40% of what number is 130? 325

Are They Getting It?

Check students' understanding of calculating percents by writing these problems on the board. Ask students to point out wrong answers and explain why they are wrong. Encourage students to use a model in their explanation.

1. 30% of what number is 150?

percent × whole = part

$0.30 \times 150 = n$

$45 = n$

This is incorrect. 150 is the part not the whole.

2. What is 62% of 240?

percent × whole = part

$0.62 \times 240 = n$

$148.8 = n$

This is correct.

3. What percent of 545 is 218?

percent × whole = part

$n \times 545 = 218$

$545n = 218$

$\frac{545n}{545} = \frac{218}{545}$

$n = 0.40$ or 40%

This is correct.

olve using the percent equation. Check each answer.

9 What is 175% of 28? 49

10 What is 45% of 80? 36

11 What percent of 3,000 is 12? 0.4%

12 What percent of 8,000 is 16? 0.2%

Step by Step Problem-Solving Practice

Problem-Solving Strategies
- ☐ Use a table.
- ☐ Look for a pattern.
- ☐ Guess and check.
- ☑ Solve a simpler problem.
- ☐ Act it out.

Solve.

13 ASTRONOMY On Mars an object weighs 38% as much as it weighs on Earth. How much would a person who weighs 150 pounds on Earth weigh on Mars?

Understand Read the problem. Write what you know.

On Mars something weighs 38% of what it does on Earth.

Plan Pick a strategy. One strategy is to solve a simpler problem.

Divide 38% into percents that are easier to compute.
38% = 30% + 5% + 3%

Solve **30%:** What is 10% of 150 pounds? 15 pounds
Multiply this by 3 because 30 = 10 × 3. 45
So, 30% of 150 is 45.

5%: 10% of 150 is 15.
Divide the amount of 10% in half to find 5%.
15 ÷ 2 = 7.5
So, 5% of 150 is $\frac{1}{2}$ × 15, or 7.5.

3%: What is 1% of 150 pounds? 1.5 pounds
Multiply this by 3. 4.5
So, 3% of 150 is 3 × 1.5, or 4.5.

38%: Add the smaller percents to find 38% of 150 pounds.
30% + 5% + 3% = 45 + 7.5 + 4.5
= 57 pounds

Check You can check your answer using estimation.
38% is close to 33%, or $\frac{1}{3}$. $\frac{1}{3}$ of 150 is 50.

GO ON

Math Challenge

Many Percents, One Whole Have students roll a number cube two times to generate a two-digit number. Example: When the first roll is 5 and the second roll is 4, it gives a two-digit number of 54. Roll the cube a third time to get a percent; multiply the number on the cube by 10. Example: For a roll of 2, you would use 20%. After the three rolls, have students find the percent of the number. Example: 20% of 54 = 10.8. Have students repeat rolls to get different percents to calculate.

English Learner Strategy

Guiding Questions Have students answer the following questions.

- What percent of 750 is 450? 60%
- What is the unknown? the percent
- What is the whole? 750
- How can you rearrange the sentence and still get the same result? Sample answer: 450 is what percent of 750?
- Explain how you can find the percent. Substitute values into the percent equation.

Math Coach Notes

Understanding Percents Percents can either be less than 100% or greater than 100%. Prompt students to notice that answers to exercises containing percents less than 100% are going to be less than the original number. Exercises containing percents greater than 100% will result in an answer greater than the original number.

Common Error *Alert*

Fractions or Decimals If students are having difficulty with calculating percents, remind them that they can choose to work with a decimal or a fraction as an equivalent for the percent.

Additional Answer

Exercise 16 percent × whole = n; when you are given the whole and the percent and need to find the percent of the whole (or part)

n = part/percent; when you are given the part and percent and need to find the whole

n = part/whole; when you are given the part and the whole and need to find the percent

Odd/Even Assignments

Exercises 17–37 are structured so that students practice the same concepts whether they are assigned the odd or even problems.

In-Class Assignment

Have students complete Exercises 19, 25, 29, 34, 37, and 41 to ensure that they understand the concept.

14 TENNIS In the city of Bridgeport, 75% of the parks have tennis courts. If 18 parks have tennis courts, how many parks does Bridgeport have altogether?
Check off each step.

✔ Understand: I underlined the key words.

✔ Plan: To solve the problem, I will solve a simpler problem

✔ Solve: The answer is 24 parks

✔ Check: I checked my answer by using estimation

15 SCHOOL There are 175 students in seventh grade at Silverado Middle School. A survey shows that 84% of them plan to volunteer during the summer. How many students plan to volunteer?

147 students

16 **Reflect** Write the percent equation in three different ways:
1. when n is the part
2. when n is the whole
3. when n is the percent
Explain when to use each form.

See TE margin.

Skills, Concepts, and Problem Solving

Write each percent as a decimal.

17 33% 0.33

18 72% 0.72

19 180% 1.8

20 4% 0.04

21 68% 0.68

22 159% 1.59

23 247% 2.47

24 57% 0.57

25 9% 0.09

26 208% 2.08

122 **Chapter 3** Percents

Intervention Strategy — Visual/Linguistic Learners

Create a Table Provide students with an exercise involving calculating percents. Prompt students to create a two-column chart. In the left-hand column, write a step-by-step guide. In the right-hand column, have students work out the corresponding step to solve the original problem.

Solve using the percent equation. Check each answer.

27 2% of what number is 5? 250

28 6% of what number is 21? 350

29 What is 110% of 60? 66

30 What is 175% of 28? 49

31 What is 250% of 40? 100

32 What is 120% of 55? 66

33 What percent of 2,000 is 14? 0.7% or $\frac{7}{10}$%

34 What percent of 84 is 63? 75%

Solve.

35 **CHESS** The chess club has 60 members. Twenty-four of the members are younger than 20 years old. What percent of the 60 members are younger than 20?

40%

36 **SHOPPING** Trevor is shopping for a new pair of shoes. The regular price is $64.99. They were on sale for 25% off. What is 25% of $64.99?

$16.25

37 **SPORTS** In a recent season, the Los Angeles Angels won 95 games and lost 67 games. What percent of games played did the Angels win? Round to the nearest tenth.

59%

Vocabulary Check **Write the vocabulary word that completes each sentence.**

38 A(n) ratio is a comparison of two numbers by division.

39 A letter or symbol used to represent a number is a(n) variable.

40 A ratio that compares a number to 100 is a(n) percent.

41 **Writing in Math** Explain how you would calculate a 15% tip.

Answers may vary. First calculate 10%. Then calculate 5%. Finally, add the two values together.

GO ON

4 Assess

See It, Do It, Say It, Write It

Step 1 Write three percentage problems that mirror Examples 1–3 in this lesson.

Step 2 Have students use the percent equation to find the unknown values.

Step 3 Arrange students in pairs and have them explain to each other how they found the unknown values in the problems above.

Step 4 Have students write in their own words the definitions of each vocabulary word and then explain how to calculate percents in their math journals.

Looking Ahead: Pre-teach

Interpret Circle Graphs In the next lesson, students will learn how to read and interpret circle graphs.

Example

The graph below shows the colors of cars in a school parking lot.

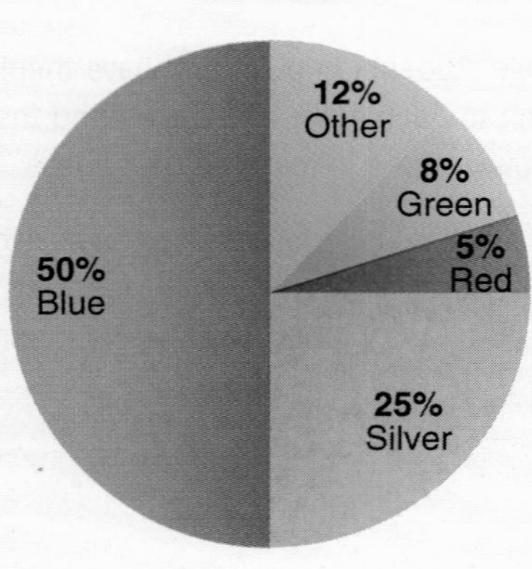

What color was one-fourth of the cars? silver

Have students answer the questions below.

1. What was the most popular car color? blue
2. What percent of the cars were green? 8%
3. If there were 200 cars in the parking lot, how many were red? 10

Spiral Review

Identify the percent shown in each model. (Lesson 3-1, p. 102)

42 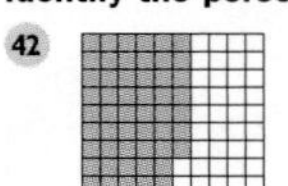 57%

43 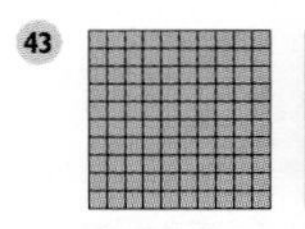 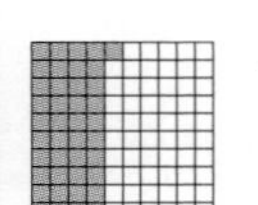 141%

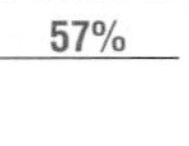

Write each percent as a fraction with 100 in the denominator and as a decimal.

44 29% $\frac{29}{100}$; 0.29

45 94% $\frac{94}{100}$; 0.94

46 137% $1\frac{37}{100}$; 1.37

47 126% $1\frac{26}{100}$; 1.26

Write each percent as a fraction or mixed number in simplest form and as a decimal. (Lesson 3-2, p. 109)

48 15% $\frac{3}{20}$; 0.15

49 30% $\frac{3}{10}$; 0.30

50 140% $1\frac{4}{10}$; 1.40

51 122% $1\frac{11}{50}$; 1.22

Write each fraction as a decimal and as a percent.

52 $\frac{2}{5}$ 0.40; 40%

53 $\frac{3}{8}$ 0.375; 37.5%

54 $\frac{7}{4}$ 1.75; 175%

55 $\frac{5}{2}$ 2.5; 250%

Solve. (Lesson 3-1, p. 102)

56 READING Ms. Roberts kept track of the number of books her students read in one school year. The results are shown in the table at the right. Write each percent as a decimal.

0.18, 0.47, 0.21, 0.14

Number of Books Read	Percent of Students
3	18%
5	47%
7	21%
9	14%

STOP

124 Chapter 3 Percents

Ticket Out the Door

Grades Instruct students to find a ficticious quiz score as a percent. Have students turn in the papers showing their work as they exit the classroom.

Lesson 3-4 Interpret Circle Graphs

KEY Concept

A **circle graph** displays data in pie-shaped sections called **sectors**. A circle graph is useful when you need to compare parts of a whole to the whole.

The whole circle represents the total of all the data. So, the whole is 100%. All the sectors added together equal 100%. (50% + 20% + 30% = 100%)

This table shows how the percents are found.

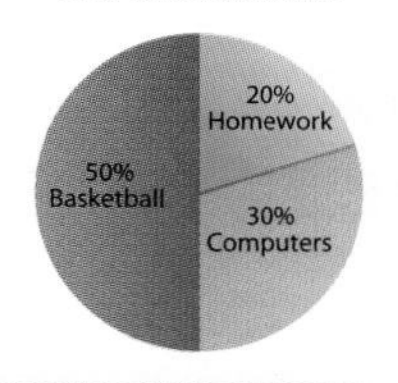

Activity	Number of Students	Fraction	Percent
Basketball	50	$\frac{50}{100}$	50%
Homework	20	$\frac{20}{100}$	20%
Computers	30	$\frac{30}{100}$	30%

VOCABULARY

circle graph a graph used to compare parts of a whole; the circle represents the whole and is separated into parts of a whole

sector pie-shaped sections in a circle graph

ne entire circle represents the way the parts of the data are related to the ntire circle. To interpret the data, it is important to be able to interpret e parts of the circle graph.

Example 1

Consuela surveyed her class to see which types of movies they liked best. She displayed the results of the survey in a circle graph. Use the graph to answer each question.

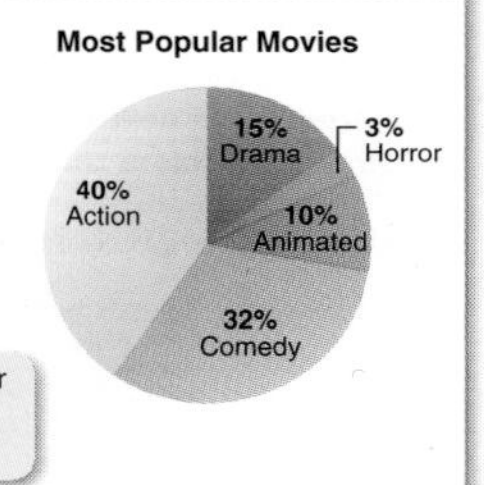

1. What is the title of the graph? Most Popular Movies
2. How many movie categories are there? 5
3. Which type of movie was most popular? Look for the largest sector. Action
4. Which type of movie was least popular? Look for the smallest sector. Horror

The size of the sector determines the size of the data.

Additional Example 1

Use the circle graph to answer each question.

1. What is the title of the graph? People's Favorite Color
2. How many color categories are there? 4
3. Which color was the most popular? Look for the largest sector. blue
4. Which color was the least favorite? Look for the smallest sector. purple

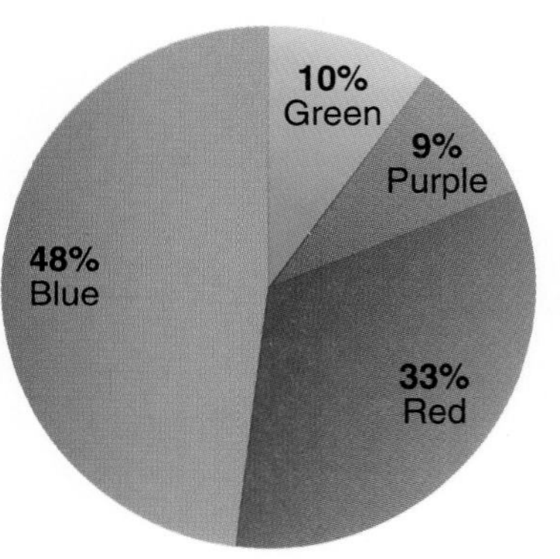

Lesson Notes

Lesson 3-4

Lesson Planner

Objective Apply percentages to make and interpret circle graphs.

Vocabulary **circle graph**, **sector**

Materials/Manipulatives fraction circles, protractors

Chapter Resource Masters

- CRM Vocabulary and English Language Development (p. A62)
- CRM Skills Practice (p. A63)
- CRM Problem-Solving Practice (p. A64)
- CRM Homework Practice (p. A65)

Vocabulary

Access Vocabulary Divide a drawn circle into four sectors, each sector a different size. Tell students that the sectors represent a part of the entire circle. Relate each sector to a piece of pie (the circle representing the whole pie). Analyze each sector to see which slice is the biggest and which is the smallest. Explain to students that they can compare the size of the sectors to other sectors in the same circle. They cannot compare the size of the sectors in one circle to sectors in a different circle.

2 Teach

Key Concept

Foundational Skills and Concepts After students have read through the Key Concept box, have them try these exercises.

1. Which sector fills the greatest part of the circle graph? Is its percent the greatest percent? basketball, yes
2. If the sectors of a circle graph were rearranged within the circle, would the graph still be a whole circle? Explain. Yes, the sectors equal 100%. The order the sectors are placed in the circle does not change that.

Note This!

Circle Graphs with Legends When the sectors of a circle graph are not labeled with the categories, you must include a legend. A legend is a key for interpreting the graph. Each category name is listed next to a patch of its color or pattern used in the circle graph.

For students that have poor hand-eye coordination or poor organizational skills, encourage them to write the percent from the circle graph next to each category name in the legend.

YOUR TURN!

The public library needed to order new books. The librarian looked at the records to see which books were borrowed most. Use the graph to answer each question.

1. What is the title of the graph? Most Borrowed Books
2. How many book categories are there? 6
3. What type of book was borrowed the most? Biography
4. What type(s) of book was borrowed the least? Look for the smallest sector. Other, Romance, and Mystery

Most Borrowed Books

10% Other
10% Romance
10% Mystery
20% Non-Fiction
20% Science Fiction
30% Biography

Example 2

Jeremy received $80 for his birthday. The graph shows how Jeremy spent his birthday money. On which two items combined did he spend as much as he did on clothes?

1. What is the percentage he spent on clothes? 25%
2. Find which two categories equal 25% when added together.

   Song Downloads + Shoes = 10% + 50% = 60% ✗

   Song Downloads + Food = 10% + 15% = 25% ✓

   Shoes + Food = 50% + 15% = 65% ✗
3. Jeremy spent the same on clothes as he did together on song downloads and food.

Birthday Spending

15% Food
10% Downloads
25% Clothes
50% Shoes

YOUR TURN!

The Recycling Company collected 100 tons of recycling materials last week. The graph shows how much of each material was collected. Which material did they collect three times more than cans?

1. What is the percentage of cans collected? 12%
2. Find which section is equal to three times more than 12%. $3 \times 12 =$ 36%
3. The Recycling Brothers collected three times more cardboard than cans.

Recycling Materials

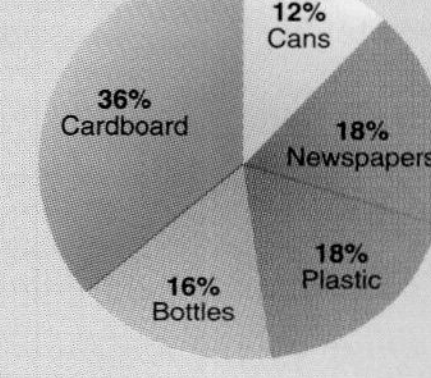

Additional *Example 2*

David's doctor gave him the circle graph shown as a guide for his daily food plan. What category does David's doctor recommend he intakes half as much as protein and dairy?

1. What is the percentage recommended for protein and dairy? 28%
2. Find which category is half of 28%, 28% ÷ 2 = 14%. Fruit is recommended half as much as protein and diary.

David's Daily Calorie Intake

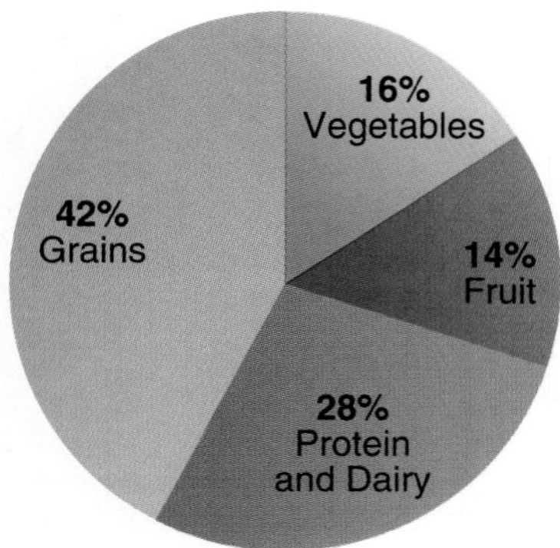

Who is Correct?

Refer to the circle graph on page 126 titled "Recycling Materials." What two items combined equal the percentage of cardboard that was collected?

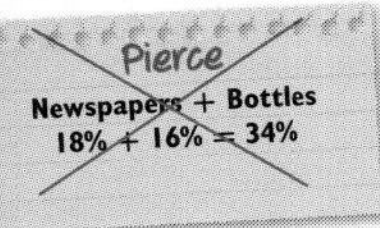

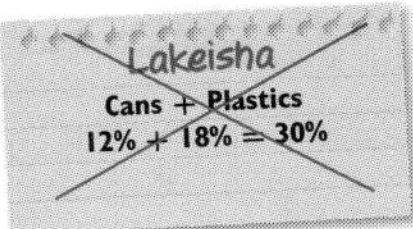

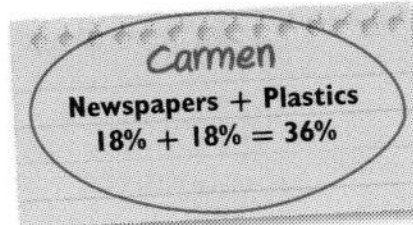

Guided Practice

The circle graph to the right shows the number of each type of pet owned by 100 middle school students. Use the circle graph to answer the questions below.

What is the title of the graph? Pet Ownership

What category of pets is the most popular? Dogs

What pet was the least popular? Snakes

Did any category have the same number of pets? Yes, fish, birds, and guinea pigs were all 20%.

Pet Ownership

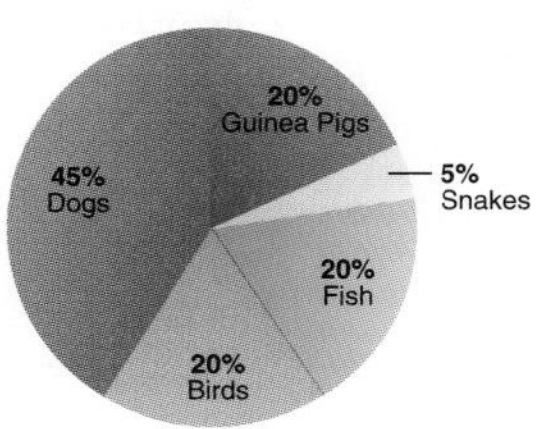

Step by Step Practice

The Student Council made food items to raise money for the school dance. The graph shows how much of each food item was made. Which food item was made two times more than the trail mix?

Step 1 What is the percentage of trail mix made? 17%

Step 2 What percentage is equal to two times more than 17%? 2 × 17% = 34%

Step 3 The Student Council made two times more cupcakes than trail mix.

Fund-raiser Food Items

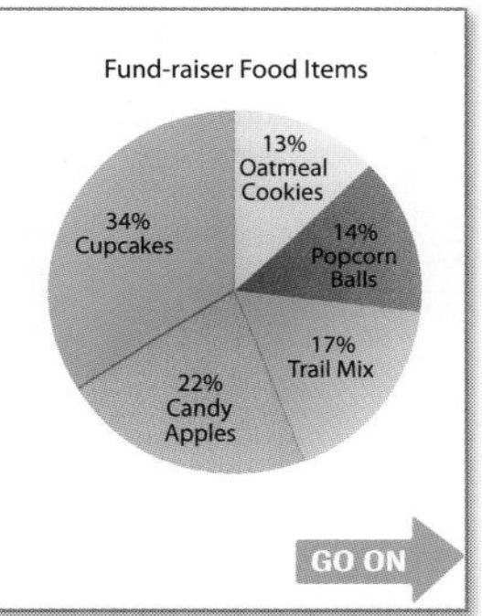

GO ON

Who *is Correct?*

Diagnostic Teaching

- Pierce is incorrect. His total is not 36%.
- Lakeisha is incorrect. Her total is not 36%.
- Carmen is correct. Her total is 36%.

3 Practice

Using Manipulatives

Fraction Circles For circle graphs with common percentages, students can make a circle graph with touchable sectors. Use the different size pieces of the fraction circles as the sectors. In this situation, students can physically place the sectors on top of each other for comparison.

Math Coach Notes

The Word "of" Teach students that the word "of" indicates to multiply. Give examples that students can answer using mental math, each time making a point to use the word "of."

For example:

Ask: What is $\frac{1}{2}$ of 10? 5

Demonstrate how multiplication is used to get this answer.

$$\frac{1}{2} \times \frac{10}{1} = \frac{1}{\cancel{2}_1} \times \frac{\cancel{10}^5}{1}$$

Ask: What is $\frac{1}{3}$ of 45? 15

$$\frac{1}{3} \times \frac{45}{1} = \frac{1}{\cancel{3}_1} \times \frac{\cancel{45}^{15}}{1}$$

Ask: What is $\frac{1}{4}$ of 300? 75

$$\frac{1}{4} \times \frac{300}{1} = \frac{1}{\cancel{4}_1} \times \frac{\cancel{300}^{75}}{1}$$

When asking questions about circle graphs, use your voice to stress the word "of" in hopes to trigger the students' memories to multiply. For example, what is 10% of 50?

Intervention Strategy — English Learners

Meaningful Categories Ask students to name three types of vegetables eaten in their native country. The students can then make their circle graph using those categories. Invite students to share their finished graphs with the class and explain a little about the types of vegetables commonly eaten. The same can be done with music or movie genres.

Math Coach Notes

Multiplying by 100 Remind students that multiplying a number by 100 moves its decimal point two places to the right. To change a percent to a decimal, move the decimal point two places to the left. When multiplying by 100, move the decimal back two places to the right.

Step by Step Problem-Solving Practice

Problem-Solving Strategies
- ☐ Draw a diagram.
- ☐ Make a table.
- ☐ Work backward.
- ☑ Use logical reasoning.
- ☐ Look for a pattern.

4 CAFETERIA The school cafeteria cooks wanted to know what vegetables to serve the junior high school students. They asked all the students to name their favorite vegetables. Which two vegetables combined equal the same percentage as green beans?

Favorite Vegetables
10% Lettuce
8% Celery
18% Green Beans
22% Broccoli
42% Carrots

Understand Read the problem. Write what you know.

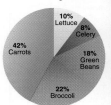

What percentage of students named green beans as their favorite vegetable? 18%

What vegetable did the students like most? carrots

What vegetable did the students like least? celery

What other vegetable was liked more than green beans? broccoli

Plan Pick a strategy. One strategy is to use logical reasoning. If you combined the carrots and lettuce or the broccoli and celery section of the circle graph, they would be larger than the green beans section.

Solve lettuce + celery = green beans

10% + 8% = 18%

Check Use subtraction to check your answer.

5 FUND-RAISER Natalie is selling candy bars for a fund-raiser at her school. She kept track of her customers with a circle graph. Who bought <u>three times more</u> candy bars than <u>Luis</u>? Check off each step.

Candy Bars Sold
10% Luis
10% Dad
10% Mom
20% Janey
20% Melanie
30% Mr. Thomas

✔ Understand: I underlined key words.

✔ Plan: To solve the problem, I will make a table.

✔ Solve: The answer is Mr. Thomas; $3 \times 10\% = 30\%$.

✔ Check: I checked my answer by using dividing 30% by 3.

128 Chapter 3 Percents

Are They Getting It?

Check students' understanding of circle graphs by writing these problems on the board. Have students explain the computation they do in each problem.

1. What percentage should be with the "Maybe" label? 43%

2. Which sector is about half the size of the "Maybe" sector? the "yes" sector

Are You Planning a Summer Vacation?

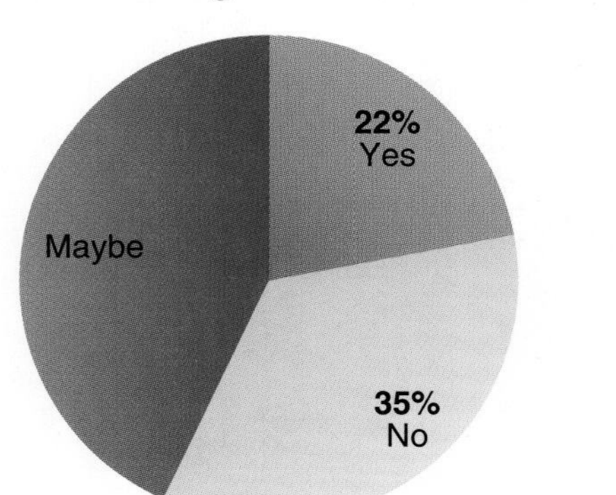

Reflect A survey of the seventh-grade class showed their favorite choice of sandwiches: 40% liked peanut butter and jelly, 25% liked ham and cheese, 20% liked grilled cheese, and 15% liked tuna salad. Why is a circle graph better to compare this data than a bar graph? Explain your thinking.

The bar graph could be used to display data because it compares data; however, it does not display the relationship of the data parts to the whole like the circle graph.

Skills, Concepts, and Problem Solving

r Exercises 7–9, use the graph at the right.

AM Mr. Hernandez surveyed his Social Studies class to see which e of assignment his students wanted to complete for their final grade. hich two types of assignments combined are equal to the percentage the group presentation assignment? Use the circle graph he created answer each question.

What percentage of students chose to complete the group presentation assignment? 40%

Which two percentages are equal to 40% when added together? 15% + 25% = 40%

The percentage of students that chose the Group Presentation is equal to the students that chose the Written Essay and Oral Exam assignment.

r questions 10–13, use the graph at the right.

IMMING EVENTS The Rolling Hills High School orter surveyed the swim team to see which types of ents they liked best. Use the circle graph to answer questions below.

What is the title of the graph? Favorite Swimming Events

How many swimming event categories are there? 5

Which swimming event was more popular than the breaststroke? Freestyle and Medley Relay

Which swimming event was liked more than the butterfly but less than the breaststroke? Backstroke

GO ON

Math Challenge

Make a Circle Graph Provide the following data to students. Instruct them to make a circle graph.

Title: *Dogs in the Rescue Shelter*

Mixed Breeds: 33, Beagles: 12, Labs: 14, Retrievers: 3, Terriers: 9

Students will need to realize that although the number of the "whole" is not given directly to them, they can find the "whole" number of dogs to be able to determine the percent for each sector.

Odd/Even Assignments

Exercises 7–16 are structured so that students practice the same concepts whether they are assigned the odd or even problems.

In-Class Assignment

Have students complete Exercises 7, 11, 12, 15, and 18 to ensure that they understand the concept.

Intervention Strategy — Interpersonal Learners

Making Class Circle Graphs Arrange the class into groups of 3 to 5 students. Have a representative from each group select the title of their assignment from the list below:

My Favorite Breakfast Cereal

Number of People in My Family

My Favorite Subject in School

My Favorite Board Game

Color of My Bedroom

My Favorite Kind of Cookie

Groups should do the following to make a circle graph of their assigned title. Each task should be assigned to an individual or a pair of students in the group. All group members need to verify the calculations.

1. Decide how to collect data from the class for their circle graphs.
2. Collect and organize the data from classmates.
3. Calculate the percentage for each category.
4. Create the circle graph to share with the class.

4 Assess

See It, Do It, Say It, Write It

Step 1 Students should look back at the circle graphs presented in this lesson. Have them name the elements that need to be included in a circle graph. List what the circle graphs have in common.

Step 2 Give the students a topic about why a circle graph would be a good choice for displaying data. Have them list categories related to the topic for a circle graph. Then have them assign a percentage to each category and create a circle graph of their data.

Step 3 Have students pair up with another student and share their graphs. Their partner can verify that the percentages total 100%.

For Exercises 14–16, use the graph at the right.

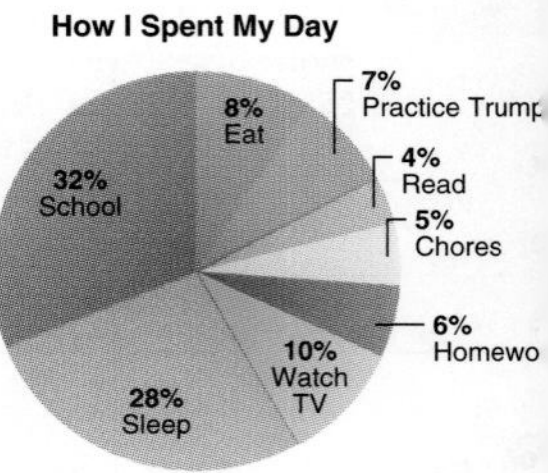

DAILY ROUTINE Angie wanted to show how she spent her time during the day. She displayed the results in the circle graph. Which activity took four times more time than trumpet practice?

14 What is the percentage spent on trumpet practice? 7%

15 What percentage is equal to four times more than 7%? $4 \times 7\% = 28\%$

16 Angie spent four times more time **sleeping** than practicing her trumpet.

Vocabulary Check **Write the vocabulary word that completes each sentence.**

17 A (n) **circle graph** is used to compare parts of a whole.

18 Writing in Math List three characteristics of circle graphs.

Sample answers: The interior of the circle represents a set of data. The percents add up to 100%. The pie-shaped sections (sectors/wedges) show the groups. The circle equals 360°.

Spiral Review

Write each percent as a fraction or mixed number in simplest form and as a decimal. (Lesson 3-2, p. 109)

19 18% $\frac{9}{50}$; 0.18

20 35% $\frac{7}{20}$; 0.35

Write each fraction as a decimal and as a percent.

21 $\frac{2}{5}$ 0.40; 40%

22 $\frac{7}{8}$ 0.875; 87.5%

Solve. (Lesson 3-3, p. 117)

23 BAKERY The local bakery made 155 muffins for the next day's sales. Sixty percent of the muffins were blueberry. How many muffins were blueberry?
93 blueberry muffins

STO

130 Chapter 3 Percents

Ticket Out the Door

Mental Math with Percents Instruct students to answer the exit question without a calculator or paper and pencil. As students exit the classroom, ask them one of the following:

1. What is 62% of 100? 62
2. What is 100% of 5? 5
3. What is 50% of 250? 125
4. What is 10% of 88? 8.8

Chapter 3

Progress Check 2 (Lessons 3-3 and 3-4)

Solve using the percent equation.

1. 13% of what number is 52? 400
2. What is 25% of 88? 22
3. What is 32% of 200? 64
4. What percent of 200 is 86? 43%
5. What percent of 350 is 245? 70%
6. 35% of what number is 49? 140

For Exercises 7–8, use the graph at the right.

VIDEO GAMES Mr. Diaz surveyed his class to see how many hours his students played video games in one week. Use the circle graph to answer the questions below.

Hours Playing Video Games

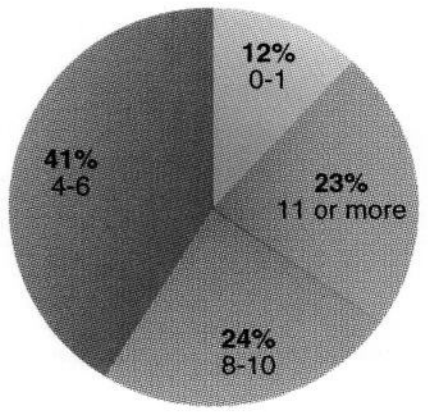

12% 0-1
23% 11 or more
24% 8-10
41% 4-6

7. How many hours did the highest percentage of students play video games in one week? 4-6 hours
8. How many hours did the lowest percentage of students play video games in one week? 0-1 hour

For Exercises 9–11, use the graph at the right.

BIRTHDAY PARTY At Lamar's birthday party, he and his four friends won 70 tickets playing games at a video arcade. Which two friends combined winnings equal the percent won by Enrico?

Tickets Won

5% Jorge
10% Lamar
35% Miles
20% Roman
30% Enrico

9. What percent of tickets did Enrico win? 30%
10. Which two percentages combined equals 30%?
    10% + 20% = 30%
11. Which two friends' combined percentage equal 30%?
    Lamar and Roman

Solve.

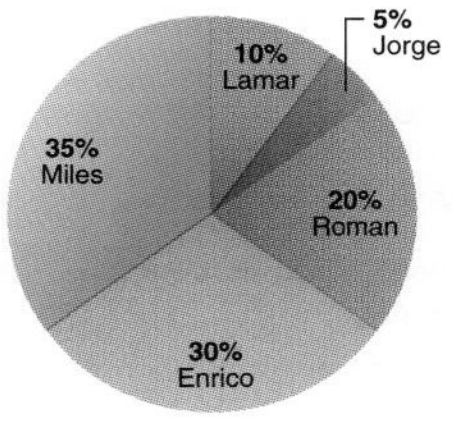

12. **MOVIES** Fourteen of the students in Ann's class prefer animated movies above all other types of movies. The rest of the students like action or mystery movies better. If there are 25 students in Ann's class, what percent do not prefer animated movies?
    44%

Progress Check 2

Chapter 3

Formative Assessment

Use the Progress Check to assess students' mastery of the previous lessons. Have students review the lesson indicated for the problems they answered incorrectly.

Odd/Even Assignments

Exercises are structured so that students practice the same concepts whether they are assigned the odd or even problems.

Common Error *Alert*

Substitute Values Correctly A challenging facet of finding percents is substituting the known values and the unknown variables into their proper locations within the percent proportion or the percent equation.

Exercise 1 The portion of the equation or proportion that is unknown is the *whole.*

Exercises 2 and 3 The portion of the equation or proportion that is unknown is the *part.*

Exercise 4 The portion of the equation or proportion that is unknown is the *percent.*

Data-Driven Decision Making

Students missing Exercises . . .	Have trouble with . . .	Should review and practice . . .
1-6	solving for varying unknowns using the percent equation.	SSG Lesson 3-3, p. 117 CRM Skills Practice, p. A59
7-11	interpreting a circle graph.	SSG Lesson 3-4, p. 125 CRM Skills Practice, p. A63
12	solving word problems involving percents and circle graphs.	CRM Problem-Solving Practice, pp. A60 and A64

Chapter 3

Study Guide
Formative Assessment

Vocabulary and Concept Check

If students have difficulty answering Exercises 1–6, remind them that they can use the page references to refresh their memories about the vocabulary terms.

Vocabulary Review Strategies

Puzzles Have students make a crossword puzzle to help them review key vocabulary words. They should interlock the words in the Vocabulary and Concept Check and then write clues that are used to determine the correct word. (For example: ____________ means hundredths or out of 100. *Answer: percent*) Have them trade puzzles with another student for additional practice.

Lesson Review

Each example walks the students through identifying percents being modeled; writing percents as percents and fractions in simplest form; and comparing fractions, decimals, and percents. If the given examples are not sufficient to review the primary concepts of the chapter, remind students that the page references tell them where to review that topic in their textbooks.

Find **Extra Practice** for these concepts in the Practice Worksheets, pages A50–A65.

Classroom Management

Group Time Have students who finish the review problems for each example create additional problems, for which they also develop a solution. Then have them gather in small groups to discuss their problems and explain the corresponding solutions. If there is ample time, you could have each group take turns presenting various problems from the different sections within the chapter.

Chapter 3

Study Guide

Vocabulary and Concept Check

circle graph, *p. 125*
decimal, *p. 102*
equivalent fractions, *p. 102*
percent, *p. 102*
ratio, *p. 102*
variable, *p. 117*

Write the vocabulary word that completes each sentence.

1. __Percent__ is a ratio that compares a number to 10(
2. A(n) __ratio__ is a comparison of two quantities by division.
3. A(n) __variable__ is a letter or symbol used to represent a number.
4. Fractions that name the same number are called __equivalent fractions__.

Write the correct vocabulary term in each blank.

5. __equivalent fractions__
$\frac{2}{3}$ and $\frac{6}{9}$

6. __ratio__
4 out of 5, 4 to 5, 4:5, or $\frac{4}{5}$

Lesson Review

3-1 Introduction to Percents (pp. 102–108)

Identify the percent shown in each model.

7. 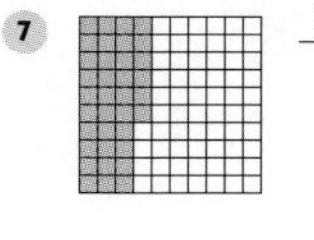 __36%__

8. 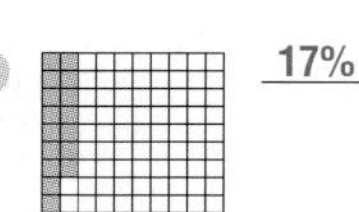 __17%__

Example 1

Identify the percent shown in the model.

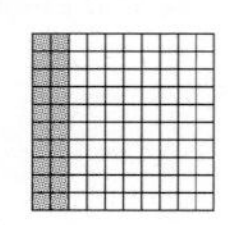

1. The model has 100 squares.
2. There are 20 squares shaded.
3. The ratio as a fraction of shaded squares to total squares is $\frac{20}{100}$.
4. The fraction is equivalent to 20%.

Write each percent as a fraction with a denominator of 100 and as a decimal.

9 44% $\frac{44}{100}$; 0.44

10 13% $\frac{13}{100}$; 0.13

11 26% $\frac{26}{100}$; 0.26

Example 2

Write 84% as a fraction with a denominator of 100 and as a decimal.

Write 84% as a fraction. $\frac{84}{100}$

Write 84% as a decimal. 0.84

3-2 Percents, Fractions, and Decimals (pp. 109–115)

Write each percent as a fraction or mixed number in simplest form and as a decimal.

12 14% $\frac{7}{50}$; 0.14

13 150% $1\frac{1}{2}$; 1.50

14 30% $\frac{3}{10}$; 0.30

Write each fraction as a decimal and as a percent.

15 $\frac{1}{2}$ 0.5, 50%

16 $\frac{9}{4}$ 2.25, 225%

17 $\frac{1}{5}$ 0.2, 20%

Example 3

Write 24% as a decimal and as a fraction in simplest form.

1. The % sign means *out of 100*. Write 24% as a fraction using this definition.

   $24\% = \frac{24}{100}$

2. $\frac{24}{100}$ is read as *24 hundredths*.

   Write this as a decimal. 0.24

3. Simplify the fraction, if possible.

   $\frac{24 \div 4}{100 \div 4} = \frac{6}{25}$

Example 4

Write $\frac{5}{8}$ as a decimal and as a percent.

1. Divide to write the fraction as a decimal.
2. Write the decimal as a percent by moving the decimal point two places to the right and adding a % sign.

$$\begin{array}{r} 0.625 \\ 8\overline{)5.000} \\ -48 \\ \hline 20 \\ -16 \\ \hline 40 \\ -40 \\ \hline 0 \end{array}$$

$\frac{5}{8} = 0.625 = 62.5\%$

FOLDABLES® Study Organizer Dinah Zike's Foldables®

Review Remind students to complete and refer to their Foldables as they progress through the Chapter 3 Study Guide. Have students share and compare their completed Foldables with a partner. You may also choose to have them use their Foldable as a study aid in preparing for the Chapter Test. (For complete instructions, see Chapter Resource Masters, p. A47.)

Fraction	Percent	Decimal
$\frac{1}{2}$ →	50% →	0.5

Intervention Strategy Kinesthetic Learners

Hands On! Create a BINGO game in which you would say, for example: "B: 25%," and the students would have to look down their ***B*** columns for either a decimal or simplest fraction equivalent of 25%. You could also call out a decimal and have students look for its equivalent percent and/or simplified fraction, or you could call out a reduced fraction and have the students look for the equivalent decimal and/or percent on their BINGO card(s).

Note This!

Create a Checklist Help students create a study checklist. The checklist should include the following items.

- Solve for the *whole* using the percent equation.
- Solve for the *part* using the percent equation.
- Solve for the *percent* using the percent equation.
- Solve percent word problems.

Students should put a checkmark next to each topic when they feel they have a good grasp of the process.

3-3 Calculate Percents (pp. 117–124)

Solve using the percent equation. Check each answer.

18. 25% of what number is 90? 360
19. 15% of what number is 33? 220
20. 30% of what number is 120? 400

Example 5

20% of what number is 32?

1. Write the percent equation. percent × whole = part
2. Substitute the known numbers and a variable into the equation. Write 20% as a decimal. $0.20 \times n = 32$; $\frac{0.20n}{0.20} = \frac{32}{0.20}$; $n = 160$
3. Solve for the variable.
4. Check your answer. $0.20 \times 160 = 32$ ✓

Solve using the percent equation. Check each answer.

21. What is 20% of 140? 28
22. What is 30% of 520? 156
23. What is 22% of 740? 162.8
24. What is 7% of 810? 56.7

Example 6

What is 12% of 400?

1. Write the percent equation. percent × whole = part
2. Substitute the known numbers and a variable into the equation. $0.12 \times 400 = n$
3. Solve for the variable. $48 = n$
4. Check your answer. $0.12 \times 400 = 48$ ✓

Solve using the percent equation. Check each answer.

25. What percent of 620 is 217? 35%
26. What percent of 4,000 is 8? 0.2%
27. What percent of 72 is 18? 25%

Example 7

What percent of 575 is 230?

1. Write the percent equation. percent × whole = part
2. Substitute the given numbers and a variable into the equation. $n \times 575 = 230$; $\frac{575n}{575} = \frac{230}{575}$
3. Solve for the variable. $n = 40$
4. Change the decimal to a percent by multiplying by 100. $0.40 = 40\%$
5. Check your answer. $0.40 \times 575 = 230$ ✓

134 **Chapter 3** Study Guide

Intervention Strategy — Auditory Learners

Verbal Game Play a verbal game with the class. You give them a phrase and they tell you which part of the percent equation is the unknown or the answer the question is looking for. Example: You say, "What number is 30% of 50?" The response you are looking for is not the numeric answer, but simply *"part,"* because that is the portion of the equation that is missing.

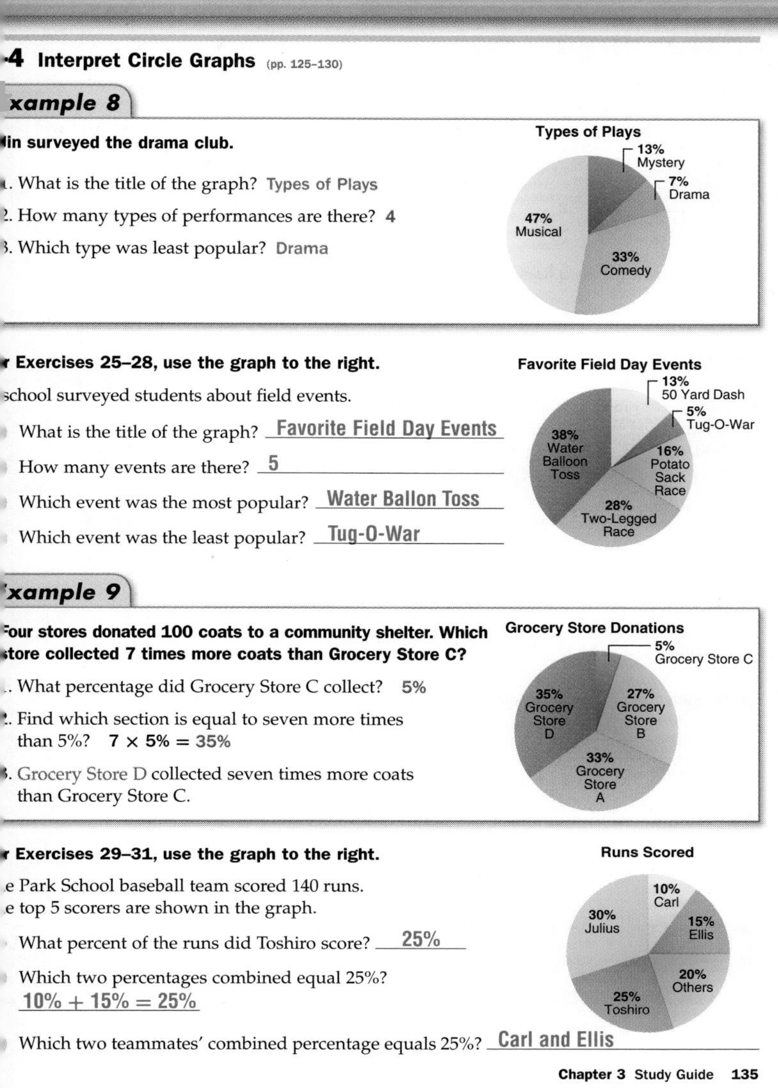

-4 Interpret Circle Graphs (pp. 125–130)

xample 8

in surveyed the drama club.

. What is the title of the graph? Types of Plays
. How many types of performances are there? 4
. Which type was least popular? Drama

Types of Plays
13% Mystery
7% Drama
47% Musical
33% Comedy

Exercises 25–28, use the graph to the right.

school surveyed students about field events.

What is the title of the graph? Favorite Field Day Events
How many events are there? 5
Which event was the most popular? Water Ballon Toss
Which event was the least popular? Tug-O-War

Favorite Field Day Events
13% 50 Yard Dash
5% Tug-O-War
38% Water Balloon Toss
16% Potato Sack Race
28% Two-Legged Race

xample 9

our stores donated 100 coats to a community shelter. Which store collected 7 times more coats than Grocery Store C?

. What percentage did Grocery Store C collect? 5%
. Find which section is equal to seven more times than 5%? 7 × 5% = 35%
. Grocery Store D collected seven times more coats than Grocery Store C.

Grocery Store Donations
5% Grocery Store C
35% Grocery Store D
27% Grocery Store B
33% Grocery Store A

Exercises 29–31, use the graph to the right.

e Park School baseball team scored 140 runs. e top 5 scorers are shown in the graph.

What percent of the runs did Toshiro score? 25%
Which two percentages combined equal 25%? 10% + 15% = 25%
Which two teammates' combined percentage equals 25%? Carl and Ellis

Runs Scored
10% Carl
15% Ellis
20% Others
25% Toshiro
30% Julius

Chapter 3 Study Guide 135

Ticket Out the Door

Do These Problems Write a percent on the board. Have students model the percent with a grid and write it as a decimal and as a fraction in simplest form. Students should hand their papers to you as they exit the classroom.

Chapter 3

Chapter Test

Chapter Resource Masters

Additional forms of the Chapter 3 Tests are available.

Test Format	Where to Find it
Chapter 3 Test	Math Online glencoe.com
Blackline Masters	Assessment Masters, p. 51

Customize and create multiple versions of your chapter tests and their answer keys. All of these questions from the chapter tests are available on ExamView® Assessment Suite.

Online Assessment and Reporting
glencoe.com

This online assessment tool allows teachers to track student progress with easily accessible comprehensive reports available for every student. Assess students using any internet-ready computer.

Alternative Assessment

Use Portfolios Have students write several sentences explaining how $\frac{3}{4}$, 0.75, and 75% are related. After they have written the paragraphs, have them demonstrate the relationships with mathematical symbols.

Chapter Test

Identify the percent shown in each model.

1 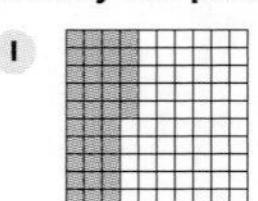 35%

2 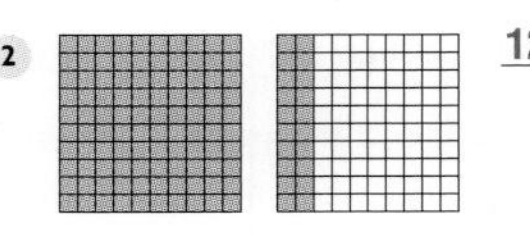 120%

Write each percent as a decimal and as a fraction in simplest form.

3 55% 0.55; $\frac{11}{20}$

4 28% 0.28; $\frac{7}{25}$

5 125% 1.25; $1\frac{1}{4}$

6 107% 1.07; $1\frac{7}{100}$

Use the circle graph to the right to answer Exercises 7–9.
The manager at Super Sports needed to order new sports equipment. She looked at the sales data to see which type of equipment was sold last month.

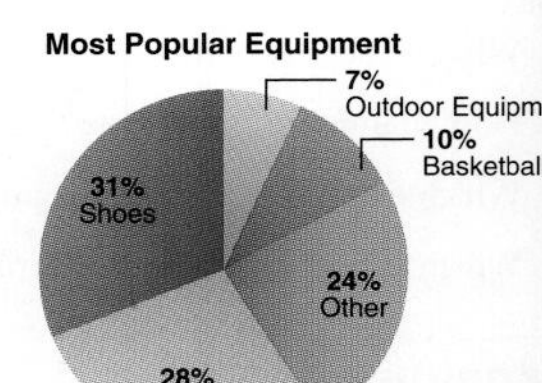

7 What type of equipment was purchased the most? shoes

8 What was purchased less than clothes but more than outdoor equipment? basketballs or other

9 What category was purchased four times more than outdoor equipment? clothes

Write each fraction as a decimal and as a percent.

10 $\frac{1}{2}$ 0.5; 50%

11 $\frac{5}{4}$ 1.25; 125%

12 $\frac{9}{8}$ 1.125; 112.5%

13 $\frac{12}{5}$ 2.4; 240%

14 $\frac{3}{5}$ 0.6; 60%

15 $\frac{6}{15}$ 0.4; 40%

Solve using the percent equation. Check each answer.

16 15% of what number is 90? 600

17 What is 6.5% of 3,600? 234

18 What percent of 625 is 125? 20%

19 What is 12% of 600? 72

20 50% of what number is 8? 16

21 What percent of 69 is 23? 33%

136 Chapter 3 Test

English Learner Strategy

Assessment Allow students time to look over the assessment. Have students take a close look at all the problem directions, as well as any terms in the word problems. Be sure students understand what is being asked of them in each problem. If there are some students struggling with terminology, try to either explain further or give them reference pages in their textbooks where the terms are presented.

se the graph to answer Exercises 22–24.

OUNTY FAIR Lydia purchased 40 ride tickets at the county ir to share with her friends. She shared them with five ifferent friends. Which two friends combined tickets equal e percentage of tickets given to Tamera?

Tickets Shared

10% Paulita
15% Laine
20% Mila
25% Tamera
30% Alisa

2 What percentage of tickets did Tamera receive? 25%

3 Which two percentages combined equal 25%?

10% + 15% = 25%

4 Which two friends' combined percentage equals 25%?

Paulita and Laine

olve.

5 **EDUCATION** In Ms. Turner's 8th-grade math classroom of 24 students, 6 students received an A on their math test. Write the ratio of the students who received an A on their test to the total number of students as a decimal and a percent.

0.25; 25%

6 **SKI CLUB** The Valley Ridge High School has 80 members in the Ski Club. Twenty of the members are in the 11th grade. What percent of the total number of members are in 11th grade?

25%

7 **BASEBALL** Matthew got 24 hits out of his last 75 at bats. Write his batting average as a decimal and as a fraction in simplest form.

0.32; $\frac{8}{25}$

orrect the mistake.

8 Adrian wanted to purchase an MP3 player. The regular price was $59.99. It was on sale for 10% off. When Adrian's mother asked him about the sale price, he told her that the discount percentage was equal to 0.12. What did Adrian do wrong?

The discount was actually equal to 0.10.

STOP

Learning from Mistakes

Review Review commonly missed questions or topics in small groups or as a class. Ask students to share their methods of answering each question. Try to find out if the mistakes are computational or whether they lack adequate understanding of the topic. Some further explanation may be required accordingly.

Data-Driven Decision Making

Students missing Exercises . . .	Have trouble with . . .	Should review and practice . . .
1–6	identifying and writing percents, fractions, and decimals and their relationships to one another.	SSG Lessons 3-1 and 3-2, pp. 102 and 109 CRM Skills Practice, pp. A51 and A55
10–15	writing fractions as decimals or percents.	SSG Lesson 3-2, p. 109 CRM Skills Practice, p. A55
16–21	calculating percents.	SSG Lesson 3-3, p. 117 CRM Skills Practice, p. A59
7–9, 22–24	interpreting circle graphs.	SSG Lesson 3-4, p. 125 CRM Skills Practice, p. A63
25–28	solving word problems involving percents, fractions, and decimals.	CRM Problem-Solving Practice, pp. A52, A56, A60, and A64

Chapter 3 Test Practice

Diagnose Student Errors

Survey student responses for each item. Class trends may indicate common errors and misconceptions.

1. A The model represents 66%.
Ⓑ correct
C The model represents 76%.
D The model represents 84%.

2. A least popular
B guess
C guess
Ⓓ correct

3. A Pepperoni is most often.
Ⓑ correct
C Cheese is not second least.
D These are most often.

4. A guess
B guess
C guess
Ⓓ correct

5. A incorrect percent
B incorrect decimal
Ⓒ correct
D incorrect decimal and percent

6. Ⓐ correct
B misinterpreted equivalent fraction
C misinterpreted equivalent fraction
D misinterpreted equivalent fraction

7. A miscalculated
Ⓑ correct
C miscalculated
D guess

8. A guess
B miscalculated
Ⓒ correct
D miscalculated

9. A tip amount
B subtracted tip from total
C misinterpreted question
Ⓓ correct

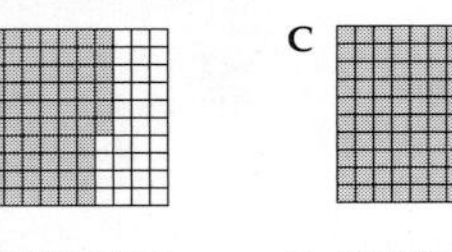

Chapter 3 Test Practice

Choose the best answer and fill in the corresponding circle on the sheet at right.

1 Which model represents 74%?

A 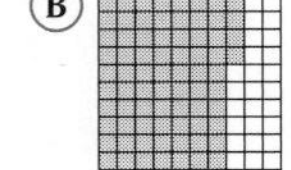

C 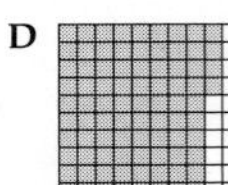

Ⓑ

D

Use the graph to answer Exercises 2–4.

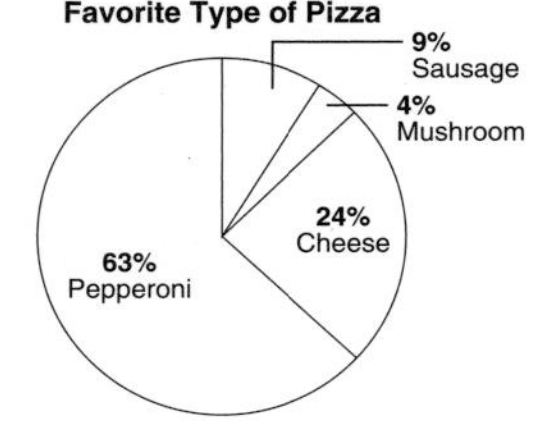

Denise surveyed her 10th grade class to see which topping on their pizza they like best. She displayed the results of the survey in a circle graph.

2 Which type of pizza was most popular?

A Mushroom
B Cheese
C Sausage
Ⓓ Pepperoni

3 Which two sections represent the types of pizza chosen least often?

A Pepperoni and Sausage
Ⓑ Sausage and Mushroom
C Mushroom and Cheese
D Cheese and Pepperoni

4 Which two types of pizza equal 33% when added together?

A Mushroom and Cheese
B Sausage and Pepperoni
C Pepperoni and Mushroom
Ⓓ Cheese and Sausage

5 Which statement is correct?

A $\frac{6}{8} = 0.75 = 7.5\%$
B $\frac{1}{10} = 1.0 = 10\%$
Ⓒ $\frac{1}{5} = 0.20 = 20\%$
D $\frac{2}{4} = 0.24 = 24\%$

6 Emilio watches a quiz show on TV every night. He guesses correctly on 70% of the questions. What fraction of the questions does Emilio answer correctly?

Ⓐ $\frac{7}{10}$
B $\frac{3}{4}$
C $\frac{7}{5}$
D $\frac{1}{2}$

10. A amount of discount
B guess
Ⓒ correct
D misplaced decimal point of discount amount

11. Ⓐ correct
B miscalculated
C miscalculated
D guess

Brittney scored $\frac{16}{20}$ on her math quiz. What is her percent?

A 70% C 75%

(B) 80% D 90%

Kyra read 320 pages of her novel this week. Samuel read 80% of Kyra's total pages. How many pages did Samuel read this week?

A 26 pages (C) 256 pages

B 240 pages D 260 pages

A meal totals $22.60, including tax. After a 20% tip is added, what is the total cost of the meal?

A $4.52

B $18.08

C $22.60

(D) $27.12

This sweater is priced at $38. What is the price after the discount?

A $9.50 (C) $28.50

B $25 D $950

---

11 In a debate club of 18 students, 10 of the students are girls. Write the ratio of girls to total number of students as a percent.

(A) 56% C 67%

B 61% D 72%

ANSWER SHEET

Directions: Fill in the circle of each correct answer.

1 A **B** C D

2 A B C **D**

3 A **B** C D

4 A B C **D**

5 A B **C** D

6 **A** B C D

7 A **B** C D

8 A B **C** D

9 A B C **D**

10 A B **C** D

11 **A** B C D

Success Strategy
Read the entire question before looking at the answer choices. Make sure you know what the question is asking.

Diagnosing Student Errors and Misconceptions

Review When working on the Test Practice problems, have students show their work on a separate sheet of notebook paper that can be used later as a reference if needed. After the class has completed the Test Practice problems, go over all the correct responses and have the students score their own responses or they can trade and grade papers.

Have students first try to correct their own mistakes. If they are still having trouble, try to determine whether or not the mistake was due to a basic computational error or whether they just misunderstood the question altogether. If the majority of errors are computational, then try to determine if the mistakes are minor and careless. If they are *not* simply the result of working too quickly or carelessly, then review some of the algorithms required in these exercises.

If the mistakes are because students do not understand the question, pair the students who have a very good grasp of the material with those who need additional help to work together on some exercises.

Common Error *Alert*

Exercise 1 Point out to students that when interpreting a model, any time one whole model is completely shaded, this automatically represents 100%. The other partially shaded models tell you how much greater than 100% the percent is.

Exercises 8–11 On word problems or situational questions, remind students to analyze their answers, asking themselves whether or not their answers are sensible. Oftentimes, especially in the case of multiple-choice questions, some answers can be thrown out because they are not reasonable within the context of the question.

Chapter 4

Chapter Overview

Chapter-at-a-Glance

Lesson	Math Objective	State/Local Standards
4-1 Metric Length (pp. 142-148)	Understand the metric system of measurement. Select and apply techniques and tools to accurately find appropriate levels of precision.	
4-2 Unit Conversions: Metric Length (pp. 149-155)	Convert units of metric length.	
Progress Check 1 (p. 156)		
4-3 Customary Length (pp. 157-162)	Understand the customary system of measurement. Select and apply techniques and tools to accurately find appropriate levels of precision.	
4-4 Unit Conversions: Customary Length (pp. 163-168)	Convert units of customary length.	
Progress Check 2 (p. 169)		

Content-at-a-Glance

The diagram below summarizes and unpacks Chapter 4 content.

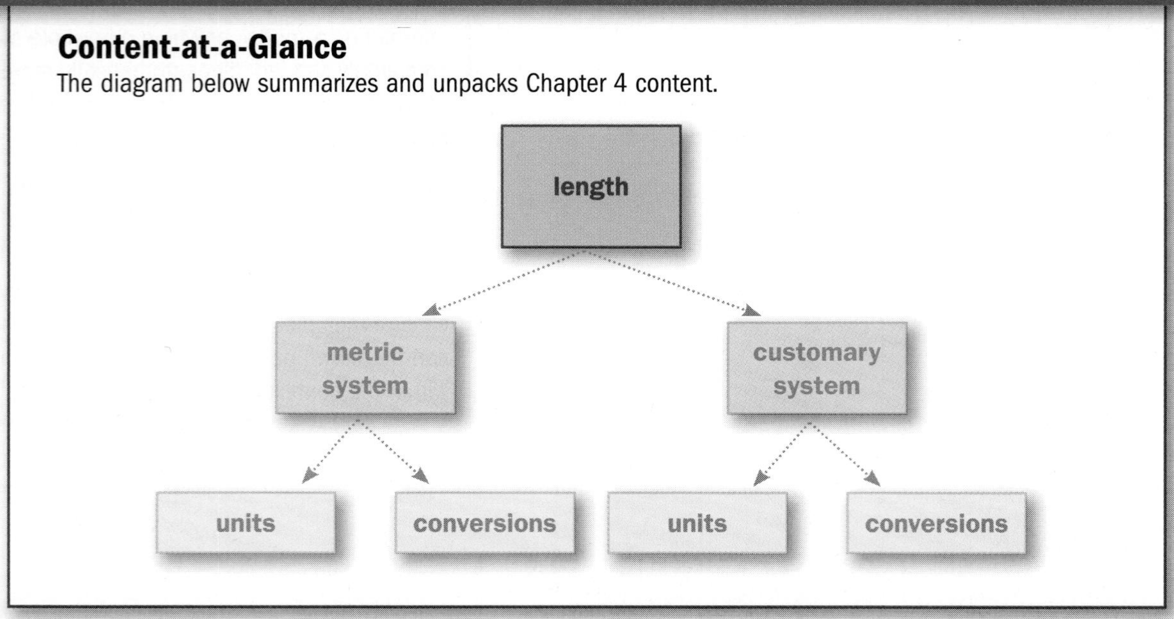

Online Assessment and Reporting
glencoe.com

Chapter Assessment Manager

Diagnostic Diagnose students' readiness.

	Student Study Guide/ Teacher Edition	Assessment Masters	Technology
Course Placement Test		1	ExamView® Assessment Suite
Book 2 Pretest		62	ExamView® Assessment Suite
Chapter 4 Pretest		65	ExamView® Assessment Suite
Quiz/Preview	SSG 141		Math Online glencoe.com StudentWorks™ Plus

Formative Identify students' misconceptions of content knowledge.

	Student Study Guide/ Teacher Edition	Assessment Masters	Technology
Progress Checks	SSG 156, 169		Math Online glencoe.com StudentWorks™ Plus
Vocabulary Review	SSG 170		Math Online glencoe.com
Lesson Assessments			ExamView® Assessment Suite
Are They Getting It?	TE 145, 152, 160, 166		

Summative Determine student success in learning concepts in the lesson, chapter, or book.

	Student Study Guide/ Teacher Edition	Assessment Masters	Technology
Chapter 4 Test	SSG 174	68	ExamView® Assessment Suite
Test Practice	SSG 176	71	ExamView® Assessment Suite
Alternative Assessment	TE 174	74	
See It, Do It, Say It, Write It	TE 148, 155, 162, 168		
Book 2 Test		98	ExamView® Assessment Suite

Back-mapping and Vertical Alignment **McGraw-Hill's *Math Triumphs*** intervention program was conceived and developed with the final result in mind: student success in grade-level mathematics, including Algebra 1 and beyond. The authors, using the **NCTM Focal Points and Focal Connections** as their guide, developed this brand-new series by backmapping from grade-level and Algebra 1 concepts, and vertically aligning the topics so that they build upon prior skills and concepts and serve as a foundation for future topics.

Chapter Resource Manager

	Lesson 4-1	Lesson 4-2	Lesson 4-3	Lesson 4-4
Concept	Metric Length	Unit Conversions: Metric Length	Customary Length	Unit Conversions: Customary Length
Objective	Understand the metric system of measurement. Select and apply techniques and tools to accurately find appropriate levels of precision.	Convert units of metric length.	Understand the customary system of measurement. Select and apply techniques and tools to accurately find appropriate levels of precision.	Convert units of customary length.
Math Vocabulary	centimeter kilometer length meter metric system millimeter	benchmark centimeter convert kilometer meter metric system millimeter	customary system foot inch length mile yard	benchmark convert customary system foot inch mile yard
Lesson Resources	**Materials** • Everyday objects • Large paperclip **Manipulatives** • Centimeter ruler • Millimeter ruler • Meter stick **Other Resources** CRM Vocabulary and English Language Development CRM Skills Practice CRM Problem-Solving Practice CRM Homework Practice	**Materials** • Everyday objects • Dime • Paper clips • Crayons • Baseball bat **Manipulatives** • Centimeter ruler • Millimeter ruler • Meter stick • Base-ten blocks **Other Resources** CRM Vocabulary and English Language Development CRM Skills Practice CRM Problem-Solving Practice CRM Homework Practice	**Materials** • Everyday objects **Manipulatives** • Inch ruler • Yardstick **Other Resources** CRM Vocabulary and English Language Development CRM Skills Practice CRM Problem-Solving Practice CRM Homework Practice	**Materials** • Everyday objects **Manipulatives** • Inch ruler • Yardstick **Other Resources** CRM Vocabulary and English Language Development CRM Skills Practice CRM Problem-Solving Practice CRM Homework Practice
Technology	Math Online glencoe.com StudentWorks™ Plus ExamView® Assessment Suite	Math Online glencoe.com StudentWorks™ Plus ExamView® Assessment Suite	Math Online glencoe.com StudentWorks™ Plus ExamView® Assessment Suite	Math Online glencoe.com StudentWorks™ Plus ExamView® Assessment Suite

Intervention Strategy

Familiar Objects

Measuring objects that are familiar to students will help them create perspective when talking about the various units in length in both the metric and customary systems.

Step 1 Have students create a chart like the one shown below.

Object	centimeters	millimeters	inches	feet

Step 2 Place stickers on various objects around the classroom. Instruct students to measure those objects in centimeters, millimeters, inches, and feet. Have students record their measurements in their tables.

Step 3 As a class, compare the lengths that each student measured. Discuss any common mistakes.

Step 4 Have students identify a pattern in their centimeter and millimeter measures. Elicit a response that the millimeter measure is about 10 times the centimeter measurement.

Step 5 Have students identify a pattern in their inches and feet measures. Elicit a response that the inch measure is about 12 times the feet measurement.

Step 6 Tell students to use their centimeter ruler and draw a line that is 10 centimeters long. Without measuring, ask students how many millimeters long the line is. Have students measure the line in millimeters to confirm the line is 100 millimeters.

Step 7 Tell students to use their inch ruler and draw a line that is 6 inches long. Without measuring, ask students how many feet long the line is. Have students measure the line in feet to confirm the line is half of a foot.

Chapter 4

Chapter Notes

Real-World Applications

Photography Pictures are often described using measurements given in either centimeters or inches. Occasionally, picture frames sold at the store are the same size, but the measurements are given with a converted unit. For example, a picture may be 24 inches by 36 inches, but the frame size is 2 feet by 3 feet. Unit conversions will show that these measures are equivalent. Have students list some other equivalent measures.

Intervention Strategy

Stair Diagrams

Step 1 Divide students into small groups.

Step 2 Review with students the topics for the lessons of the chapter. For each lesson they will need to come up with a diagram showing the relationships between the units. A common diagram used with measurement is a stair diagram. Each diagram should include the base unit and at least the three units above and the three units below the base unit.

Step 3 Students should also include next to each unit an example that describes the unit.

Step 4 Each group should present their diagrams and examples to the class. Students should compare diagrams for accuracy.

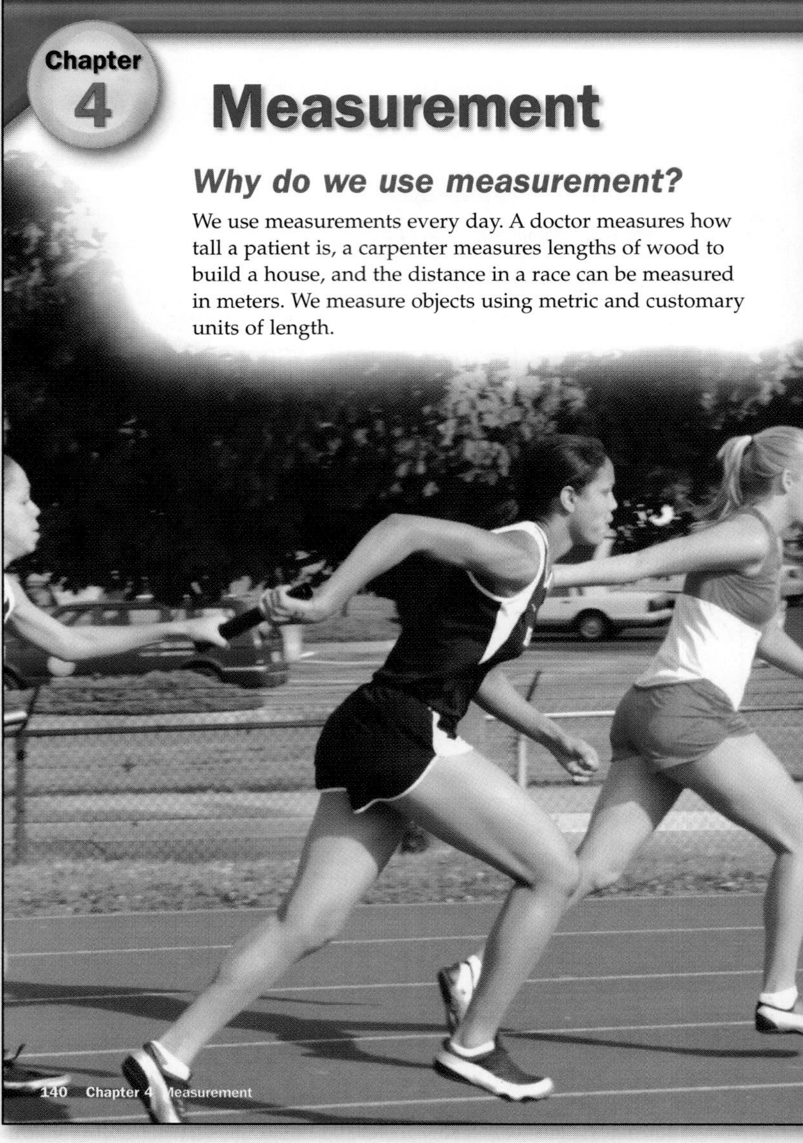
Chapter 4

Measurement

Why do we use measurement?

We use measurements every day. A doctor measures how tall a patient is, a carpenter measures lengths of wood to build a house, and the distance in a race can be measured in meters. We measure objects using metric and customary units of length.

140 Chapter 4 Measurement

Key Vocabulary

Find interactive definitions in 13 languages in the **eGlossary** at glencoe.com.

English **Español** *Introduce the most important vocabulary terms from Chapter 4.*

benchmark **parámetro**
an object or number used as a guide to estimate or reference (p. 149)

convert **convertir**
to find an equivalent measure (p. 149)

customary system **sistema inglés**
a measurement system that includes units such as foot, pound, and quart (p. 157)

inch **pulgada**
a customary measure of length (p. 157)

length **longitude**
a measurement of the distance between two points (p. 142)

meter **metro**
the base unit of length in the metric system (p. 142)

metric system **sistema métrico**
a decimal system of weights and measures (p. 142)

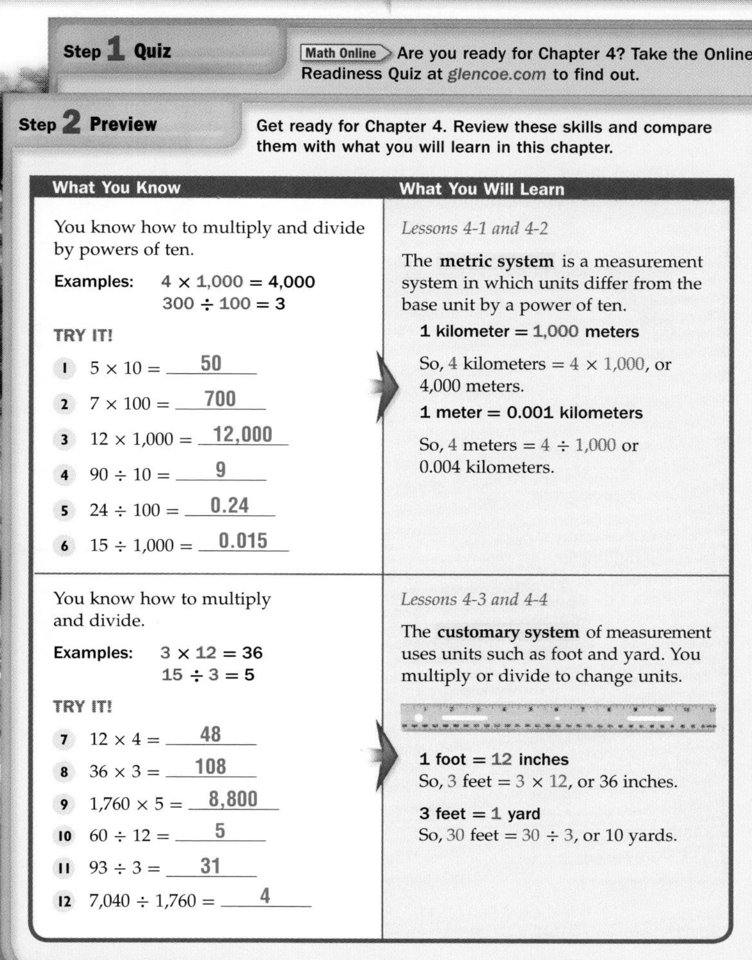

Step 1 Quiz

Math Online Are you ready for Chapter 4? Take the Online Readiness Quiz at *glencoe.com* to find out.

Step 2 Preview

Get ready for Chapter 4. Review these skills and compare them with what you will learn in this chapter.

What You Know	What You Will Learn
You know how to multiply and divide by powers of ten. Examples: 4 × 1,000 = 4,000 300 ÷ 100 = 3 **TRY IT!** 1 5 × 10 = 50 2 7 × 100 = 700 3 12 × 1,000 = 12,000 4 90 ÷ 10 = 9 5 24 ÷ 100 = 0.24 6 15 ÷ 1,000 = 0.015	*Lessons 4-1 and 4-2* The **metric system** is a measurement system in which units differ from the base unit by a power of ten. **1 kilometer = 1,000 meters** So, 4 kilometers = 4 × 1,000, or 4,000 meters. **1 meter = 0.001 kilometers** So, 4 meters = 4 ÷ 1,000 or 0.004 kilometers.
You know how to multiply and divide. Examples: 3 × 12 = 36 15 ÷ 3 = 5 **TRY IT!** 7 12 × 4 = 48 8 36 × 3 = 108 9 1,760 × 5 = 8,800 10 60 ÷ 12 = 5 11 93 ÷ 3 = 31 12 7,040 ÷ 1,760 = 4	*Lessons 4-3 and 4-4* The **customary system** of measurement uses units such as foot and yard. You multiply or divide to change units. **1 foot = 12 inches** So, 3 feet = 3 × 12, or 36 inches. **3 feet = 1 yard** So, 30 feet = 30 ÷ 3, or 10 yards.

141

Vocabulary Preview

- As students complete the Chapter Preview, have them make a list of important terms and prefixes throughout the chapter.
- Using graph paper, have students create a stair diagram to define each prefix associated with unit measurement.
- Below the stair diagram, have them list the various base units and definitions.
- Once students are finished, pair them up and have them challenge each other to define words that are a combination of a prefix and base unit such as *kilometer*.

Step 1 Quiz

Pretest/Prescribe Students can take the Online Readiness Quiz or the Diagnostic Pretest in the Assessment Masters.

Step 2 Preview

Use this pre-chapter activity to activate students' prior knowledge, build confidence, and help students preview the lessons.

Dinah Zike's Foldables®

Guide students through the directions on p. A66 in the Chapter Resource Masters to create their own Foldable graphic organizer for use with this chapter.

Home Connections

- Find and name three tools that are used frequently in your home to measure length. Also, tell what they measure and the units used for the measurement.

Mc Graw Hill Professional Development

Targeted professional development has been articulated throughout **McGraw-Hill's *Math Triumphs*** intervention program. **The McGraw-Hill Professional Development Video Library** provides short videos that support the **NCTM Focal Points and Focal Connections.** For more information, visit glencoe.com.

Lesson 4-1 Lesson Notes

Lesson Planner

Objective Understand the metric system of measurement. Select and apply techniques and tools to accurately find length to appropriate levels of precision.

Vocabulary **centimeter**, **kilometer**, **length**, **meter**, **metric system**, **millimeter**

Materials/Manipulatives centimeter ruler, millimeter ruler, meter stick, large paperclip

Chapter Resource Masters

- CRM Vocabulary and English Language Development (p. A69)
- CRM Skills Practice (p. A70)
- CRM Problem-Solving Practice (p. A71)
- CRM Homework Practice (p. A72)

1 Introduce

Vocabulary

Prefixes Students should be able to relate the prefixes for the metric system across other concepts of measurement. The prefixes centi-, milli-, and kilo- are probably the most commonly used metric prefixes. A chart like the one below may help students associate the magnitudes represented by the prefixes.

milli	centi	deci	UNIT	deca	hecto	kilo
$\frac{1}{1000}$	$\frac{1}{100}$	$\frac{1}{10}$	1	10	100	1000

2 Teach

Key Concept

Foundational Skills and Concepts After students have read through the Key Concept box, have them try these exercises.

1. Which is a larger unit, a centimeter or a kilometer? kilometer
2. If you were going to measure the distance from your seat in the classroom to the door of the classroom, what unit would you use? meter

Lesson 4-1 Metric Length

KEY Concept

The metric system is a decimal system of weights and measures. A **meter** is the base unit of length in the **metric system**.

The most commonly used metric units of **length** are shown below.

Metric Units of Length

Metric Unit	Symbol	Real-World Benchmark	Meaning
millimeter	mm	thickness of a dime	one-thousandth
centimeter	cm	half the width of a penny	one-hundredth
meter	m	height of a doorknob	one
kilometer	km	six city blocks	one-thousand

Units on a centimeter ruler are divided into ten parts. Each part is a millimeter.

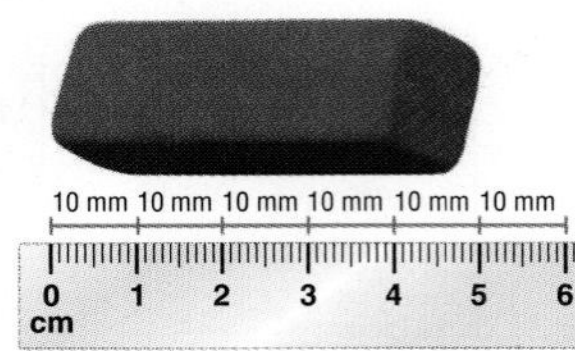

To read millimeters, count each individual mark on the centimeter ruler. There are ten millimeter marks for each centimeter mark.

The eraser is about 5 centimeters or 50 millimeters long.

VOCABULARY

centimeter a metric unit of length; one centimeter equals one-hundredth of a meter

kilometer a metric unit of length; one kilometer equals one thousand meters

length a measurement of the distance between two points

meter the base unit of length in the metric system; one meter equals one-thousandth of a kilometer

metric system a decimal system of weights and measures

millimeter a metric unit of length; one millimeter equals one-thousandth of a meter

English Learner Strategy

Worldwide Length Length is a measured distance that is used in every culture throughout the world. The difference is the units that people use to measure the distance. Arrange students into groups with at least one EL student in every group, if possible. Have the EL student explain to the other students the measuring units that their native country uses. This is a way for the EL student to bring in prior knowledge of measuring to math class.

Example 1

Find the length of the golf tee to the nearest centimeter.

1. Line up the "zero mark" of a ruler with the left end of the golf tee.

2. Read the number on the ruler that lines up with the right end of the golf tee.

The golf tee is 5 centimeters long.

YOUR TURN!

Find the length of the paper clip to the nearest centimeter.

1. Line up the "zero mark" of a ruler with the left end of the paper clip.

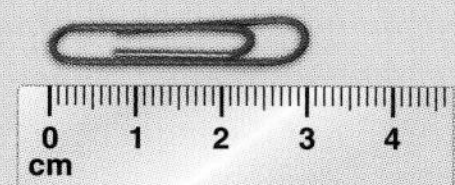

2. Read the number on the ruler that lines up with the right end of the paper clip.

The paper clip is about <u>3</u> centimeters long.

Example 2

Find the length of the ticket to the nearest millimeter.

1. Line up the "zero mark" of the ruler with the left end of the ticket.

2. Read the mark on the ruler that lines up with the right end of the ticket by counting each individual mark.

The ticket is about 59 millimeters long.

YOUR TURN!

Find the length of the quarter to the nearest millimeter.

1. Line up the "zero mark" of a ruler with the left end of the quarter.

2. Read the mark on the ruler that lines up with the right end of the quarter by counting each individual mark.

The quarter is about <u>24</u> millimeters long.

Intervention Strategy — Visual Learners

Number Lines and Rulers Number lines prepare students for rulers because students often get confused about the intervals of rulers. Preparation for measuring with metric rulers can be made with a number line. Introduce the number line first or at the same time as the ruler.

Additional *Example 1*

Find the length of the eraser to the nearest centimeter.

1. Line up the "zero mark" of the ruler with the left end of the eraser.

2. Read the number on the ruler that lines up with the right end of the eraser by counting each individual mark.

The eraser is about 6 centimeters long.

Additional *Example 2*

Find the length of the rubber band to the nearest millimeter.

1. Line up the "zero mark" of the ruler with the left end of the rubber band.

2. Read the mark on the ruler that lines up with the right end of the rubber band by counting each individual mark.

The rubber band is 27 millimeters long.

Additional **Example 3**

Which unit would you use to measure the distance from Chicago to Atlanta: *millimeter*, *centimeter*, *meter*, or *kilometer*?

The distance from Chicago to Atlanta is ...

1. greater than the thickness of a dime. millimeter
2. greater than half the width of a penny. centimeter
3. greater than the height of a doorknob. meter

The kilometer is an appropriate unit of measure.

3 Practice

Using Manipulatives

Because millimeters and centimeters are not units that most students are familiar with, give students a common, everyday item in which they can reference.

A millimeter is approximately equal to the thickness of a dime. Have a dime to show the students.

- To picture a centimeter, think of a stack of ten dimes.
- To picture a meter, think of a stack of 1,000 dimes.

A centimeter is approximately equal to the width of a large paperclip. Have a large paperclip to show the students.

- To picture a meter, think of 100 large paperclips lying side by side.
- To picture a kilometer, think of 100,000 large paperclips lying side by side.

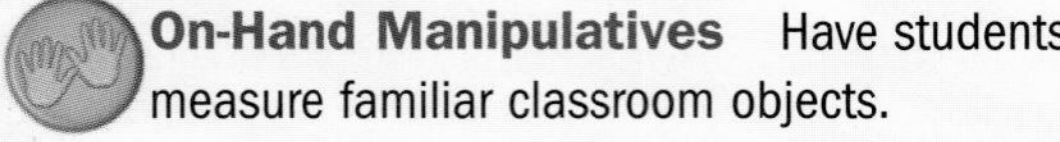

On-Hand Manipulatives Have students measure familiar classroom objects.

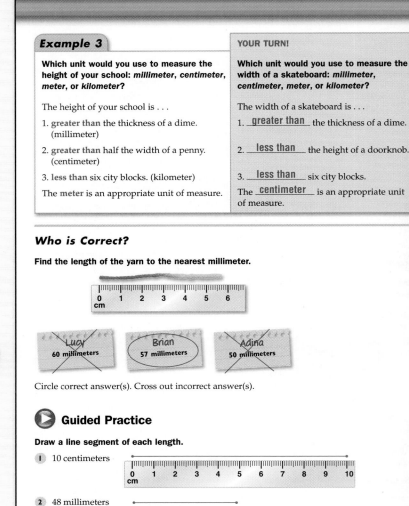

Example 3

Which unit would you use to measure the height of your school: *millimeter*, *centimeter*, *meter*, or *kilometer*?

The height of your school is . . .

1. greater than the thickness of a dime. (millimeter)
2. greater than half the width of a penny. (centimeter)
3. less than six city blocks. (kilometer)

The meter is an appropriate unit of measure.

YOUR TURN!

Which unit would you use to measure the width of a skateboard: *millimeter*, *centimeter*, *meter*, or *kilometer*?

The width of a skateboard is . . .

1. greater than the thickness of a dime.
2. less than the height of a doorknob.
3. less than six city blocks.

The centimeter is an appropriate unit of measure.

Who is Correct?

Find the length of the yarn to the nearest millimeter.

0 1 2 3 4 5 6 cm

Lucy: 60 millimeters | Brian: 57 millimeters | Adina: 50 millimeters

Circle correct answer(s). Cross out incorrect answer(s).

Guided Practice

Draw a line segment of each length.

1. 10 centimeters
2. 48 millimeters

144 Chapter 4 Measurement

Who *is Correct?*

Diagnostic Teaching

- Lucy wrote 60 millimeters. This is not correct because Lucy did not give an exact measurement. Guide students who make this mistake to count each mark on the ruler to the right end of an object.
- Brian wrote 57 millimeters. This is correct.
- Adina wrote 50 millimeters. This is not correct because it is not a precise measurement.

Remind students that a metric ruler is divided into centimeters and millimeters. The smaller units are millimeters.

Step by Step Practice

3 Find the width of the golf ball to the nearest centimeter.

Step 1 Line up the "zero mark" of the ruler with the left end of the golf ball.

Step 2 Read the number on the ruler that lines up with the right end of the golf ball.

The golf ball is about 4 centimeters wide.

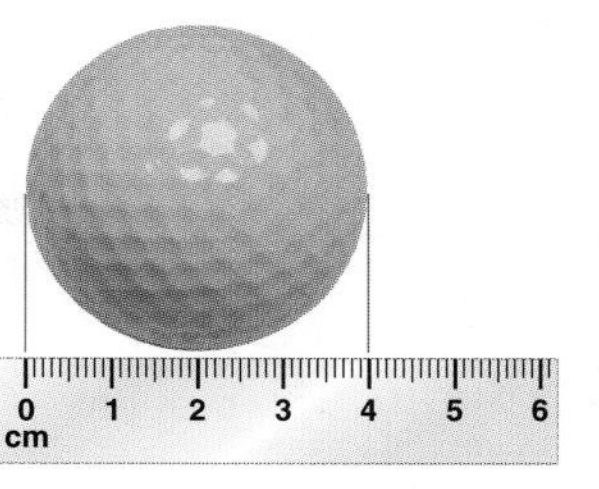

ind the length of each line segment.

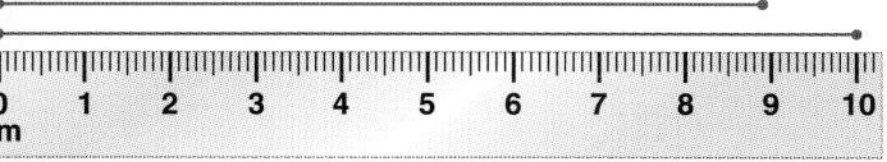

4 Red line segment to the nearest millimeter: 89 mm

5 Blue line segment to the nearest centimeter: 10 cm

ind the length of each object to the nearest centimeter r millimeter.

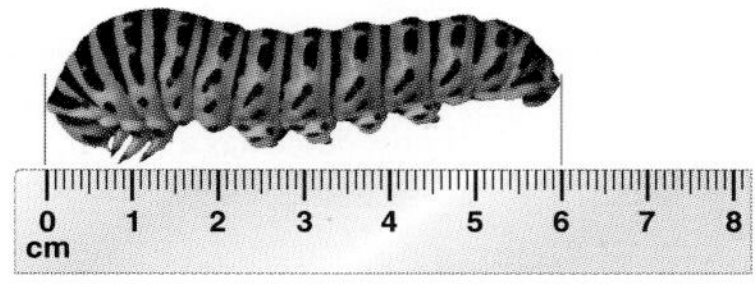

6 43 mm

7 6 cm

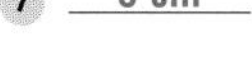

Common Error Alert

Exercises 4 and 5 If students do not write the correct answers for Exercises 4 or 5, they might be confusing centimeters with millimeters. Point out to students that millimeter is a smaller unit, so it will take more millimeters to reach the end of the line segment than centimeters. For students that are confusing millimeters with centimeters, have them give some equivalents that are multiples of 10, such as 30 mm = 3 cm and 7 cm = 70 mm.

Note This!

Real-World Length In this lesson, students are introduced to using length to measure distance. Suggest that students create a list of real-world items and common units of length used to measure those items.

Are They Getting It?

Check students' understanding of measuring length by writing these problems on the board. Ask students to point out wrong answers. Tell them to use a ruler to show why the answers are correct or not correct.

1. The length of this line segment to the nearest millimeter is 64 millimeters. This is not correct. The length is 79 millimeters.

2. The length of this line segment to the nearest centimeter is 10 centimeters. This is correct.

3. The most appropriate unit to use to measure the length of the cafeteria is centimeters. This is not correct. The most appropriate unit to use is meters.

Common Error *Alert*

Multi-Step Problem If students are having difficulty with word problems, explain that word problems involve many steps. First, students may need to pick a strategy when solving the problem. Then, they need to use the correct side of the ruler and know the preciseness of the measurement.

Math Coach Notes

Patterns on Rulers Students should understand that for every centimeter mark on a metric ruler, there are 10 millimeters. However, they should not assume that for every meter there are 10 centimeters. Show students a meter stick. Point out that there are 100 centimeters for every meter. Explain to them that while metric units do increase by powers of 10, not all metric units are commonly used. There are 10 centimeters in 1 decimeter and 10 decimeters in 1 meter. Ask students how many meters are in 1 kilometer. There are 1,000 meters in 1 kilometer.

Common Error *Alert*

Exercise 13 Students may struggle to get an accurate measurement of an object that does not align directly against the ruler, such as the flag in Exercise 13. Demonstrate to students how to place a straightedge, such as another ruler, a pencil, or a line directly against the bottom and top of the figure. The bottom line ensures the base of the object aligns with zero on the ruler. Where the top straightedge or line crosses the ruler is the most accurate measure of length of the object.

Select the proper unit to measure the length of each object. Write *millimeter, centimeter, meter,* or *kilometer.*

8. thickness of a calculator millimeter
9. width of a notebook centimeter
10. height of a flag pole meter
11. distance from home to school kilometer

Step by Step Problem-Solving Practice

Problem-Solving Strategies
- ☐ Look for a pattern.
- ☐ Guess and check.
- ☑ Act it out.
- ☐ Solve a simpler problem.
- ☐ Work backward.

Solve.

12. **BASEBALL** Gloria has a model of a baseball bat. What is the length of the model baseball bat to the nearest centimeter?

Understand Read the problem. Write what you know. Measure the length to the nearest centimeter.

Plan Pick a strategy. One strategy is to act it out. Line up the 0 on a centimeter ruler with the bat.

Solve Read the closest number on the ruler that lines up with the right end of the baseball bat.

The baseball bat is about 11 centimeters.

Check The baseball bat is greater than 11 centimeters and less than 12 centimeters long. The answer makes sense.

13. **MODELS** The post office has a model of a flagpole. What is the <u>height</u> to the <u>nearest</u> <u>millimeter</u>? Check off each step.

✔ Understand: I underlined the key words.

✔ Plan: To solve the problem, I will act it out.

✔ Solve: The answer is 32 millimeters.

✔ Check: I checked my answer by estimating the length in millimeters

Intervention Strategy — Kinesthetic Learners

Measure It Cut yarn into various lengths. Distribute a piece of yarn and a ruler marked with millimeters and centimeters to each student. Instruct students to measure the length of the yarn in both millimeters and centimeters. Repeat the process with other lengths of yarn.

14 **SHOPPING** Darcy bought a ribbon for a dress. What is the length of the ribbon to the nearest centimeter? 9 centimeters

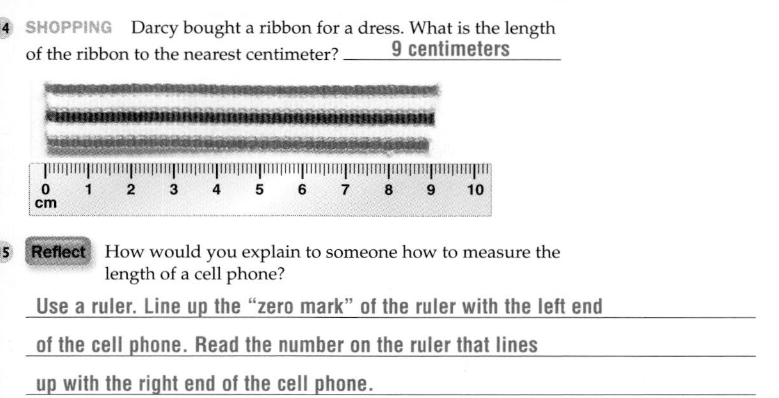

15 **Reflect** How would you explain to someone how to measure the length of a cell phone?

Use a ruler. Line up the "zero mark" of the ruler with the left end of the cell phone. Read the number on the ruler that lines up with the right end of the cell phone.

Skills, Concepts, and Problem Solving

Draw a line segment of each length.

16 4 centimeters

17 95 millimeters

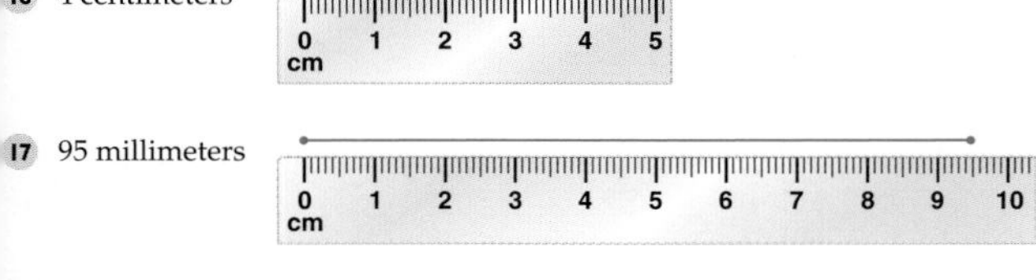

Find the length of each line segment.

18 To the nearest millimeter: 75 mm

19 To the nearest centimeter: 5 cm

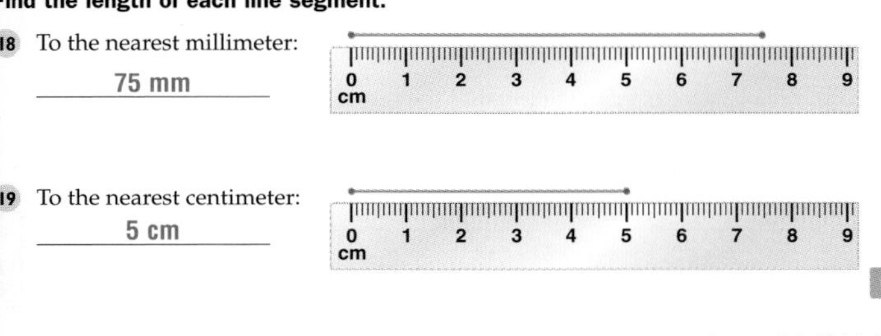

GO ON

Math Challenge

Measure List Instruct each student to create a list with two columns. In the first column they are to list various objects in the classroom. Distribute a ruler marked in centimeters to each student. Have students work with a partner to measure the length of the items listed in the first column. In the second column, list the measurement.

Odd/Even Assignments

Exercises 16–27 are structured so that students practice the same concepts whether they are assigned the odd or even problems.

In-Class Assignment

Have students complete Exercises 16, 18, 21, 22, 27, and 30 to ensure that they understand the concept.

Exercises 22–25 If students struggle with exercises 22-25, review the units of measure. For Exercise 25, show students a dime. Also show students a meter stick. Ask students whether they would prefer to count the number of stacked dimes it would take to reach the top of the house, or the number of stacked meter sticks it would take to reach the top of the house.

See It, Do It, Say It, Write It

Step 1 Show students how to measure the length of an item using a ruler. Draw a line on the board and ask what the length is in centimeters. Have student volunteers measure the line a few times to get an accurate measure. Guide students to the correct answer, using this and other lengths.

Step 2 Ask students to draw a line on paper. Ask them to write a brief explanation of how to measure it in millimeters. Have students draw a line 5 cm long and a line 32 mm long.

Step 3 Have students list three items that should be measured in meters. Have them also list three items that should be measured in millimeters. Select student volunteers to share their items.

Looking Ahead: Pre-teach

Unit Conversions: Metric Length In the next lesson, students will learn how to convert from one metric unit of length to another metric unit of length.

The metric system is a base ten system. This means that conversions within the metric system are made by multiplying or dividing by a power of 10. Students will need to learn the order of the metric units from smallest to largest unit.

smallest unit	millimeter (mm)	
↓	centimeter (cm)	10 mm = 1 cm
	decimeter (dm)	10 cm = 1 dm
	meter (m)	10 dm = 1 m
	decameter (dkm)	10 m = 1 dkm
	hectometer (hm)	10 dkm = 1 hm
largest unit	kilometer (km)	10 hm = 1 km

Find the length of each object to the nearest centimeter or millimeter.

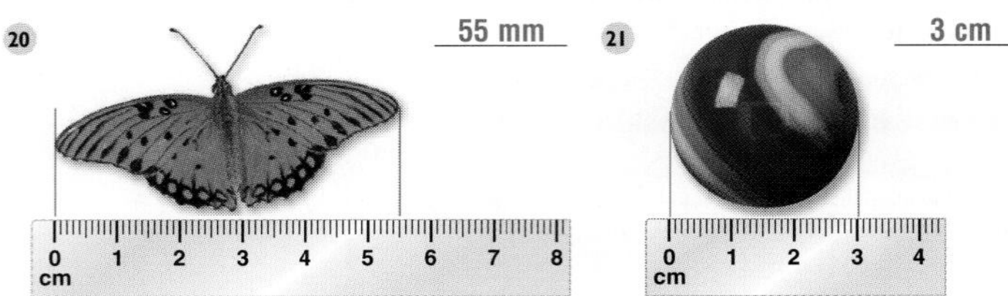

Write the metric unit of length that you would use to measure each of the following.

22 distance between two cities kilometer

23 length of a ladybug millimeter

24 width of a baseball card centimeter

25 height of a house meter

Solve.

26 SCHOOL After Seth sharpened his pencil, it was 101 millimeters long. Draw a line segment to show the length of Seth's pencil.

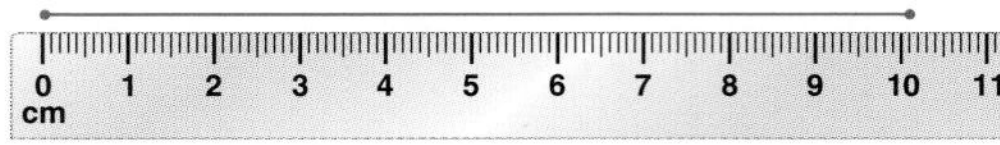

27 SCIENCE A snail traveled 5 centimeters in an hour. Draw a line segment to show this distance.

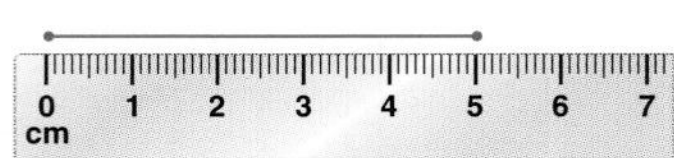

Vocabulary Check **Write the vocabulary word that completes each sentence.**

28 One kilometer equals one thousand meters.

29 The meter is the base unit of length in the metric system.

30 Writing in Math Carlie said she was going to measure the length of her bedroom in millimeters. Is this a good choice? Explain.

No; A millimeter is too small to measure the length of a bedroom. A meter would be better.

Ticket Out the Door

List Items Instruct students to give an example of items found in the classroom that are about 2 mm, 2 cm, and 2 m in length. Have students share their ideas and measure the items, if needed. Students turn in their papers as they exit the classroom.

Lesson 4-2

Unit Conversions: Metric Length

KEY Concept

Prefixes used for units of metric measurement always have the same meaning. The **meter** is the base unit of length in the **metric system**. Each prefix shows the size of a unit compared to a meter.

Prefix	Meaning	Metric Unit	Symbol	Real-World Benchmark
milli	one-thousandth	millimeter	mm	thickness of a dime
centi	one-hundredth	centimeter	cm	half the width of a penny
deci	one-tenth	decimeter	dm	length of a crayon
	one	meter	m	height of a doorknob
kilo	one thousand	kilometer	km	six city blocks

Sometimes it is necessary to **convert** from one unit of measurement to another. A metric place-value chart can be useful.

1000	100	10	1	0.1	0.01	0.001
thousands	hundreds	tens	ones	tenths	hundredths	thousandths
			•			
kilo (km)			meters (m)	deci (dm)	centi (cm)	milli (mm)

The following metric conversion diagram can also be used to help convert metric units of measure. To convert a larger unit to a smaller unit, you should multiply. To convert a smaller unit to a larger unit, you should divide.

× 1000 × 100 × 10

larger units → km ⇄ m ⇄ cm ⇄ mm ← smaller units

÷ 1000 ÷ 100 ÷ 10

VOCABULARY

benchmark
an object or number used as a guide to estimate or reference

centimeter
a metric unit of length; one centimeter equals one-hundredth of a meter

convert
to find an equivalent measure

kilometer
a metric unit of length; one kilometer equals one thousand meters

meter
the base unit of length in the metric system; one meter equals one-thousandth of a kilometer

metric system
a decimal system of weights and measures

millimeter
a metric unit of length; one millimeter equals one-thousandth of a meter

GO ON

Intervention Strategy — Visual Learners

When students are first learning to make conversions within the metric system, have them practice using a chart like the one shown below with a natural number meter measurement. Point out to students the blue decimal points and how they move to the right and left. After students have enough practice to understand how the decimal point needs to move when converting, then they can make a modified chart to use with any metric measurements.

			Unit				
			km	0	0	0.	0
			hm	0	0.	0	
			dkm	0.	0		
			m 8.	0			
		0.	dm				
	0.	0	cm				
0.	0	0	mm				

From this chart, you can see what 8 m equals as other metric units. Simply move the 8 up and down to the desired unit and read the number in that row.

Lesson Notes

Lesson 4-2

Lesson Planner

Objective Convert units of metric length.

Vocabulary **benchmark**, **centimeter**, **convert**, **kilometer**, **meter**, **metric system**, **millimeter**

Materials/Manipulatives centimeter ruler, millimeter ruler, meter stick, base-ten blocks, dimes, paperclips, crayons, baseball bat

Chapter Resource Masters

- CRM Vocabulary and English Language Development (p. A73)
- CRM Skills Practice (p. A74)
- CRM Problem-Solving Practice (p. A75)
- CRM Homework Practice (p. A76)

Vocabulary

Explore Vocabulary Hand out a *meter stick* to each student or student pair. Ask students to describe the patterns they see. Guide students to realize that the *metric system* is a base-ten or decimal system based on the meter. Why is it easy to convert metric units? Discuss the purpose of *benchmarks*. What are nonexamples of benchmarks?

2 Teach

Key Concept

Foundational Skills and Concepts After students have read through the Key Concept box, have them try these exercises.

1. To convert km to m, what should you multiply by? 1,000
2. To convert m to km, what should you divide by? 1,000

Point out the last column of the table in the Key Concept box to students. Tell them to use the last column to help them understand the relative size of a unit by comparing it to everyday objects.

Additional **Example 1**

Convert 5 centimeters to meters.

1. Use a chart. Place 5 in the cm column.

1,000			1	.	0.1	0.01	0.001
thousands			ones	.	tenths	hundredths	thousandths
			0	.	0	5	
kilo (km)			meters (m)		deci (dm)	centi (cm)	milli (mm)

2. Place zeros in the m and dm columns.

3. Read the number from the chart for the conversion. 5 cm = 0.05 m

Additional **Example 2**

Convert 1.6 kilometers to meters.

1. Use a chart. Place 1 in the km column and 6 in the next column to the right.

1,000			1	.	0.1	0.01	0.001
thousands			ones	.	tenths	hundredths	thousandths
1	6	0	0	.			
kilo (km)			meters (m)		deci (dm)	centi (cm)	milli (mm)

2. Place zeros in the columns between 6 and the decimal point.

3. Read the number from the chart for the conversion. 1.6 km = 1,600 m

Note This!

Prefixes Students may have difficulty remembering the definition of each prefix used in the metric system. Tell students to list the prefixes and their meanings in their notes. Have students write the prefixes on one side of an index card and the meanings of the prefix on the other.

Example 1

Convert 8 centimeters to meters.

1. Use a chart. Place 8 in the cm column.

1000			1	0.1	0.01	0.001
thousands			ones	tenths	hundredths	thousandths
			0.	0	8	
kilo (km)			meters (m)	deci (dm)	centi (cm)	milli (mm)

The chart is set up this way because a centimeter is $\frac{1}{100}$ of a meter. A decimeter is $\frac{1}{10}$ of a meter.

2. Place zeros in the m and dm columns.

3. Read the number from the chart for the conversion. 8 cm = 0.08 m

YOUR TURN!

Convert 9.7 decimeters to meters.

1. Use a chart. Place 9 in the dm column and 7 in the cm column.

1000			1	0.1	0.01	0.001
thousands			ones	tenths	hundredths	thousandths
			0.	9	7	
kilo (km)			meters (m)	deci (dm)	centi (cm)	milli (mm)

2. Place a zero in the m column.

3. Read the number from the chart for the conversion.

9.7 dm = 0.97 m

Example 2

Convert 6.4 kilometers to meters.

1. Use a chart. Place 6 in the km column and 4 in the next column to the right.

1000			1	0.1	0.01	0.001
thousands			ones	tenths	hundredths	thousandths
6	4	0	0.			
kilo (km)			meters (m)	deci (dm)	centi (cm)	milli (mm)

2. Place zeros in the columns between 4 and the decimal point.

3. Read the number from the chart for the conversion. 6.4 km = 6,400 m

YOUR TURN!

Convert 3 meters to millimeters.

1. Use a chart. Place 3 in the m column.

1000			1	0.1	0.01	0.001
thousands			ones	tenths	hundredths	thousandths
			3.	0	0	0
kilo (km)			meters (m)	deci (dm)	centi (cm)	milli (mm)

2. Place zeros in the dm, cm, and mm columns.

3. Read the number from the chart for the conversion.

3 m = 3,000 mm

English Learner Strategy

Guiding Questions Use a meter stick as a model. Then ask students the following questions to ensure that they understand the concept.

- How many centimeters are in 1 meter? 100
- How many centimeters are in 2 meters? 200

Point to 6 decimeters.

- Why would you multiply to convert meters to decimeters? Meters are larger than decimeters and to convert from a larger unit to a smaller one, you multiply.
- Explain how to convert 725 millimeters to meters. Divide 725 by 1,000 to get 0.725.
- Describe how to use the place-value chart to convert 3 decimeters to meters. Place a zero in the m column and 3 in the dm column. Read from the chart for the conversion, which is 0.3 meters.

Example 3

Convert 3 meters to centimeters.

1. **1** meter is equal to 100 centimeters.
2. You are converting from a **larger** unit to a **smaller** unit, so **multiply**.

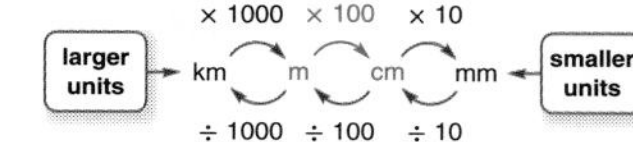

3. Convert.
   $3 \times 100 = 300$
   $3 \text{ m} = 300 \text{ cm}$

YOUR TURN!

Convert 7 meters to kilometers.

1. <u>1,000</u> m is equal to 1 kilometer.
2. You are converting from a <u>smaller</u> unit to a <u>larger</u> unit, so <u>divide</u>.
3. Convert.
   7 <u>÷ 1,000</u> = <u>0.007</u>
   7 m = <u>0.007</u> km

Who is Correct?

Convert 8.4 meters to millimeters.

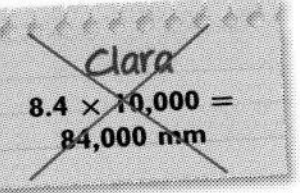

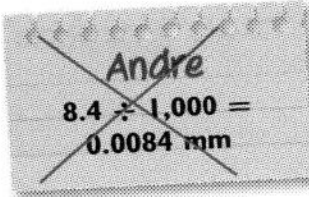

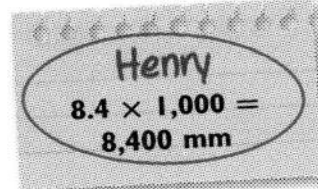

Circle correct answer(s). Cross out incorrect answer(s).

Additional Example 3

Convert 12 kilometers to meters.

1. 1 kilometer is equal to 1,000 meters.
2. You are converting from a **larger** unit to a **smaller** unit, so **multiply**.

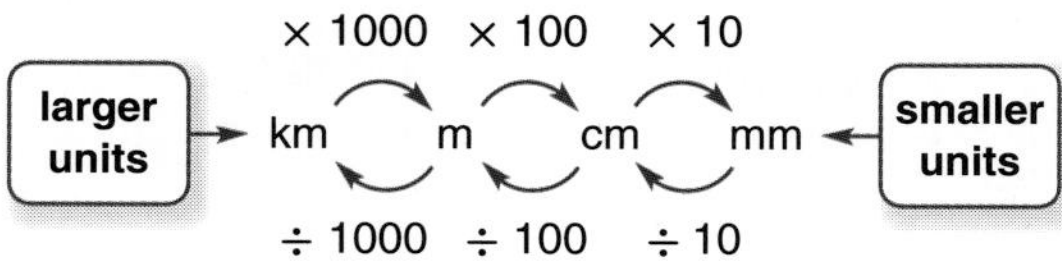

3. Convert.
   $12 \times 1{,}000 = 12{,}000$
   $12 \text{ km} = 12{,}000 \text{ m}$

Math Coach Notes

Strategies

1. Start this lesson with a hands-on practice as an anchoring experience. Gather items such as dimes and paper clips for students to use as benchmarks. Students can also measure natural measures, for instance, the length of their fingers or forearms. Discuss how having an idea of the relative size of the units has real-life applications.
2. Encourage students to use the meter stick or a drawing to represent units until automaticity occurs.
3. Some students might understand the relationship between units better if they are written in fractional form. For example, there are 100 cm in 1 meter, so 1 cm is $\frac{1}{100}$ m.

Who is Correct?

Diagnostic Teaching

- Clara wrote 84,000 mm. This is not correct because there are 1,000 millimeters in a meter. $8.4 \times 1{,}000 = 8{,}400$
- Andre wrote 0.0084 mm. This is not correct because there are 1,000 millimeters in 1 meter. The number of units will increase when going from a larger to smaller unit.
- Henry wrote 8,400 mm. This is correct.

Common Error *Alert*

Conversions When students are converting in the metric system from smaller units to larger units, they should divide (which moves the decimal point to the left).
When students are converting in the metric system from larger units to smaller units, they should multiply (which moves the decimal point to the right).

3 Practice

Using Manipulatives

Meter Stick When presenting Example 1, model the units on a meter stick.

Base-Ten Blocks If the cube represents a meter, what does 1 unit represent? A rod?

On-Hand Manipulatives When presenting the concept of benchmarks, have dimes, paper clips, crayons, and a baseball bat available for benchmark comparisons.

Common Error *Alert*

Exercises 1 and 2 If students do not arrive at the correct answers for Exercises 1 or 2, they might not understand how to use a place-value chart to convert metric units. One method to help students understand the chart is to use both fractions and decimals to represent parts of a meter. Another method is to have students convert with a metric ruler, then write the conversion onto a chart.

Guided Practice

Convert using a place-value chart.

1. 7 km = 7,000 m

1000			1	0.1	0.01	0.001
thousands			ones	tenths	hundredths	thousandths
7	0	0	0.	0	0	0
kilo (km)			meters (m)	deci (dm)	centi (cm)	milli (mm)

2. 3 dm = 0.3 m

1000			1	0.1	0.01	0.001
thousands			ones	tenths	hundredths	thousandths
			0.	3	0	0
kilo (km)			meters (m)	deci (dm)	centi (cm)	milli (mm)

Step by Step Practice

Convert.

3. 8 m = ______ mm

Step 1 1,000 millimeters is equal to 1 meter.

larger units → km ×1000 m ×100 cm ×10 mm ← smaller units; ÷ 1000 ÷ 100 ÷ 10

Step 2 You are converting from a larger unit to a smaller unit, so you multiply.

Step 3 Convert. 8 × 100 × 10 = 8,000

8 m = 8,000 mm

Convert.

4. 5 m = ______ cm
1 m = 100 cm
Multiply or divide? multiply
5 × 100 = 500
5 m = 500 cm

5. 8 m = ______ km
1 km = 1,000 m
Multiply or divide? divide
8 ÷ 1,000 = 0.008
8 m = 0.008 km

6. 8.5 cm = 0.085 m

7. 0.5 m = 5 dm

8. 93 dm = 9.3 m

9. 2 km = 2,000 m

152 Chapter 4 Measurement

Are They Getting It?

Check students' understanding of the metric system of length by writing these problems on the board. Ask students to point out wrong answers. Tell them to use a metric ruler or a place-value chart to show why the answers are correct or not correct.

1. 0.5 m = 5 cm
This is not correct, because there are 100 centimeters in 1 meter.
0.5 × 100 = 50 cm

2. 725 mm is 72.5 centimeters.
This is correct. 725 ÷ 10 = 72.5

3. Convert 7 km to cm using a place-value chart.

1,000			1	.	0.1	0.01	0.001
thousands			ones	.	tenths	hundredths	thousandths
0	0	0	0	.	0	7	0
kilo (km)			meters (m)		deci (dm)	centi (cm)	milli (mm)

This is not correct. The 7 should be written in the kilometers column, not the centimeter column. 7 km = 700,000 cm

Step by Step Problem-Solving Practice

Problem-Solving Strategies
- ☐ Draw a diagram.
- ☑ Look for a pattern.
- ☐ Act it out.
- ☐ Solve a simpler problem.
- ☐ Work backward.

Solve.

10 SPORTS A soccer field is 120 meters long. How many decimeters long is a soccer field?

Understand Read the question. Write what you know.
A soccer field is 120 meters long.

Plan Pick a strategy. One strategy is to look for a pattern.
10 decimeters is equal to 1 meter. Find a rule. One rule is to add 10 for each meter.

Solve The pattern is to add 10, 120 times. This is repeated addition, which is the same as 10 × 120.

The soccer field is 1,200 decimeters long.

Check Think: Decimeters are a smaller unit of measure than meters, so the number of decimeters of a soccer field is greater than the number of meters.

11 SEWING Booker bought 1,850 millimeters of ribbon to make a pillow. The pillow required 170 centimeters of ribbon. In centimeters, how much extra ribbon is left?

larger units → km (× 1000 / ÷ 1000) m (× 100 / ÷ 100) cm (× 10 / ÷ 10) mm ← smaller units

Check off each step.

✔ Understand: I underlined key words.

✔ Plan: To solve the problem, I will use a diagram.

✔ Solve: The answer is 15 cm.

✔ Check: I checked my answer by working backward using multiplication.

Common Error Alert

Multi-Step Problem If students are having difficulty converting units, begin with concrete materials. It is imperative that students recognize the relative sizes of the units. Then have students estimate the answers. For example, 0.7 cm is how many meters? Use the statement 1 cm = __ m. (0.01 m) This will help students see how the correct answer should look.

Math Coach Notes

Study Tips When it is time for a test, have students go through the lessons and choose key concepts, definitions, and examples to write on index cards. The answers, or definitions, go on the back of each card. Pair students to quiz each other using both sets of student-made cards. Switch partners to ensure students are quizzed thoroughly. Use any disputes or questions as whole-class discussion and review points. Students can also create a game using their cards.

Intervention Strategy

Intrapersonal/ Kinesthetic Learners

Circle Conversions Divide students into groups of four. Provide each student with an index card. Students should sit in a circle. First, each student writes a number on the index card and passes the card to the student on his or her right. Then, the next student writes a metric unit of length next to the number and passes the card to the student on his or her right. The next student writes a different unit of measure on the other side of the card and passes the card to the student on his or her right. Finally, the last student converts the number and unit to the unit of measure on the back of the card. Have students rearrange the order until each student has completed a conversion.

Odd/Even Assignments

Exercises 14–27 are structured so that students practice the same concepts whether they are assigned the odd or even problems.

In-Class Assignment

Have students complete Exercises 14, 17, 18, 21, 26, and 30 to ensure that they understand the concept.

Additional Answer

Exercise 13 No; 1,000 millimeters are equal to 1 meter. So, you can count by 1,000s to find the number of millimeters equal to 7 meters: 1,000; 2,000; 3,000; 4,000; 5,000; 6,000; 7,000. The seventh number in the pattern is 7,000. Therefore, 7 m = 7,000 mm, not 700 mm.

Math Coach Notes

Skills Review Converting metric units of length involves multiplication and division by decimals or fractions. Have students practice multiplying and dividing by decimals and fractions as preparation for this lesson.

12 SHOES The sales clerk measured Robert's foot to be 3.2 decimeters long. How many millimeters long is Robert's foot?

320 mm

13 **Reflect** Is 700 millimeters equal to 7 meters? Use patterns to explain.

See TE margin

Skills, Concepts, and Problem Solving

Convert using a place-value chart.

14 7 cm = 0.07 m

1000			1	0.1	0.01	0.001
thousands			ones	tenths	hundredths	thousandths
			0.	0	7	
kilo (km)			meters (m)	deci (dm)	centi (cm)	milli (mm)

15 6 km = 6,000 m

1000			1	0.1	0.01	0.001
thousands			ones	tenths	hundredths	thousandths
6	0	0	0.			
kilo (km)			meters (m)	deci (dm)	centi (cm)	milli (mm)

16 73 dm = ______ cm

1 dm = 10 cm

Multiply or divide? multiply

73 × 10 = 730

73 dm = 730 cm

17 6 m = ______ mm

1 m = 1,000 mm

Multiply or divide? multiply

6 × 1,000 = 6,000

6 m = 6,000 mm

Convert.

18 70 m = 700 dm

19 58.6 cm = 0.586 m

20 92.7 mm = 9.27 cm

21 360 m = 0.36 km

22 4.3 m = 4,300 mm

23 0.021 km = 21 m

24 4.9 dm = 49 cm

25 6.4 cm = 0.064 m

Math Challenge

Measurement Match-Up Before class, measure 20 items in the classroom and list them on the board. Then write each item on one side of an index card and its measure on the other side. Students lay the cards in a stack with the measures faceup. To play, students write the item they believe the measure belongs to on paper. Whoever gets the item correct gets a point. Whoever gets to 5 points first wins.

olve.

6 TRAVEL It is 63 kilometers from Grady's house to his cousin's house. How many meters is it to Grady's cousin's house? 63,000 m

7 PETS Marni's cat was found wandering around the high school which is 4,700 meters from her home. How many kilometers away was Marni's cat? 4.7 km

ocabulary Check **Write the vocabulary word that completes each sentence.**

8 The metric system is a decimal system of weights and measures.

9 A meter is the base unit of length in the metric system.

0 Writing in Math Explain how to convert 5.2 meters to centimeters.

There are 100 cm in 1 m. Multiply because you are going from a larger unit to a smaller unit: $5.2 \times 100 = 520$. There are 520 cm in 5.2 m.

Spiral Review (Lesson 4-1 p. 142)

ind the length of the line segment to the nearest millimeter r centimeter.

0 1 2 3 4 5 6 7 8 9
cm

1 7 cm

32 72 mm

elect the proper unit to measure the length of each object. Write *illimeter, centimeter, meter,* or *kilometer.*

3 length of an ant millimeter

34 height of a giraffe meter

5 SWIMMING Which is the most appropriate estimate for the depth of a swimming pool: 3 millimeters, 3 meters, or 3 kilometers? Explain.

3m; 3 millimeters is not even an inch and is not deep enough, and 3 kilometers is about $1\frac{1}{2}$ miles and is too deep.

STOP

Lesson 4-2 Unit Conversions: Metric Length 155

Ticket Out the Door

From Greatest to Least Have students make a one-row table that lists, from least to greatest, the metric units for measuring length. Students should show their tables as they exit the classroom, but keep to use as a reference when converting metric measurements.

See It, Do It, Say It, Write It

Step 1 Show students how to convert using a meter stick. Write 4.6 dm on the board. Demonstrate where 4.6 dm is on a meter stick. About what part of the meter stick is it? What would the decimal look like? Guide students to the correct answer, using this and other lengths.

Step 2 Draw a model or number line on paper that shows how to convert centimeters to millimeters, kilometers to millimeters, kilometers to meters, and so on. Write several conversions on the board for students to demonstrate.

Step 3 Go around the class and have students explain how they made their conversions.

Step 4 Have students write about the metric system. Tell them to include the length units in their paragraphs.

Looking Ahead: Pre-teach

Customary Length In the next lesson, students will learn how to read a customary measuring tool.

The customary system is not a base ten system. Students will need to memorize how many of each unit equals the next larger unit.

12 inches = 1 foot
3 feet = 1 yard
1,750 yards = 1 mile   5,280 feet = 1 mile

Have students list the customary units of length from the smallest unit to the largest unit. inch, foot, yard, mile

Chapter 4 Progress Check 1

Formative Assessment

Use the Progress Check to assess students' mastery of the previous lessons. Have students review the lesson indicated for the problems they answered incorrectly.

Odd/Even Assignments

Exercises are structured so that students practice the same concepts whether they are assigned the odd or even problems.

Common Error *Alert*

Decimal Placement If students are getting some of the metric conversions incorrect due to decimal placement, you may want to refer them to look at their conversion charts again.

Exercise 7 If students struggle with Exercise 7, it might be because they are having difficulty converting from centimeters to decimeters. Some students might include the extra step of converting from centimeters to meters and then to decimeters.

Chapter 4 Progress Check 1 (Lessons 4-1 and 4-2)

Draw a line segment of each length.

1. 52 millimeters

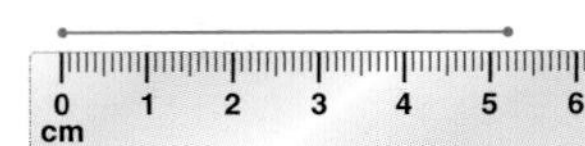

2. 7 centimeters

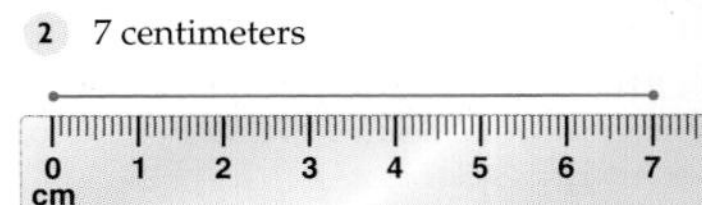

Find the length of each line segment to the nearest millimeter or centimeter.

3. The line segment is about __79__ millimeters long.

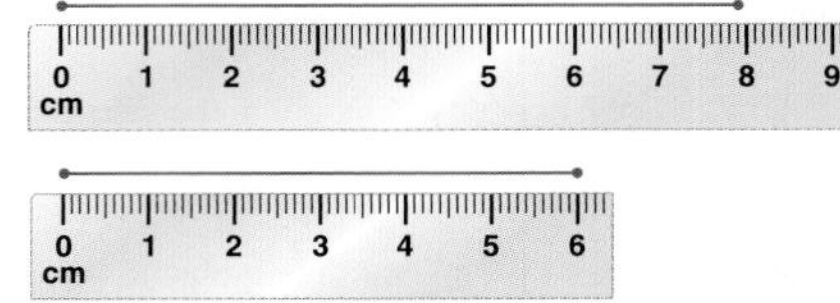

4. The line segment is about __6__ centimeters long.

Convert using a place-value chart.

5. 73 km = __73,000__ m

10,000	1000			1	0.1	0.01	0.001
ten thousands	thousands			ones	tenths	hundredths	thousandths
7	3	0	0	0.			
	kilo (km)			meters (m)	deci (dm)	centi (cm)	milli (mm)

6. 45 mm = __0.045__ m

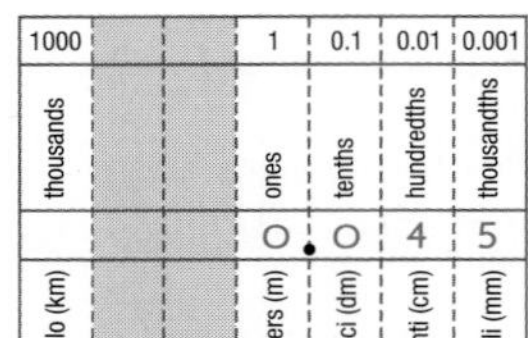

1000			1	0.1	0.01	0.001
thousands			ones	tenths	hundredths	thousandths
			0.	0	4	5
kilo (km)			meters (m)	deci (dm)	centi (cm)	milli (mm)

Convert.

7. 0.68 cm = __0.068__ dm
8. 103 mm = __0.103__ m
9. 439 dm = __43,900__ mm
10. 1,800 m = __1.8__ km

Solve.

11. **LAND** The road on Rachel's farm is 2,475 meters long. How many kilometers long is the road? __2.475 kilometers__

156 Chapter 4 Measurement

Data-Driven Decision Making

Students missing Exercises . . .	Have trouble with . . .	Should review and practice . . .
1–4	drawing and measuring the length of segments.	SSG Lesson 4–1, p. 142 CRM Skills Practice, p. A70
5–6	unit conversions using a chart and/or table.	SSG Lesson 4–2, p. 149 CRM Skills Practice, p. A74
7–10	conversion factors.	SSG Lesson 4–2, p. 149 CRM Skills Practice, p. A74
11	solving a word problem by converting units of measure.	CRM Problem-Solving Practice, pp. A71 and A75

Lesson 4-3 Customary Length

KEY Concept

The units of **length** most often used in the United States are the inch, foot, yard, and mile. These units are part of the customary system.

Units of Length		
Customary Unit	Symbol	Real-World Benchmark
1 inch	in.	width of a quarter
1 foot	ft	length of a large adult foot
1 yard	yd	length from nose to fingertip
1 mile	mi	four laps around a running track

You can use a ruler to measure objects to the nearest half inch or quarter inch.

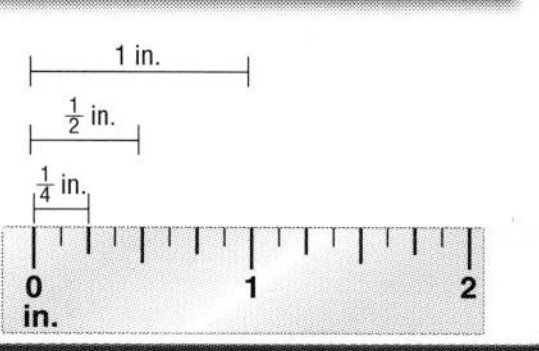

VOCABULARY

customary system
a measurement system that includes units such as foot, pound, and quart

foot
a customary unit of length equal to 12 inches

inch
a customary unit of length; 12 inches equal 1 foot

length
a measurement of the distance between two points

mile
a customary unit of length equal to 5,280 feet or 1,760 yards

yard
a customary unit of length equal to 3 feet, or 36 inches

Example 1

Find the length of the nail to the nearest $\frac{1}{2}$ inch.

1. Line up the "zero mark" of the ruler with the left end of the nail.

2. Find the $\frac{1}{2}$ inch mark that is closest to the right end.

The nail is $2\frac{1}{2}$ inches long.

YOUR TURN!

Find the length of the grasshopper to the nearest $\frac{1}{2}$ inch.

1. Line up the "zero mark" of a ruler with the left end of the grasshopper.

2. Find the $\frac{1}{2}$ inch mark that is closest to the right end.

The grasshopper is $2\frac{1}{2}$ inches long.

GO ON

Additional Example 1

Find the length of the golf ball to the nearest $\frac{1}{2}$ inch.

1. Line up the "zero mark" of the ruler with the left end of the golf ball.

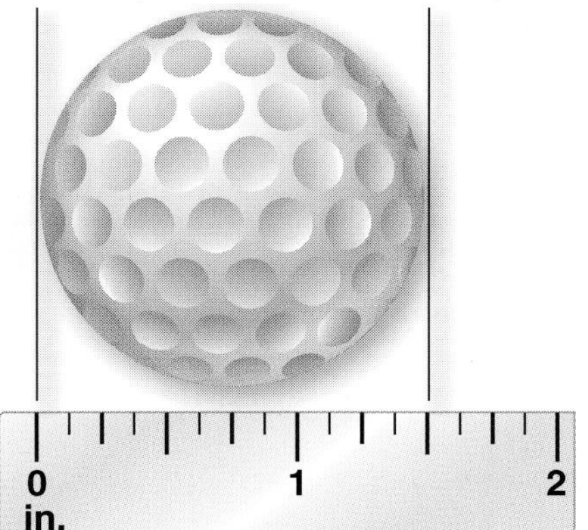

2. Find the $\frac{1}{2}$ inch mark that is closest to the right end.

The golf ball is $1\frac{1}{2}$ inches long.

Lesson Notes

Lesson 4-3

Lesson Planner

Objective Understand the customary system of measurement. Select and apply techniques and tools to accurately find length to appropriate levels of precision.

Vocabulary **customary system**, **foot**, **inch**, **length**, **mile**, **yard**

Materials/Manipulatives inch ruler, yardstick

Chapter Resource Masters

- CRM Vocabulary and English Language Development (p. A77)
- CRM Skills Practice (p. A78)
- CRM Problem-Solving Practice (p. A79)
- CRM Homework Practice (p. A80)

1 Introduce

Vocabulary

Model Vocabulary Show students a yard stick. Point out the inch marks. Have students indicate which mark represents 1 foot. Ask students to indicate which mark represents 1 yard.

2 Teach

Key Concept

Foundational Skills and Concepts After students have read through the Key Concept box, have them try these exercises.

1. Which is a larger unit, an inch or a foot? foot
2. How many half-inch sections make one inch? 2
3. How many quarter-inch sections make one inch? 4

Additional **Example 2**

Find the length of the player to the nearest $\frac{1}{4}$ inch.

1. Line up the "zero mark" of the ruler with the left end of the player.

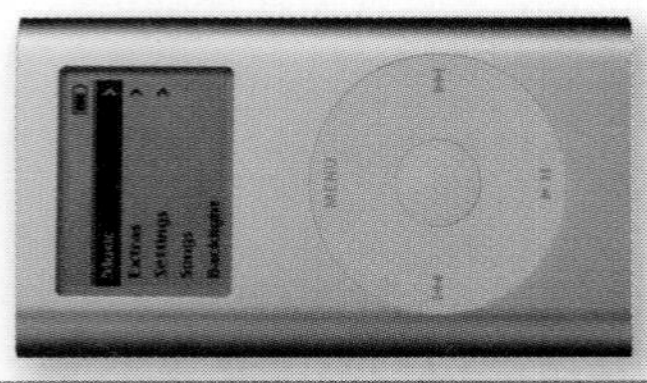

2. Find the $\frac{1}{4}$-inch mark that is closest to the right end.

The player is about $3\frac{1}{2}$ inches long.

Math Coach Notes

Using Resources When measuring an object where a ruler cannot easily be placed next to it, use a piece of string to mark the length of the object. Then place the string next to a ruler to find the length of the object.

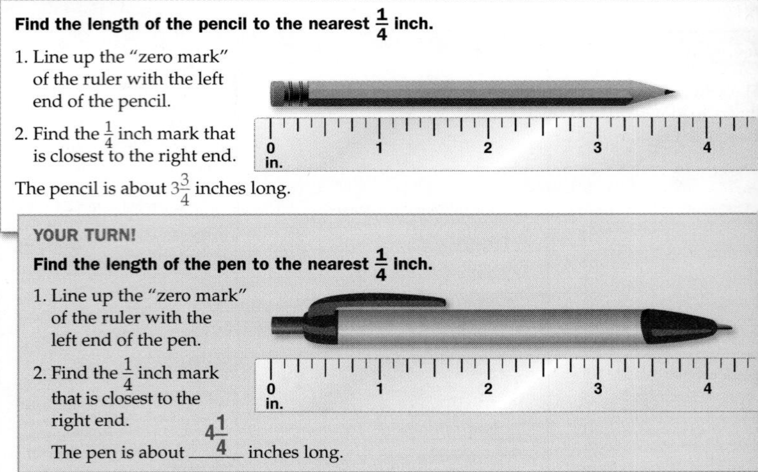

Example 2

Find the length of the pencil to the nearest $\frac{1}{4}$ inch.

1. Line up the "zero mark" of the ruler with the left end of the pencil.
2. Find the $\frac{1}{4}$ inch mark that is closest to the right end.

The pencil is about $3\frac{3}{4}$ inches long.

YOUR TURN!

Find the length of the pen to the nearest $\frac{1}{4}$ inch.

1. Line up the "zero mark" of the ruler with the left end of the pen.
2. Find the $\frac{1}{4}$ inch mark that is closest to the right end.

The pen is about $4\frac{1}{4}$ inches long.

Example 3

Which unit would you use to measure the length of a bicycle: *inch*, *foot*, *yard*, or *mile*?

The length of a bicycle is . . .

1. greater than the width of a quarter.
2. less than the length from nose to fingertip.
3. less than four laps around a running track.

The foot is an appropriate unit of measure.

YOUR TURN!

Which unit would you use to measure the length of a football field: *inch*, *foot*, *yard*, or *mile*?

The length of a football field is . . .

1. greater than the width of a quarter.
2. greater than the length of a large adult foot.
3. less than four laps around a running track.

The yard is an appropriate unit of measure.

158 Chapter 4 Measurement

Additional **Example 3**

Which unit would you use to measure the length of a pair of scissors: *inch*, *foot*, *yard*, or *mile*?

The length of a pair of scissors is ...

1. greater than the width of a quarter.

2. less than the length of a large adult foot.

3. less than 4 laps around a running track.

The inch is an appropriate unit of measure.

Who is Correct?

Find the length of the chalk to the nearest $\frac{1}{4}$ inch.

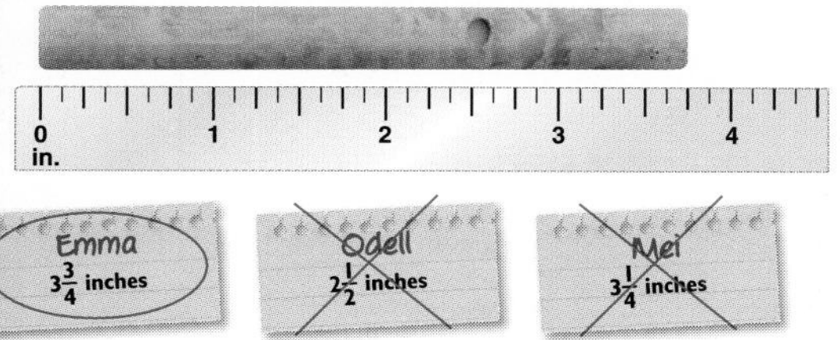

Circle correct answer(s). Cross out incorrect answer(s).

Guided Practice

Draw a line segment of each length.

1. $5\frac{1}{4}$ inches

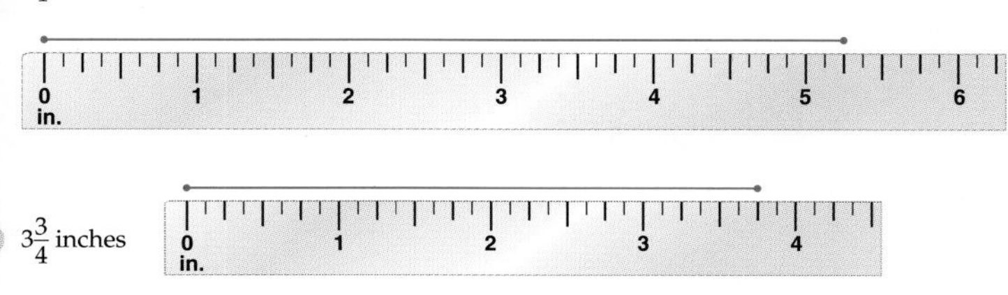

2. $3\frac{3}{4}$ inches

0 in. 1 2 3 4

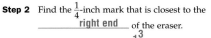

Step by Step Practice

3. Find the length of the eraser to the nearest $\frac{1}{4}$-inch.

Step 1 Line up the "zero mark" of the ruler with the left end of the eraser.

Step 2 Find the $\frac{1}{4}$-inch mark that is closest to the right end of the eraser.

The eraser is about $1\frac{3}{4}$ inches long.

GO ON

Lesson 4-3 Customary Length **159**

Who *is Correct?*

Diagnostic Teaching

- Emma wrote $3\frac{3}{4}$ inches. That is correct.
- Odell wrote $2\frac{1}{2}$ inches. That is not correct because the chalk is longer than 3 inches. Guide students who make this mistake to count the quarter marks to the right end of the object.
- Mei wrote $3\frac{1}{4}$ inches. That is not correct. She looked at each $\frac{1}{4}$-inch mark as $\frac{1}{4}$. The $\frac{1}{4}$-inch mark that is at the right end of the object is $\frac{3}{4}$ of the way past $3\frac{1}{2}$, or $3\frac{3}{4}$.

3 Practice

Using Manipulatives

Relating a Ruler to Fractions Students often struggle to distinguish the marks that subdivide an inch. Have students make a reference ruler like the one shown below (enlarge for easier viewing). Teach them to count all the marks and then reduce the fraction, if it can be reduced.

2 4 6 8 10 12 14 16
1 3 5 7 9 11 13 15
0 in. 1

Count the number of marks from the edge to the 1 inch mark. 16

There are $\frac{16}{16}$ in one inch.

If a measurement lines up with the green rule: $\frac{2}{16} = \frac{1}{8}$

If a measurement lines up with the blue rule: $\frac{6}{16} = \frac{3}{8}$

If a measurement lines up with the orange rule: $\frac{8}{16} = \frac{1}{2}$

If a measurement lines up with the purple rule: $\frac{12}{16} = \frac{3}{4}$

If a measurement lines up with the yellow rule: $\frac{15}{16}$

On-Hand Manipulatives Have students measure familiar classroom objects.

Note This!

Real-World Length In this lesson, students are introduced to using length to measure distance. Suggest that students create a list of real-world items and common units of length used to measure those items.

Common Error *Alert*

Multi-Step Problem If students are having difficulty with word problems, explain that word problems involve many steps. First, students need to identify key words. Then they need to pick a strategy to solve the problem. Then they need to use the correct side of the ruler and know the preciseness of the measurement.

Math Coach Notes

Rulers Length can be measured in metric and customary units. Inches and centimeters can be mistaken for one another on a ruler. Allow students to study a ruler to view the difference between these two systems of measurement.

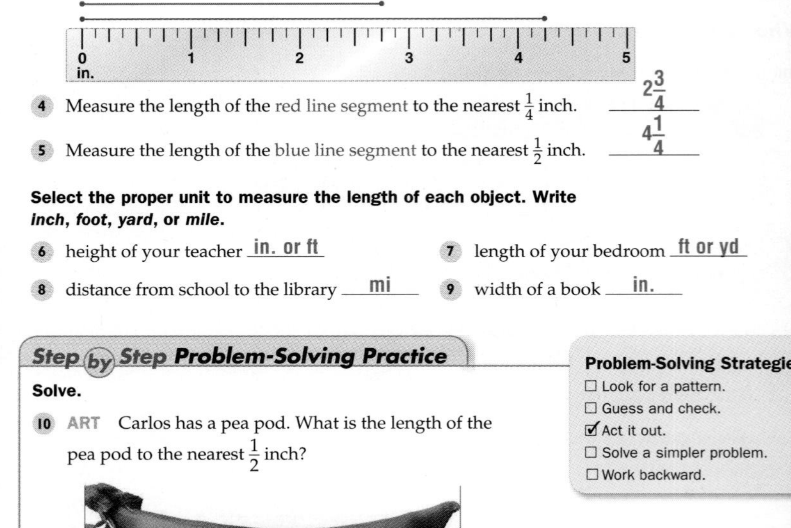

4. Measure the length of the red line segment to the nearest $\frac{1}{4}$ inch. $2\frac{3}{4}$

5. Measure the length of the blue line segment to the nearest $\frac{1}{2}$ inch. $4\frac{1}{4}$

Select the proper unit to measure the length of each object. Write *inch, foot, yard,* or *mile*.

6. height of your teacher in. or ft
7. length of your bedroom ft or yd
8. distance from school to the library mi
9. width of a book in.

Step by Step Problem-Solving Practice

Problem-Solving Strategies
- ☐ Look for a pattern.
- ☐ Guess and check.
- ☑ Act it out.
- ☐ Solve a simpler problem.
- ☐ Work backward.

Solve.

10. ART Carlos has a pea pod. What is the length of the pea pod to the nearest $\frac{1}{2}$ inch?

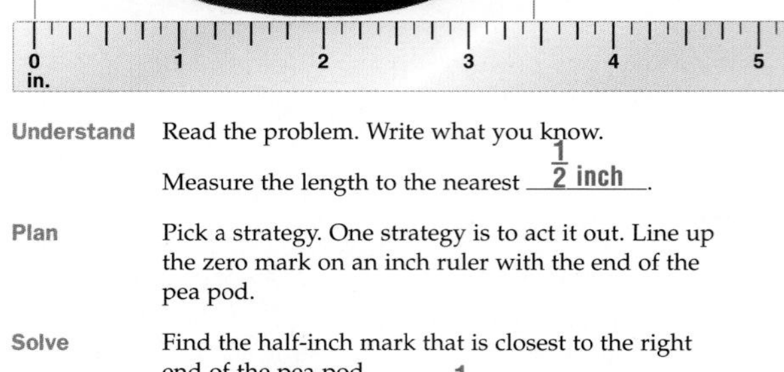

Understand Read the problem. Write what you know.
Measure the length to the nearest $\frac{1}{2}$ inch.

Plan Pick a strategy. One strategy is to act it out. Line up the zero mark on an inch ruler with the end of the pea pod.

Solve Find the half-inch mark that is closest to the right end of the pea pod.
The pea pod is about $3\frac{1}{2}$ inches long.

Check The pea pod is greater than 3 and less than 4 inches long. The answer makes sense.

Are They Getting It?

Check students' understanding of measuring length by writing these problems on the board. Ask students to point out wrong answers. Tell them to use a ruler or coordinate plane to show why the answers are correct or are not correct.

1. The length of this line segment to the nearest inch is 4 inches. This is not correct, the length is 3 inches.

2. The length of this line segment to the nearest $\frac{1}{4}$ inch is $3\frac{1}{4}$ inches. This is correct.

3. The most appropriate unit to use to measure the length of a tennis court is miles. This is not correct. The most appropriate unit to use is yards (or feet).

1 SCIENCE Ryan is collecting shells to make a craft. What is the length of the shell shown to the nearest $\frac{1}{4}$ inch? Check off each step.

✔ Understand: I underlined the key words.

✔ Plan: To solve the problem, I will act it out

✔ Solve: The answer is $1\frac{3}{4}$ inches

✔ Check: I checked my answer by estimating the length in inches

2 WOODWORKING Maria is using screws to build a doghouse. What is the length of the screws to the nearest $\frac{1}{4}$ inch?

$2\frac{1}{4}$ inch

3 Reflect How would you explain to someone what customary system unit to use when measuring the distance from Tampa, Florida, to Miami, Florida?

Sample answer: The distance from Tampa to Miami is longer than several yards, so you would measure in miles.

Skills, Concepts, and Problem Solving

raw a line segment of each length.

4 $5\frac{1}{2}$ inches

15 $4\frac{1}{4}$ inches

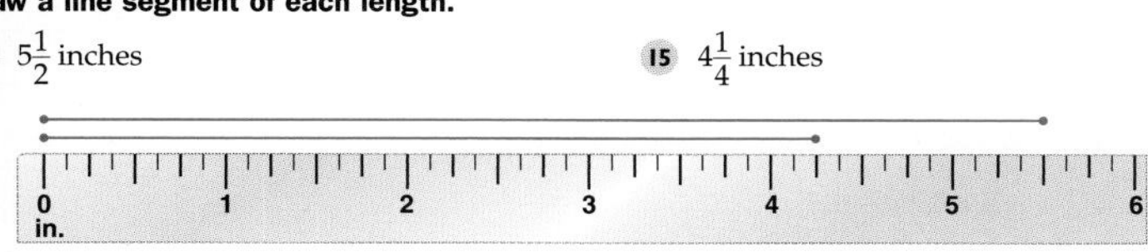

leasure the length of each line segment to the nearest $\frac{1}{4}$ or $\frac{1}{2}$ inch.

6 Red line segment to the nearest $\frac{1}{2}$ inch: $1\frac{1}{2}$ in.

17 Blue line segment to the nearest $\frac{1}{4}$ inch: $3\frac{3}{4}$ in.

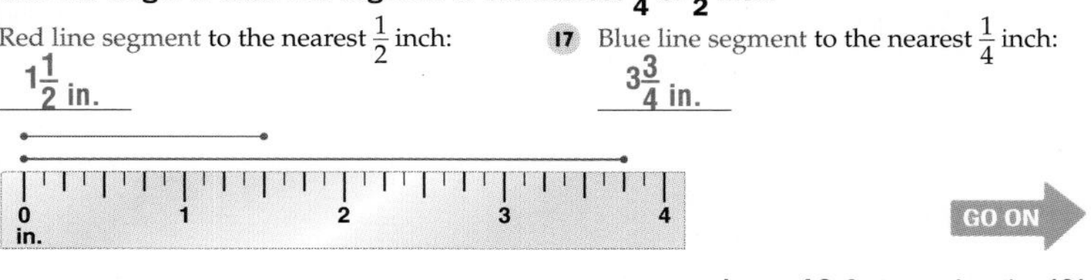

GO ON

Odd/Even Assignments

Exercises 14–22 are structured so that students practice the same concepts whether they are assigned the odd or even problems.

In-Class Assignment

Have students complete Exercises 14, 17, 18, 20, 22, and 23 to ensure that they understand the concept.

Common Error Alert

Reading Rulers If students struggle with any exercise where they are reading a ruler, have them count marks, use sixteen as the denominator, and reduce the fraction.

Intervention Strategy — Kinesthetic Learners

Measure It Use uncooked spaghetti broken into various lengths. Distribute a piece of spaghetti and a ruler marked with inches to each student. Instruct students to measure the length of the spaghetti to the nearest $\frac{1}{4}$ inch, $\frac{1}{2}$ inch, and inch.

Math Challenge

Draw Line Segments Instruct students to draw line segments of the following lengths.

1. $3\frac{1}{4}$ inches
2. $1\frac{1}{8}$ inches
3. $2\frac{3}{4}$ inches
4. $4\frac{5}{16}$ inches
5. $5\frac{1}{8}$ inches
6. $9\frac{3}{16}$ inches

See It, Do It, Say It, Write It

Step 1 Draw three line segments on the board of different lengths. Invite a different student to the board to measure each of the line segments. The members of the class should watch and verify that each measurement is correct.

Step 2 Arrange students in pairs. Have them walk about the classroom and find an item that is about the same length of each of the line segments on the board. Students can share their items with the class.

Step 3 Tell students to write about how they found items of a specific length. Encourage them to include strategies they used for narrowing their choices before they confirmed the actual lengths of the items.

Looking Ahead: Pre-teach

Unit Conversions: Customary Length In the next lesson, students will learn about converting units of length using customary units.

Example

Convert 5 yards to feet. 15 feet

Have students convert each of the following.

1. 60 inches to feet 5 feet
2. 12 feet to yards 4 yards
3. 2 yards to inches 72 inches

Find the length of each object.

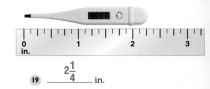

18 $\frac{1}{2}$ in.

19 $2\frac{1}{4}$ in.

Solve.

20 TECHNOLOGY The screen on Tamika's new video player measured $3\frac{1}{2}$ inches long. Draw a line segment to show its width.

0 in. 1 2 3 4

Vocabulary Check **Write the vocabulary word that completes each sentence.**

21 A(n) mile is a unit of length equal to 5,280 feet or 1,760 yards.

22 A(n) foot is a unit of length equal to 12 inches.

23 Writing in Math Explain how to measure a line segment to the nearest $\frac{1}{2}$ inch.

Sample answer: Line up the "zero mark" with the left end of the object. Find the $\frac{1}{2}$-inch mark that is closest to the right end.

Spiral Review

Convert using a place-value chart. (Lesson 4-2, p. 149)

24 3 m = 300 cm

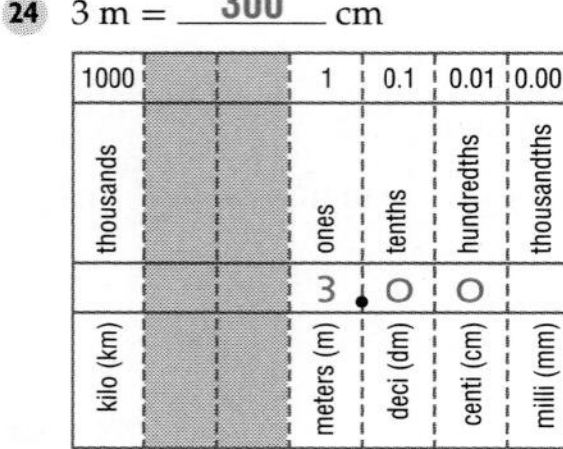

25 9 m = 0.009 km

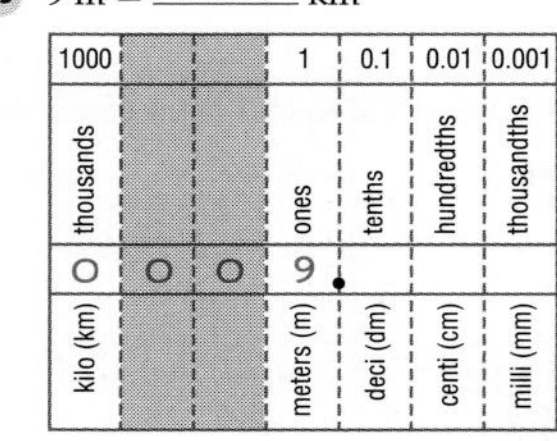

STOP

Ticket Out the Door

Choose the Right Unit Write a list of 10 things on the board that can be measured. Examples include a penny, the distance across an ocean, a student's height, and so on. Ask students to write which customary unit would be best to measure each item. Then ask the students to estimate the lengths using the unit they chose. Have students turn to a partner to share their estimations. Students will turn in their papers as they exit the classroom.

Lesson 4-4

Unit Conversions: Customary Length

KEY Concept

Unit for Length	Abbreviation	Equivalents	Real-World Benchmark
inch	in.		small paper clip
foot	ft	1 ft = 12 in.	standard ruler
yard	yd	1 yd = 3 ft 1 yd = 36 in.	baseball bat
mile	mi	1 mi = 1,760 yd 1 mi = 5,280 ft	about eight city blocks

Use the last column of the table to help you understand the relative size of a unit by comparing it to everyday objects.

Use a ruler to see how the units of length compare.

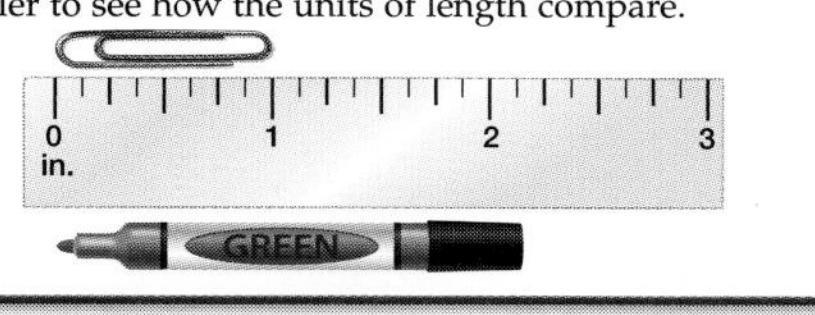

Sometimes it is necessary to **convert** from one unit of measure to another. Knowing customary conversions can help you understand the relationship between two units.

VOCABULARY

benchmark
an object or number used as a guide to estimate or reference

convert
to find an equivalent measure

customary system
a measurement system that includes units such as foot, pound, and quart

foot
a customary unit of length equal to 12 inches

inch
a customary unit of length; 12 inches equal 1 foot

mile
a customary unit of length equal to 5,280 feet or 1,760 yards

yard
a customary unit of length equal to 3 feet or 36 inches

Example 1

Convert 60 inches to feet using a table.

feet	1	2	3	4	5
inches	12	24	36	48	60

1. There are 12 inches in 1 foot.
2. Fill in the table.

2 feet = 2 × 12 inches
3 feet = 3 × 12 inches
4 feet = 4 × 12 inches
5 feet = 5 × 12 inches

60 inches are equal to 5 feet.

YOUR TURN!

Convert 15 feet to yards using a table.

yards	1	2	3	4	5
feet	3	6	9	12	15

1. There are 3 feet in 1 yard. Complete the chart by using multiples of three.
2. Fill in the table.

15 feet are equal to 5 yards.

Additional *Example 1*

Convert 48 inches to feet using a table.

feet	1	2	3	4
inches	12	24	36	48

1. There are 12 inches in 1 foot.
2. Fill in the table.

2 feet = 2 × 12 inches
3 feet = 3 × 12 inches
4 feet = 4 × 12 inches

4 feet is equal to 48 inches.

Lesson Notes

Lesson 4-4

Lesson Planner

Objective Convert units of customary length.

Vocabulary **benchmark**, **convert**, **customary system**, **foot**, **inch**, **mile**, **yard**

Materials/Manipulatives inch ruler, yardstick

Chapter Resource Masters

CRM Vocabulary and English Language Development (p. A81)

CRM Skills Practice (p. A82)

CRM Problem-Solving Practice (p. A83)

CRM Homework Practice (p. A84)

1 Introduce

Vocabulary

Vocabulary Review Hand out a ruler to each student, and then a yardstick. Have students demonstrate how to use the yardstick and ruler to *convert* between inches, feet, and yards.

2 Teach

Key Concept

Foundational Skills and Concepts After students have read through the Key Concept box, have them try these exercises.

1. What unit(s) would be best for measuring the length of a street? mile
2. How many feet are in 1 yard? 3
3. How many inches are in 1 foot? 12

Additional **Example 2**

Convert 7,040 yards to miles.

1. You are converting from yards to miles, which is a smaller unit to a larger unit. You should divide.
2. 1,760 yards are equal to 1 mile.

   So, 7,040 yards are equal to 7,040 ÷ 1,760, or 4 miles.

Math Coach Notes

Customary Rulers Students often become confused with the intervals in customary measures. Use a number line first to demonstrate a unit divided into twelfths or thirty-sixths.

Using Manipulatives

Yardstick When presenting Example 2, model the units on a yardstick.

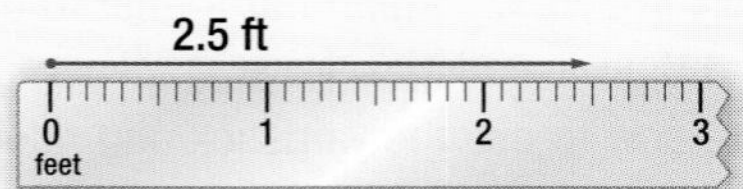

On-Hand Manipulatives Let students measure objects, arm lengths, and heights to acquire their own benchmarks with customary units.

To convert a larger unit to a smaller unit, multiply.
To convert a smaller to a larger unit, divide.

Example 2

Convert 2.5 feet to inches.

1. You are converting from feet to inches, which is a larger unit to a smaller unit. You should multiply.
2. 1 foot is equal to 12 inches.

So, 2.5 feet are equal to 2.5 × 12, or 30 inches.

YOUR TURN!

Convert 156 feet to yards.

1. You are converting from feet to yards, which is a smaller unit to a larger unit. You should divide.
2. 3 feet are equal to 1 yard.

So, 156 feet are equal to 156 ÷ 3, or 52 yards.

Who is Correct?

Convert 48 inches to feet.

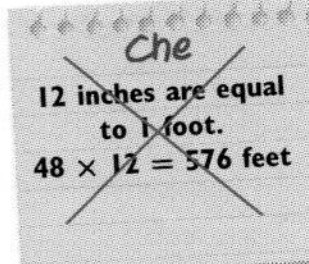

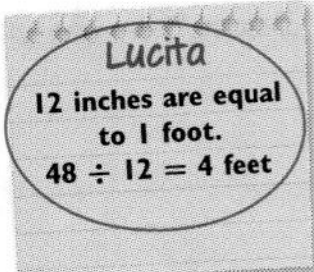

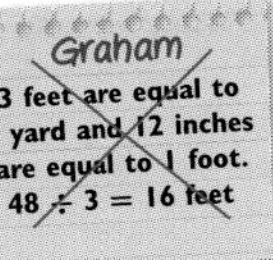

Circle correct answer(s). Cross out incorrect answer(s).

Guided Practice

Convert using a table.

1. 6 yd = 216 in.

yards	1	2	3	4	5	6
inches	36	72	108	144	180	216

2. 4 mi = 7,040 yd

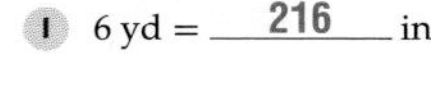

miles	1	2	3	4
yards	1,760	3,520	5,280	7,040

Who *is Correct?*

Diagnostic Teaching

- Che wrote 48 × 12 = 576 feet. This is not correct because converting from a smaller unit to a larger unit indicates division, not multiplication.
- Lucita wrote 48 ÷ 12 = 4 feet. This is correct.
- Graham wrote 48 ÷ 3 = 16 feet. This is not correct because he divided inches by the number of feet in a yard.

Step by Step Practice

Convert.

9 yd = ________ ft

Step 1 You are converting from a **larger** unit to a **smaller** unit, so you should **multiply**.

Step 2 1 yard is equal to **3** feet.

Step 3 So, 9 yards are 9 **×** 3, or **27** feet.

Convert.

2 mi = ________ ft
1 mi = **5,280** ft
Multiply or divide? **multiply**
2 **×** 5,280 = **10,560**
2 mi = **10,560** ft

5 72 in. = ________ ft
1 ft = **12** in.
Multiply or divide? **divide**
72 **÷** 12 = **6**
72 in. = **6** ft

8,800 yd = **5** mi

7 3 mi = **5,280** yd

5 yd = **15** ft

9 5 mi = **26,400** ft

9 yd = **27** ft

11 1 mi = **1,760** yd

60 in. = **5** ft

13 15 ft = **180** in.

9 ft = **108** in.

15 12 ft = **144** in.

108 in. = **3** yd

17 93 ft = **31** yd

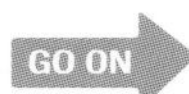

Intervention Strategy

Interpersonal/ Kinesthetic Learners

Estimate Distances Instruct students to determine the distances between different locations. Sample locations can be the distance between their school and their homes. Other locations can be the distance between two cities. This information can be researched from the Internet or other references. Have students convert their distances in miles to yards, feet, and inches.

Math Coach Notes

Strategies

1. Gather items for students to use as benchmarks. Students can also measure natural measures, for instance, the length of their arm spans or forearms.
2. Have students estimate an answer before calculating it. This will give them an idea of the approximate size and ensure their answer is correct.

English Learner Strategy

Guiding Questions Ask students the following questions to ensure that they understand the concept. Use a yardstick.

- Point to 2 feet.
- How many feet are in 1 yard? 3 ft How many inches are in 1 yard? 36 in.
- Would you multiply or divide to convert yards to inches? You would multiply because you are converting from a larger unit to a smaller unit.
- Explain how to convert feet to miles. 5,280 feet is equal to 1 mile. Divide the given number of feet by 5,280 to get miles.
- Describe how to use a table to convert inches to yards. Place the conversions in the table using the equivalency 36 in. is equal to 1 yd.

Math Coach Notes

Draw Diagrams Suggest to students that they draw diagrams to represent conversions in the exercises. For example, if a problem requires converting from feet to inches, the student can draw a segment for each foot. Then the student can divide each segment into 12 parts and count the number of sections formed.

Common Error *Alert*

Establish a Concrete Connection If students are having difficulty knowing whether to divide or multiply, use concrete materials. From base-ten blocks, take a rod and a unit. Ask: If you wanted to represent the rod in terms of units, would there be more or less than the number of units you start with? Guide students to understand that when moving to a smaller unit, there will be more of the smaller unit, so you will multiply. When moving to a larger unit there will be less, so you would divide.

Step by Step Problem-Solving Practice

Problem-Solving Strategies
- ☐ Draw a diagram.
- ☐ Look for a pattern.
- ☐ Guess and check.
- ☐ Solve a simpler problem.
- ☑ Work backward.

Solve.

18 HOMES The bedroom in Tenisha's apartment is 144 inches long. How many yards long is the room?

Understand Read the question. Write what you know.
The bedroom is 144 inches long.

Plan Pick a strategy. One strategy is to work backward.

You know the total number of inches.
Subtract repeatedly until the answer is 0.
Count the number of times you subtracted 36.

Solve

144	− 36 =	108	1 yard
108	− 36 =	72	2 yards
72	− 36 =	36	3 yards
36	− 36 =	0	4 yards

The room is 4 yards long.

Check Think: An inch is a smaller unit of measure than a yard. So the number of inches should be greater than the number of yards. The answer makes sense.

19 SCHOOL Justina's desk is 42 inches wide. How many feet wide is her desk? Check off each step.

✔ Understand: I underlined the words.

✔ Plan: To solve the problem, I will work backward

✔ Solve: The answer is 3.5 ft

✔ Check: I checked my answer by multiplying 3.5 by 12 inches

20 SPORTS During Saturday's football game, James set the school record by running 96 yards to score a touchdown. How many feet did James run for the touchdown?

288 ft

Are They Getting It?

Check students' understanding of the customary system of length by writing these problems on the board. Ask students to point out wrong answers. Tell them to use a yardstick or a table to show why the answers are correct or not correct.

1. 2 ft = 12 in.
   This is not correct, because $2 \times 12 = 24$ in.
2. 9 mi = 15,840 yd
   This is correct. $5{,}280 \times 9 = 47{,}520 \div 3 = 15{,}840$ yd.
3. 5 yd = 60 in.
   This is not correct. $5 \times 36 = 180$ in.

21 **Reflect** Is 108 inches equal to 9 feet? Explain.

Yes; Convert 9 feet to inches: $9 \times 12 = 108$; $108 = 108$.

Skills, Concepts, and Problem Solving

Convert using a table.

22 8 ft = 96 in.

feet	1	2	3	4	5	6	7	8
inches	12	24	36	48	60	72	84	96

23 4 yd = 144 in.

yards	1	2	3	4
inches	36	72	108	144

Convert.

24 2 mi = 10,560 ft

25 39 ft = 13 yd

26 26,400 ft = 5 mi

27 10 mi = 52,800 ft

28 360 in. = 10 yd

29 17,600 yd = 10 mi

30 1,821 ft = 607 yd

31 17 yd = 612 in.

32 45 ft = 15 yd

33 2.5 yd = 90 in.

34 Ruben made a toy chest for his little sister. What are the dimensions in inches?

1 ft = 12 in.

1.5 ft = 18 in.

2 ft = 24 in.

GO ON

Math Challenge

Judging Lengths Provide students with cards with varying lengths in different units written on them. Students divide the cards. Simultaneously, each student turns one card over. Whichever student has the greater length gets the point. The first student to get 5 points wins.

Odd/Even Assignments

Exercises 22–36 are structured so that students practice the same concepts whether they are assigned the odd or even problems.

In-Class Assignment

Have students complete Exercises 22, 26, 36, 37, and 39 to ensure that they understand the concept.

Common Error Alert

Miles to Inches If students are having difficulty converting miles to inches, suggest they create a flow chart or sequence map on their papers. Tell them to include each step to move from miles to inches. Then, have them do the work.

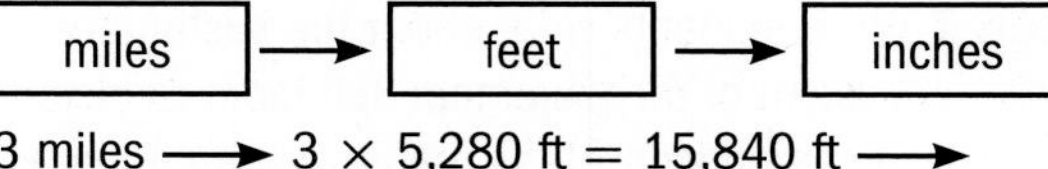

3 miles ⟶ $3 \times 5{,}280$ ft = 15,840 ft ⟶ $15{,}840 \times 12$ in. = 190,080 in.

Students can also make a table to help with conversions.

Intervention Strategy — Visual Learners

Visual Reminder Have students create a visual reminder of whether to divide or multiply when converting units. Their ideas can be drawn on paper or poster board. One example is:

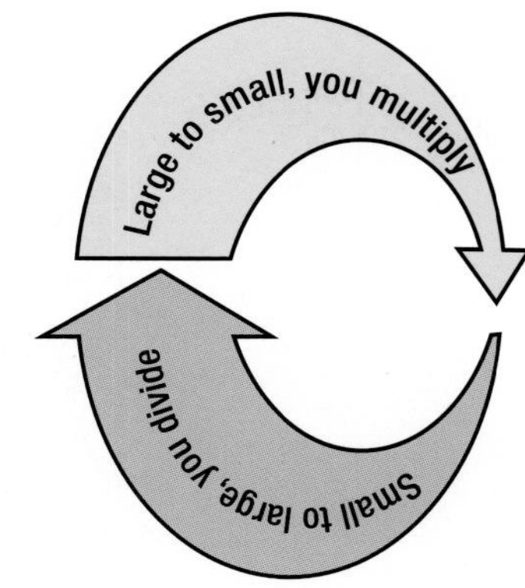

4 Assess

See It, Do It, Say It, Write It

Step 1 Draw a number line labeled from 0 to 3 on the board. Divide the first interval into twelfths. Hold up a yardstick and compare it with the number line. Ask students to locate certain lengths, such as 30 in., 0.75 ft, and 0.5 yd.

Step 2 Ask students to make a table to convert 84 inches to feet. Tell them to turn to a partner when they are finished to share their results. Discuss with students other methods to convert inches to feet.

Step 3 Have students write about the customary system of measurement. Tell them to include a comparison of the metric system. Then ask them to write how to find the number of yards in 6 miles. Tell them to include the answer.

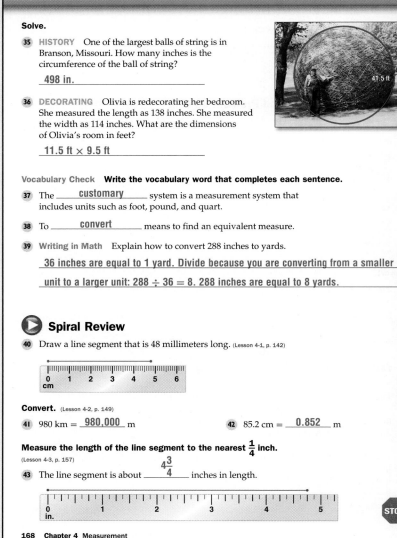

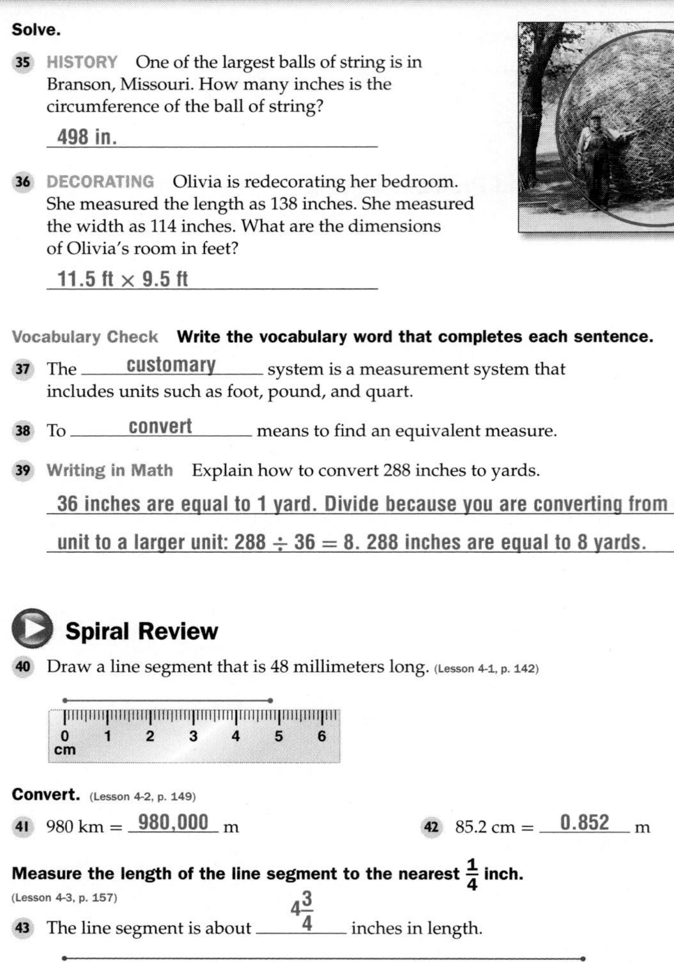

Solve.
35 HISTORY One of the largest balls of string is in Branson, Missouri. How many inches is the circumference of the ball of string?
498 in.
41.5 ft
36 DECORATING Olivia is redecorating her bedroom. She measured the length as 138 inches. She measured the width as 114 inches. What are the dimensions of Olivia's room in feet?
11.5 ft × 9.5 ft
Vocabulary Check Write the vocabulary word that completes each sentence.
37 The customary system is a measurement system that includes units such as foot, pound, and quart.
38 To convert means to find an equivalent measure.
39 Writing in Math Explain how to convert 288 inches to yards.
36 inches are equal to 1 yard. Divide because you are converting from a smaller unit to a larger unit: 288 ÷ 36 = 8. 288 inches are equal to 8 yards.
Spiral Review
40 Draw a line segment that is 48 millimeters long. (Lesson 4-1, p. 142)
0 1 2 3 4 5 6
cm
Convert. (Lesson 4-2, p. 149)
41 980 km = 980,000 m
42 85.2 cm = 0.852 m
Measure the length of the line segment to the nearest 1/4 inch. (Lesson 4-3, p. 157)
43 The line segment is about 4 3/4 inches in length.
0 1 2 3 4 5
in.
STOP
168 Chapter 4 Measurement

Ticket Out the Door

Equivalences As students exit the classroom, ask them to answer each of these questions:

1 foot = ? inches 12

1 yd = ? inches 36

1 yd = ? feet 3

1 mile = ? feet 5,280

1 mile = ? yards 1,760

Chapter 4

Progress Check 2 (Lessons 4-3 and 4-4)

1. Draw a line segment that has a length of $4\frac{1}{2}$ inches.

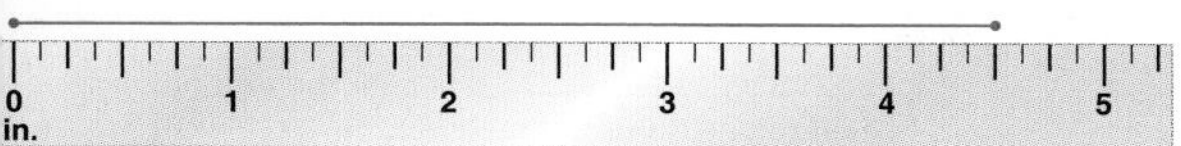

2. Measure the length of the line segment to the nearest $\frac{1}{4}$ inch.

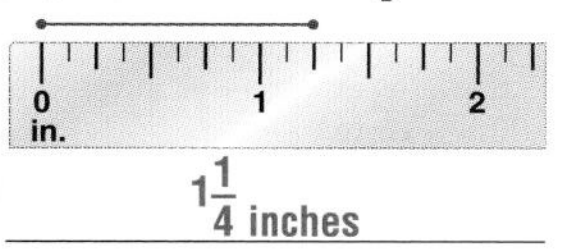

$1\frac{1}{4}$ inches

3. Measure the length of the dragonfly to the nearest $\frac{1}{2}$ inch.

$1\frac{1}{2}$ inches

onvert using a table.

4. 3 mi = 190,080 in.

miles	1	2	3
yards	1,760	3,520	5,280

5. 15 ft = 5 yd

yards	1	2	3	4	5
feet	3	6	9	12	15

onvert.

6. 12 yd = 432 in.
7. 2 mi = 3,520 yd
8. 96 in. = 8 ft
9. 42 ft = 14 yd

olve.

10. **NUMBER SENSE** The community pool measures 25 yards long. How many inches long is the pool?

900 in.

Progress Check 2

Chapter 4

Formative Assessment

Use the Progress Check to assess students' mastery of the previous lessons. Have students review the lesson indicated for the problems they answered incorrectly.

Odd/Even Assignments

Exercises are structured so that students practice the same concepts whether they are assigned the odd or even problems.

Common Error *Alert*

Conversions If students are getting some of the conversions incorrect, you may want to refer them to look at their conversion charts again.

Exercises 5, 8, 9 When students are converting in the customary system from smaller units to larger units, they should divide.

Exercises 4, 6, 7 When students are converting in the customary system from larger units to smaller units, they should multiply.

Data-Driven Decision Making

Students missing Exercises . . .	Have trouble with . . .	Should review and practice . . .
1-3	drawing and measuring the length of a segment.	SSG Lesson 4-3, p. 157 CRM Skills Practice, p. A78
4-5	unit conversions using a chart and/or table.	SSG Lesson 4-4, p. 163 CRM Skills Practice, p. A82
6-9	conversion factors.	SSG Lesson 4-4, p. 163 CRM Skills Practice, p. A82
10	solving word problems by converting units of measure.	CRM Problem-Solving Practice, pp. A79 and A83

Chapter 4

Study Guide
Formative Assessment

Vocabulary and Concept Check

If students have difficulty answering Exercises 1–11, remind them that they can use the page references to refresh their memories about the vocabulary terms.

Vocabulary Review Strategies

Puzzles Have students make a crossword puzzle to help them review key vocabulary words. They should interlock the words in the Vocabulary and Concept Check and then write clues that are used to determine the correct word. Have them trade puzzles with another student.

Lesson Review

If the given examples are not sufficient to review the questions, have students design their own examples from a particular section of the chapter. When finished, have them share their examples and explanations with partners, small groups, or the entire class.

Find **Extra Practice** for these concepts in the Practice Worksheets, pages A69–A84.

Classroom Management

Pair and Share Pair a student who has a good grasp of the material with another student who could use some support. Have students take turns explaining the examples to each other. In this case they will both benefit, whether by doing the explaining or having it explained to them.

Study Guide

Vocabulary and Concept Check

benchmark, *p. 149*
centimeter, *p. 142*
convert, *p. 149*
customary system, *p. 157*
foot, *p. 157*
inch, *p. 157*
kilometer, *p. 142*
length, *p. 142*
meter, *p. 142*
metric system, *p. 142*
mile, *p. 157*
millimeter, *p. 142*
yard, *p. 157*

Write the vocabulary word that completes each sentence.

1. The __kilometer__ is a metric unit of length equal to one thousand meters.
2. The __customary system__ includes units such as foot, pound, and quart.
3. A(n) __foot__ is a customary unit of length equal to 12 inches.
4. A(n) __benchmark__ is an object or number used as a guide to estimate or reference.
5. The __metric system__ is a decimal system of weights and measures.
6. To __convert__ is to find an equivalent measure.
7. A(n) __mile__ is a customary unit of length equal to 5,280 feet or 1,760 yards.

Label each diagram below by writing the word for the abbreviation.

8. __meter__
9. __millimeter__

$1 \text{ m} = 1{,}000 \text{ mm}$

10. __yard__
11. __inch__

$1 \text{ yd} = 36 \text{ in.}$

Lesson Review

4-1 Metric Length (pp. 142–148)

Measure the length of the object to the nearest centimeter.

2 The orange slice is 6 centimeters long.

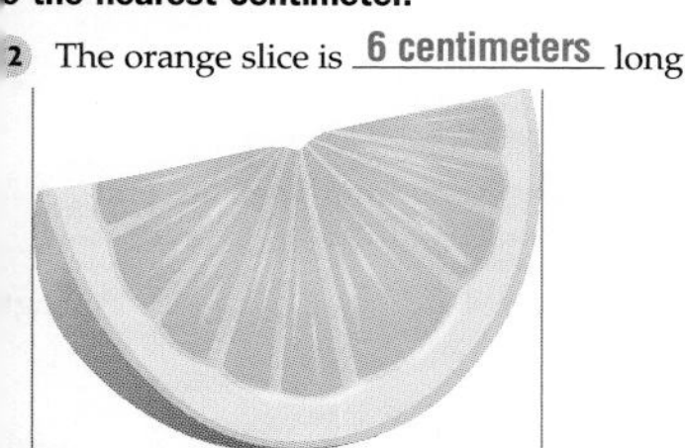

Measure the length of the object to the nearest millimeter.

3 The earthworm is 90 millimeters long.

Example 1

Find the length of the pencil to the nearest millimeter.

1. Line up the "zero mark" of the ruler with the left end of the pencil.

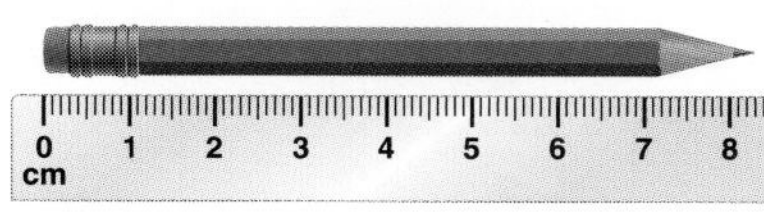

2. Read the number on the ruler that lines up with the right end.

The pencil is about 83 millimeters long.

4-2 Unit Conversions: Metric Length (pp. 149–155)

4 Convert 6.5 meters to millimeters.

1000			1	0.1	0.01	0.001
thousands			ones	tenths	hundredths	thousandths
			6.	5	0	0
kilo (km)			meters (m)	deci (dm)	centi (cm)	milli (mm)

6.5 m = 6,500 mm

Example 2

Convert 4 centimeters to meters.

1. Use a chart. Place 4 in the cm column.

1000			1	0.1	0.01	0.001
thousands			ones	tenths	hundredths	thousandths
			0.	0	4	
kilo (km)			meters (m)	deci (dm)	centi (cm)	milli (mm)

2. Place zeros in the m and dm columns.
3. Read the number from the chart for the conversion. 4 cm = 0.04 m

Chapter 4 Study Guide 171

Intervention Strategy Visual Learners

Name That Measure Point to different objects around the classroom and have the students respond by saying whether they can use the object to find length, perimeter, area, or volume. Example: Hold up a pencil, and the correct response would be "length."

FOLDABLES Study Organizer Dinah Zike's Foldables®

Review Remind students to complete and refer to their Foldables as they progress through the Chapter 4 Study Guide. Have students share and compare their completed Foldables with a partner. You may also choose to have them use their Foldable as a study aid in preparing for the Chapter Test. (For complete instructions, see Chapter Resource Masters, p. A66.)

Measurement	Length	Area and Volume
Metric		
Customary		

Math Coach Notes

Study Tables Give students metric conversion charts and standard conversion tables that are partially filled in. Like a puzzle, the students can fill in the pieces from their memories, using the ones already provided as a guideline.

Math Coach Notes

Different Rulers Be sure students know how to determine if the ruler they have is precise enough to make the requested measurement. If a measurement is to be to the nearest $\frac{1}{4}$ then the ruler must show the inches divided into fourths. If the measurement is to be to the nearest $\frac{1}{8}$ then the ruler must show the inches divided into eighths.

Most rulers used beyond primary school show inches divided into at least eighths, usually sixteenths. If a student is not sure of the precision of a ruler, have them count the number of lines, of any length, from the zero to the one-inch mark. That number identifies the smallest unit marked on a ruler.

Common Error *Alert*

Exercises 16–19 Students need to be familiar with the order from least to greatest of the metric units for measuring length. It is helpful to write the units in a horizontal table with the smallest unit on the left. By setting up the units this way, moving from the starting unit to the ending unit mimics the necessary movement of the decimal point.

Convert.

15 larger units → km (× 1000 / ÷ 1000) m (× 100 / ÷ 100) cm (× 10 / ÷ 10) mm ← smaller units

3 km = ________ m

__1,000__ m = 1 km

Multiply or divide? __multiply__

3 × 1,000 = __3,000__

3 km = __3,000__ m

Convert.

16 4.5 mm = __0.0045__ m

17 3 m = __0.003__ km

18 57 mm = __5.7__ cm

19 7 m = __700__ cm

Example 3

Convert 9.5 millimeters to centimeters.

larger units → km (× 1000 / ÷ 1000) m (× 100 / ÷ 100) cm (× 10 / ÷ 10) mm ← smaller units

1. 1 mm is equal to 10 centimeters.
2. You are converting from a smaller unit to a larger unit, so divide.
3. Convert.

9.5 ÷ 10 = 0.95

9.5 mm = 0.95 cm

4-3 Customary Length (pp. 157–162)

Measure the length of the item to the nearest $\frac{1}{4}$ inch.

20 The domino is __$2\frac{1}{4}$ inches__ long.

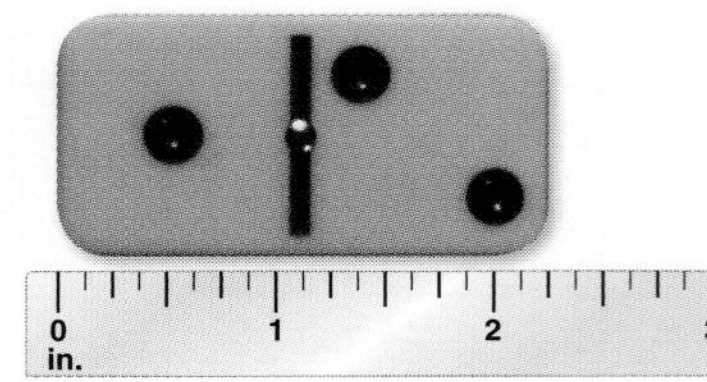

Example 4

Find the length of the battery to the nearest $\frac{1}{2}$ inch.

1. Line up the "zero mark" of the ruler with the left end of the battery.

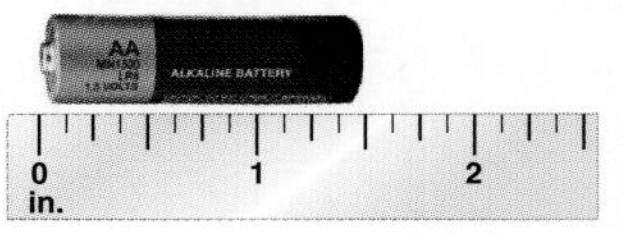

2. Read the number on the ruler that lines up with the right end.

The battery is about $1\frac{1}{2}$ inches long.

Intervention Strategy **Visual Learners**

Color Code Until the students have a grasp (especially with the metric system) of which units are larger and which are smaller, assign a color to each to aid them in determining whether to multiply or divide. For example, consistently code the smaller unit in blue and the larger unit in red.

4-4 Unit Conversions: Customary Length (pp. 163–168)

Convert using a table.

21 5 ft = 60 in.

feet	1	2	3	4	5
inches	12	24	36	48	60

Convert.

22 6 yd = ____ ft

1 yd = 3 feet

Multiply or divide? multiply

6 × 3 = 18

6 yd = 18 ft

23 7 ft = 84 in.

24 15 yd = 45 ft

Example 6

Convert 3 feet to inches.

1. You are converting from feet to inches, which is a larger unit to a smaller unit. You should multiply.
2. 1 foot is equal to 12 inches.

So, 3 feet are equal to 3 × 12, or 36 inches.

Convert using a table.

25 60 in. = 5 ft

feet	1	2	3	4	5
inches	12	24	36	48	60

Convert.

26 30 ft = ____ yd

1 yd = 3 ft

Multiply or divide? divide

30 ÷ 3 = 10

30 ft = 10 yd

27 24 ft = 8 yd

28 72 in. = 6 ft

Example 7

Convert 48 inches to feet.

1. You are converting from inches to feet, which is a smaller unit to a larger unit. You should divide.
2. 12 inches are equal to 1 foot.

So, 48 inches are equal to 48 ÷ 12, or 4 feet.

Math Coach Notes

Metric and Customary Although the two systems are very different, remind students the act of converting measurements is the same in both units. What is the same is that you multiply when converting from a larger unit to a smaller unit, and you divide when converting from a smaller unit to a larger unit. What is different is that you multiply or divide by factors other than 10. Stress the similarities to students so that they can focus on learning the equivalences in the customary system and realize that the procedure is the same.

Ticket Out the Door

Conversions As students approach you to exit the classroom, have them name a unit in the customary system, such as inches. You ask them for a conversion that they should be able to do using mental math. For example, the student approaches and says *yards*; you ask *how many feet are in 2 yards?*

Chapter 4 Chapter Test

Chapter Resource Masters

Additional forms of the Chapter 4 Tests are available.

Test Format	Where to Find it
Chapter 4 Test	Math Online glencoe.com
Blackline Masters	Assessment Masters, p. 68

Customize and create multiple versions of your chapter tests and their answer keys. All of these questions from the chapter tests are available on ExamView® Assessment Suite.

Online Assessment and Reporting
glencoe.com

This online assessment tool allows teachers to track student progress with easily accessible comprehensive reports available for every student. Assess students using any internet-ready computer.

Alternative Assessment

Use Portfolios Ask students to write examples of unit conversions in their portfolios. They should include a brief description of the steps used to make each conversion. They should also state whether the conversion is metric or customary. Encourage students to list as many conversions from each system as they can.

Chapter Test

Solve.

1. What is the height of the toy soldier at the right to the nearest centimeter? 7 cm

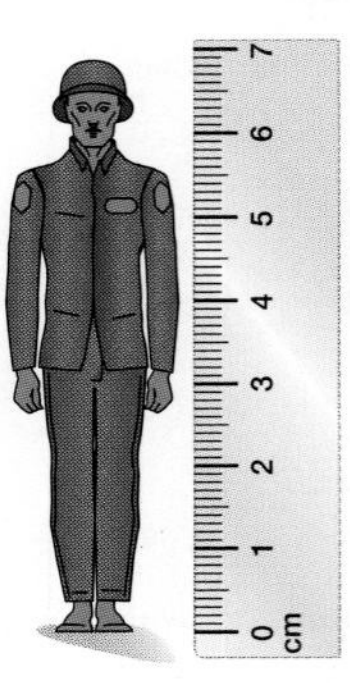

2. Draw a line segment that has a length of 59 millimeters.

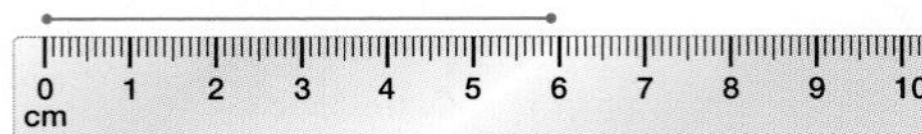

3. Measure the length of the three buttons to the nearest $\frac{1}{2}$ inch. $3\frac{1}{2}$ inches

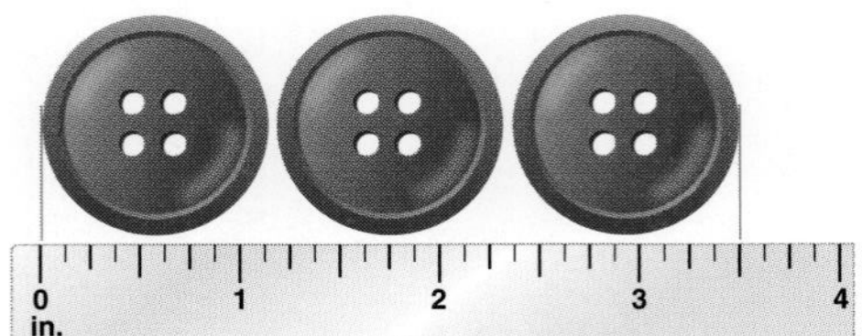

Convert using a place-value chart or table.

4. 9 cm = 0.09 m

1000 thousands kilo (km)			1 ones meters (m)	0.1 tenths deci (dm)	0.01 hundredths centi (cm)	0.001 thousandths milli (mm)
			.	0	9	

5. 8.3 km = 8,300 m

1000 thousands kilo (km)			1 ones meters (m)	0.1 tenths deci (dm)	0.01 hundredths centi (cm)	0.001 thousandths milli (mm)
8	3	0	0.			

6. 5 yd = 180 in.

yard	1	2	3	4	5
inches	36	72	108	144	180

7. 7 ft = 21 yd

feet	1	2	3	4	5	6	7
yards	3	6	9	12	15	18	21

174 Chapter 4 Test

English Learner Strategy

Assessment Allow students time to look over the assessment. Have the students find math vocabulary terms used in the assessment. After listing all the vocabulary terms on the board that the students identify, have the students look up those they do not remember by turning back to the section in which the term was introduced. If needed, review these terms and their meanings prior to answering the questions.

onvert.

8 0.28 km = 280 m

9 5 cm = 0.5 dm

10 3 mi = 15,840 ft

11 48 in. = 4 ft

elect the appropriate unit to measure the length of each object.
/rite millimeters, inches, meters, or miles.

12 height of your school meters

13 width of a calculator millimeters

14 length of a skateboard inches

15 length of Lake Okeechobee miles

olve.

16 **TRAVEL** It is 12 kilometers from Tayshan's house to the community swimming pool. How many meters is it to the pool?

12,000 m

Football stadium near Petaluma, California

17 **SPORTS** A football field is 100 yards long. How many feet long is the football field?

300 feet

18 **ART** Kenisha needed strips of cloth $3\frac{3}{4}$ inches long for an art project. Draw a line segment to show the length of each piece of cloth.

0 1 2 3 4
in.

orrect the mistakes.

19 Mr. Hopkins went to a hardware store to buy 8 yards of rope for his garden. The rope was measured in feet, so he purchased 96 feet instead. What was wrong with the purchase Mr. Hopkins made?

The mistake by Mr. Hopkins was he thought there were 12 feet per yard, when there are actually 3 feet per yard.

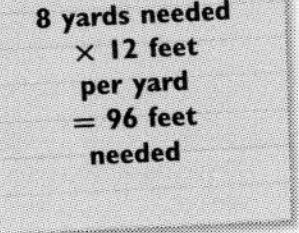

20 Show how you would correct Mr. Hopkins' mistake.

Since there are actually 3 feet per yard, Mr. Hopkins needed to do the following calculation: 8 yards needed × 3 feet per yard = 24 feet needed.

Math Coach Notes

Test-Taking Tip Have students underline the smaller unit measure and circle the larger unit measure in each conversion question. This will force them to think about each unit carefully before they decide whether it is necessary to multiply or divide.

Data-Driven Decision Making

Students missing Exercises . . .	Have trouble with . . .	Should review and practice . . .
1–3	drawing and measuring objects.	SSG Lesson 4–1 and 4–3, pp. 142 and 157 CRM Skills Practice, pp. A70 and A78
4–11	converting units of measure with the use of tables or charts.	SSG Lesson 4–2 and 4–4, pp. 149 and 163 CRM Skills Practice, pp. A74 and A82
12–15	determining an appropriate measure to use.	SSG Lesson 4–1 and 4–3, pp. 142 and 157 CRM Skills Practice, pp. A70 and A78
16–20	solving word problems that involve unit of measure conversions.	CRM Problem-Solving Practice, pp. A71, A75, A79 and A83

Chapter 4 Test Practice

Diagnose Student Errors

Survey student responses for each item. Class trends may indicate common errors and misconceptions.

1. A measured to nearest centimeter
(B) correct
C rounded up
D used end of ruler, not end of line

2. A conversion to kilometers
(B) correct
C conversion to decimeters
D conversion to millimeters

3. A did not look at whole number
B measured incorrectly
(C) correct
D measured incorrectly

4. A divided with conversion factor instead of multiplied
B used wrong conversion factor
C used wrong conversion factor
(D) correct

5. A used wrong conversion factor
(B) correct
C used wrong conversion factor
D used wrong conversion factor

6. A measured incorrectly
B measured incorrectly
(C) correct
D measured incorrectly

7. A divided inches by 20 instead of 12
(B) correct
C divided inches by 10 instead of 12
D divided incorrectly

8. (A) correct
B misinterpreted conversion of miles to feet
C did not convert total miles to feet
D misinterpreted conversion of miles to feet

9. A guess
(B) correct
C rounded up
D read ruler in reverse

Chapter 4 Test Practice

Choose the best answer and fill in the corresponding circle on the sheet at right.

1 Find the length of the line to the nearest millimeter.

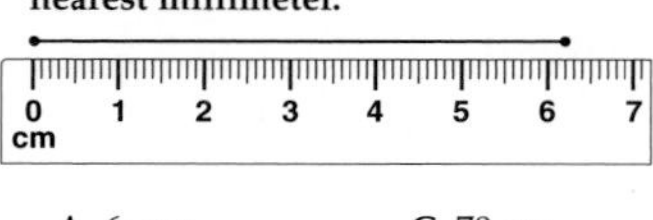

A 6 mm C 70 cm
(B) 62 mm D 72 mm

2 246 centimeters = _____ meters

A 0.00246 C 24.6
(B) 2.46 D 2,460

3 Find the length of the line to the nearest $\frac{1}{2}$ inch.

0 1 2 3
in.

A $1\frac{1}{2}$ in. (C) $2\frac{1}{2}$ in.
B $3\frac{1}{2}$ in. D $4\frac{1}{2}$ in.

4 When completed, a road will be 7.36 kilometers long. What is the length in meters?

A 0.736 m C 736 m
B 73.6 m (D) 7,360 m

5 803 millimeters = _____ meters

A 0.0803 C 8.03
(B) 0.803 D 80.3

6 Find the length of the line to the nearest centimeter.

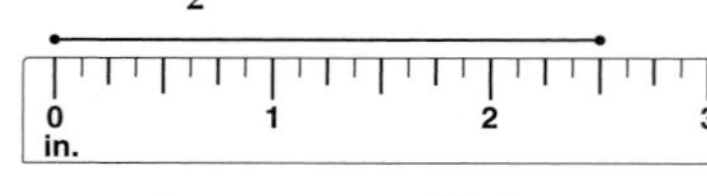

A 3 cm (C) 5 cm
B 4 cm D 6 cm

7 The ladder is 60 inches long. How many feet long is the ladder?

A 3 ft
(B) 5 ft
C 6 ft
D 7 ft

8 Javon rode his bike 2 miles to Zina's house. Together they rode another 3 miles to the park. Which sentence shows how many feet Javon traveled to get to the park?

(A) $5 \times 5{,}280 = 26{,}400$ ft
B $5 \times 12 = 60$ ft
C $2 + 3 = 5$ ft
D $5 \times 100 = 500$ ft

GO ON

176 Chapter 4 Test Practice

10. A unit too small
B unit too large
(C) correct
D unit much too large

11. (A) correct
B divided incorrectly
C divided incorrectly
D divided incorrectly

12. (A) correct
B unit too large
C unit much too large
D unit much too large

9 Find the length of the line to the nearest $\frac{1}{4}$ inch.

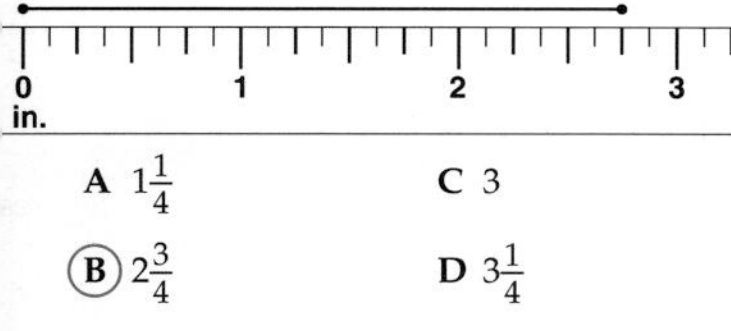

A $1\frac{1}{4}$ C 3

(B) $2\frac{3}{4}$ D $3\frac{1}{4}$

10 What customary unit of length would you use to measure a person's height?

A centimeters (C) foot

B yard D mile

11 Berto and his friends are enjoying the outdoor activity shown at the right. Their sled traveled 42 feet. Convert 42 feet to yards.

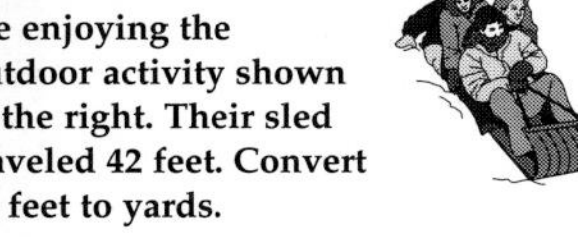

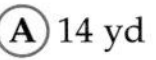 14 yd C 17 yd

B 15 yd D 20 yd

12 What metric unit of length would you use to measure the length of an ant?

(A) millimeter C meter

B centimeter D kilometer

ANSWER SHEET

Directions: Fill in the circle of each correct answer.

1	A	**B** (filled)	C	D
2	A	**B** (filled)	C	D
3	A	B	**C** (filled)	D
4	A	B	C	**D** (filled)
5	A	**B** (filled)	C	D
6	A	B	**C** (filled)	D
7	A	**B** (filled)	C	D
8	**A** (filled)	B	C	D
9	A	**B** (filled)	C	D
10	A	B	**C** (filled)	D
11	**A** (filled)	B	C	D
12	**A** (filled)	B	C	D

Success Strategy
Find key words or phrases in each question that will help you choose the correct answer. For example, pay attention to the units the question is asking you to convert.

Diagnosing Student Errors and Misconceptions

Review When working on the Test Practice problems, have students show their work on a separate sheet of notebook paper that can be used later as a reference. After the class has completed the Test Practice problems, go around the room and solicit answers to each question. After each question, take an informal poll of how many students answered each question correctly. If you notice a significant number of students who did not get the problem correct, then you should review the method or thought process behind the question with the entire class. If a very small number of students miss the question, ask the student(s) individually if he or she knows what went wrong or where the error occurred. Repeat this process throughout the Test Practice problems as time permits.

Common Error *Alert*

Using Benchmarks For Exercises 10 and 12 remind students to think of the benchmark length they established earlier in the chapter.

Chapter 5

Chapter Overview

Chapter-at-a-Glance

Lesson	Math Objective	State/Local Standards
5-1 Quadrilaterals (pp. 180-186)	Identify and draw quadrilaterals.	
5-2 Triangles (pp. 187-193)	Identify and draw triangles.	
Progress Check (p. 194)		
5-3 Introduction to Area (pp. 195-200)	Find areas of figures on grids.	
5-4 Area of a Rectangle (pp. 201-207)	Find areas of rectangles.	
Progress Check (p. 208)		
5-5 Area of a Parallelogram (pp. 209-214)	Find areas of parallelograms.	
5-6 Area of a Triangle (pp. 215-222)	Find areas of triangles.	
5-7 Circles (pp. 223-229)	Find circumferences and areas of circles.	
Progress Check (p. 230)		

Content-at-a-Glance

The diagram below summarizes and unpacks Chapter 5 content.

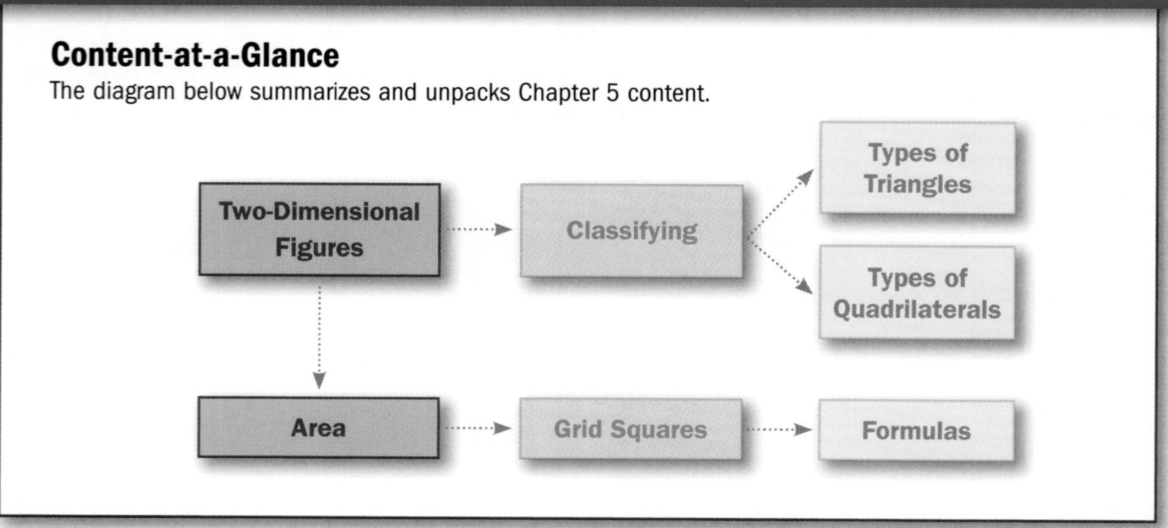

Online Assessment and Reporting
glencoe.com

Chapter Assessment Manager

Diagnostic

Diagnose students' readiness.

	Student Study Guide/ Teacher Edition	Assessment Masters	Technology
Course Placement Test		1	ExamView® Assessment Suite
Book 2 Pretest		62	ExamView® Assessment Suite
Chapter 5 Pretest		76	ExamView® Assessment Suite
Quiz/Preview	SSG 179		Math Online glencoe.com StudentWorks™ Plus

Formative

Identify students' misconceptions of content knowledge.

	Student Study Guide/ Teacher Edition	Assessment Masters	Technology
Progress Checks	SSG 194, 208, 230		Math Online glencoe.com StudentWorks™ Plus
Vocabulary Review	SSG 231		Math Online glencoe.com
Lesson Assessments			ExamView® Assessment Suite
Are They Getting It?	TE 183, 190, 198, 204, 212, 218, 226		Math Online glencoe.com

Summative

Determine student success in learning concepts in the lesson, chapter, or book.

	Student Study Guide/ Teacher Edition	Assessment Masters	Technology
Chapter 5 Test	SSG 236	79	ExamView® Assessment Suite
Test Practice	SSG 238	82	ExamView® Assessment Suite
Alternative Assessment	TE 236	85	
See It, Do It, Say It, Write It	TE 186, 193, 200, 207, 214, 222, 229		
Book 2 Test		98	ExamView® Assessment Suite

Back-mapping and Vertical Alignment **McGraw-Hill's *Math Triumphs*** intervention program was conceived and developed with the final result in mind: student success in grade-level mathematics, including Algebra 1 and beyond. The authors, using the **NCTM Focal Points and Focal Connections** as their guide, developed this brand-new series by backmapping from grade-level and Algebra 1 concepts, and vertically aligning the topics so that they build upon prior skills and concepts and serve as a foundation for future topics.

Chapter Resource Manager

	Lesson 5-1	Lesson 5-2	Lesson 5-3	Lesson 5-4
Concept	Quadrilaterals	Triangles	Introduction to Area	Area of a Rectangle
Objective	Identify and draw quadrilaterals.	Identify and draw triangles.	Find areas of figures on grids.	Find areas of rectangles.
Math Vocabulary	congruent parallel lines parallelogram quadrilateral rhombus trapezoid	acute angle congruent obtuse angle right angle	area square unit	area square unit
Lesson Resources	**Materials** • Grid paper • Ruler • Index cards **Manipulatives** • Geoboards • Pattern blocks **Other Resources** CRM Vocabulary and English Language Development CRM Skills Practice CRM Problem-Solving Practice CRM Homework Practice	**Materials** • Centimeter grid paper • Colored pencils • Colored construction paper • Protractors • Rubber bands **Manipulatives** • Geoboards • Tangrams **Other Resources** CRM Vocabulary and English Language Development CRM Skills Practice CRM Problem-Solving Practice CRM Homework Practice	**Materials** • Grid paper **Manipulatives** • Geoboards **Other Resources** CRM Vocabulary and English Language Development CRM Skills Practice CRM Problem-Solving Practice CRM Homework Practice	**Materials** • Ruler • Index cards **Manipulatives** • Base-ten blocks • Connecting cubes • Geoboards **Other Resources** CRM Vocabulary and English Language Development CRM Skills Practice CRM Problem-Solving Practice CRM Homework Practice
Technology	Math Online glencoe.com StudentWorks™ Plus ExamView® Assessment Suite	Math Online glencoe.com StudentWorks™ Plus ExamView® Assessment Suite	Math Online glencoe.com StudentWorks™ Plus ExamView® Assessment Suite	Math Online glencoe.com StudentWorks™ Plus ExamView® Assessment Suite

SSG Student Study Guide
CRM Chapter Resource Masters

TE Teacher Edition
DVD

	Lesson 5-5	Lesson 5-6	Lesson 5-7
Concept	Area of a Parallelogram	Area of a Triangle	Circles
Objective	Find areas of parallelograms.	Find areas of triangles.	Find circumferences and areas of circles.
Math Vocabulary	area parallelogram square unit	area parallelogram square unit triangle	circle circumference diameter pi radius
Lesson Resources	**Materials** • Cardboard or cardstock • Square tiles • Grid paper **Manipulatives** • Geoboards • Pattern blocks • Tangrams **Other Resources** CRM Vocabulary and English Language Development CRM Skills Practice CRM Problem-Solving Practice CRM Homework Practice	**Materials** **Manipulatives** • Geoboards • Pattern blocks • Tangrams **Other Resources** CRM Vocabulary and English Language Development CRM Skills Practice CRM Problem-Solving Practice CRM Homework Practice	**Materials** **Manipulatives** • Fraction circles **Other Resources** CRM Vocabulary and English Language Development CRM Skills Practice CRM Problem-Solving Practice CRM Homework Practice
Technology	Math Online glencoe.com StudentWorks™ Plus ExamView® Assessment Suite	Math Online glencoe.com StudentWorks™ Plus ExamView® Assessment Suite	Math Online glencoe.com StudentWorks™ Plus ExamView® Assessment Suite

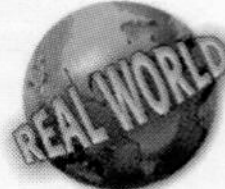

Chapter 5 Chapter Notes

Real-World Applications

Decorating Marty is painting his bedroom so that three walls are blue and one wall is tan. Marty's room has dimensions of 13 feet by 15 feet with 8-foot ceilings. What is the area of each wall?

Intervention Strategy

Equal Areas

Step 1 Have students form four groups.

Step 2 Using graph paper, groups of students need to draw as many triangles and rectangles as they can find with an area equal to a number assigned to that group. Numbers should be even numbers between 10 and 24.

Step 3 Group members should write the dimensions of each of their figures on their drawings.

Step 4 Have each group discuss the relationship between the dimensions and the area. Can each group establish a formula for the area of a triangle and a rectangle that would work with each figure they drew?

Step 5 Have groups share their figures, dimensions, area, and the formulas discovered. Verify that each group arrived at the same formulas for the area of a triangle and the area of a rectangle.

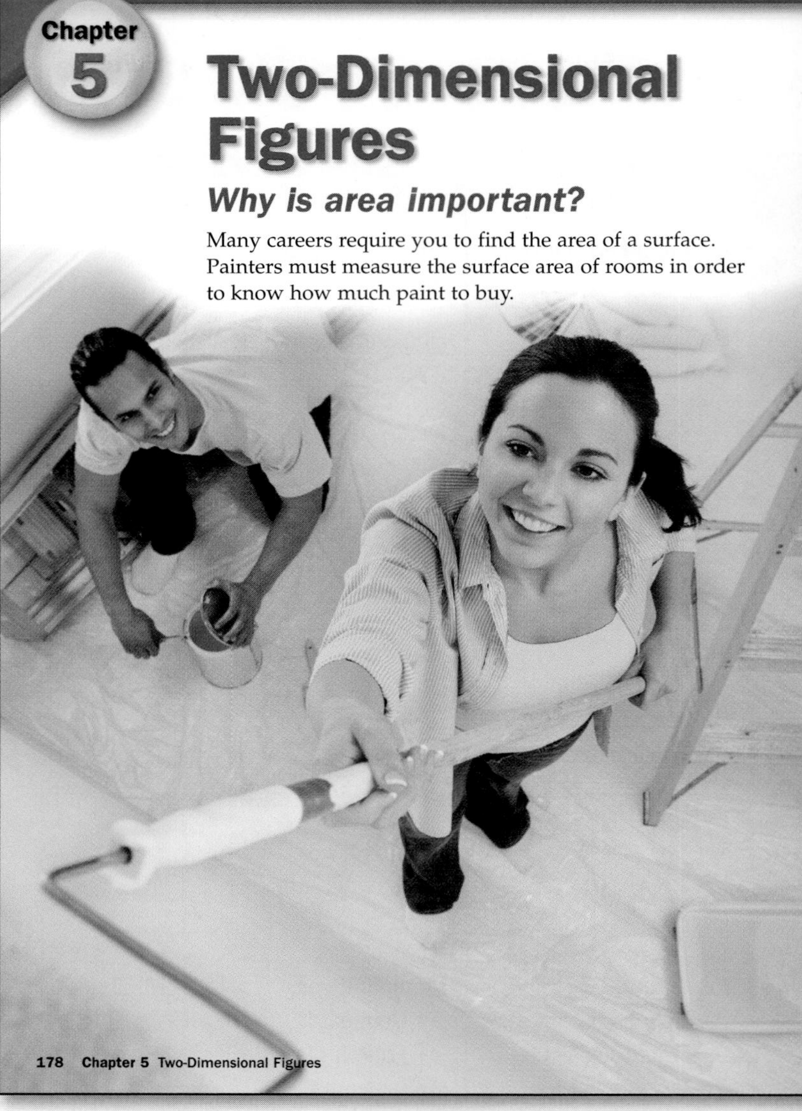

Chapter 5

Two-Dimensional Figures

Why is area important?

Many careers require you to find the area of a surface. Painters must measure the surface area of rooms in order to know how much paint to buy.

178 Chapter 5 Two-Dimensional Figures

Key Vocabulary

Find interactive definitions in 13 languages in the **eGlossary** at glencoe.com.

English **Español** *Introduce the most important vocabulary terms from Chapter 5.*

area **área**
the number of square units needed to cover the surface enclosed by a geometric figure (p. 195)

parallelogram **paralelogramo**
a quadrilateral that has both pairs of opposite sides congruent and parallel (p. 180)

quadrilateral **cuadrilátero**
a shape that has four sides and four angles (p. 180)

rhombus **rombo**
a parallelogram with four congruent sides (p. 180)

square unit **unidad cuadrada**
a unit for measuring area (p. 195)

trapezoid **trapecio**
a quadrilateral with one pair of opposite sides parallel (p. 180)

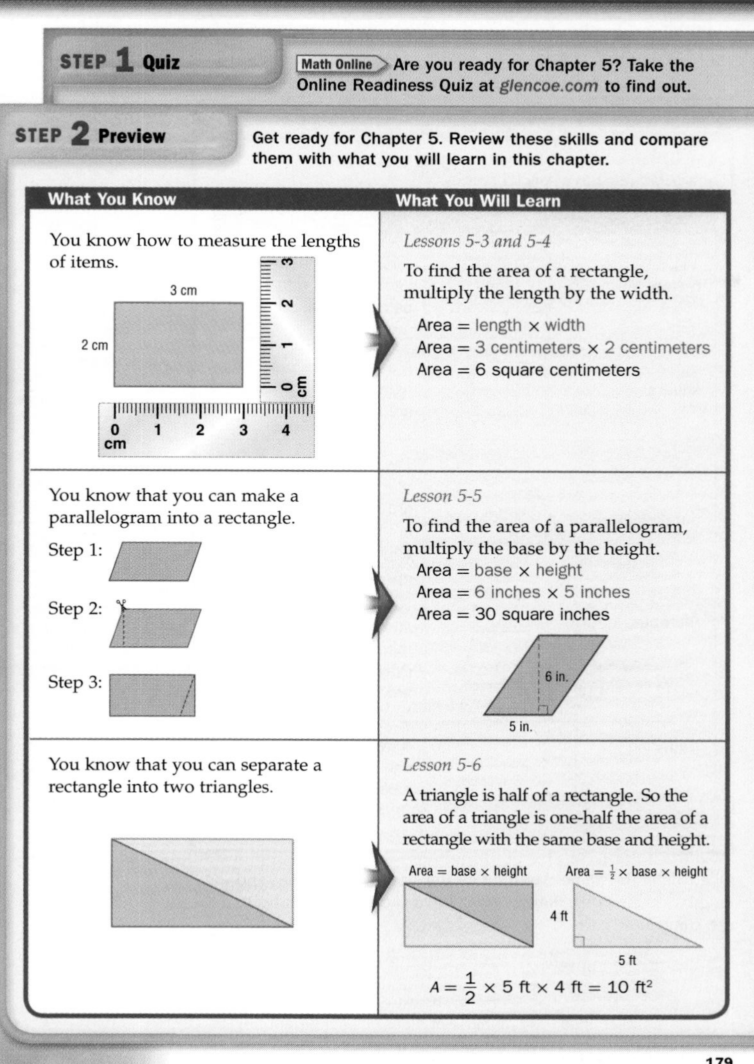

STEP 1 Quiz

Math Online Are you ready for Chapter 5? Take the Online Readiness Quiz at *glencoe.com* to find out.

STEP 2 Preview

Get ready for Chapter 5. Review these skills and compare them with what you will learn in this chapter.

What You Know	What You Will Learn
You know how to measure the lengths of items. (3 cm, 2 cm; ruler 0 1 2 3 4 cm)	*Lessons 5-3 and 5-4* To find the area of a rectangle, multiply the length by the width. Area = length × width Area = 3 centimeters × 2 centimeters Area = 6 square centimeters
You know that you can make a parallelogram into a rectangle. Step 1: Step 2: Step 3:	*Lesson 5-5* To find the area of a parallelogram, multiply the base by the height. Area = base × height Area = 6 inches × 5 inches Area = 30 square inches (6 in., 5 in.)
You know that you can separate a rectangle into two triangles.	*Lesson 5-6* A triangle is half of a rectangle. So the area of a triangle is one-half the area of a rectangle with the same base and height. Area = base × height Area = $\frac{1}{2}$ × base × height (4 ft, 5 ft) $A = \frac{1}{2} \times 5 \text{ ft} \times 4 \text{ ft} = 10 \text{ ft}^2$

179

Vocabulary Preview

- As students complete the Chapter Preview, have them make a list of important terms throughout the chapter.
- Divide students into pairs. Have the pairs compare their lists of terms to make one list.
- Then have students take turns defining the terms aloud to each other.
- Finally, have students take turns looking up the terms in the Glossary and reading the definitions out loud.

Step 1 Quiz

Pretest/Prescribe Students can take the Online Readiness Quiz or the Diagnostic Pretest in the Assessment Masters.

Step 2 Preview

Use this pre-chapter activity to activate students' prior knowledge, build confidence, and help students preview the lessons.

Dinah Zike's Foldables®

Guide students through the directions on p. A85 in the Chapter Resource Masters to create their own Foldable graphic organizer to use with this chapter.

Home Connections

- Find two figures that you think may have the same or close-to-the-same area but different dimensions. (No calculations should be done.)

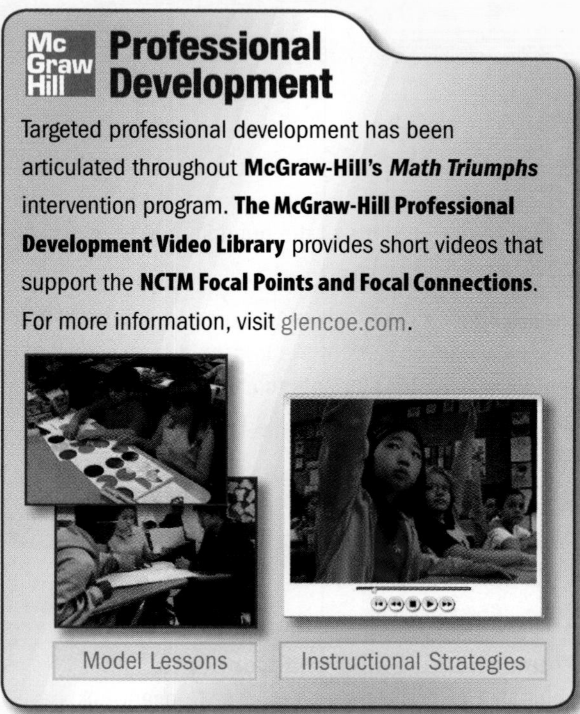

Professional Development

Targeted professional development has been articulated throughout **McGraw-Hill's *Math Triumphs*** intervention program. **The McGraw-Hill Professional Development Video Library** provides short videos that support the **NCTM Focal Points and Focal Connections**. For more information, visit glencoe.com.

Lesson 5-1

Lesson Notes

Lesson Planner

Objective Identify and draw quadrilaterals.

Vocabulary **congruent**, **parallel lines**, **parallelogram**, **quadrilateral**, **rhombus**, **trapezoid**

Materials/Manipulatives pattern blocks, grid paper, geoboards, ruler, index cards

Chapter Resource Masters

- CRM Vocabulary and English Language Development (p. A88)
- CRM Skills Practice (p. A89)
- CRM Problem-Solving Practice (p. A90)
- CRM Homework Practice (p. A91)

1 Introduce

Vocabulary

Explore Vocabulary Draw a *quadrilateral* on the board. Have a student volunteer come to the board and change a part or parts of the quadrilateral to make it a *trapezoid.*

Have another student volunteer come to the board and change a part or parts of the trapezoid to make it a *parallelogram.* Ask students to continue the pattern until all the vocabulary words are used.

2 Teach

Key Concept

Foundational Skills and Concepts After students have read through the Key Concept box, have them try these exercises.

1. How many sides does a quadrilateral have? four
2. What quadrilaterals have two pairs of congruent sides? parallelogram, rectangle, rhombus, square
3. What quadrilaterals have four congruent sides? rhombus, square

Lesson 5-1

Quadrilaterals

KEY Concept

Quadrilaterals have four sides and four angles. Some quadrilaterals have special names.

Type	Example	Description
rectangle		A rectangle has four right angles, with two pairs of equal sides.
square		A square has four right angles. All sides are equal.
parallelogram		The opposite sides of a parallelogram are parallel and equal in length. Opposite angles of each side are also congruent.
rhombus (These marks show equal sides.)		All four sides of a rhombus are equal. Opposite sides are parallel.
trapezoid (This symbol indicates parallel sides.)		A trapezoid has only one pair of opposite sides parallel.

VOCABULARY

congruent line segments that have the same length or angles that have the same measure

parallel lines lines that are the same distance apart; parallel lines do not meet or cross

parallelogram a quadrilateral that has both pairs of opposite sides congruent and parallel

quadrilateral a shape that has four sides and four angles

rhombus a parallelogram with four congruent sides

trapezoid a quadrilateral with one pair of opposite sides parallel

Quadrilaterals can be classified by the size of their angles and the length of their sides. Figures often have symbols that indicate if there are **congruent** parts.

parallel lines

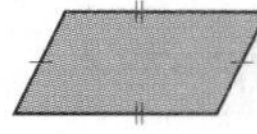
congruent sides

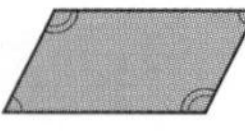
congruent angles

180 Chapter 5 Two-Dimensional Figures

English Learner Strategy

Reference Cards Have EL students use definitions (in their native languages) of angles to help them classify quadrilaterals. Allow them to write the classification on one side of an index card. They should draw the figure on the other side of the card for reference.

Example 1

Classify the figure in as many ways as possible.

1. Look at the figure.
2. Are opposite sides equal?
   yes
3. Are any of the opposite sides parallel?
   yes
4. Does the figure have exactly one pair of parallel sides? no
5. The figure can be classified as a parallelogram and a rectangle.

YOUR TURN!

Classify the figure in as many ways as possible.

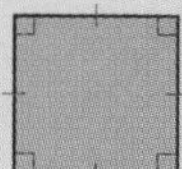

1. Look at the figure.
2. Are opposite sides equal? yes
3. Are any of the opposite sides parallel?
   yes
4. Does the figure have exactly one pair of parallel sides? no
5. The figure can be classified as a square.

Example 2

Identify the figure.

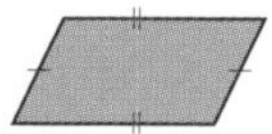

1. The figure has four sides.
   The figure is a quadrilateral.
2. The opposite sides are parallel and equal in length.
   The figure is a parallelogram or a rectangle.
3. The opposite angles of each side are congruent.
   The figure is a parallelogram.

YOUR TURN!

Identify the figure.

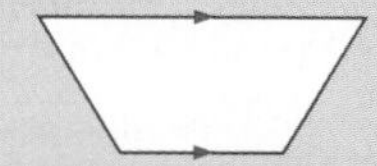

1. The figure has four sides.
   The figure is a(n) quadrilateral.
2. There is one pair of parallel sides.
3. There are zero right angles.
   The figure is a(n) trapezoid.

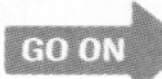

Additional Example 1

Classify the figure in as many ways as possible.

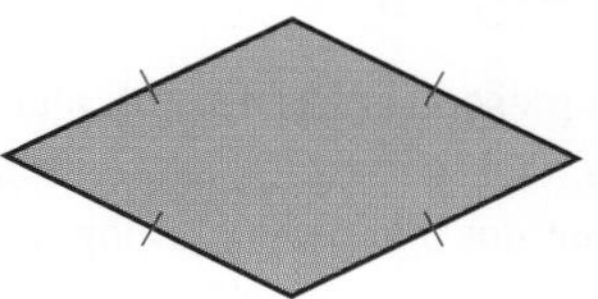

1. Look at the figure.
2. Are opposite sides equal? yes, two pairs
3. Are any of the opposite sides parallel? yes, two pairs
4. The figure can be classified as a parallelogram and rhombus.

Additional Example 2

Identify the figure.

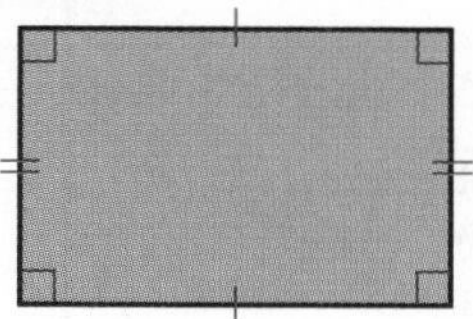

1. The figure has four sides. The figure is a quadrilateral.
2. The figure has two sets of parallel lines and four right angles. The figure is a rectangle.

Intervention Strategy

Visual Learners

Concept Map List the different types of quadrilaterals. Have students create a concept map listing the different types of quadrilaterals and then describe the processes they used in creating them.

Using Manipulatives

Ruler When presenting Examples 1 and 2, have students use a ruler to draw the figures accurately in their notes. Point out that when drawing a model, students should make sure that they accurately meet the classifications.

On-Hand Manipulatives Show students that there are many real-world items that are quadrilaterals. Have students list real-world examples of quadrilaterals in this lesson to help them classify and remember the figures.

Math Coach Notes

Classify Quadrilaterals Provide a table to students that helps them to classify and name quadrilaterals.

Quadrilateral	Sides	Angles
Trapezoid	one set of parallel sides	
Parallelogram	two sets of parallel sides	
Rhombus	two sets of parallel sides; four congruent sides	
Rectangle	two sets of parallel sides	four right angles
Square	two sets of parallel sides; four congruent sides	four right angles

Who is Correct?

Draw a trapezoid.

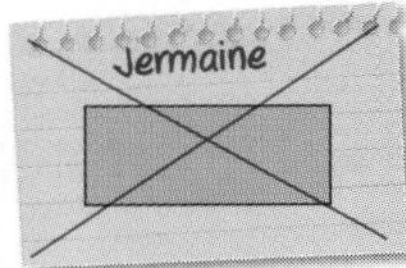

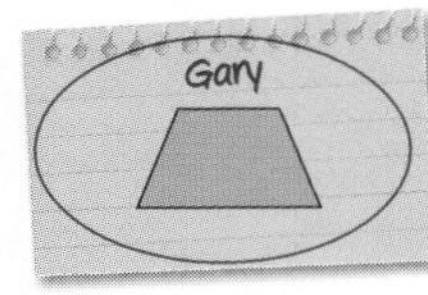

Circle correct answer(s). Cross out incorrect answer(s).

Guided Practice

Classify each quadrilateral in as many ways as possible.

1

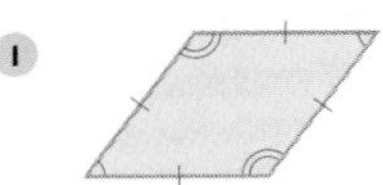

1. Are opposite sides equal? yes
2. Are any of the opposite sides parallel? yes
3. Are all the angles equal in size? no
4. The figure is a rhombus.

2

1. Are opposite sides equal? no
2. Are any of the opposite sides parallel? yes
3. Does the figure have exactly one pair of parallel sides? yes
4. The figure is a trapezoid.

182 **Chapter 5** Two-Dimensional Figures

Who *is Correct?*
Diagnostic Teaching

- Jermaine is incorrect. He drew a rectangle.
- Gary is correct.
- Ashley is incorrect. She drew a parallelogram.

Remind students that trapezoids have one and only one pair of parallel sides.

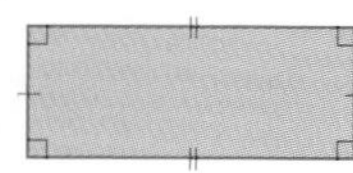

3 Identify the figure.

Step 1 The figure has four sides.

The figure is a(n) quadrilateral.

Step 2 Are any of the sides parallel? yes

Step 3 There are two pairs of parallel sides.

The figure is a(n) rectangle.

entify the figure.

The figure has four sides.

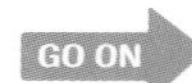

The figure is a(n) quadrilateral.

The opposite sides are parallel and equal in length.

The opposite angles of each side are congrent.

The figure is a(n) parallelogram.

The figure has four sides.

The figure is a(n) quadrilateral.

All four sides are equal.

The opposite sides are parallel.

The figure is a(n) rhombus.

GO ON

Intervention Strategy — Logical Learners

Check Figures When students are identifying figures, they can use logic to help them. For example, if they are trying to find out whether sides of a figure are congruent, then they do not need a ruler. Have students pick a side and place a piece of paper along the side so they can see the line. Then have students put a mark on the paper, which will represent the length of the side. Compare the marks with another side of the figure to see if they are congruent.

Are They Getting It?

Check students' understanding of quadrilaterals by writing these problems on the board. Have students explain the incorrect information in each problem.

Identify the figure.

1. 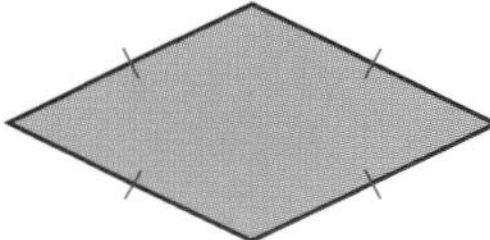

The figure is a parallelogram. This is correct.

2. The figure is a square. This is incorrect. The figure has two pairs of parallel sides and four congruent sides. It does not have right angles.

The figure is a rhombus.

Common Error *Alert*

Different Trapezoids Students get accustomed to seeing trapezoids that have the parallel sides shown as horizontal lines where the shortened base is the side along the top of the figure. They can overlook that trapezoids can be oriented differently. These figures are trapezoids. Students also do not think of trapezoids that have one right angle. The figure on the far right is also a trapezoid.

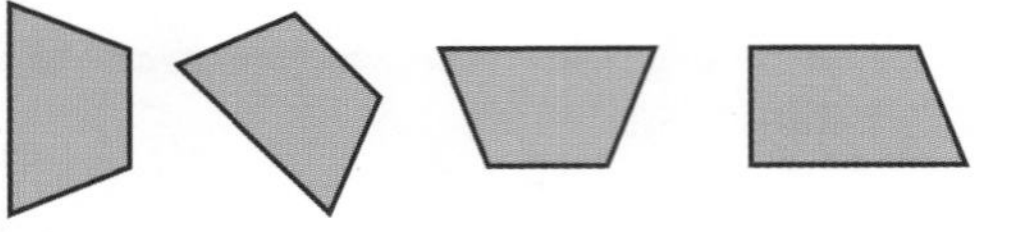

Note This!

Review Materials Suggest that students refer to their notes within 24 hours after taking them. Have students edit their notes for words and phrases that are illegible or do not make sense. Instruct them to edit with a different-colored pen to distinguish between what they wrote in class and what they filled in later.

Step by Step Problem-Solving Practice

Problem-Solving Strategies
- ☑ Use a diagram.
- ☐ Look for a pattern.
- ☐ Guess and check.
- ☐ Act it out.
- ☐ Work backward.

Solve.

6 MUSIC Alonso plays the glockenspiel in the marching band. What quadrilateral figure describes the shape of his instrument?

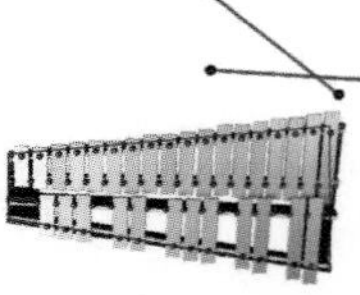

Understand Read the problem. Write what you know. The figure of the glockenspiel is a quadrilateral.

Plan Pick a strategy. One strategy is to use a diagram.

Solve Trace the outline of the figure. There are four sides. There is one pair of parallel sides. The figure is a(n) trapezoid.

Check Review the definition of the figure you named.

7 PLANTS Stella planted flowers in a pot. Viewed from the side, the flower pot has four sides. There is one pair of parallel sides and no right angles. What figure is Stella's flower pot? Check off each step.

✓ Understand: I underlined key words.

✓ Plan: To solve the problem, I will use a diagram.

✓ Solve: The answer is a(n) trapezoid.

✓ Check: I checked my answer by reviewing the definition.

8 **Reflect** The word *quadrilateral* has two parts. *Quad* means "four" and *lateral* means "side or relating to the side." In your own words, explain the meaning of the word quadrilateral.

Sample answer: Quadrilateral means a figure that has four sides.

Intervention Strategy — Visual Learners

Real-World Quadrilaterals Provide students with pictures of architecture from around the world. Have students find examples of quadrilaterals in the buildings. Students should trace the figures onto a sheet of paper. Prompt students to classify the quadrilaterals.

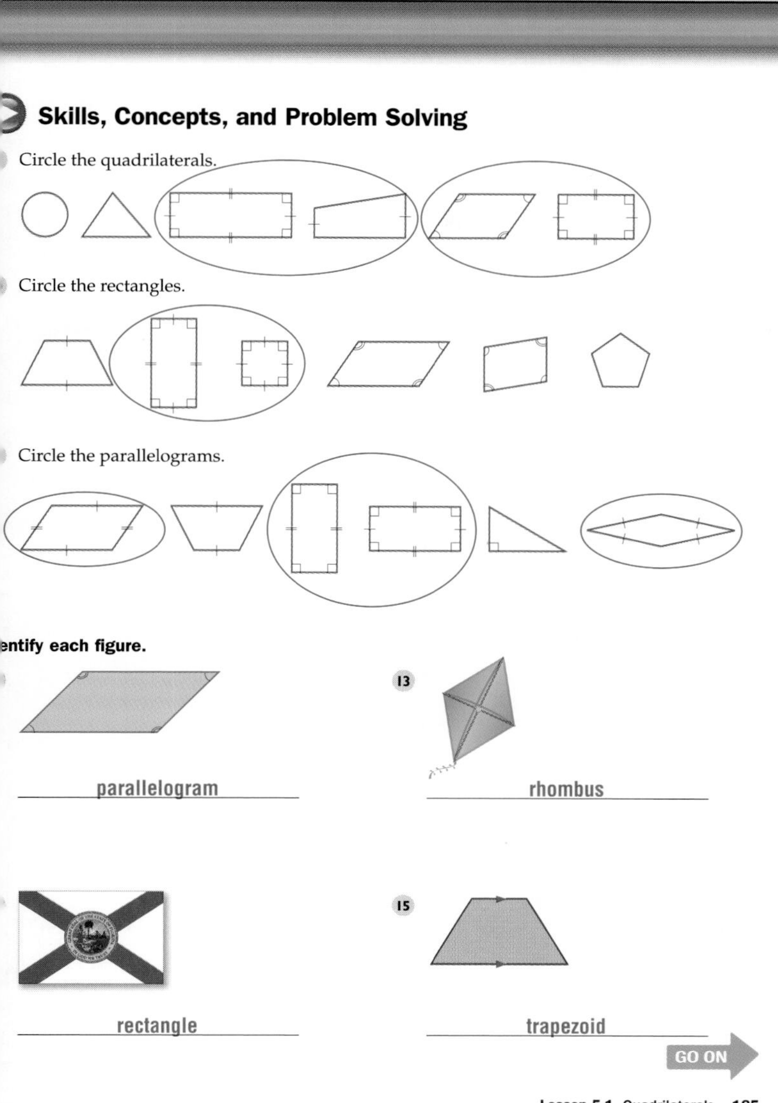

Skills, Concepts, and Problem Solving
Circle the quadrilaterals.
Circle the rectangles.
Circle the parallelograms.
entify each figure.
13
parallelogram
rhombus
15
rectangle
trapezoid
GO ON
Lesson 5-1 Quadrilaterals 185

Odd/Even Assignments

Exercises 9–19 are structured so that students practice the same concepts whether they are assigned the odd or even problems.

In-Class Assignment

Have students complete Exercises 10, 13, 16, 18, and 24 to ensure that they understand the concept.

Intervention Strategy

Kinesthetic Learners

Create Figures Arrange students into pairs and give each group a geoboard. Have one student select a figure from the Key Concept box. The other student makes the figure on the geoboard. Point out that finding an angle measure on a geoboard is difficult, so try to classify the figures by side lengths and parallel sides.

Math Challenge

Draw and Identify Have students create a sketch of a parallelogram, a rhombus, a rectangle, a square, and a trapezoid. Then have students name each figure with as many names as they can. For example, a square meets the classifications of a quadrilateral, parallelogram, rhombus, rectangle, and square.

4 Assess

See It, Do It, Say It, Write It

Step 1 Draw the following figure on the board.

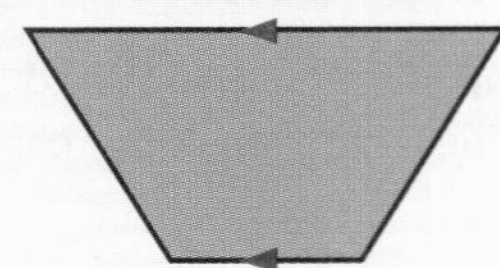

Step 2 Have students classify the figure. trapezoid

Step 3 Arrange students into pairs and have them explain to each other how they classified the figure.

Step 4 Have students write in their own words how to classify quadrilaterals.

Looking Ahead: Pre-teach

Triangles In the next lesson, students will learn about classifying triangles. Triangles can be classified by their angles and by their side lengths.

Example

Which description best represents the term *equilateral triangle*? C

A. All the sides of the triangle are of different lengths.

B. Two of the sides of the triangle have the same lengths.

C. All of the sides of the triangle are of the same lengths.

Match each triangle name with the description that is likely to fit it best.

A. acute triangle B. right triangle C. obtuse triangle

1. a triangle that has a right angle B

2. a triangle that has all acute angles A

3. a triangle that has an obtuse angle C

Identify each figure.

16 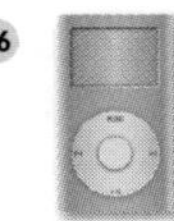

rectangle

17 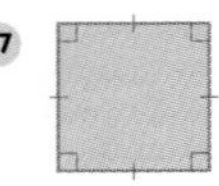

square

18 SAFETY Alan's science teacher asked him to tape a safety sign on the wall. All four sides of the sign are equal, and the opposite sides are parallel. What is the name of this figure?

rhombus

19 HOMEWORK Tanisha's math teacher asks her to explain the differences between parallelograms and trapezoids. Tanisha says, "A parallelogram has only one pair of opposite parallel sides. A trapezoid has two pair of opposite parallel sides." Is Tanisha correct? Explain.

No; both pairs of opposite sides of a parallelogram are parallel, and a trapezoid has only one pair of opposite sides parallel.

Vocabulary Check **Write the vocabulary word that completes each sentence.**

20 Line segments that have the same length are congruent.

21 A(n) quadrilateral has four sides and four angles.

22 A parallelogram with four congruent sides is called a(n) rhombus.

23 Parallel lines are lines that are the same distance apart; they do not meet or cross.

24 Writing in Math Describe a rectangle in words.

Sample answer: A rectangle has four sides and four angles. Its opposite sides are equal and parallel. The angles are all right angles. Some rectangles have two longer sides and two shorter sides.

STO

186 Chapter 5 Two-Dimensional Figures

Ticket Out the Door

Connect Vocabulary Tell students to give an example of an item found in the class that represents a vocabulary word from this lesson. Have students show you their examples as they exit the classroom.

Lesson 5-2 Triangles

KEY Concept

Triangles can be named by the measure of their angles and lengths of their sides.

For example, a triangle with one **right angle** and two congruent sides is called an isosceles right triangle.

Classify Triangles by Angles

acute triangle
three angles less than 90°

obtuse triangle
one angle greater than 90°

right triangle
one 90° angle

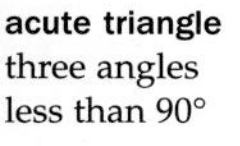

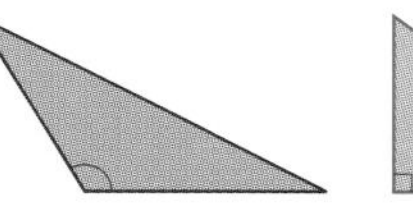

Classify Triangles by Sides

equilateral triangle
all sides are congruent

isosceles triangle
at least two sides are congruent

scalene triangle
no congruent sides

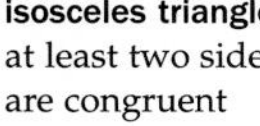

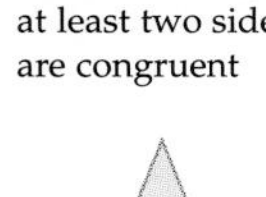

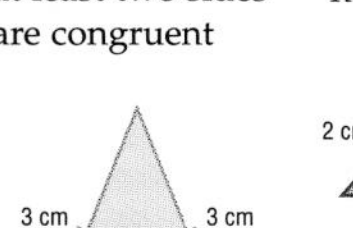

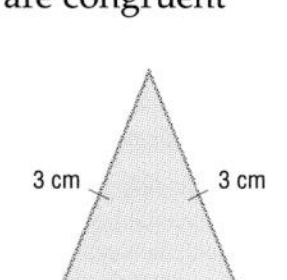

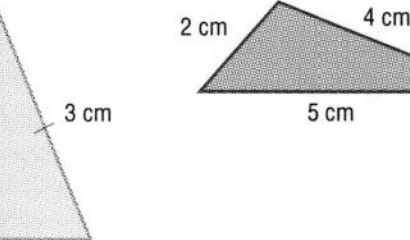

VOCABULARY

acute angle
an angle with a measure greater than 0° and less than 90°

congruent
line segments that have the same length, or angles that have the same measure

obtuse angle
an angle that measures greater than 90° but less than 180°

right angle
an angle with the measure of 90°

GO ON

Intervention Strategy — Kinesthetic Learners

Model Triangles

Have students work in pairs. Give each student a geoboard, a few rubber bands, and a piece of grid paper. Model how to make a triangle on the geoboard with a rubber band and then transfer that image to the grid paper. Tell students to classify and label each triangle they create. Then have students explain to their partners how each triangle meets the criteria for its classification.

Lesson Notes

Lesson 5-2

Lesson Planner

Objective Identify and draw triangles.

Vocabulary **acute angle**, **congruent**, **obtuse angle**, **right angle**

Materials/Manipulatives geoboards, rubber bands, centimeter grid paper, colored pencils or colored construction paper, protractors, tangrams

Chapter Resource Masters

- CRM Vocabulary and English Language Development (p. A92)
- CRM Skills Practice (p. A93)
- CRM Problem-Solving Practice (p. A94)
- CRM Homework Practice (p. A95)

1 Introduce

Vocabulary

Basic Vocabulary Draw three different triangles on the board—acute, obtuse, and right. Discuss what makes these figures triangles, using terms such as sides, vertices or corners, and angles. Compare a right angle to sitting upright in a chair. Then compare an acute angle to leaning forward and an obtuse angle to reclining back in a chair.

2 Teach

Key Concept

Foundational Skills and Concepts After students have read through the Key Concept box, have them try these exercises.

1. Which kind of triangle has one angle greater then 90°? obtuse triangle
2. Can a triangle have two obtuse angles? Explain. No; it would not be a closed figure with two obtuse angles.
3. Which kind(s) of triangle(s) have at least two congruent sides? isosceles and equilateral triangles

Additional **Example 1**

Name the triangle by its sides.

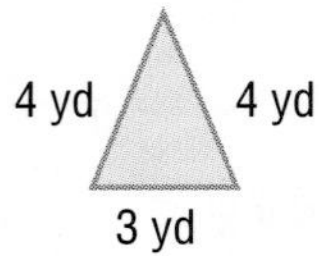

1. The triangle has two congruent sides.

2. The triangle is a(n) isosceles triangle.

Additional **Example 2**

Name the triangle by its angles.

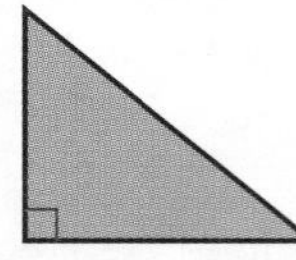

1. Use a right angle to show 90°. Compare the right angle to the angles of the triangle.

2. There are two angles less than 90°.

3. There are no angles greater than 90°.

4. There is one right angle.

5. The triangle is a(n) right triangle.

Example 1

Name the triangle by its sides.

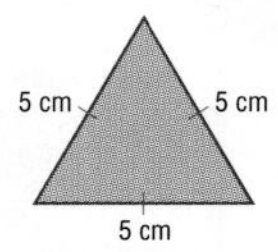

1. The triangle has 3 congruent sides.
2. The triangle is an equilateral triangle.

YOUR TURN!

Name the triangle by its sides.

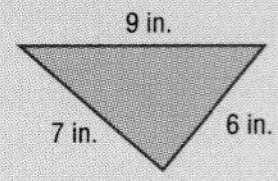

1. The triangle has __no__ congruent sides.
2. The triangle is a(n) __scalene triangle__.

Example 2

Name the triangle by its angles.

1. Use a right angle to show 90°. Compare the right angle to the angles of the triangle.
2. There are two angles less than 90°.
3. There is one angle greater than 90°.
4. There are no right angles.
5. The triangle is an obtuse triangle.

greater than 90° | less than 90°

YOUR TURN!

Name the triangle by its angles.

1. Use a right angle to show 90°. Compare the right angle to the angles of the triangle.
2. There are __three__ angles less than 90°.
3. There are __no__ angles greater than 90°.
4. There are __no__ right angles.
5. The triangle is a(n) __acute__ triangle.

greater than 90° | less than 90°

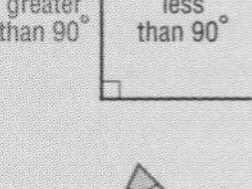

English Learner Strategy

Write three examples from the list below on the board. Discuss the prefix *tri-*. Examine each word and explain the three "parts" of each example. Challenge students to brainstorm words beginning with this prefix. Point out that the term triangle has three angles but also has three sides and three vertices or corners.

triathlon	tricolor	trimester
tricycle	trifecta	tripod
triceps	trifocal	trisect

Who is Correct?

Draw an acute triangle.

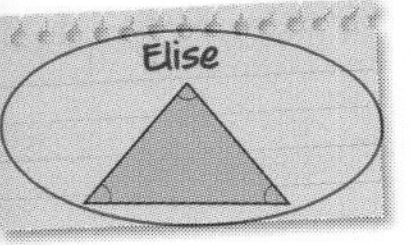

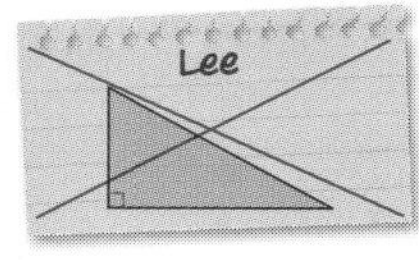

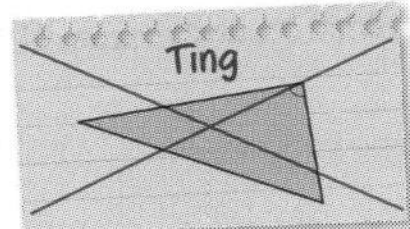

Circle correct answer(s). Cross out incorrect answer(s).

Guided Practice

Name each triangle by its sides.

1 The triangle has three congruent sides.

The triangle is a(n) equilateral triangle.

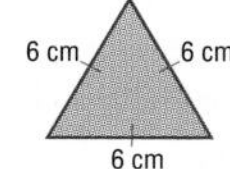

2

isosceles triangle

3

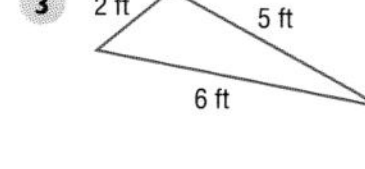

scalene triangle

Name the triangle by its angles.

4 There are three angles less than 90°.

There are no angles greater than 90°.

There are no right angles.

The triangle is a(n) acute triangle.

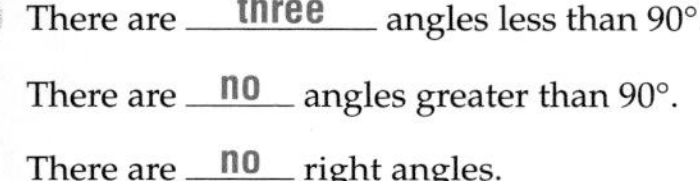

5

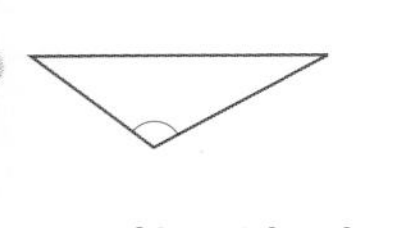

obtuse triangle

6

right triangle

GO ON

Lesson 5-2 Triangles 189

Using Manipulatives

Protractors To construct triangles that have angles of specific measures, students can use protractors. Model how to use the angle measurements to draw the different kinds of triangles and the straight edge to make the sides.

On-Hand Manipulatives Use tangrams to identify types of triangles. Have students combine the triangle pieces to create other figures and polygons, including larger triangles.

Math Coach Notes

Order of Naming Teach students that the proper order in triangle classification is angles first, then sides. For example, if a triangle has three angles less than 90° and three congruent sides, students should consider the angles first to determine that it is an acute triangle. Then consider the sides to determine that it is an equilateral triangle. The order of naming would be an *acute equilateral triangle*.

Who *is Correct?*

Diagnostic Teaching

- Elise is correct. Her triangle has three acute angles.
- Lee is incorrect. His triangle has a right angle.
- Ting is incorrect. His triangle has an obtuse angle.

English Learner Strategy

Everyday Triangles After teaching the Key Concept and discussing the examples, ask students to point out different kinds of triangles in their home and school environment. Tell them to explore large images as well as smaller designs within structures. Ask students to try to name the kinds of triangles they find. Discuss their examples together as a group.

Math Coach Notes

Hash Marks Point out the symbols used in the figures to identify triangles. Tell them the curved line indicates an angle measure and the hash mark on two sides indicate these sides are congruent. In a triangle with unlabeled sides, teach students to look for these symbols to help them classify the type of triangle.

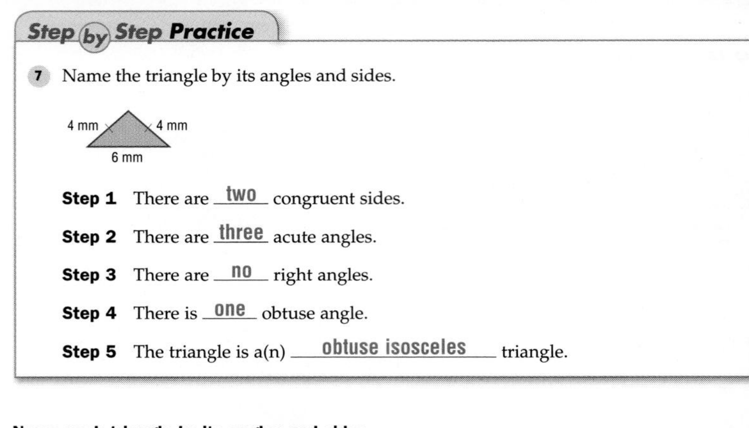

Step by Step Practice

7 Name the triangle by its angles and sides.

Step 1 There are two congruent sides.

Step 2 There are three acute angles.

Step 3 There are no right angles.

Step 4 There is one obtuse angle.

Step 5 The triangle is a(n) obtuse isosceles triangle.

Name each triangle by its angles and sides.

8 number of congruent sides 3

number of acute angles 3

number of right angles 0

number of obtuse angles 0

The triangle is a(n) equilateral triangle.

7 in. 7 in. 7 in.

9 obtuse scalene triangle

10 right scalene triangle

190 **Chapter 5** Two-Dimensional Figures

Are They Getting It?

Check students' understanding of triangles by drawing this figure and writing these problems on the board.

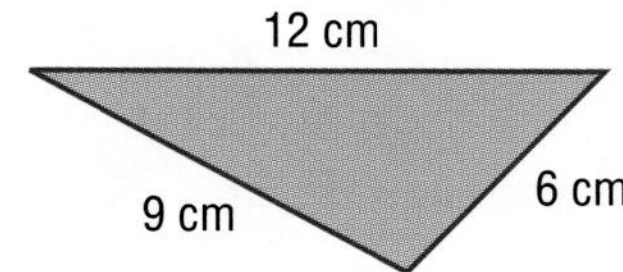

1. Name the triangle by its angles. obtuse triangle
2. Name the triangle by its angles and sides. obtuse scalene triangle
3. Explain why this figure is NOT an acute isosceles triangle. The triangle has one obtuse angle and no congruent sides.

Step by Step Problem-Solving Practice

Solve.

Problem-Solving Strategies
- ☑ Use a diagram.
- ☐ Look for a pattern.
- ☐ Guess and check.
- ☐ Act it out.
- ☐ Work backward.

11 **HOME ARTS** Rondell made an apple turnover in Home Arts that looked like the photo at the right. He thought it looked like a triangle so he traced it. Classify the triangle he traced by its angles.

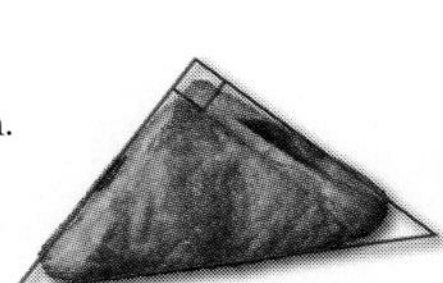

Understand Read the problem. Write what you know.
Rondell made an apple turnover.

Plan Pick a strategy. One strategy is to use a diagram.

Solve There are two angles less than 90°.
There are no angles greater than 90°.
There is one right angle.
The figure is a(n) right triangle.

Check Review the definition of the figure you named.

BASEBALL Desiree bought a pennant banner at a baseball game. If the triangle is classified by its angles, what type of triangle is shown? Check off each step.

✔ Understand: I underlined key words.

✔ Plan: To solve the problem, I will use a diagram.

✔ Solve: The answer is an acute triangle.

✔ Check: I checked my answer by reviewing the definition.

Reflect Can a triangle be both isosceles and obtuse? Explain.

Sample answer: Yes; an obtuse triangle can have two equal sides connecting at the obtuse angle, making it obtuse and isosceles.

Intervention Strategy — Visual Learners

Triangle Use colored pencils or colored construction paper to make triangles. Write a variety of triangle names from the list below on the board. Tell students to make several sizes of each kind of triangle from the list. Have students use the same colors for the same types of triangles. Then have students work in small groups. Each student should use their creations to help their group members practice identifying and naming types of triangles. Have students give proof for their classifications.

right isosceles
right scalene
acute equilateral
acute scalene
acute isosceles
obtuse isosceles
obtuse scalene

Odd/Even Assignments

Exercises 14–24 are structured so that students practice the same concepts whether they are assigned the odd or even problems.

In-Class Assignment

Have students complete Exercises 14, 18, 19, 22, and 28 to ensure that they understand the concept.

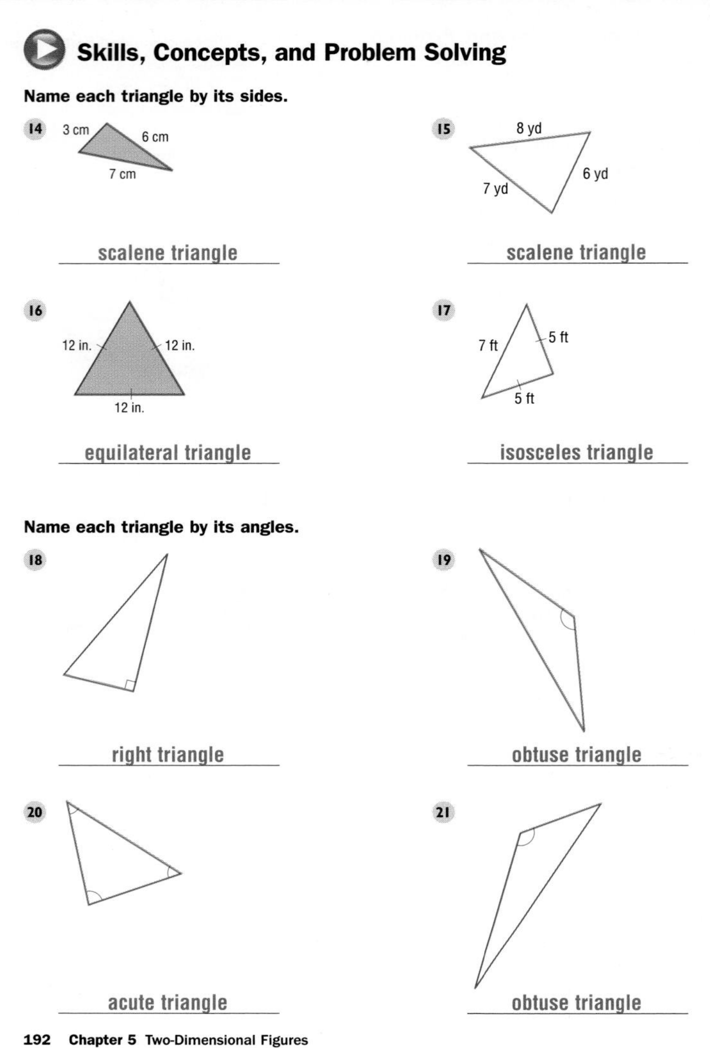

Math Challenge

Determine if each statement is true or false. For false sentences, have students explain their reasoning.

1. A triangle with three congruent sides can have one obtuse angle. false; the three sides would never meet with one obtuse angle.
2. A triangle with one right angle can have two congruent sides. true
3. Scalene triangles can be either acute or obtuse. true
4. A right triangle can have an obtuse angle. false; the other two angles in a right triangle must be acute.

ART Sandy's art teacher asked her class to cut out a triangle with sides that measure 9 inches, 7 inches, and 12 inches. What type of triangle did the students cut out? scalene triangle

Name the triangle by its angles and sides. acute isosceles triangle

6 m, 6 m, 7 m

MUSIC The musical instrument pictured on the right is in the shape of a triangle. All three angles of the triangle are less than 90°. Name the type of triangle pictured.

acute triangle

Vocabulary Check **Write the vocabulary word that completes each sentence.**

Angles that have the same measure are congruent.

A triangle with an angle that measures greater than 90° but less than 180° is a(n) obtuse triangle.

A(n) equilateral triangle has three equal sides.

Writing in Math Can a triangle be both a right triangle and an acute triangle?

Sample Answer: No; a right triangle has one angle that measures 90°. An acute triangle has three angles that all measure less than 90°.

Spiral Review

Identify each figure. (Lesson 5-1, p. 180)

square

30 parallelogram

STOP

Ticket Out the Door

Classifying Triangles Draw the following triangle on the board. As students exit, alternate asking them to name the triangle by its angles, sides, or both.

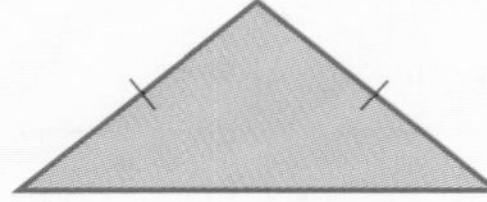

obtuse isosceles triangle

See It, Do It, Say It, Write It

Step 1 Write the following names on the board: right isosceles triangle, right scalene triangle, acute equilateral triangle, acute scalene triangle, acute isosceles triangle, obtuse isosceles triangle, and obtuse scalene triangle.

Step 2 Ask students to draw an example of each of the types of triangles on the board. Tell them to label each of their drawings.

Step 3 Have students pair up with another student and share their drawings. They should explain what makes each of their triangles match its classification.

Step 4 Instruct students to write out the criteria for each of their classifications. Encourage them to use clear language and correct vocabulary.

Looking Ahead: Pre-Teach

Introduction to Area In the next lesson, students will be introduced to the concept of area.

Area is a measurement in square units.

Draw each figure described on grid paper and count the number of unit squares inside the figure.

1. a rectangle that is 3 units by 4 units 12
2. a rectangle that is 1 unit by 8 units 8
3. a rectangle that is 4 units by 4 units 16
4. a rectangle that is 6 units by 2 units 12

Chapter 5 Progress Check 1

Formative Assessment

Use the Progress Check to assess students' mastery of the previous lessons. Have students review the lesson indicated for the problems they answered incorrectly.

Odd/Even Assignments

Exercises are structured so that students practice the same concepts whether they are assigned the odd or even problems.

Common Error Alert

Identify Shapes Students need to be careful when identifying the characteristics of quadrilaterals and triangles. Remind students to look for the small differences between each type.

Exercises 9–10 Students may need to be reminded of the properties of quadrilaterals and triangles. Direct students to the charts made in their notes for assistance.

Chapter 5 Progress Check 1 (Lessons 5-1 and 5-2)

Write the name of each figure.

1 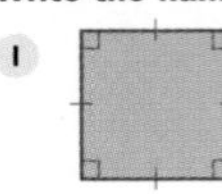

square

2 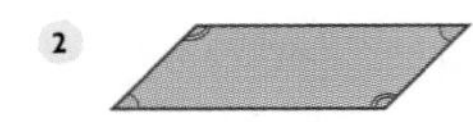

parallelogram

3 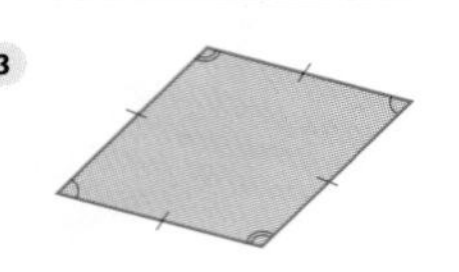

rhombus (parallelogram)

4 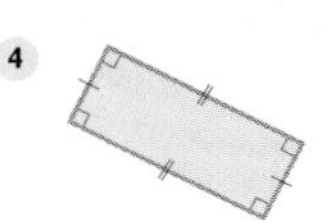

rectangle

Name each triangle by its sides or angles.

5 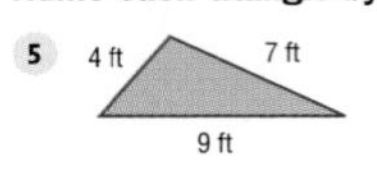

scalene triangle

6 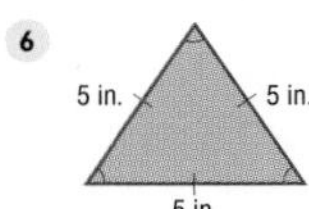

equilateral triangle

7 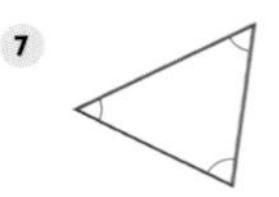

acute triangle

8 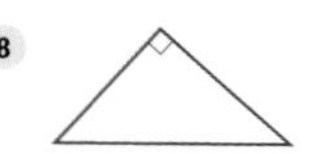

right triangle

Solve.

9 **FIGURES** Mindy bought a purse for her friend's birthday. What type of quadrilateral is the red part of the purse?

trapezoid

10 Can a right triangle also be equilateral? Explain.

Sample answer: No; a right triangle has an angle that measures exactly 90°, so the other two angles must be smaller than 90°. Equilateral triangles have all sides the same length and all angles the same size.

194 Chapter 5 Two-Dimensional Figures

Data-Driven Decision Making

Students missing Exercises . . .	Have trouble with . . .	Should review and practice . . .
1–4	classifying quadrilaterals.	SSG Lesson 5-1, p. 180 CRM Skills Practice, p. A89
5–8	classifying triangles by sides or angles.	SSG Lesson 5-2, p. 187 CRM Skills Practice, p. A93
9–10	solving word problems involving classifying quadrilaterals or triangles.	CRM Problem-Solving Practice, pp. A90 and A94

Lesson 5-3 Introduction to Area

KEY Concept

The **area** of a figure is the number of **square units** needed to cover a surface.

To find the area of a figure, you can count the number of square units the figure covers.

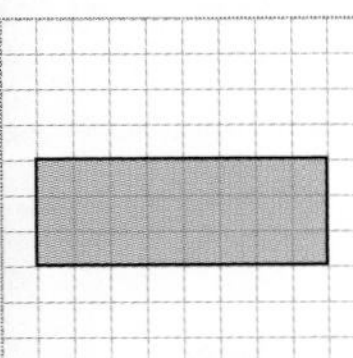

The area of the rectangle is 24 square units.

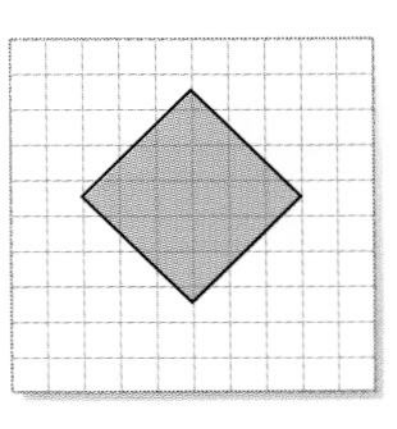

The area of the figure is about 18 square units.

VOCABULARY

area
the number of square units needed to cover the surface enclosed by a geometric figure

square unit
a unit for measuring area

ʼe units of area are square units.

Example 1

Find the area of the rectangle.

1. Count the number of squares the rectangle covers.
2. The area of the rectangle is 30 square units.
3. Check your answer.
   Count the squares in the top row. 6
   Count the number of rows. 5
4. Add the rows to find the area.
   6 + 6 + 6 + 6 + 6 = 30
   The area of the figure is about 30 square units.

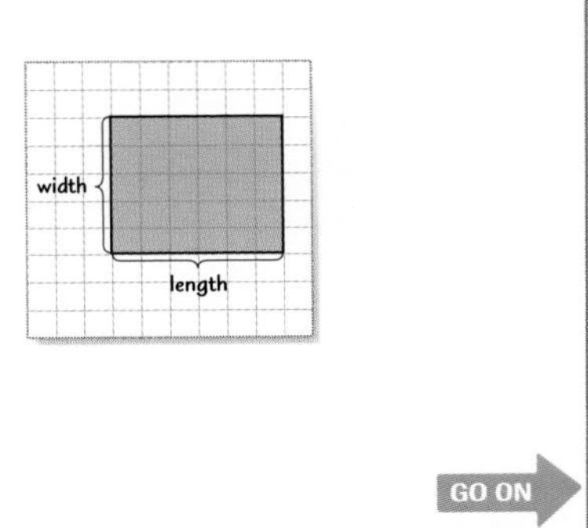

GO ON

Additional Example 1

Find the area of the rectangle.

1. Count the number of squares the rectangle covers.

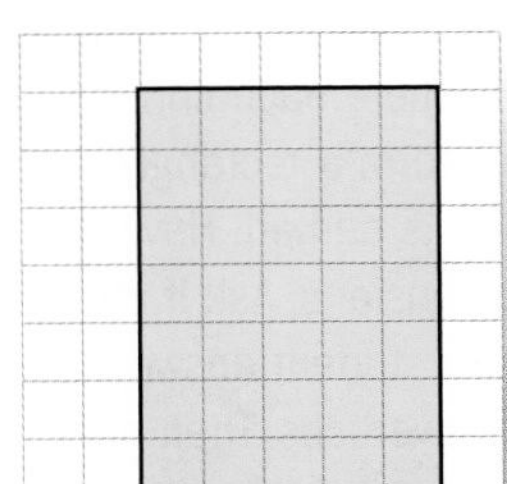

2. The area of the rectangle is 35 square units.
3. Check your answer.
   Count the squares in the top row. 5
   Count the number of rows. 7
4. Add the rows to find the area.
   5 + 5 + 5 + 5 + 5 + 5 + 5 = 35 ✔
   The area of the figure is 35 square units.

Lesson Notes

Lesson 5-3

Lesson Planner

Objective Find areas of figures on grids.

Vocabulary **area**, **square unit**

Materials/Manipulatives grid paper, geoboards

Chapter Resource Masters

- CRM Vocabulary and English Language Development (p. A96)
- CRM Skills Practice (p. A97)
- CRM Problem-Solving Practice (p. A98)
- CRM Homework Practice (p. A99)

1 Introduce

Vocabulary

Explore Vocabulary Hand out a sheet of grid paper to each student. Inform students that one square is one *square unit.* Ask students to make a rectangle that is 5 squares by 6 squares and count the number of squares inside the rectangle. Guide students to realize that the number of squares, or *square units*, inside the rectangle is the area.

2 Teach

Key Concept

Fundamental Skills and Concepts After students have read through the Key Concept box, have them try these exercises.

1. Draw another figure on grid paper that has the same area as the figure on the left. possible answer: 6 units by 4 units
2. If the figure on the right was rotated 90° on the grid paper, what would the area of the figure be? 18 square units

Additional *Example 2*

Estimate the area of the figure.

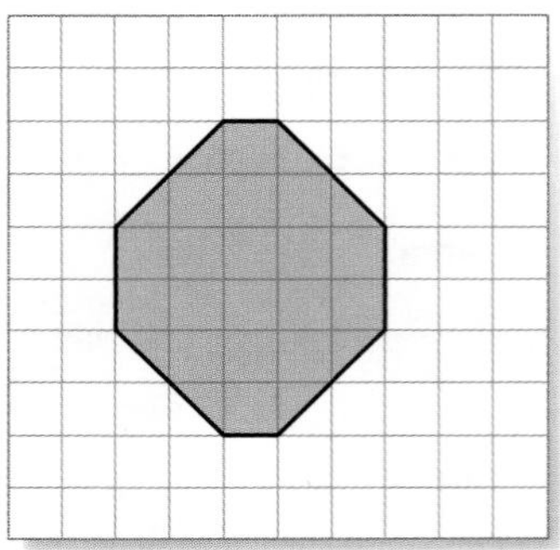

1. Count the number of whole squares the figure covers. The figure covers 18 whole squares.
2. Count the number of half squares the figure covers.
   The figure covers 8 half squares.
   8 half squares = 4 whole squares
3. Add the number of whole squares.
   $18 + 4 = 22$
   The area of the figure is about 22 square units.

Math Coach Notes

Common Error One of the most common errors students make is to believe that area is defined by formulas. If the students see a figure for which they do not know a formula for determining the area, they will have no idea how to proceed with finding the area.

YOUR TURN!

Find the area of the rectangle.

width

length

1. Count the number of squares the rectangle covers.
2. The area of the rectangle is _36_ square units.
3. Check your answer. Count the squares in the top row. _4_
   Count the number of rows. _9_
4. Add the rows to find the area.

_4_ + _4_ + _4_ + _4_ + _4_ + _4_ + _4_ + _4_ + _4_ = _36_

Example 2

Estimate the area of the figure.

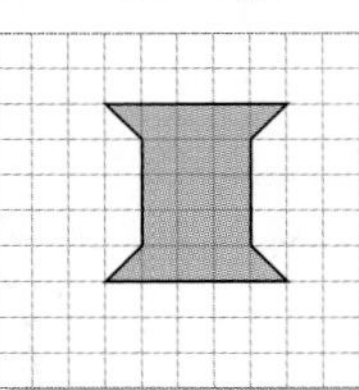

1. Count the number of whole squares the figure covers.
   The figure covers 15 whole squares.
2. Count the number of half squares the figure covers.
   The figure covers 4 half squares.
   4 half squares = 2 whole square(s)
3. Add the number of whole squares.
   $15 + 2 = 17$

The area of the figure is about 17 square units.

YOUR TURN!

Estimate the area of the figure.

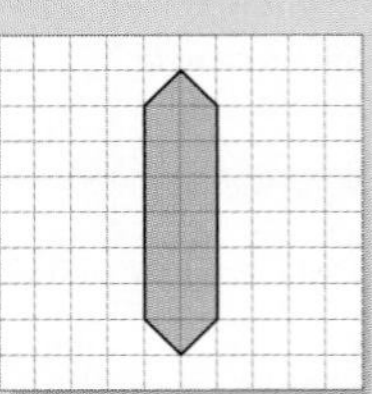

1. Count the number of whole squares the figure covers.
   The figure covers _12_ whole squares.
2. Count the number of half squares the figure covers.
   The figure covers 4 _half_ square(s).
   _4_ half squares = _2_ whole square(s)
3. Add the number of whole squares.
   _12_ + _2_ = _14_

The area of the figure is about _14_ square units.

196 Chapter 5 Two-Dimensional Figures

Intervention Strategy — Kinesthetic Learners

Tiled Floor Locate an area where the floor has square tiles. Explain to students that the floor will serve as a sheet of grid paper for this activity. Select four students to act as the vertices of a rectangle. Select a fifth student to name a whole number, not prime, less than 30. Have the four students determine where each can stand (using the tiled floor as the grid) so that they form a rectangle that has a area equal to the number of square units named. Have the class verify that the rectangle is of the correct dimensions. Ask if a different size rectangle could have been made. If any student answers yes, invite them forward to replace any one of the vertices. Then have the new student and the other three students work together to adjust the other three vertices.

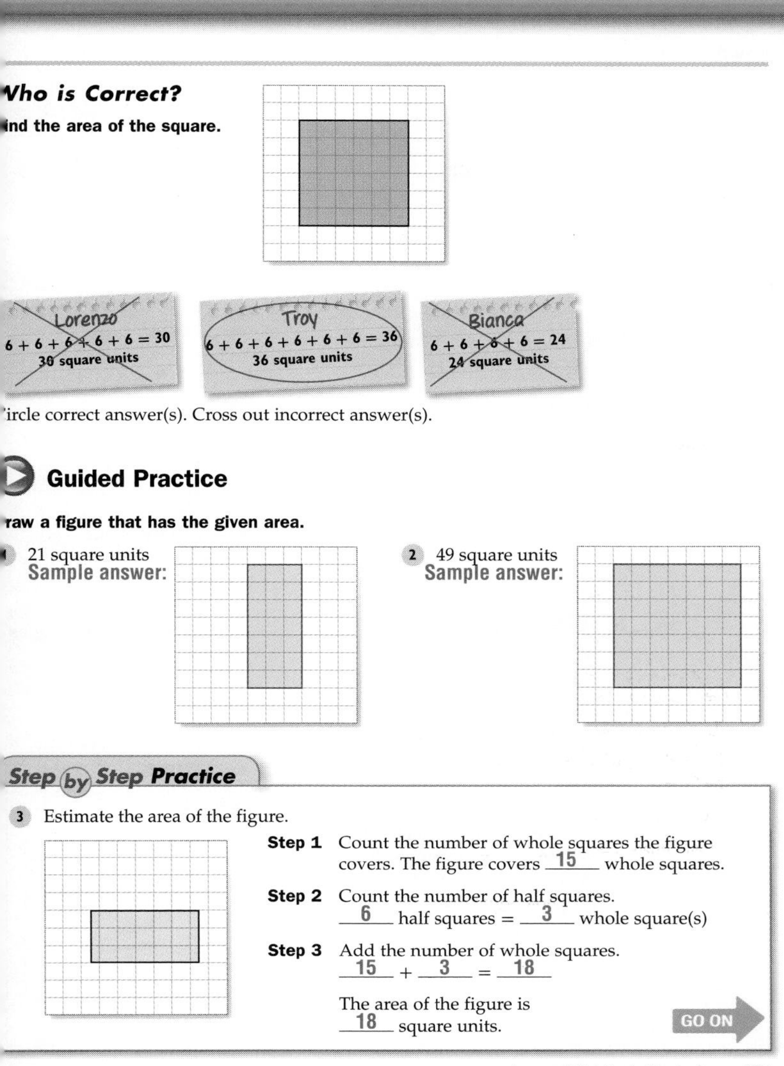

Who is Correct?
Find the area of the square.
Lorenzo
6 + 6 + 6 + 6 + 6 = 30
30 square units
Troy
6 + 6 + 6 + 6 + 6 + 6 = 36
36 square units
Bianca
6 + 6 + 6 + 6 = 24
24 square units
Circle correct answer(s). Cross out incorrect answer(s).
Guided Practice
Draw a figure that has the given area.
1 21 square units
Sample answer:
2 49 square units
Sample answer:
Step by Step Practice
3 Estimate the area of the figure.
Step 1 Count the number of whole squares the figure covers. The figure covers 15 whole squares.
Step 2 Count the number of half squares.
6 half squares = 3 whole square(s)
Step 3 Add the number of whole squares.
15 + 3 = 18
The area of the figure is 18 square units.
GO ON
Lesson 5-3 Introduction to Area 197

Who *is Correct?*

Diagnostic Teaching

- Lorenzo is incorrect. He counted only five rows of squares.
- Troy is correct.
- Bianca is incorrect. She counted only four rows of squares.

Remind students to count the units inside of the rectangle to find the area.

Using Manipulatives

Geoboard When assigning Example 1, model how to use a geoboard to make a rectangle that is 5 units by 6 units. Point out to the students that they can either count the units or multiply the length by the width.

Coordinate Plane/Grid Paper When presenting Example 2, model the units on a grid. Emphasize to students that when they are asked to estimate, they need to count the whole units and then count the partial units.

On-Hand Manipulatives Draw figures or have students draw figures on grid paper to practice counting the units within the figures to find the areas.

Math Coach Notes

Geoboards When students use geoboards be sure they understand that they are not counting the pegs on the inside of the figure. Guide them to realize that they need to count the squares on the inside of the figure.

Partial Units Discuss with students that when partial units are in a figure, they will calculate a more accurate estimate if they pair or group the partial units that come close to one whole unit. For example, if one partial unit covers only the tip of a corner of the square unit, do not pair that partial with a partial unit that covers only half of a square unit. It would be better to pair the small tip partial with a partial that covers three-fourths or more of the square unit.

Note This!

Keeping Track of Counts One method that students can use when counting with units is to mark each whole unit with a black dot. When counting partial units, use different color dots to group two or more partial units for a count of one unit. If two square units are each about half covered, mark those squares with a red dot. If three units are each about one-third covered, mark those squares with a blue dot. Continue this pattern using colors until all units are dotted. Then count the whole dots and the groups of dots that represent a whole unit.

Find the area of each figure.

4 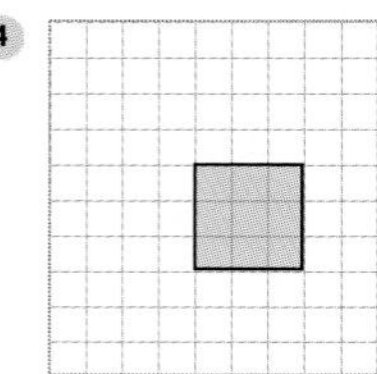

The area of the square is 9 square units.

5 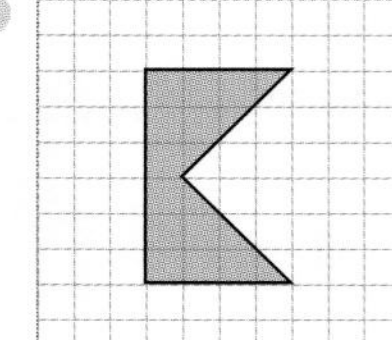

The area of the figure is about 15 square units.

6 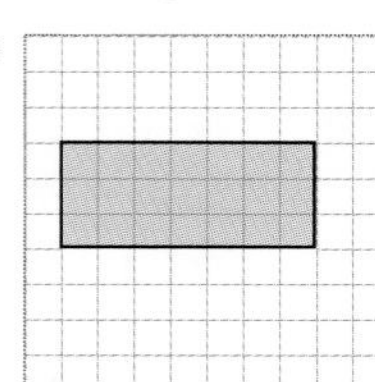

The area of the rectangle is 21 square units.

7 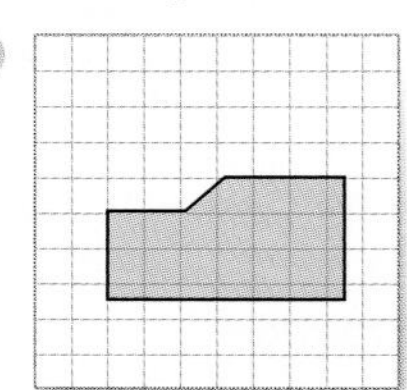

The area of the figure is about 20 square units.

Step by Step Problem-Solving Practice

Problem-Solving Strategies
- ☑ Draw a diagram.
- ☐ Look for a pattern.
- ☐ Guess and check.
- ☐ Act it out.
- ☐ Solve a simpler problem.

Solve.

8 GEOMETRY What is the area of a rectangle that has sides of 8 units and 4 units?

Understand Read the problem. Write what you know. A rectangle has sides of 8 units and 4 units.

Plan Pick a strategy. One strategy is to draw a diagram. Draw a rectangle that has sides of 8 units and 4 units.

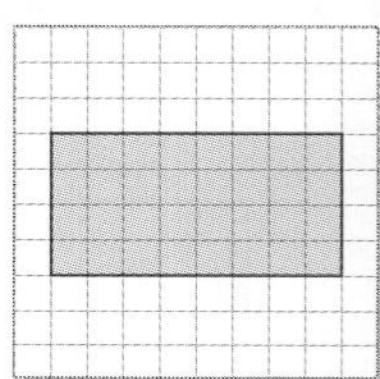

Solve Count the number of squares the figure covers. The area of the rectangle is 32 square units.

Check You can multiply 8 and 4 because there are 4 rows of 8 units. $8 \times 4 =$ 32

198 Chapter 5 Two-Dimensional Figures

Are They Getting It?

Check students' understanding of finding the area by writing these problems on the board. Ask students to point out each wrong answer. Tell them to use a grid to show why the answers are correct or not correct.

Find the area of each figure.

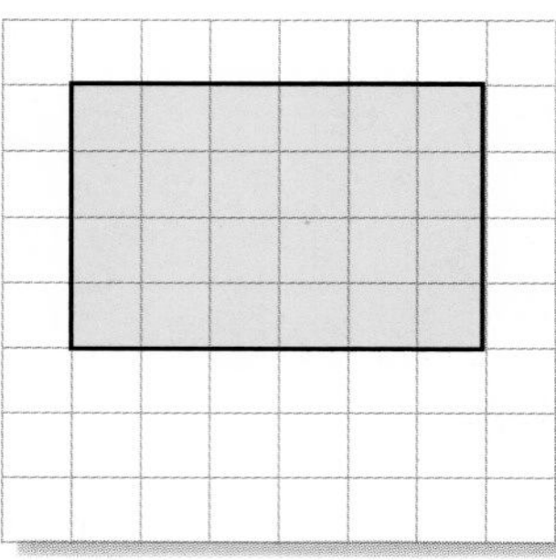

The area of the rectangle is 24 square units. This is correct.

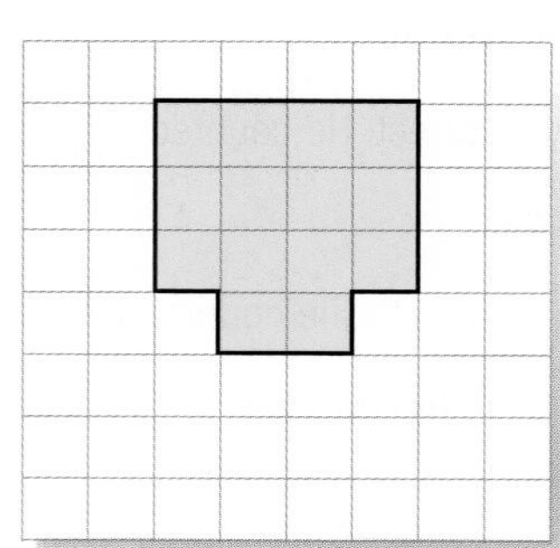

The area of the figure is 16 square units. This is incorrect. The area is 14 square units.

9 PATIOS Talia's patio in her backyard measures 9 feet by 7 feet. What is the area of the patio in Talia's backyard? Check off each step.

✔ Understand: I underlined the keywords.

✔ Plan: To solve the problem I will draw a diagram.

✔ Solve: The answer is 63 square feet.

✔ Check: I checked my answer by adding the number of squares in each row.

10 ART Selina is using one-inch square clay tiles to create a plate in ceramics class. She wants her plate to have 8 rows of 8 tiles. What is the area of her plate? 64 square inches

11 Reflect Is the area of the figure at the right 23 square units? Explain.

Yes; $4 \times 5 + 1 + \frac{1}{2} + \frac{1}{2} + \frac{1}{2} + \frac{1}{2} = 23$

Skills, Concepts, and Problem Solving

Draw a figure that has the given area.

12 16 square units
Sample answer:

13 24 square units
Sample answer:

Find the area of each figure.

14 48 square units

15 42 square units

GO ON

Math Challenge

The Dot Game Group students into pairs. Demonstrate how to make a Dot game board. Explain the rules and allow students time to play one game. When that game is over explain that the second game should be played trying to cover the least area of the game board possible.

A partial game board is shown here. The object of the game is to complete a square and then write your initial inside the square. Each player's turn continues as long as he or she can complete a square. A partial game is also shown (on the right).

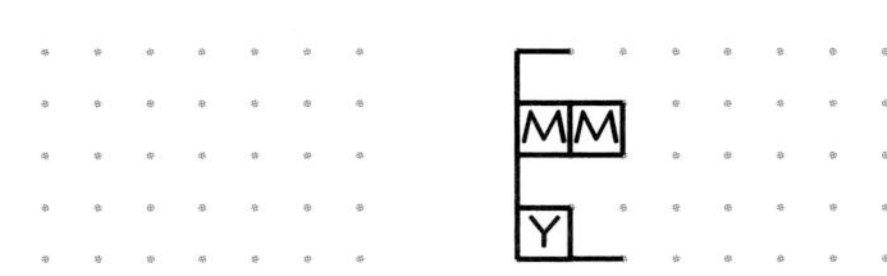

Odd/Even Assignments

Exercises 12–16 are structured so that students practice the same concepts whether they are assigned the odd or even problems.

In-Class Assignment

Have students complete Exercises 12, 14, 16, and 19 to ensure that they understand the concept.

Common Error *Alert*

Area and Perimeter

Students may confuse finding the perimeter with finding the area. Draw a rectangle on a grid on the board. Use a piece of string to show the perimeter, which goes around the figure. Use a sheet of paper to show the area, which goes over the figure. Have the students use a string and a sheet of paper to visualize perimeter and area. When you present perimeter problems, show only the outline of a figure. When you present area problems, shade the figure. Consistently presenting the two types of problems this way will reinforce the concepts of perimeter and area.

Other Visual Aids for finding area:

Coordinate Plane

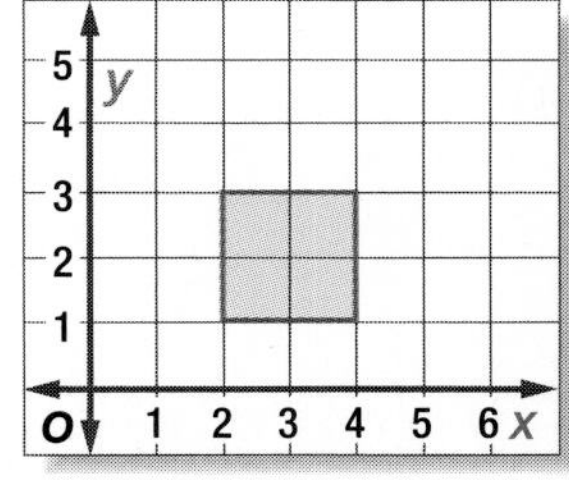

The rectangle covers 4 square units.

Geoboard

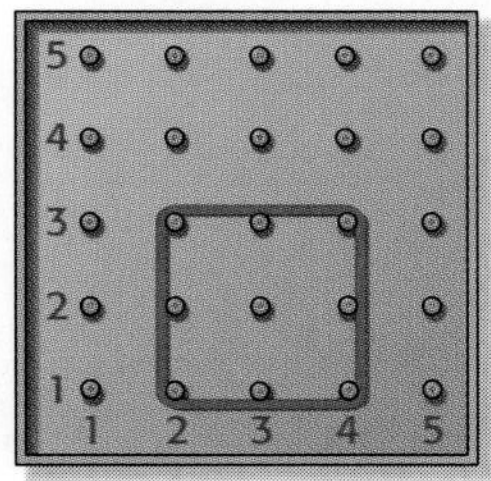

There are 4 squares of pegs inside the rectangle.

See It, Do It, Say It, Write It

Step 1 Draw the following figure on the board.

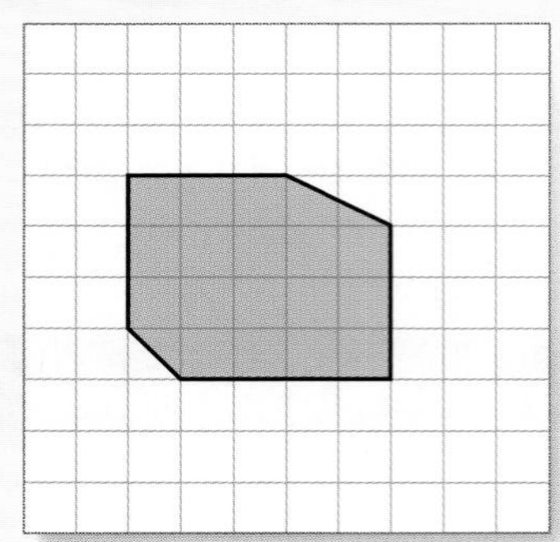

Step 2 Have students estimate the area of the figure on the board.

Step 3 Arrange the students in pairs and have them explain to each other how they found the area of the figure.

Step 4 Have students write in their journals how to find the area of a figure.

Looking Ahead: Pre-teach

Area of a Rectangle In the next lesson, students will learn to use a formula to find the area of a rectangle.

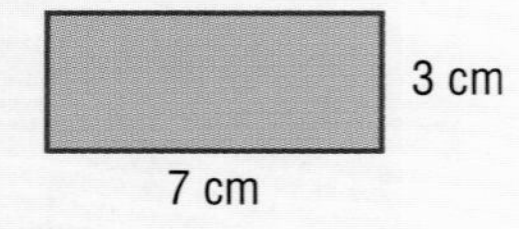

$A = \ell \times w$
$A = 7 \times 3$
$A = 21\ \text{cm}^2$

Write the multiplication fact that finds the area for each rectangle.

1.

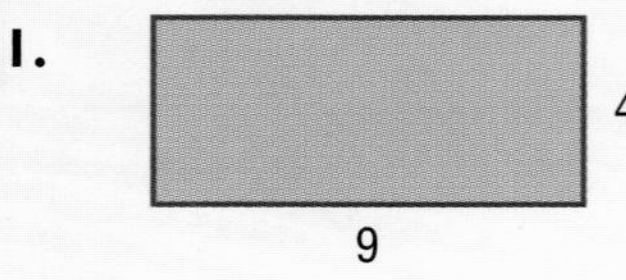

9×4

2. 1 × 3 rectangle

3

3×1

Solve.

16 BASEBALL The batter's box in baseball measures about 6 feet by 4 feet. What is the area of the batter's box? 24 square feet

Vocabulary Check **Write the vocabulary word that completes each sentence.**

17 A(n) square unit is a unit for measuring area.

18 Area is the number of square units needed to cover the surface enclosed by a geometric figure.

19 **Writing in Math** Explain how to find the length and width of a rectangle with an area of 36 square units.

The area of a rectangle is found by multiplying length times width. Any two factors of 36 can be the length and width of the rectangle. For example, 3×12, 6×6, or 9×4 could be the dimensions of the rectangle.

Spiral Review

Identify each figure. (Lesson 5-1, p. 180)

20 trapezoid

21 parallelogram

Name the triangle by its sides. (Lesson 5-2, p. 187)

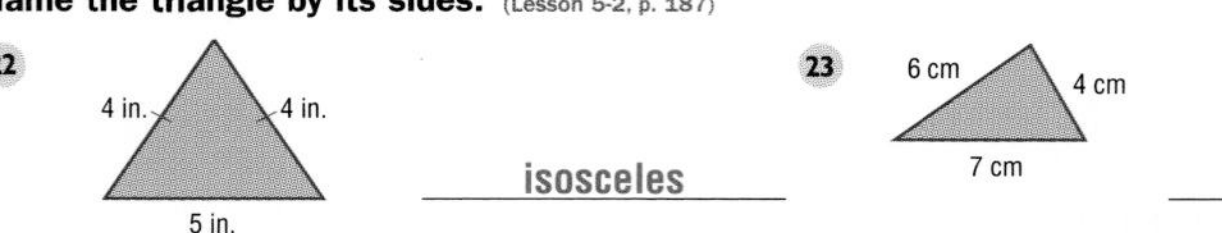

22 isosceles

23 scalene

Solve.

24 SCHOOL BAND The high school marching band made a triangular formation during their routine. All the angles they formed were less than 90°. What type of triangle did they form? acute triangle

STOP

Ticket Out the Door

Defining Area Have students write the meaning of *area* in their own words. Encourage them to include a sketch if it makes their definition more complete. As they exit the classroom, collect their definitions.

Lesson 5-4 Area of a Rectangle

KEY Concept

Find the **area** of a rectangle using the formula below.

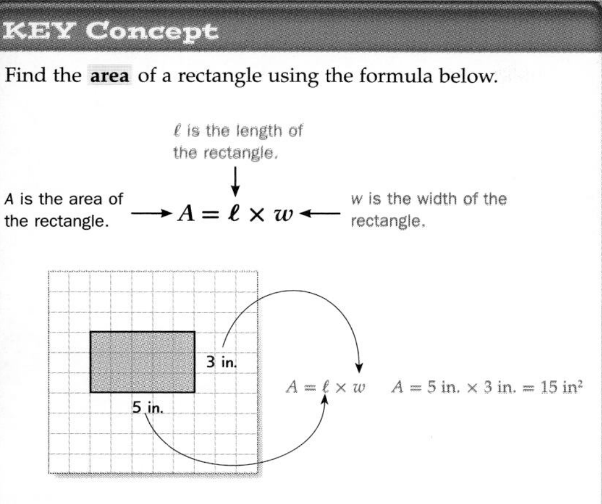

The area of the rectangle is 15 square inches.

VOCABULARY

area
the number of square units needed to cover the surface enclosed by a geometric figure

square unit
a unit for measuring area

The units of area are **square units**.

Example 1

What is the area of the rectangle?

1. The length of the rectangle is 6 centimeters, and the width is 4 centimeters.

2. Substitute these values into the formula. Multiply.

$A = \ell \times w$
$A = 6 \text{ cm} \times 4 \text{ cm}$
$A = 24 \text{ cm}^2$

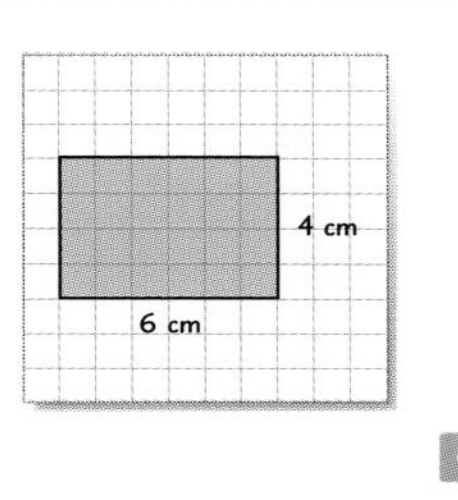

The area of the rectangle is 24 square centimeters.

GO ON

Additional *Example 1*

What is the area of the rectangle?

1. The length of the rectangle is 5 inches, and the width is 3 inches.

2. Substitute these values into the formula. Multiply.

$A = \ell \times w$
$A = 5 \text{ in.} \times 3 \text{ in.}$
$A = 15 \text{ in}^2$

3 in.
5 in.

The area of the rectangle is 15 square inches.

Lesson Notes

Lesson 5-4

Lesson Planner

Objective Find areas of rectangles.

Vocabulary **area**, **square unit**

Materials/Manipulatives geoboards, base-ten blocks, connecting cubes, ruler, index cards

Chapter Resource Masters

- CRM Vocabulary and English Language Development (p. A100)
- CRM Skills Practice (p. A101)
- CRM Problem-Solving Practice (p. A102)
- CRM Homework Practice (p. A103)

1 Introduce

Vocabulary

Length and Width Discuss as a class how to determine which dimension is the length and which is the width. Talk about the affects of assigning the dimensions differently than another person. Have students consider this question as they work through this lesson. By the end of the lesson, students should realize that because of the Commutative Property, the dimensions can be reversed and the area of the rectangle remains the same. Caution students this is not the case for all figures, but it is for rectangles.

2 Teach

Key Concept

Foundational Skills and Concepts After students have read through the Key Concept box, have them try these exercises.

1. What is the area of a rectangle with length 13 meters and width 6 meters? 78 m^2

2. What is the area of a square with length and width 9 yd? 81 yd^2

Additional **Example 2**

What is area of the square?

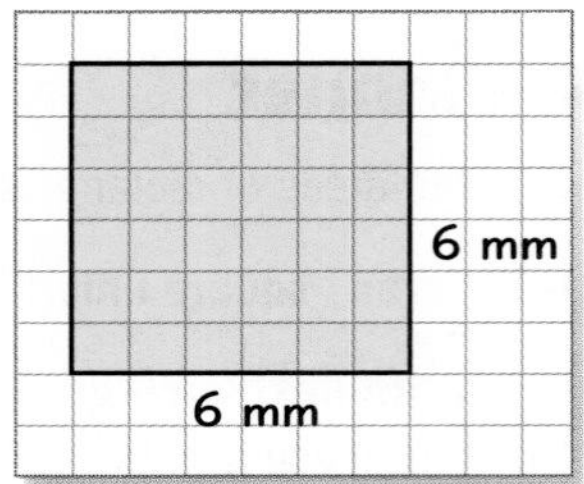

1. The length of the square is 6 millimeters, and the width is 6 millimeters.

2. Substitute these values into the formula. Multiply.

$A = \ell \times w$

$A = 6 \text{ mm} \times 6 \text{ mm}$

$A = 36 \text{ mm}^2$

The area of the square is 36 square millimeters.

Common Error *Alert*

Units Be sure students realize that their answers are not complete nor correct if they omit the units. Show students that you can write square units using whole words, abbreviated words, or abbreviated words and symbols, such as square feet, sq ft, and ft^2.

YOUR TURN!

What is the area of the rectangle?

1. The length of the rectangle is __7__ feet, and the width is __3__ feet.
2. Substitute these values into the formula. Multiply.

$A = \ell \times w$

$A =$ __7__ feet × __3__ feet

$A =$ __21__ feet^2

The area of the rectangle is __21__ square feet.

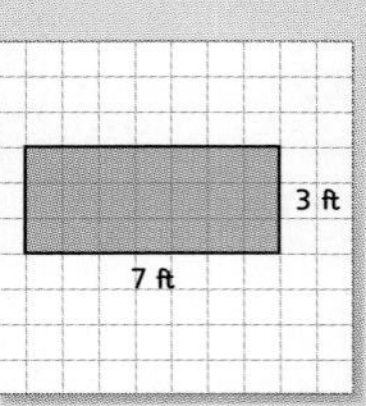

Example 2

What is the area of the square?

1. The length of the square is 5 km, and the width is 5 km.
2. Substitute these values into the formula. Multiply.

5 km

5 km

$A = \ell \times w$

$A = 5 \text{ km} \times 5 \text{ km}$

$A = 25 \text{ km}^2$

The area of the square is 25 square km.

YOUR TURN!

What is the area of the square?

1. The length of the square is __4__ feet, and the width is __4__ feet.
2. Substitute these values into the formula. Multiply.

4 ft

4 ft

$A = \ell \times w$

$A =$ __4__ ft × __4__ ft

$A =$ __16__ ft^2

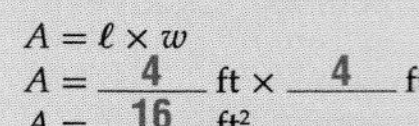

The area of the square is __16__ square feet.

Who is Correct?

What is the area of the rectangle at the right?

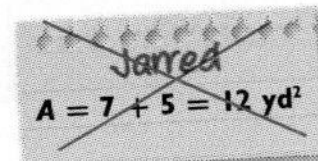

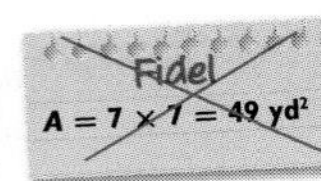

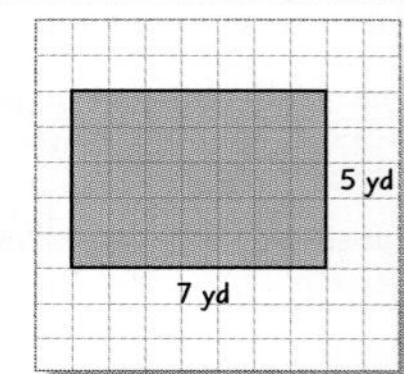

Circle correct answer(s). Cross out incorrect answer(s).

202 Chapter 5 Two-Dimensional Figures

Who ***is Correct?***

Diagnostic Teaching

- Juan wrote 35 yd^2. This is correct.
- Jarred wrote 12 yd^2. This is incorrect. He added the length and width.
- Fidel wrote 49 yd^2. This is incorrect. He multiplied the length times the length and not the length times the width.

Guided Practice

aw a rectangle for each given area.

12 in² **Sample answer:**

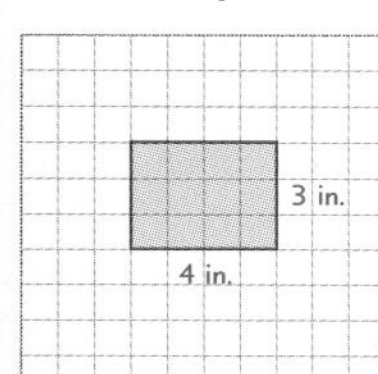

2 32 m² **Sample answer:**

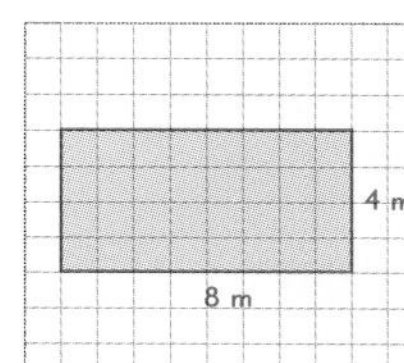

tep by Step Practice

What is the area of the square?

Step 1 The length of the square is __6__ centimeters, and the width __6__ centimeters.

Step 2 Substitute these values into the formula. Multiply.

$A = \ell \times w$

$A =$ __6__ cm $\times$ __6__ cm

$A =$ __36__ cm²

The area of the rectangle is __36__ square centimeters.

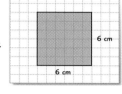

6 cm

6 cm

nd the area of each rectangle.

The length is __9__ meters. The width is __3__ meters.

$A =$ __9__ m $\times$ __3__ m

$A =$ __27__ m²

The length of the rectangle is __8__ inches. The width is __6__ inches.

$A = \ell \times w$

$A =$ __8__ in. $\times$ __6__ in.

$A =$ __48__ in²

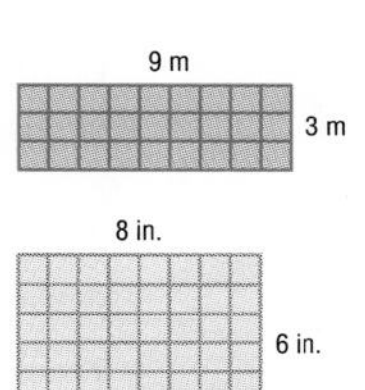

GO ON

Intervention Strategy — Visual Learners

Put a Ruler to Use On a sheet of paper, use a straightedge to draw a rectangle. Be sure students draw rectangles with dimensions that can be measured. Have students use the inch scale or the centimeter scale on a ruler and mark off the units along the length and the width of the rectangle. Then have students use a straightedge to sketch in the square units by connecting the marks made for the units with the opposite side of the rectangle. As all lines get drawn, students will see the outlined area covered in square units.

3 Practice

Using Manipulatives

Geoboard When presenting area problems, model the rectangle by using a geoboard.

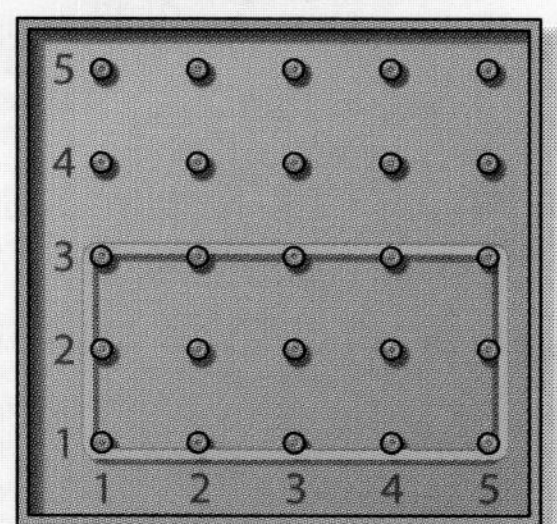

Base-Ten Blocks Base-ten blocks can be used in a single layer as square units.

Connecting Cubes Connecting cubes can be used in a single layer to represent the length and width of rectangles.

On-Hand Manipulatives Use children's toy blocks or squares cut out from construction paper to show square units of area.

Math Coach Notes

Strategies

1. Start this lesson with a hands-on practice as an anchoring experience. Tell students to get out a rectangular piece of paper. Have students measure the length and width using the unit of their choice. Have them represent their figure on grid paper. Guide them to find the area.

2. Area is the number of equal squares that covers a surface. Use the word "cover" occasionally in place of "area" to remind students of what the area really is.

3. When possible, present nonexamples. If a rectangle measures 4 units by 5 units, why is the area not 9 square units? Continuously offering nonexamples reminds students of what area is not.

4. Point out that when a student uses linear measurements to represent area, that area is measured in square units, while length is measured in linear units (like inches).

Find the area of each figure.

6 $A =$ 40 mi^2

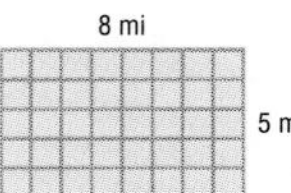

7 $A =$ 100 cm^2

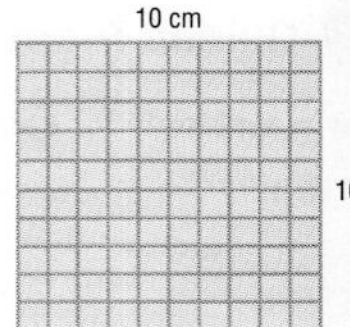

8 $A =$ 72 m^2

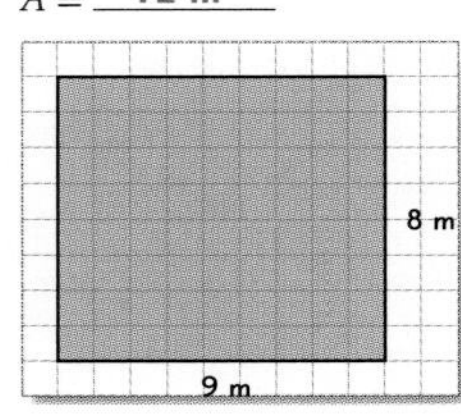

9 $A =$ 33 yd^2

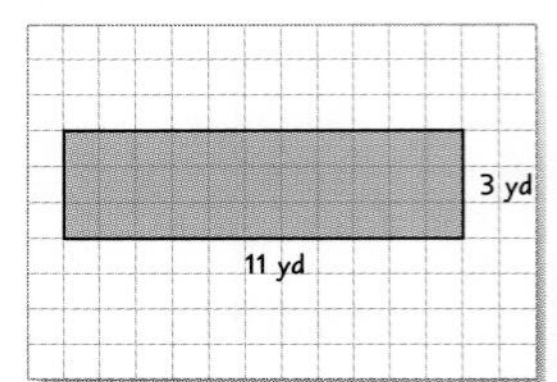

Step by Step Problem-Solving Practice

Problem-Solving Strategies
- ☑ Use a formula.
- ☐ Look for a pattern.
- ☐ Guess and check.
- ☐ Act it out.
- ☐ Solve a simpler problem.

Solve.

10 TENNIS A singles match in tennis is played on a court that measures 78 feet long and 27 feet wide. What is the area of the tennis court?

Understand Read the problem. Write what you know. The length of the tennis court is 78 feet, and the width of the court is 27 feet.

Plan Pick a strategy. One strategy is to use a formula. Substitute values for length and width into the area formula.

Solve Use the formula.

$A = \ell \times w$

$A =$ 78 ft × 27 ft

$A =$ 2,106 ft^2

The area of a tennis court is 2,106 square feet.

Check Use a calculator to check your answer.

Are They Getting It?

Check students' understanding of the area of rectangles by writing these problems on the board. Have students explain the incorrect information in each problem. Tell them to use a drawing or model to show why the answers are correct or incorrect.

1. A rectangle that is 9 m by 3 m has an area of 27 m^2. This is correct.

2. A rectangle with an area of 16 cm^2 could have a length of 6 cm and a width of 3 cm. This is incorrect because $6 \times 3 = 18$.

3. The area of this square is 64 in^2. This is correct.

11 **NURSING HOME** Ms. Guzman's art class made quilts for the community nursing home. Each quilt was 60 inches long and 80 inches wide. What is the area of each quilt the class made for the nursing home?

Check off each step.

✔ Understand: I underlined the key words.

✔ Plan: To solve the problem I will use a formula

✔ Solve: The answer is $4,800\text{ in}^2$

✔ Check: I checked my answer by working backward, I divided 4,800 by 80 to get 60

12 **BAKING** Randall made garlic bread for dinner. He put the garlic bread on a baking sheet that measured 9 inches wide by 13 inches long. What was the area of the baking sheet? 117 in^2

13 **Reflect** Can two rectangles have the same area but different lengths and widths? Explain.

Sample answer: Yes; A rectangle with side lengths of 1 inch and 6 inches has an area of 6 in^2. A rectangle with side lengths of 2 inches and 3 inches also has an area of 6 in^2.

Skills, Concepts, and Problem Solving

Draw a rectangle that has the given area.

14 16 square units Sample answer:

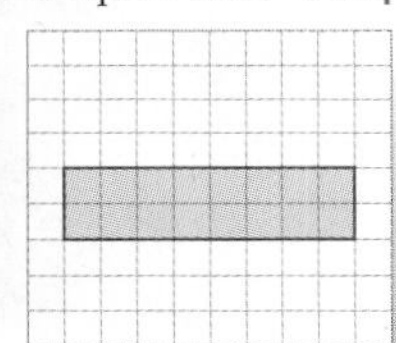

15 30 square units Sample answer:

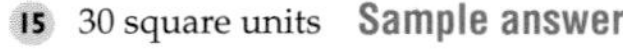

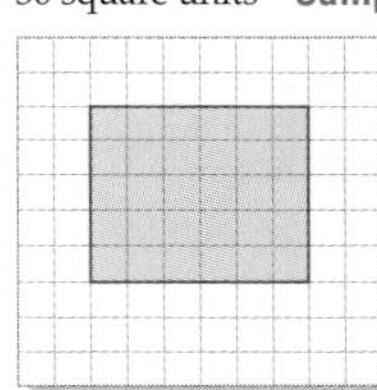

GO ON

Odd/Even Assignments

Exercises 14–25 are structured so that students practice the same concepts whether they are assigned the odd or even problems.

In-Class Assignment

Have students complete Exercises 15, 17, 21, 24, and 29 to ensure that they understand the concept.

English Learner Strategy

Guiding Questions Use index cards that have been cut into squares. Then ask students the following:

- Cover your desk (or textbook) with the cards. Count the cards.
- How many cards did it take to cover your desk (or textbook)?
- How can you find the number of cards without counting them?
- Explain how to use a formula to find the area of a rectangle that has a length of 5 centimeters and a width of 4 centimeters.
- Describe how you would find the area of the classroom (or the counter top).

Common Error *Alert*

Exercise 25 Students should not get distracted by the image in the photo. Rather, they should focus their attention on the caption below the photo.

Find the area of each figure.

16 A = 28 mi²

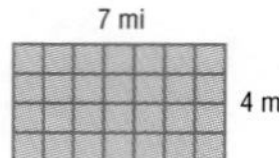

17 A = 18 yd²

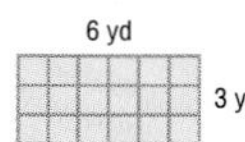

18 $A =$ 14 m²

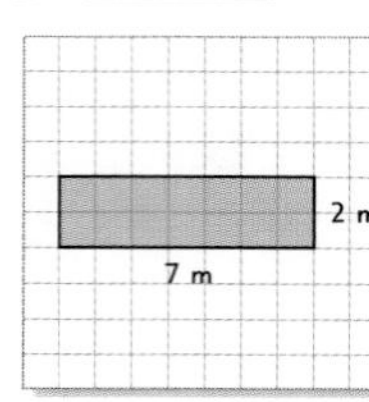

19 $A =$ 49 in²

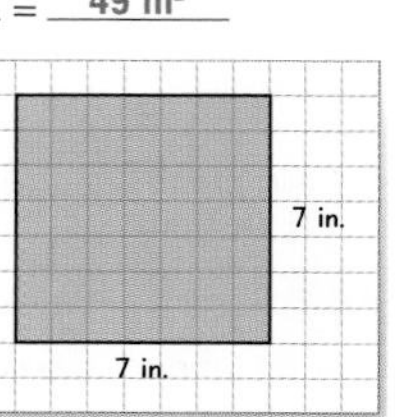

20 $A =$ 42 mm²

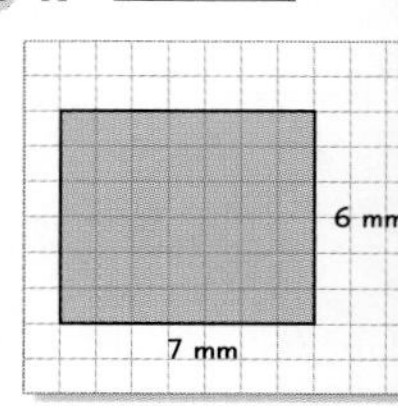

21 $A =$ 81 mi²

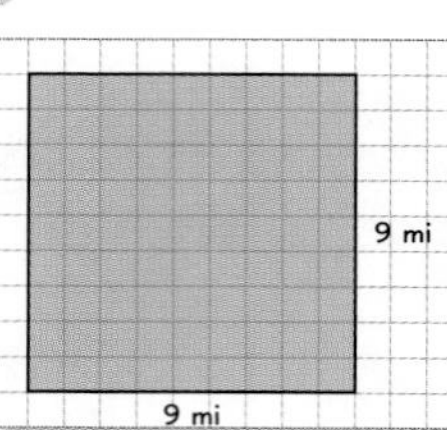

22 $A =$ 54 yd²

6 yd

9 yd

23 $A =$ 144 m²

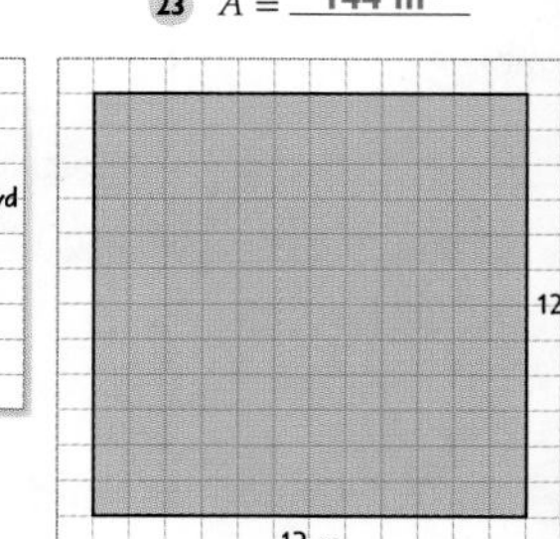

Solve.

24 VOLUNTEERS Ed received a certificate for his community volunteer work from the mayor of his city. The certificate was 28 cm long and 22 cm wide. What is the area of Ed's certificate?

616 cm²

25 GARDENING Marcie made a vegetable garden in her backyard shown at the right. What is the area of Marcie's garden?

810 ft²

GARDENING **The vegetable garden is 30 feet long and 27 feet wide.**

Math Challenge

Rectangle Madness Write the composite numbers between 12 and 50 on small pieces of paper and place in a box or pile where students can see the number being drawn. The object of the game is to name the dimensions of the most rectangles with a given area. Have students section a sheet of paper into eight parts and label the sections *Rounds 1 – 8*. From the pile of papers, draw a number. Announce the number and give students 15 seconds to write all the whole number dimensions of a rectangle with that area. For example, if your number was 20, students could write 5×4. After 15 seconds, call stop. The student(s) with the most correct dimensions get a point for that round. Do not replace the numbers drawn from the pile. The student with the most points after 8 rounds, wins.

ocabulary Check **Write the vocabulary word that completes each entence.**

26 A(n) ___rectangle___ has opposite sides that are equal and parallel. It is a quadrilateral with four right angles.

27 ___Area___ is the number of square units needed to cover the surface enclosed by a geometric figure.

28 A(n) ___square___ is a rectangle with four congruent sides.

29 **Writing in Math** Explain how to find the area of a rectangle.

Sample answer: Identify the length and width of the rectangle. Substitute values of the length and width into the formula for the area of a rectangle. Multiply to find the area of the rectangle. Express the answer in square units.

Spiral Review

olve.

30 **CONSTRUCTION** Jen and her friends built a tree house in her backyard. The floor of the tree house was 12 feet long by 8 feet wide. What was the area of the tree house's floor? (Lesson 5-3, p. 195)

___96 ft²___

dentify the figure. (Lesson 5-1, p. 180)

31

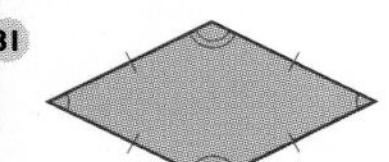

___rhombus___

ame the triangle by its angles. (Lesson 5-2, p. 187)

32

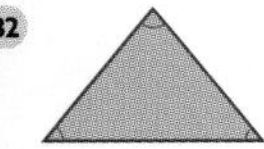

___acute triangle___

ind the area of the figure. (Lesson 5-3, p. 195)

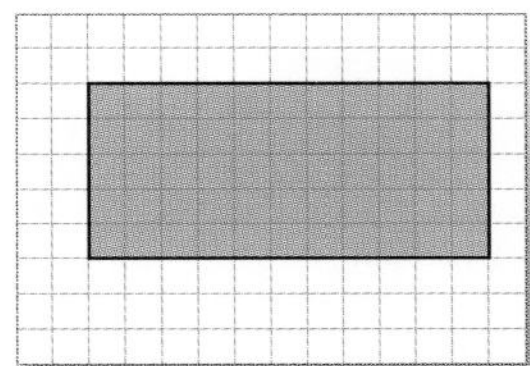

33 $A =$ ___55___ square units

STOP

Lesson 5-4 Area of a Rectangle 207

Ticket Out the Door

Say the Width As students approach the door to exit, ask a question in the following format, changing the area and the length given for each student.

What is the width of a rectangle that has an area of 34 in² and a length of 2 inches?

See It, Do It, Say It, Write It

Step 1 Use an overhead and draw a rectangle on grid paper. Label the length and width. Show students how you can use the formula to find the area. Show them how the area can be verified by counting the square units.

Step 2 Have students name household objects for which they can find the area. Examples may include a rug or a table top. Have them explain how to find the area of each object.

Step 3 Give students rectangular shapes that they can measure or trace on grid paper. Tell them to find the areas. Have them share their methods with the class.

Step 4 Have students write the definition of *area.* Tell them to imagine they are writing the information for a student who was absent that day and to use a lot of details, pictures, and examples.

Looking Ahead: Pre-teach

Area of a Parallelogram In the next lesson, students will learn about the area of a parallelogram. A parallelogram looks like this:

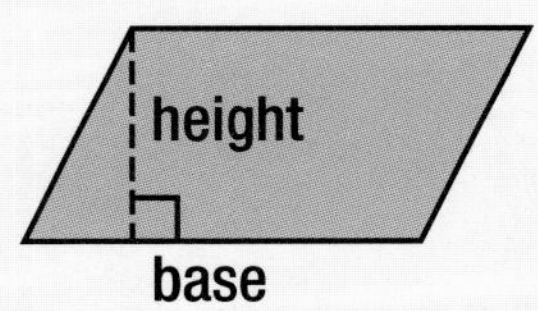

The formula for the area is $A = base \times height$.

Example

What is the area of a parallelogram with a base of 8 feet and a height of 2 feet? 16 ft²

Have students find the area of each parallelogram.

1. a base of 13 m and a height of 4 m 52 m²
2. a base of 10 in. and a height of 3 in. 30 in²
3. a base of 9 yd and a height of 1 yd 9 yd²

Chapter 5

Progress Check 2

Formative Assessment

Use the Progress Check to assess students' mastery of the previous lessons. Have students review the lesson indicated for the problems they answered incorrectly.

Odd/Even Assignments

Exercises are structured so that students practice the same concepts whether they are assigned the odd or even problems.

Common Error *Alert*

Find Area If students are having difficulties with finding the areas, remind them that the answers to most of these questions can be found by *multiplying* the dimensions of the shaded area or by *adding* the shaded squares because multiplication is repeated addition.

Progress Check 2 (Lessons 5-3 and 5-4)

Draw a figure that has the given area.

1. 54 square units
Sample answer:

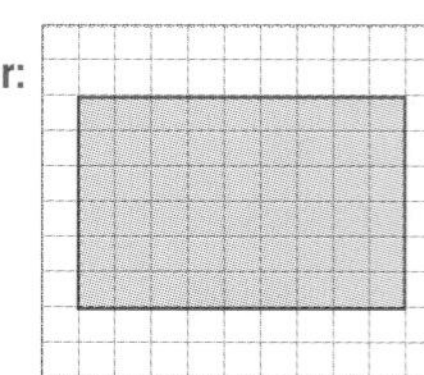

2. 42 square units
Sample answer:

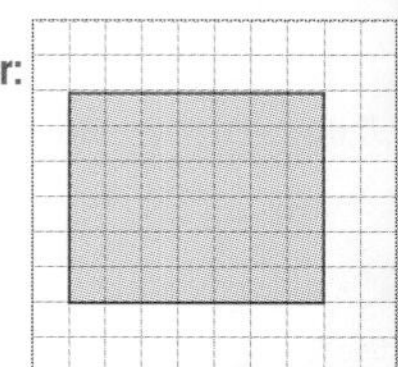

Find the area of each figure.

3. 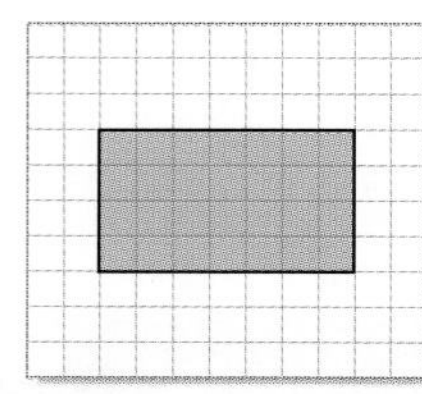

The area of the rectangle is 28 square units.

4. 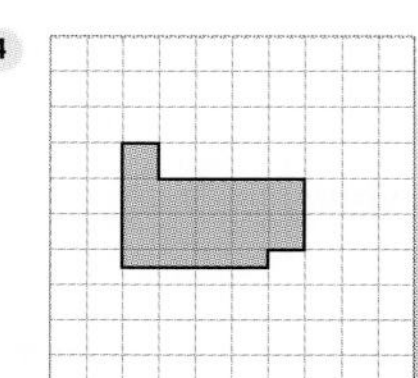

The area of the figure is 13 square units.

Find the area of each rectangle.

5. $A =$ 77 m^2

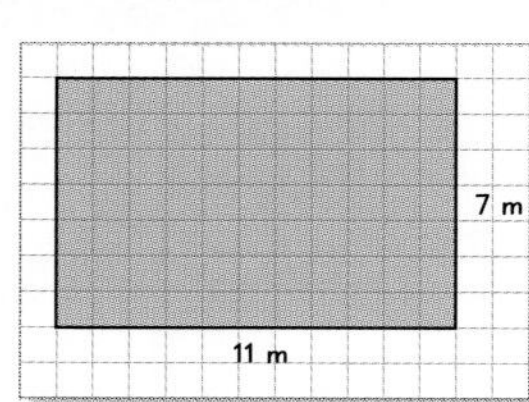

6. $A =$ 60 yd^2

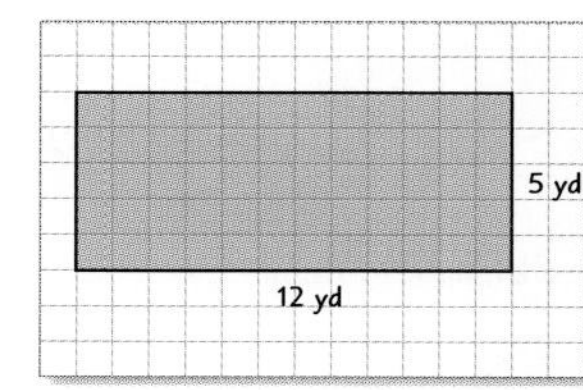

Solve.

7. **ROOMS** The ceiling tiles in Toni's kitchen are the shape of a square. Each tile has sides that measure 54 centimeters. What is the area of each tile? 2,916 square cm

208 Chapter 5 Two-Dimensional Figures

Data-Driven Decision Making

Students missing Exercises . . .	Have trouble with . . .	Should review and practice . . .
1–2	drawing figures with a given area.	SSG Lesson 5-3, p. 195 CRM Skills Practice, p. A97
3–6	finding area by counting the total of shaded units.	SSG Lesson 5-3 and 5-4, pp. 195 and 201 CRM Skills Practice, pp. A97 and A101
7	solving word problems that involve area.	CRM Problem-Solving Practice, pp. A98 and A102

Lesson 5-5

Area of a Parallelogram

KEY Concept

parallelogram

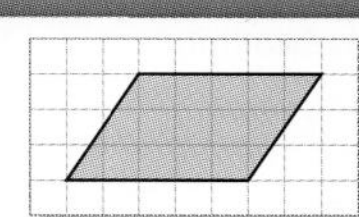

In a parallelogram, b represents the base, and h represents the height. Cut a triangle from the parallelogram along the dashed line. Place the triangle on the other side, next to the right edge of the parallelogram.

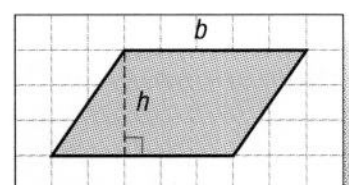

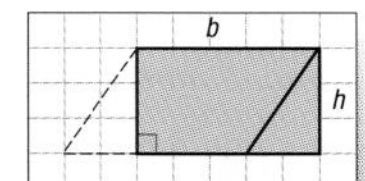

Notice that the new shape is a rectangle. So, the formulas for the areas of parallelograms and rectangles are similar.

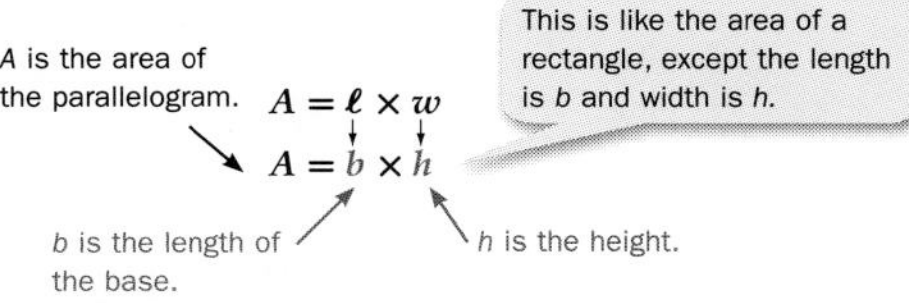

VOCABULARY

area
the number of square units needed to cover the surface enclosed by a geometric figure

parallelogram
a quadrilateral that has both pairs of opposite sides congruent and parallel

square unit
a unit for measuring area

Example 1

Find the area of the parallelogram.

1. The base is 7 feet. The height is 6 feet.
2. Substitute these values into the formula. Multiply.

$A = b \times h$
$A = 7 \text{ ft} \times 6 \text{ ft}$
$A = 42 \text{ ft}^2$

The area of the parallelogram is 42 square feet.

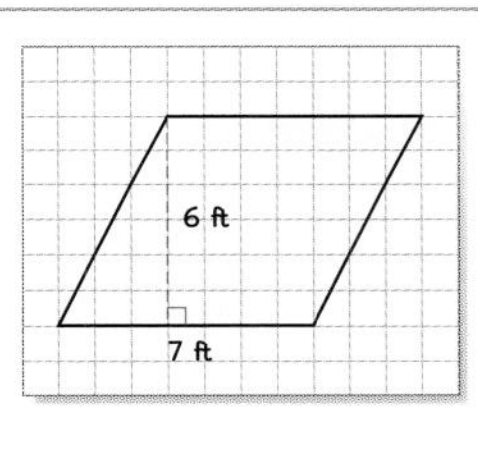

GO ON

Additional Example 1

Find the area of the parallelogram.

1. The base is 4 inches.
The height is 5 inches.
2. Substitute these values into the formula. Multiply.

$A = b \times h$
$A = 4 \text{ in.} \times 5 \text{ in.}$
$A = 20 \text{ in}^2$

The area of the parallelogram is 20 square inches.

5 in.
4 in.

Lesson Notes

Lesson 5-5

Lesson Planner

Objective Find areas of parallelograms.

Vocabulary **area**, **parallelogram**, **square unit**

Materials/Manipulatives geoboards, tangrams, pattern blocks, cardboard or cardstock, square tiles, grid paper

Chapter Resource Masters

- CRM Vocabulary and English Language Development (p. A104)
- CRM Skills Practice (p. A105)
- CRM Problem-Solving Practice (p. A106)
- CRM Homework Practice (p. A107)

1 Introduce

Vocabulary

Reenact Vocabulary Draw a *parallelogram* on the board. Illustrate the example in the Key Concept box, showing how the figure can be made into a *rectangle.* Ask students what unit the area of a *parallelogram* would be expressed in.

2 Teach

Key Concept

Foundational Skills and Concepts After students have read through the Key Concept box, have them try these exercises.

1. What shape can you cut off and move on a parallelogram to form a rectangle? triangle
2. What is the difference between a parallelogram and a rectangle? A rectangle has 4 right angles, and a parallelogram does not.
3. How is the area of a parallelogram like the area of a rectangle? The length is b and the height is h.

Additional **Example 2**

Find the area of the parallelogram.

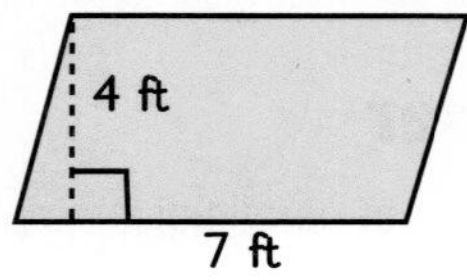

1. The base is 7 feet.
   The height is 4 feet.
2. Substitute these values into the formula. Multiply.

   $A = b \times h$
   $A = 7 \text{ ft} \times 4 \text{ ft}$
   $A = 28 \text{ ft}^2$

   The area of the parallelogram is 28 square feet.

Intervention Strategy — Logical Learners

Area The most common error of students is that they define area by the formulas. Move figures around to show students where the formulas come from. Show them how the formulas are derived so they can always find the area.

YOUR TURN!

Find the area of the parallelogram.

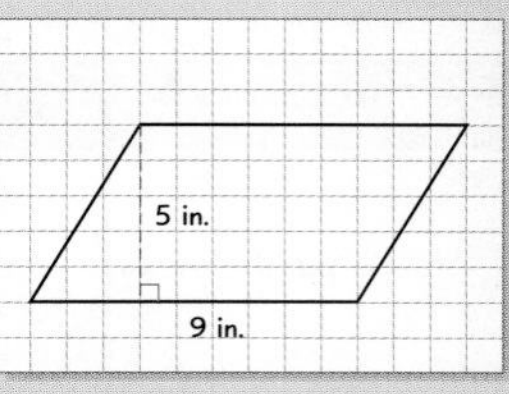

1. The base is __9__ inches. The height is __5__ inches.
2. Substitute these values into the formula. Multiply.

   $A = b \times h$
   $A =$ __9__ in. × __5__ in.
   $A =$ __45__ in^2

The area of the parallelogram is __45__ square inches.

Example 2

Find the area of the parallelogram.

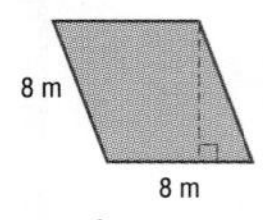

1. The base is 8 meters.
   The height is 8 meters.
2. Substitute these values into the formula. Multiply.

   $A = b \times h$
   $A = 8 \text{ m} \times 8 \text{ m}$
   $A = 64 \text{ m}^2$

The area of the parallelogram is 64 square centimeters.

YOUR TURN!

Find the area of the parallelogram.

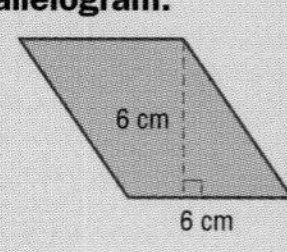

1. The base is __6__ centimeters.
   The height is __6__ centimeters.
2. Substitute these values into the formula. Multiply.

   $A = b \times h$
   $A =$ __6__ cm × __6__ cm
   $A =$ __36__ cm^2

The area of the parallelogram is __36__ square centimeters.

Who is Correct?

Find the area of the parallelogram.

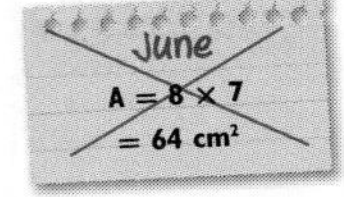

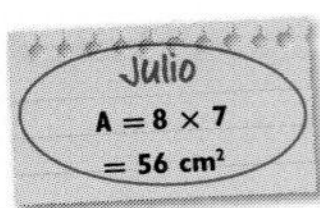

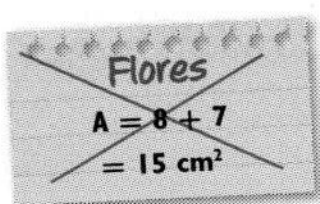

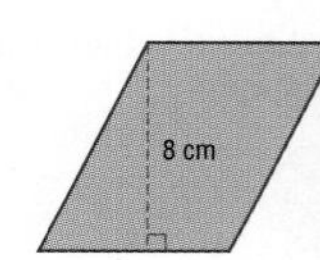

Circle correct answer(s). Cross out incorrect answer(s).

210 Chapter 5 Two-Dimensional Figures

Who *is Correct?*

Diagnostic Teaching

- June wrote 64 cm^2. She multiplied incorrectly.
- Julio wrote 56 cm^2. This is correct.
- Flores wrote 15 cm^2. She added instead of multiplied.

Guided Practice

Draw a parallelogram that has the given area.

1 36 mm² Sample answer:

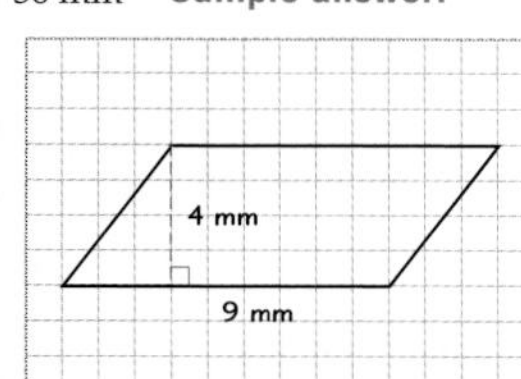

2 80 yd² Sample answer:

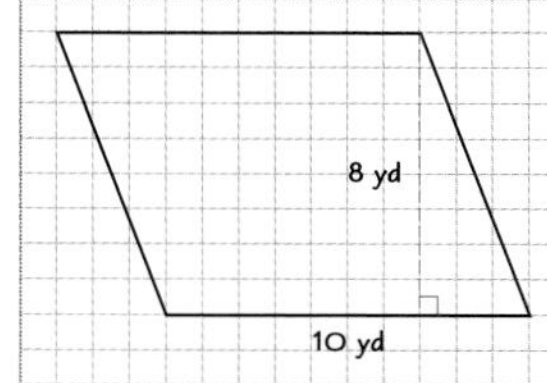

Step by Step Practice

Find the area of the parallelogram.

3 **Step 1** The base is 9 centimeters.
The height is 8 centimeters.

Step 2 Substitute these values into the formula. Multiply.

$A = b \times h$

$A = 9$ cm $\times$ 8 cm

$A = 72$ cm²

The area of the parallelogram is 72 square centimeters.

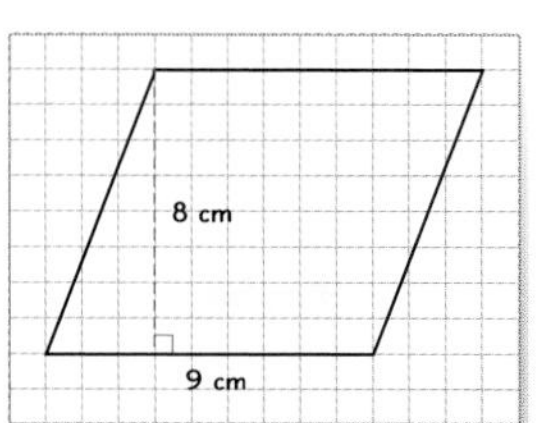

Find the area of each parallelogram.

4 The base is 8 kilometers.
The height is 5 kilometers.

$A = b \times h$

$A =$ 8 km $\times$ 5 km

$A =$ 40 km²

The area of the parallelogram is 40 squares kilometers.

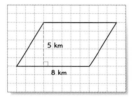

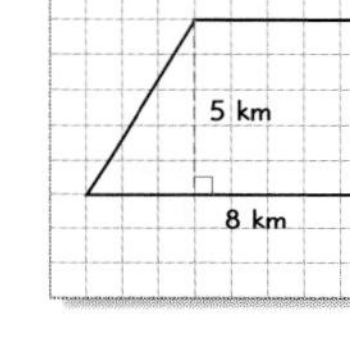

5 The base is 5 inches.
The height is 3 inches.

$A =$ 5 in. $\times$ 3 in.

$A =$ 15 in²

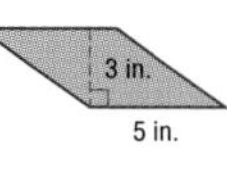

GO ON

Intervention Strategy

Kinesthetic/Visual Learners

Estimate Area Create several parallelograms cut from cardboard or cardstock. Distribute a parallelogram and several congruent square tiles to each student. Using the tiles, have students estimate the area of the parallelogram by placing the tiles on top of the cardboard parallelogram. Create a chart on the board in which students can fill in the estimated area of their parallelogram.

3 Practice

Using Manipulatives

Geoboard When presenting area problems, model the parallelogram using a geoboard.

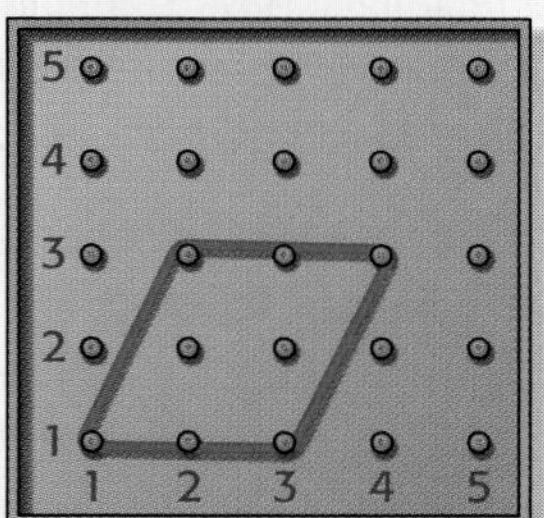

Tangram Tangram pieces can be used to show the relationships between areas of triangles, rectangles, and parallelograms.

On-Hand Manipulatives Cut out shapes using paper to show the relationships between areas of rectangles and parallelograms.

Common Error Alert

Exercises 1 and 2 If students do not arrive at the correct answers for Exercises 1 or 2, they might not understand how to proceed. Give the students grid paper. Have them practice making parallelograms and finding the areas. Ask: What dimensions would be needed for an area of 30 cm² or 200 cm²? Guide students to realize that they are looking for two factors with a product of the required areas.

Math Coach Notes

Strategies

1. Start this lesson with hands-on practice as an anchoring experience. Give students grid paper. Have them draw a parallelogram and then cut it out. Tell them to snip off the end triangle and move it to make a rectangle. Have students find the areas of both the parallelogram and rectangle. Allow them to do this with a variety of different-sized figures.
2. Experiment with a tangram. If needed, make one using an online pattern. Tell students to cover the parallelogram in the puzzle with the two small triangles. What other shape can they cover with the two triangles (the square)? Use the square and the small triangles to form a rectangle, then move the triangles onto each end to make a parallelogram. Trace these on grid paper. Prove the area relationship between parallelograms and rectangles.

Note This!

Area Formula When reading the lesson on the area of a parallelogram, encourage students to write the formula for area in their notes. Also, have students list the characteristics of a parallelogram in their notes. Having a better understanding of parallelograms can help students determine which formula is appropriate for finding area.

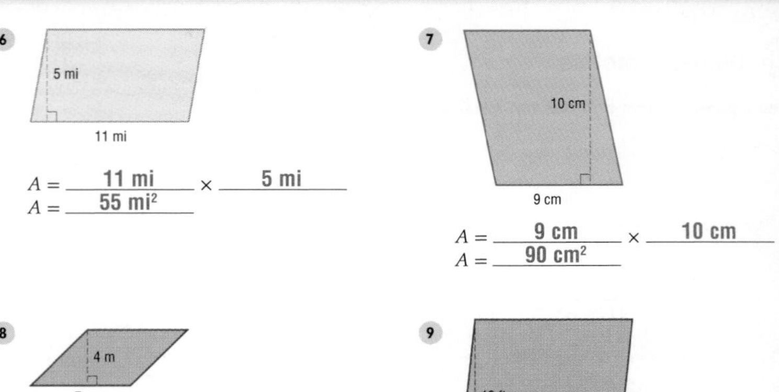

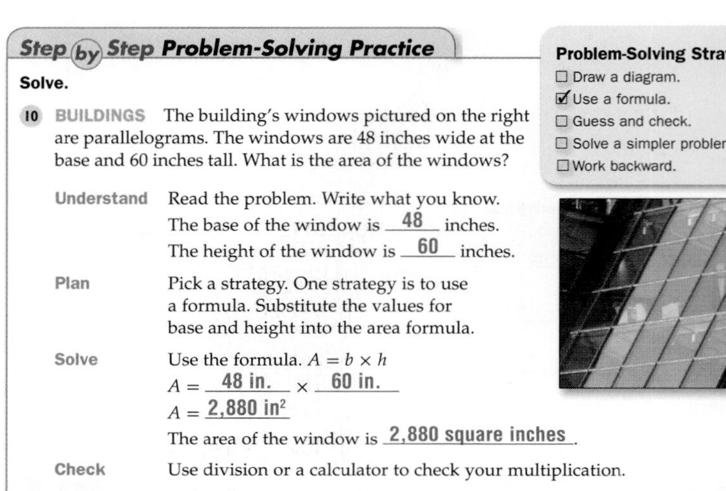

Step by Step Problem-Solving Practice

Problem-Solving Strategies
- ☐ Draw a diagram.
- ☑ Use a formula.
- ☐ Guess and check.
- ☐ Solve a simpler problem.
- ☐ Work backward.

Solve.

10 BUILDINGS The building's windows pictured on the right are parallelograms. The windows are 48 inches wide at the base and 60 inches tall. What is the area of the windows?

Understand Read the problem. Write what you know.
The base of the window is 48 inches.
The height of the window is 60 inches.

Plan Pick a strategy. One strategy is to use a formula. Substitute the values for base and height into the area formula.

Solve Use the formula. $A = b \times h$
$A =$ 48 in. × 60 in.
$A =$ 2,880 in²
The area of the window is 2,880 square inches.

Check Use division or a calculator to check your multiplication.

Are They Getting It?

Check students' understanding of the area of parallelograms by writing these problems on the board. Ask students to point out wrong answers. Tell them to use a drawing or model to show why the answers are correct or are not correct.

1. A parallelogram with base 9 mm and height 9 mm has area 81 mm. This is incorrect, because units should be mm².
2. A parallelogram with area of 56 cm² could have a base of 8 cm and a height of 7 cm. This is correct.
3. The area of this parallelogram is 35 yd². This is incorrect. The height is not known. 5 yd is the measure of the width, not the height.

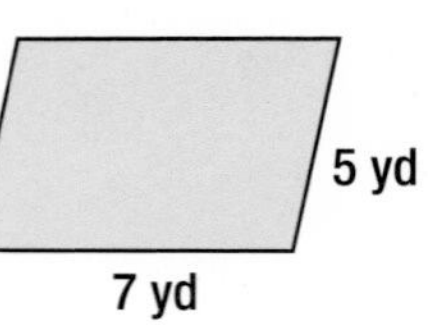

PETS The roof of Wesley's doghouse is shaped like a parallelogram. The roof has a base of 9 feet and a height of 7 feet. What is the area of the roof of the doghouse? Check off each step.

✔ Understand: I underlined key words.

✔ Plan: To solve the problem, I will use a formula.

✔ Solve: The answer is 63 square feet.

✔ Check: I checked my answer by using division or a calculator.

WATCHES Rita received a watch as a present for her birthday. The face of the watch is shaped like a parallelogram with a base of 30 mm and a height of 40 mm. What is the area of the face of Rita's watch?

1,200 mm²

Reflect Compare the area of the parallelogram to the area of the rectangle at the right. Explain.

See TE margin.

6 in.

8 in.

16 in.

3 in.

Skills, Concepts, and Problem Solving

aw a parallelogram that has the given area.

27 in²

mple swer:

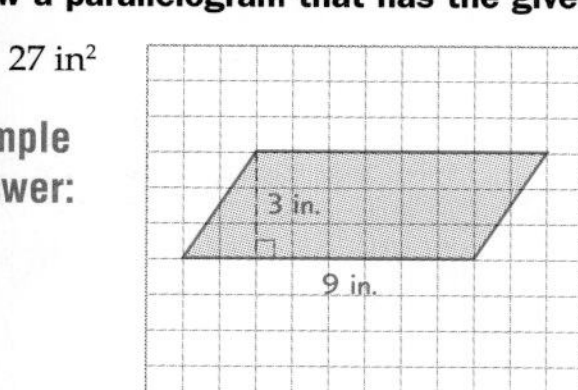

15 40 mm²

Sample answer:

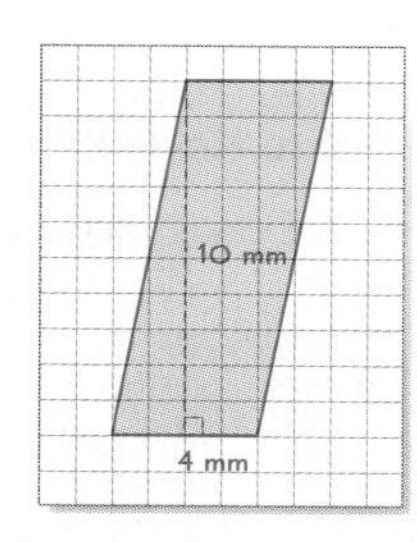

d the area of each parallelogram.

$A =$ 119 ft²

17 $A =$ 108 yd²

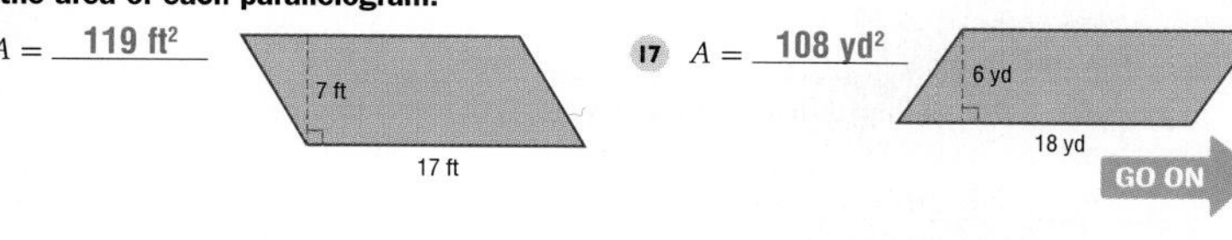

GO ON

Odd/Even Assignments

Exercises 14–19 are structured so that students practice the same concepts whether they are assigned the odd or even problems.

In-Class Assignment

Have students complete Exercises 15, 16, 18, and 22 to ensure that they understand the concept.

Additional Answer

Exercise 13 The area of the parallelogram is found by using the formula $A = b \times h$. Since $8 \times 6 = 48$, the area of the parallelogram is 48 in². The area of the rectangle is found by using the formula $A = \ell \times w$. Since $16 \times 3 = 48$, the area of the rectangle is 48 in². The figures have different dimensions, but their areas are the same.

Math Challenge

Making Parallelograms out of Rectangles Have students use grid paper to make a rectangle that has an area of 40 square units and cut it out. Students should compare rectangles and arrange themselves into groups so that all students with the same dimensions of rectangle are together. Within the group, form a different parallelogram for each person with a rectangle. Each group should present to the class the dimensions of their original rectangle and all of the parallelograms made. Ask whether each group should be able to make a parallelogram for each rectangle brought into the group. If not, have students explain the limitations.

Additional Answer

Exercise 22 Substitute the values of the base and height into the formula for the area of a parallelogram. $A = b \times h$; $A = 12 \text{ ft} \times 7 \text{ ft} = 84 \text{ ft}^2$. The area of the parallelogram is 84 ft^2.

See It, Do It, Say It, Write It

Step 1 Use an overhead projector and draw a parallelogram on grid paper. Draw a line that is perpendicular to the base and count the units of the height. Label the base and height. Ask a student what the area of the figure is. Verify by counting units.

Step 2 Give students geoboards. Challenge them to make rectangles and determine the areas. Then students can move the bands to make a parallelogram. Have students explain how they know what the area of the parallelogram is.

Step 3 Tell students to draw a parallelogram on grid paper. Ask them to draw a line where they would cut to make it into a rectangle. They can use an arrow to show where they would place the part they cut.

Step 4 On the same paper, ask students to write about what they have learned about area. Also tell them to write about the relationship between the areas of a rectangle and a parallelogram.

Looking Ahead: Pre-teach

Area of a Triangle In the next lesson, students will learn about the area of a triangle. You can cut a rectangle into two triangles like this.

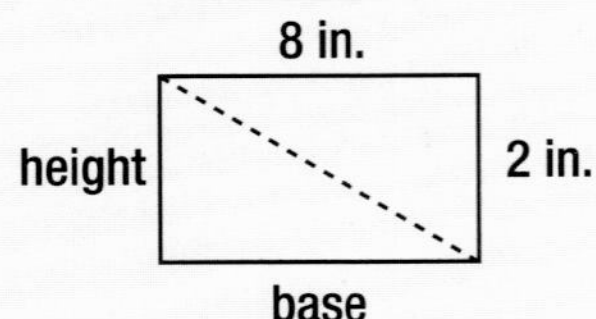

The formula for the area is $A = \frac{1}{2}$ *base* $\times$ *height.*

Example

What is the area of the triangle? 8 in^2

Solve.

18 STUDENT COUNCIL Alfonso made posters in the shape of a parallelogram for the student council election. The posters were 11 inches long and 9 inches tall. What is the area of each poster?

99 in^2

19 HATS The top of Mateo's graduation hat is the shape of a parallelogram. The cap has a height of 18 centimeters and a base of 23 centimeters. What is the area of the cap?

414 cm^2

Vocabulary Check **Write the vocabulary word that completes each sentence.**

20 A(n) parallelogram is a quadrilateral that has both pairs of opposite sides congruent and parallel.

21 A(n) square unit is a unit for measuring area.

22 Writing in Math Explain how to find the area of a parallelogram with a base of 12 feet and a height of 7 feet.

See TE margin.

Spiral Review

Find the area of each figure. (Lesson 5-3, p. 193)

23 54 square units

24 56 square unit

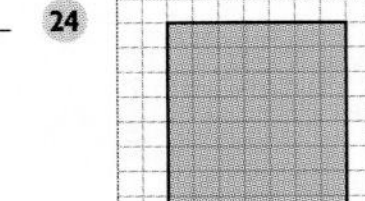

Solve. (Lesson 5-4, p. 201)

25 BASKETBALL The high-school basketball court needed to be replaced. It is 94 feet long and 50 feet wide. What is the area of the court?

4,700 square feet

STO

214 Chapter 5 Two-Dimensional Figures

Ticket Out the Door

Parallelograms All Around Have students sketch two parallelograms that have the same area and at least one dimension different in each parallelogram. Students should trade sketches with a classmate. If both students agree that each other's work is correct, they can proceed to the door to be checked.

Lesson 5-6

Area of a Triangle

KEY Concept

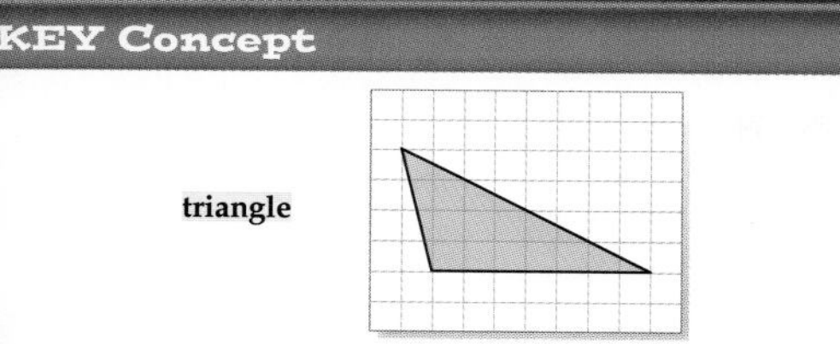

To find the area of a triangle, use what you know about the area of a **parallelogram**. You can cut a parallelogram to create two **triangles**.

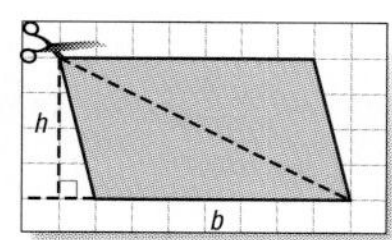

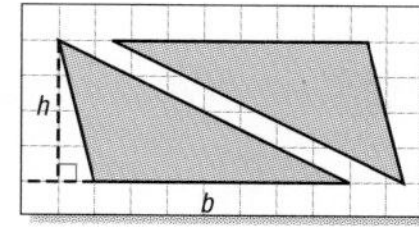

You know each triangle is $\frac{1}{2}$ the size of the parallelogram. You know the formula for the area of a parallelogram is $A = b \times h$. So, you can multiply the area of a parallelogram by $\frac{1}{2}$ to find the area of a triangle.

$$A = \frac{1}{2} \times b \times h$$

h is the height.
A is the area of the triangle.
b is the length of the base.

The location of the height of a triangle can vary. There are three possibilities.

The height is one side of the triangle.	The height is inside the triangle.	The height is outside the triangle.

VOCABULARY

area
the number of square units needed to cover the surface enclosed by a geometric figure

parallelogram
a quadrilateral that has both pairs of opposite sides congruent and parallel

square unit
a unit for measuring area

triangle
a polygon with three sides and three angles

GO ON

Intervention Strategy — Linguistic Learners

Real-World Triangles Have students go through magazines, newspapers, and other printed material to find examples of triangles in the real world. Have students cut out or copy these examples and share their results with the class. They should measure each triangle found and calculate its area.

Lesson Notes

Lesson 5-6

Lesson Planner

Objective Find areas of triangles.

Vocabulary **area**, **parallelogram**, **square unit**, **triangle**

Materials/Manipulatives geoboards, tangrams, pattern blocks

Chapter Resource Masters

- CRM Vocabulary and English Language Development (p. A108)
- CRM Skills Practice (p. A109)
- CRM Problem-Solving Practice (p. A110)
- CRM Homework Practice (p. A111)

1 Introduce

Vocabulary

Relationships Draw a *triangle* on the board. Tell students that any two identical *triangles* will always form a *parallelogram.* If that is so, what is the formula for area of a *triangle?* $A = \frac{1}{2} \times b \times h$

2 Teach

Key Concept

Foundational Skills and Concepts After students have read through the Key Concept box, have them try these exercises.

1. True or false; the side length is always the height of a triangle. false
2. The parallelogram has an area of 80 square units. What is the area of one of the triangles? 40 square units

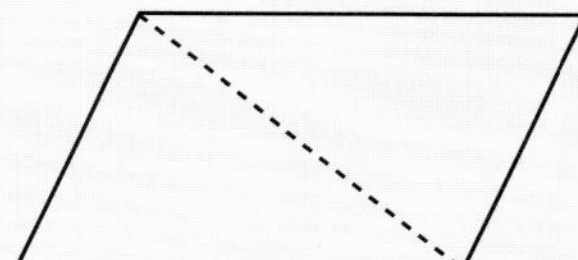

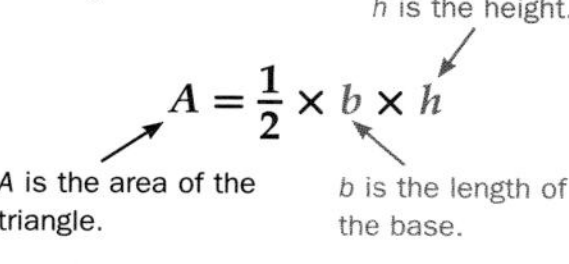

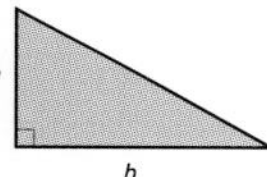

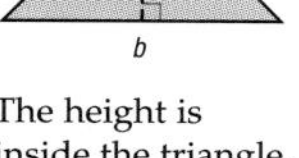

Additional **Example 1**

Find the area of the triangle.

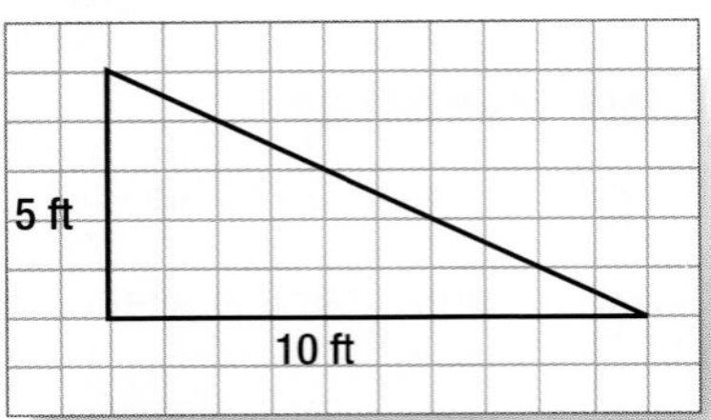

1. The base is 10 feet.
   The height is 5 feet.
2. Substitute these values into the formula.
   $A = \frac{1}{2} \times b \times h$
   $A = \frac{1}{2} \times 10 \text{ ft} \times 5 \text{ ft}$
3. Multiply to find the area of the triangle.
   $A = 25 \text{ ft}^2$

   The area of the triangle is 25 square feet.

Additional **Example 2**

Find the area of the triangle.

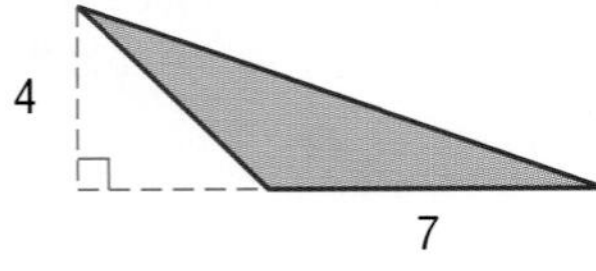

1. This base is 7 units long.
2. The height is 4 units long.
3. Substitute these values into the formula.
   $A = \frac{1}{2} \times b \times h$
   $A = \frac{1}{2} \times 7 \times 4$
4. Multiply to find the area of the triangle.
   $A = 14 \text{ units}^2$

   The area of the triangle is 14 square units.

Example 1

Find the area of the triangle.

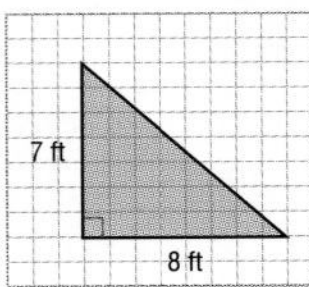

1. The base is 8 feet.
2. The height is 7 feet.
3. Substitute these values into the formula.
   $A = \frac{1}{2} \times b \times h$
   $A = \frac{1}{2} \times 8 \text{ ft} \times 7 \text{ ft}$
4. Multiply to find the area of the triangle.
   $A = 28 \text{ ft}^2$

   The area of the triangle is 28 square feet.

YOUR TURN!

Find the area of the triangle.

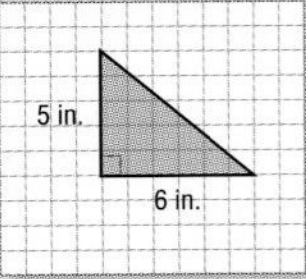

1. The base is __6__ inches.
2. The height is __5__ inches.
3. Substitute these values into the formula.
   $A = \frac{1}{2} \times b \times h$
   $A = \frac{1}{2} \times$ __6__ in. $\times$ __5__ in.
4. Multiply to find the area of the triangle.
   $A =$ __15__ in²

   The area of the triangle is __15__ square inches.

Example 2

Find the area of the triangle.

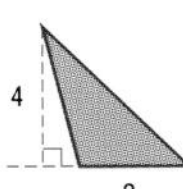

1. The base is 3 units long.
2. The height is 4 units long.
3. Substitute these values into the formula.
   $A = \frac{1}{2} \times b \times h$
   $A = \frac{1}{2} \times 3 \times 4$
4. Multiply to find the area of the triangle.
   $A = 6 \text{ units}^2$

   The area of the triangle is 6 square units.

216 Chapter 5 Two-Dimensional Figures

Intervention Strategy — Linguistic Learners

Area of a Triangle Have students write a list of steps for determining the area of a triangle. They should use complete sentences, appropriate grammar, and punctuation. After their instructions are complete, student volunteers can share their directions with the class verbally, while drawing illustrations as needed on the board.

YOUR TURN!

Find the area of the triangle.

1. The base is 6 units long.
2. The height is 2 units long.
3. Substitute these values into the formula.

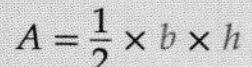

$A = \frac{1}{2} \times b \times h$

$A = \frac{1}{2} \times$ 6 $\times$ 2

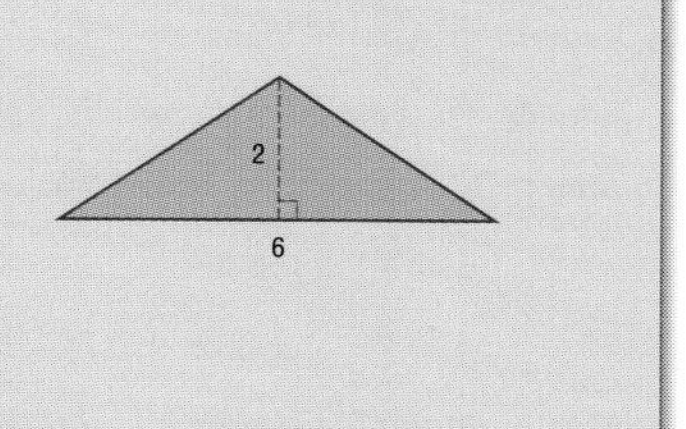

4. Multiply to find the area of the triangle.

$A =$ 6

The area of the triangle is 6 square units.

ho is Correct?

nd the area of the triangle.

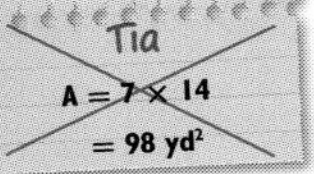

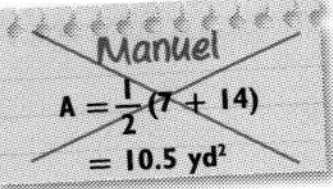

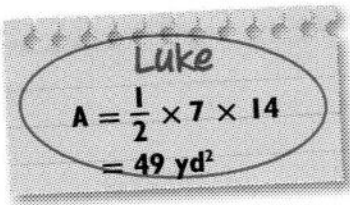

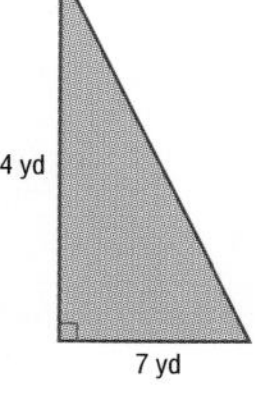

rcle correct answer(s). Cross out incorrect answer(s).

Guided Practice

aw a triangle that has the given area.

12 units² **Sample answer:**

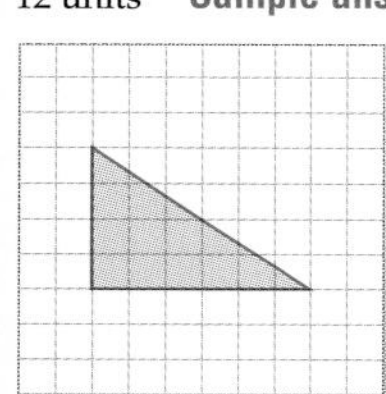

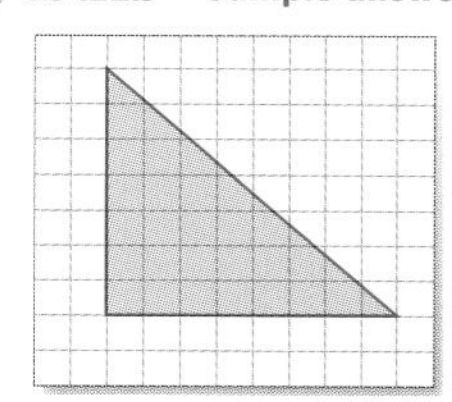

GO ON

Using Manipulatives

Geoboard When presenting area problems, model the given triangle with one color band using a geoboard. Model the rectangle that makes up the triangle in another color band.

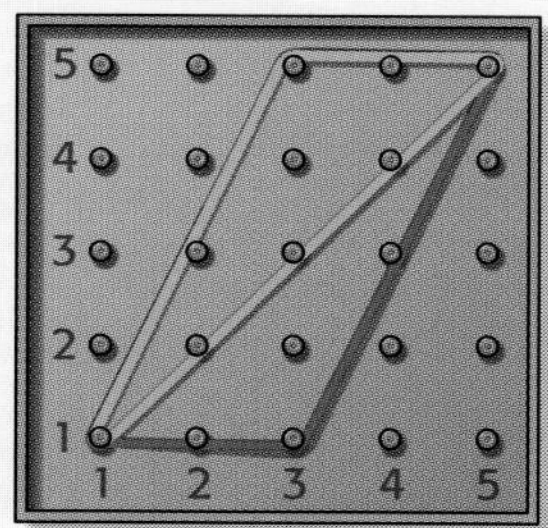

Tangram Tangram pieces can be used to show the relationships between areas of triangles, rectangles, and parallelograms.

On-Hand Manipulatives Cut out shapes using paper to show the relationships between areas of triangles, rectangles, and parallelograms.

Who *is Correct?*

Diagnostic Teaching

- Tia wrote 98 yd². This is incorrect because she forgot to multiply by $\frac{1}{2}$.
- Manual wrote 10.5 yd². This is incorrect because he added the dimensions when he should have multiplied.
- Luke wrote 49 yd². This is correct.

Math Coach Notes

Identifying the Height Use the same triangle three times to show how the base determines the location of the height in a triangle. Identify the side to use as the base and then have students sketch in the height. Use the following examples.

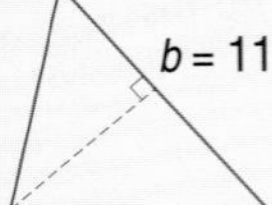

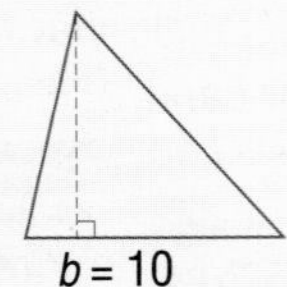

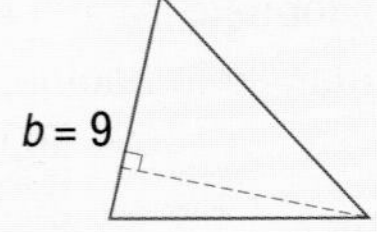

Step by Step Practice

3 Find the area of the triangle.

Step 1 The base is 4 meters. The height is 17 meters.

Step 2 Substitute these values into the formula.

$A = \frac{1}{2} \times b \times h$

$A = \frac{1}{2} \times$ 4 m $\times$ 17 m

Step 3 Multiply to find the area of the triangle.

$A =$ 34 m^2

The area of the triangle is 34 square meters.

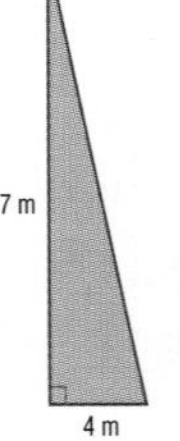

Find the area of each triangle.

4 The base is 12 inches. The height is 5 inches.

5 in.
12 in.

$A = \frac{1}{2} \times b \times h$

$A = \frac{1}{2} \times$ 12 in. $\times$ 5 in.

$A =$ 30 in^2

The area of the triangle is 30 square inches.

5 The base is 6 centimeters. The height is 14 centimeters.

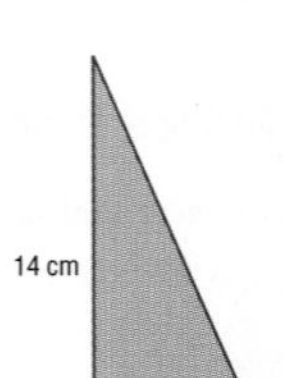

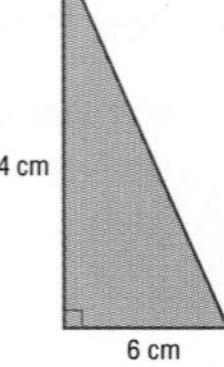

$A = \frac{1}{2} \times b \times h$

$A = \frac{1}{2} \times$ 6 cm $\times$ 14 cm

$A =$ 42 cm^2

The area of the triangle is 42 square centimeters.

218 **Chapter 5** Two-Dimensional Figures

Are They Getting It?

Check students' understanding of the area of triangles by writing these problems on the board. Ask students to point out wrong answers and explain why they are wrong. Tell them to use a drawing or model to show why the answers are correct or incorrect.

1. A triangle with base 3 mm and height 6 mm has an area of 9 mm^2. This is correct.

2. A triangle with an area of 24 m^2 could have a base of 6 m and a height of 4 m. This is incorrect. The dimensions should be multiplied, then divided by 2. For example, $6 \times 8 = 48$, and $48 \div 2 = 24$.

3. The area of this triangle is 75 m^2. This is incorrect. The area is one-half of 75 m^2, or 37.5 m^2.

15 m
5 m

6 The area of the triangle is

20 square units.

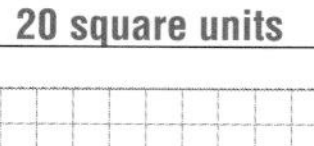

7 The area of the triangle is

45 square inches.

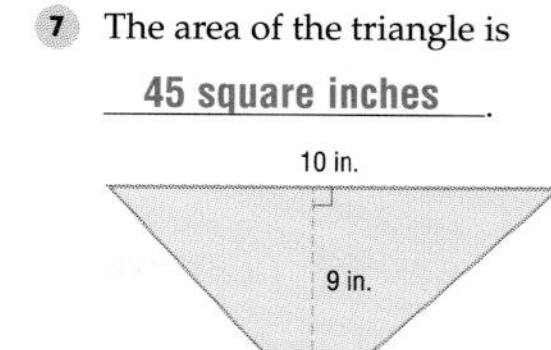

Step by Step Problem-Solving Practice

Problem-Solving Strategies
- ☐ Draw a diagram.
- ☐ Look for a pattern.
- ☐ Guess and check.
- ☑ Use a formula.
- ☐ Solve a simpler problem.

Solve.

8 **FLAGS** Mirna raises the flag every morning at summer camp. The flag is the shape of a triangle. It is 48 inches long at its base and has a height of 72 inches. What is the area of the camp flag?

Understand Read the problem. Write what you know.

The base of the flag is 48 inches.
The height of the flag is 72 inches.

Plan Pick a strategy. One strategy is to use a formula.

Substitute these values into the formula.

Solve Use the formula.

$A = \frac{1}{2} \times b \times h$

$A = \frac{1}{2} \times$ 48 in. $\times$ 72 in.

$A =$ 1,728 in^2

The area of the flag is 1,728 square inches.

Check Use a calculator to check your answer.

Common Error *Alert*

When a student is consistently getting the wrong value for the area of a triangle and their answer is 2 times greater than the actual area, the student is forgetting to multiply the product of the base and height by $\frac{1}{2}$. Point out to students that either the base can be multiplied by $\frac{1}{2}$, or the height can be multiplied by $\frac{1}{2}$, or the product of the base and height can be multiplied by $\frac{1}{2}$. Remind students that multiplying by $\frac{1}{2}$ produces the same result as dividing by 2.

Intervention Strategy

Logical/Visual/ Kinesthetic Learners

Different Triangles, Same Area Give each student pair a ruler. Tell them to draw a triangle with an area of 20 square inches. Have students share their results. Guide students to see that the dimensions of the triangles can be different, while the areas are the same. Ask student volunteers to draw their triangles on the board. Note that the triangles can have different shapes and still have the same areas.

Odd/Even Assignments

Exercises 12–21 are structured so that students practice the same concepts whether they are assigned the odd or even problems.

In-Class Assignment

Have students complete Exercises 12, 15, 17, 20, and 24 to ensure that they understand the concept.

9 ART The art teacher asked the students to cut out triangles for their 3-D collage. Each triangle had to be 62 millimeters long at its base and have a height of 47 millimeters. What is the area of each triangle? Check off each step.

✔ Understand: I underlined key words.

✔ Plan: To solve the problem, I will use a formula.

✔ Solve: The answer is 1,457 mm².

✔ Check: I checked my answer by using a calculator.

10 Belinda bought a key chain in the shape of a triangle. The key chain is 40 millimeters tall and has a base of 55 millimeters. What is the area of the key chain?

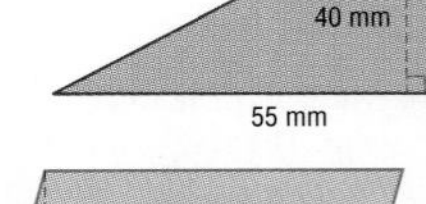

1,100 mm²

11 **Reflect** Compare the area of the triangle to the area of the parallelogram at the right.

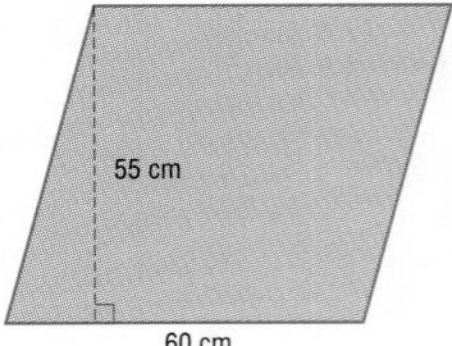

The parallelogram's area is three times the triangle's area.

Skills, Concepts, and Problem Solving

Draw a triangle that has the given area.

12 9 units² **Sample answer:**

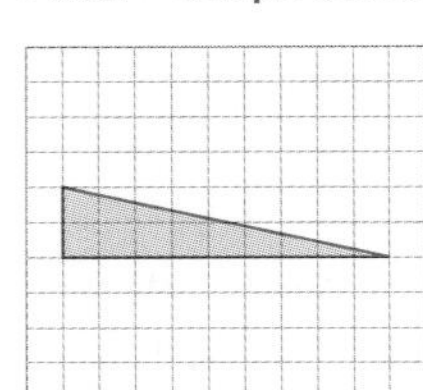

13 20 units² **Sample answer:**

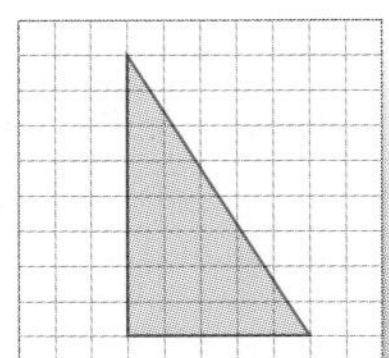

English Learner Strategy

Guiding Questions Give students two index cards each. Fold and cut one along the diagonal. Then ask the following questions.

- How many of the triangles make a rectangle?
- What is the formula for the area of a rectangle?
- How can you use the formula for the area of a rectangle to write the formula for the area of a triangle?
- How would you use the formula to find the area of a triangle with base length of 4 ft and height of 5 ft?

Find the area of each triangle.

14 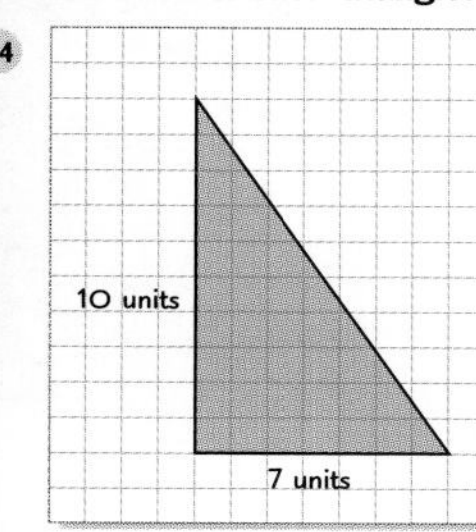

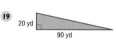

$A =$ 35 units^2

15 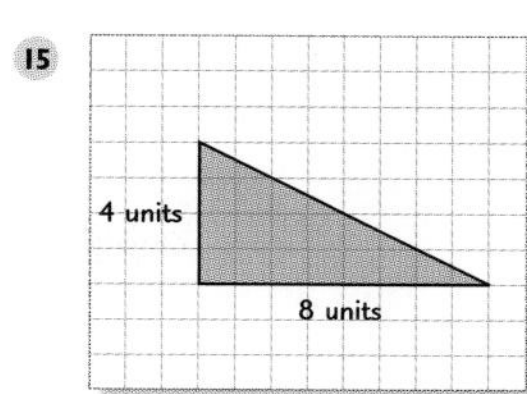

$A =$ 16 units^2

16 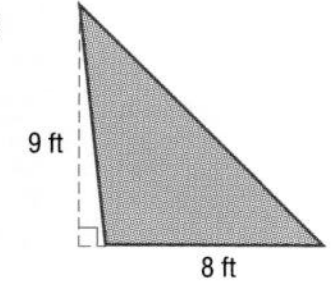

$A =$ 36 ft^2

17 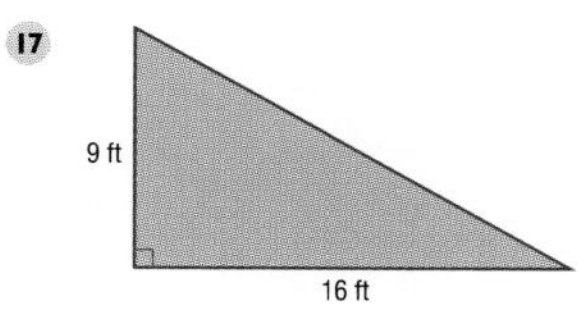

$A =$ 72 ft^2

18 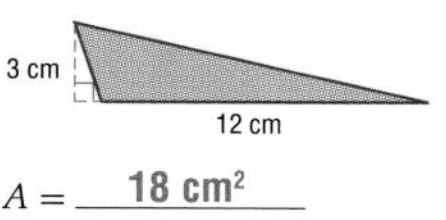

$A =$ 18 cm^2

19 20 yd, 90 yd

$A =$ 900 yd^2

Solve.

20 **WEATHER** Pearl watched a video recording of a weather report in science class. The meterologist reported on a region that had a thunderstorm watch. The region was shaped like a triangle. It measured 34 miles at the base and a height of 41 miles. What was the area of the region with the thunderstorm watch?

697 mi^2

Common Error *Alert*

Exercise 20 If a student struggles with Exercise 20, it might be because he or she is having difficulty visualizing the situation. Suggest the student sketch and label the triangle.

Note This!

Chart of Formulas In this chapter, students have learned three formulas. Tell students to make a content frame. Have them include a picture of the figure, its name, the formula, and examples. Students can add to their content frame after future lessons. An example is shown below for triangles.

Name	Picture	Area Formula	Example
Triangle	△	$A = \frac{1}{2}b \times h$	$b = 5; h = 4$ $A = \frac{1}{2} \times 5 \times 4 = 10$

Math Challenge

Given an Area Have students work independently at their desks, but compare the results of all class members. When you give the area of a triangle, each student should write the base and height of a triangle with that area. As a class, try to list all possible combinations of triangles that have whole number dimensions.

See It, Do It, Say It, Write It

Step 1 Draw an equilateral, acute, and scalene triangle on the board. Discuss with students what is different and the same about the triangles. Tell students to copy the triangles onto graph paper. Tell them to find the area of each using two methods.

Step 2 Ask students to use one of the triangles from the step above. Tell them to describe the two methods they used to find the area.

Step 3 Draw a right triangle on the board. Label its dimensions. Have a student volunteer explain how to find the area using a formula. Repeat using equilateral and acute triangles. Let students explain where the height would be measured.

Step 4 Draw a right triangle on the board. Extend the triangle to a rectangle. Have a student write an explanation of how to find the area using what he or she knows about the area of a rectangle. Do this with different types of triangles.

Looking Ahead: Pre-teach

Circles In the next lesson, students will learn about circles.

Example

What is the area of the circle?

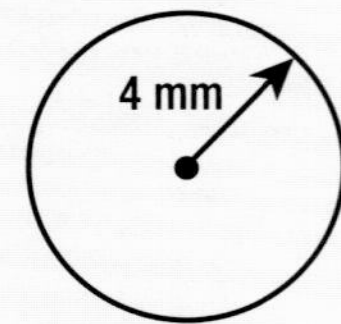

1. The radius is 4 mm, so $r = 4$.
2. Substitute 4 for r and 3.14 for π in the formula for the area of a circle, which is $A = \pi r^2$.
3. The area of the circle is about 50.24 mm^2.

---

21 RACE Fillmore Junior High School had a relay race on field day. The race was arranged in a triangular formation. It had a base of 25 yards and a height of 50 yards. What was the area of the race?

625 yd^2

Vocabulary Check **Write the vocabulary word that completes each sentence.**

22 Area is the number of square units needed to cover the surface enclosed by a geometric figure.

23 A(n) triangle is a polygon with three sides and three angles.

24 **Writing in Math** Explain how the area of a triangle is related to the area of a rectangle.

Sample answer: A rectangle can be cut into two equal triangles. So, the area of a triangle is half the area of a rectangle.

Spiral Review

Solve.

25 PAINTING Paige painted parallelograms on her two-dimensional painting. The parallelograms were 46 millimeters wide at the base and 63 millimeters tall. What was the area of each parallelogram? (Lesson 5-5, p. 209)

2,898 mm^2

26 TILES Sean is placing new ceramic tiles on his bathroom floor. The ceramic tiles have four sides and four right angles. There are two sets of lines equal in length and the opposite sides are parallel. What is the name of the figure that describes the ceramic tiles? (Lessons 5-1, p. 180)

rectangle

STOP

Ticket Out the Door

Student Created Assessment Have each student sketch a triangle on paper with the base and height given. On the back side of their papers, have students write the area of their triangles. Then each student should exchange triangles with another student to find the area of the triangle. As students exit the classroom, have them show you that the area they calculated matches the area calculated by the student that created the triangle.

Lesson 5-7 Circles

KEY Concept

A **circle** is the set of all points in a plane that are the same distance from a point called the center.

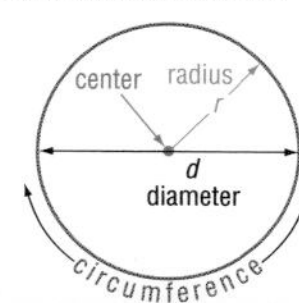

Measurement	Description	Formula
diameter and radius	The length of the **diameter** is twice the length of the **radius** of a circle.	$d = 2r$ or $r = \frac{d}{2}$ (diameter, radius)
circumference	The **circumference** of a circle is equal to π times its diameter or π times twice its radius.	circumference: $C = \pi d$ or $C = 2\pi r$; π is approximately **3.14**
area	The area of any circle is always equal to π times the radius squared.	$A = \pi r^2$ (Area, radius squared)

Pi (π) is a Greek letter used to represent the ratio of the circumference to the diameter. It is not possible to write the exact value of π. To calculate using π, either use a calculator with a π button, or substitute an approximate value of π, such as 3.14.

VOCABULARY

circle
the set of all points in a plane that are the same distance from a given point called the center

circumference
the distance around a circle

diameter
the distance across a circle through its center

pi (π)
the ratio of the circumference of a circle to the diameter of the same circle; the value of π is approximately 3.14

radius
the distance from the center of a circle to any point on the circle

hen you make a substitution for π, you have to change the = symbol ≈ symbol to show that you are making an estimate.

Lesson 5-7 Circles 223

Intervention Strategy — Interpersonal Learners

Solve and Explain Special formulas are used to find the circumference and the area of a circle. Encourage students to write the appropriate formula on their papers and substitute in the appropriate values. Also, remind students that area is measured in square units. Have student volunteers complete several problems on the board, explaining each step as they go.

Lesson Notes

Lesson 5-7

Lesson Planner

Objective Find circumferences and areas of circles.

Vocabulary **circle**, **circumference**, **diameter**, **pi**, **radius**

Materials/Manipulatives fraction circles

Chapter Resource Masters

- CRM Vocabulary and English Language Development (p. A112)
- CRM Skills Practice (p. A113)
- CRM Problem-Solving Practice (p. A114)
- CRM Homework Practice (p. A115)

1 Introduce

Vocabulary

Explore Vocabulary Draw a circle on the board and ask a student volunteer to identify the *diameter* of the circle with arrows and blue chalk. Have another student identify the *radius* of the circle with arrows and red chalk. Finally, have another student identify the *circumference* of the circle with arrows and green chalk. Show how to use pi (π) and the other vocabulary words to find the area and circumference of a circle.

2 Teach

Key Concept

Foundational Skills and Concepts After students have read through the Key Concept box, have them try these exercises.

1. What statement can you make about the relationship between the radius and diameter of a circle? The radius is half the diameter.
2. Can you substitute d for r^2? Explain. No; twice the radius equals the diameter, not the radius squared.

Additional **Example 1**

Find the radius of the circle.

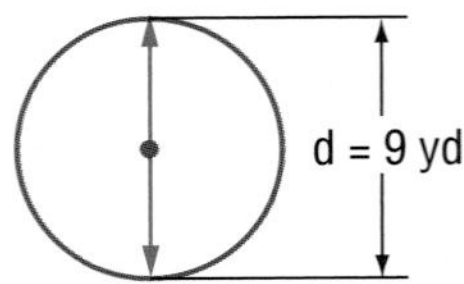

1. The radius is $\frac{1}{2}$ as long as the diameter.
2. One-half of 9 yd is 4.5 yd.
   9 yd ÷ 2 = 4.5 yd
3. The radius of the circle is 4.5 yd.

Additional **Example 2**

What is the circumference of the circle?

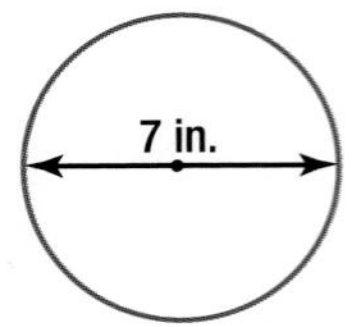

1. The diameter is 7 inches; $d = 7$.
2. Substitute 7 for d and 3.14 for π in the formula for circumference.
   $C = \pi d$
   $C \approx 3.14 \times 7$
   $C \approx 21.98$

The circumference of the circle is about 21.98 inches.

Example 1

Find the radius of the circle.

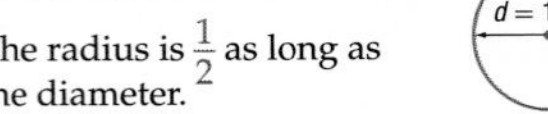

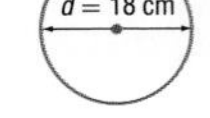

1. The radius is $\frac{1}{2}$ as long as the diameter.
2. One-half of 18 cm is 9 cm.
   18 cm ÷ 2 = 9 cm
3. The radius of the circle is 9 cm.

YOUR TURN!

Find the radius of the circle.

d = 46 ft

1. The radius is $\underline{\frac{1}{2}}$ as long as the diameter.
2. One-half of __46 ft__ is __23 ft__.
   __46 ft__ ÷ __2__ = __23 ft__
3. The radius of the circle is __23 ft__.

Example 2

What is the circumference of the circle?

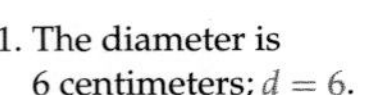

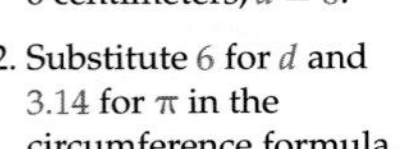

1. The diameter is 6 centimeters; $d = 6$.
2. Substitute 6 for d and 3.14 for π in the circumference formula.

$C = \pi d$
$C \approx 3.14 \times 6$
$C \approx 18.84$

The circumference of the circle is about 18.84 centimeters.

YOUR TURN!

What is the circumference of the circle?

8 ft

1. The radius is __8__ feet, so r = __8__.
2. Substitute __8__ for r and 3.14 for π in the circumference formula.

$C = 2\pi r$
$C \approx 2 \times 3.14 \times$ __8__
$C \approx$ __50.24__

When you know the radius, use $C = 2\pi r$.

The circumference of the circle is about __50.24__ feet.

Example 3

What is the area of the circle?

10 yd

1. The radius is 10 yards; $r = 10$.
2. Substitute 10 for r and 3.14 for π in the area formula.

$A = \pi r^2$
$A \approx 3.14 \times 10^2$
$A \approx 3.14 \times 100$
$A \approx 314$

The area of the circle is about 314 square yards.

224 Chapter 5 Two-Dimensional Figures

Additional **Example 3**

What is the area of the circle?

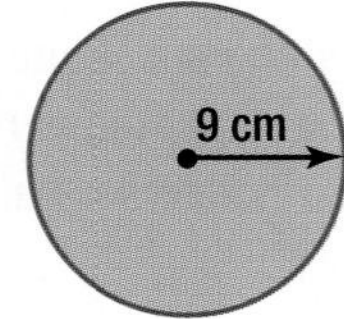

1. The radius is 9 centimeters; $r = 9$.
2. Substitute 9 for r and 3.14 for π in the formula for area.
   $A = \pi r^2$
   $A \approx 3.14 \times 9^2$
   $A \approx 3.14 \times 81$
   $A \approx 254.34$

The area of the circle is about 254.34 square centimeters.

YOUR TURN!

What is the area of the circle?

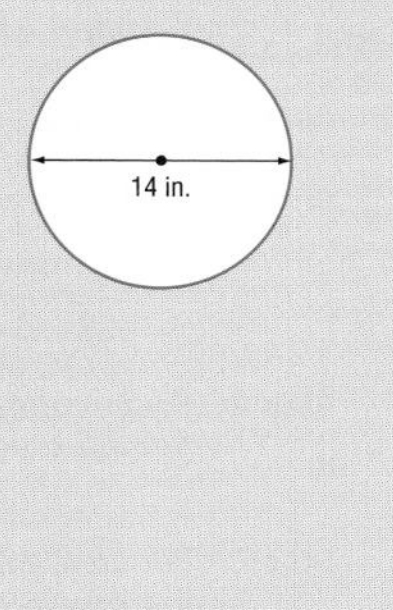

14 in.

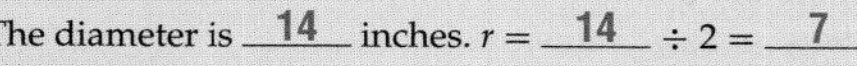

1. Find the length of the radius.

The diameter is 14 inches. $r =$ 14 $\div 2 =$ 7.

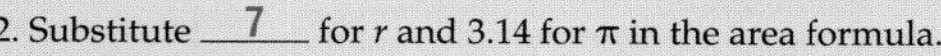

2. Substitute 7 for r and 3.14 for π in the area formula.

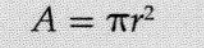

$A = \pi r^2$

$A \approx 3.14 \times 7^2$

$A \approx 3.14 \times 49$

$A \approx 153.86$

The area of the circle is about 153.86 square inches.

ho is Correct?

hat is the circumference of a circle with a radius of 5 yards?

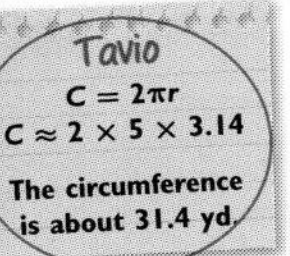

Tavio
C = 2πr
C ≈ 2 × 5 × 3.14
The circumference is about 31.4 yd.

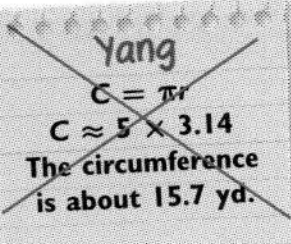

Yang
C = πr
C ≈ 5 × 3.14
The circumference is about 15.7 yd.

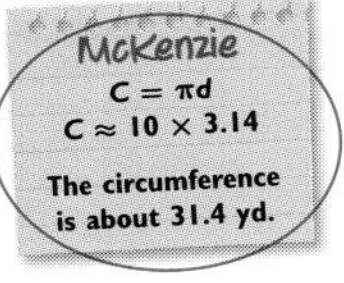

McKenzie
C = πd
C ≈ 10 × 3.14
The circumference is about 31.4 yd.

ırcle correct answer(s). Cross out incorrect answer(s).

Guided Practice

entify the length of the radius and the diameter of each circle.

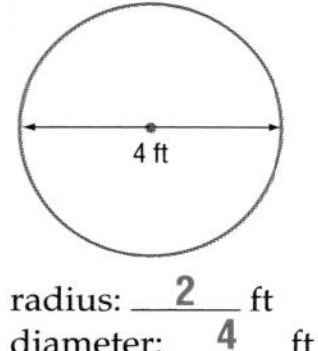

4 ft

radius: 2 ft
diameter: 4 ft

2

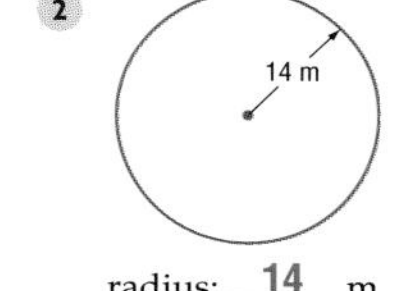

14 m

radius: 14 m
diameter: 28 m

3

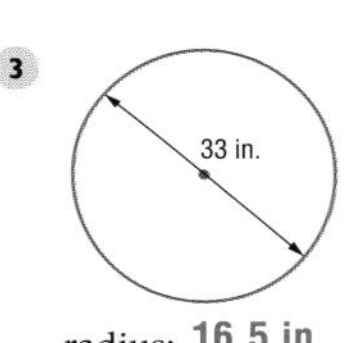

33 in.

radius: 16.5 in.
diameter: 33 in.

GO ON

Who *is Correct?*

Diagnostic Teaching

- Tavio is correct.
- Yang is incorrect. He needed to multiply the radius by 2 to find the diameter.
- McKenzie is correct.

Remind students that the diameter of a circle is two times the radius.

Note This!

Draw a Diagram Several terms used with circles are introduced in this lesson. Tell students to draw a circle in their notes and label the parts of the circle introduced in this lesson.

3 Practice

Using Manipulatives

Fraction Circles When presenting Examples 1 and 2, have students outline a fraction circle to help them draw the circle accurately. Point out that when drawing circles, students should make sure they know whether they are using the radius or the diameter. (Also, have students use a compass if you have them draw the circles.)

On-Hand Manipulatives String is a great way to find the circumference of a circle. Have students draw the circle with the appropriate values and then place the string on the circle. Mark or cut the string and measure the string with a ruler. Make sure the units are correct.

Also illustrate circumference by wrapping a tape measure around a circular object, such as a soup can. Read the measurement. Then roll the object for one complete turn along a flat surface and measure the distance it traveled. The two measurements should be the same.

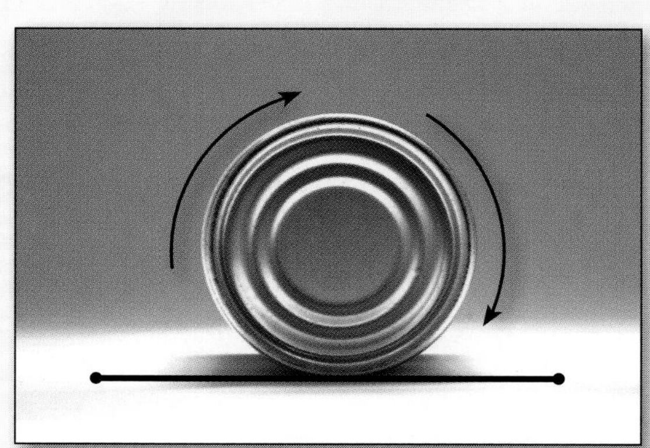

Math Coach Notes

Strategies

1. Define *radius, diameter,* and *circumference.* When explaining or reviewing these definitions, emphasize that these measurements are the lengths of parts of the circle. These lengths should be written in units and not square units.
2. Arrange students into pairs and give each student a ruler and a piece of string. Have each group use their string and rulers to measure each part of a circle. Each group needs to write down their measurements.
3. As a class, compare the measurements and discuss any common mistakes.

Step by Step Practice

4 Find the circumference and area of the circle.

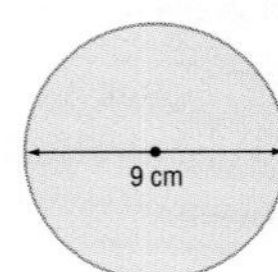

Step 1 Find the length of the diameter and radius.

The diameter is <u>9</u> centimeters.

$r =$ <u>9</u> $\div 2 =$ <u>4.5</u>

Step 2 For circumference, substitute <u>9</u> for d and 3.14 for π in the circumference formula.

$C = \pi d$
$C \approx 3.14 \times$ <u>9</u>
$C \approx$ <u>28.26</u>

Step 3 For area, substitute <u>4.5</u> for r and 3.14 for π in the area formula.

$A = \pi r^2$
$A \approx 3.14 \times$ <u>4.5</u>^{2}
$A \approx 3.14 \times$ <u>20.25</u>
$A \approx$ <u>63.585</u>

The circumference of the circle is about <u>28.26</u> centimeters, and the area of the circle is about <u>63.585</u> square centimeters.

Find the circumference and area of each circle. Use 3.14 for π.

5 $d =$ <u>26</u> in. $r =$ <u>13</u> in.

13 in.

$C = \pi d$	$A = \pi r^2$
$C \approx 3.14 \times$ <u>26</u>	$A \approx 3.14 \times$ <u>13</u>^{2}
$C \approx$ <u>81.64</u>	$A \approx 3.14 \times$ <u>169</u>
	$A \approx$ <u>530.66</u>

The circumference of the circle is about <u>81.64</u> inches, and the area of the circle is about <u>530.66</u> square inches.

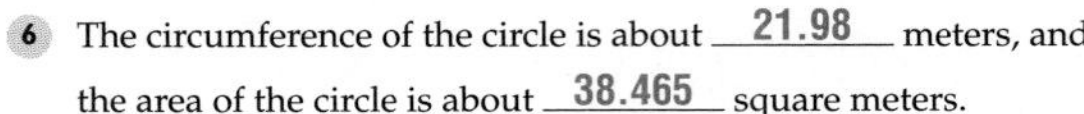

6 The circumference of the circle is about <u>21.98</u> meters, and the area of the circle is about <u>38.465</u> square meters.

7 m

$d =$ <u>7</u> m $r =$ <u>3.5</u> m

$C = \pi d$	$A = \pi r^2$
$C \approx 3.14 \times$ <u>7</u>	$A \approx 3.14 \times$ <u>3.5</u>^{2}
$C \approx$ <u>21.98</u>	$A \approx 3.14 \times$ <u>12.25</u>
	$A \approx$ <u>38.465</u>

226 **Chapter 5** Two-Dimensional Figures

Are They Getting It?

Check students' understanding of circles by writing these problems on the board. Ask students to point out wrong answers and explain why they are wrong.

Find the circumference and area of the circle. Use 3.14 for π.

1.

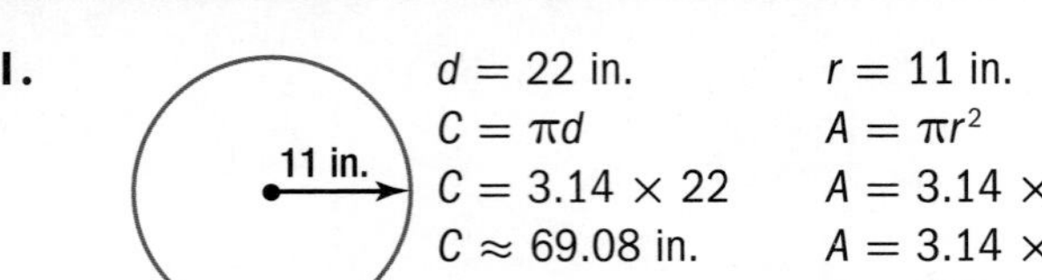

$d = 22$ in. | $r = 11$ in.
$C = \pi d$ | $A = \pi r^2$
$C = 3.14 \times 22$ | $A = 3.14 \times 11^2$
$C \approx 69.08$ in. | $A = 3.14 \times 121$
$A \approx 379.94 \text{ in}^2$

The circumference of the circle is about 69.08 inches and the area of the circle is about 379.94 inches². This is correct.

2.

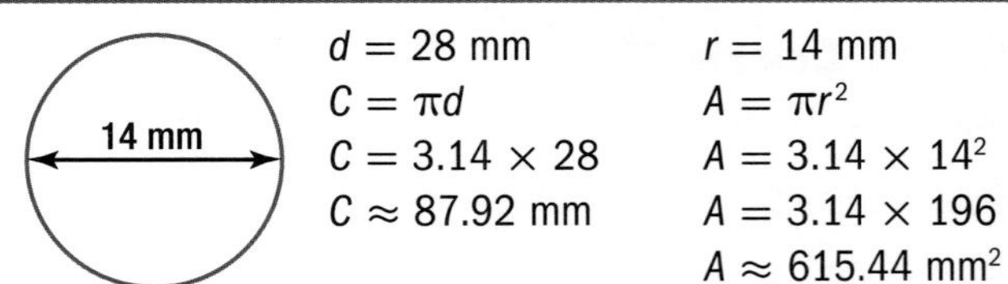

$d = 28$ mm | $r = 14$ mm
$C = \pi d$ | $A = \pi r^2$
$C = 3.14 \times 28$ | $A = 3.14 \times 14^2$
$C \approx 87.92$ mm | $A = 3.14 \times 196$
$A \approx 615.44 \text{ mm}^2$

The circumference of the circle is about 87.92 millimeters and the area of the circle is about 615.44 millimeters². This is incorrect. The lengths used for the diameter and the radius were incorrect.

ıd the circumference and area of each circle. Use 3.14 for π.

The circumference of the circle is about 37.68 yards, and the area of the circle is about 113.04 square yards.

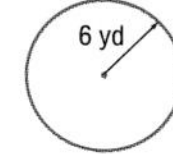

8 The circumference of the circle is about 12.56 feet, and the area of the circle is about 12.56 square feet.

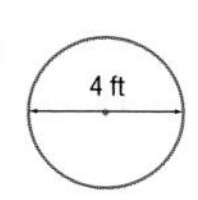

The circumference of the circle is about 69.08 inches, and the area of the circle is about 379.94 square inches.

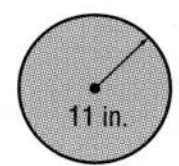

10 The circumference of the circle is about 53.38 centimeters, and the area of the circle is about 226.865 square centimeters.

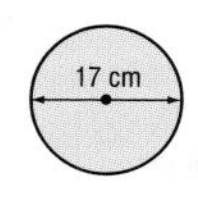

tep by Step Problem-Solving Practice

Problem-Solving Strategies

- ☐ Draw a diagram.
- ☑ Use a formula.
- ☐ Guess and check.
- ☐ Act it out.
- ☐ Solve a simpler problem.

ılve.

CARS Octavia's tires each have a diameter of 35 inches. What is the circumference of each tire?

Understand Read the problem. Write what you know. Alana's tires have a diameter of 35 inches.

Plan Pick a strategy. One strategy is to use a formula. Use the formula for the circumference of a circle.

Solve Substitute 35 for d and 3.14 for π in the circumference formula.

$C = \pi d$

$C \approx 3.14 \times 35$

$C \approx 109.9$

The circumference of each tire is about 109.9 inches.

Check Estimate the circumference by substituting 3 for π and 35 for d.

$C = \pi d$

$C \approx 3 \times 35$

$C \approx 105$

The circumference of each tire is close to the estimate, so the answer is reasonable.

Intervention Strategy

Visual/Logical Learners

Sketch and Solve Have students create a circle on the upper half of a sheet of construction or poster paper. Have students label the radius, diameter, and center of the circle. In the lower half of the paper, have students show the steps for finding the area and circumference of a circle.

Math Coach Notes

Real-World Connections Have students find three circular items in their home. Trace the circles onto a sheet of paper. Label and measure the parts of the circle—radius, diameter, center, area, and circumference.

Common Error Alert

Pi

A common error is that students do not really understand how pi (π) is a ratio. Use a piece of string to represent the circumference of a circle and another piece to represent the diameter of the circle. Have students explore and prompt them to figure out that the circumference is about 3 times the diameter.

Discuss with students that the size of the circle does not matter. The ratio illustrated in the activity above remains constant.

Arrange the class into three groups. Assign one group to demonstrate the ratio of π using a circle that has a diameter of 2 inches. Assign another group to demonstrate the ratio using a circle that has a diameter of 5 inches. Assign the third group a circle that has a diameter of 10 inches.

Odd/Even Assignments

Exercises 15–19 are structured so that students practice the same concepts whether they are assigned the odd or even problems.

In-Class Assignment

Have students complete Exercises 15, 17, 19, and 22 to ensure that they understand the concept.

Intervention Strategy

Kinesthetic Learners

Model the Answer Provide students with circles cut out of cardboard and a piece of yarn or string larger than the circumference of the circles. Instruct students to cut a piece of yarn that is equal to the distance around the circle and measure the string. Then ask students to determine the circumference of the circle using the formula by finding the radius (or diameter) of the circle. Answers should be approximately the same.

12 SPORTS The skating rink has a radius of 8 yards. What is the circumference of the skating rink? Use 3.14 for π. Check off each step.

✓ Understand: I underlined key words.

✓ Plan: To solve the problem I will use a formula

✓ Solve: The answer is 50.24 yards

✓ Check: I checked my answer by estimating the circumference by substituting 3 for π and 16 for d.

13 HOBBIES Darin collects clocks. The face of his largest clock has a radius of 23 inches. What is the area of Darin's largest clock? Use 3.14 for π. 1,661.06 in^2

14 **Reflect** Using an appropriate measuring tool and the centimeter grid shown, find the circumference and area using the formulas $C = 2\pi r$ and $A = \pi r^2$. Write down both sets of numbers. How do the two sets of numbers compare?

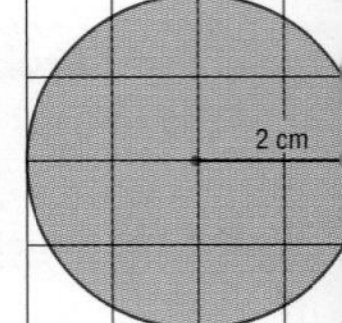

The circumference of this circle is $2 \times \pi \times 2$, or $4\pi \approx 12.56$. The area of the circle is πr^2 or $\pi 2^2$, which is also equal to $4\pi = 12.56$. Both the circumference and area of the figure equal 12.56.

Skills, Concepts, and Problem-Solving

Identify the length of the radius and diameter of each circle.

15 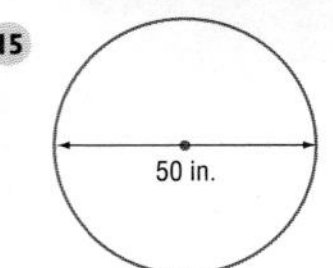

radius = 25 in.
diameter = 50 in.

16 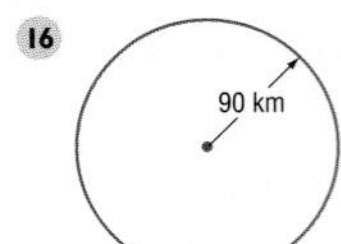

radius = 90 km
diameter = 180 k

Find the circumference and area of the circle. Use 3.14 for π.

17 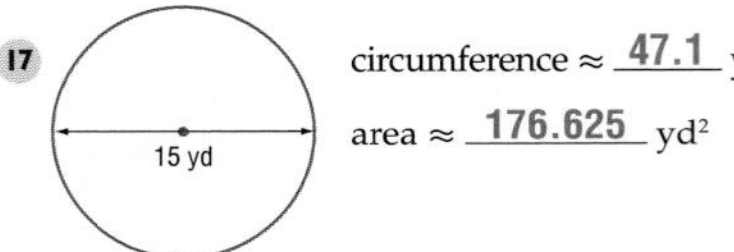

circumference ≈ 47.1 yd
area ≈ 176.625 yd^2

18 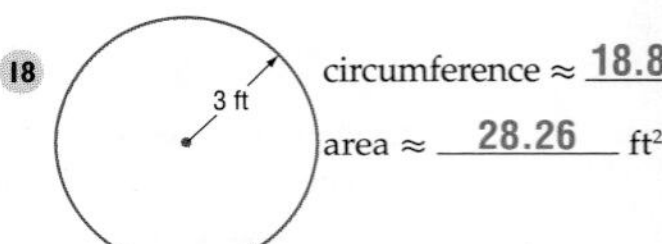

circumference ≈ 18.84
area ≈ 28.26 ft^2

Math Challenge

Circles for Partners Arrange students into pairs. Instruct one member of each pair to draw a circle and write the circumference and area. Have the other student find the diameter and radius of the circle. Have the students switch roles. Advise them to work out the problems to make sure they are giving a workable problem.

Solve.

19 HOBBIES Dane's grandmother used a circular canvas last week while painting a collage. The canvas had a diameter of 14 inches. What was the area of the canvas? Use 3.14 for π.

$153.86\ in^2$

Vocabulary Check **Write the vocabulary word that completes each sentence.**

20 Circumference is the distance around a circle.

21 Pi (π) is the ratio of the circumference of a circle to the diameter of the same circle. Its value is approximately 3.14.

22 Writing in Math Explain how to find the area of a circle.

Find the length of the radius. Substitute the length of the radius for r and 3.14 for π in the area formula. $A = \pi r^2$

Spiral Review

Name each figure by its angles. (Lesson 5-2, p. 187)

23

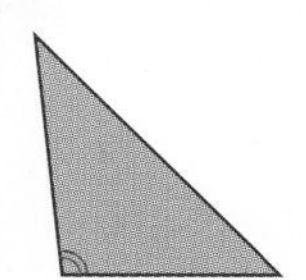

obtuse triangle

24

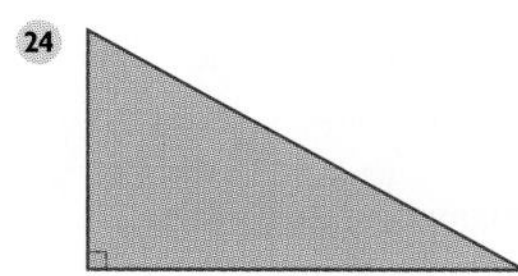

right triangle

Solve. (Lesson 5-5, p. 209)

25 SAILBOATS The traditional boats found on Lake Tai in China have sails shaped like parallelograms. Refer to the photo caption at the right. What is the area of the sail?

$400\ ft^2$

SAILBOATS **The height of the large sail is 25 feet. The base is 16 feet.**

See It, Do It, Say It, Write It

Step 1 Draw the following figure on the board.

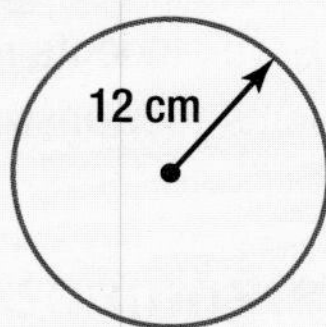

Step 2 Have students find the circumference and area of the circle using the formulas provided in this lesson. $C = 75.36$ cm, $A = 452.16\ cm^2$

Step 3 Arrange students into pairs and have them explain to each other how they found the circumference and area using the formulas.

Step 4 Have students write in their own words how they find the circumference and area of circles.

Ticket Out the Door

Vocabulary Modeled in Classroom Instruct each student to give an example of an item found in the classroom that represents a vocabulary word from this lesson. Have students show you their example as they exit the classroom.

Chapter 5

Progress Check 3

Formative Assessment

Use the Progress Check to assess students' mastery of the previous lessons. Have students review the lesson indicated for the problems they answered incorrectly.

Odd/Even Assignments

Exercises are structured so that students practice the same concepts whether they are assigned the odd or even problems.

Common Error Alert

Formulas More than likely, one of the biggest difficulties encountered will be working with the different formulas required to answer the questions.

Exercises 1 and 2 Students might not recall the formula for area of a parallelogram.

Exercises 3 and 4 Students might not recall the formula for area of a triangle.

Exercises 5 and 6 Review the formulas for finding the circumference and area of a circle.

Chapter 5

Progress Check 3 (Lessons 5-5, 5-6, and 5-7)

Find the area of each parallelogram.

1 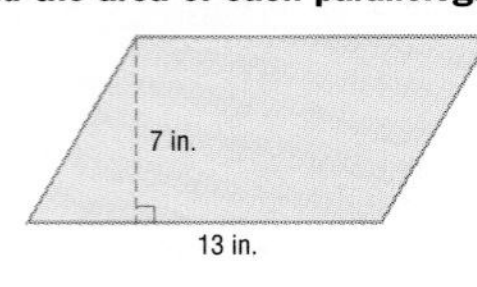

$A =$ 91 in²

2 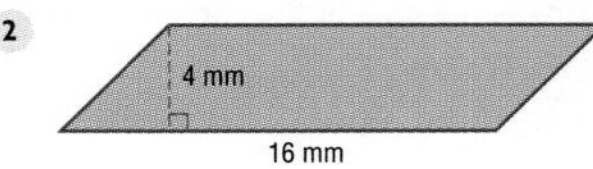

$A =$ 64 mm²

Find the area of each triangle.

3 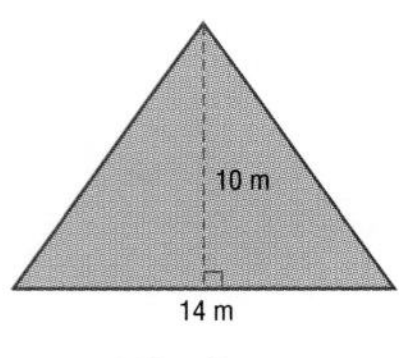

$A =$ 70 m²

4 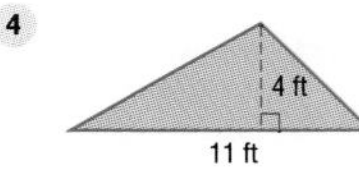

$A =$ 22 ft²

Find the circumference and area of each circle. Use 3.14 for π.

5 The circumference of the circle is about 25.12 yards, and the area of the circle is about 50.24 square yards.

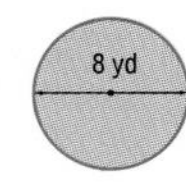

6 The circumference of the circle is about 75.36 feet. The area of the circle is about 452.16 square feet.

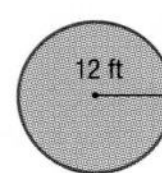

Solve.

7 **ARCHITECTURE** The owners of this house would like to paint the front and need to know how much paint to buy. What is the area if it has a height of 25 feet and a base of 40 feet?
500 ft²

8 **BASEBALL** According to baseball regulations, the pitcher's mound, which is circular, must have a diameter of 18 feet. What is the approximate area of a pitcher's mound?
254.34 ft²

230 Chapter 5 Two-Dimensional Figures

Data-Driven Decision Making

Students missing Exercises . . .	Have trouble with . . .	Should review and practice . . .
1–2	finding the area of a parallelogram.	SSG Lesson 5-5, p. 209 CRM Skills Practice, p. A105
3–4	finding the area of a triangle.	SSG Lesson 5-6, p. 215 CRM Skills Practice, p. A109
5–6	finding the circumference and area of a circle.	SSG Lesson 5-7, p. 223 CRM Skills Practice, p. A113
7–8	solving word problems that involve finding circumferences and areas.	CRM Problem-Solving Practice, pp. A106, A110, and A114

Study Guide

Vocabulary and Concept Check

cute angle, p. 187
ircumference, p. 223
btuse angle, p. 187
(π), p. 223
adius, p. 223
hombus, p. 180
quare unit, p. 195
apezoid, p. 180

Write the vocabulary word that completes each sentence.

1. Circumference is the distance around a circle.
2. An angle that measures greater than 90° but less than 180° is called a(n) obtuse angle.
3. The unit used for measuring area is called a(n) square unit.
4. A(n) trapezoid has only one pair of opposite sides parallel.
5. The distance from the center of a circle to any point on the circle is the radius.

dentify the correct figure for each formula.

6. $A = \pi r^2$ circle
7. $A = \ell \times w$ rectangle
8. $A = b \times h$ parallelogram
9. $A = \frac{1}{2} \times b \times h$ triangle

esson Review

-1 Quadrilaterals (pp. 180–186)

dentify each figure.

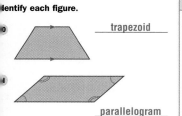

10. 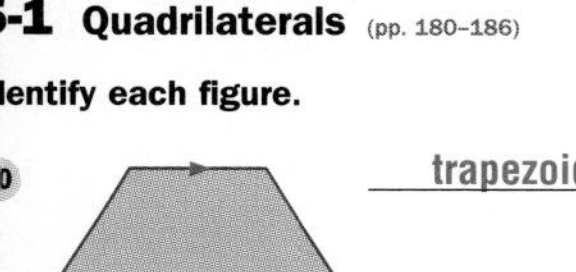
trapezoid

11. 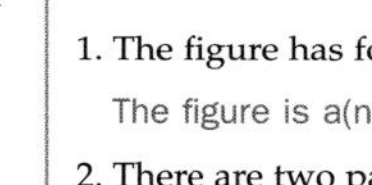
parallelogram

Example 1

Identify the figure.

1. The figure has four sides.
The figure is a(n) quadrilateral.
2. There are two pairs of parallel sides.
3. There are no right angles.
The figure is a(n) rhombus.

Classroom Management

Early Finishers Have students who finish the review problems for each example create additional problems. They should create the problem and include an answer, including a labeled diagram. When complete, have these students exchange problems and double-check each other's work.

Chapter 5

Study Guide
Formative Assessment

Vocabulary and Concept Check

If students have difficulty answering Exercises 1–9, remind them that they can use the page references to refresh their memories about the vocabulary terms.

Vocabulary Review Strategies

Vocabulary Frames Students can create Vocabulary Frames for the words. Have the students make two index cards for each vocabulary word.

- On one set of cards, state the definition, and on the other side write the vocabulary term. Students can study these either by looking at the vocabulary term and stating its definition (flipping the card over to see if they got the definition correct), or students can read the side with the definition and try to state the corresponding vocabulary term (flipping the card over to see if they got the correct term).
- On the other set of cards, have the vocabulary terms on one side and have a drawing or sketch of the term on the other side. Students can quiz themselves with the same technique as described with the first set of index cards. It will be beneficial if the students not only know the *word* definitions of the vocabulary terms, but that they also recognize a sketch that represents the term.

Lesson Review

Each example walks the students through finding areas of a rectangle, parallelogram, or triangle and the circumference and area of circles. Have students write out the formula for each problem. They can explain the steps in each example as they perform them.

Find **Extra Practice** for these concepts in the Practice Worksheets, pages A88–A115.

Dinah Zike's Foldables®

Review Remind students to complete and refer to their Foldables as they progress through the Chapter 5 Study Guide. Have students share and compare their completed Foldables with a partner. You may also choose to have them use their Foldable as a study aid in preparing for the Chapter Test. (For complete instructions, see Chapter Resource Masters, p. A85.)

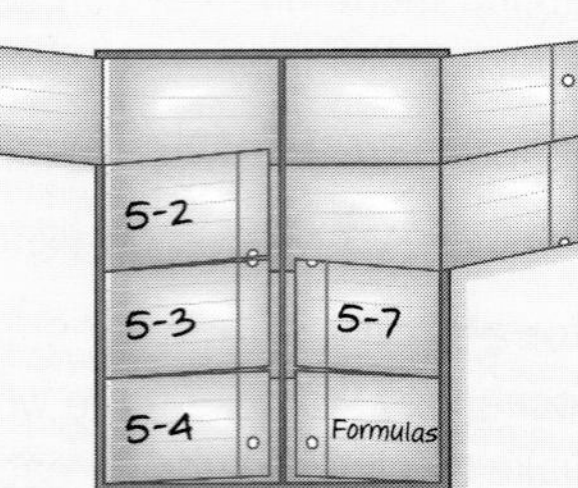

5-2 Triangles (pp. 187–193)

Name each triangle by its sides or angles.

12 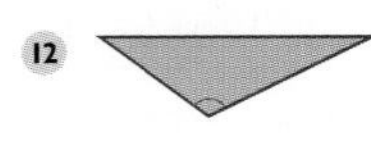

obtuse triangle

13 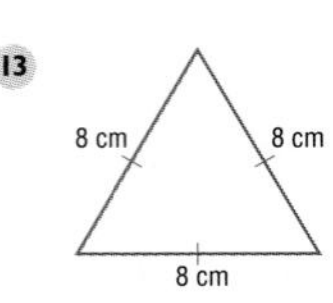

equilateral triangle

Example 2

Name the triangle by its sides.

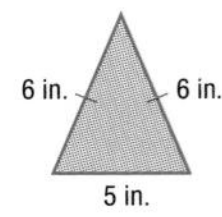

1. The triangle has 2 congruent sides.
2. The triangle is an isosceles triangle.

5-3 Introduction to Area (pp. 195–200)

Find the area of each figure.

14 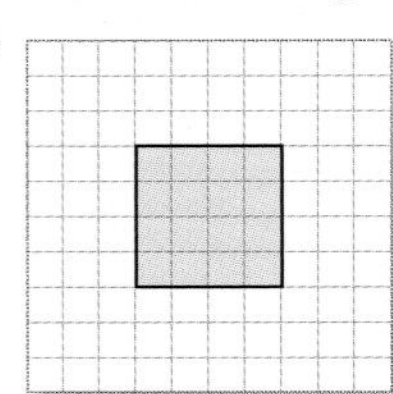

The area of the square is 16 square units.

15 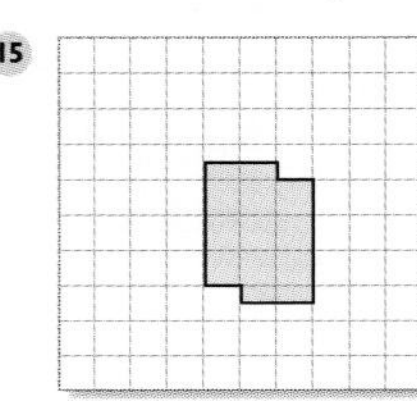

The area of the figure is about 11 square units.

Example 3

Find the area of the rectangle.

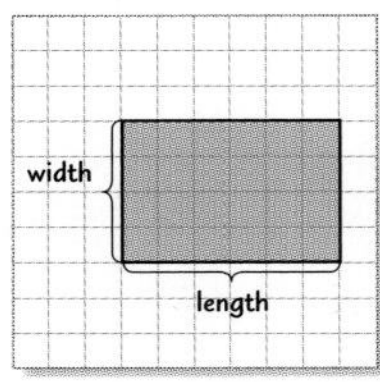

1. Count the squares the rectangle covers.
2. The area of the rectangle is **24** square units.
3. Check your answer.
   Count the squares in the top row. **6**
   Count the number of rows. **5**
4. Add the rows to find the area.
   $6 + 6 + 6 + 6 = 24$

The area of the rectangle is about 24 square units.

232 Chapter 5 Study Guide

5-4 Area of a Rectangle (pp. 201–207)

Find the area of each rectangle.

16

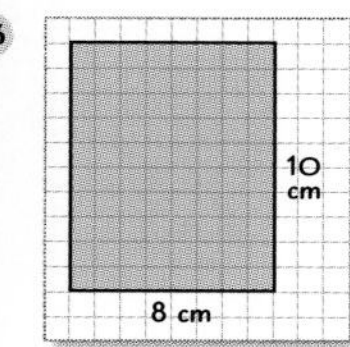

$A =$ 80 square centimeters or 80 cm^2

17

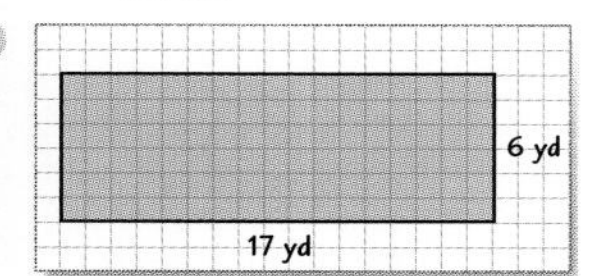

$A =$ 102 square yards or 102 yd^2

Example 4

What is the area of the rectangle?

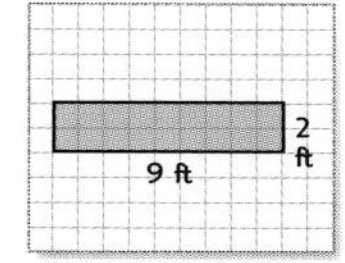

1. The length of the rectangle is 9 feet, and the width is 2 feet.
2. Substitute these values into the formula. Multiply.

$A = \ell \times w$
$A = 9 \text{ ft} \times 2 \text{ ft}$
$A = 18 \text{ ft}^2$

The area of the rectangle is 18 square feet.

Find the area of each square.

18

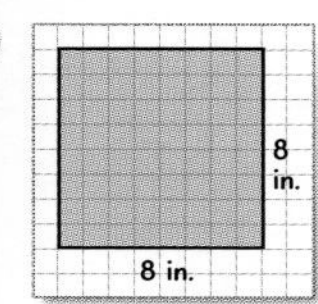

$A =$ 64 square inches or 64 in^2

19

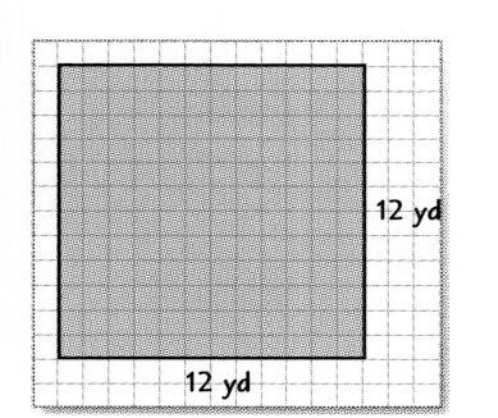

$A =$ 144 square yards or 144 yd^2

Example 5

What is the area of the square?

1. The length of the square is 4 meters, and the width is 4 meters.
2. Substitute these values into the formula. Multiply.

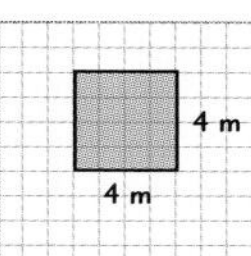

$A = \ell \times w$
$A = 4 \text{ m} \times 4 \text{ m}$
$A = 16 \text{ m}^2$

The area of the square is 16 square meters.

Math Coach Notes

More than One Way Have students check their work by finding the areas of rectangles two ways. First by using the formula, then by counting the grid squares.

Common Error *Alert*

Exercises 22 and 23 If students are not finding the areas in Exercises 22 and 23 correctly, remind them to pay close attention to the $\frac{1}{2}$ that is in the formula when finding the area of a triangle. If they omitted the $\frac{1}{2}$, ask them what shape's area did they actually find?

Math Coach Notes

Formula for Triangle If a student does not like calculating with fractions, suggest they include the following variations of the formula in their notes. These formulas are the same formula as $A = \frac{1}{2}b \times h$, simply using alternative symbols and notations.

$A = 0.5 \times b \times h$ $\quad$ $A = b \times h \div 2$

5-5 Area of a Parallelogram (pp. 209–214)

Find the area of each parallelogram.

20 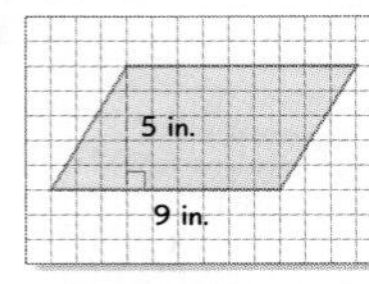

$A =$ 45 square inches or 45 in^2

21 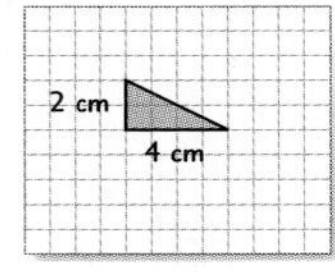

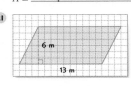

$A =$ 78 square meters or 78 m^2

Example 6

Find the area of the parallelogram.

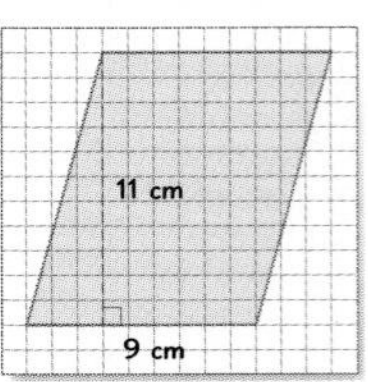

1. The base is 9 centimeters. The height is 11 centimeters.
2. Substitute these values into the formula. Multiply.

$A = b \times h$
$A = 9 \text{ cm} \times 11 \text{ cm}$
$A = 99 \text{ cm}^2$

The area of the parallelogram is 99 square centimeters.

5-6 Area of a Triangle (pp. 215–222)

Find the area of each triangle.

22 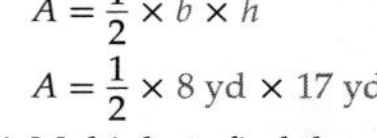

$A =$ 4 square centimeters, or 4 cm^2

23 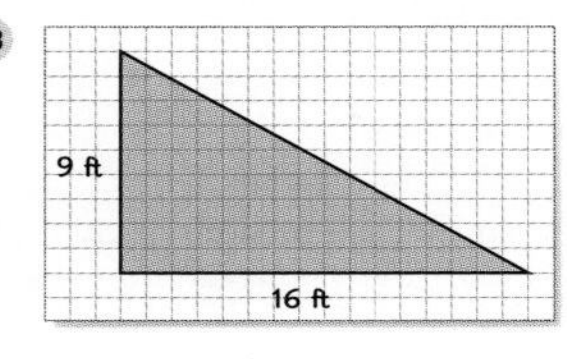

$A =$ 72 square feet, or 72 ft^2

Example 7

Find the area of the triangle.

17 yd

8 yd

1. The base is 8 yards long.
2. The height is 17 yards long.
3. Substitute these values into the formula.

$A = \frac{1}{2} \times b \times h$

$A = \frac{1}{2} \times 8 \text{ yd} \times 17 \text{ yd}$

4. Multiply to find the area of the triangle.

$A = 68 \text{ yd}^2$

The area of the triangle is 68 square yards.

-7 Circles (pp. 223–229)

Find the circumference of the circle. Use 3.14 for π.

$C \approx \pi d$

$C \approx 3.14 \times 7$

$C \approx$ **21.98 ft**

Find the circumference of the circle. Use 3.14 for π.

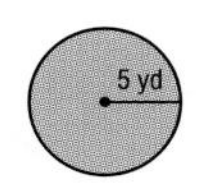

$C \approx 2\pi r$

$C \approx 2 \times 3.14 \times 5$

$C \approx$ **31.4 yd**

Example 8

What is the circumference of the circle?

The diameter is 12 meters; $d = 12$.

Substitute 12 for d and 3.14 for π in the circumference formula.

$C \approx \pi d$

$C \approx 3.14 \times 12$

$C \approx 37.68$

The circumference of the circle is about 37.68 meters.

What is the area of the circle? Use 3.14 for π.

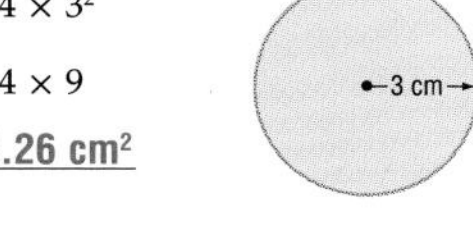

$A \approx 3.14 \times 3^2$

$A \approx 3.14 \times 9$

$A \approx$ **28.26 cm²**

What is the area of the circle? Use 3.14 for π.

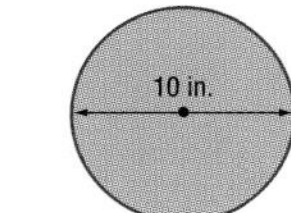

$A \approx 3.14 \times 5^2$

$A \approx 3.14 \times 25$

$A \approx$ **78.5 in²**

Example 9

What is the area of the circle?

1. The radius is 9 ft; $r = 9$.
2. Substitute 9 for r and 3.14 for π in the area formula.

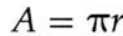

$A = \pi r^2$

$A \approx 3.14 \times 9^2$

$A \approx 3.14 \times 81$

$A \approx 254.34$

The area of the circle is about 254.34 ft².

Chapter 5 Study Guide 235

Note This!

Study Checklist Help students create a study checklist. The checklist should include the following items.

- State the formula for the area of a rectangle and parallelogram.
- Find the area of a rectangle.
- Find the area of a parallelogram.
- State the formula for the area of a triangle.
- Find the area of a triangle.
- State the formulas for circumference and area of a circle.
- Find the circumference and area of a circle.

Students should put a check mark next to each topic when they feel they have a good grasp of the process.

Ticket Out the Door

Review Area Have students answer a total of five questions that you give them on a half-sheet of paper. Have one question from each concept.

- finding the area of a rectangle
- finding the area of a parallelogram
- finding the area of a triangle
- finding the circumference of a circle
- finding the area of a circle

Chapter 5 Chapter Test

Chapter Resource Masters

Additional forms of the Chapter 5 Tests are available.

Test Format	Where to Find it
Chapter 5 Test	Math Online glencoe.com
Blackline Masters	Assessment Masters, p. 79

Customize and create multiple versions of your chapter tests and their answer keys. All of these questions from the chapter tests are available on ExamView® Assessment Suite.

Online Assessment and Reporting
glencoe.com

This online assessment tool allows teachers to track student progress with easily accessible comprehensive reports available for every student. Assess students using any internet-ready computer.

Alternative Assessment

Use Portfolios Ask students to write examples of each type of problem from this chapter in their portfolios. Require them to include a diagram or picture with each example.

Have students write the answer to each example in their portfolios and describe the steps taken, *in their own words,* to solve or simplify each one.

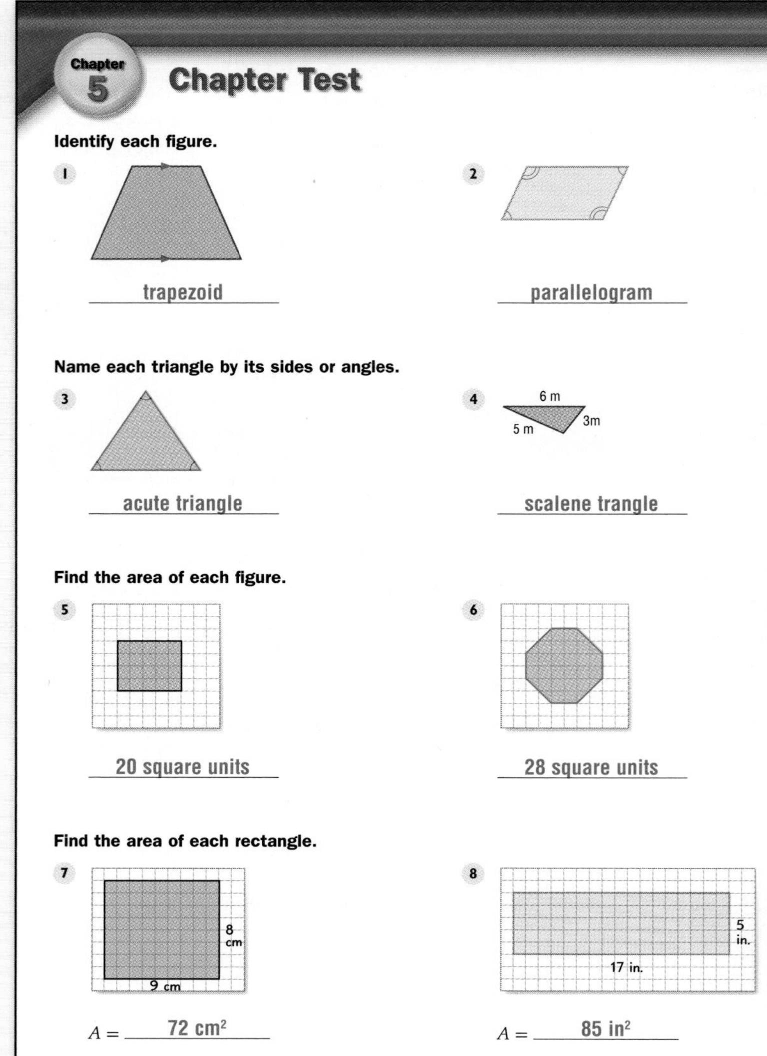

Chapter 5 Chapter Test

Identify each figure.

1. trapezoid
2. parallelogram

Name each triangle by its sides or angles.

3. acute triangle
4. 6 m, 5 m, 3m — scalene trangle

Find the area of each figure.

5. 20 square units
6. 28 square units

Find the area of each rectangle.

7. 8 cm, 9 cm — $A =$ 72 cm^2
8. 5 in., 17 in. — $A =$ 85 in^2

236 Chapter 5 Test

English Learner Strategy

Assessment Allow students time to look over the assessment. Have students take a close look at all the problem directions, as well as any terms in the word problems. Provide an opportunity for students to clarify any words they think they do not understand by conducting a brief question-and-answer period.

nd the area of each parallelogram.

$A =$ 108 m²

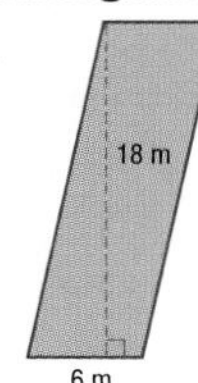

10 $A =$ 667 yd²

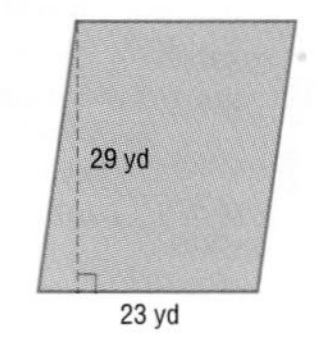

nd the area of each triangle.

$A =$ 12 units²

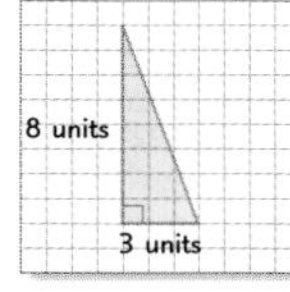

12 $A =$ 76 in²

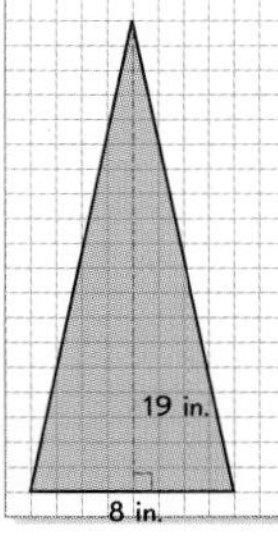

nd the circumference and area of the circle. Use 3.14 for π.

The circumference of the circle is about 50.24 cm,

and the area of the circle is about 200.96 square cm.

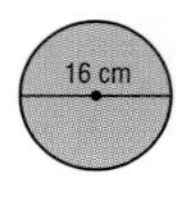

lve.

FLAGS Lakita hung a flag shaped like a parallelogram in her bedroom. The flag is 60 inches wide at the base and 36 inches tall. What is the area of her flag? 2,160 in²

MEASUREMENT Steve uses a measuring tool to measure angles of wood while building a deck. The measuring tool is shaped like a triangle. The base is 20 millimeters and it is 26 millimeters tall. What is the area of the measuring tool? 260 mm²

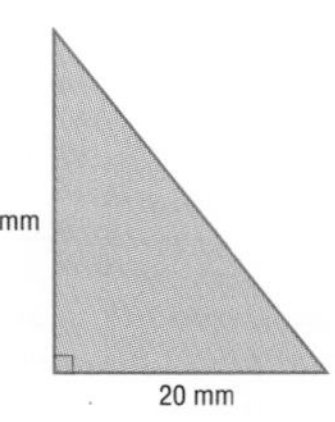

rrect the mistake.

Mia measured the area of a base of a cylinder in math class. The base of the cylinder had a radius of 6 centimeters. Mia said the area of the base of the cylinder was 18.84 square centimeters. Was she correct? Why or why not?

Sample Answer: No; To find the area of the base of the cylinder, you multiply πr^2. $3.14 \times 6^2 = 113.04$ square centimeters

Learning from Mistakes

Missed Questions Review commonly missed questions as a small group or class. Ask students to share their methods of answering each question. Try to point out when any errors occur and take corrective measures.

Data-Driven Decision Making

Students missing Exercises . . .	Have trouble with . . .	Should review and practice . . .
1–4	identifying and classifying figures.	SSG Lessons 5-1 and 5-2, pp. 180 and 187 CRM Skills Practice, pp. A88 and A93
5–8	finding the area of figures on grids.	SSG Lessons 5-3 and 5-4, pp. 195 and 201 CRM Skills Practice, pp. A97 and A101
9–10	finding the area of a parallelogram.	SSG Lesson 5-5, p. 209 CRM Skills Practice, p. A105
11–12	finding the area of a triangle.	SSG Lesson 5-6, p. 215 CRM Skills Practice, p. A109
13	finding the circumference and area of a circle.	SSG Lesson 5-7, p. 223 CRM Skills Practice, p. A113
14–16	solving word problems involving finding area.	CRM Problem-Solving Practice, pp. A106, A110, and A114

Chapter 5 Test Practice

Diagnose Student Errors

Survey student responses for each item. Class trends may indicate common errors and misconceptions.

1. A used radius in formula, $c = \pi d$
   (B) correct
   C doubled diameter in formula, $c = \pi d$
   D found area using diameter instead of radius
2. (A) correct
   B guess
   C guess
   D guess
3. A added dimensions
   (B) correct
   C miscalculated
   D miscalculated
4. A added dimensions and incorrect unit
   B incorrect unit
   (C) correct
   D multiplied by 2 instead of multiplying by $\frac{1}{2}$
5. A added dimensions
   B miscounted number of rows
   (C) correct
   D miscounted number of rows
6. A added dimensions
   B multiplied incorrectly
   C multiplied base times base
   (D) correct
7. A found perimeter
   B added dimensions
   (C) correct
   D multiplied incorrectly
8. A multiplied by $\frac{1}{4}$ instead of $\frac{1}{2}$
   (B) correct
   C did not multiply by $\frac{1}{2}$
   D multiplied by 2
9. A not a triangle
   (B) correct
   C acute triangle
   D no right angle

Chapter 5 Test Practice

Choose the best answer and fill in the corresponding circle on the sheet at right.

1 What is the circumference of the circle? Use 3.14 for π.

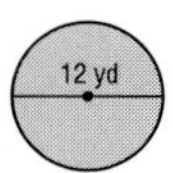

A 18.84 yd (B) 37.68 yd C 75.36 yd D 452.16 yd

2 Choose the correct name of the triangle by the measure of its angles.

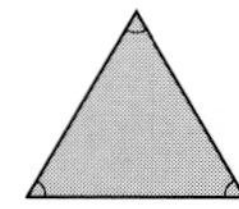

(A) acute triangle
B obtuse triangle
C right triangle
D none of the above

3 Devon has a parallelogram-shaped wallet. It has a base length of 9 cm and a height of 8 cm. What is the area of the wallet?

A 17 cm² (B) 72 cm² C 90 cm² D 144 cm²

4 What is the area of the triangle?

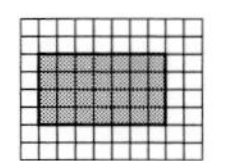

A 19 km B 44 km (C) 44 km² D 88 km²

5 What is the area of the figure?

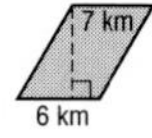

A 11 square units B 21 square units (C) 28 square units D 35 square units

6 What is the area of the parallelogram?

7 km
6 km

A 13 km² B 30 km² C 36 km² (D) 42 km²

7 Elliott's 9th grade class painted a wall of the gymnasium. The wall measures 10 feet by 36 feet. What is the area of this wall?

A 92 ft² B 46 ft² (C) 360 ft² D 3,600 ft²

238 Chapter 5 Test Practice

10. A forgot to square radius
    B found circumference
    C guess
    (D) correct
11. A no right angles
    B guess
    (C) correct
    D guess

8 What is the area of the triangle?

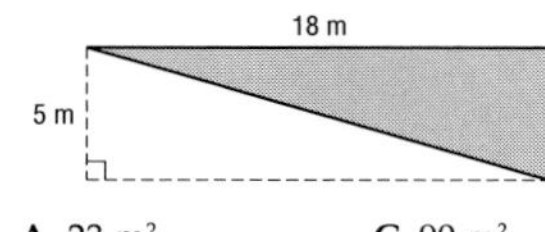

A 23 m^2 (B) 45 m^2 C 90 m^2 D 180 m^2

---

9 Which of the following shows a right scalene triangle?

A

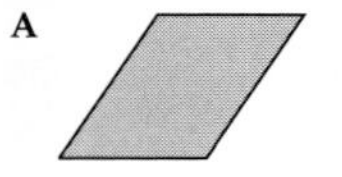

C

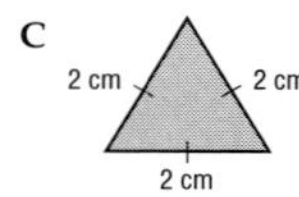

(B)

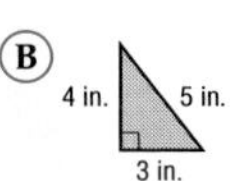

D

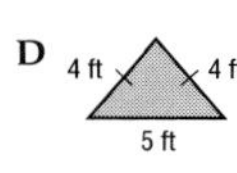

---

10 What is the area of the circle? Use 3.14 for π.

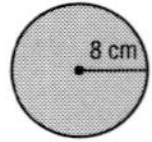

A 25.12 cm^2 B 50.24 cm^2 C 67.14 cm^2 (D) 200.96 cm^2

---

11 Choose the correct name of the figure.

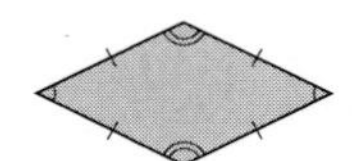

A rectangle   B triangle   (C) rhombus   D trapezoid

ANSWER SHEET

Directions: Fill in the circle of each correct answer.

1	A	●B	C	D
2	●A	B	C	D
3	A	●B	C	D
4	A	B	●C	D
5	A	B	●C	D
6	A	B	C	●D
7	A	B	●C	D
8	A	●B	C	D
9	A	●B	C	D
10	A	B	C	●D
11	A	B	●C	D

Success Strategy

Read the entire question before looking at the answer choices. Make sure you know what the question is asking.

Diagnosing Student Errors and Misconceptions

Scoring When working on the Test Practice problems, have students show their work on a separate sheet of notebook paper that can be used later as a reference as needed. After the class has completed the Test Practice problems, go over all the correct responses and have the students score their own responses.

Have students try to find and correct their mistakes. If they are still having trouble, try to determine whether the mistake was due to a basic computational error or whether there is a misunderstanding of the concept. Try to resolve as many of these errors as time permits.

Chapter 6

Chapter Overview

Chapter-at-a-Glance

Lesson	Math Objective	State/Local Standards
6-1 Introduction to Three-Dimensional Figures (pp. 242-246)	Classify three-dimensional figures.	
6-2 Surface Area of Rectangular Solids (pp. 247-255)	Determine surface area of prisms.	
Progress Check 1 (p. 256)		
6-3 Introduction to Volume (pp. 257-262)	Determine volume of prisms.	
6-4 Volume of Rectangular Solids (pp. 263-268)	Determine volume of prisms.	
Progress Check 2 (p. 269)		

Content-at-a-Glance

The diagram below summarizes and unpacks Chapter 6 content.

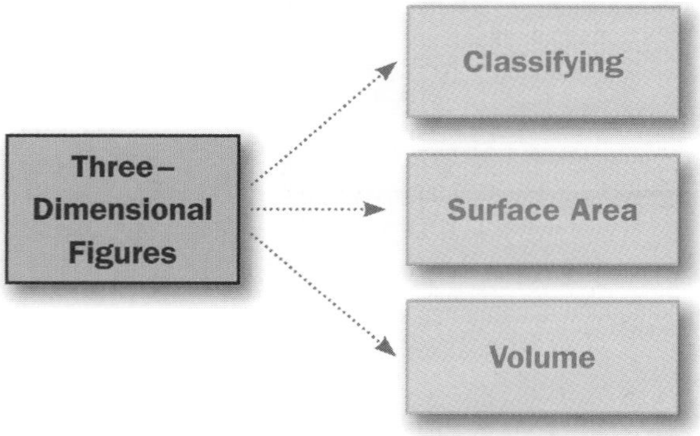

Online Assessment and Reporting
glencoe.com

Chapter Assessment Manager

Diagnostic

Diagnose students' readiness.

	Student Study Guide/ Teacher Edition	Assessment Masters	Technology
Course Placement Test		1	ExamView® Assessment Suite
Book 2 Pretest		62	ExamView® Assessment Suite
Chapter 6 Pretest		87	ExamView® Assessment Suite
Quiz/Preview	SSG 241		Math Online glencoe.com StudentWorks™ Plus

Formative

Identify students' misconceptions of content knowledge.

	Student Study Guide/ Teacher Edition	Assessment Masters	Technology
Progress Checks	SSG 256, 269		Math Online glencoe.com StudentWorks™ Plus
Vocabulary Review	SSG 270		Math Online glencoe.com
Lesson Assessments			ExamView® Assessment Suite
Are They Getting It?	TE 244, 250, 260, 266		Math Online glencoe.com

Summative

Determine student success in learning concepts in the lesson, chapter, or book.

	Student Study Guide/ Teacher Edition	Assessment Masters	Technology
Chapter 6 Test	SSG 274	90	ExamView® Assessment Suite
Test Practice	SSG 276	93	
Alternative Assessment	TE 274	96	ExamView® Assessment Suite
See It, Do It, Say It, Write It	TE 246, 255, 262, 268		
Book 2 Test		98	ExamView® Assessment Suite

Back-mapping and Vertical Alignment **McGraw-Hill's *Math Triumphs*** intervention program was conceived and developed with the final result in mind: student success in grade-level mathematics, including Algebra 1 and beyond. The authors, using the **NCTM Focal Points and Focal Connections** as their guide, developed this brand-new series by backmapping from grade-level and Algebra 1 concepts, and vertically aligning the topics so that they build upon prior skills and concepts and serve as a foundation for future topics.

Chapter Resource Manager

	Lesson 6-1	Lesson 6-2	Lesson 6-3	Lesson 6-4
Concept	Introduction to Three-Dimensional Figures	Surface Area of Rectangular Solids	Introduction to Volume	Volume of Rectangular Solids
Objective	Classify three-dimensional figures.	Determine surface area of prisms.	Determine volume of prisms.	Determine volume of prisms.
Math Vocabulary	congruent figures edge face three-dimensional figure vertex	face net square unit surface area	cube cubic unit rectangular prism volume	cube cubic unit volume
Lesson Resources	**Materials** • Compass • Construction paper • Ruler • Scissors • Tape **Manipulatives** • Connecting cubes • Geometric solids • Unit cubes **Other Resources** CRM Vocabulary and English Language Development CRM Skills Practice CRM Problem-Solving Practice CRM Homework Practice	**Materials** • Tissue box • Real-world solids • Index cards **Manipulatives** • Grid paper • Geometric solids • Base-ten blocks • Connecting cubes **Other Resources** CRM Vocabulary and English Language Development CRM Skills Practice CRM Problem-Solving Practice CRM Homework Practice	**Materials** • Real-world solids • Toy blocks **Manipulatives** • Geometric solids • Unit cubes **Other Resources** CRM Vocabulary and English Language Development CRM Skills Practice CRM Problem-Solving Practice CRM Homework Practice	**Materials** • Real-world solids **Manipulatives** • Geometric solids • Base-ten blocks • Unit cubes • Connecting cubes **Other Resources** CRM Vocabulary and English Language Development CRM Skills Practice CRM Problem-Solving Practice CRM Homework Practice
Technology	Math Online glencoe.com StudentWorks™ Plus ExamView® Assessment Suite	Math Online glencoe.com StudentWorks™ Plus ExamView® Assessment Suite	Math Online glencoe.com StudentWorks™ Plus ExamView® Assessment Suite	Math Online glencoe.com StudentWorks™ Plus ExamView® Assessment Suite

Intervention Strategy

Learn through Questioning

Have students work together to explore the properties of three-dimensional figures in an entertaining way that will help them to learn more effectively in a social, relaxed setting.

Step 1: Divide students evenly into groups of 4 to 6 students. Each group will choose a spokesperson.

Step 2: Secretly assign a three-dimensional figure to one group. This group will stand at the front of the class. Groups will take turns being in front of the class.

Step 3: The groups that remain seated will consult within their groups on a question to ask the group standing about their figure. Students must ask a question in a format that requires only a yes or no response. For example, instead of "How many bases does the figure have?" the question would be "Does the figure have 2 bases?" The spokesperson for each group will ask the agreed upon questions.

Step 4: The group that is standing will quietly discuss with one another before answering the questions asked, but only the spokesperson will answer.

Step 5: Rotate from group to group in an organized fashion, keeping track of the total number of questions asked. If 20 questions are asked and the figure has not been guessed, the standing group wins.

Step 6: Each time a group's figure is guessed, have all groups switch spokespersons so each student has an opportunity to be the speaker.

Step 7: Keep track of the times that students correctly guess a figure or stump the other groups.

Chapter Notes

Real-World Applications

Exercise A committee is trying to decide on which three-dimensional figures to use along an exercise trail as stretching/resting stations. Give advice as if you were hired by the committee. Justify your response using what you know about three-dimensional figures.

Intervention Strategy

Objects in our World

Step 1 Divide the class into small groups or pairs. Assign each group a three-dimensional figure that will be covered in this chapter. Tell each group to find a photograph that shows their figure.

Step 2 Place the photos around the room. Have students look at the designs and write down at least two comments regarding each figure that are related to a geometric property of the figure.

Step 3 Have a class discussion regarding the comments each group made. This can be a nice lead-in acitivity when discussing the attributes of each figure.

Three-Dimensional Figures

There are triangles, circles, rectangles, and other figures all around us.

You see figures every day. Everywhere you go there are different figures. Some may be flat, or solid. Shrubs can be formed into different three-dimensional figures.

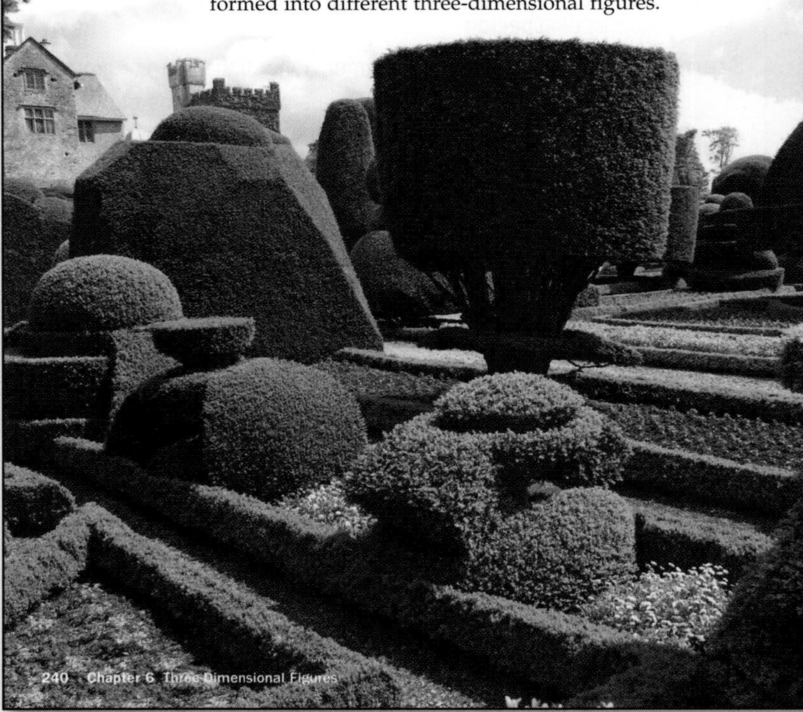

Key Vocabulary

Find interactive definitions in 13 languages in the **eGlossary** at glencoe.com.

English **Español** *Introduce the most important vocabulary terms from Chapter 6.*

edge **borde**

the line segment where two faces of a three-dimensional figure meet (p. 242)

face **cara**

the flat side of a three-dimensional figure (p. 242)

net **red**

a two-dimensional figure that can be used to build a three-dimensional figure (p. 247)

rectangular prism **prisma rectangular**

a three-dimensional figure that has two parallel and congruent bases in the shape of polygons (p. 257)

vertex **vértice**

the point on a three-dimensional figure where three or more edges meet (p. 242)

volume **volumen**

the amount of space that a three-dimensional figure contains (p. 257)

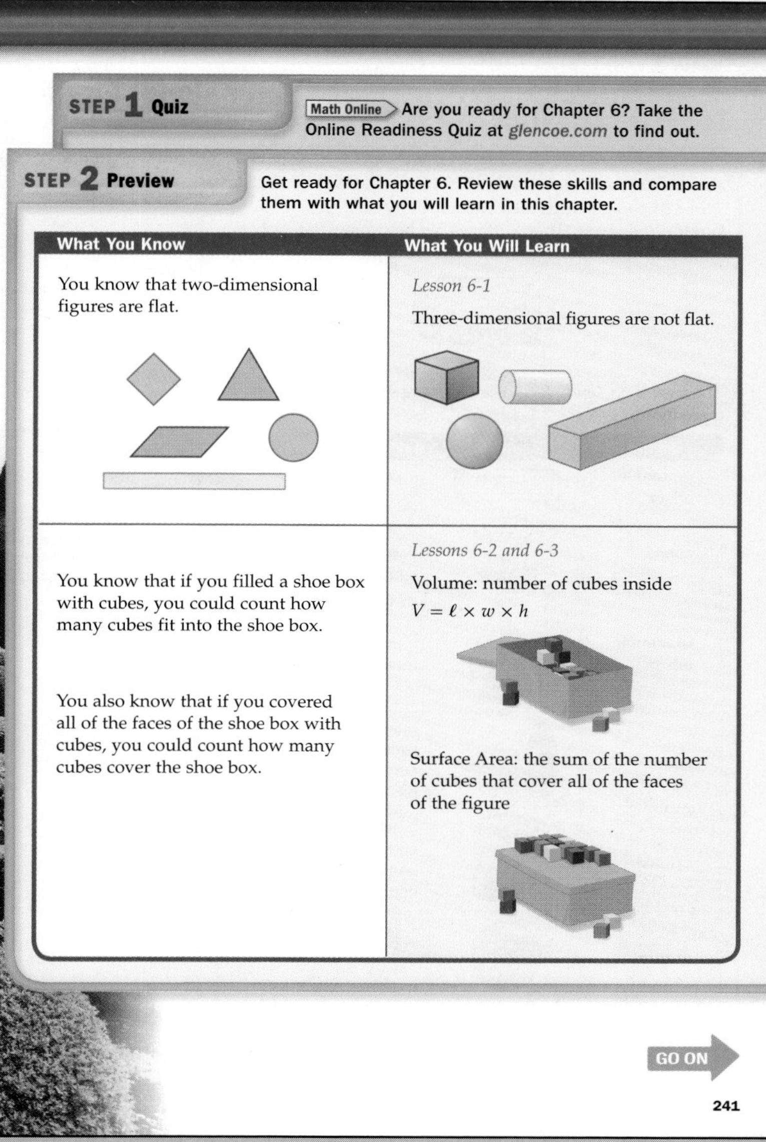

STEP 1 Quiz

Math Online Are you ready for Chapter 6? Take the Online Readiness Quiz at *glencoe.com* to find out.

STEP 2 Preview

Get ready for Chapter 6. Review these skills and compare them with what you will learn in this chapter.

What You Know	What You Will Learn
You know that two-dimensional figures are flat.	*Lesson 6-1* Three-dimensional figures are not flat.
You know that if you filled a shoe box with cubes, you could count how many cubes fit into the shoe box. You also know that if you covered all of the faces of the shoe box with cubes, you could count how many cubes cover the shoe box.	*Lessons 6-2 and 6-3* Volume: number of cubes inside $V = \ell \times w \times h$ Surface Area: the sum of the number of cubes that cover all of the faces of the figure

GO ON

241

Vocabulary Preview

- As students complete the Chapter Preview, have them make a list of important terms throughout the chapter. Include a sketch if appropriate.
- Using index cards, have students write terms on one side of the cards and definitions and sketches of terms on the other side. Ask them to also include any other information that will help them identify the figures.
- Once students are finished, have them trade their cards with other students to challenge their knowledge of the vocabulary in this chapter.

Step 1 Quiz

Pretest/Prescribe Students can take the Online Readiness Quiz or the Diagnostic Pretest in the Assessment Masters.

Step 2 Preview

Use this pre-chapter activity to activate students' prior knowledge, build confidence, and help students preview the lessons.

Dinah Zike's Foldables®

Guide students through the directions on p. A116 in the Chapter Resource Masters to create their own Foldable graphic organizer for use with this chapter.

Home Connections

Ask students to look around their homes and write down at least five different items that represent three-dimensional figures that they see or use regularly.

Have students talk to their parents or caregivers to write down one example of how three-dimensional figures play a part in their everyday lives. Have students share their examples with the class.

Mc Graw Hill
Professional Development
Targeted professional development has been articulated throughout McGraw-Hill's Math Triumphs intervention program. The McGraw-Hill Professional Development Video Library provides short videos that support the NCTM Focal Points and Focal Connections. For more information, visit glencoe.com.
Model Lessons
Instructional Strategies

Lesson 6-1

Lesson Notes

Lesson Planner

Objective Classify three-dimensional figures.

Vocabulary **congruent**, **edge**, **face**, **three-dimensional figure**, **vertex**

Materials/Manipulatives circle compass, connecting cubes, construction paper, geometric solids, ruler, scissors, tape, unit cubes

Chapter Resource Masters

- CRM Vocabulary and English Language Development (p. A119)
- CRM Skills Practice (p. A120)
- CRM Problem-Solving Practice (p. A121)
- CRM Homework Practice (p. A122)

Vocabulary

Explore Vocabulary Use a tissue box to demonstrate the location of the faces, vertices, and edges of a rectangular prism. Have students locate other rectangular prisms in the classroom and count the number of faces, vertices, and edges on these prisms. Students should share their findings with the class so that everyone realizes that all rectangular prisms have the same number of faces, vertices, and edges.

Key Concept

Foundational Skills and Concepts After students have read through the Key Concept box, have them try these exercises.

1. What two-dimensional figure represents the base of a cone? circle
2. How many faces are there in a triangular prism? 5
3. How many faces are on a cube? 6

Lesson 6-1

Introduction to Three-Dimensional Figures

KEY Concept

Three-dimensional figures are named by the types of surfaces they have. Their surfaces can be curved, flat, or both.

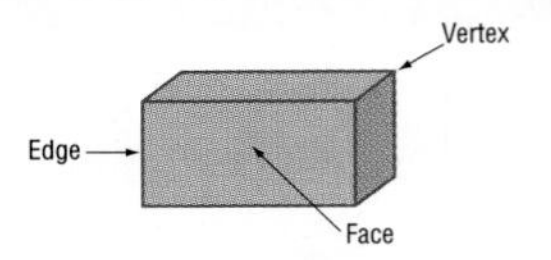

The base is an "end" face. The bases are shaded in the first three figures below.

Figure	Example	Description
rectangular prism		a prism with six rectangular faces
cube		a prism with six faces that are congruent squares
triangular prism		a prism that has triangular bases
cone		a solid that has a circular base and one curved surface from the base to a vertex
cylinder		a solid with two parallel, congruent, circular bases; a curved surface connects the bases
sphere		a solid figure that is a set of all points that are the same distance from the center

VOCABULARY

congruent figures figures having the same size and the same shape

edge the line segment where two faces of a three-dimensional figure meet

face the flat side of a three-dimensional figure

three-dimensional figure a solid figure that has length, width, and height

vertex the point on a three-dimensional figure where three or more edges meet

242 Chapter 6 Three-Dimensional Figures

Intervention Strategy — Visual Learners

Figures in the Media Gather enough magazines, newspapers, and catalogs so that each student can have at least one, preferably two. Instruct students to find images of the objects that are shaped like each of the three-dimensional figures in this lesson. Ask students to locate at least two images of each figure. Have the students discuss how the images are the same and how the images are different.

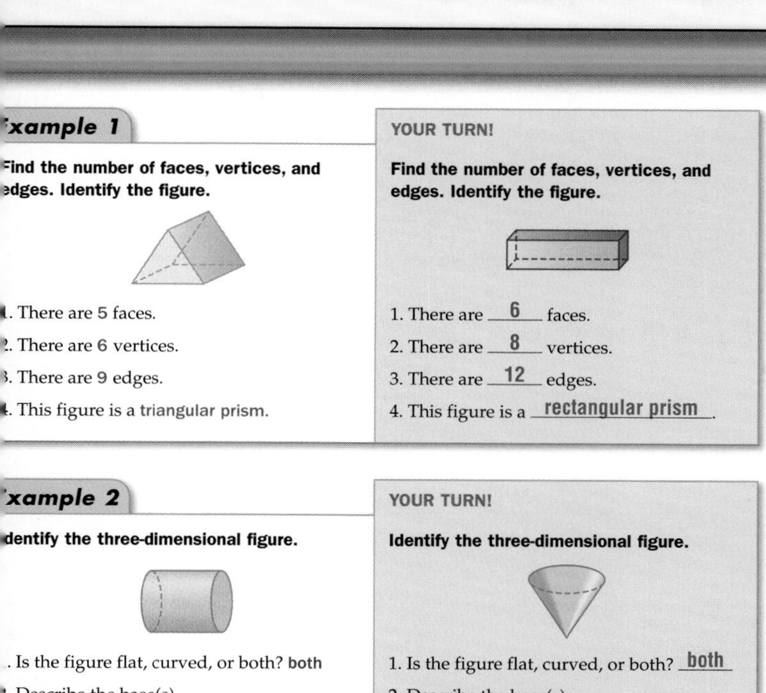

xample 1

Find the number of faces, vertices, and edges. Identify the figure.

1. There are 5 faces.
2. There are 6 vertices.
3. There are 9 edges.
4. This figure is a triangular prism.

YOUR TURN!

Find the number of faces, vertices, and edges. Identify the figure.

1. There are 6 faces.
2. There are 8 vertices.
3. There are 12 edges.
4. This figure is a rectangular prism.

xample 2

dentify the three-dimensional figure.

1. Is the figure flat, curved, or both? both
2. Describe the base(s). two congruent circular bases
3. The figure is a cylinder.

YOUR TURN!

Identify the three-dimensional figure.

1. Is the figure flat, curved, or both? both
2. Describe the base(s). one circular base
3. The figure is a(n) cone.

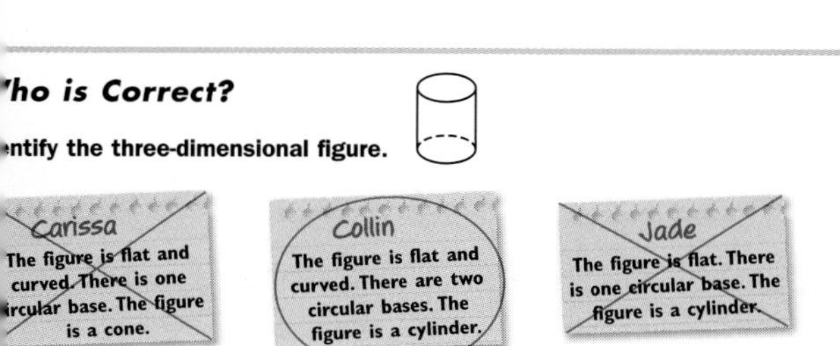

ho is Correct?

ntify the three-dimensional figure.

cle correct answer(s). Cross out incorrect answer(s).

Carissa
The figure is flat and curved. There is one circular base. The figure is a cone.
Collin
The figure is flat and curved. There are two circular bases. The figure is a cylinder.
Jade
The figure is flat. There is one circular base. The figure is a cylinder.

GO ON

Lesson 6-1 Introduction to Three-Dimensional Figures 243

Additional *Example 1*

Find the number of faces, vertices, and edges. Identify the figure.

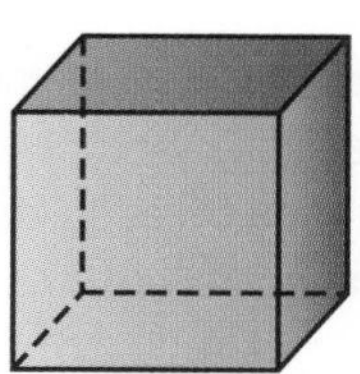

1. How many faces? 6
2. How many vertices? 8
3. How many edges? 12
4. The figure is a rectangular prism.
5. The faces appear to be congruent, so the figure is also a cube.

Additional *Example 2*

Identify the three-dimensional figure.

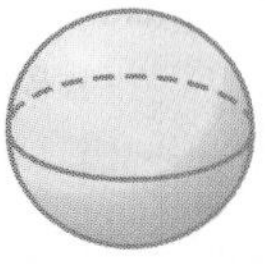

1. Is the figure flat, curved, or both? curved
2. Describe the base(s). There is no base.
3. The figure is a sphere.

Who *is Correct?*

Diagnostic Teaching

- Carissa is incorrect. A cone has a vertex and the given figure does not have a vertex.
- Collin is correct.
- Jade is incorrect. The figure is curved and it has two circular bases.

Remind students that any figure with a curved surface is not a prism.

Math Coach Notes

New Vocabulary The concept of an edge, face, or vertex of a figure is new to students, as are many concepts in this chapter. Stress the importance of learning the vocabulary. Assist students by periodically quizzing them on the vocabulary.

3 Practice

Using Manipulatives

Geometric Solids Use geometric models to show students three-dimensional views of a cube, rectangular prism, sphere, cone, and cylinder. Make sure to point out the bases on the models as well as the faces, edges, and vertices.

Unit Cubes/Connecting Cubes Allow students to experiment with rectangular prisms using unit cubes. Students can see how the shape may change, but the number of faces, edges, and vertices remain the same as long as the shape of the base is the same.

On-Hand Manipulatives Have students practice constructing their own geometric solids by creating the faces and bases on grid paper and then assembling the solids. The models will also help students study for tests and quizzes.

Intervention Strategy — Kinesthetic Learners

Sketching Figures Students will need to be able to sketch three-dimensional shapes for their assignments. Give the following guidelines for how to draw each type of figure.

Prisms (of any kind) – draw one base; draw the second base to match, but offset slightly from the first; draw straight lines to connect the vertices.

Cylinder – draw an oval; draw a second oval to match slightly above the first oval; draw a straight line on the outside of both sides of the ovals so that the line just touches the ovals.

Cone – draw an oval; place a point above the oval; draw a straight line from the point to each side of the oval.

Sphere – draw a circle; draw an oval inside the circle so that it touches the circle in two places.

Guided Practice

Find the number of faces, vertices, and edges.

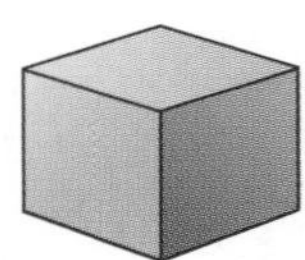

1. Count the faces. There are 6 faces.
   Count the vertices. There are 8 vertices.
   Count the edges. There are 12 edges.

Step by Step Practice

2. Identify the three-dimensional figure.

   Step 1 Is the figure flat, curved, or both? flat

   Step 2 Describe the base(s). rectangular and opposite sides are congruent

   Step 3 The figure is a(n) rectangular prism.

Identify each three-dimensional figure.

3. 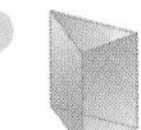

   The figure is flat.

   Describe the base(s). triangular and bases are congruent

   The figure is a(n) triangular prism.

4. 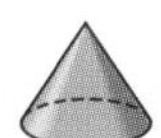

   The figure is curved and flat

   Describe the base(s). one circular bas

   The figure is a(n) cone

5. 

   The figure is flat.

   Describe the base(s). square and all sides are congruent

   The figure is a(n) cube.

6. 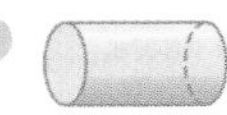

   The figure is curved and flat

   Describe the base(s). two congruent bases

   The figure is a(n) cylinder

244 **Chapter 6** Three-Dimensional Figures

Are They Getting It?

Check students' understanding of three-dimensional figures by writing these problems on the board. Have students explain the incorrect information in each problem.

1. Find the number of faces, vertices, and edges.
   - There are 5 faces. This is correct.
   - There are 3 vertices. This is incorrect. There are 6 vertices.
   - There are 9 edges. This is correct.
2. Identify the three-dimensional figure. The figure is a rectangular prism. This is incorrect. The two identical bases are triangles, so this is a triangular prism.

Step by Step Problem-Solving Practice

Solve.

Problem-Solving Strategies
- ☑ Use a diagram.
- ☐ Look for a pattern.
- ☐ Guess and check.
- ☐ Solve a simpler problem.
- ☐ Work backward.

7 PARTY Dante served a wedge of cheese at his party. The block of cheese is a three-dimensional figure. What is the name of the figure?

Understand Read the problem. Write what you know.
Dante served a wedge of cheese in the shape of a three-dimensional figure.

Plan Pick a strategy. One strategy is to use a diagram.

Solve Look at the photo. Describe the shape.
The figure has 2 triangular bases, 3 rectangular faces, 6 vertices, and 9 edges.

The three-dimensional figure is a triangular prism.

Check Compare the figure to other figures in the lesson.

8 HISTORY Samantha's 8th-grade class visited the Lincoln Memorial in Washington D.C. The columns of the structure are three-dimensional figures. What is the name of the three-dimensional figures? Check off each step.

✓ Understand: I underlined key words.

✓ Plan: To solve the problem, I will use a diagram.

✓ Solve: The answer is cylinders.

✓ Check: I will check my answer by comparing the figures in the lesson.

9 DINNER Benito's family had spaghetti and meatballs for dinner. He wanted to identify the shape of the meatballs. What figure are the meatballs? sphere

10 **Reflect** What is the difference between three-dimensional figures and two-dimensional figures? Explain. Give an example of each.

Sample answer: Three-dimensional figures have width, length, and height, and can be solid. Two-dimensional figures have only two of the three dimensions and are flat. A ball is a three-dimensional figure. A circle is a two-dimensional figure.

GO ON

Lesson 6-1 Introduction to Three-Dimensional Figures 245

Math Coach Notes

Self-Check The concepts introduced in this lesson and chapter are often difficult ones for students. If students are having difficulty, perform a self-check to see what other strategies might help them. Ask yourself some of the following questions:

- Do I clearly establish the purpose for learning these concepts?
- What is the area in which my students struggle consistently?
- What am I doing to address this?
- What types of assessments do I give students?
- What information do the results of these assessments give me?
- How am I using that information to improve students' comprehension?
- Am I modeling concepts and assignments?
- Am I providing examples to show students how to do the problems?

Reference Cards On one side of an index card draw a three-dimensional figure. On the other side of the card, list the distinguishing attributes. List any other important facts relating to the figure. To study, take turns with each side of the card to make sure that students are comfortable with the information.

English Learner Strategy

Guiding Questions Draw a cylinder and a cone. Then ask the students the following questions.

- Which figure is a cylinder?
- What figure has only one vertex?
- How many circular bases does the cylinder have?
- How many circular bases does the cone have?

Note This!

Draw and Label Several terms used with three-dimensional figures are introduced in this lesson. Encourage students to draw each figure and label the edges, faces, vertices, bases, and any additional information that helps them distinguish the shapes.

Odd/Even Assignments

Exercises 11–18 are structured so that students practice the same concepts whether they are assigned the odd or even problems.

In-Class Assignment

Have students complete Exercises 11, 14, 17, and 21 to ensure that they understand the concept.

See It, Do It, Say It, Write It

Step 1 Draw a rectangular prism on the board. Ask the students to identify as many parts of the prism as they can.

Step 2 Ask the students to draw a cone. Have the students justify why the figure they have drawn is a cone.

Step 3 In pairs, ask students to take turns choosing a figure and then reciting the most common attributes.

Step 4 In their math journals, have students write down the important information about each figure that distinguishes it from the other. Also list similarities in figures that will help students classify them.

Looking Ahead: Pre-teach

Surface Area of Rectangular Solids In the next lesson, students will learn about the surface area of a rectangular solid. Show students a cube and a rectangular prism. The sum of the area of each of the six faces equals the surface area.

Example

What is the surface area of a cube that has one face with an area of 10 square units? 60 units^2

How many faces does a rectangular prism have? 6

Ask students: What is the surface area of each prism?

1. 52 units^2 **2.** 148 units^2

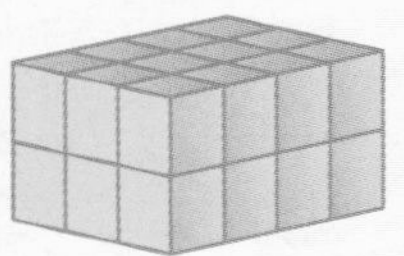

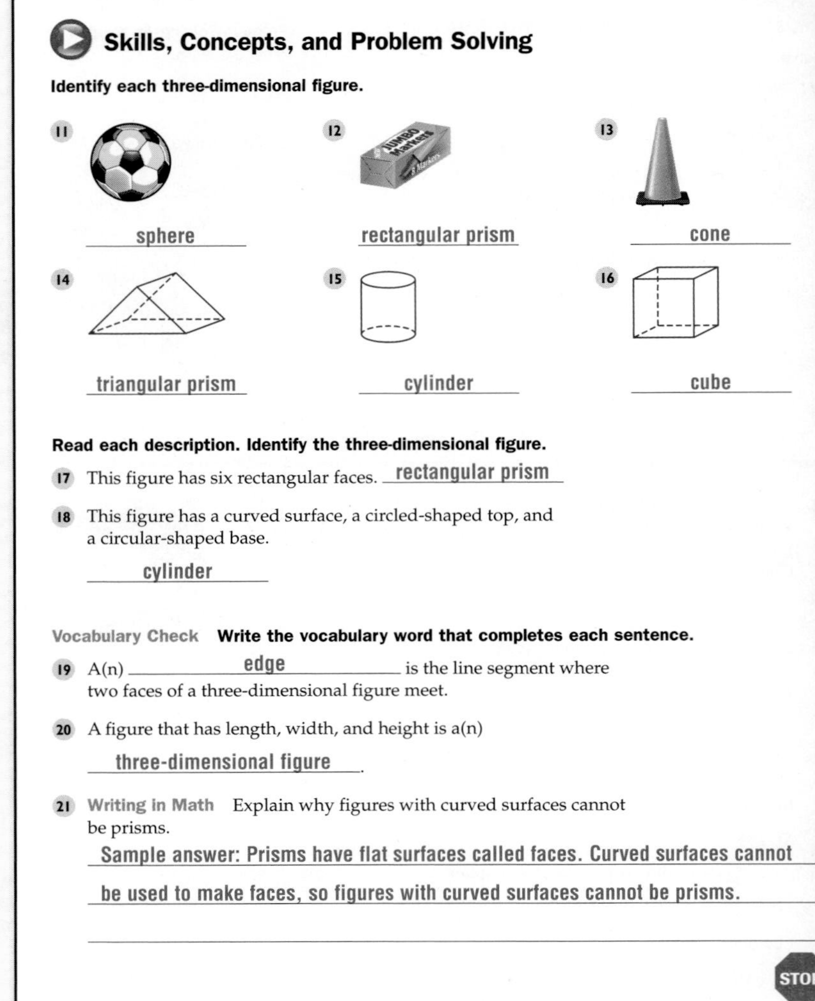

Skills, Concepts, and Problem Solving

Identify each three-dimensional figure.

11 sphere

12 rectangular prism

13 cone

14 triangular prism

15 cylinder

16 cube

Read each description. Identify the three-dimensional figure.

17 This figure has six rectangular faces. rectangular prism

18 This figure has a curved surface, a circled-shaped top, and a circular-shaped base.

cylinder

Vocabulary Check **Write the vocabulary word that completes each sentence.**

19 A(n) edge is the line segment where two faces of a three-dimensional figure meet.

20 A figure that has length, width, and height is a(n) three-dimensional figure.

21 Writing in Math Explain why figures with curved surfaces cannot be prisms.

Sample answer: Prisms have flat surfaces called faces. Curved surfaces cannot be used to make faces, so figures with curved surfaces cannot be prisms.

STOP

246 Chapter 6 Three-Dimensional Figures

Ticket Out the Door

Drawing Three-Dimensional Figures Have students sketch one of the three-dimensional figures in this lesson. Below the sketch, they should write the name of the figure, the number of faces, the number of vertices, and the number of edges. Students should turn in their sketches as they exit the room.

Lesson 6-2

Surface Area of Rectangular Solids

KEY Concept

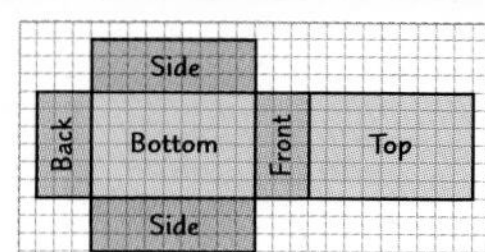

The **net** can be folded to make a rectangular prism.

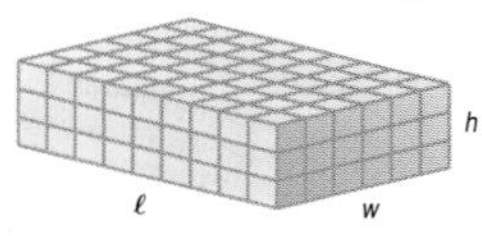

The **surface area** of a rectangular prism is the sum of the areas of all the **faces** of the figure. A rectangular prism has six faces.

The following formula can be used to find surface area:

$S = (\ell \times w) + (\ell \times h) + (w \times h) + (\ell \times w) + (\ell \times h) + (w \times h)$

VOCABULARY

face
the flat part of a three-dimensional figure

net
a two-dimensional figure that can be used to build a three-dimensional figure

surface area
the sum of the areas of all the surfaces (faces) of a three-dimensional figure

square unit
a unit for measuring area

Example 1

Find the surface area of the rectangular prism.

1. Use a net of the rectangular prism.
2. Find the area of faces A and F.
   $A = \ell \times w$
   $A = 6 \times 5 = 30$
3. Find the area of faces B and D.
   $A = \ell \times w$
   $A = 5 \times 2 = 10$
4. Find the area of faces C and E.
   $A = \ell \times w$ $A = 6 \times 2 = 12$
5. Find the sum of all the areas of all the faces. $30 + 10 + 12 + 30 + 10 + 12 = 104$

The surface area of the rectangular prism is 104 square units.

Additional Example 1

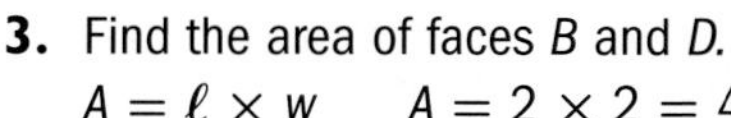

Find the surface area of the rectangular prism.

1. Use a net of the rectangular prism.
2. Find the area of faces A and F.
   $A = \ell \times w$ $A = 3 \times 2 = 6$
3. Find the area of faces B and D.
   $A = \ell \times w$ $A = 2 \times 2 = 4$
4. Find the area of faces C and E.
   $A = \ell \times w$ $A = 3 \times 2 = 6$
5. Find the sum of all the areas of all the faces. $6 + 4 + 6 + 6 + 4 + 6 = 32$

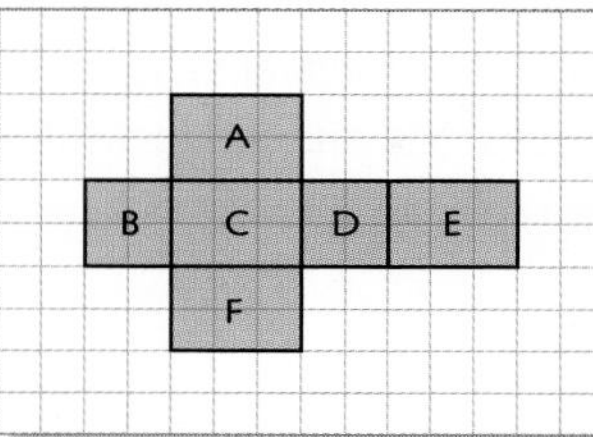

The surface area of the rectangular prism is 32 square units.

Lesson Notes

Lesson 6-2

Lesson Planner

Objective Determine surface area of prisms.

Vocabulary **face**, **net**, **square unit**, **surface area**

Materials/Manipulatives grid paper, geometric solids, base-ten blocks, connecting cubes, tissue box, real-world solids, index cards

Chapter Resource Masters

- CRM Vocabulary and English Language Development (p. A123)
- CRM Skills Practice (p. A124)
- CRM Problem-Solving Practice (p. A125)
- CRM Homework Practice (p. A126)

1 Introduce

Vocabulary

Demonstrate Vocabulary Use an empty cardboard box as a visual for the class. Ask students to imagine unfolding the box so that it can lay flat. Have students make a drawing of what they think the box will look like when it lays out flat. Then carefully break the box down and lay it flat. Discuss how closely the students drawings match the unfolded box and why there might be differences.

2 Teach

Key Concept

Foundational Skills and Concepts After students have read through the Key Concept box, have them try these exercises.

1. How many faces does a rectangular solid have? 6
2. How many faces are used to find the surface area of a rectangular prism? 6

Additional *Example 2*

Find the surface area of the cube.

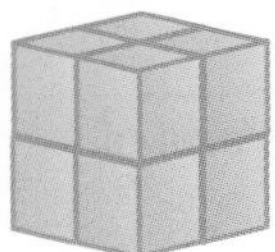

1. Find the area of each face.

$A = \ell \times w$
$A = 2 \times 2 = 4$

2. There are six faces on the cube. Find the sum of the areas of all six faces.

$4 + 4 + 4 + 4 + 4 + 4 = 24$

The surface area of the cube is 24 square units.

Math Coach Notes

Formulas Some students will benefit from having a formula so that they can substitute values for variables and compute. Guide students to see that formulas for the areas of the faces are $A = \ell \times w$, $A = \ell \times h$, and $A = w \times h$; and that there are two of each of these faces. The formula can be written as $SA = 2(\ell \times w) + 2(\ell \times h) + 2(w \times h)$ or $SA = 2(\ell \times w + \ell \times h + w \times h)$

YOUR TURN!

Find the surface area of the rectangular prism.

1. Use a net of the rectangular prism.
2. Find the area of faces A and F.

$A = \ell \times w$
$A =$ 3 $\times$ 6 $=$ 18

3. Find the area of faces B and D.

$A = \ell \times w$
$A =$ 6 $\times$ 5 $=$ 30

4. Find the area of faces C and E.

$A = \ell \times w$
$A =$ 3 $\times$ 5 $=$ 15

5. Find the sum of the areas of all the faces.

18 + 30 + 15 + 18 + 30 + 15 = 126

The surface area of the rectangular prism is 126 square units.

Example 2

Find the surface area of the cube.

1. Find the area of each face.

$A = \ell \times w$

$A = 3 \times 3 = 9$

2. There are six faces on the cube. Find the sum of the areas of all six faces.

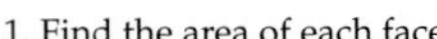

9 + 9 + 9 + 9 + 9 + 9 = 54

The surface area of the cube is 54 square units.

YOUR TURN!

Find the surface area of the cube.

1. Find the area of each face.

$A = \ell \times w$

$A =$ 4 $\times$ 4 $=$ 16

2. Find the sum of the areas of all six faces.

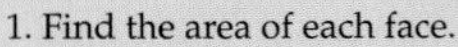

16 + 16 + 16 + 16 + 16 + 16 = 96

The surface area of the cube is 96 square units.

248 Chapter 6 Three-Dimensional Figures

Intervention Strategy — Linguistic/Interpersonal Learners

Students as Teacher/Teacher as Student Group students in pairs. Have each pair select a rectangular prism that is in the classroom or one that they can bring from home. The students should prepare a demonstration on how to find the surface area of their prism. You can become a member of the class and allow each pair to present their mini-lesson to the class. After each lesson, conduct a question/answer session where you and the other students ask questions and the presenters answer the questions.

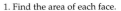

Vho is Correct?

ind the surface area of the rectangular prism.

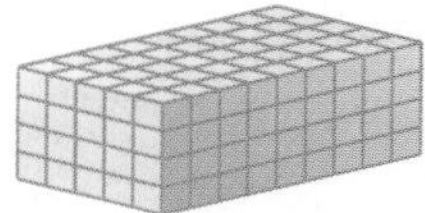

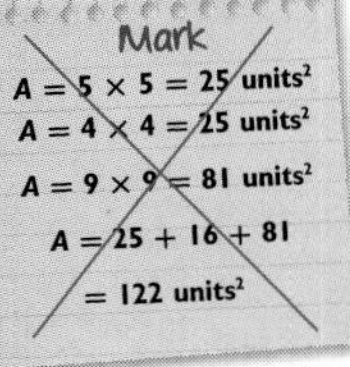

Mark
A = 5 × 5 = 25 units²
A = 4 × 4 = 25 units²
A = 9 × 9 = 81 units²
A = 25 + 16 + 81
= 122 units²

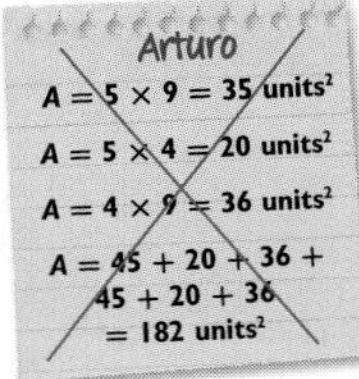

Arturo
A = 5 × 9 = 35 units²
A = 5 × 4 = 20 units²
A = 4 × 9 = 36 units²
A = 45 + 20 + 36 +
45 + 20 + 36
= 182 units²

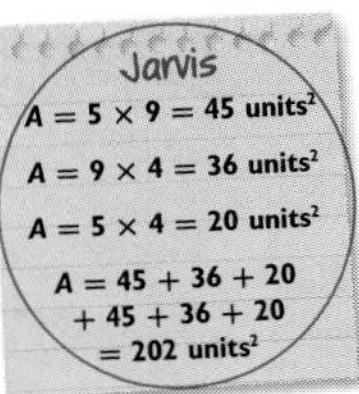

Jarvis
A = 5 × 9 = 45 units²
A = 9 × 4 = 36 units²
A = 5 × 4 = 20 units²
A = 45 + 36 + 20
+ 45 + 36 + 20
= 202 units²

ircle correct answer(s). Cross out incorrect answer(s).

Guided Practice

raw a net for a rectangular prism with the given length, width, id height.

$7 \times 8 \times 2$ **Sample answer:**

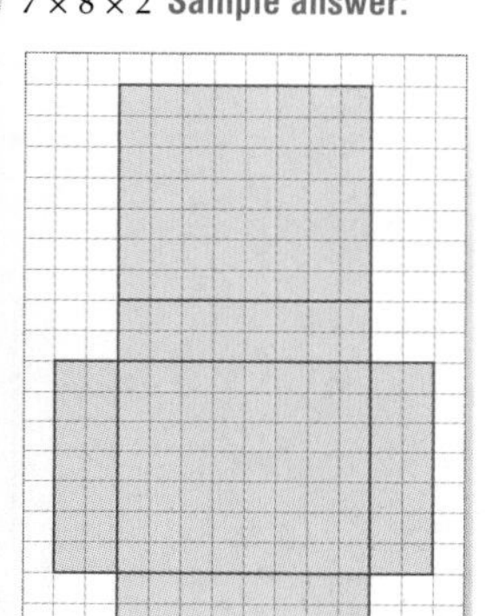

2 $3 \times 4 \times 2$ **Sample answer:**

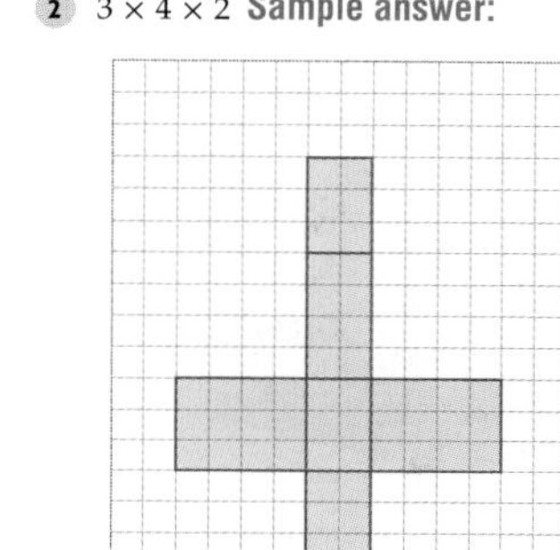

GO ON

Who *is Correct?*

Diagnostic Teaching

- Mark wrote 122 units². This is not correct because he multiplied each dimension by itself.
- Arturo wrote 182 units². This is not correct because he multiplied 5×9 for a product of 35, and it is 45.
- Jarvis wrote 202 units². This is correct.

Remind students that prisms have six faces so they will need to find the sum of six addends to find the surface area.

3 Practice

Base-Ten Blocks Base-ten blocks can be useful in showing prisms and surface area.

Grid Paper Use a solid and grid paper to make a net.

Connecting Cubes Increase the number of connecting cubes and note how the surface area changes.

Using Manipulatives

Geometric Solids When presenting Examples 1 and 2, model the solids. Show students how you can trace the sides of the faces to make the net, and then fill in the square units.

On-Hand Manipulatives Take six index cards and make a net. Use the net to make a prism.

Common Error *Alert*

Multi-Step Problems If students struggle with Exercises 1 and 2, it might be because they do not know what the dimensions of the figure represent. To remedy this problem, hold a prism and show students the height, the length, and the width. Now tell them to use blocks and build a prism with a height of 2 units, a length of 7 units, and a width of 8 units. Once they have made the figure, they can then draw the net. To check their work, encourage students to draw the answer on grid paper and use the net to make the prism. Does it match the figure they built? Does it have the correct dimensions?

Math Coach Notes

Connections When students use graph paper to create nets for the prism, point out to them that counting the number of units along each side of the rectangle and multiplying is the same thing as counting each unit in the rectangle.

Step by Step Practice

Find the surface area of the rectangular prism.

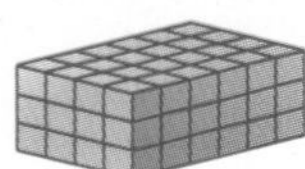

Step 1 Use a net of the rectangular prism.

Step 2 Find the area of faces A and F.

$A = \ell \times w$

$A = \underline{\ 4\ } \times \underline{\ 3\ } = \underline{\ 12\ }$

Step 3 Find the area of faces B and D.

$A = \ell \times w$

$A = \underline{\ 3\ } \times \underline{\ 6\ } = \underline{\ 18\ }$

Step 4 Find the area of faces C and E.

$A = \ell \times w$

$A = \underline{\ 4\ } \times \underline{\ 6\ } = \underline{\ 24\ }$

Step 5 Find the sum of the areas of all the faces.

$\underline{\ 12\ } + \underline{\ 18\ } + \underline{\ 24\ } + \underline{\ 12\ } + \underline{\ 18\ } + \underline{\ 24\ } = \underline{\ 108\ }$

The surface area of the rectangular prism is __108__ square units.

4 Find the surface area of the rectangular prism.

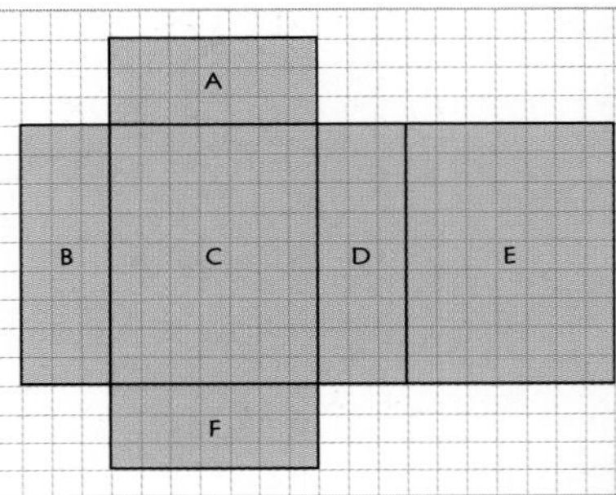

Use a net of the rectangular prism. Follow the steps at the top of page 251 to find the surface area. The surface area of the rectangular prism is __222__ square units.

Are They Getting It?

Check students' understanding of the surface area of rectangular solids by writing these problems on the board. Have students explain the incorrect information in each problem. Tell them to use a model or drawing to show why the answer is correct or not correct.

1. A cube that has a face with area 9 mm^2 has a total surface area of 54 mm^2. This is correct.
2. A rectangular prism with height 5 in., length 3 in., and width 4 in. has a surface area of 47 in^2. This is not correct because only three faces were used.
3. The surface area of this prism is 40 units^2. This is not correct. It is 76 units^2.

Find the area of faces A and F.
$A = \ell \times w$
$A = \underline{7} \times \underline{3} = \underline{21}$

Find the area of faces B and D.
$A = \ell \times w$
$A = \underline{3} \times \underline{9} = \underline{27}$

Find the area of faces C and E.
$A = \ell \times w$
$A = \underline{7} \times \underline{9} = \underline{63}$

Find the sum of the area of all the faces.

$\underset{A}{\underline{21}} + \underset{B}{\underline{27}} + \underset{C}{\underline{63}} + \underset{D}{\underline{21}} + \underset{E}{\underline{27}} + \underset{F}{\underline{63}} = \underline{222}$

The surface area of the rectangular prism is 222 square units.

ind the surface area of the rectangular prism.

Find the area of faces A and F.
$A = \ell \times w$
$A = \underline{7} \times \underline{9} = \underline{63}$

Find the area of faces B and D.
$A = \ell \times w$
$A = \underline{9} \times \underline{6} = \underline{54}$

Find the area of faces C and E.
$A = \ell \times w$
$A = \underline{7} \times \underline{6} = \underline{42}$

Find the sum of the area of all the faces.

$\underline{63} + \underline{54} + \underline{42} + \underline{63} + \underline{54} + \underline{42} = \underline{318}$

The surface area of the rectangular prism is 318 square units.

The surface area of the rectangular prism is 202 square units.

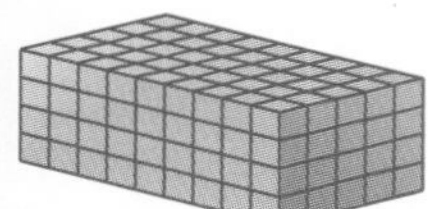

7 The surface area of the rectangular prism is 158 square units.

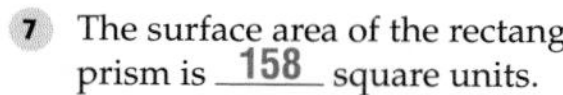

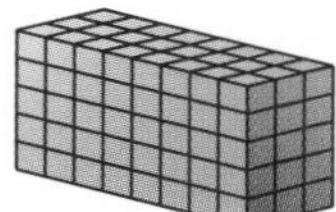

GO ON

Common Error *Alert*

Multi-Step Problem If students struggle with finding the surface area of the figure in Exercise 5, they may benefit from using a sheet of grid or dot paper to make a net. First, have them number the sides of the figure. Then, have them outline each one and create the net. Finally, have them find the area of each face as directed to solve the problem.

Intervention Strategy Naturalistic Learners

Naming Units

1. Remind students that area is a two-dimensional measure, and therefore measured in square units. Many students struggle with this idea for surface area because they are working with three-dimensional figures. Relate the idea of surface area to wrapping a birthday gift box, and the wrapping paper they use has a length and width.
2. Point out to students that the examples have been given in units, not specifically inches, feet, centimeters, etc. Explain that when a unit is given with the measurement, then the answer needs to be given using that specific unit squared. For example, when the dimensions are given in meters, the surface area should be given in square meters.

Note This!

Showing Steps Suggest to students that they include each step of an example in their notes with call out boxes describing the action being taken. This will help when students return after several weeks or even months to review this topic.

Intervention Strategy

Logical Learners

More Than One Way Give an example of a prism. Ask students to identify the dimensions. Choose three students who identified the dimensions differently. Then have these students show their work on the board to find the surface area of the prism. Discuss how each answer is the same even though they used the dimensions differently.

Step by Step Problem-Solving Practice

Solve.

8 TISSUES Megan bought a box of tissues shaped like a cube. Each side measures 6 inches. What is the surface area of the box of tissues?

Understand Read the problem. Write what you know. Each side of the box of tissues is __6__ inches.

Plan Pick a strategy. One strategy is to draw a diagram. Use a net of the cube.

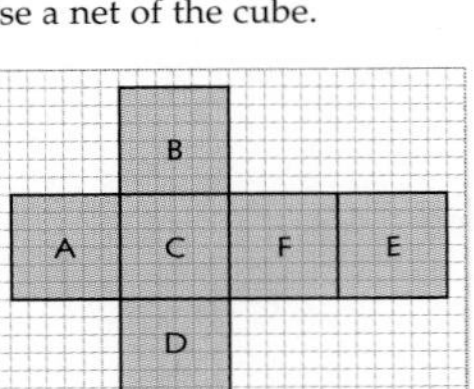

Solve Find the area of each face.

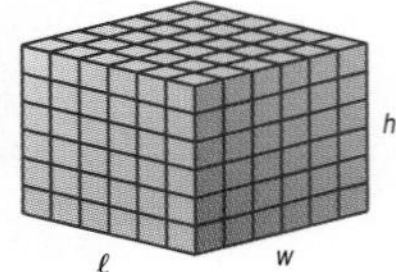

$A = \ell \times w$

$A =$ __6__ $\times$ __6__ $=$ __36__

Find the sum of the areas of all the faces.

__36__ + __36__ + __36__ + __36__ +
__36__ + __36__ = __216__

The surface area of Megan's box of tissues is __216__ square inches.

Check Use a calculator to check your multiplication and addition.

252 Chapter 6 Three-Dimensional Figures

English Learner Strategy

Guiding Questions Set out a rectangular prism and a cube. Then ask the following questions. Point to the rectangular prism.

- Point to an edge and ask if this edge is the length, the width, or the height of the prism. Discuss that their answers may depend on how they "see" the prism.
- Point to a face and ask if this edge is the length by the width, the length by the height, or the width by the height. Again, discuss that their answers may depend on how they "see" the prism.
- Guide students to realize that if they view the prism differently than another person, their calculated surface areas will be equal. Multiplication is commutative so the order the factors are multiplied does not affect their products.

PETS Julieta put her pet hamster in the aquarium shown. What is the surface area of the aquarium? Check off each step.

✔ Understand: I underlined the key words.

✔ Plan: To solve this problem, I will draw a diagram.

✔ Solve: The answer is 736 in^2.

✔ Check: I checked my answer by using a calculator to check multiplication and addition.

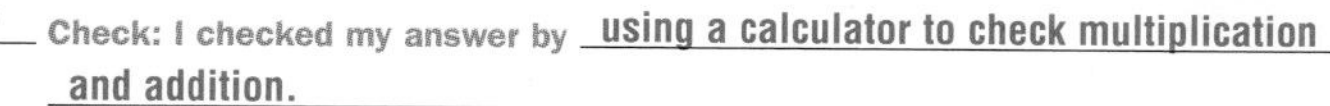

GEOMETRY What is the surface area of a number cube that has 13 millimeter edges? 1,014 mm^2

Reflect Use what you know about finding the area of triangles and rectangles to find the surface area of this triangular prism. (Hint: This triangular prism has 2 sides that are triangles, and 3 sides that are rectangles.)

See TE margin.

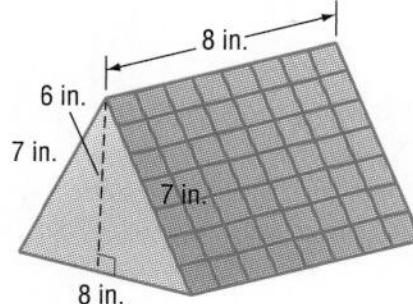

Skills, Concepts, and Problem Solving

...w a net for a rectangular prism with the given length, width, ... height.

$4 \times 4 \times 8$ Sample answer:

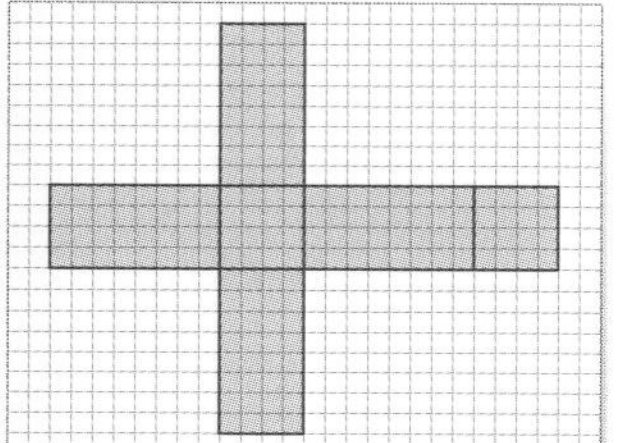

13 $3 \times 5 \times 7$ Sample answer:

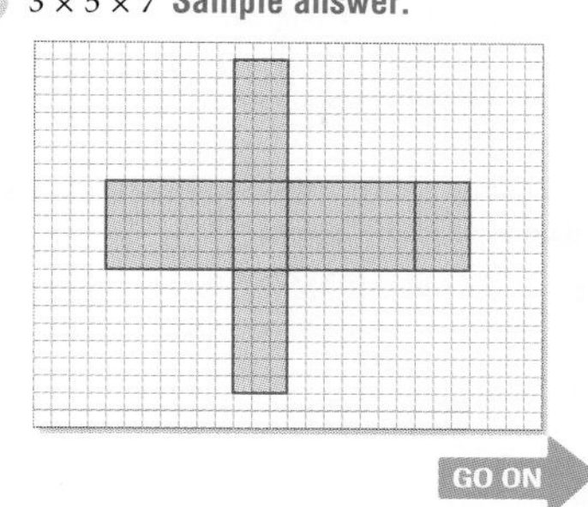

GO ON

Common Error *Alert*

Triangular Prisms Students need to include in their notes a heading for prisms, draw a rectangular prism and a triangular prism under it, and label the drawings. Next, draw a triangular pyramid and a square pyramid and put an ✗ over them. These figures are not prisms. Students have a tendency to confuse triangular prisms with pyramids.

Additional Answer

Exercise 11 To find the area of the triangles, use the formula $A = \frac{1}{2} \times b \times h$. Since $\frac{1}{2} \times 8 \times 6 = 24$, the area of each triangle is 24 in^2. To find the area of the rectangles, use the formula $A = \ell \times w$. Two of the rectangles have a length of 8 and a width of 7. The area is $8 \times 7 = 56$ in^2. The third rectangle has a length of 8 and a width of 8. The area is $8 \times 8 = 64$ in^2. To find the surface area of the triangular prism, add the area of each side. Since $24 + 24 + 56 + 56 + 64 = 224$, the surface area is 224 in^2.

Odd/Even Assignments

Exercises 12–19 are structured so that students practice the same concepts whether they are assigned the odd or even problems.

In-Class Assignment

Have students complete Exercises 12, 15, 19, and 23 to ensure that they understand the concept.

Math Coach Notes

Label the Sides When learning about surface area, encourage students to label the faces of the figure and write the area of that side next to the letter or number. This will help students organize their work and determine which areas of the figure still need to be determined. They may also use colored pencils to color-code the faces.

Find the surface area of each rectangular prism.

14 The surface area of the rectangular prism is **160** square units.

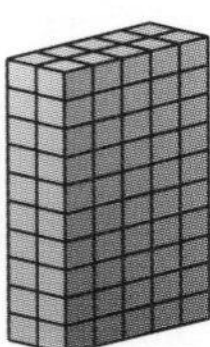

15 The surface area of the rectangular prism is **340** square units.

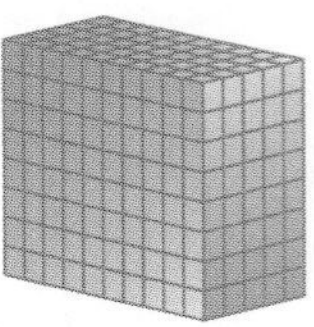

16 The surface area of the rectangular prism is **216** square units.

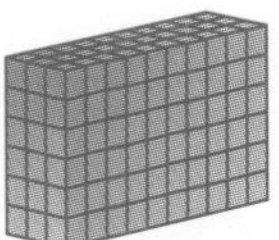

17 The surface area of the rectangular prism is **254** square units.

Solve.

18 ALARM CLOCK Juanita bought the alarm clock shown. What is the surface area of the alarm clock? **1,176 cm²**

ALARM CLOCK **Juanita's alarm clock is shaped like a cube. The sides measure 14 centimeters each.**

19 ART Quinn decorated a rectangular-shaped chest with wallpaper. The length of the chest is 4 feet, the width is 6 feet, and the height is 3 feet. What is the least amount of wallpaper Quinn used? **108 ft²**

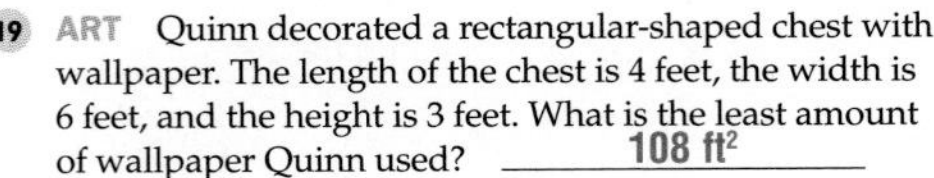

Vocabulary Check **Write the vocabulary word that completes each sentence.**

20 **Surface area** is the sum of the areas of all the surfaces (faces) of a three-dimensional figure.

21 A(n) **net** is a two-dimensional figure that can be used to build a three-dimensional figure.

22 A(n) **face** is the flat side of a three-dimensional figure.

Math Challenge

Triangular Prism Refer students to Question 11 in the exercises. Have students use graph paper to draw a net for this triangular prism. Then they can show the calculations for the area of each face and the calculation for the surface area of the prism.

3 **Writing in Math** Explain how to find the surface area of a rectangular prism.

Sample answer: To find the surface area of a rectangular prism, find the sum of the areas of all the faces of the rectangular prism.

Spiral Review

Identify each three-dimensional figure. (Lesson 6-1, p. 242)

4 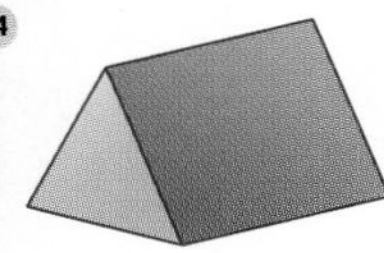

Count the faces. There are 5 faces.

Count the vertices. There are 6 vertices.

Count the edges. There are 9 edges.

5 

The figure is curved and flat.

Describe the base(s). circular and congruent

The figure is a(n) cylinder.

6 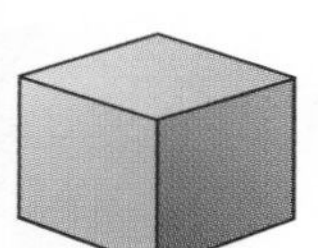

The figure is flat.

Describe the bases. square and opposite sides are congruent

The figure is a(n) rectangular prism.

Solve.

7 GEOGRAPHY Elena's geography class is learning how to find countries on the globe. Her teacher asks her to find Algeria. What figure is the globe? sphere

8 DONATIONS Rose's school is donating food to the local shelter. She brought in soup cans to donate. What figure are the soup cans she donated? cylinder

STOP

Lesson 6-2 Surface Area of Rectangular Solids 255

Ticket Out the Door

Surface Area Given Give students the dimensions of a rectangular prism. Students should draw a net, label the dimensions, and show the calculation to find the surface area. Have students turn in papers as they exit the classroom.

See It, Do It, Say It, Write It

Step 1 Draw a cube on grid paper using an overhead. Show students how you can add the area of the faces to get the total surface area. Is there a way to multiply to arrive at the answer quicker? Now draw a rectangular solid. Point out the dimensions. Have students help you calculate the surface area. Repeat this several times with cubes and prisms.

Step 2 Have students work in pairs. Give them rectangular prisms of varying dimensions. Ask them to draw a net. Then give them only the dimensions of another prism and have them draw another net.

Step 3 Give each student the dimensions of a rectangular prism. Ask students to explain the method they would use to draw a net for the figure.

Step 4 Have students draw the net of the prism with the given dimensions. Tell them to find the surface area.

Looking Ahead: Pre-teach

Introduction to Volume In the next lesson, students will learn how to find the volume of an object.

Example

What is the volume of the rectangular prism?

1. Count the number of layers of cubes in the prism.
   2 layers
2. Count the number of cubes in the top layer.
   6 cubes
3. Each layer has the same number of cubes.
   $6 + 6 = 12$ cubes

The volume of the rectangular prism is 12 cubic units.

Chapter 6

Progress Check 1

Formative Assessment

Use the Progress Check to assess students' mastery of the previous lessons. Have students review the lesson indicated for the problems they answered incorrectly.

Odd/Even Assignments

Exercises are structured so that students practice the same concepts whether they are assigned the odd or even problems.

Common Error *Alert*

Exercises 3–4 Students may have difficulty visualizing how to draw a net when given its dimensions. Remind them of what the dimensions represent and how it will help to think of the net as several pieces or sides of the prism flattened out and laid together.

Exercises 5–6 Students may forget one or more of the sides when totaling the prism's surface area. Remind students that a rectangular prism has 6 sides.

Chapter 6

Progress Check 1 (Lessons 6-1 and 6-2)

Identify each three-dimensional figure.

1 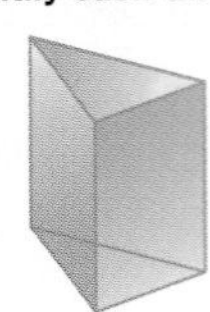 triangular prism

2 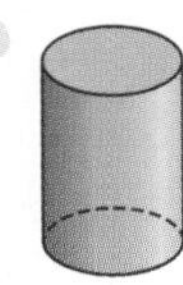 cylinder

Draw a net for a rectangular prism with the given length, width, and height.

3 $3 \times 7 \times 6$ Sample answer:

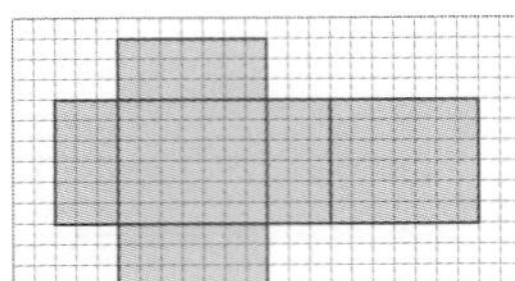

4 $2 \times 8 \times 5$ Sample answer:

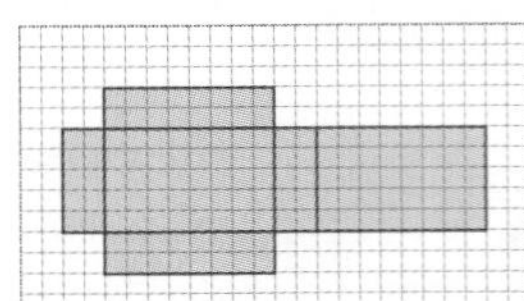

Find the surface area of each rectangular prism.

5 The surface area of the rectangular prism is 268 square units.

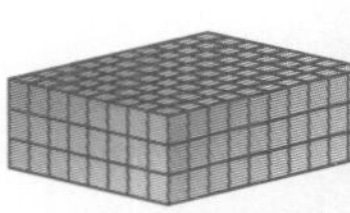

6 The surface area of the rectangular prism is 178 square units.

Solve.

7 **ART** Ms. Jackson asked her students to draw three-dimensional figures. She told students to use objects as models for their figures. Maurice decided to draw a cereal box. What three-dimensional figure did Maurice draw?

rectangular prism

8 **STORAGE** A storage cabinet is 24 inches wide, 26 inches long, and 40 inches high. What is the surface area of the storage cabinet?

5,248 in^2

256 **Chapter 6** Three-Dimensional Figures

Data-Driven Decision Making

Students missing Exercises . . .	Have trouble with . . .	Should review and practice . . .
1–2	identifying a three-dimensional figure.	SSG Lesson 6-1, p. 242 CRM Skills Practice, p. A120
3–4	drawing a net given its dimensions.	SSG Lesson 6-2, p. 247 CRM Skills Practice, p. A124
5–6	finding the surface area of a prism.	SSG Lesson 6-2, p. 247 CRM Skills Practice, p. A124
7–8	solving word problems involving three-dimensional figures and/or finding surface area of a prism.	CRM Problem-Solving Practice, pp. A121 and A125

Lesson 6-3 Introduction to Volume

KEY Concept

The amount of space inside a three-dimensional figure is the **volume** of the figure. Volume is measured in **cubic units**. To find the volume of a solid figure, determine the number of cubic units the solid figure contains.

One way to determine the volume of a **rectangular prism** is to think about the number of **cubes** in each layer.

This figure has 2 layers. Each layer has 9 cubes.

2 layers of 9 cubes = 9 + 9 = 18

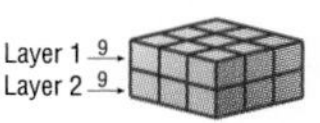

This rectangular prism has a volume of 18 cubic units.

VOCABULARY

cube a rectangular prism with six faces that are congruent squares

cubic unit used to measure volume; tells the number of cubes of a given size it will take to fill a three-dimensional figure

rectangular prism a three-dimensional figure that has two parallel and congruent bases in the shape of polygons; the shape of the bases tells the name of the prism

volume the amount of space that a three-dimensional figure contains; volume is expressed in cubic units

ıe volume of a figure is related to its dimensions, length, width, and height.

Example 1

Find the volume of the rectangular prism.

1. Count the number of cube layers in the prism. There are 2 layers of cubes. (Layer 1 8, Layer 2 8)
2. Count the number of cubes in the top layer. There are 8 cubes in the top layer.
3. Each layer has the same number of cubes. There are 8 + 8 = 16 cubes.

The volume of the rectangular prism is 16 cubic units.

YOUR TURN!

Find the volume of the rectangular prism.

1. Count the number of cube layers in the prism. There are __3__ layers of cubes. (Layer 1 4, Layer 2 4, Layer 3 4)
2. Count the number of cubes in the top layer. There are __4__ cubes in the top layer.
3. Each layer has the same number of cubes. There are __4__ + __4__ + __4__ = __12__ cubes.

The volume of the rectangular prism is __12__ cubic units.

GO ON

Lesson 6-3 Introduction to Volume 257

Additional Example 1

Find the volume of the rectangular prism.

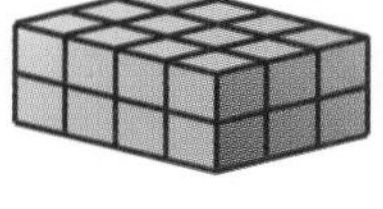

1. Count the number of cube layers in the prism. There are 2 layers of cubes.
2. Count the number of cubes in the top layer. There are 12 cubes in the top layer.
3. Each layer has the same number of cubes. There are 12 + 12 = 24 cubes.

The volume of the rectangular prism is 24 cubic units.

Lesson Notes

Lesson 6-3

Lesson Planner

Objective Determine volume of prisms.

Vocabulary **cube**, **cubic unit**, **rectangular prism**, **volume**

Materials/Manipulatives geometric solids, unit cubes, real-world solids, toy blocks

Chapter Resource Masters

- CRM Vocabulary and English Language Development (p. A127)
- CRM Skills Practice (p. A128)
- CRM Problem-Solving Practice (p. A129)
- CRM Homework Practice (p. A130)

1 Introduce

Vocabulary

Model Vocabulary Provide each student with 12 unit cubes. Explain that these 12 cubes have a combined *volume* of 12 cubic units. Ask students to rearrange the cubes to show a figure that has a volume of 12 cubic units. Share with the class the different figures that students made. Students could have made several different figures, including prisms with dimensions 1 by 1 by 12, 1 by 2 by 6, 1 by 3 by 4, and 2 by 2 by 3.

2 Teach

Key Concept

Foundational Skills and Concepts After students have read through the Key Concept box, have them try these exercises.

1. What is *volume?* The amount of space inside a three-dimensional figure.
2. Would the volume change if you rotated the rectangular prism? no

Additional **Example 2**

Find the volume of the rectangular prism.

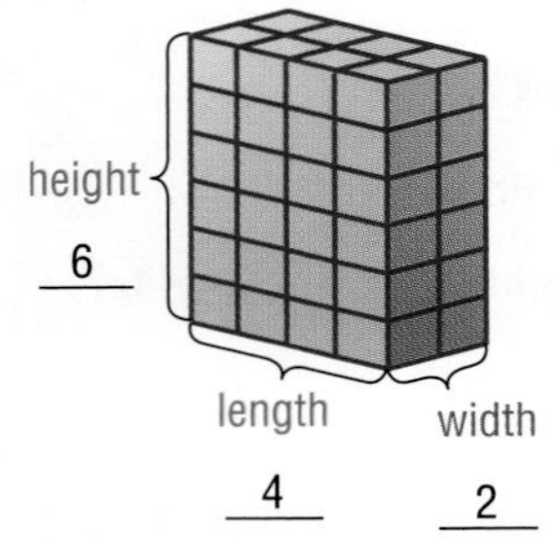

1. Look at the top layer of cubes on the prism. The length of the rectangular prism has 4 cubes. The width of the prism has 2 cubes.
2. Area $= \ell \times w$, so the area of the top layer is $4 \times 2 = 8$. There are 8 cubes on the top layer.
3. Each layer has the same number of cubes. There are 6 layers, so there are $8 + 8 + 8 + 8 + 8 + 8 = 48$ cubes in the prism.
4. The volume of the rectangular prism is 48 cubic units.

Note This!

Sketches Encourage students to sketch and label the three-dimensional figures in this lesson. Labeling figures with the appropriate dimensions can help students in the future when they must substitute those values into formulas.

Example 2

Find the volume of the rectangular prism.

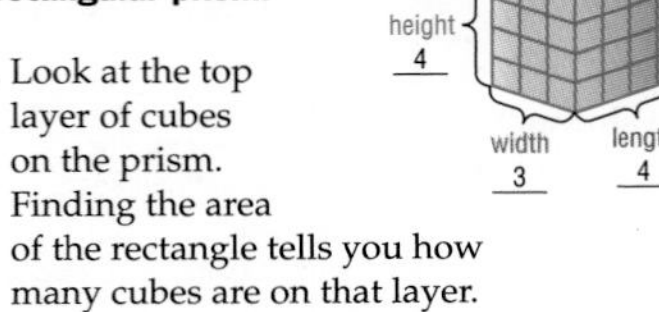

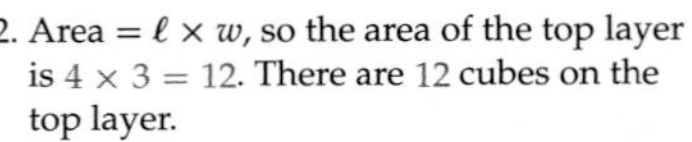

1. Look at the top layer of cubes on the prism. Finding the area of the rectangle tells you how many cubes are on that layer.
2. Area $= \ell \times w$, so the area of the top layer is $4 \times 3 = 12$. There are 12 cubes on the top layer.
3. Each layer has the same number of cubes. There are 4 layers, so there are $12 + 12 + 12 + 12 = 48$ cubes in the prism.
4. The volume of the rectangular prism is 48 cubic units.

YOUR TURN!

Find the volume of the rectangular prism.

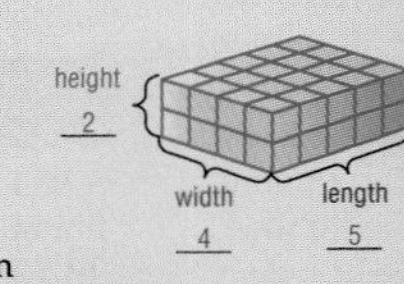

1. Look at the top layer of cubes on the prism. The length of the prism has __5__ cubes. The width of the prism has __4__ cubes.
2. Area $= \ell \times w$, so the area of the top layer is __5__ × __4__ = __20__. There are __20__ cubes on the top layer.
3. Each layer has the same number of cubes. There are __2__ layers, so there are __20__ + __20__ = __40__ cubes in the prism.
4. The volume of the rectangular prism is __40__ cubic units.

Who is Correct?

Find the volume of the rectangular prism.

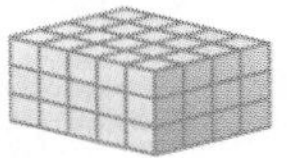

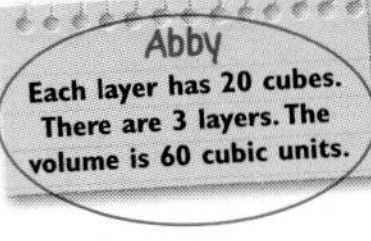

Abby
Each layer has 20 cubes. There are 3 layers. The volume is 60 cubic units.

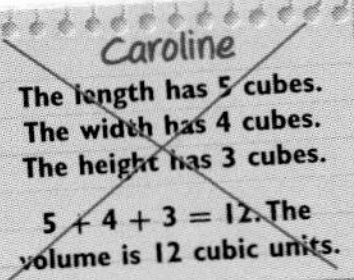

Caroline
The length has 5 cubes.
The width has 4 cubes.
The height has 3 cubes.
5 + 4 + 3 = 12. The volume is 12 cubic units.

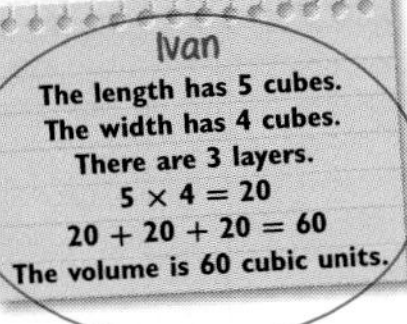

Ivan
The length has 5 cubes.
The width has 4 cubes.
There are 3 layers.
5 × 4 = 20
20 + 20 + 20 = 60
The volume is 60 cubic units.

Circle correct answer(s). Cross out incorrect answer(s).

Who *is Correct?*

Diagnostic Teaching

- Abby is correct. She counted the cubic units the figure contains.
- Caroline is incorrect. She added instead of multiplying the length, width, and height.
- Ivan is correct. He found the area of the top layer, and then found the sum of the areas of all the layers.

Suggest to students that the volume of a prism is the product of its length, width, and height.

Guided Practice

1 How many cubes are in this rectangular prism?

16

2 How many cubes are in this rectangular prism?

45

Remember, you can find the volume of a solid figure by counting the number of cubic units it contains.

Step by Step Practice

3 Find the volume of the rectangular prism.

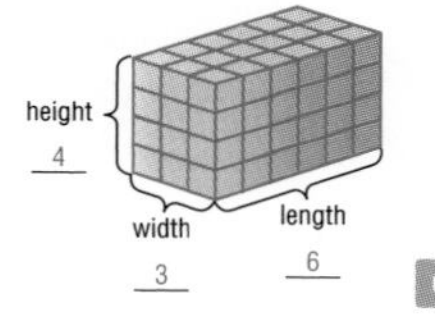

Step 1 Count the number of cubes along the length.
The length of the rectangular prism has 6 cubes.

Step 2 Count the number of cubes along the width.
The width of the rectangular prism has 2 cubes.

Step 3 The area of the top layer is 6 × 2 = 12.

Step 4 There are 3 layers in the prism.
12 + 12 + 12 = 36 cubes in the prism
The volume of the rectangular prism is 36 cubic units.

Find the volume of each rectangular prism.

4 Count the number of cubes along the length, width, and height of the rectangular prism.

Find the area of the top layer. Add that number four times. The volume of the rectangular prism is 72 cubic units.

height 4

width 3

length 6

GO ON

Intervention Strategy Kinesthetic Learners

Along the Edges Provide students with a small box, such as a paperclip box, and several unit cubes. Have students line unit cubes along the one edge of the box and record the number of cubes used. Then have students do the same for the other two dimensions of the box. Students should multiply the three numbers to find the volume of the box in cubic units. Have students place cubes in a pile that equal the product they just found. Explain to students that if all sets were completed accurately, all the cubes in the pile will fit inside the box. Have students fill their boxes with the piles of cubes.

3 Practice

Using Manipulatives

Unit Cubes When presenting Examples 1 and 2, model the three-dimensional figures by using unit cubes. Allow students to model the figures and count the unit cubes to have a deeper understanding of volume. Point out to students that they can either count the units, or multiply the length, width, and height. (They will learn this in the next lesson.)

On-Hand Manipulatives Use children's toy blocks instead of unit cubes.

Math Coach Notes

Strategies

Ask students to list all sets of three whole-number factors that have a product of 12. Their lists should include:

1 × 1 × 12	2 × 1 × 6	3 × 1 × 4
1 × 2 × 6	2 × 2 × 3	3 × 2 × 2
1 × 3 × 4	2 × 3 × 2	3 × 4 × 1
1 × 4 × 3	2 × 6 × 1	
1 × 6 × 2		
1 × 12 × 1		
4 × 1 × 3	6 × 1 × 2	12 × 1 × 1
4 × 3 × 1	6 × 2 × 1	

Refer to the figure building activity in the Lesson Introduction. Ask students to picture 18 prisms, each having the same volume. Discuss if each of the 18 prisms are different. Help students to see that even though the two or three prisms have the same three numbers as their dimensions, the prisms are oriented differently, and therefore, are different shaped prisms. Select the dimensions 1, 3, 4 and demonstrate that there are 6 different shaped prisms with these dimensions. Show a table with column headings *length*, *width*, and *height* and fill in the rows with the different combinations.

Common Error Alert

Remember the Units Volume is measured in cubic units. Remind students that their final answers should be in units cubed.

5 Count the number of cubes along the length, width, and height of the rectangular prism.

Find the area of the top layer. Add that number eight times. The volume of the rectangular prism is 96 cubic units.

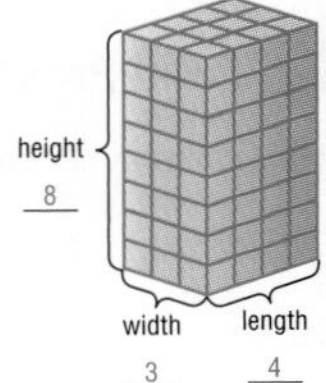

6 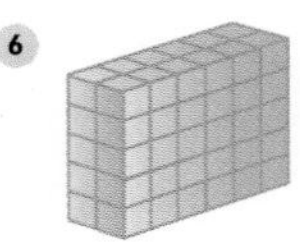 The volume of the rectangular prism is 60 cubic units.

7 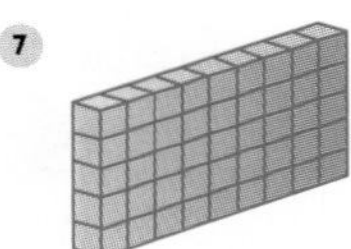 The volume of the rectangular prism is 45 cubic units.

Step by Step Problem-Solving Practice

Problem-Solving Strategies
- ☐ Draw a diagram.
- ☐ Look for a pattern.
- ☑ Use a model.
- ☐ Solve a simpler problem.
- ☐ Work backward.

Solve.

8 PHOTOTGRAPHY A camera that is shaped like a rectangular prism has a length of 9 centimeters, a width of 3 centimeters, and a height of 6 centimeters. What is its volume?

Understand Read the problem. Write what you know.
A rectangular prism has a length of 9 centimeters, a width of 3 centimeters, and a height of 6 centimeters.

3 cm
6 cm
9 cm

Plan Pick a strategy. One strategy is to use a model.

Solve Use unit blocks to build the rectangular prism. Count the number of blocks used.

Check The length is 9 centimeters.
The width is 3 centimeters.
There are 6 layers.
Multiply then add.

$9 \times 3 = 27$

$27 + 27 + 27 + 27 + 27 + 27 = 162$

The volume of the rectangular prism is 162 cubic centimeters.

260 Chapter 6 Three-Dimensional Figures

Are They Getting It?

Check students' understanding of finding the volume by writing these problems on the board. Ask students to point out wrong answers. Instruct them to use a grid or cubes to show why the answers are correct or are not correct.

Find the volume of each rectangular prism.

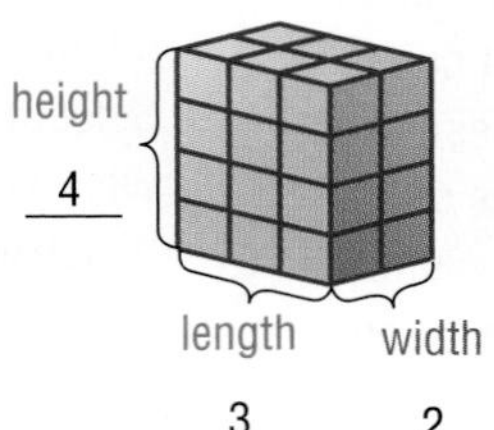

The volume of the rectangular prism is 12 cubic units. This is incorrect. The volume is 24 cubic units.

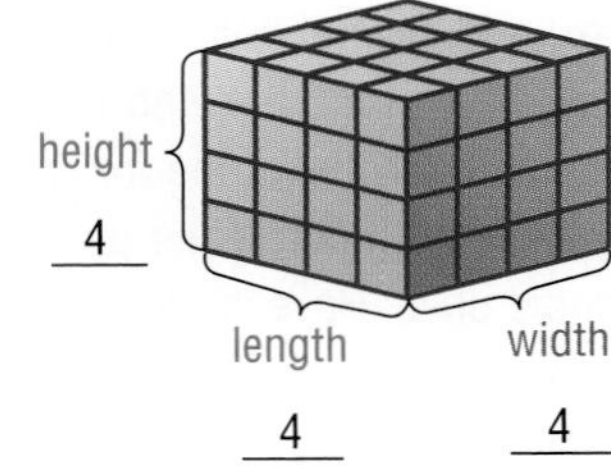

The volume of the cube is 64 cubic units. This is correct.

9 MODELS Pedro's model house is 15 inches long, 20 inches wide, and 10 inches tall. What is the volume of Pedro's house? 3,000 cubic inches

Check off each step.

✔ Understand: I underlined the key words.

✔ Plan: To solve this problem, I will use a model.

✔ Solve: The answer is 3,000 cubic inches.

✔ Check: I checked my answer by multiplying and adding.

10 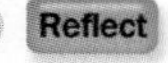 Give the length, width, and height of a rectangular prism that has a volume of 36 cubic units. Explain.

See TE margin.

Skills, Concepts, and Problem Solving

Find the volume of each rectangular prism.

11 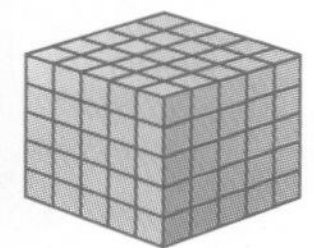

The volume of the rectangular prism is 125 cubic units.

12 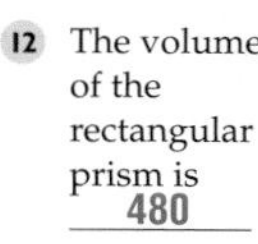 The volume of the rectangular prism is 480 cubic units.

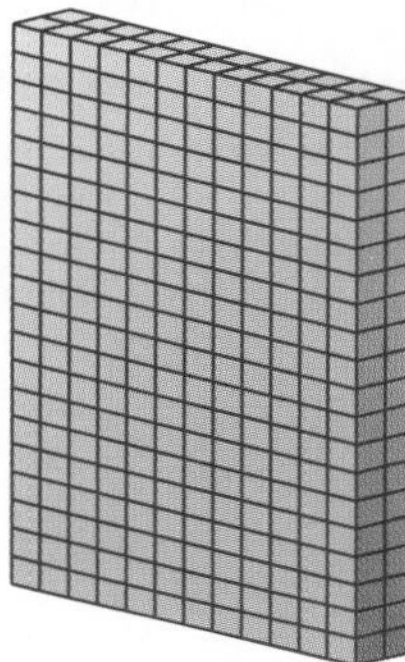

13 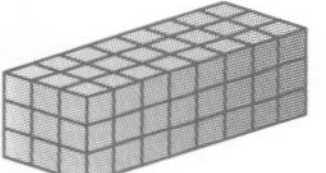

The volume of the rectangular prism is 72 cubic units.

14 

The volume of the rectangular prism is 140 cubic units.

GO ON

Lesson 6-3 Introduction to Volume 261

Math Challenge

Prisms on Graph Paper Arrange students in pairs. Students can use graph paper to draw a net for a rectangular prism. Each student should draw a net for a prism different than their partner's. On each face of the net write the dimensions of the face and the area of the face. Use the nets to name the dimensions of the prisms. Have students discuss how to use this information to find the volume of each prism, and compare the volumes and surface areas of the prisms.

Additional Answer

Exercise 10 Sample answer: A rectangular prism that has a volume of 36 cubic units could have a length of 9 units, a width of 1 unit, and a height of 4 units. There are 4 layers of 9 square units.

$9 + 9 + 9 + 9 = 36$

Odd/Even Assignments

Exercises 11–15 are structured so that students practice the same concepts whether they are assigned the odd or even problems.

In-Class Assignment

Have students complete Exercises 11, 15, and 18 to ensure that they understand the concept.

English Learner Strategy

Guiding Questions Ask students the following questions to ensure that they understand the concept. Show students a prism.

- What is the length of the prism? What is the width of the prism? What is the height of the prism?
- How do you find the volume?
- Describe to another student how to find the volume of a prism. If another student of the same native language is available, have the student explain the process to him or her in the native language.

Additional Answer

Exercise 18 Count the number of cubes along the length, width, and height of the rectangular prism. Write your answer in cubic units.

See It, Do It, Say It, Write It

Step 1 Draw the following figure on the board.

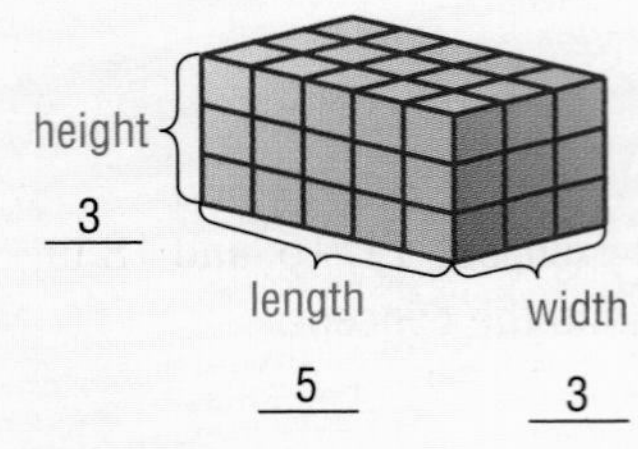

Step 2 Have students estimate the volume of the figure on the board.

Step 3 Arrange the students into pairs and have them explain to each other how they found the volume of the figure.

Step 4 Have students write in their journals how to find the volume of a figure.

Looking Ahead: Pre-teach

Volume of Rectangular Solids In the next lesson, students will learn about the volume of a rectangular solid. The formula $V = \ell \times w \times h$ can be used. The units are cubic units.

Example

A cube has edges 3 cm long. What is the volume of the cube? 27 cm^3

Have students find the volume of each rectangular prism.

1. length 7 cm, width 4 cm, height 3 cm 84 cm^3
2. length 9 cm, width 2 cm, height 2 cm 36 cm^3
3. length 5 cm, width 5 cm, height 5 cm 125 cm^3

Solve.

15 STORAGE What is the volume of the storage chest shown at the right?

72 cubic feet

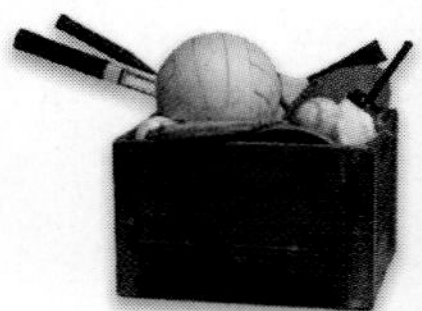

STORAGE CHEST The chest is 6 feet long, 3 feet wide, and 4 feet tall.

Vocabulary Check Write the vocabulary word that completes each sentence.

16 ___Volume___ is the number of cubic units needed to fill a three-dimensional figure.

17 A(n) ___cubic unit___ is a unit for measuring volume.

18 **Writing in Math** Explain how to find the volume of a rectangular prism.

See TE margin.

Spiral Review

Find the surface area of each rectangular prism. (Lesson 6-2, p. 247)

19 The surface area of the rectangular prism is ___142___ square units.

20 The surface area of the rectangular prism is ___208___ square units.

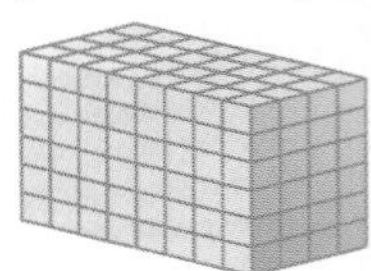

21 SUITCASE Tao packed his clothes in a rectangular-shaped suitcase for his trip to Florida. The length of his suitcase is 18 inches, the width is 10 inches, and the height is 12 inches. What is the surface area of his suitcase?

___1,032___ cubic inches

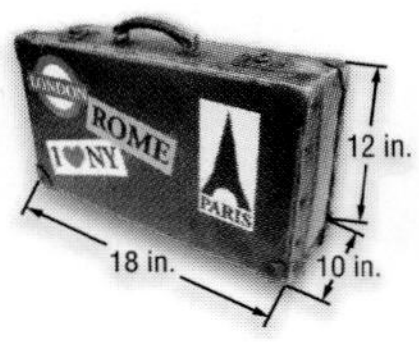

Ticket Out the Door

Birthday Volume Ask students to write the date of their birthdays in the upper right corner on a half sheet of paper. For example, if a birthday is January 24, write 24 in the upper right corner of the paper. Students should sketch a prism that has a volume equal to the number written in the corner of the paper. Students will turn in their papers as they leave the classroom.

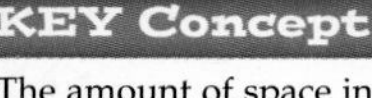

Lesson 6-4 Volume of Rectangular Solids

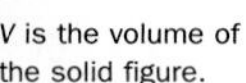

KEY Concept

The amount of space inside a three-dimensional figure is the **volume** of the figure.

The volume of a rectangular solid is the product of its length, width, and height.

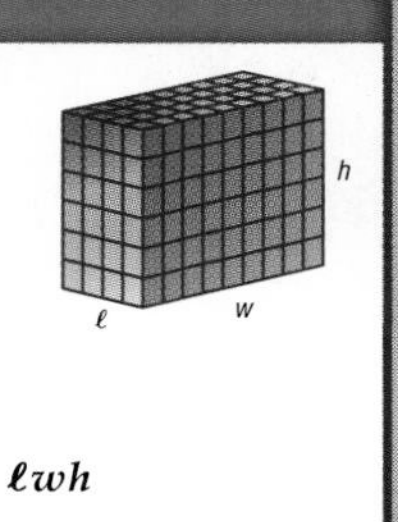

V is the volume of the solid figure. w is the width.

$$V = \ell \times w \times h \quad \text{or} \quad V = \ell wh$$

ℓ is the length. h is the height.

VOCABULARY

cube
a rectangular prism with six faces that are congruent squares

cubic unit
used to measure volume; tells the number of cubes of a given size it will take to fill a three-dimensional figure

volume
the amount of space that a three-dimensional figure contains; volume is expressed in cubic units

olume is measured in **cubic units**.

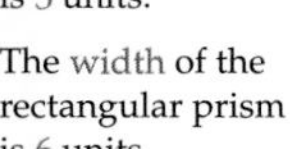

Example 1

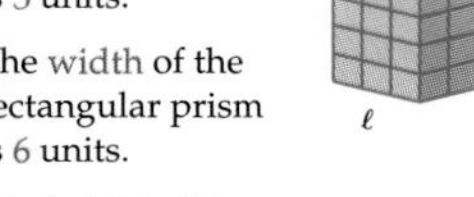

Find the volume of the rectangular prism.

1. The length of the rectangular prism is 3 units.
   The width of the rectangular prism is 6 units.
   The height of the rectangular prism is 5 units.
2. Substitute the length, width, and height into the volume formula.
   $V = \ell \times w \times h$
   $V = 3 \times 6 \times 5$
3. Multiply.
   $V = 90$

The volume of the rectangular prism is 90 cubic units.

YOUR TURN!

Find the volume of the rectangular prism.

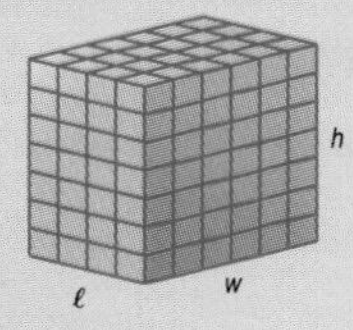

1. The length of the rectangular prism is __4__ units.
   The width of the rectangular prism is __6__ units.
   The height of the rectangular prism is __7__ units.
2. Substitute the length, width, and height into the volume formula.
   $V = \ell \times w \times h$
   $V = $ __4__ $\times$ __6__ $\times$ __7__
3. Multiply.
   $V = $ __168__

The volume of the rectangular prism is __168__ cubic units.

GO ON

Lesson Notes

Lesson 6-4

Lesson Planner

Objective Determine volume of prisms.

Vocabulary **cube**, **cubic unit**, **volume**

Materials/Manipulatives geometric solids, base-ten blocks, unit cubes, connecting cubes, real-world solids

Chapter Resource Masters

- CRM Vocabulary and English Language Development (p. A131)
- CRM Skills Practice (p. A132)
- CRM Problem-Solving Practice (p. A133)
- CRM Homework Practice (p. A134)

1 Introduce

Vocabulary

Recognizing Dimensions Gather several different rectangular solids from around the classroom to use as visual aids in a discussion about dimensions. One by one, hold up a solid and have students identify its length, width, and height. Discuss if others would have identified the dimensions differently. Question students if the volume of the solid changes when the dimensions are assigned differently.

Additional *Example 1*

Find the volume of the rectangular prism.

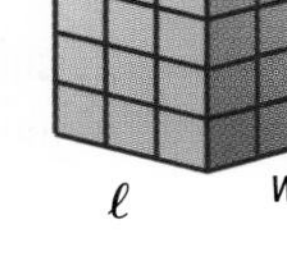

1. The length of the rectangular prism is 3 units.
   The width of the rectangular prism is 3 units.
   The height of the rectangular prism is 4 units.
2. Substitute the length, width, and height into the formula for volume.
   $V = \ell \times w \times h$
   $V = 3 \times 3 \times 4$
3. Multiply.
   $V = 36$
   The volume of the rectangular prism is 36 cubic units.

2 Teach

Key Concept

Foundational Skills and Concepts After students have read through the Key Concept box, have them try these exercises.

1. What is volume? the amount of space that a three-dimensional figure contains
2. What is the unit for volume? cubic units

Additional **Example 2**

Find the volume of the cube.

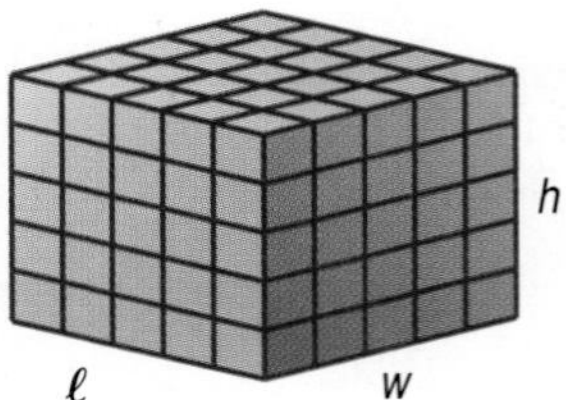

h
ℓ
w

1. The length of the cube is 5 units.
The width of the cube is 5 units.
The height of the cube is 5 units.

2. Substitute the length, width, and height into the formula for volume.
$V = \ell \times w \times h$
$V = 5 \times 5 \times 5$
$V = 5^3$

3. Multiply.
$V = 125$
The volume of the cube is 125 cubic units.

Math Coach Notes

Units Make the connection that the word *cubic* means three and that volume is measured in cubic units because you are finding the measurement of a three-dimensional object.

Example 2

Find the volume of the cube.

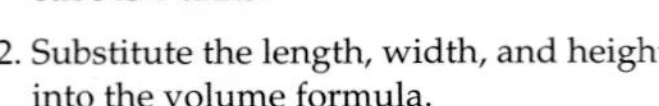

1. The length of the cube is 6 units.

   The width of the cube is 6 units.

   The height of the cube is 6 units.
2. Substitute the length, width, and height into the volume formula.

   $V = \ell \times w \times h$
   $V = 6 \times 6 \times 6$
   $V = 6^3$
3. Multiply.

   $V = 216$

The volume of the cube is 216 cubic units.

YOUR TURN!

Find the volume of the cube.

1. The length of the cube is __4__ units.

   The width of the cube is __4__ units.

   The height of the cube is __4__ units.
2. Substitute the length, width, and height into the volume formula.

   $V = \ell \times w \times h$
   $V =$ __4__ $\times$ __4__ $\times$ __4__
   $V =$ __4^3__
3. Multiply.

   $V =$ __64__

The volume of the cube is __64__ cubic units.

Who is Correct?

Find the volume of the rectangular prism.

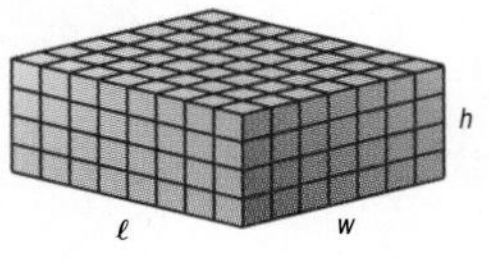

h
ℓ
w

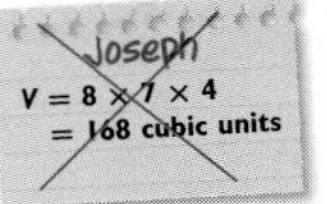

Joseph
V = 8 × 7 × 4
= 168 cubic units

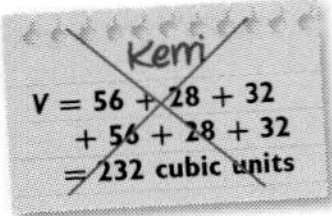

Kerri
V = 56 + 28 + 32
+ 56 + 28 + 32
= 232 cubic units

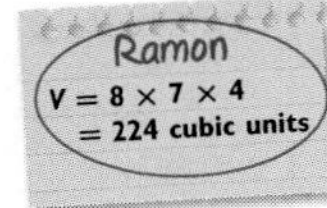

Ramon
V = 8 × 7 × 4
= 224 cubic units

Circle correct answer(s). Cross out incorrect answer(s).

Who *is Correct?*

Diagnostic Teaching

- Joseph wrote 168 cubic units. This is incorrect. He made an error in multiplying.
- Kerri wrote 232 cubic units. This is incorrect. She added for surface area instead of multiplying the dimensions to find the volume.
- Ramon wrote 224 cubic units. This is correct.

Guided Practice

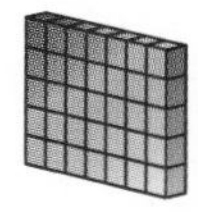

1. How many cubes are in this rectangular prism? 35
2. How many cubes are in this rectangular prism? 8

Check your answer. Remember, you can find the volume of a solid figure by counting the number of cubic units it contains.

Step by Step Practice

Find the volume of the rectangular prism.

3

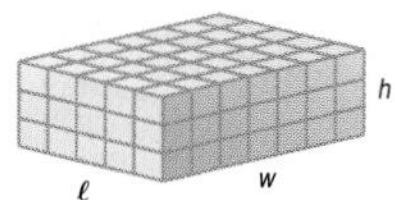

Step 1 The length of the rectangular prism is 5 units.

The width of the rectangular prism is 7 units.

The height of the rectangular prism is 3 units.

Step 2 Substitute the length, width, and height into the volume formula.

$V = \ell \times w \times h$

$V = 5 \times 7 \times 3$

Step 3 Multiply.

$V = 105$

The volume of the rectangular prism is 105 cubic units.

Find the volume of each rectangular prism.

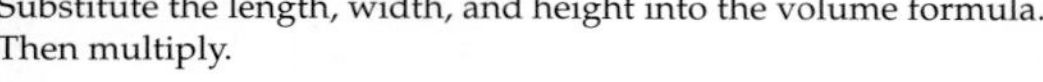

4. Substitute the length, width, and height into the volume formula. Then multiply.

$V = \ell \times w \times h$

$V = 10 \times 6 \times 3$

$V = 180$

The volume of the rectangular prism is 180 cubic units.

Intervention Strategy

Kinesthetic/Visual/Logical Learners

Fill the Box Select two different sizes of boxes that can be filled. To reinforce the idea that volume is the space inside the box, use uncooked rice or sand to fill each box. Have students measure the dimensions of a box and calculate the volume. Find the volume of the second box. Locate a bucket larger than either of the boxes. Empty the contents of the box with the lesser volume into the bucket. Mark the level of the rice and then pour the rice out of the bucket. Empty the rice from the second box into the bucket to verify that it was the box with the greater volume. The level of the rice will be higher than the mark made from the content of the first box.

3 Practice

Using Manipulatives

Geometric Solids When presenting Example 1, model with geometric solids. Show students how to fill the solid with cubes to find the volume.

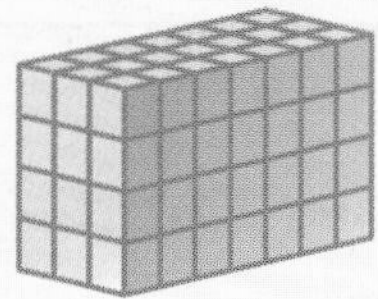

Base-Ten Blocks Base-ten blocks can be used to show how cubic units make up the volume of a prism.

Connecting Cubes Increase the number of connecting cubes and look how the volume changes.

On-Hand Manipulatives Build solids with alphabet blocks or unit cubes.

Math Coach Notes

Exercise 2 If cubes are available, have students build the cube shown in Exercise 2. They will notice that they used 8 centimeter cubes to build the cube.

Common Error *Alert*

Labeling Because the rectangular solids in this lesson do not have unit labels, students often forget to indicate their answers as cubic units. This label is critical to the concept of volume, and answers need to be complete with the label cubic units for the answer to be complete and correct.

English Learner Strategy

Guiding Questions

- Point to a dimension on a rectangular solid and ask if this edge represents length, width, or height.
- Point to a different dimension on the solid and ask if this edge represents length, width, or height.
- Point to the last dimension on the solid and ask the name of this dimension.
- Ask for the formula for the volume of a rectangular solid using the names of the dimensions.

5 $V = \ell \times w \times h$

$V =$ <u>3</u> $\times$ <u>10</u> $\times$ <u>5</u>

$V =$ <u>150</u>

The volume of the rectangular prism is <u>150</u> cubic units.

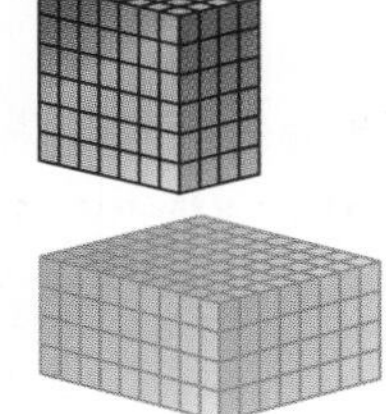

6 The volume of the rectangular prism is <u>168</u> cubic units.

7 The volume of the rectangular prism is <u>288</u> cubic units.

Step by Step Problem-Solving Practice

Problem-Solving Strategies
- ☑ Use a model.
- ☐ Look for a pattern.
- ☐ Guess and check.
- ☐ Act it out.
- ☐ Work backward.

Solve.

8 Ruthie has a pool in her backyard that is 30 feet long, 15 feet wide, and 6 feet deep. What is the volume of Ruthie's pool?

Understand Read the problem. Write what you know.

The pool has a length of <u>30</u> feet, a width of <u>15</u> feet, and a height of <u>6</u> feet.

Plan Pick a strategy. One strategy is to use a model.

Stack cubes to model the pool.

Solve Use the formula.

$V = \ell \times w \times h$

$V =$ <u>30</u> ft $\times$ <u>15</u> ft $\times$ <u>6</u> ft

$V =$ <u>2,700</u> ft^3

The volume of Ruthie's pool is <u>2,700</u> cubic feet.

Check Use a calculator to check your multiplication.

Are They Getting It?

Check students' understanding of the volume of rectangular solids by writing these problems on the board. Have students explain the incorrect information in each problem. Tell them to use a model or drawing to show why the answer is correct or not correct.

1. A cube that has a base of area 9 mm^2 has a volume of 27 mm^3. This is correct.
2. A rectangular prism with width 2 in., length 4 in., and height 5 in. has a volume of 40 in^2. This is not correct because the units should be cubic units.
3. The volume of this prism is 24 m^3. This is not correct. The volume is 36 m^3.

9 CONSTRUCTION Marion's family has a storage shed that is 5 yards wide, 8 yards long, and 5 yards high. What is the volume of the shed?
Check off each step.

✔ Understand: I underlined the key words.

✔ Plan: To solve the problem, I will use a model.

✔ Solve: The answer is 200 yd^3.

✔ Check: I checked my answer by using a calculator to check my multiplication.

10 PACKAGING Mrs. Romero put together a card box for her daughter's graduation party. The card box shape is a cube. Each side measures 48 centimeters. What is the volume of the card box? 110,592 cm^3

11 **Reflect** Compare the volume of the rectangular prism shown at the right to its surface area.

See TE margin.

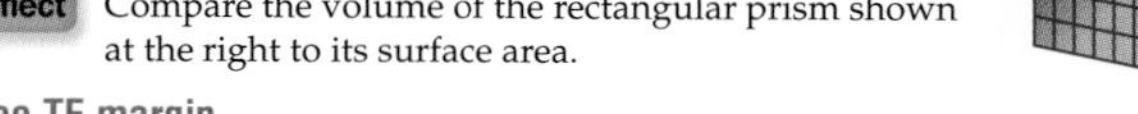

Skills, Concepts, and Problem Solving

Find the volume of each rectangular prism.

12 The volume of the rectangular prism is 162 cubic units.

13 The volume of the rectangular prism is 30 cubic units.

14 The volume of the rectangular prism is 140 cubic units.

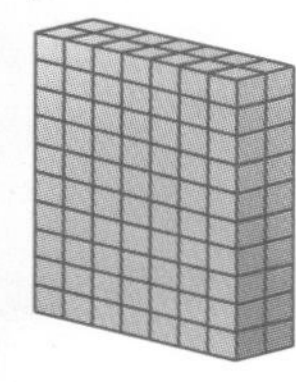

15 The volume of the rectangular prism is 240 cubic units.

Math Challenge

Unknown Dimensions Give students the following information about three different rectangular solids and have them find the unknown dimension.

The volume of a rectangular solid that has a length of 5 units and width of 3 units has a volume of 75 units cubed. What is the height of the solid? 5 units

The volume of a rectangular solid that has a height of 12 units and width of 2 units has a volume of 144 units cubed. What is the length of the solid? 6 units

The volume of a rectangular solid that has a length of 8 units and height of 5 units has a volume of 280 units cubed. What is the width of the solid? 7 units

Common Error *Alert*

Exercises 9 and 10 If a student struggles with Exercises 9 or 10, it might be because he or she is having difficulty visualizing the figure. Suggest the student draw the figure and label the dimensions.

Additional Answer

Exercise 11 The volume of the rectangular prism is found by using the formula $V = \ell \times w \times h$. Since $9 \times 1 \times 4 = 36$, the volume is 36 cubic units. The surface area of the rectangular prism is found by adding the areas of all six sides. Two sides have areas of $9 \times 1 = 9$ square units. Two sides have areas of $4 \times 1 = 4$ square units. The remaining two sides have areas of $9 \times 4 = 36$ square units. The surface area is $9 + 4 + 36 + 9 + 4 + 36$ or 98 square units. Volume describes how many cubic units are within the rectangular prism. Surface area describes how many square units cover the outside surface of the rectangular prism.

Odd/Even Assignments

Exercises 12–17 are structured so that students practice the same concepts whether they are assigned the odd or even problems.

In-Class Assignment

Have students complete Exercises 12, 14, 17, and 20 to ensure that they understand the concept.

See It, Do It, Say It, Write It

Step 1 Hold up a rectangular tissue box. Point to one dimension and name it as the length. Tell students this dimension is 10 units. Repeat this action with the other two dimensions giving the width as 6 units and the height as 2 units.

Step 2 Tell students to find the volume of the tissue box, given the dimensions named in Step 1.

Step 3 Arrange students into pairs. Hold up the rectangular tissue box again, but tell students that each one should name the dimensions and give their units. (Different than those given in Step 1.) Students should trade papers and find the volume of these solids.

Step 4 Have students use the solid from Step 1 and the two solids from Step 3 to write a comparison about the dimensions of these rectangular solids and their volumes.

Solve.

16 FLOWER BOX Tabitha has a flower box sitting on her windowsill. What is the volume of the flower box?
54 ft^3

FLOWER BOX **The flower box has a length of 6 feet, width of 3 feet, and height of 3 feet.**

17 GIFT Lana wrapped a present to give to her mom for her birthday. The present was 12 inches long, 8 inches wide, and 3 inches high. What was the volume of the present?
288 in^3

Vocabulary Check **Write the vocabulary word that completes each sentence.**

18 Volume is the number of cubic units needed to fill a three-dimensional figure.

19 Cubic unit is a unit for measuring volume.

20 Writing in Math Explain how to find the volume of a rectangular prism.
Sample answer: Find the length, width, and height of the rectangular prism. Substitute the length, width, and height into the formula for the volume of a rectangular prism. Then multiply.

Spiral Review

Read each description. Identify each three-dimensional figure. (Lesson 6-1, p. 242)

21 This figure has triangular bases. triangular prism

22 This figure has a circular base and one curved surface from the base to a vertex. cone

Solve. (Lesson 6-2, p. 247)

23 CONSTRUCTION Oleta's dresser is 4 feet long, 2 feet wide, and 4 feet tall. What is the surface area of Oleta's dresser?
64 ft^2

24 MUSIC Tobias' stereo speakers are cube-shaped. Each side measures 20 millimeters. What is the surface area of each speaker?
2,400 mm^2

STOP

Ticket Out the Door

Find Volume Ask students to sketch a rectangular solid on paper and label each dimension. Students should show their work using the formula to find the volume of the solid. Students can turn in their papers as they exit the classroom.

Progress Check 2 (Lessons 6-3 and 6-4)

Find the volume of each rectangular prism.

1  How many cubes are in this rectangular prism? 24

2 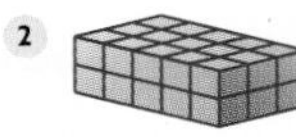 How many cubes are in this rectangular prism? 30

3 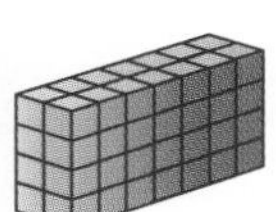 The volume of the rectangular prism is 56 cubic units.

4  The volume of the rectangular prism is 36 cubic units.

5 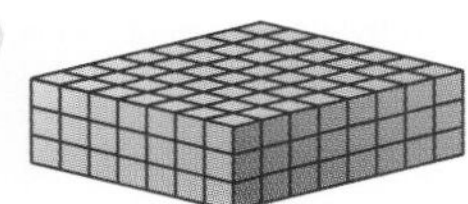

The volume of the rectangular prism is 168 cubic units.

6 

The volume of the rectangular prism is 252 cubic units.

Solve.

7 **PETS** Read the caption below the photo. What is the volume of Theo's fish tank?

2,520 cubic inches

8 **CONSTRUCTION** Vito needed his tool box to make repairs around his house. His tool box is 36 centimeters long, 15 centimeters wide, and 8 centimeters tall. What is the volume of the tool box?

4,320 cubic centimeters

9 **RECYCLING** Gregory's recycling bin is full and ready to be picked up. The bin is 21 inches long, 14 inches wide, and 25 inches tall. What is the volume of his recycling bin?

7,350 cubic inches

PETS **Theo's fish tank is 12 inches long, 14 inches wide, and 15 inches tall.**

Progress Check 2

Chapter 6

Formative Assessment

Use the Progress Check to assess students' mastery of the previous lessons. Have students review the lesson indicated for the problems they answered incorrectly.

Odd/Even Assignments

Exercises are structured so that students practice the same concepts whether they are assigned the odd or even problems.

Common Error *Alert*

Exercises 1-2 Remind students that not all cubes are visible in the picture. They cannot simply count the ones they see. Remind them to count the cubes along the edges to identify the dimensions and then use the formula to find the volume.

Exercises 3-6 Tell students to think about slicing "a piece" off of the solid along the longest dimension. For Exercise 4, the piece would have 6 cubes in it. Then they can imagine how many slices of the same size they could cut. Each slice would have 6 cubic units. Add 6 for each slice to find the volume of the solid.

Data-Driven Decision Making

Students missing Exercises . . .	Have trouble with . . .	Should review and practice . . .
1-6	finding volumes of prisms.	SSG Lessons 6-3 and 6-4, pp. 257 and 263 CRM Skills-Practice, pp. A128 and A132
7-9	solving word problems that involve volume.	CRM Problem-Solving Practice, pp. A129 and A133

Chapter 6

Study Guide
Formative Assessment

Vocabulary and Concept Check

If students have difficulty answering Exercises 1–10, remind them that they can use the page references to refresh their memories about the vocabulary terms.

Vocabulary Review Strategies

Vocabulary Frames Have students create Vocabulary Frames for the words. Have the students make two index cards for each vocabulary word.

- On one set of cards, state the definition, and on the other side write the vocabulary term. The students can study these either by looking at the vocabulary term and having to state its definition (flipping the card over to see if they got the definition correct), or the students read the side with the definition and try to state the corresponding vocabulary term (flipping the card over to see if they got the correct term).
- On the other set of cards, have the vocabulary terms on one side and on the other side have a drawing or sketch of the term. The students can quiz themselves with the same technique as described with the first set of index cards. It will be beneficial if the students not only know the *word* definitions of the vocabulary terms, but that they also recognize a sketch that represents the term.

Lesson Review

Each example walks the students through identifying three-dimensional figures and finding the surface areas and volumes of rectangular solids. Have the students write out the formula for each problem. Have students explain the steps in each example as they perform them.

Find **Extra Practice** for these concepts in the Practice Worksheets, pages A119–A134.

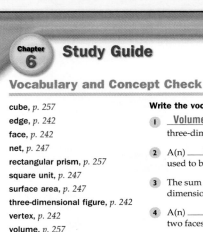

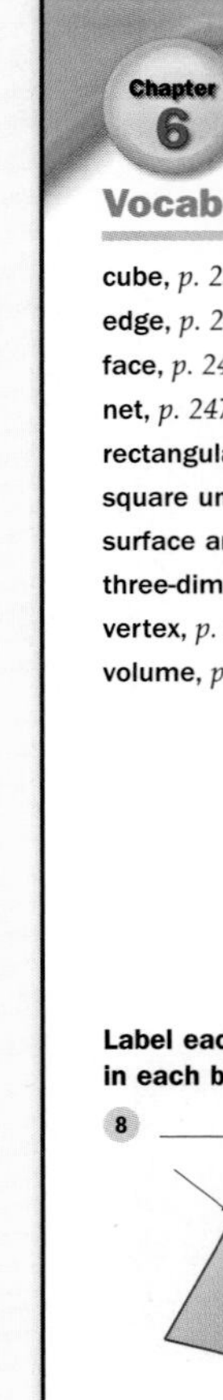

Chapter 6

Study Guide

Vocabulary and Concept Check

Write the vocabulary word that completes each sentence.

1. __Volume__ is the number of cubic units needed to fill a three-dimensional figure.
2. A(n) __net__ is a two-dimensional figure that can be used to build a three-dimensional figure.
3. The sum of the areas of all the surfaces (faces) of a three-dimensional figure is the __surface area__.
4. A(n) __edge__ is the line segment where two faces of a three-dimensional figure meet.
5. The point on a three-dimensional figure where three or more edges meet is the __vertex__.
6. The __face__ is the flat side of a three-dimensional figure.
7. A(n) __rectangular prism__ is a three-dimensional figure with six faces that are rectangles.

Label each diagram below. Write the correct vocabulary term in each blank.

8. __vertex__

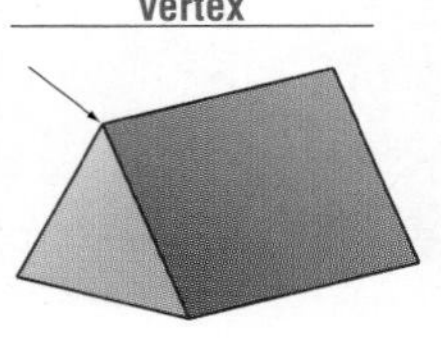

9. __face__

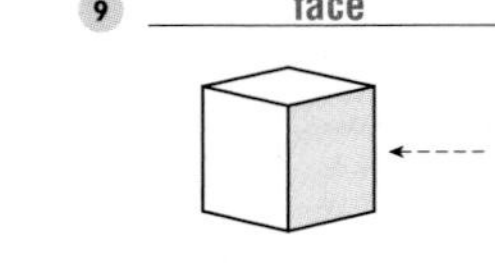

10. The net shown is of a __cube__ with 6 __faces__.

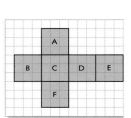

A B C D E F

GO ON

Classroom Management

Early Finishers Have students who finish the review problems for each example create additional problems. They should create the problem and include an answer (including a labeled diagram). When complete, have these students exchange their problems and double-check each other's work.

esson Review

-1 Introduction to Three-Dimensional Figures (pp. 242–246)

dentify each three-dimensional figure.

1 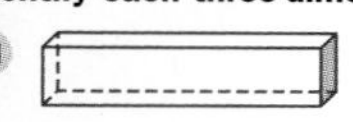

rectangular prism

2 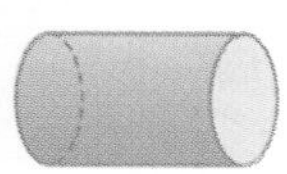

cylinder

Example 1

Identify the three-dimensional figure.

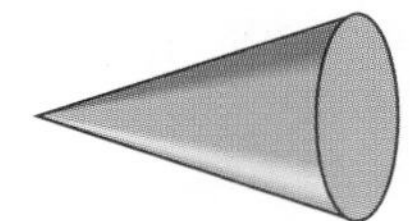

1. Is the shape flat, curved, or both? both
2. Describe the base(s). one circular base
3. The three-dimensional figure is a cone.

-2 Surface Area of Rectangular Solids (pp. 247–255)

ind the surface area of each ectangular prism.

3 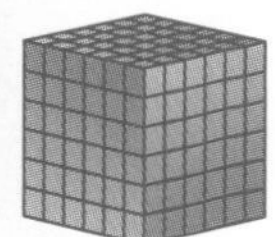

The surface area of the cube is 216 square units.

4 

The surface area of the rectangular prism is 382 square units.

Example 2

What is the surface area of the rectangular prism?

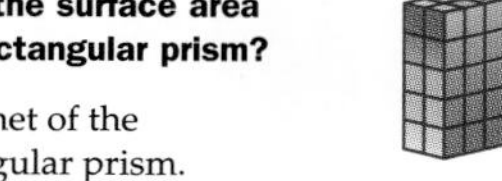

1. Use a net of the rectangular prism.
2. Find the area of faces A and F.

   $A = \ell \times w$
   $A = 2 \times 4 = 8$
3. Find the area of faces B and D.

   $A = \ell \times w$
   $A = 4 \times 5 = 20$
4. Find the area of faces C and E.

   $A = \ell \times w$
   $A = 2 \times 5 = 10$
5. Find the sum of the areas of all the faces.

   $8 + 20 + 10 + 8 + 20 + 10 = 76$

   The surface area of the rectangular prism is 76 square units.

Dinah Zike's Foldables®

Review Remind students to complete and refer to their Foldables as they progress through the Chapter 6 Study Guide. Have students share and compare their completed Foldables with a partner. You may also choose to have them use their Foldable as a study aid in preparing for the Chapter Test. (For complete instructions, see Chapter Resource Masters, p. A116.)

Ch. 6	Rectangular Prisms	Cylinders
Draw Examples		
Find Volume		
Find Surface Area		

Note This!

Solids in the Real World Suggest students write the different types of solids introduced. Next to each name, students should draw the figure and then think of some real-world examples that will help them remember the figure. They should also write in their own words the steps necessary to find the surface area and volume of that figure.

Common Error *Alert*

Liquid or Solid Students are sometimes confused with the word *volume* because they have also seen it in science class. Explain to students that volume is a capacity and can be either a solid or a liquid.

Intervention Strategy

Visual/ Linguistic Learners

Real-World Volume In a descriptive paragraph, have students describe in their own words how volume is used. Have students include examples of how they have used volume in their everyday lives. Have them list multiple ways to calculate volume.

6-3 Introduction to Volume (pp. 257–261)

15 Find the volume of the rectangular prism.

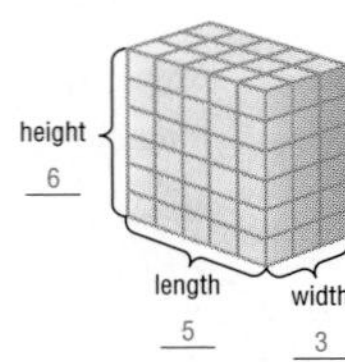

The volume of the rectangular prism is 90 cubic units.

16 Find the volume of the rectangular prism.

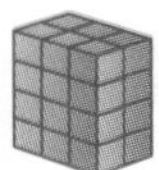

The volume of the rectangular prism is 24 cubic units.

17 Find the volume of the rectangular prism.

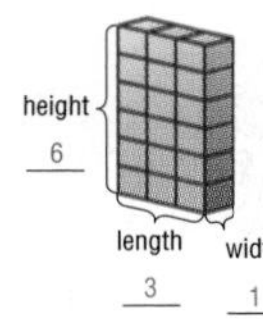

The volume of the rectangular prism is 18 cubic units.

Example 3

Find the volume of the rectangular prism.

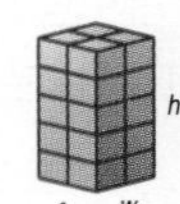

1. Count the number of layers of cubes in the prism. There are 5 layers of cubes in the rectangular prism.
2. Count the number of cubes in the top layer. There are 4 cubes in the top layer.
3. Each layer has the same number of cubes. There are $4 + 4 + 4 + 4 + 4$ cubes.

The volume of the rectangular prism is 20 cubic units.

Example 4

Find the volume of the rectangular prism.

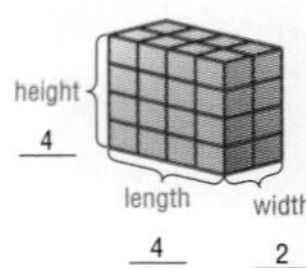

1. Look at the top layer of cubes on the prism. Finding the area of a rectangle would tell you how many cubes are on that layer.
2. Area $= \ell \times w$, so the area of the top layer is $4 \times 2 = 8$, there are 8 cubes on the top layer.
3. Each layer has the same number of cubes. There are 4 layers so there are $8 + 8 + 8 + 8 = 32$ cubes in the prism.

The volume of the rectangular prism is 32 cubic units.

6-4 Volume of Rectangular Solids (pp. 263–268)

ind the volume of each ectangular prism.

8 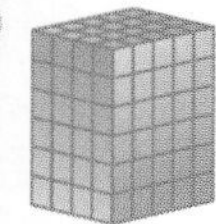

The volume of the rectangular prism is 120 cubic units.

9 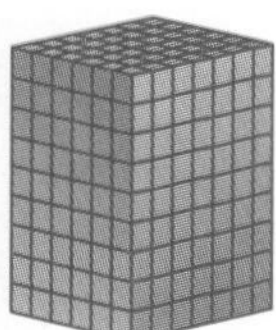

The volume of the rectangular prism is 378 cubic units.

0 

The volume of the rectangular prism is 48 cubic units.

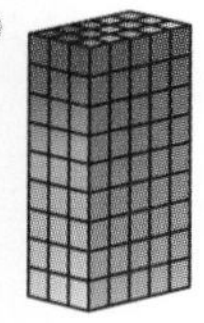

The volume of the rectangular prism is 135 cubic units.

Example 5

Find the volume of the rectangular solid.

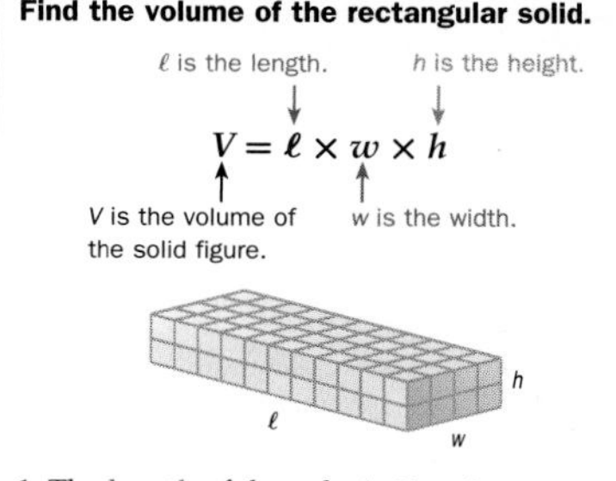
ℓ is the length.
h is the height.
$V = \ell \times w \times h$
V is the volume of the solid figure.
w is the width.
ℓ
w
h

1. The length of the cube is 11 units.

   The width of the cube is 4 units.

   The height of the cube is 2 units.

2. Substitute the length, width, and height into the volume formula.

   $V = \ell \times w \times h$
   $V = 11 \times 4 \times 2$

3. Multiply.

   $V = 88$

   The volume of the rectangular prism is 88 cubic units.

STOP

Note This!

Study Checklist Help students create a study checklist. The checklist should include the following items.

- Identify three-dimensional figures.
- Find the surface area of a rectangular solid.
- Find the volume of a rectangular solid.

Students should put a check mark next to each topic when they feel they have a good grasp of the process.

Ticket Out the Door

Review Surface Area and Volume Have students answer a total of four questions that you give them on a half-sheet of paper.

- identifying a cylinder, cone, or a sphere
- finding the surface area of a rectangular prism
- finding the volume of a rectangular prism
- finding the volume of a cube

Chapter 6

Chapter Test

Chapter Resource Masters

Additional forms of the Chapter 6 Tests are available.

Test Format	Where to Find it
Chapter 6 Test	Math Online glencoe.com
Blackline Masters	Assessment Masters, p. 90

Customize and create multiple versions of your chapter tests and their answer keys. All of these questions from the chapter tests are available on ExamView® Assessment Suite.

Online Assessment and Reporting
glencoe.com

This online assessment tool allows teachers to track student progress with easily accessible comprehensive reports available for every student. Assess students using any internet-ready computer.

Alternative Assessment

Use Portfolios Ask students to write examples of each type of problem from this chapter in their portfolios. Require them to include a diagram or picture with each example.

Have students write the answer to each example in their portfolios and describe the steps taken *(in their own words)* to solve or simplify each one.

Chapter 6

Chapter Test

Find the surface area of each rectangular prism.

1 The surface area of the rectangular prism is 122 square units.

2 The surface area of the rectangular prism is 234 square units.

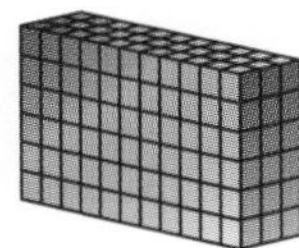

3 The surface area of the rectangular prism is 318 square units.

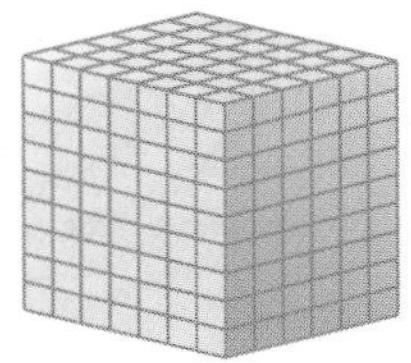

4 The surface area of the rectangular prism is 202 square units.

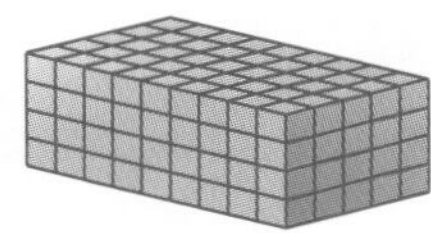

Find the volume of each rectangular prism.

5 How many cubes are in this rectangular prism? 20

6 How many cubes are in this rectangular prism? 36

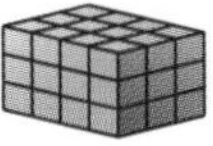

7 The volume of the rectangular prism is 180 cubic units.

8 The volume of the rectangular prism is 168 cubic units.

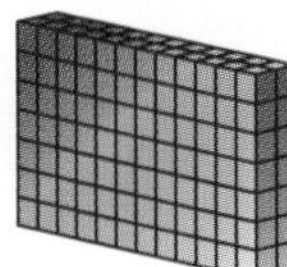

274 Chapter 6 Test

English Learner Strategy

Assessment Allow students time to look over the assessment. Have students take a close look at all the problem directions, as well as any terms in the word problems. Provide an opportunity for students to clarify any words they think they do not understand by conducting a brief question-and-answer period.

entify each three-dimensional figure.

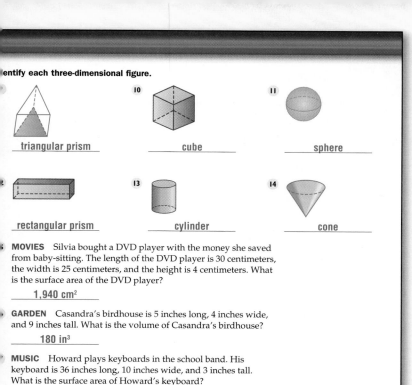

10 11

triangular prism

cube

sphere

13 14

rectangular prism

cylinder

cone

MOVIES Silvia bought a DVD player with the money she saved from baby-sitting. The length of the DVD player is 30 centimeters, the width is 25 centimeters, and the height is 4 centimeters. What is the surface area of the DVD player?

1,940 cm^2

GARDEN Casandra's birdhouse is 5 inches long, 4 inches wide, and 9 inches tall. What is the volume of Casandra's birdhouse?

180 in^3

MUSIC Howard plays keyboards in the school band. His keyboard is 36 inches long, 10 inches wide, and 3 inches tall. What is the surface area of Howard's keyboard?

996 in^2

rrect the mistakes.

Ms. Blackwell asked students in her math class to draw three-dimensional figures. She set some objects on a table. She told students to use the objects as models for their figures. Yolanda decided to use the roll of paper towels as a model. Look at Yolanda's drawing. What did she do wrong?

Sample answer: She drew a cone, not a cylinder.

A cylinder should be a curved figure with two flat ends.

Chapter 6 Test 275

Learning from Mistakes

Missed Questions Review commonly missed questions as a small group or class. Ask students to share their methods of answering each question. Try to point out when any errors occur and take corrective measures.

Data-Driven Decision Making

Students missing Exercises . . .	Have trouble with . . .	Should review and practice . . .
1–4	finding the surface area of a rectangular prism.	SSG Lesson 6-2 p. 247 CRM Skills Practice, p. A124
5–8	finding the volume of a rectangular prism.	SSG Lessons 6-3 and 6-4, pp. 257 and 263 CRM Skills Practice, pp. A128 and A132
9–14	identifying three-dimensional figures.	SSG Lesson 6-1, p. 242 CRM Skills Practice, p. A120
15–18	solving word problems involving finding surface area and volume.	CRM Problem Solving Practice, pp. A121, A125, A129, and A133

Chapter 6

Test Practice

Chapter 6 Test Practice

Choose the best answer and fill in the corresponding circle on the sheet at right.

1 What is the volume of the solid figure?

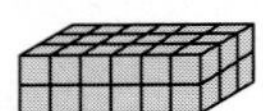

A 12 cubic units C 30 cubic units
B 18 cubic units (D) 36 cubic units

2 Which of the following best describes the shape of a soccer ball?

A cone
B rectangular prism
(C) sphere
D vertex

3 Ray has a closed shoe box that measures 10 inches by 7 inches by 5 inches. What is the volume of the shoe box?

A 22 in^3 C 350 in^2
(B) 350 in^3 D 350 in

4 Which of the following figures shows a cone?

A  C 
B  (D) 

5 What is the surface area of the rectangular solid?

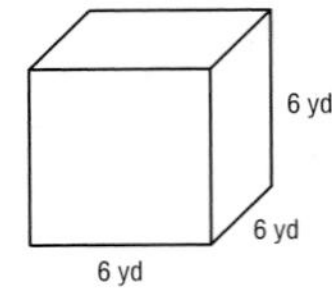

A 18 yd^2
B 186 yd^2
(C) 216 yd^2
D 248 yd^2

6 What is the volume of the solid figure

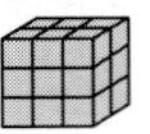

A 9 cubic units C 16 cubic units
B 12 cubic units (D) 18 cubic units

7 What is the surface are of the rectangular solid?

(A) 108 square units
B 72 square units
C 54 square units
D 13 square units

276 **Chapter 6** Test Practice

Diagnose Student Errors

Survey student responses for each item. Class trends may indicate common errors and misconceptions.

1. A only counted cubes in front
B only counted cubes on top layer
C miscounted
(D) correct

2. A did not understand attributes of a sphere
B guess
(C) correct
D guess

3. A added measurements instead of multiplying
(B) correct
C incorrect units
D incorrect units

4. A did not understand attributes of a cone
B guess
C guess
(D) correct

5. A added measurements instead of multiplying
B multiplication error
(C) correct
D guess

6. A only counted cubes in front
B miscounted
C miscounted
(D) correct

7. (A) correct
B found volume
C found $\frac{1}{2}$ the surface area
D added dimensions

8. A added measurements instead of multiplying
B multiplication error
(C) correct
D guess

9. A did not understand attributes of a three-dimensional figure
(B) correct
C did not understand attributes of a three-dimensional figure
D did not understand correct terms for three-dimensional figures

10. A guess
B added dimensions
C found volume
(D) correct

11. A guess
(B) correct
C guess
D guess

12. (A) correct
B guess
C guess
D picked incorrect base shape

Patty has a jewelry box that measures 15 centimeters long by 10 centimeters wide by 8 centimeters tall. What is the volume of the jewelry box?

A 33 cm^3 | (C) $1{,}200\text{ cm}^3$

B $1{,}500\text{ cm}^3$ | D 800 cm^3

Choose the correct name of the three-dimensional figure.

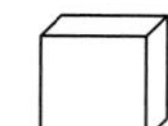

A square | C rectangle

(B) cube | D box

What is the surface area of the rectangular prism?

A 47 square units | C 60 square units

B 12 square units | (D) 94 square units

Omar built a storage chest for his bedroom that is 5 feet long, 4 feet wide and 2 feet tall. What is the surface area of the chest?

A 47 square feet | C 94 square feet

(B) 76 square feet | D 141 square feet

12 Which of the following describes the object below?

(A) triangular prism

B sphere

C cube

D rectangular prism

ANSWER SHEET

Directions: Fill in the circle of each correct answer.

1	A	B	C	**D**
2	A	B	**C**	D
3	A	**B**	C	D
4	A	B	C	**D**
5	A	B	**C**	D
6	A	B	C	**D**
7	**A**	B	C	D
8	A	B	**C**	D
9	A	**B**	C	D
10	A	B	C	**D**
11	A	**B**	C	D
12	**A**	B	C	D

Success Strategy
After answering all the questions, go back and check your work. Make sure you circled the correct answer to each problem.

Diagnosing Student Errors and Misconceptions

Labels The most common error in measurement problems, other than computational mistakes, is the misuse of labels. Help students understand the differences in the units of each measure.

Surface area is measured in square units.

- It is a measure of two dimensions.
- The standard unit of measure is a specific-sized square.

Volume is measure in cubic units.

- It is a measure of three dimensions.
- The standard unit of measure is a specific-sized cube.

Chapter 7

Chapter Overview

Chapter-at-a-Glance

Lesson	Math Objective	State/Local Standards
7-1 Read and Write Whole Numbers In the Millions (pp. 280–286)	Write and expand whole numbers in the millions and be able to identify place value.	
7-2 Round and Compare Whole Numbers In the Millions (pp. 287–292)	Round and compare whole numbers.	
Progress Check (p. 293)		
7-3 Model Integers (pp. 294–300)	Understand and model integers.	
7-4 Absolute Value and Zero Pairs (pp. 301–306)	Evaluate operations with absolute value; use absolute value to operate with integers.	
Progress Check (p. 307)		

Content-at-a-Glance

The diagram below summarizes and unpacks Chapter 7 content.

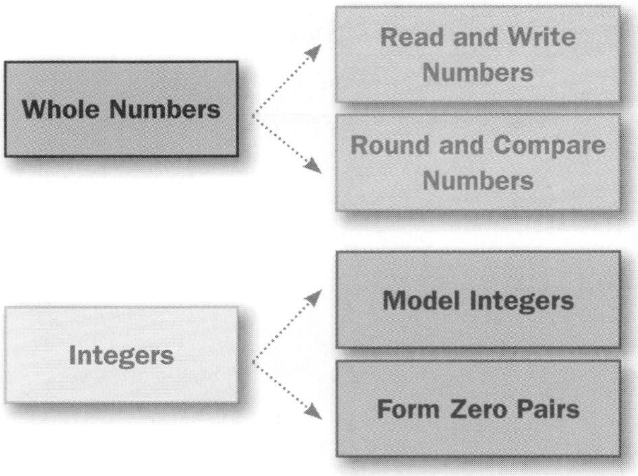

Whole Numbers → Read and Write Numbers; Round and Compare Numbers

Integers → Model Integers; Form Zero Pairs

Online Assessment and Reporting
glencoe.com

Chapter Assessment Manager

Diagnostic

Diagnose students' readiness.

	Student Study Guide/ Teacher Edition	Assessment Masters	Technology
Course Placement Test		1	ExamView® Assessment Suite
Book 3 Pretest		101	ExamView® Assessment Suite
Chapter 7 Pretest		104	ExamView® Assessment Suite
Quiz/Preview	SSG 279		Math Online glencoe.com StudentWorks™ Plus

Formative

Identify students' misconceptions of content knowledge.

	Student Study Guide/ Teacher Edition	Assessment Masters	Technology
Progress Checks	SSG 293, 307		Math Online glencoe.com StudentWorks™ Plus
Vocabulary Review	SSG 308		Math Online glencoe.com
Lesson Assessments			ExamView® Assessment Suite
Are They Getting It?	TE 282, 290, 297, 304		Math Online glencoe.com

Summative

Determine student success in learning concepts in the lesson, chapter, or book.

	Student Study Guide/ Teacher Edition	Assessment Masters	Technology
Chapter 7 Test	SSG 312	107	ExamView® Assessment Suite
Test Practice	SSG 314	110	
Alternative Assessment	TE 312	113	ExamView® Assessment Suite
See It, Do It, Say It, Write It	TE 286, 292, 300, 306		
Book 3 Test		148	ExamView® Assessment Suite

Back-mapping and Vertical Alignment **McGraw-Hill's *Math Triumphs*** intervention program was conceived and developed with the final result in mind: student success in grade-level mathematics, including Algebra 1 and beyond. The authors, using the **NCTM Focal Points and Focal Connections** as their guide, developed this brand-new series by backmapping from grade-level and Algebra 1 concepts, and vertically aligning the topics so that they build upon prior skills and concepts and serve as a foundation for future topics.

Chapter Resource Manager

	Lesson 7-1	Lesson 7-2	Lesson 7-3	Lesson 7-4
Concept	Read and Write Whole Numbers in the Millions	Round and Compare Whole Numbers in the Millions	Model Integers	Absolute Values and Zero Pairs
Objective	Write and expand whole numbers in the millions and be able to identify place value.	Round and compare whole numbers.	Understand and model integers.	Evaluate operations with absolute value; use absolute value to operate with integers.
Math Vocabulary	period standard form word form	compare greater than (>) less than (<) round	integers negative numbers opposites positive numbers whole numbers	absolute value opposites zero pairs
Lesson Resources	**Materials** • Construction paper • Number lines • Place-value charts • Decks of cards • Colored pencils **Manipulatives** • Base-ten blocks **Other Resources** CRM Vocabulary and English Language Development CRM Skills Practice CRM Problem-Solving Practice CRM Homework Practice	**Materials** • Place-value charts **Manipulatives** • Base-ten blocks • Unit cubes **Other Resources** CRM Vocabulary and English Language Development CRM Skills Practice CRM Problem-Solving Practice CRM Homework Practice	**Materials** • Number lines • Rulers • Decks of cards • Thermometers **Manipulatives** • Algebra tiles **Other Resources** CRM Vocabulary and English Language Development CRM Skills Practice CRM Problem-Solving Practice CRM Homework Practice	**Materials** • Number lines • Deck of cards • Counstruction paper • Balance scale **Manipulatives** • Algebra tiles • Counters • Unit cubes **Other Resources** CRM Vocabulary and English Language Development CRM Skills Practice CRM Problem-Solving Practice CRM Homework Practice
Technology	Math Online glencoe.com StudentWorks™ Plus ExamView® Assessment Suite	Math Online glencoe.com StudentWorks™ Plus ExamView® Assessment Suite	Math Online glencoe.com StudentWorks™ Plus ExamView® Assessment Suite	Math Online glencoe.com StudentWorks™ Plus ExamView® Assessment Suite

Intervention Strategy

Place Value and Number Magnitude

Playing a number cube game that requires students to think ahead about how to make the greatest number will help them to understand how the place of a digit can affect its magnitude.

Step 1: While students sit at their desks, draw lines on the board with commas to represent digits and periods. For example, to represent 153,126 you would write __ __ __, __ __ __. Students will copy the lines and commas exactly on plain paper. You can choose any number of lines you want, but vary the number each game.

Step 2: Toss a number cube. When a number comes up, announce it and write it on the board. Students will choose, based on the size of the number tossed, which line to write the number on. If the number is a 1 or 2, students would place it in a smaller place value and if it were larger, in a larger place value. Once the number has been written down, students may not erase it or change their minds.

Step 3: Once all students have chosen a place value, keep involved with the class by asking specific students where they decided to write the last number. Make sure each student has committed the digit to a place-value before continuing.

Step 4: Repeat the process of rolling the number cube and having students write the digit in their chosen place-value until all the places are filled. For example, for the unknown number __ __ __, __ __ __ you would roll the die a total of 6 times. The student or students that have the greatest number wins.

Step 5: You can vary the game by telling students at the beginning that they want to make the smallest instead of the largest number they can. You can use a 9- or 10-sided die for advanced students.

Chapter Notes

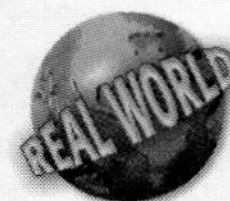

Real-World Applications

Round Numbers According to the U.S. Census Bureau, the state of California had a population of over 36 million people in 2005. Large numbers like state and country populations are often rounded. Ask students to name other situations in which numbers are often rounded. Sample answers: exports, imports, averages (like batting averages), surveys, to make mental calculations easier, and so on.

Intervention Strategy

Place Value and Rounding

Step 1 Divide students into small groups.

Step 2 Have each group create a poster that displays a place-value chart covering the ones place through the millions place. Insert numbers in the chart to illustrate the value of each digit.

Step 3 Give each group the following set of five numbers:

5,463,261	1,962,034	610,335
8,225,000	7,050,891	

Step 4 Using the set of numbers from above, each group should round each number to the nearest tens place, hundreds place, thousands place, ten-thousands place, hundred-thousands place, and millions place.

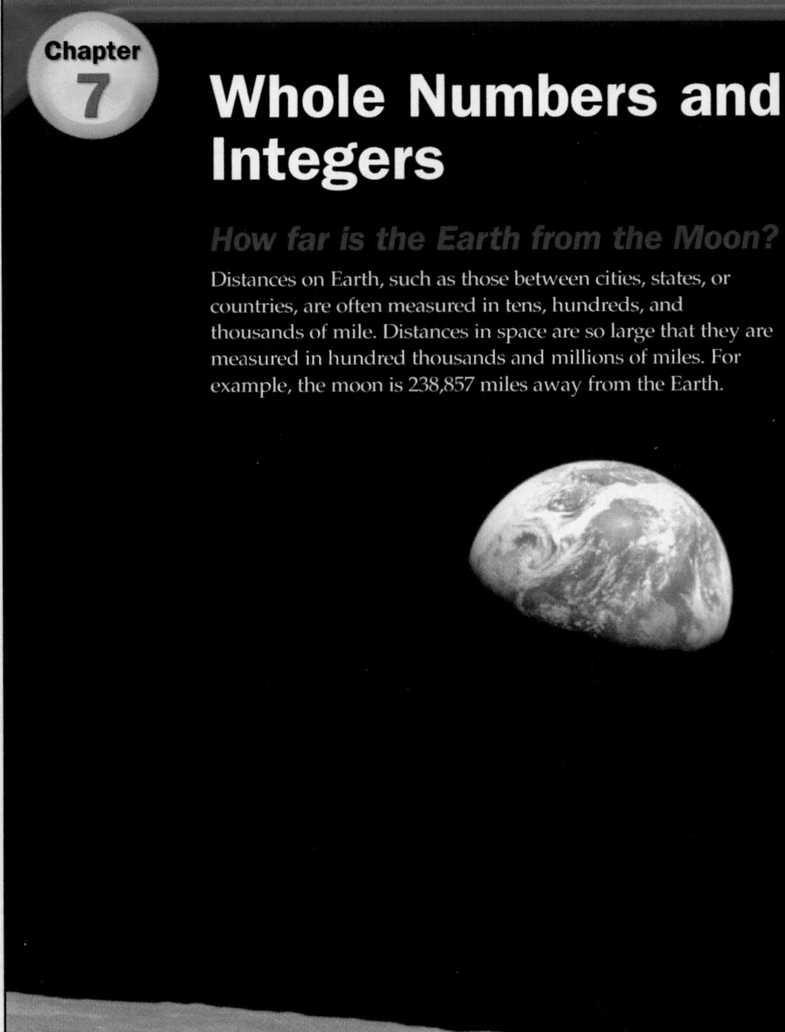
Chapter 7

Whole Numbers and Integers

How far is the Earth from the Moon?

Distances on Earth, such as those between cities, states, or countries, are often measured in tens, hundreds, and thousands of mile. Distances in space are so large that they are measured in hundred thousands and millions of miles. For example, the moon is 238,857 miles away from the Earth.

278 Chapter 7 Whole Numbers and Integers

Key Vocabulary

Find interactive definitions in 13 languages in the **eGlossary** at glencoe.com.

English **Español** *Introduce the most important vocabulary terms from Chapter 7.*

absolute value **valor absoluto**
the distance between a number and 0 on a number line (p. 301)

integers **número entero**
the whole numbers and their opposites (p. 294)
Example:
{... −3, −2, −1, 0, 1, 2, 3, ...}.

opposites **lo contrario**
numbers that are the same distance from zero in opposite directions (p. 294)

period **periodo**
a group of three digits in the place-value chart (p. 280)

round **redondear**
to find the nearest number based on a given place value (p. 287)

standard form **forma estándar**
writing a number using only digits (p. 280)

word form **en palabras**
a way to write numbers using only words (p. 280)

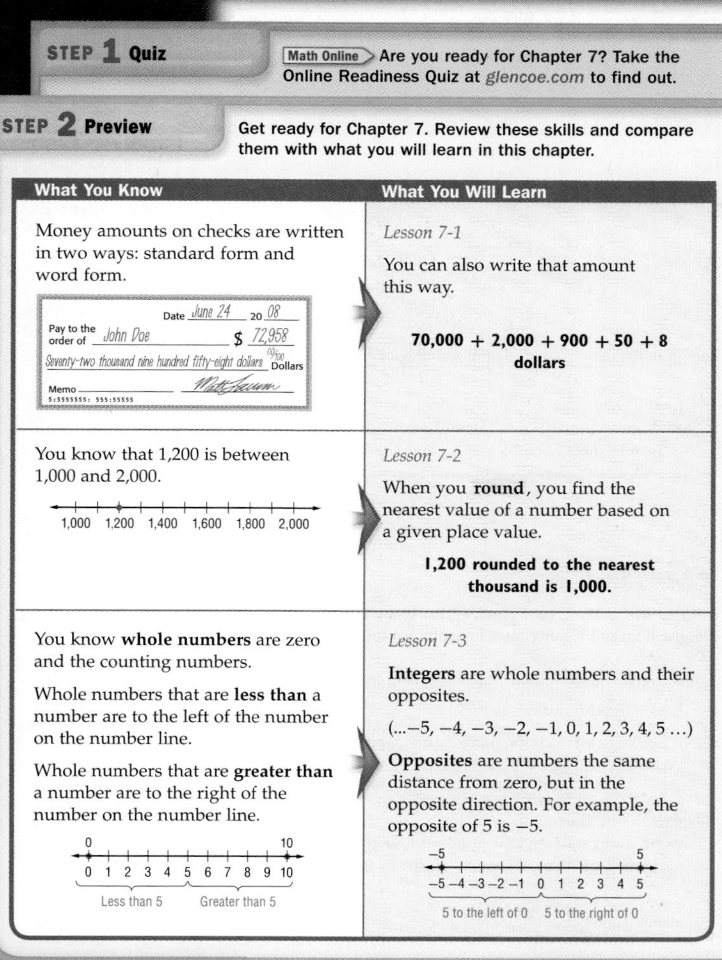

STEP 1 Quiz

Math Online Are you ready for Chapter 7? Take the Online Readiness Quiz at glencoe.com to find out.

STEP 2 Preview

Get ready for Chapter 7. Review these skills and compare them with what you will learn in this chapter.

What You Know	What You Will Learn
Money amounts on checks are written in two ways: standard form and word form. (Check: Date June 24 20 08; Pay to the order of John Doe $ 72,958; Seventy-two thousand nine hundred fifty-eight dollars 00/100 Dollars; Memo)	*Lesson 7-1* You can also write that amount this way. **70,000 + 2,000 + 900 + 50 + 8 dollars**
You know that 1,200 is between 1,000 and 2,000. (Number line: 1,000 1,200 1,400 1,600 1,800 2,000)	*Lesson 7-2* When you **round**, you find the nearest value of a number based on a given place value. **1,200 rounded to the nearest thousand is 1,000.**
You know **whole numbers** are zero and the counting numbers. Whole numbers that are **less than** a number are to the left of the number on the number line. Whole numbers that are **greater than** a number are to the right of the number on the number line. (Number line: 0 1 2 3 4 5 6 7 8 9 10; Less than 5, Greater than 5)	*Lesson 7-3* **Integers** are whole numbers and their opposites. (...−5, −4, −3, −2, −1, 0, 1, 2, 3, 4, 5 ...) **Opposites** are numbers the same distance from zero, but in the opposite direction. For example, the opposite of 5 is −5. (Number line: −5 −4 −3 −2 −1 0 1 2 3 4 5; 5 to the left of 0, 5 to the right of 0)

279

Step 1 Quiz

Pretest/Prescribe Students can take the Online Readiness Quiz or the Diagnostic Pretest in the Assessment Masters.

Step 2 Preview

Use this pre-chapter activity to activate students' prior knowledge, build confidence, and help students preview the lessons.

Dinah Zike's Foldables®

Guide students through the directions on p. A135 in the Chapter Resource Masters to create their own Foldable graphic organizer for use with this chapter.

Home Connections

- Have students find items in their homes that contain, hold, or have about 10; 100; 1,000; or 10,000 of something.
- Have students name three things in which the order is very important to the overall outcome.

Vocabulary Preview

- As students complete the Chapter Preview, have them make a list of important terms throughout the chapter.
- Relate the importance of the location of a digit in place value to the location of a letter in a crossword puzzle. Pass out graph paper and have students make a crossword puzzle that includes the key words and any other important terms throughout the chapter.
- The clues used for the puzzle should be given using definitions and examples.
- Once students are finished, have them trade and complete each other's crossword puzzles.

McGraw Hill Professional Development

Targeted professional development has been articulated throughout **McGraw-Hill's *Math Triumphs*** intervention program. **The McGraw-Hill Professional Development Video Library** provides short videos that support the **NCTM Focal Points and Focal Connections**. For more information, visit glencoe.com.

Model Lessons

Instructional Strategies

Lesson 7-1

Lesson Notes

Lesson Planner

Objective Write and expand whole numbers in the millions and be able to identify place value.

Vocabulary **period**, **standard form**, **word form**

Materials/Manipulatives base-ten blocks, construction paper, number lines, place-value charts, decks of cards, colored pencils

Chapter Resource Masters

- CRM Vocabulary and English Language Development (p. A138)
- CRM Skills Practice (p. A139)
- CRM Problem-Solving Practice (p. A140)
- CRM Homework Practice (p. A141)

Vocabulary

Standard Form Tell students that standard form is the typical way to write numbers. Each digit holds a place value, and together the digits represent a number. Practice reading numbers in standard form and identifying their place values.

Key Concept

Foundational Skills and Concepts After students have read through the Key Concept box, have them try these exercises.

1. How are place values grouped? into periods
2. What is the value of the 7 in 172,506? 70,000
3. What is the value of the 8 in 6,874,513? 800,000

Lesson 7-1

Read and Write Whole Numbers in the Millions

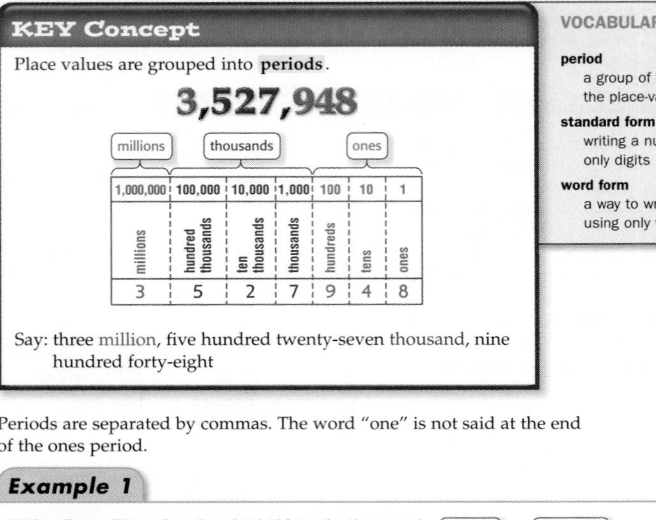

KEY Concept

Place values are grouped into **periods**.

3,527,948

millions	thousands			ones		
1,000,000	100,000	10,000	1,000	100	10	1
millions	hundred thousands	ten thousands	thousands	hundreds	tens	ones
3	5	2	7	9	4	8

Say: three million, five hundred twenty-seven thousand, nine hundred forty-eight

VOCABULARY

period
a group of three digits in the place-value chart

standard form
writing a number using only digits

word form
a way to write numbers using only words

Periods are separated by commas. The word "one" is not said at the end of the ones period.

Example 1

Write five million, four hundred thirty-six thousand, eight hundred twenty-nine in standard form.

1. Rewrite the number using digits and periods.
   5 million, 436 thousand, 829
2. Fill in each period of a place-value chart.
   Write the number. 5,436,829

millions	thousands			ones		
1,000,000	100,000	10,000	1,000	100	10	1
millions	hundred thousands	ten thousands	thousands	hundreds	tens	ones
5	4	3	6	8	2	9

YOUR TURN!

Write eight million, two hundred four thousand, nine hundred thirty-seven in standard form.

1. Rewrite the number using digits and periods.
   8 million, 204 thousand, 937
2. Fill in each period of a place-value chart.
   Write the number. 8,204,937

millions	thousands			ones		
1,000,000	100,000	10,000	1,000	100	10	1
millions	hundred thousands	ten thousands	thousands	hundreds	tens	ones
8	2	0	4	9	3	7

280 Chapter 7 Whole Numbers and Integers

Additional *Example 1*

Write nine million, six hundred seventy thousand, four hundred three in standard form.

1. Rewrite the number using digits and periods.
   9 million, 670 thousand, 403
2. Fill in each period of a place-value chart.
   Write the number. 9,670,403

1,000,000	100,000	10,000	1,000	100	10	1
millions	hundred thousands	ten thousands	thousands	hundreds	tens	ones
9	6	7	0	4	0	3

Example 2

Write 7,859,436 in word form.

1. Rewrite the number using digits and periods.
   7 million, 859 thousand, 436
2. Write the words for the millions period.
   seven million
3. Write the words for the thousands period.
   eight hundred fifty-nine thousand
4. Write the words for the ones period.
   four hundred thirty-six
5. Write the periods in order. Separate each period with a comma.
   seven million, eight hundred fifty-nine thousand, four hundred thirty-six

YOUR TURN!

Write 4,618,053 in word form.

1. Rewrite the number using digits and periods. 4 million, 618 thousand, 53
2. Write the words for the millions period. four million
3. Write the words for the thousands period. six hundred eighteen thousand
4. Write the words for the ones period. fifty-three
5. Write the periods in order. Separate each period with a comma.
   four million, six hundred eighteen thousand, fifty-three

Who is Correct?

Write 5,704,600 in word form.

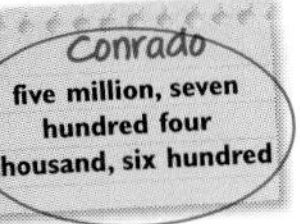

Conrado
five million, seven hundred four thousand, six hundred

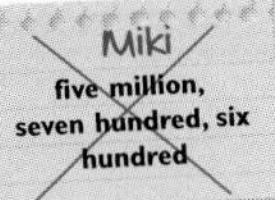

Miki
five million, seven hundred, six hundred

Selena
5 million, 704 hundred thousand, six

Circle correct answer(s). Cross out incorrect answer(s).

GO ON

Additional Example 2

Write 7,032,154 in word form.

1. Rewrite the number using digits and periods.
   7 million, 32 thousand, 154
2. Write the words for the millions period.
   seven million
3. Write the words for the thousands period.
   thirty-two thousand
4. Write the words for the ones period.
   one hundred fifty-four
5. Write the periods in order. Separate each period with a comma.
   seven million, thirty-two thousand, one hundred fifty-four

English Learner Strategy

Reading and Writing Numbers Alternate writing seven-digit numbers in standard and word form. Ask students to read aloud each number they write and identify which form they are giving. Have students write the numbers in their own language before writing them in English.

Common Error *Alert*

Place Value Remind students to focus on one period at a time to avoid missing a place value. Point out the importance of a zero placeholder and model the effect of a dropped zero.

Who *is Correct?*

Diagnostic Teaching

- Conrado wrote five million, seven hundred four thousand, six hundred. This is correct.
- Miki wrote five million, seven hundred, six hundred. This is incorrect because there are seven hundred four thousands, not seven hundred.
- Selena wrote 5 million, 704 hundred thousand, six. This is incorrect because there are numbers and words in her answer.

Remind students to use place-value charts to help them read numbers.

3 Practice

Using Manipulatives

Base-Ten Blocks To help students get a visual understanding of place value, show how ten unit blocks are equivalent to a rod, and how ten rods are equivalent to a flat. Have students use their imaginations to visualize representations for the greater place values. Be sure that students understand that the common element is always 10. Explain why that is the reason the number system they use is called a base-ten number system.

On-Hand Manipulatives Use a deck of playing cards to practice reading and writing numbers in the millions. Have students work in pairs. One student uses the cards to create a large number, while the partner reads and then writes the number in various forms.

Guided Practice

Use the place-value chart to answer each question. Then write each number in the chart.

1. How many zeros are in 8 millions? 6
2. How many zeros are in 4 hundred thousands? 5
3. How many zeros are in 9 ten thousands? 4

	1,000,000 millions	100,000 hundred thousands	10,000 ten thousands	1,000 thousands	100 hundreds	10 tens
1.	8	0	0	0	0	0
2.		4	0	0	0	0
3.			9	0	0	0

Write the missing number in each equation.

4. 4,000,000 + 500,000 + 9,000 + 20 + 8 = 4,509,028
5. 9,000,000 + 600,000 + 50,000 + 3,000 + 4 = 9,653,004

Write each number in standard form.

6. two million, seven hundred three thousand, eighty-five 2,703,085
7. eight million, two hundred thousand, three 8,200,003

Step by Step Practice

8. Write 621,050 in word form.

Step 1 Rewrite the number using digits and periods.

621 thousand, 50

When the digit is 0, its value is zero, so you do not write that place value.

Step 2 Write the words for the thousands period. six hundred twenty-one thousand

Step 3 Write the words for the ones period. fifty

Step 4 Write the periods in order. Separate each period with a comma.

six hundred twenty-one thousand, fifty

Write each number in word form.

9. 9,310,628 9 million 310 thousand 628
nine million, three hundred ten thousand, six hundred twenty-eight

10. 34,007,600
thirty-four million, seven thousand, six hundred

Are They Getting It?

Check students' understanding of reading and writing whole numbers by writing these problems on the board. Have students explain the incorrect information in each problem. Tell them to use a number line or a place-value chart to show why the answers are correct or incorrect.

1. The value of the 3 in the number 8,053,175 is thirty thousand. This is incorrect, because the 3 is in the thousands place. The value of the 3 is 3,000.
2. 1,764,329 is one million, seven hundred sixty-four thousand, three hundred twenty-nine in word form. This is correct.
3. The number line shows 340,000. This is correct.

Step by Step Problem-Solving Practice

Problem-Solving Strategies
- ☐ Draw a diagram.
- ☐ Make a table.
- ☐ Work backward.
- ☑ Solve a simpler problem.
- ☐ Look for a pattern.

Solve.

11 RECREATION The Apalachicola National Forest in Florida covers about five hundred sixty-four thousand, nine hundred sixty-one acres. What is this number in standard form?

Understand Read the problem. Write what you know. What is the greatest period in the number of acres in the Apalachicola National Forest? thousands

Plan Pick a strategy. One strategy is to solve a simpler problem.

Solve Break the number into the thousands period and the ones period.

Write the thousands period in digits. 564

Write the ones period in digits. 961

Write the periods together, separated by a comma. 564,961

Check Read the standard form aloud. Follow along with the word form to make sure the forms match.

12 SPACE The distance from the Earth to the Moon is about three hundred eighty-four thousand, four hundred kilometers. Write this distance in standard form. Check off each step.

✔ Understand: I underlined key words.

✔ Plan: To solve the problem, I will solve a simpler problem.

✔ Solve: The answer is 384,400.

✔ Check: I checked my answer by reading it aloud.

13 GEOGRAPHY Look at the map at the right. Write the area of Lake Michigan in word form.

twenty-two thousand, three hundred sq mi

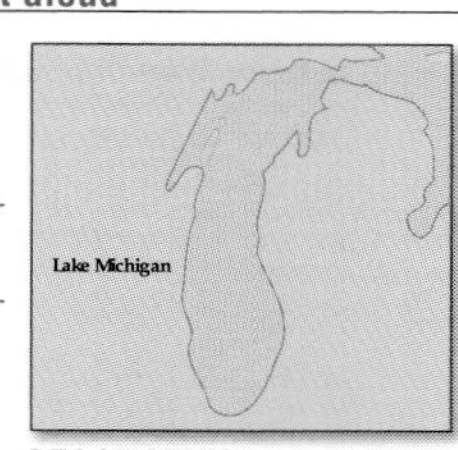

GEOGRAPHY Lake Michigan is 22,300 sq miles in area.

GO ON

Math Coach Notes

Using Color

Use colored pencils to differentiate periods in large numbers. Write a seven- or eight-digit number using three different colored pencils. Then write the word form of the number, writing the place value names in the same colors as the corresponding periods. Have students practice writing the word and standard forms of large numbers using these colored pencils.

Intervention Strategy — Naturalist/Kinesthetic Learners

Real-Life Applications

Brainstorm real-life examples of reading and writing numbers in a variety of forms. Use the example of writing checks. Create a check template and have students practice writing large payments. Include mistakes in both the standard and written forms, and challenge students to find the errors. Discuss how accuracy affects not only their personal account balances, but also the businesses to which their checks are written.

Odd/Even Assignments

Exercises 16–39 are structured so that students practice the same concepts whether they are assigned the odd or even problems.

In-Class Assignment

Have students complete Exercises 17, 21, 25, 29, 32, 38, and 43 to ensure that they understand the concept.

14 EARTH SCIENCE The continent of Asia is about 17,212,000 square miles. Write this number in word form.

seventeen million, two hundred twelve thousand sq mi

15 Reflect Place commas in the number 8245603. Then write the number in word form.

8,245,603; eight million, two hundred forty-five thousand, six hundred three

Skills, Concepts, and Problem Solving

Use the place-value chart to answer each question. Then write each number in the chart.

16 How many zeros are in 7 thousands?

3; 7,000

17 How many zeros are in 5 hundred thousands?

5; 500,000

18 How many zeros are in 2 ten thousands?

4; 20,000

19 How many zeros are in 9 millions?

6; 9,000,000

	1,000,000 millions	100,000 hundred thousands	10,000 ten thousands	1,000 thousands	100 hundreds	10 tens	1 ones
16.				7	0	0	0
17.		5	0	0	0	0	0
18.			2	0	0	0	0
19.	9	0	0	0	0	0	0

Write the missing number in each equation.

20 5,000,000 + 900,000 + 40,000 + 7,000 + 300 + 20 + 6 = 5,947,326

1,000,000 millions	100,000 hundred thousands	10,000 ten thousands	1,000 thousands	100 hundreds	10 tens	1 ones
5	9	4	7	3	2	?

21 3,000,000 + 70,000 + 90 + 4 = 3,070,094

Math Challenge

Missing Digits Have students create seven- or eight-digit numbers with zeroes in several place values. Ask them to write an answer key of the numbers in three different forms: standard, word, and using digits and period names. Encourage students to exchange with one another to write their classmates' numbers or post one of their problems as a challenge for the class.

Example:

40,080,307 40 million, 80 thousand, 307; forty million, eighty thousand, three hundred seven

rite the missing number in each equation.

5,000,000 + 700,000 + 10,000 + 200 + 90 = 5,710,290

8,000,000 + 200,000 + 3,000 + 500 + 7 = 8,203,507

7,000,000 + 500,000 + 20,000 + 600 + 3 = 7,520,603

9,000,000 + 300,000 + 1,000 + 50 = 9,301,050

rite each number in standard form.

six hundred thirty-seven thousand, ninety-two 637,092

nine hundred five thousand, one hundred four 905,104

two million, three hundred eight thousand, nine hundred sixty-five
2,308,965

seven million, forty-nine thousand, two hundred three 7,049,203

fifty-two million, three hundred nine thousand, sixty-seven 52,309,067

forty nine million, seven thousand, five hundred eight 49,007,508

rite each number in word form.

406,129
four hundred six thousand, one hundred twenty-nine

952,038
nine hundred fifty-two thousand, thirty-eight

8,214,765
eight million, two hundred fourteen thousand, seven hundred sixty-five

6,940,387
six million, nine hundred forty thousand, three hundred eighty-seven

Common Error *Alert*

Exercises 26-37 Demonstrate how easy it is to skip words when writing numbers in word form and the effect it has on the number's standard form. Remind students to read carefully and look for the place value word cues to help correctly write the standard form.

4 Assess

See It, Do It, Say It, Write It

Step 1 Write a seven-digit number on the board. Ask students to copy it on their papers.

Step 2 Have students rewrite the number using digits and periods.

Step 3 Ask students to work in pairs or small groups. Have each student show their group members the rewritten number and explain how to write it in word form.

Step 4 Have students work alone to explain how to write the number in word form. Encourage students to use lesson vocabulary such as period and place value names in their written explanations.

Looking Ahead: Pre-Teach

Round and Compare Whole Numbers in the Millions In the next lesson, students will learn how to round and compare whole numbers up to the millions. The rounding rules will be reviewed.

Example

Round 38,621,097 to the nearest million. 39,000,000

Have students round each number to the nearest hundred thousand.

1. 508,243 500,000
2. 964,017 1,000,000
3. 7,213,650 7,200,000

Write each number in word form.

36 7,908,260

seven million, nine hundred eight thousand, two hundred sixty

37 3,096,047

three million, ninety-six thousand, forty-seven

Solve.

38 GEOGRAPHY The Arctic Ocean is the smallest ocean in the world. Its area is about five million, four hundred twenty-six thousand square miles. Write this number in standard form.

5,426,000 sq mi

39 GEOGRAPHY Write the area of the United States in standard form, using the map at the right.

3,537,441 sq km

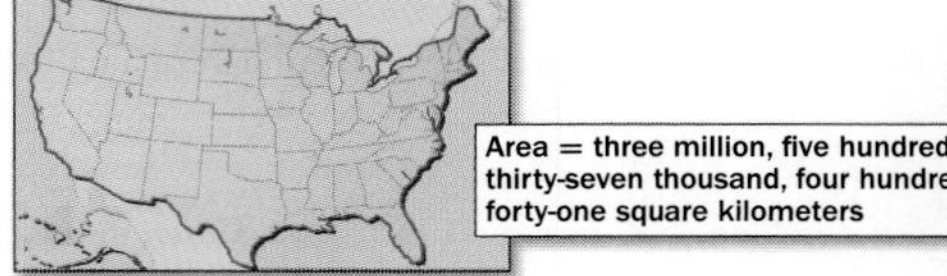

Vocabulary Check **Write the vocabulary word that completes each sentence.**

40 A group of three digits in the place value chart is called a(n) period.

41 Word form is a way to write numbers using only words.

42 Standard form is when numbers are written using only digits.

43 Writing in Math Divide a sheet of paper into four sections. Write the number 4,436,500 in one section of the paper. Use the other three sections to represent the number in three other ways.

Sample answer: 4,000,000 + 400,000 + 30,000 + 6,000 + 500; four million, four hundred thirty-six thousand, five hundred; 4 millions, 436 thousands, 5 hundreds

STOP

286 Chapter 7 Whole Numbers and Integers

Ticket Out the Door

Place Value and Number Forms Write the following on the board. Tell students to write each number in standard form. As students approach the classroom door to exit, alternate asking them to identify the form in which one of the examples is written or a specific period of a number from the board.

1. 11 million, 905 thousand, 723 11,905,723
2. six million, four hundred fifty thousand, eight hundred ninety-two 6,450,892
3. 3,000,000 + 100,000 + 50,000 + 2,000 + 400 + 80 + 6 3,152,486

Lesson 7-2 Round and Compare Whole Numbers in the Millions

KEY Concept

To **round** greater numbers, underline the place value being rounded and circle the digit to its right.

If the circled digit < 5, the underlined digit does not change. All digits to the right of the underlined digit change to 0.

If the circled digit = 5, the underlined digit increases by 1. All digits to the right of the underlined digit change to 0.

If the circled digit > 5, the underlined digit increases by 1. All digits to the right of the underlined digit change to 0.

Round to the nearest million.

2,(3)45,678   3 < 5

So, 2,345,678 rounds to 2,000,000.

To **compare** numbers, look at each place value until you find a place value where the digits are not the same.

Compare 8,765,432 to 8,654,321.

8,765,432
8,654,321

The digits differ in the hundred-thousands place. 7 > 6

8,765,432 > 8,654,321

VOCABULARY

compare to note the differences, such as which number is greater

greater than (>) the number on the left side of the symbol is greater than the number on the right side

less than (<) the number on the left side of the symbol is less than the number on the right side

round to find the nearest number based on a given place value

emember that when rounding, the circled digit and all digits to the ght of it become 0.

Example 1

Round 1,632,700 to the nearest ten thousand.

1. Underline the digit in the ten-thousands place. 1,6<u>3</u>2,700
2. Circle the digit to the right of 3. 1,6<u>3</u>(2),700
3. Compare 2 and 5. 2 < 5
4. Leave 3 unchanged. Change all digits to the right of 3 to 0. 1,630,000

YOUR TURN!

Round 7,436,956 to the nearest ten thousand.

1. Underline the digit in the ten-thousands place. 7,436,956
2. Circle the digit to the right. 7,43(6),956
3. Compare the circled digit to 5. 6 > 5
4. What happens to the 3? It increases by 1 to 4.

Write the rounded number. 7,440,000

Lesson 7-2 Round and Compare Whole Numbers in the Millions 287

Additional *Example 1*

Round 4,387,812 to the nearest ten-thousand.

1. Underline the digit in the ten-thousands place. 4,3<u>8</u>7,812
2. Circle the digit to the right of 8. 4,3<u>8</u>(7),812
3. Compare 7 and 5. 7 > 5
4. Increase the 8 by 1. Change all digits to the right to 0. 4,390,000

Lesson Notes

Lesson 7-2

Lesson Planner

Objective Round and compare whole numbers.

Vocabulary **compare**, **greater than (>)**, **less than (<)**, **round**

Materials/Manipulatives place-value charts, base-ten blocks, unit cubes

Chapter Resource Masters

CRM Vocabulary and English Language Development (p. A142)

CRM Skills Practice (p. A143)

CRM Problem-Solving Practice (p. A144)

CRM Homework Practice (p. A145)

1 Introduce

Vocabulary

Vocabulary Connections The concepts of *greater than, less than,* and *rounding* should be familiar to most students. Ask students for strategies to remember that ">" means *greater than* and "<" means *less than*. Guide students to see the symbol points to the lesser number.

2 Teach

Key Concept

Foundational Skills and Concepts After students have read through the Key Concept box, have them try these exercises.

1. In 13,455,016, what number is in the hundred-thousands place? 4
2. When rounding to the nearest millions place, what place value decides whether the number in the millions place rounds up or stays the same? hundred-thousands

Additional **Example 2**

Use <, =, or > to compare 5,687,000 and 5,697,000.

1. Write both numbers in a place-value chart.

1,000,000	100,000	10,000	1,000	100	10	1
millions	hundred thousands	ten thousands	thousands	hundreds	tens	ones
5	6	8	7	0	0	0
5	6	9	7	0	0	0

2. Begin on the left. Compare the digits in the millions places.
   5 = 5
3. Compare the digits in the hundred-thousands places.
   6 = 6
4. Compare the digits in the ten-thousands places.
   8 < 9
   Because the digits in the ten-thousands places are different, there is no need to compare any more digits.
5. Write a statement using the < symbol.
   5,687,000 < 5,697,000

Using Manipulatives

Base-Ten Blocks Put the 10 cubes together from the base-ten block kits and ask how much they represent. If there are 100 cubes available, repeat with differing amounts.

On-Hand Manipulatives Have students create place-value models out of construction paper. For example, one large block equals 1,000 and one small block equals 100.

Example 2

Use <, =, or > to compare 3,653,000 and 3,663,000.

1. Write both numbers in a place-value chart.

1,000,000	100,000	10,000	1,000	100	10	1
millions	hundred thousands	ten thousands	thousands	hundreds	tens	ones
3	6	5	3	0	0	0
3	6	6	3	0	0	0

2. Begin on the left. Compare the digits in the millions places. 3 = 3
3. Compare the digits in the hundred-thousands places. 6 = 6
4. Compare the digits in the ten-thousands places. 5 < 6

   Because the digits in the ten-thousands places are different, there is no need to compare any more digits.
5. Write a statement using the < symbol.

   3,653,000 < 3,663,000

YOUR TURN!

Use <, =, or > to compare 8,544,543 and 8,544,343.

1. Use a place-value chart.

1,000,000	100,000	10,000	1,000	100	10	1
millions	hundred thousands	ten thousands	thousands	hundreds	tens	ones
8	5	4	4	5	4	3
8	5	4	4	3	4	3

2. Begin on the left. Compare the digits in the millions places. 8 = 8
3. Compare the digits in the hundred-thousands places. 5 = 5
4. Compare the digits in the ten-thousands places. 4 = 4
5. Compare the digits in the thousands places. 4 = 4
6. Compare the digits in the hundreds places. 5 > 3
7. Write a statement using <, =, or >.
   8,544,543 > 8,544,343

Who is Correct?

Use <, =, or > to compare 1,362,980 and 1,362,982.

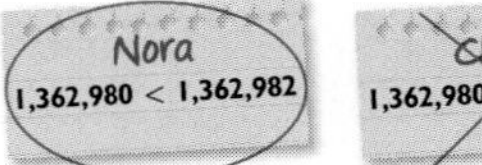

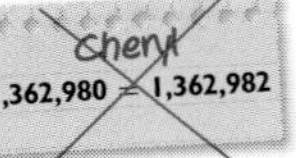

Circle correct answer(s). Cross out incorrect answer(s).

Guided Practice

1. Is 268,233 closer to 200,000 or 300,000? 300,000
2. Is 5,298,637 closer to 5,000,000 or 6,000,000? 5,000,000

Who *is Correct?*

Diagnostic Teaching

- Nora wrote the < symbol. This is correct.
- Cheryl wrote the = sign. This is not correct because 1,362,980 is not equal to 1,362,982.
- Melisa wrote the > symbol. This is not correct because 1,362,980 is less than, not greater than, 1,362,982.

Vrite the ten thousands each number is between.

3 203,670 is between 200,000 and 210,000.

4 692,549 is between 690,000 and 700,000.

Step by Step Practice

5 Round 256,049 to the nearest ten thousand.

Step 1 Underline the digit in the ten-thousands place. What digit do you underline? 5

Step 2 Circle the digit in the thousands place. What digit do you circle? 6

Step 3 Is the circled digit greater than, equal to, or less than 5? greater than

Step 4 Increase the underlined digit by 1. What digit is in the ten-thousands place now? 6

Step 5 What digit(s) get changed to zeros? 6, 4, and 9

Step 6 256,049 rounded to the nearest ten thousand is 260,000.

ound each number to the given place value.

6 603,252, ten thousands
Underline the digit in the ten-thousands place.
Circle the digit in the thousands place.
What is 603,252 rounded to the nearest ten thousand? 600,000

7 726,509, ten thousands 730,000

8 898,761, hundred thousands 900,000

se <, =, or > to complete each statement.

9 1,304,987 < 1,895,823

10 4,340,900 > 2,949,800

1 266,907 < 266,990

12 928,840 > 927,840

Vrite the numbers in order from least to greatest.

3 3,356,000; 2,359,000; 2,937,000 2,359,000; 2,937,000; 3,356,000

4 2,009,000; 2,037,000; 2,006,000 2,006,000; 2,009,000; 2,037,000

Math Coach Notes

Study Tip Tell students that when they study, they should do so in the same place. If they have a special spot where they always study, they will get into the mindset more readily each time they sit there. Suggest that students keep or even write a goal for how long they plan to study. This keeps a little pressure on them to pay attention to what they are doing and to continue moving to meet their goals.

Zeros as Placeholders Zeros are not just placeholders but represent a power of 10. For instance, in the number 8,506,789, the zero represents $0 \times 10{,}000$. Use this notation until students are secure in their understanding of zero.

Note This!

Proofread Instruct students to proofread their notes at the end of class, if not during. Often students get distracted, even for just a moment, and make an error in their notes. Sometimes the error is an outright mistake; other times it is an omission of information. Proofreading before the class ends ensures that the information in their notes is complete and accurate.

Intervention Strategy

Auditory/Linguistic Learners

Strategies

1. Have seven students stand in front of the class. They will represent a place value for a number in the millions. Ask each student to call out a digit. Tell them to round to the nearest ten-thousands, then call out their digits. Repeat with different sets of students.
2. In groups or pairs, have students use a map, atlas, or reference book to choose five countries. Have them find the population or area of each. Tell them to compare the population or square miles of each country using number sentences and a short paragraph. They can round the figures.
3. Have students research the distance from Earth to each planet. Ask them to write number sentences comparing distances and round to the nearest million miles.

Math Coach Notes

Model Large Numbers

1. Concrete materials are not practical to model large numbers, but visual aids such as place-value charts and number lines can be used.
2. To give students opportunities to compare and round large numbers, use the distances between planets, and populations or areas of states and countries as a source of real-world large numbers. Ask students to come up with other examples on which they can gather data.

Common Error *Alert*

Rounding Up When 9 is Involved

When the digit 9 is in the place being rounded to, students often know that 9 rounds up to 10, but they do not remember to increase the digit to the left of the rounding place by 1. Show students various examples, such as:

Round 79,834 to the nearest thousand. 80,000
Round 123,970 to the nearest hundred. 124,000
Round 974,032 to the nearest hundred-thousand. 1,000,000

Step by Step Problem-Solving Practice

Problem-Solving Strategies
- ☐ Work backward.
- ☐ Draw a picture.
- ☑ Make a chart.
- ☐ Solve a simpler problem.
- ☐ Act it out.

Solve.

15 GEOGRAPHY The total land area of Canada is about 3,855,103 square miles. A news article said the total area was about 3,860,000 square miles. To what place value was the area rounded?

Understand Read the problem. Write what you know.

The actual land area is 3,855,103 square miles.

The rounded area is 3,860,000 square miles.

Plan Pick a strategy. One strategy is to make a chart.

Solve Write both the actual land area and the rounded area in a place-value chart.

1,000,000	100,000	10,000	1,000	100	10	1
millions	hundred thousands	ten thousands	thousands	hundreds	tens	ones
3	8	5	5	1	0	3
3	8	6	0	0	0	0

Digits to the right of the place being rounded change to 0. What non-zero digit of the rounded number is farthest right? 6

It is in the ten-thousands place. For the article, the land area was rounded to the nearest ten thousand.

Check Round the total land area to the place value you identified. Is your rounded number the same as the number used in the article?

16 NATURE Each year it is estimated that 42,225 Canada geese migrate south to warmer climates. A news reporter stated that 42,000 Canada geese migrate each year. To what place value did the news reporter round? Check off each step.

✓ Understand: I underlined key words.

✓ Plan: To solve the problem, I will make a chart

✓ Solve: The answer is thousands

✓ Check: I checked my answer by making sure the rounded number is the same as the rounded amount

Are They Getting It?

Check students' understanding of rounding and comparing whole numbers in the millions by writing these problems on the board. Have students explain the incorrect information in each problem. Tell them to draw a number line or a place-value chart to show why the answers are correct, or are not correct.

1. 4,553,800 rounded to the nearest ten-thousand is 4,500,000. This is not correct. The number is rounded to the hundred-thousands, not the ten-thousands.
2. 15,819,405 < 15,809,405 This is not correct because 15,819,405 has a 1 in the ten-thousands digit, and 15,809,405 has a zero.
3. 3,456,054 to the nearest million is 3,000,000. This is correct.

TRAVEL The average distance by car from California to Florida is 2,795 miles. What is this distance rounded to the nearest hundred? 2,800 miles

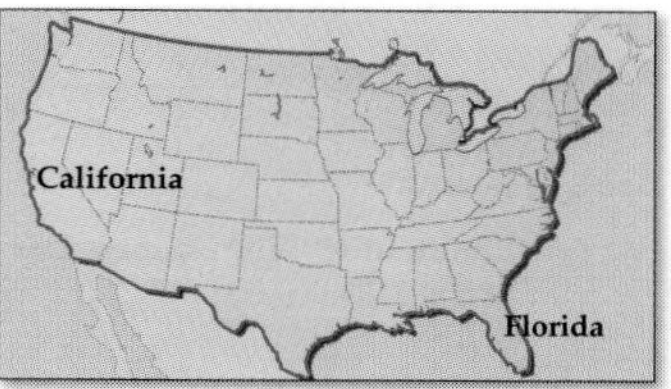

Reflect Tell how many digits are in the standard form of 15 million. How many of those digits are zeros?

8 digits; 6 zeros

Skills, Concepts, and Problem Solving

rite *true* or *false* for each statement. If a statement is false, change e statement to make it true.

The digits in the thousand period represent hundred thousand, ten thousand, and thousand. true

0 When comparing numbers, the greatest number will have the greatest ones digit. False; you have to look at all of the place values to determine the greatest number.

rite the hundred thousands that each number is between.

312,003 is between 300,000 and 400,000.

427,900 is between 400,000 and 500,000.

ound each number to the given place value.

445,700, hundred thousands 400,000

100,000	10,000	1,000	100	10	1
hundred thousands	ten thousands	thousands	hundreds	tens	ones
4	4	5	7	0	0

24 285,008, hundred thousands 300,000

100,000	10,000	1,000	100	10	1
hundred thousands	ten thousands	thousands	hundreds	tens	ones
2	8	5	0	0	8

254,900, hundred thousands 300,000

26 107,306, hundred thousands 100,000

445,700, ten thousands 450,000

28 285,008, ten thousands 290,000

2,987,549, millions 3,000,000

30 5,705,600, millions 6,000,000

GO ON

Odd/Even Assignments

Exercises 19–34 are structured so that students practice the same concepts whether they are assigned the odd or even problems.

In-Class Assignment

Have students complete Exercises 20, 22, 24, 28, 32, 33, and 37 to ensure that they understand the concept.

Common Error *Alert*

Exercise 20 If students struggle with Exercise 20, they may not understand what the question is asking. Write down two numbers in the millions, for instance 5,890,819 and 6,809,236. Ask if the number with the 9 in the ones place is greater than the other number. Using a place-value chart may also be helpful in solving this problem. Give an example of when Exercise 20 would be true (8,056,891 and 8,056,892, for example).

Math Challenge

Number Game Divide students into pairs. Have each student pair neatly write random numbers between 1 and 99 million on 20 index cards. Student pairs then trade cards. After they shuffle the deck and place it facedown, each player takes a turn by choosing a card. Whoever has the *greater* number gets a point. The first student to 10 points wins.

4 Assess

See It, Do It, Say It, Write It

Step 1 Draw a number line. Plot two numbers, for instance, 2,500,000 and 2,300,000. Ask which number is greater. Do the same using a place-value chart, with numbers such as 5,801,456 and 5,835,322. Have students explain their process for comparing large numbers.

Step 2 Tell students to draw a number line on paper and plot 1,600,000. Make certain they understand how to label it. Have a student volunteer share his or her work.

Step 3 Have students begin at 100,000 and count off by 100,000s to 1 million (or higher if desired).

Step 4 Ask students to write the rules for rounding. Tell them to use an example. Then ask them to write three number sentences that compare numbers in the millions using the *greater than, less than,* and *equal* symbols.

Looking Ahead: Pre-teach

Model Integers In the next lesson, students will learn how to model integers. Integers are the positive whole numbers and their opposites.

Example

Write an integer to represent "a loss of $80." −80

Have students write an integer to represent each situation.

1. 4,000 feet below sea level −4,000
2. a deposit of $55 55
3. a temperature of 6 degrees Celsius below zero −6

Write *true* or *false* for each statement.

31. 4,315,000 < 4,382,000 true

32. 530,019 > 610,710 false

Solve.

33. CONSTRUCTION The estimated cost to build a new baseball stadium is $458,000,000. What is this amount rounded to the nearest ten million? $460,000,000

34. OCEANOGRAPHY The Pacific Ocean covers an area of about sixty-four million, one hundred eighty-six thousand, three hundred square miles. How many square miles is the Pacific Ocean rounded to the nearest hundred thousand? 64,200,000

Vocabulary Check **Write the vocabulary word that completes each sentence.**

35. To round a number is to find its nearest number based on a given place value.

36. The greater than, or > symbol means that the greater number is left of the symbol.

37. Writing in Math Create a place-value chart with millions, thousands, and ones periods. Write three 7-digit numbers in your table. Write each of your numbers in words. Write the numbers in order from least to greatest.

Sample answer: 1,560,500; 2,300,900; 6,700,345

one million, five hundred sixty thousand, five hundred;

two million, three hundred thousand, nine hundred;

six million, seven hundred thousand, three hundred forty-five

Spiral Review

Solve. (Lesson 7-1, p. 280)

38. SCHOOL Vik was asked to write 5,305,707 in words on his homework assignment. He wrote "five million, three hundred five thousand, seven hundred." What mistake did Vik make?

Vik forgot the last 7 in the ones period. The number is five million, three hundred five thousand, seven hundred seven.

STOP

Ticket Out the Door

Write and Compare Have students work in two pairs. Two students in one pair will each draw a place-value chart and write a number between 1 and 99 million in the chart. The pair will give the two charts to the other pair. The other pair will write a number sentence comparing the two numbers. Students will turn in their papers as they exit the classroom.

Progress Check 1 (Lessons 7-1 and 7-2)

Write each number in word form.

1. 6,324,015 six million, three hundred twenty-four thousand, fifteen
2. 1,447,398 one million, four hundred forty-seven thousand, three hundred ninety-eight
3. 26,700,000 twenty-six million, seven hundred thousand

Write each number in standard form.

4. thirteen million, four hundred five thousand 13,405,000
5. thirty-three million, one hundred twelve thousand 33,112,000

Round each number to the given place value.

6. 573,234, hundred thousands 600,000
7. 3,454,900, millions 3,000,000

Use <, =, or > to complete each statement.

8. 634,920 (>) 632,920
9. 5,372,649 (<) 5,927,036

Write the numbers in order from least to greatest.

10. 834,000; 843,000; 804,000 804,000; 834,000; 843,000
11. 3,005,000; 2,987,000; 2,908,000 2,908,000; 2,987,000; 3,005,000

Solve.

12. **POPULATION** The 2006 estimated population for California was thirty-six million, four hundred fifty-seven thousand, five hundred forty-nine. Write this number in standard form.

    36,457,549

13. **SPORTS** The Boston Garden hosted basketball games from 1946 until 1995. It could seat fourteen thousand, eight hundred ninety fans. What is this amount rounded to the nearest thousand?

    15,000

Chapter 7 Progress Check 293

Progress Check 1

Chapter 7

Formative Assessment

Use the Progress Check to assess students' mastery of the previous lessons. Have students review the lesson indicated for the problems they answered incorrectly.

Odd/Even Assignments

Exercises are structured so that students practice the same concepts whether they are assigned the odd or even problems.

Common Error Alert

Symbols Be sure students know < reads "less than," and > reads "greater than," and that place values are grouped into periods separated by commas.

Exercises 1–3 Tell students to break down the numbers at the commas for simplification.

Data-Driven Decision Making

Students missing Exercises . . .	Have trouble with . . .	Should review and practice . . .
1-5	writing numbers in word and standard form.	SSG Lesson 7-1, p. 280 CRM Skills Practice, p. A139
6-7	rounding numbers.	SSG Lesson 7-2, p. 287 CRM Skills Practice, p. A143
8-9	comparing numbers.	SSG Lesson 7-2, p. 287 CRM Skills Practice, p. A143
10-11	ordering numbers.	SSG Lesson 7-2, p. 287 CRM Skills Practice, p. A143
12-13	solving word problems involving writing numbers in standard form and/or rounding numbers.	CRM Problem-Solving Practice, pp. A140 and A144

Lesson 7-3

Lesson Notes

Lesson Planner

Objective Understand and model integers.

Vocabulary **integers**, **negative number**, **opposites**, **positive number**, **whole numbers**

Materials/Manipulatives number lines, rulers, algebra tiles, decks of cards, thermometers

Chapter Resource Masters

- CRM Vocabulary and English Language Development (p. A146)
- CRM Skills Practice (p. A147)
- CRM Problem-Solving Practice (p. A148)
- CRM Homework Practice (p. A149)

Vocabulary

Number Families Write the following list of numbers vertically on the board: –3, 4, 0, –2, 5, 1, –1, 3, –5. In a different area of the board write *integer, even number, odd number, positive number, negative number, whole number,* and *zero.* Ask for volunteers to write as many vocabulary words as possible that describe each integer in the vertical list. Then ask for volunteers to identify any *opposites* in the vertical list.

Key Concept

Foundational Skills and Concepts After students have read through the Key Concept box, have them try these exercises.

1. Write the opposite of each number.
   –2 2 4 –4 5 –5
   –6 6 –9 9 –1 1
2. Circle the positive integers in the group:
   –2, –5, 7, 1, –4, 0, 2, –3 circle: 7, 1, 2
3. Name one whole number that is neither positive nor negative. zero

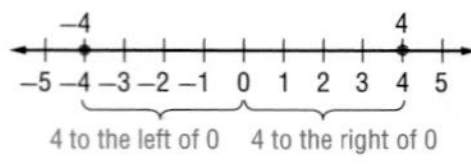

Lesson 7-3

Model Integers

KEY Concept

Whole numbers are zero and the counting numbers.

Opposites are numbers the same distance from zero, but in the opposite direction. For example, the opposite of 4 is –4.

–4 is read "negative 4" not "minus 4." "Minus" indicates the operation of subtraction, and "negative" indicates a number less than 0.

Integers are whole numbers and their opposites.

...–5, –4, –3, –2, –1, 0, 1, 2, 3, 4, 5,...

Positive numbers are numbers that are greater than zero, and **negative numbers** are numbers that are less than zero.

The number zero is neither positive nor negative.

VOCABULARY

integers
the whole numbers and their opposites
Example: ...–3, –2, –1, 0, 1, 2, 3,...

negative number
a number that is less than zero

opposites
numbers that are the same distance from 0 in opposite directions
Example: 3 and –3

positive number
a number that is greater than zero

whole numbers
the set of all counting numbers and zero

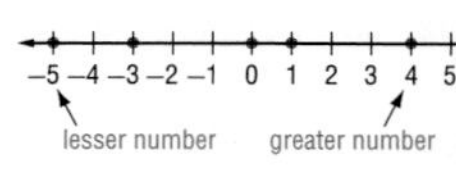

Example 1

Graph the integers 4, –3, 0, –5, and 1 on a number line. Then write them in order from least to greatest.

1. On the number line, place a dot at each of the numbers.
2. The numbers in order from least to greatest are –5, –3, 0, 1, 4.

YOUR TURN!

Graph the integers 3, –2, 1, 5, and –1 on a number line. Then write them in order from least to greatest.

1. On the number line, place a dot at 3, –2, 1, 5, –1.
2. The numbers in order from least to greatest are –2, –1, 1, 3, 5.

Additional *Example 1*

Graph the integers –1, 2, –3, and 4 on a number line. Then write them in order from least to greatest.

1. On the number line, place a dot at each of the numbers.

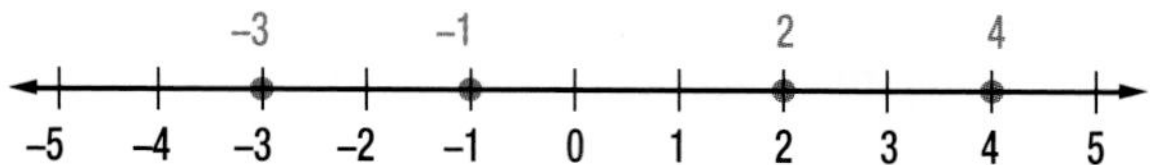

2. The numbers in order from least to greatest are –3, –1, 2, 4.

Example 2

Use $<$, $=$, or $>$ to compare −4 and 4.

1. Graph both numbers on the number line.
2. The number farther to the right is 4, so it is the greater number.
3. Since −4 is less than 4, you need to use the *less than* symbol. **$-4 < 4$**

YOUR TURN!

Use $<$, $=$, or $>$ to compare 1 and −1.

1. Graph both numbers on the number line.
2. The number farther to the right is __1__, so it is the greater number.
3. Write a comparison statement. 1 (>) −1

Example 3

Write an integer to represent the sentence.

"A shipwreck is 250 feet below sea level."

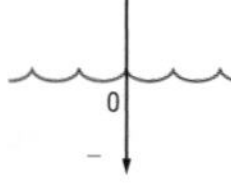

1. Underline the key words.
2. Decide if the number is positive or negative. negative
   Imagine a number line that is vertical instead of horizontal.
   Sea level is "0." Below sea level is negative.
   Above sea level is positive.
3. Write the number. −250

YOUR TURN!

Write an integer to represent the sentence.

"A mountain climber is 375 feet above sea level."

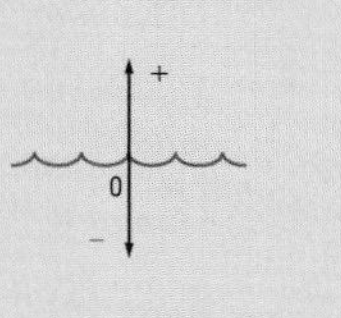

1. Underline key words.
2. Decide if the number is positive or negative. __positive__
   Imagine a number line that is vertical instead of horizontal.
   Sea level is 0. Below sea level is negative.
   Above sea level is positive.
3. Write the number. __375__

GO ON

Additional Example 2

Use $<$, $=$, or $>$ to compare –3 and 3.

1. Graph both numbers on the number line.

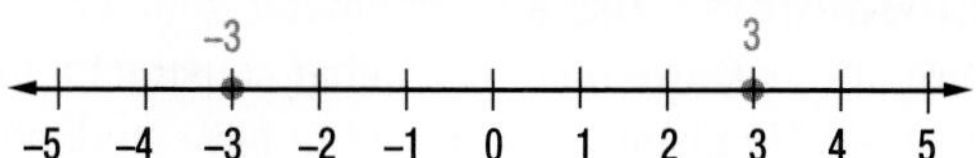

2. The number farther to the right is 3, so it is the greater number.
3. Since –3 is less than 3, you need to use the *less than* symbol. $-3 < 3$

Additional Example 3

Write an integer to represent the sentence.

"The coral reef was 18 feet below sea level."

1. Underline the key words. 18 feet below sea level
2. Decide if the number is positive or negative. negative Imagine a vertical number line. Sea level is 0. Below sea level is negative. Above sea level is positive.

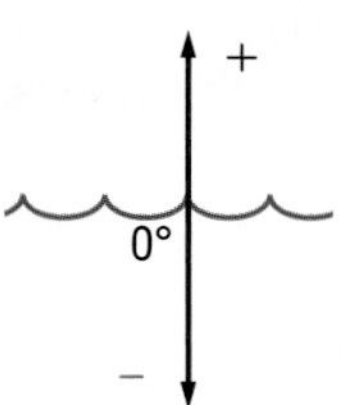

3. Write the number. –18

Intervention Strategy — Logical Learners

Classifying Integers List the following vocabulary terms on the board: integer, whole number, positive number, negative number. Write several integers on the board to model how to classify each number, using as many terms as possible. Ask students to work in pairs. Tell them to create a set of numbers and then classify each example. Invite volunteers to share their sets and classifications with the class.

3 Practice

Using Manipulatives

Thermometers Use a thermometer to model positive and negative numbers. Either construct a large thermometer to display on a board or have students draw their own to label.

On-Hand Manipulatives Use a bulletin board to create a number line. Invite students to label and classify integers along the number line, using lesson vocabulary while plotting points.

English Learner Strategy

Comparing Numbers Write an assortment of integers on a piece of paper. Ask students to identify which numbers are greater than zero and which are less than zero. Review the meaning of the negative sign. Have students find each integer on a number line. Explain how to compare two of the integers and determine which one is greater or lesser. Use lesson vocabulary to identify each of the integers. Relate the terms *greater than* and *less than* to terms in each student's native language.

Who is Correct?

Write −4, 3, 2, and −1 in order from least to greatest.

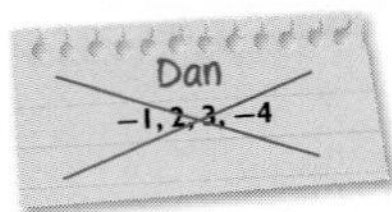

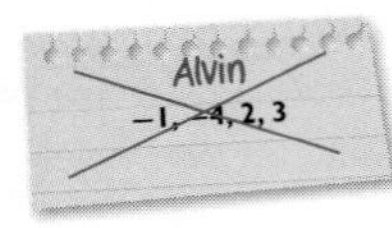

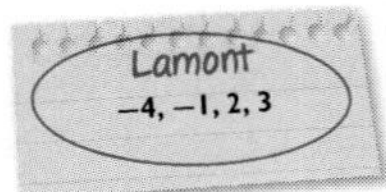

Circle correct answers. Cross out incorrect answers.

Guided Practice

Graph the integers on a number line. Then write them in order from least to greatest.

1. 5, −2, 1, 4, −1

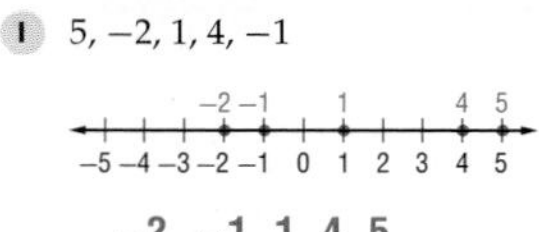

−2, −1, 1, 4, 5

2. 4, 3, 2, −5, −2

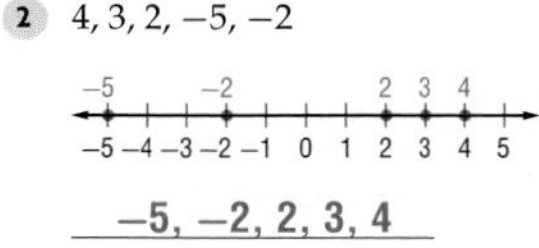

−5, −2, 2, 3, 4

Step by Step Practice

3. Use <, =, or > to compare −8 and −3.

Step 1 Graph both numbers on the number line.

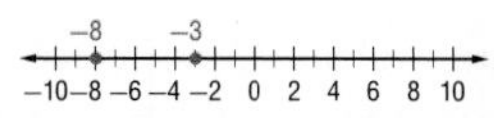

Step 2 What number is farther to the right?

−3

Step 3 Write a comparison statement.

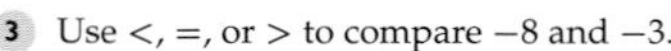
−8 < −3

Who *is Correct?*

Diagnostic Teaching

- Dan's work is incorrect. He wrote the numbers in order, not considering the negative signs.
- Alvin's work is incorrect. −4 is less than −1.
- Lamont's work is correct. The numbers are ordered correctly.

Remind students that the numbers that are farther left on the number line are less in value.

Write <, =, or > in each circle to compare each number pair.

4 $-1 \,\textcircled{<}\, 0$

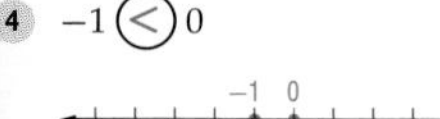
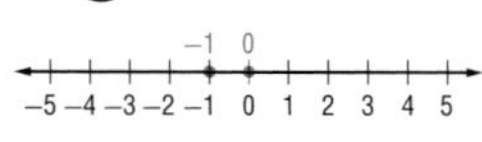

5 $-2 \,\textcircled{>}\, -4$

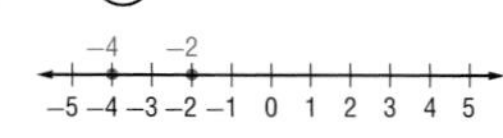

6 $3 \,\textcircled{<}\, 4$

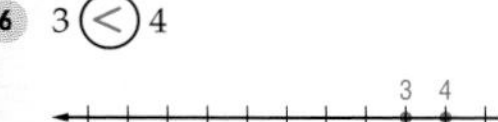

7 $-6 \,\textcircled{>}\, -7$

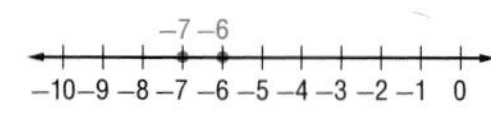

8 $-3 \,\textcircled{<}\, 1$

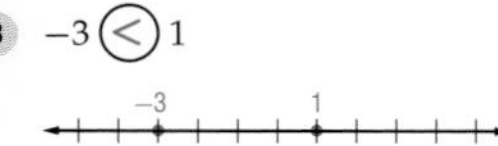

9 $5 \,\textcircled{>}\, -1$

Step by Step Problem-Solving Practice

Problem-Solving Strategies
- ☑ Draw a diagram.
- ☐ Use logical reasoning.
- ☐ Make a table.
- ☐ Solve a simpler problem.
- ☐ Work backward.

Solve.

10 WEATHER The temperature in the morning was 5°F (Fahrenheit). The temperature at noon was 10°F. By the evening, the temperature was −5°F. What was the highest temperature?

Understand Read the problem. Write what you know. The temperature began at 5°F. Then it was 10°F. By evening, the temperature was −5°F.

Plan Pick a strategy. One strategy is to draw a diagram. Make a line to represent a thermometer. Mark the 0. Then mark it in 5-degree increments.

Solve Begin at 5°F. Then mark 10°F and −5° F. The highest temperature was 10°F.

Check Does the answer make sense? Look over your solution. Did you answer the question?

A vertical number line is often used when measuring temperature. When this happens, the positive numbers go up, and the negative numbers go down.

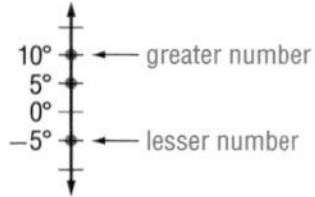

GO ON

Common Error *Alert*

Exercises 4–9 If students have difficulty with Exercises 4-9, they might be confused about the negative sign. Sometimes students have difficulty grasping the concept of –4 being less than –2, since 4 is greater than 2. Relate each negative number to 0 and discuss how moving left on the number line means the integers are becoming less.

Intervention Strategy

Kinesthetic/ Visual Learners

Real-World Integers Take students on a walking field trip through their school. Ask students to carry journals or paper to take notes as they look for positive and negative numbers in their environment. Have students try to identify where they see integers being used. Encourage students to draw and write examples as they observe places such as the office, library, cafeteria, gymnasium, other classrooms, playgrounds, or recess areas. When students return to their classroom, have them spend a few minutes writing or drawing their observations. Allow time for students to share their experiences and notes in small groups or with the class.

Are They Getting It?

Check students' understanding of integers by writing these problems on the board. Ask students to point out wrong answers and explain why they are wrong.

1. Negative numbers include 5, – 6, –4, –2, and 7. This is incorrect. Negative numbers are numbers less than 0, so 5 and 7 are not negative numbers.
2. –9 is greater than –15. This is correct.
3. Jessica gave away $75. This means she has $75 less than she used to have. This is correct.

Odd/Even Assignments

Exercises 14–34 are structured so that students practice the same concepts whether they are assigned the odd or even problems.

In-Class Assignment

Have students complete Exercises 14, 21, 24, 26, 33, and 38 to ensure that they understand the concept.

Note This!

Watch the Signs Remind students to look for the negative sign when comparing numbers. Students may focus on the whole number part of an integer and not consider the negative sign when comparing or ordering a set of numbers. Discuss how this impacts the comparison and affects the ordering. Review this using a number line for visual reinforcement.

11 SCUBA DIVING Griff was scuba diving. He went 30 feet below the surface. What integer represents his depth?
Check off each step.

✓ Understand: I underlined the key words.

✓ Plan: To solve the problem, I will draw a diagram

✓ Solve: The answer is −30

✓ Check: I checked my answer by counting back from 0 to 30 on the diagram

12 MONEY Theresa gives her mother $68. What integer represents Theresa's money? −68

13 **Reflect** How does graphing integers on a number line help in comparing them?

The order the integers are placed on a number line from left to right is the order of their value from least to greatest.

Skills, Concepts, and Problem Solving

Graph the integers on a number line. Then write them in order from least to greatest.

14 −9, 8, 2, −5, 1

−10 −8 −6 −4 −2 0 2 4 6 8 10

−9, −5, 1, 2, 8

15 9, −4, 5, −1, 8

−10 −8 −6 −4 −2 0 2 4 6 8 10

−4, −1, 5, 8, 9

16 −3, −1, 5, 0, −5

−5 −4 −3 −2 −1 0 1 2 3 4 5

−5, −3, −1, 0, 5

17 2, 0, −3, 4, −5

−5 −4 −3 −2 −1 0 1 2 3 4 5

−5, −3, 0, 2, 4

18 −3, 10, −2, 4, −6

−10 −8 −6 −4 −2 0 2 4 6 8 10

−6, −3, −2, 4, 10

19 7, −4, −5, 3, −2

−10 −8 −6 −4 −2 0 2 4 6 8 10

−5, −4, −2, 3, 7

Intervention Strategy — Interpersonal Learners

Partner Practice Have students work in pairs or small groups. Have one student write down a list of 6 integers. The partner plots the integers on a number line and then orders the list from least to greatest. Ask students to repeat the process, switching roles so each student gets a chance to order a set of integers. Partners should practice explaining how they determined the order of their set.

rite the integers from least to greatest.

0 −18, −10, 20, 14, −13 −18, −13, −10, 14, 20

1 −10, −15, 5, 25, −25 −25, −15, −10, 5, 25

2 68, −42, 91, −19, 35 −42, −19, 35, 68, 91

rite the integers from greatest to least.

3 −105, −106, 100, 50, −35 100, 50, −35, −105, −106

4 −805, −900, 500, 450, −350 500, 450, −350, −805, −900

5 244, −301, 187, −24, −256 244, 187, −24, −256, −301

se <, =, or > to compare each number pair.

6 14 (>) −16	27 −9 (<) −7
8 25 (>) −25	29 −98 (<) 99
0 0 (>) −6	31 3 (>) 0

olve.

2 WEATHER The temperature at noon was 18°F. What integer represents the temperature?

18

3 FINANCES You spend $25. What integer represents your money?

−25

4 MUSIC Reynaldo downloaded sixteen songs to his MP3 player. What integer represents the songs?

16

GO ON

Common Error *Alert*

Exercise 33 If students struggle with Exercise 33, encourage them to use concrete materials such as number lines or money manipulatives to visualize the concept of a negative dollar amount. Relate negative money to borrowing $10 from a friend, and then repaying him when you get some money. Show these relationships on a number line, moving left to represent negative numbers and moving right to represent positive numbers.

Math Challenge

Real-Life Applications Have students solve the following problems by writing the integer each situation represents.

1. A student deposits $37 into his savings account. 37
2. A quarterback loses 12 yards during a play. −12
3. Kylie donates four pairs of her shoes. −4
4. Marcel lives on the fifteenth floor of his apartment building. 15
5. She finished the race 29 seconds faster than her time last week. −29

See It, Do It, Say It, Write It

Step 1 Write several integers on the board. Include positive and negative integers, zero, and opposites.

Step 2 Ask volunteers to identify and classify each number using correct vocabulary terms and concise language. Have them compare and order the numbers.

Step 3 Ask students to work in pairs or small groups. Have students discuss real-life examples of each integer.

Step 4 Have students work alone to write a sentence to represent each integer. Tell them to include the integer that represents the situation. Students can share their sentences in small groups or with the class.

Looking Ahead: Pre-teach

Absolute Value and Zero Pairs In the next lesson, students will learn about absolute value and zero pairs. Use a number line to teach the concept of absolute value.

The absolute value of 4 is 4 because it is 4 units from 0 on a number line.

The absolute value of -4 is 4 because it is 4 units from 0 on a number line.

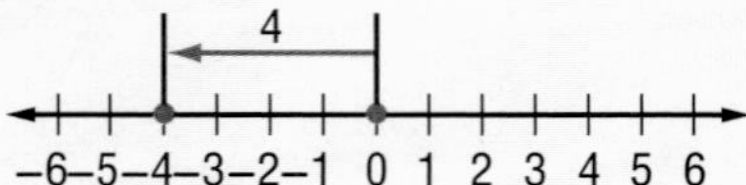

Two numbers that are the same number of units from 0 on a number line, but in opposite directions, are zero pairs.

Have students try the following problems.

How many units from 0 on a number line is each number given.

1. 5 5
2. -3 3
3. -1 1
4. 3 3
5. Which numbers from Questions 1-4 form a zero pair? 3 and -3

Vocabulary Check **Write the vocabulary word that completes each sentence.**

35 A(n) ___negative___ number is a number that is less than 0.

36 ___Integers___ are the whole numbers and their opposites.

37 Numbers that are the same distance from 0 on a number line are ___opposite___ integers.

38 **Writing in Math** Explain how to list integers from greatest to least.

Sample answer: Graph them on a number line and then write the integers as they appear from right to left.

Spiral Review

Solve. (Lesson 7-1, p. 280)

39 GEOGRAPHY The Caspian Sea is the world's largest sea. Its area covers about three hundred seventy-one thousand square kilometers. Write this number in standard form.

371,000

40 The 2005 estimated population for Miami, Florida was 386,417. Write this number in word form.

three hundred eighty-six thousand, four hundred seventeen

Round each number to the given place value. (Lesson 7-2, p. 287)

41 374,295, ten thousands ___370,000___

42 583,067, hundred thousands ___600,000___

Use <, =, or > to compare each number pair.

43 739,528 (<) 739,782

44 2,599,786 (<) 3,002,413

300 Chapter 7 Whole Numbers and Integers

Ticket Out the Door

Ordering Integers Write the following list on the board. Ask students to write the numbers in order from least to greatest. Have them include an explanation of how they determined the order. As students leave, ask them to make a comparison statement using two of the numbers from the board.

−13, −2, 8, −12, 16, 0, 12

Lesson 7-4 Absolute Value and Zero Pairs

KEY Concept

The **absolute value** of a number is the distance between the number and zero on a number line. Vertical bars on both sides of an integer are used to indicate absolute value.

–5 –4 –3 –2 –1 0 1 2 3 4 5 (2, 2)

$|-2| = 2$ and $|2| = 2$, so $|-2| = |2|$

You can use **zero pairs** to prove that the absolute value of a number and the absolute value of its opposite are equal.

Each yellow algebra tile represents +1. Each red algebra tile represents –1.

Each pair of red and yellow algebra tiles cancels each other. It has a value of zero and is called a zero pair.

The value shown on the mat is 0. So, the absolute values of $|-2|$ and $|+2|$ are equal.

VOCABULARY

absolute value
the distance between a number and 0 on a number line
Example: the absolute value of both –5 and 5 is 5

opposites
numbers that are the same distance from 0 in opposite directions
Example: 3 and –3

zero pair
the result when one positive number is paired with one negative number

A number and its opposite always have the same absolute value. For example, the absolute value of –8 and +8 is 8 because they are both 8 units away from zero on a number line.

Example 1

Evaluate the expression $|-7|$.

1. On a number line, plot points at 0 and –7.
2. Count the units between the points. 7
3. The distance between the points is 7 units, so $|-7| = 7$.

GO ON

Additional Example 1

Evaluate the expression $|-3|$.

1. On a number line, plot points at 0 and –3.

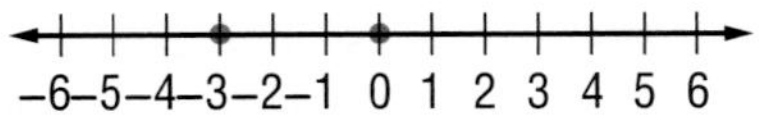

2. Count the units between the points. 3

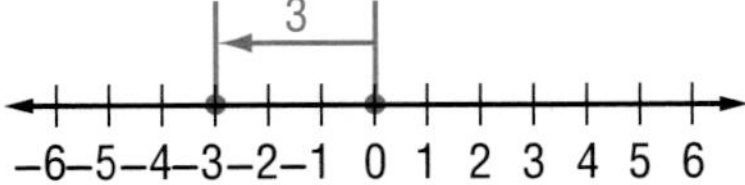

3. The distance between the points is 3 units, so $|-3| = 3$.

Lesson Notes

Lesson 7-4

Lesson Planner

Objective Evaluate operations with absolute value; use absolute value to operate with integers.

Vocabulary **absolute value**, **opposites**, **zero pair**

Materials/Manipulatives number lines, algebra tiles, decks of cards, counters, construction paper, balance scales, unit cubes

Chapter Resource Masters

- CRM Vocabulary and English Language Development (p. A150)
- CRM Skills Practice (p. A151)
- CRM Problem-Solving Practice (p. A152)
- CRM Homework Practice (p. A153)

1 Introduce

Vocabulary

Absolute Value Notation The symbol for absolute value looks like two goalposts surrounding a number. Point out that the Integer Mat shows $|2|$ and its opposite, $|-2|$, using the absolute value symbol.

2 Teach

Key Concept

Foundational Skills and Concepts After students have read through the Key Concept box, have them try these exercises.

1. What is absolute value? the distance a number is from zero on a number line
2. Which two integers have an absolute value of 4? 4 and –4
3. How many zero pairs can you form if you have 5 negative tiles and 3 positive tiles? 3

Additional **Example 2**

Use algebra tiles to model +6 and –6. Form zero pairs to find the sum.

1. Each yellow counter represents +1. Each red counter represents –1.

2. Place 6 yellow algebra tiles and 6 red algebra tiles on the mat. Make 6 zero pairs using yellow and red algebra tiles.

3. Each pair of red and yellow algebra tiles equals 0 and cancels each other.

4. There are 0 remaining algebra tiles, so the sum is 0.

YOUR TURN!

Evaluate the expression |+6|.

1. On a number line, plot points at __0__ and __6__.
2. Count the units between the points. __6__
3. The distance between the points is __6__ units, so |+6| = __6__.

Example 2

Use algebra tiles to model +3 and –3. Form zero pairs to find the sum.

1. Each yellow algebra tile represents +1. Each red algebra tile represents –1.
2. Place 3 yellow algebra tiles and 3 red algebra tiles on the mat. Make 3 zero pairs using yellow and red algebra tiles.
3. Each pair of red and yellow algebra tiles equals 0 and cancels each other.
4. There are 0 remaining algebra tiles, so the sum is 0.

A pair made of +1 and –1 has a value of zero. This is called a zero pair.

YOUR TURN!

Use algebra tiles to model +5 and –5. Form zero pairs to find the sum.

1. Each yellow algebra tile represents __+1__. Each red algebra tile represents __–1__.
2. Place __5__ yellow algebra tiles and __5__ red algebra tiles on the mat. Make __5__ zero pairs using red and yellow algebra tiles.
3. Each pair of red and yellow algebra tiles equals __0__ and cancels each other out.
4. There are __0__ remaining algebra tiles, so the sum is __0__.

Intervention Strategy — Kinesthetic Learners

Real-Life Examples Have students work in pairs. Each group needs to create real-life situations that model zero pairs or absolute value. Groups should develop a representation to demonstrate to the class. Presentations can include drawings, models, or physical examples of their situations. Give suggestions such as temperature changes, weights on a scale, or an elevator moving to floors above and below ground. Students should write sentences using absolute value notation to accompany their situations.

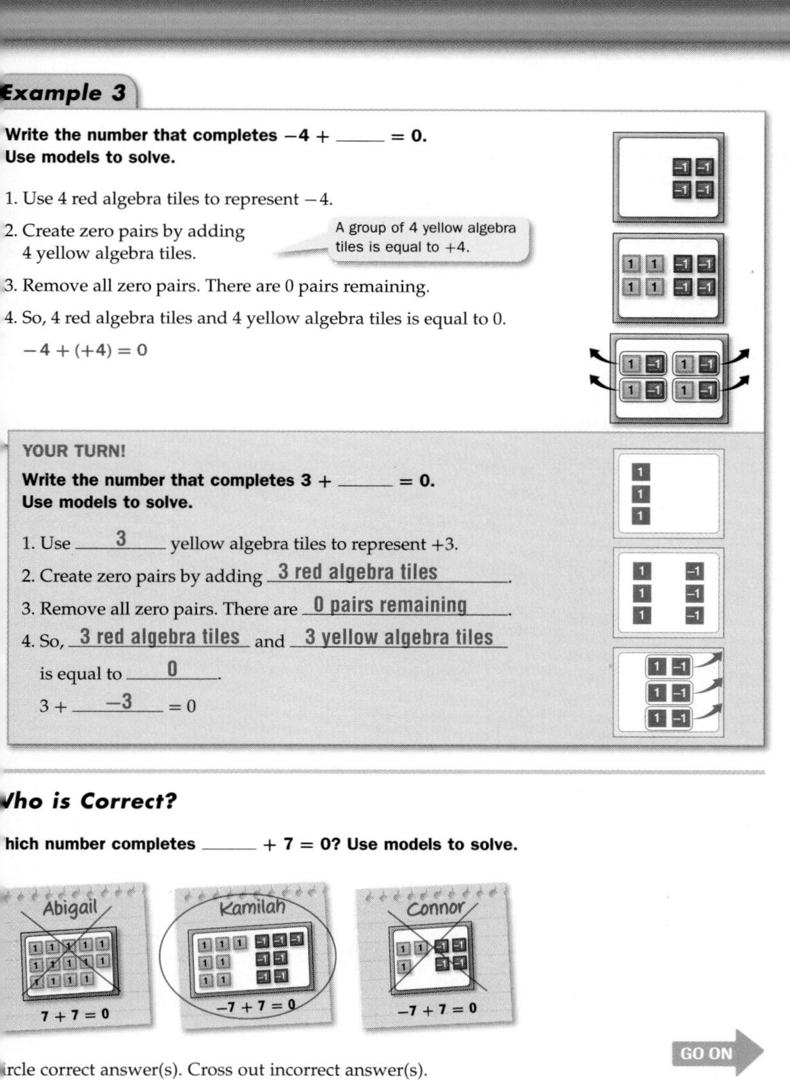

Example 3

Write the number that completes −4 + _____ = 0. Use models to solve.

1. Use 4 red algebra tiles to represent −4.
2. Create zero pairs by adding 4 yellow algebra tiles.
3. Remove all zero pairs. There are 0 pairs remaining.
4. So, 4 red algebra tiles and 4 yellow algebra tiles is equal to 0.

A group of 4 yellow algebra tiles is equal to +4.

$-4 + (+4) = 0$

YOUR TURN!

Write the number that completes 3 + _____ = 0. Use models to solve.

1. Use 3 yellow algebra tiles to represent +3.
2. Create zero pairs by adding 3 red algebra tiles.
3. Remove all zero pairs. There are 0 pairs remaining.
4. So, 3 red algebra tiles and 3 yellow algebra tiles is equal to 0.

$3 + -3 = 0$

ho is Correct?

hich number completes _____ + 7 = 0? Use models to solve.

ircle correct answer(s). Cross out incorrect answer(s).

GO ON

Lesson 7-4 Absolute Value and Zero Pairs 303

Additional *Example 3*

Write the number that completes the sentence −5 + ___ = 0. Use models to solve.

1. Use 5 red algebra tiles to represent −5.

2. Create zero pairs by adding 5 yellow algebra tiles.

3. Remove all zero pairs. There are 0 pairs remaining.

4. So, 5 red algebra tiles and 5 yellow algebra tiles is equal to 0.

$-5 + (+5) = 0$

Who *is Correct?*

Diagnostic Teaching

- Abigail is incorrect. She formed her zero pairs with positive tiles instead of negative tiles.
- Kamilah is correct. She had 7 pairs of zero pairs. There are no tiles left.
- Connor is incorrect. He did not model the number sentence correctly.

3 Practice

Using Manipulatives

Deck of Cards To demonstrate absolute value, students can use a deck of playing cards to model zero pairs. Use red cards for negative numbers and black cards for positive numbers.

On-Hand Manipulatives Have students make two-color counters out of construction or bulletin board paper. Ask students to use their counters to form zero pairs and explain absolute value.

Math Coach Notes

Partner Practice Ask students to practice explaining to one another how to use a number line to demonstrate absolute value and zero pairs. Encourage the use of core vocabulary and clear language. Invite partners to model their demonstrations for the class.

Common Error *Alert*

Exercise 1–6 Students may confuse absolute value with opposite. Remind students that absolute value reflects the distance a number is from zero. Distance is always positive.

Guided Practice

Evaluate each expression.

1. $|-4| =$ 4

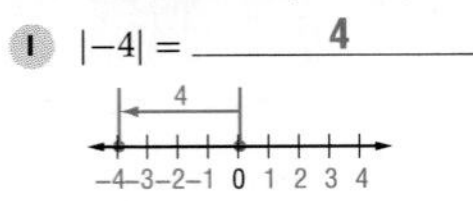

2. $|+5| =$ 5

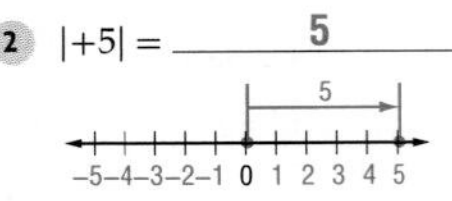

3. $|-13| =$ 13
4. $|+9| =$ 9
5. $|-11| =$ 11
6. $|+18| =$ 18

Step by Step Practice

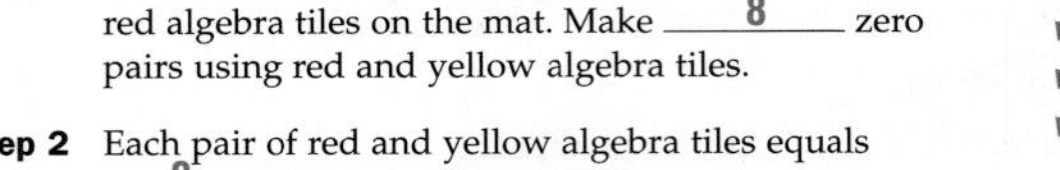

7. Use algebra tiles to model +8 and –8. Form zero pairs to find the sum.

Step 1 Place 8 yellow algebra tiles and 8 red algebra tiles on the mat. Make 8 zero pairs using red and yellow algebra tiles.

Step 2 Each pair of red and yellow algebra tiles equals 0 and cancels each other.

Step 3 There are 0 remaining algebra tiles, so the sum is 0.

Use algebra tiles to model. Form zero pairs to find the sum.

8. -1 and $+1 =$ 0
9. $+9$ and $-9 =$ 0
10. -20 and $+20 =$ 0
11. $+12$ and $-12 =$ 0

Write the number that completes each sentence.

12. $-5 + 5 = 0$
13. $-24 + 24 = 0$
14. $62 + (-62) = 0$
15. $-76 + 76 = 0$

Are They Getting It?

Check students' understanding of absolute value by writing these problems on the board. Ask them to point out wrong answers and explain why they are wrong.

1. $|-8| = -8$ This is incorrect. Absolute value is always positive; $|-8| = 8$.
2. The absolute value of $|+4|$ and $|-4|$ are equal. This is correct.
3. –15 and –15 form a zero pair. This is incorrect. $-15 + (-15) = -30$; Zero pairs cancel one another out and yield a sum of 0.

Step by Step Problem-Solving Practice

Problem-Solving Strategies

- ☑ Draw a diagram.
- ☐ Use logical reasoning.
- ☐ Make a table.
- ☐ Solve a simpler problem.
- ☐ Work backward.

SCUBA DIVING Andrea went scuba diving in Hanauma Bay in Hawaii. The deepest Andrea dove was −10 feet. What is the absolute value of the distance of Andrea's deepest dive?

Understand Read the problem. Write what you know. Andrea dove to a depth of −10 feet into Hanauma Bay.

Plan Pick a strategy. One strategy is to draw a diagram.

Solve Draw a diagram using a number line.

−10 −9 −8 −7 −6 −5 −4 −3 −2 −1 0 1 2 3 4 5 6 7 8 9 10

What point would represent the distance of the depth of Andrea's dive? −10 feet

What point would represent the distance of sea level? 0 feet

The distance between sea level and Andrea's deepest depth is 10 feet.

Check Count the units between 0 to −10.

ELEVATOR An elevator takes its passengers three flights down from the lobby to the parking garage. What integer represents this distance? What is the absolute value of this distance? Check off each step.

✔ Understand: I underlined key words.

✔ Plan: To solve this problem, I will draw a diagram.

✔ Solve: The answer is −3 flights; $|-3| = 3$.

✔ Check: I checked my answer by using counting the units between 0 to −3 on a number line.

Reflect What are some situations in which you might need to measure absolute value?

Sample answers: changes in temperature, loss of yardage in football, score-keeping in golf, changes in altitude in a plane

Intervention Strategy — Visual Learners

Demonstration Use a balance scale and unit cubes to demonstrate zero pairs. Assign one color unit cube to represent positive numbers and a different color to represent negative numbers. Have students place several negative cubes on one side of the balance scale and determine how many of the positive cubes are needed to balance the scale. Ask students to write a sentence that matches the demonstration and explain why the absolute values are equal.

Math Coach Notes

Reviewing Number Lines Use a number line to reinforce vocabulary and concepts. Draw and label a number line with integers –10 through 10. Differentiate the terms zero, positive numbers, negative numbers, and integers. Review how positive numbers move to the right of 0 on the number line, while negative numbers move to the left of 0. Plot different points and ask students to identify the integers needed to form their zero pairs. Use the number line to model how absolute value shows the distance from 0 and is always positive.

Math Challenge

Applying Absolute Value Have students read and solve real-life situations in pairs. Ask them to use absolute value in their answers. Students should practice explaining their solutions with their partners.

Carina is -$53 from her fundraising goal. How much does she have to earn in order to make her goal? She must earn $53 to make her goal. $|-53| = 53$

Joel lost 12 yards during the last football play. How many yards does he need to make up to reach the starting line? He must make up 12 yards to return to the starting line. $|-12| = 12$

Odd/Even Assignments

Exercises 19–27 are structured so that students practice the same concepts whether they are assigned the odd or even problems.

In-Class Assignment

Have students complete Exercises 19, 22, 23, 27, and 30 to ensure that they understand the concept.

See It, Do It, Say It, Write It

Step 1 Write any positive or negative integer on the board enclosed in absolute value brackets.

Step 2 Have students draw and label a number line to evaluate and model the expression.

Step 3 Ask students to work in pairs or small groups. Have each student show their group members the number line they created, and explain how this demonstrates absolute value.

Step 4 Have students work alone to write the evaluation of the expression on the board, including how their number lines support their answers. Encourage students to use the correct vocabulary terms in their explanations.

Skills, Concepts, and Problem Solving

Evaluate each expression. Use a number line to model.

19 $|+10| =$ 10

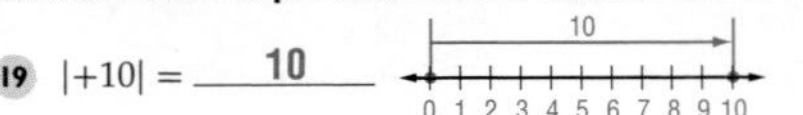

20 $|-6| =$ 6

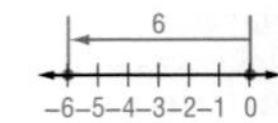

Form zero pairs to find the sum.

21 $+12$ and $-12 =$ 0

22 -23 and $+23 =$ 0

Write the number that completes each sentence.

23 $14 +$ −14 $= 0$

24 $-18 +$ 18 $= 0$

25 −17 $+ 17 = 0$

26 −23 $+ 23 = 0$

27 **BANK ACCOUNT** Brent currently has 15 dollars in his bank account. How much does he have to withdraw in order to have a zero balance? Use absolute value.

He must withdraw $15 dollars. $|-15| = 15$

Vocabulary Check **Write the vocabulary word that completes each sentence.**

28 The absolute value is the distance between a number and zero on a number line.

29 A(n) zero pair is the result when one positive number is paired with one negative number.

30 **Writing in Math** If you modeled −35 with algebra tiles, how can you model the rest of the zero pair?

Use 35 yellow algebra tiles to create zero pairs with the 35 red algebra tiles.

Spiral Review

Write each number in standard form. (Lesson 7-1, p. 280)

31 five hundred thirty-nine thousand, six hundred forty-seven 539,647

Use <, =, or > to compare each number pair. (Lesson 7-3, p. 294)

32 $13 \; (>) \; -15$

33 $-4 \; (>) \; -9$

STOP

306 Chapter 7 Whole Numbers and Integers

Ticket Out the Door

Values and Pairs Write the following integers on the board. Tell students to write each integer's absolute value and the number needed to create its zero pair. As students approach the classroom door to exit, alternate asking them to name the absolute value or zero pair partner of an integer from the board.

-17, 3, -24, -59, 82

Progress Check 2 (Lessons 7-3 and 7-4)

Graph the integers on a number line. Then write them in order from least to greatest.

1 −8, −2, 3, −3 −8, −3, −2, 3

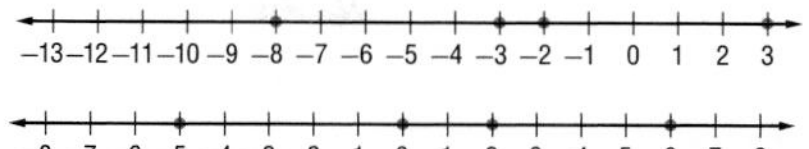

2 6, 2, −5, 0 −5, 0, 2, 6

Write <, =, or > to compare each number pair.

3 −6 (<) −4 4 5 (>) −5 5 0 (>) −1

Evaluate each expression. Use a number line to model.

6 |−3| = 3 7 |−1| = 1

8 |+14| = 14 9 |−17| = 17

10 |+28| = 28 11 |−31| = 31

Form zero pairs to find the sum.

12 −4 and +4 = 0 13 +18 and −18 = 0 14 −27 and +27 = 0

Write the number that completes each sentence.

15 11 + −11 = 0 16 −15 + 15 = 0 17 25 + −25 = 0

Solve.

18 **WEATHER** The temperature of three cities in New York was taken. In Rochester, the temperature was 7°F. In Buffalo, the temperature was −7°F. In New York City, the temperature was 0°F. What was the lowest temperature? −7°F

Chapter 7 Progress Check 307

Progress Check 2

Chapter 7

Formative Assessment

Use the Progress Check to assess students' mastery of the previous lessons. Have students review the lesson indicated for the problems they answered incorrectly.

Odd/Even Assignments

Exercises are structured so that students practice the same concepts whether they are assigned the odd or even problems.

Common Error Alert

Use Diagrams Students should try to make a transition between using a diagram to solve the problems to solving the problems abstractly.

Exercise 3 If students look at Exercise 3 and see the 6 and the 4 (not taking into account the negative signs) and select −6 as the greater of the two numbers, they can refer to a number line to visualize the answer.

Data-Driven Decision Making

Students missing Exercises . . .	Have trouble with . . .	Should review and practice . . .
1-2	graphing integers on a number line, and writing them in order from least to greatest.	SSG Lesson 7-3, p. 294 CRM Skills Practice, p. A147
3-5	comparing pairs of integers.	SSG Lesson 7-3, p. 294 CRM Skills Practice, p. A147
6-11	evaluating absolute value expressions.	SSG Lesson 7-4, p. 301 CRM Skills Practice, p. A151
12-17	using absolute value concepts.	SSG Lesson 7-4, p. 301 CRM Skills Practice, p. A151
18	solving a word problem involving comparing integers.	CRM Problem-Solving Practice, pp. A148 and A152

Chapter 7

Study Guide
Formative Assessment

Vocabulary and Concept Check

If students have difficulty answering Exercises 1–6, remind them that they can use the page references to refresh their memories about the vocabulary terms.

Vocabulary Review Strategies

Puzzles Have students make a crossword puzzle to help them review key vocabulary words. They should interlock the words in the Vocabulary and Concept Check and then write clues that are used to determine the correct word. (Example: In the number 4,783, the digit 7 is in the ____________ place. *Answer: hundreds)* Have them trade puzzles with another student for additional practice.

Lesson Review

Each example walks students through writing numbers in various forms, comparing numbers, rounding numbers to specified place values, modeling integers, and using absolute value. If the given examples are not sufficient to review the primary concepts of the chapter, remind students that the page references tell them where to review that topic in their textbooks.

Find **Extra Practice** for these concepts in the Practice Worksheets, pages A138–A153.

Classroom Management

Group Time Have students who finish the review problems for each example create additional problems, for which they also develop solutions. Then have them gather in small groups to discuss their problems and explain the corresponding solutions.

Study Guide

Vocabulary and Concept Check

absolute value, *p. 301*
integers, *p. 294*
round, *p. 287*
standard form, *p. 280*
word form, *p. 280*
zero pair, *p. 301*

Write the vocabulary word that completes each sentence.

1. If you have 472,319 and you __round__ it to the nearest hundred thousand, you will get 500,000.
2. The numbers −3, −2, −1, 0, 1, 2, and 3 are examples of __integers__.
3. Writing numbers using only digits is called __standard form__.
4. The __absolute value__ is the distance between a number and 0 on a number line.

Write the correct place value in each blank.

5. __hundred thousands__ — **523,496**
6. __millions__ — **78,419,650**

Lesson Review

7-1 Read and Write Whole Numbers in the Millions (pp. 280–286)

Write each number in word form.

7. 6,387,495
__six million, three hundred eighty-seven thousand, four hundred ninety-five__

8. 943,257
__nine hundred fourty-three thousand, two hundred fifty-seven__

Example 1

Write 7,426,983 in word form.

1. Rewrite the number using digits and words.
   7 million, 426 thousand, 983
2. Write the words for the millions period.
   seven million
3. Write the words for the thousands period.
   four hundred twenty-six thousand
4. Write the words for the ones period.
   nine hundred eighty-three
5. Write the periods in order. Separate each period with a comma.
   seven million, four hundred twenty-six thousand, nine hundred eighty-three

308 Chapter 7 Study Guide

'-2
ound and Compare Whole Numbers the Millions (pp. 287-292)

ound the number to the given lace value.

9 772,491, hundred thousands 800,000

100,000	10,000	1,000	100	10	1
hundred thousands	ten thousands	thousands	hundreds	tens	ones
7	7	2	4	9	1

10 529,800, hundred thousands 500,000

11 438,197, ten thousands 440,000

12 7,198,000, millions 7,000,000

se <, =, or > to compare ach number pair.

13 4,795,600 (<) 4,795,620

14 8,915,324 (>) 8,914,324

15 1,112,846 (<) 1,211,846

16 7,893,142 (=) 7,893,142

17 3,003,413 (<) 3,103,412

18 5,901,997 (>) 5,901,907

Example 2

Round 5,279,463 to the nearest ten thousand.

1. Underline the digit in the ten-thousands place. 5,279,463
2. Circle the digit to the right of 7. 5,27(9),463
3. Compare the 9 and 5. 9 > 5
4. The 7 increases by 1 to 8. Write the rounded number. 5,280,000

Example 3

Use <, =, or > to compare 2,685,797 and 2,684,999.

1. Begin on the left. Compare the digits in the millions places. 2 = 2
2. Compare the digits in the hundred thousands places. 6 = 6
3. Compare the digits in the ten thousands places. 8 = 8
4. Compare the digits in the thousands places. 5 > 4

   Because the digits in the thousands places are different, there is no need to compare any more digits.
5. Write a statement using the > symbol. 2,685,797 > 2,684,999

Intervention Strategy Kinesthetic Learners

Number Cards Have students play a game using two sets of cards. One stack of cards will be numbered from 0 to 9. The other stack of cards will include the directions, such as "Draw six number cards and make the greatest number possible with them." This game could be played alone or in small groups with students taking turns.

Dinah Zike's Foldables®

Review Remind students to complete and refer to their Foldables as they progress through the Chapter 7 Study Guide. Have students share and compare their completed Foldables with a partner. You may also choose to have them use their Foldable as a study aid in preparing for the Chapter Test. (For complete instructions, see Chapter Resource Masters, p. A135.)

Note This!

Create Place-Value Charts Help students create place-value charts to go with each type of example in this study guide. Give them a *skeletal* outline of the chart and have the students fill in the missing parts or places.

Math Coach Notes

Code the Problems If students are having trouble with the rounding in Exercises 9–12, have them underline the digit to which they are rounding. Then have the students circle the digit one place to the right of the underlined digit. Now tell them to evaluate the circled digit. If it is greater than or equal to 5, then they will increase the underlined digit; if it is less than 5, the underlined digit will remain the same. This will force them to think about what they are doing one step at a time, hopefully decreasing the number of mistakes made.

Common Error Alert

Compare Numbers If students are having difficulty comparing the numbers in Exercises 13–18, have them describe their thought processes for comparing the numbers digit by digit. Having them verbalize the process of comparing the numbers should help them complete the exercises with fewer mistakes.

Math Coach Notes

Representing Negatives Although negative numbers are represented using two symbols, students need to see it as one value. Until they get into the habit of seeing the negative sign as part of the value, they will not be able to get past their experiences with the digits. From the beginning of their math instruction, 3 has always been greater than 1. When students are given a value of –3, they need to be trained to see the negative sign and not just the 3.

You will be able to tell which students are not thinking of the negative sign as an integral part of the number because these students will order integers from least to greatest incorrectly, such as –2, –4, –7, –10, 0, 3, 6, 8, and 12.

Provide a lot of practice of ordering integers from least to greatest until you are sure that students understand the values of the integers.

7-3 Model Integers (pp. 294–300)

Graph the integers on a number line. Then write them in order from least to greatest.

19 −7, 6, 4, −3, 3

−7, −3, 3, 4, 6

20 −4, −1, 5, 2, −3

−4, −3, −1, 2, 5

Write the integers in order from greatest to least.

21 68, −23, −71, 47, 52

68, 52, 47, −23, −71

22 −147, 123, 172, −160, −154

172, 123, −147, −154, −160

Example 4

Graph the integers 4, −3, 2, 6, and −2 on a number line. Then write them in order from least to greatest.

1. On the number line, place a dot at 4, −3, 2, 6, and −2.
2. The numbers in order from least to greatest are −3, −2, 2, 4, 6.

Write $<$, $=$, or $>$ to compare each number pair.

23 3 (>) −3

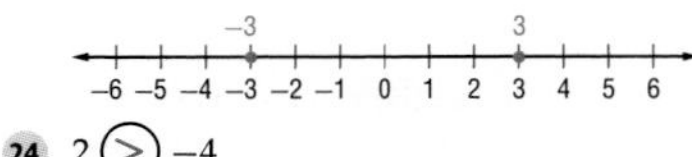

24 2 (>) −4

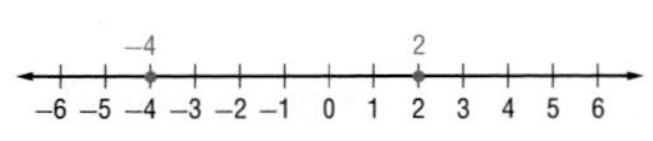

Example 5

Use $<$, $=$, or $>$ to compare −5 and 5.

1. Graph both numbers on the number line.

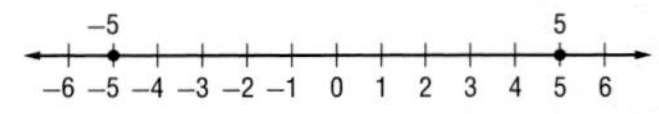

2. The number farther to the right is 5, so it is the greater number.
3. Since −5 is less than 5, you need to use the *less than* symbol.

$-5 < 5$

310 Chapter 7 Study Guide

-4 Absolute Value and Zero Pairs (pp. 301–306)

aluate each expression.
e a number line to model.

|+2| = 2

−2 −1 0 1 2

|−8| = 8

|−15| = 15

Example 6

Evaluate the expression |−5|.

1. On the number line, plot points at 0 and −5.

−5 −4 −3 −2 −1 0 1 2 3 4 5

2. Count the units between the points. 5

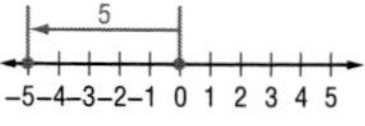

3. The distance between the points is 5 units, so |−5| = 5.

e algebra tiles to model.
rm zero pairs to find
e sum.

−7 and +7 = 0

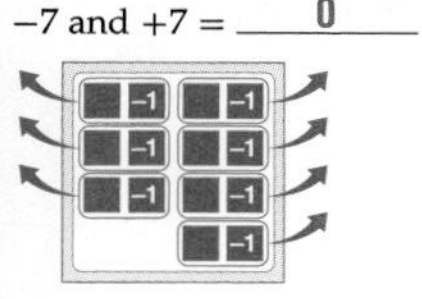

−16 and +16 = 0

+21 and −21 = 0

Example 7

Use algebra tiles to model +9 and −9. Form zero pairs to find the sum.

1. Each yellow algebra tile represents +9. Each red algebra tile represents −9.
2. Place 9 yellow algebra tiles and 9 red algebra tiles on the mat. Make 9 zero pairs using red and yellow algebra tiles.
3. Each pair of red and yellow algebra tiles equals 0 and cancels each other.
4. There are 0 remaining algebra tiles, so the sum is 0.

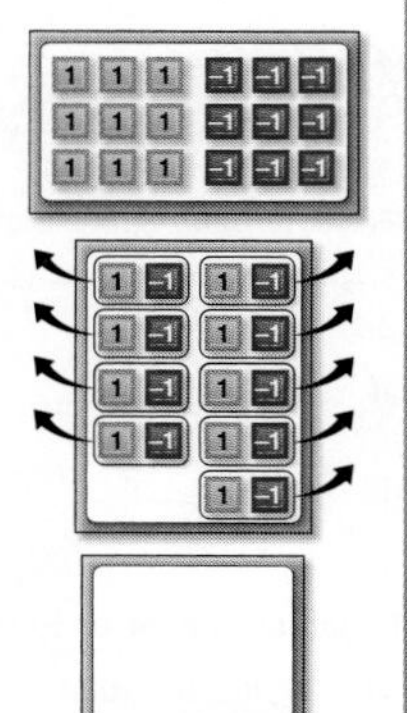

Ticket Out the Door

Ordering Cards Arrange students into groups of 3 to 5. Use the hearts and spades from a standard deck of playing cards, but omit the face cards. The hearts represent negative numbers, and the spades represent positive numbers. Have each student select a card from the deck and line up in order from least to greatest in their small groups. At the end of class, each small group should exit together in order from least to greatest showing their playing card as they reach the door. Collect the cards from the group members if they are ordered correctly when they exit. If their order is incorrect, have the students reorder themselves correctly and approach the exit again.

Chapter Test

Chapter Resource Masters

Additional forms of the Chapter 7 Tests are available.

Test Format	Where to Find it
Chapter 7 Test	Math Online glencoe.com
Blackline Masters	Assessment Masters, p. 107

Customize and create multiple versions of your chapter tests and their answer keys. All of these questions from the chapter tests are available on ExamView® Assessment Suite.

Online Assessment and Reporting
glencoe.com

This online assessment tool allows teachers to track student progress with easily accessible comprehensive reports available for every student. Assess students using any internet-ready computer.

Alternative Assessment

Use Portfolios Ask students to write examples of all the different forms of a number in their portfolios. Also have them include some examples of number rounding (including a place-value chart), as well as comparing.

Chapter Test

Write each number in standard form.

1. seven hundred forty-six thousand, two hundred eighty-five **746,285**
2. three million, eight hundred nine thousand, seventy-four **3,809,074**
3. five million, two hundred sixty-seven thousand, three hundred forty-nine **5,267,349**

Graph the numbers on the number line. Then write the numbers in order from least to greatest.

4. −1, −7, 6, 0, 4, −3

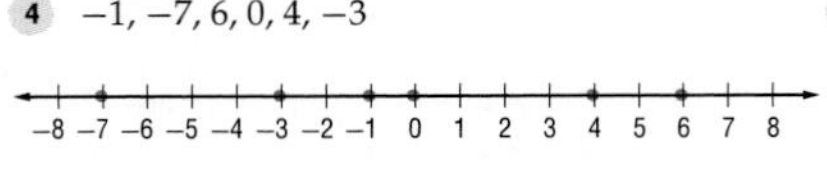

−7, −3, −1, 0, 4, 6

5. −1, 5, 3, −2, −4, 6

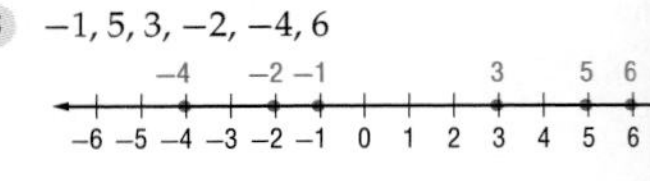

−4, −2, −1, 3, 5, 6

Write <, =, or > to compare each number pair.

6. 547,392 (<) 547,932
7. 6,301,974 (>) 6,013,974
8. −2 (>) −5
9. −8 (<) 2

Evaluate each expression. Use a number line to model.

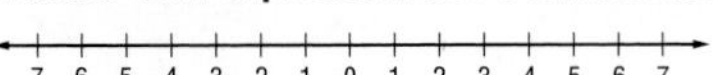

10. $|+3| =$ **3**
11. $|-5| =$ **5**
12. $|-2| =$ **2**
13. $|+7| =$ **7**

Round each number to the given place value.

14. 827,400, hundred thousands **800,000**
15. 578,916, ten thousands **580,000**
16. 3,914,000, millions **4,000,000**
17. 85,732,100, millions **86,000,000**

English Learner Strategy

Assessment Allow students time to look over the assessment. Have the students take a close look at all the problem directions, as well as any terms in the word problems. Provide an opportunity for students to clarify any words they think they do not understand by conducting a brief question-and-answer period or by allowing them to look them up in their textbooks.

rite each number in word form.

8 496,570

four hundred ninety-six thousand, five hundred seventy

9 3,487,382

three million, four hundred eighty-seven thousand, three hundred eighty-two

0 52,365,200

fifty-two million, three hundred sixty-five thousand, two hundred

rm zero pairs to find the sum.

−7, +7 = 0	22 +25, −25 = 0
3 +38, −38 = 0	24 −16, +16 = 0

rite the number that completes each sentence.

5 12 + −12 = 0	26 −24 + 24 = 0

lve.

FINANCES You have $100 in your bank account. You spend $37 on a video game. What integer represents how much you spent on a video game?

−37

3 **SPORTS** The high school football team is 17 yards from the end zone. How many yards do they need to travel to score a touchdown? Use absolute value in your answer.

The football team must travel 17 yards to score a touchdown. |+17| = 17

rrect the Mistakes.

Lola wrote 4,506,803 in words on her homework paper. She wrote "four million, five hundred thousand, eight hundred three." What mistake did Lola make?

Lola forgot the 6 in the thousands period. The number is

four million, five hundred six thousand, eight hundred three.

Learning from Mistakes

Review Review commonly missed questions or topics in small groups or as a class. Ask students to share their methods of answering each question. Try to point out when any errors occur and take corrective measures.

Data-Driven Decision Making

Students missing Exercises . . .	Have trouble with . . .	Should review and practice . . .	
1–3, 18–20	writing numbers in standard and word form.	SSG Lesson 7-1, p. 280	CRM Skills Practice, p. A139
4–9	ordering and comparing numbers.	SSG Lesson 7-2, p. 287	CRM Skills Practice, p. A143
10–13	finding absolute values of numbers.	SSG Lesson 7-4, p. 301	CRM Skills Practice, p. A151
14–17	rounding numbers to a given place value.	SSG Lesson 7-2, p. 287	CRM Skills Practice, p. A143
21–26	using absolute value concepts.	SSG Lesson 7-4, p. 301	CRM Skills Practice, p. A151
27–29	solving word problems that involve integers.	CRM Problem-Solving Practice, pp. A140, A144, and A152	

Chapter 7 Test Practice

Diagnose Student Errors

Survey student responses for each item. Class trends may indicate common errors and misconceptions.

1. (A) correct
B used wrong place value in thousands, hundreds and tens
C numbers 3 and 2 omitted
D placed too many zero placeholders

2. (A) correct
B compared only millions place, 8 = 8
C compared incorrectly
D guess

3. A represents −5
(B) correct
C represents 1
D represents 4

4. A rounded to millions place
B rounded to ten-thousands place
C rounded to thousands place
(D) correct

5. A misread number
B incorrect sign
(C) correct
D guess

6. A rounds correctly
B rounds correctly
C rounds correctly
(D) correct

7. A did not consider negative
B guess
(C) correct
D guess

8. A guess
(B) correct
C opposite, not absolute value
D doubled integer

9. A wrong place value of 7
B wrong place values of 6 and 7
C wrong place values of 6 and 7
(D) correct

Test Practice

Choose the best answer and fill in the corresponding circle on the sheet at right.

1 Which number shows nine hundred thirty-six thousand, seven hundred twenty written in standard form?

(A) 936,720 C 906,700
B 930,270 D 900,020

2 Which symbol makes the sentence true?

8,541,937 ◯ 8,514,937

(A) > C <
B = D +

3 Which letter on the number line represents −3?

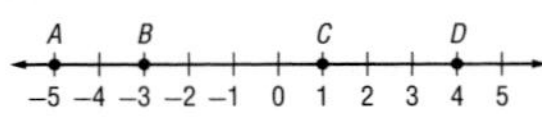

A *A* C *C*
(B) *B* D *D*

4 Round 3,081,524 to the nearest hundred thousand.

A 3,000,000 C 3,082,000
B 3,080,000 (D) 3,100,000

5 Which number completes the sentence

$-19 + \square = 0$

A 17 (C) 19
B −19 D −17

6 Which does *not* round to 4,920,000 when rounded to the nearest ten thousand?

A 4,916,273
B 4,918,872
C 4,922,066
(D) 4,927,105

7 Which symbol makes the sentence tru

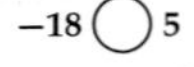

A > (C) <
B = D +

8 An elevator takes its passengers five floors up from the parking garage. If t integer that represents this distance is +5, which is the absolute value?

A 0 C −5
(B) 5 D 10

314 **Chapter 7** Test Practice

10. A models integer, not absolute value
B guess
(C) correct
D guess

11. A guess
(B) correct
C guess
D guess

12. A rounded to nearest hundred-thousands
B truncated instead of rounding
(C) correct
D truncated millions place

9 Which of these is the word form for the number 6,007,017?

A six million, seven hundred, seventeen

B six thousand, seven hundred, seventeen

C six billion, seven million, seventeen

(D) six million, seven thousand, seventeen

---

10 Rudy went scuba diving in the ocean. He dove 55 feet below sea level to explore a cave. What is the absolute value of the distance of Rudy's dive?

A −55 (C) 55

B 0 D 5

---

11 Which list is written in order from greatest to least?

A −32, 38, −27, 19, −41

(B) 59, 17, −34, −71, −97

C 87, −59, −62, 74, 23

D −16, −45, 73, 95, −52

---

12 Round 74,601,003 to the nearest million.

A 74,600,000 (C) 75,000,000

B 74,000,000 D 70,000,000

ANSWER SHEET

Directions: Fill in the circle of each correct answer.

1	**(A)**	B	C	D
2	**(A)**	B	C	D
3	A	**(B)**	C	D
4	A	B	C	**(D)**
5	A	B	**(C)**	D
6	A	B	C	**(D)**
7	A	B	**(C)**	D
8	A	**(B)**	C	D
9	A	B	C	**(D)**
10	A	B	**(C)**	D
11	A	**(B)**	C	D
12	A	B	**(C)**	D

Success Strategy

Double check your answers after you finish. Read each problem and all of the answer choices. Put your finger on each bubble you filled in to make sure it matches the answer for each problem.

Diagnosing Student Errors and Misconceptions

Review Understanding place value is the foundation for being able to order numbers. If students are consistently missing problems about ordering, have students review the place-value chart and expanded form.

Chapter 8

Chapter Overview

Chapter-at-a-Glance

Lesson	Math Objective	State/Local Standards
8-1 Add Integers (pp. 318-324)	Add integers.	
8-2 Subtract Integers (pp. 325-332)	Subtract integers.	
Progress Check (p. 333)		
8-3 Add and Subtract Groups of Integers (pp. 334-340)	Add and subtract groups of integers.	
8-4 Multiply Integers (pp. 341-346)	Multiply integers.	
Progress Check (p. 347)		
8-5 Divide Integers (pp. 348-352)	Divide integers.	
8-6 Exponents (pp. 353-358)	Recognize and use exponents.	
8-7 Order of Operations (pp. 359-364)	Use the order of operations to simplify expressions.	
Progress Check (p. 365)		

Content-at-a-Glance

The diagram below summarizes and unpacks Chapter 8 content.

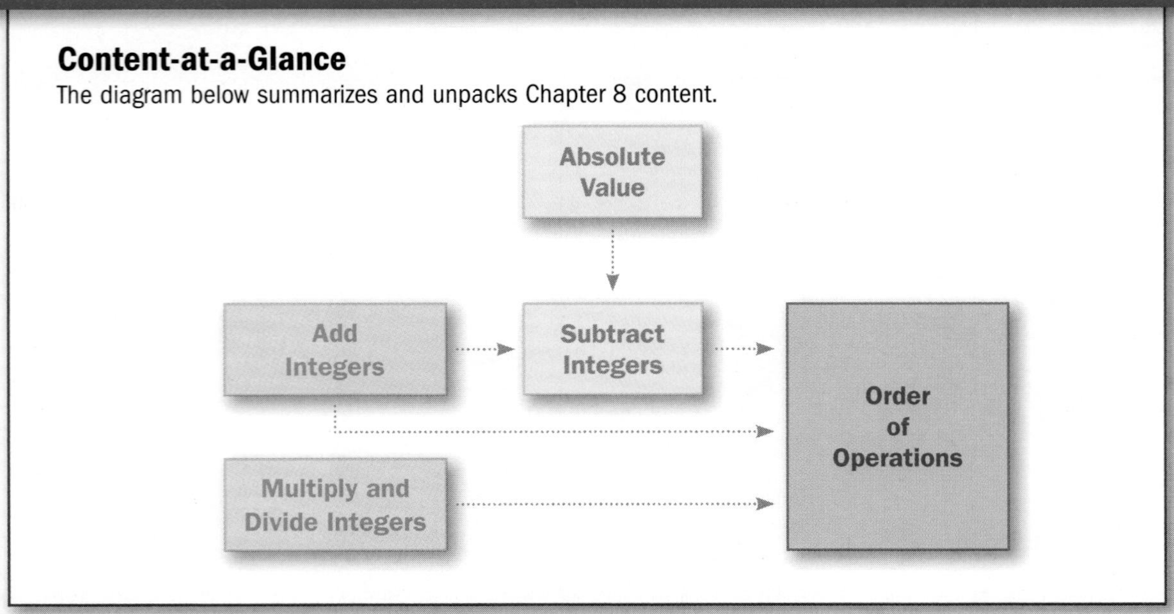

Online Assessment and Reporting
glencoe.com

Chapter Assessment Manager

Diagnostic

Diagnose students' readiness.

	Student Study Guide/ Teacher Edition	Assessment Masters	Technology
Course Placement Test		1	ExamView® Assessment Suite
Book 3 Pretest		101	ExamView® Assessment Suite
Chapter 8 Pretest		115	ExamView® Assessment Suite
Quiz/Preview	SSG 317		Math Online glencoe.com StudentWorks™ Plus

Formative

Identify students' misconceptions of content knowledge.

	Student Study Guide/ Teacher Edition	Assessment Masters	Technology
Progress Checks	SSG 333, 347, 365		Math Online glencoe.com StudentWorks™ Plus
Vocabulary Review	SSG 366		Math Online glencoe.com
Lesson Assessments			ExamView® Assessment Suite
Are They Getting It?	TE 321, 329, 337, 342, 350, 356, 361		Math Online glencoe.com

Summative

Determine student success in learning concepts in the lesson, chapter, or book.

	Student Study Guide/ Teacher Edition	Assessment Masters	Technology
Chapter 8 Test	SSG 370	118	ExamView® Assessment Suite
Test Practice	SSG 372	121	ExamView® Assessment Suite
Alternative Assessment	TE 370	124	
See It, Do It, Say It, Write It	TE 324, 332, 340, 346, 352, 358, 364		
Book 3 Test		148	ExamView® Assessment Suite

Back-mapping and Vertical Alignment **McGraw-Hill's *Math Triumphs*** intervention program was conceived and developed with the final result in mind: student success in grade-level mathematics, including Algebra 1 and beyond. The authors, using the **NCTM Focal Points and Focal Connections** as their guide, developed this brand-new series by backmapping from grade-level and Algebra 1 concepts, and vertically aligning the topics so that they build upon prior skills and concepts and serve as a foundation for future topics.

Chapter Resource Manager

	Lesson 8-1	Lesson 8-2	Lesson 8-3	Lesson 8-4
Concept	Add Integers	Subtract Integers	Add and Subtract Groups of Integers	Multiply Integers
Objective	Add integers.	Subtract integers.	Add and subtract groups of integers.	Multiply integers.
Math Vocabulary	Commutative Property of Addition integers Inverse Property of Addition negative number positive number	absolute value opposites	Associative Property of Addition	Associative Property of Multiplication Commutative Property of Multiplication factor Identity Property of Multiplication product Zero Property of Multiplication
Lesson Resources	**Materials** • Number lines • Nickels • Pennies • Thermometer (with only one measurement scale) • Playing cards **Manipulatives** • Algebra tiles • Two-color counters **Other Resources** CRM Vocabulary and English Language Development CRM Skills Practice CRM Problem-Solving Practice CRM Homework Practice	**Materials** • Number lines • Index cards • Money • Thermometer **Manipulatives** • Pattern blocks • Two-color counters • Algebra tiles **Other Resources** CRM Vocabulary and English Language Development CRM Skills Practice CRM Problem-Solving Practice CRM Homework Practice	**Materials** • Black marker • Money • Plastic cups • Red marker • Number cubes **Manipulatives** • Connecting cubes • Pattern blocks • Two-color counters • Algebra tiles **Other Resources** CRM Vocabulary and English Language Development CRM Skills Practice CRM Problem-Solving Practice CRM Homework Practice	**Materials** • 4 or 5 decks of cards • Index cards • Hundreds chart **Manipulatives** • Algebra tiles • Geoboards **Other Resources** CRM Vocabulary and English Language Development CRM Skills Practice CRM Problem-Solving Practice CRM Homework Practice
Technology	Math Online glencoe.com StudentWorks™ Plus ExamView® Assessment Suite	Math Online glencoe.com StudentWorks™ Plus ExamView® Assessment Suite	Math Online glencoe.com StudentWorks™ Plus ExamView® Assessment Suite	Math Online glencoe.com StudentWorks™ Plus ExamView® Assessment Suite

SSG Student Study Guide
CRM Chapter Resource Masters

TE Teacher Edition
DVD

Lesson 8-5	Lesson 8-6	Lesson 8-7	
Divide Integers	Exponents	Order of Operations	**Concept**
Divide integers.	Recognize and use exponents.	Use the order of operations to simplify expressions.	**Objective**
dividend divisor quotient	base cubed exponent squared	base (of a power) exponent order of operations	**Math Vocabulary**
Materials • Hundreds chart **Manipulatives** • Fraction circles • Geoboards • Algebra tiles **Other Resources** CRM Vocabulary and English Language Development CRM Skills Practice CRM Problem-Solving Practice CRM Homework Practice	**Materials** • Counters • Index cards • Scissors **Manipulatives** • Pattern blocks • Two-color counters **Other Resources** CRM Vocabulary and English Language Development CRM Skills Practice CRM Problem-Solving Practice CRM Homework Practice	**Materials** • Colored markers **Manipulatives** • Algebra tiles **Other Resources** CRM Vocabulary and English Language Development CRM Skills Practice CRM Problem-Solving Practice CRM Homework Practice	**Lesson Resources**
Math Online glencoe.com StudentWorks™ Plus ExamView® Assessment Suite	Math Online glencoe.com StudentWorks™ Plus ExamView® Assessment Suite	Math Online glencoe.com StudentWorks™ Plus ExamView® Assessment Suite	**Technology**

Chapter 8

Chapter Notes

Real-World Applications

Apartment Living Juan lives on the sixth floor of an apartment building. Ira lives 3 floors below Juan and 2 floors above Tony. Greg lives 3 floors above Tony and 4 floors below Kia. Marco lives the same number of floors from Angie and William. Angie lives in the basement. Assign an integer, –1 to 6, and a name to each floor of the apartment building to show where each person lives.

Intervention Strategy

Rolling Integers

Step 1 Distribute either a red number cube or a white number cube to each student. Arrange students in pairs, one having a red cube and the other having a white cube.

Step 2 Explain to students that the red number cube will represent negative integers, while the white cube represents positive integers.

Step 3 The students in each pair should roll their cubes and then find the sum of the two numbers rolled. Each student should write down the sum and then compare the sum with the partner. Do not roll again until both students agree on the sum. Repeat until each pair has computed ten addition sentences.

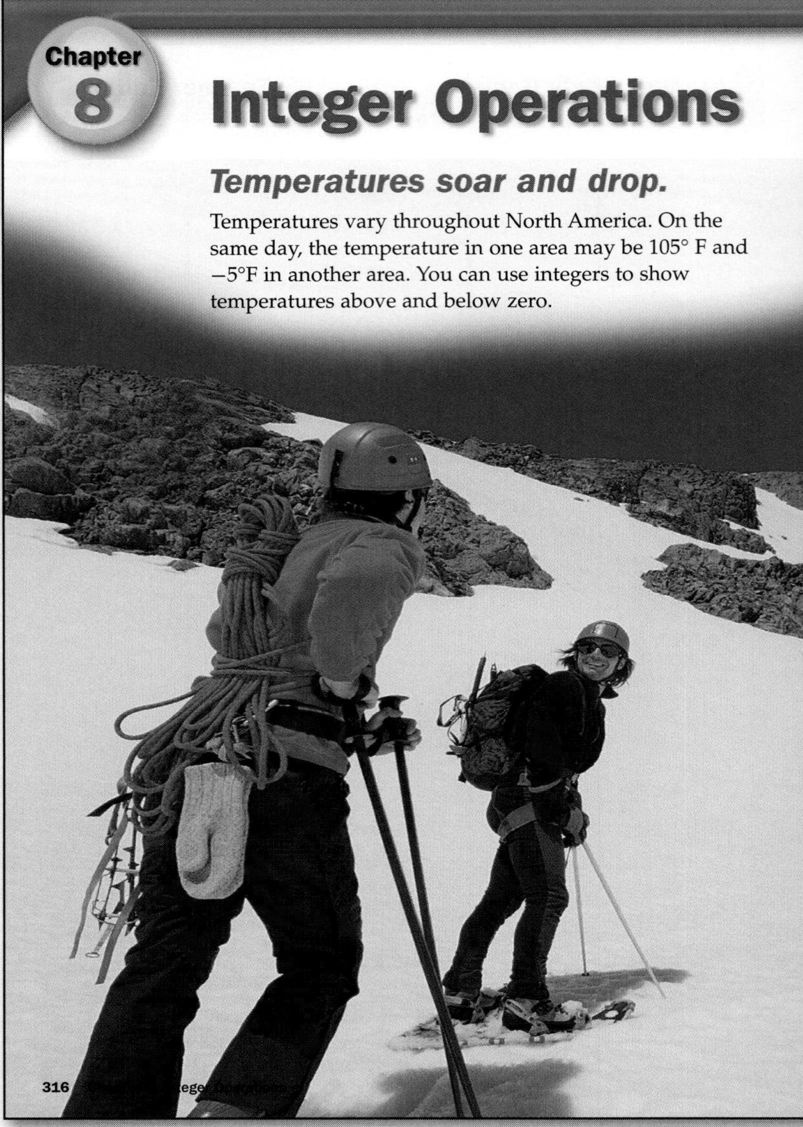

Chapter 8

Integer Operations

Temperatures soar and drop.

Temperatures vary throughout North America. On the same day, the temperature in one area may be 105° F and –5°F in another area. You can use integers to show temperatures above and below zero.

316

Key Vocabulary

Find interactive definitions in 13 languages in the **eGlossary** at glencoe.com.

English **Español** *Introduce the most important vocabulary terms from Chapter 8.*

absolute value **valor absoluto**
the distance between a number and 0 on a number line (p. 325)

Associative Property of Addition **priopedad asociativa de la adición**
the way addends are grouped does not change the sum (p. 334)

Commutative Property of Addition **propiedad conmutativa de la adición**
the order in which two numbers are added does not change the sum (p. 318)

integers **enteros**
the whole numbers and their opposites (p. 318)

Inverse Property of Addition **priopedad inversa de la adición**
for any number, the sum of that number and its opposite is zero (p. 318)

negative number **número negativo**
a number less than zero (p. 318)

positive number **número positivo**
a number that is greater than zero (p. 318)

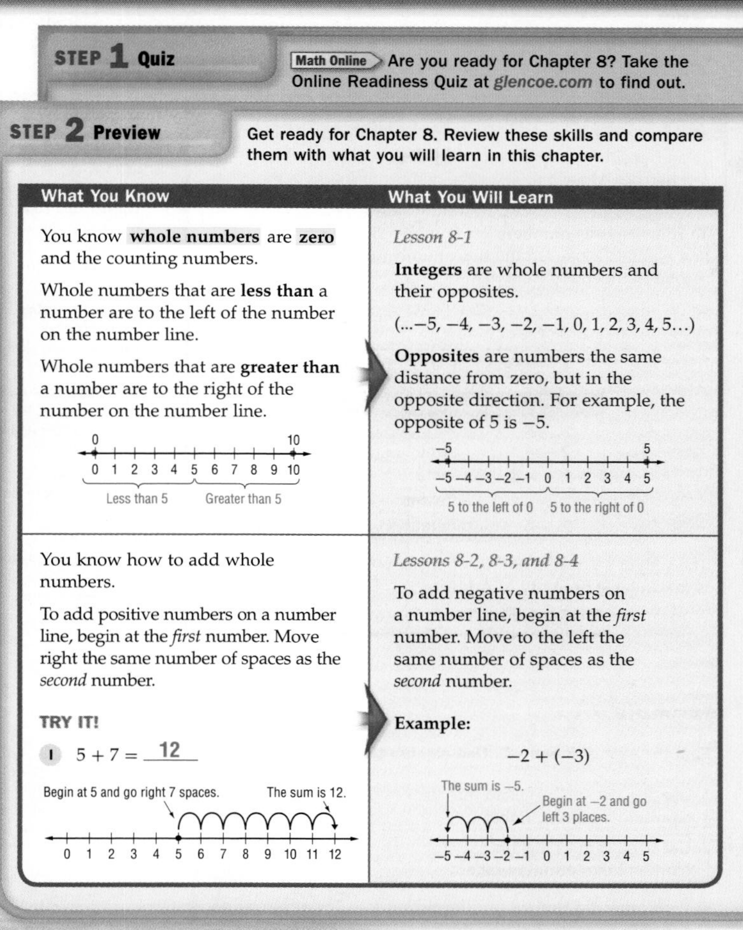

STEP 1 Quiz

Math Online Are you ready for Chapter 8? Take the Online Readiness Quiz at glencoe.com to find out.

STEP 2 Preview

Get ready for Chapter 8. Review these skills and compare them with what you will learn in this chapter.

What You Know	What You Will Learn
You know **whole numbers** are **zero** and the counting numbers. Whole numbers that are **less than** a number are to the left of the number on the number line. Whole numbers that are **greater than** a number are to the right of the number on the number line.	*Lesson 8-1* **Integers** are whole numbers and their opposites. (...−5, −4, −3, −2, −1, 0, 1, 2, 3, 4, 5...) **Opposites** are numbers the same distance from zero, but in the opposite direction. For example, the opposite of 5 is −5.
You know how to add whole numbers. To add positive numbers on a number line, begin at the *first* number. Move right the same number of spaces as the *second* number. **TRY IT!** 1 $5 + 7 =$ 12	*Lessons 8-2, 8-3, and 8-4* To add negative numbers on a number line, begin at the *first* number. Move to the left the same number of spaces as the *second* number. **Example:** $-2 + (-3)$

317

Vocabulary Preview

- As students complete the Chapter Preview, have them make a list of important terms throughout the chapter.
- Have students work in groups to create vocabulary posters. Each poster should list the key vocabulary terms, along with examples and definitions.
- Groups can present their posters to the class.
- Hang posters for reference during the study of Chapter 8.

Step 1 Quiz

Pretest/Prescribe Students can take the Online Readiness Quiz or the Diagnostic Pretest in the Assessment Masters.

Step 2 Preview

Use this pre-chapter activity to activate students' prior knowledge, build confidence, and help students preview the lessons.

Dinah Zike's Foldables®

Guide students through the directions on p. A154 in the Chapter Resource Masters to create their own Foldable graphic organizer for use with this chapter.

Home Connections

- Record the outside temperature every hour for a four-hour period. Describe the hourly change in temperature using integers.

Mc Graw Hill Professional Development

Targeted professional development has been articulated throughout **McGraw-Hill's *Math Triumphs*** intervention program. **The McGraw-Hill Professional Development Video Library** provides short videos that support the **NCTM Focal Points and Focal Connections**. For more information, visit glencoe.com.

Model Lessons

Instructional Strategies

Lesson 8-1 Lesson Notes

Lesson Planner

Objective Add integers.

Vocabulary **Commutative Property of Addition**, **integers**, **Inverse Property of Addition**, **negative number**, **positive number**

Materials/Manipulatives number lines, algebra tiles, two-color counters, nickels, pennies, thermometer, playing cards

Chapter Resource Masters

- CRM Vocabulary and English Language Development (p. A157)
- CRM Skills Practice (p. A158)
- CRM Problem-Solving Practice (p. A159)
- CRM Homework Practice (p. A160)

1 Introduce

Vocabulary

Integers on Number Lines Ask students to think of the number –5 and to visualize moving 5 units to the left of zero on a number line to locate that number. Now ask them to visualize moving to the right on the number line from the point made for –5. They should picture stopping after moving right 3 units. Are they on a positive number? Have them return to –5 and picture moving right 8 units. Are they on a positive number now? Explain that they just modeled the addition sentences $-5 + 3 = -2$ and $-5 + 8 = 3$.

2 Teach

Key Concept

Foundational Skills and Concepts After students have read through the Key Concept box, have them try these exercises.

1. $-9 + \_\_\_\_ = 0$ 9
2. Write an addition sentence that shows the opposite of 2 and justifies it. $2 + (-2) = 0$
3. $-7 + 9 = \_\_\_\_$ 2

Lesson 8-1 Add Integers

KEY Concept

To add **positive numbers** on a number line, begin at the *first* number. Move right the same number of spaces as the *second* number.

To add **negative numbers** on a number line, begin at the *first* number. Move left the same number of spaces as the second number. For example:

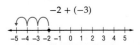

$-2 + (-3)$

–5 –4 –3 –2 –1 0 1 2 3 4 5

Adding Integers

Addition	Signs	Answer
2 + 4	same	6
−2 + −4	same	−6
2 + −4	different	−2
−2 + 4	different	2

The sum of an integer and its opposite is always zero. This is the **Inverse Property of Addition**.

$5 + (-5) = 0$ or $(-5) + 5 = 0$

VOCABULARY

Commutative Property of Addition
the order in which two numbers are added does not change the sum
Example: 12 + 15 = 15 + 12

integers
the whole numbers and their opposites
Example: ...-3, -2, -1, 0, 1, 2, 3,...

Inverse Property of Addition
for any number, the sum of that number and its opposite is zero

negative number
a number that is less than zero

positive number
a number that is greater than zero

Example 1

Find the sum of 3 and –5. Use algebra tiles.

1. Use three positive algebra tiles to represent the first number.
2. Use five negative algebra tiles to represent the second number.
3. A zero pair is made up of 1 negative and 1 positive algebra tile. You can make 3 zero pairs.
4. There are two negative algebra tiles left.
5. Write the sum. **3 + (–5) = –2**

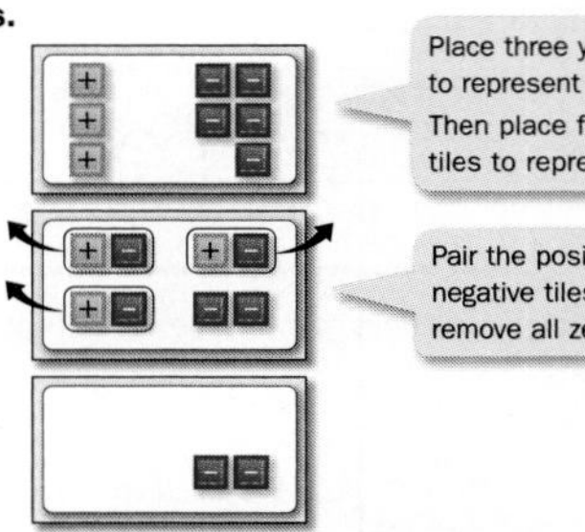

Place three yellow tiles to represent +3. Then place five red tiles to represent –5.
Pair the positive and negative tiles. Then remove all zero pairs.

Additional Example 1

Find the sum of –4 and 6. Use algebra tiles.

1. Use four negative algebra tiles to represent the first number.
2. Use six positive algebra tiles to represent the second number.

3. A zero pair is made up of 1 negative and 1 positive algebra tile. You can make 4 zero pairs.

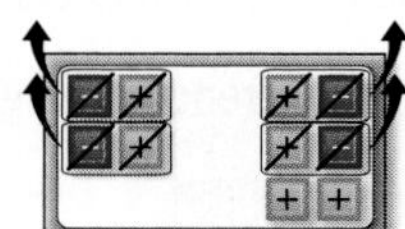

4. There are two positive algebra tiles left.

5. Write the sum. $-4 + 6 = 2$

YOUR TURN!

Find the sum of 8 and −3. Use algebra tiles.

1. Use eight positive algebra tiles to represent the first number.
2. Use three negative algebra tiles to represent the second number.
3. You can make 3 zero pairs.
4. There are five positive algebra tiles left.
5. Write the sum.

$8 + (-3) = 5$

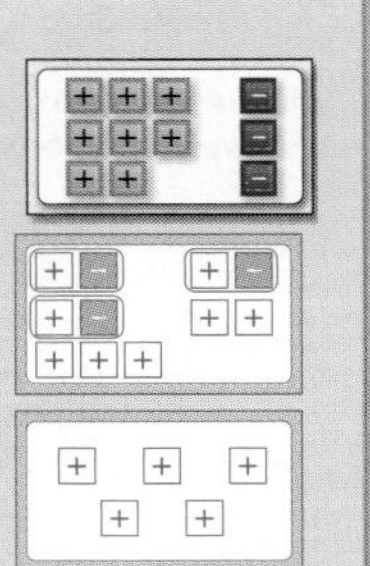

Example 2

Find the sum of −1 and −3. Use a number line.

1. Graph the first number.
2. Start at −1.
3. Since −3 is a negative integer, move left 3 spaces.

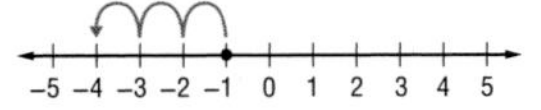

4. Write the sum. $-1 + (-3) = -4$

YOUR TURN!

Find the sum of −2 and 5. Use a number line.

1. Graph the first number.
2. Start at −2.
3. Since 5 is a positive integer, move right 5 spaces.

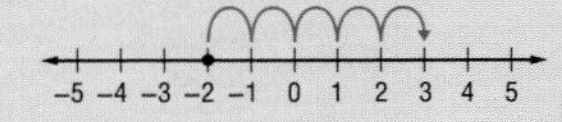

4. Write the sum. $-2 + 5 = 3$

Additional *Example 2*

Find the sum of −1 and 3. Use a number line.

1. Graph the first number.

2. Start at −1.

3. Since 3 is a positive integer, move right 3 spaces.

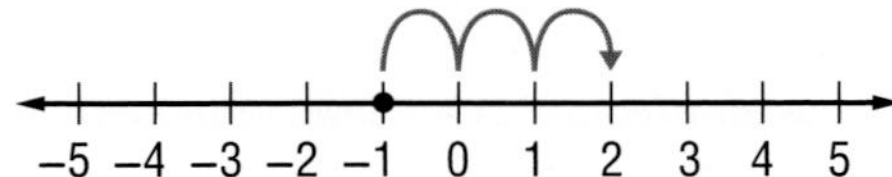

4. Write the sum. $-1 + 3 = 2$

Math Coach Notes

Number Properties Reteaching and reinforcing the Associative, Commutative, and Distributive properties of numbers will enable students to extend and apply arithmetic processes for counting numbers to integers. If students are familiar and comfortable with these properties and processes for counting numbers, applying them to integers, fractions, and decimals will be a smoother transition.

Intervention Strategy

Naturalist Learners

Use a display in the classroom such as a whiteboard, chalkboard, or bulletin board to make a list of the letters of the alphabet. There should be space to write a few words next to each letter. Ask students to name an activity that people do in their daily lives that deal with positive and negative numbers. Over the next few days, students should try to name one activity for each letter. Some examples include B as banking, F as football, G as gardening, and R as rainfall.

Additional **Example 3**

What is the opposite of 4? Use it to show the Inverse Property of Addition.

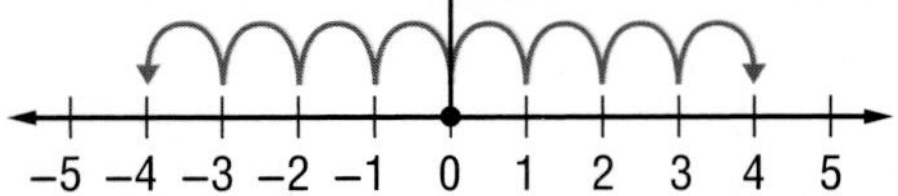

1. Graph the number. What number is the same distance from zero as 4? −4
2. Write an example of the inverse property using the two numbers. $4 + (-4) = 0$

3 Practice

Using Manipulatives

Algebra Tiles When presenting the addition of integers, use concrete materials such as counters or algebra tiles to model positive and negative integers.

$-2 + 6 = 4$

Thermometer Use a thermometer that shows only one measurement scale, such as Fahrenheit, to help students visualize positive and negative temperatures and temperature changes during the day.

On-Hand Manipulatives Use two types of everyday objects as coins, such as pennies and nickels. Pennies could represent negative integers, while nickels represent positive integers.

Example 3

What is the opposite of −3? Use it to show the Inverse Property of Addition.

1. Graph the number. What number is the same distance from zero as −3? 3

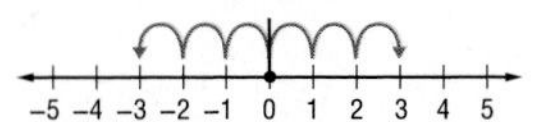

2. Write an example of the inverse property using the two numbers.

$-3 + 3 = 0$

YOUR TURN!

What is the opposite of 2? Use it to show the Inverse Property of Addition.

1. Graph the number. What number is the same distance from zero as 2? −2

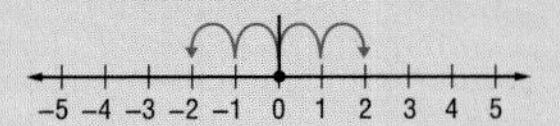

2. Write an example of the inverse property using the two numbers.

$2 + \underline{-2} = 0$

Who is Correct?

Find the sum of 7 and −3.

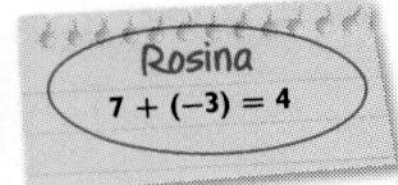

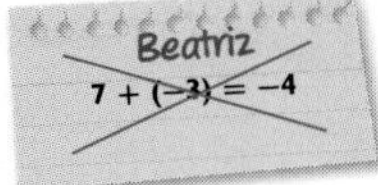

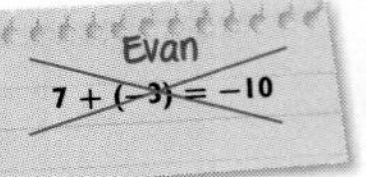

Circle correct answer(s). Cross out incorrect answer(s).

Guided Practice

Find each sum. Use algebra tiles.

1. $4 + (-1) = \underline{3}$

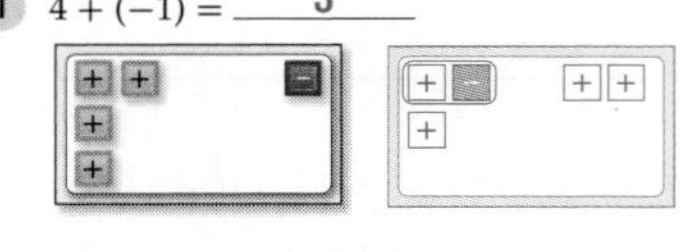

2. $-6 + (-3) = \underline{-9}$

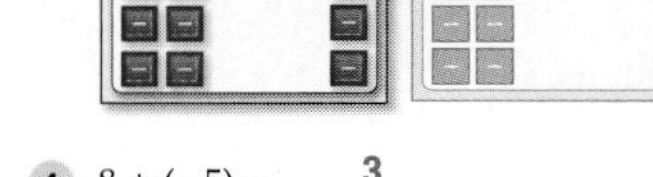

3. $-10 + 7 = \underline{-3}$

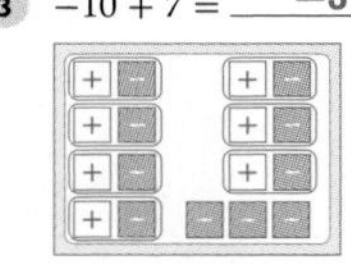

4. $8 + (-5) = \underline{3}$

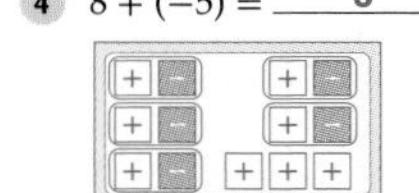

Who *is Correct?*

Diagnostic Teaching

- Rosina's work is correct. She added correctly.
- Beatriz's work is incorrect. She moved in the opposite direction for negative and positive numbers.
- Evan's work is incorrect. He added the digits without regard to the signs.

Remind students to look carefully at the signs of both numbers.

Step by Step Practice

5 Find the sum of −6 and −3. Use the number line.

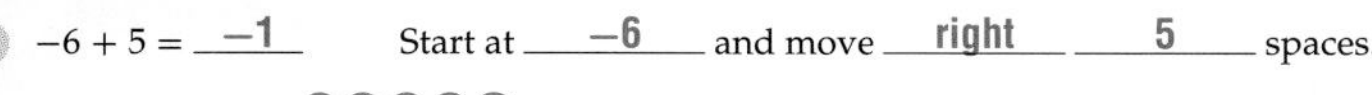

Step 1 Graph the first number.

Step 2 Start at −6.

Step 3 Since 3 is a negative integer, move left 3 spaces.

Step 4 Write the sum. −6 + (−3) = −9

Find each sum. Use the number line.

6 −6 + 5 = −1 Start at −6 and move right 5 spaces.

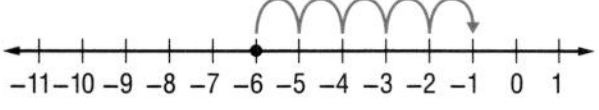

7 −3 + 0 = −3

8 −4 + (−2) = −6

Find each sum.

9 3 + (−3) = 0

10 2 + (−3) = −1

11 −6 + (−1) = −7

12 −4 + 7 = 3

13 −6 + 9 = 3

14 −4 + (−4) = −8

What is the opposite of each number? Use it to show the Inverse Property of Addition.

15 14 −14; 14 + (−14) = 0

16 −48 48; −48 + 48 = 0

17 −92 92; −92 + 92 = 0

18 5 −5; 5 + (−5) = 0

GO ON

Are They Getting It?

Check students' understanding of adding integers by writing these problems on the board. Have students state which are correct and which are not correct. Encourage them to use drawings or examples in their explanations.

1. −8 + 3 = −11 This is incorrect. −8 + 3 = −5

2. The number line shows −2 + 5 = 3. This is correct.

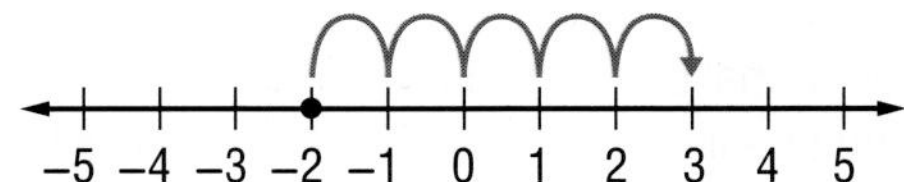

3. The sum of −6 and −9 is −15. This is correct.

English Learner Strategy

Temperature and Integers Use a thermometer to discuss negative integers. Make sure the thermometer only shows one measurement scale such as Fahrenheit. Ask students to identify degrees above zero such as 20°F on the thermometer. Ask: Which is colder, 20°F or 12°F? Make comparisons verbally and then write the numbers on a sheet of paper. Practice making comparisons using the terms *colder* or *warmer.* Then move to math terms such as *greater than* and *less than.* Gradually move into negative numbers by asking: Which is colder (or less), 0°F or 15°F? Continue comparing negative temperatures or numbers to zero until students understand that even though the numbers look like they are getting greater, when they are less than zero, they are actually lesser numbers.

Common Error *Alert*

Exercise 20 Students may not read the word problem carefully. They may see the 10 and not read the word quarters after the number. Before subtracting $1, the 10 quarters that Tammy put into the pinball machine needs to be converted to dollars and cents. Have students think of 4 quarters equal to $1, so 8 quarters is equal to $2. The two quarters left make a total of $2.50.

Additional Answer

Exercise 22 Inverse Property: Add any number and its opposite and get 0. $7 + (-7) = 0$

Commutative Property: The order of the addends does not change the sum. $9 + 1 = 10$ and $1 + 9 = 10$

Step by Step Problem-Solving Practice

Problem-Solving Strategies
- ☑ Draw a picture.
- ☐ Use logical reasoning.
- ☐ Make a table.
- ☐ Solve a simpler problem.
- ☐ Work backward.

Solve.

19 HIKING Two friends start out on a day-long hike on a hill. They begin at an elevation of 500 feet. Their hike takes them to an altitude that is 200 feet lower than where they began. What is their current altitude?

Understand Read the problem. Write what you know.
The hikers begin at an altitude of **500 ft**.
They walk down **200 ft** feet in altitude.

Plan Pick a strategy. One strategy is to draw a picture.

Solve Begin at 500 feet and go down 200 feet.
$500 + (-200) =$ **300 ft**

Check Does the answer make sense? Look over your solution. Did you answer the question?

20 GAMES Tammy puts 10 quarters into a pinball machine. She uses $1 of her credit. How much credit does she have left?

Check off each step.

✔ Understand: I underlined key words.

✔ Plan: To solve the problem, I will **draw a diagram**.

✔ Solve: The answer is **$2.50 + (−$1.00) = $1.50**.

✔ Check: I checked my answer by **working backward**.

21 HEALTH Julio had a fever of 102°F. At the end of the day, his temperature had gone down 2 degrees. What was his temperature at the end of the day?

102 + (−2) = 100; 100°F

22 **Reflect** Give examples of the Inverse Property and Commutative Property of Addition. Explain each property.

See TE margin.

English Learner Strategy

Understanding Credit You can make the following statements and ask the following questions to help students that are not familiar with the meaning of credit or have not played video games to understand the situation in Exercise 20.

- When you put $1 into a vending machine to buy a $0.75 snack, what happens to the extra quarter that you put into the machine?
- Video games work differently than vending machines. Video game machines do not make change. Tammy put 10 quarters into the machine. Without earning more credits, how many $1 games will she be able to play?
- If she plays well she can earn credits to play more. How many credits does she need to earn to be able to play a third game?

Skills, Concepts, and Problem Solving

Find each sum. Use algebra tiles.

23 $5 + (-6) =$ **−1**

24 $-2 + 4 =$ **2**

Find each sum. Use the number line.

25 $-7 + 3 =$ **−4**

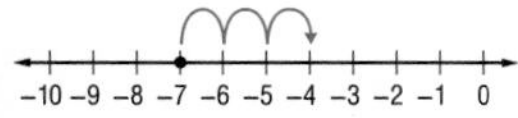

26 $-2 + (-3) =$ **−5**

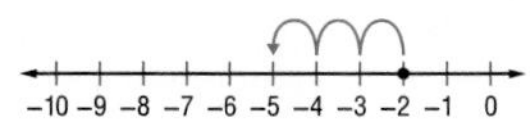

27 $2 + (-5) =$ **−3**

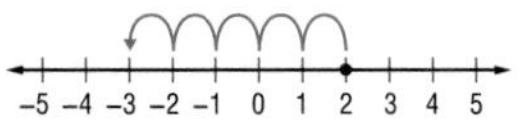

28 $-3 + (-1) =$ **−4**

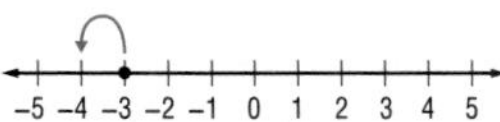

What is the opposite of each number? Use it to show the Inverse Property of Addition.

29 6 **-6; $6 + (-6) = 0$**

30 −5 **5; $-5 + 5 = 0$**

31 −28 **28; $-28 + 28 = 0$**

32 37 **-37; $37 + (-37) = 0$**

Find each sum.

33 $8 + (-4) =$ **4**

34 $-6 + (-3) =$ **−9**

35 $-7 + 4 =$ **−3**

36 $9 + (-7) =$ **2**

37 $-17 + (-5) =$ **−22**

38 $-24 + 8 =$ **−16**

39 $27 + (-9) =$ **18**

40 $-15 + (-8) =$ **−23**

41 $28 + (-39) =$ **−11**

42 $37 + (-24) =$ **13**

GO ON

Math Challenge

Addition Sentences Arrange students into groups of three. Give each group a standard deck of playing cards and have them remove the face cards. Explain that the red cards represent positive numbers 1–10 and the black cards represent negative numbers 1–10. Have the group deal out all of the cards to each other. Each player should make as many true addition sentences as they can from the cards they were dealt. Each sentence should have one positive addend and one negative addend. With the remaining cards in hand, play a modified version of Go Fish, but without a draw pile in the middle. As long as a player can make another sentence, his or her turn continues. The first player to use all the cards wins. If the game reaches a stalemate, it is a tie game.

Odd/Even Assignments

Exercises 23–46 are structured so that students practice the same concepts whether they are assigned the odd or even problems.

In-Class Assignment

Have students complete Exercises 23, 26, 30, 34, 35, 43, and 49 to ensure that they understand the concept.

See It, Do It, Say It, Write It

Step 1 Write several integers on the board. Ask students to write two addition sentences using numbers from the list. Tell them to determine the sum for each of their sentences.

Step 2 Ask students to model the problems using a number line.

Step 3 Have students share their number line models in small groups.

Step 4 Write an addition sentence using negative integers on the board. Have students work in pairs. Tell them to write a word problem to represent the addition sentence. Include the solution and a model that represents the situation.

Looking Ahead: Pre-teach

Subtract Integers In the next lesson, students will learn how to subtract integers. Subtraction can be defined as adding the opposite.

Example

Find the difference of 2 and 5.

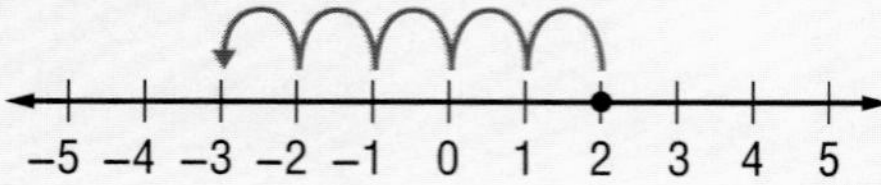

2 – 5 is the same as 2 + (–5).
Find the sum. 2 + (–5) = –3

Have students find the difference of each pair of integers. Write each as a sentence showing an addition of the opposite.

1. 1 and –4 1 – (–4) = 1 + (4) = 5
2. –3 and 2 –3 – 2 = –3 + (–2) = –5
3. –6 and –5 –6 – (–5) = –6 + (5) = –1

Solve.

43 TRAVEL Thirty-two people got on a bus. Ten people got off at the next stop. How many people were on the bus then?

32 + (–10) = 22; There were 22 people on the bus.

44 BUILDINGS John was on the fourteenth floor. He got on the elevator and went down 8 floors. What floor was John on then?

14 + (–8) = 6; John was on the sixth floor.

45 TEMPERATURE When Demetrius went to school the temperature was –3°F. When he got home from school the temperature raised 16°. What was the actual temperature when he got home from school?

–3 + 16 = 13; 13°F

46 BANKING Ariana's bank account statement said she had –$35. She deposited $57 into her account. What is Ariana's balance after she made the deposit?

–35 + 57 = 22; $22

Vocabulary Check **Write the vocabulary word that completes each sentence.**

47 The property that states that the order in which numbers are added does not affect the sum is the

Commutative Property of Addition.

48 The Inverse Property of Addition states that the sum of an integer and its opposite is zero.

49 Writing in Math Explain what is wrong with how the sum of –7 and –3 is found on the number line shown on the right.

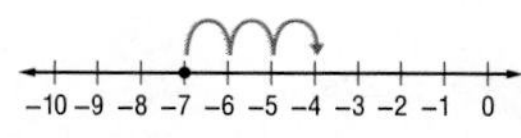

The mistake is that the second number is a negative. You should move to the left 3 spaces. The answer is –10, not –4.

Ticket Out the Door

Unscramble the Sentence Write the following numbers on the board.

–18 –22 –23 23 28 –37 –41 –45 65

Explain to students that these nine numbers can be arranged into three addition sentences. When each student has unscrambled the numbers to make three true equations, they can write them on a paper and turn them in as they exit the classroom.
65 + (–37) = 28; –45 + 23 = –22; –23 + (–18) = –41

Lesson 8-2

Subtract Integers

KEY Concept

The first step in subtracting integers is to rewrite the subtraction expression as an addition expression.

2 – 5 can be written as the addition expression 2 + (–5).

You can use the number line to show the sum.

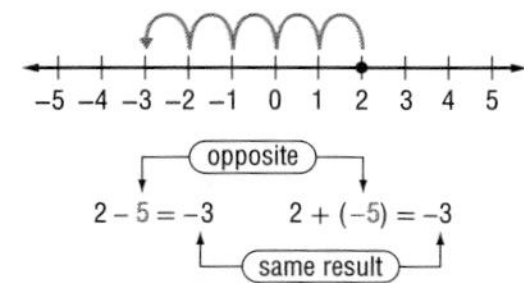

VOCABULARY

absolute value
the distance between a number and 0 on a number line
Example: The absolute value of both –5 and 5 is 5.

opposites
numbers that are the same distance from zero in opposite directions
Example: 3 and –3

Subtracting Integers

Subtraction	Rewritten as Addition	Signs	Answer
–3 – 5	–3 + (–5)	same	–8
3 – 5	3 + (–5)	different	–2
–3 – (–5)	–3 + 5	different	2
3 – (–5)	3 + 5	same	8

Rewrite subtraction problems as adding the opposite. The rules given above for determining the sign of an answer are used for both addition and subtraction problems.

The **absolute value** of a number is the distance the number is from zero. All absolute values are positive numbers or zero. The symbol for absolute value of the number 3 is |–3|.

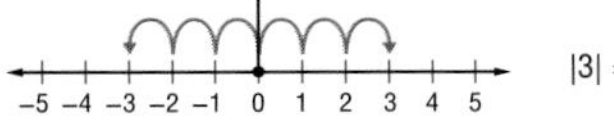

|3| = 3 and |–3| = 3

An easy way to think of absolute value of a negative number is to drop the negative sign.

Finding the absolute value of numbers can help you when adding and subtracting integers.

GO ON

Intervention Strategy

Interpersonal/ Kinesthetic Learners

Matching Expressions Hand out three index cards to every student. Each student needs to write a subtraction expression on one card, the equivalent addition expression on another card, and the answer on the third card. Arrange students into groups of four. Each group should mix up their cards and lay them out face down in 4 rows by 4 columns. Each group should play a modified version of the Memory Game turning over three cards at each turn. After the first game concludes, groups should trade sets of cards with each other and play again.

Lesson Notes

Lesson 8-2

Lesson Planner

Objective Subtract integers.

Vocabulary **absolute value**, **opposites**

Materials/Manipulatives number lines, algebra tiles, two-color counters, pattern blocks, money, index cards, thermometer

Chapter Resource Masters

- CRM Vocabulary and English Language Development (p. A161)
- CRM Skills Practice (p. A162)
- CRM Problem-Solving Practice (p. A163)
- CRM Homework Practice (p. A164)

Vocabulary

Adding and Subtracting Remind students that the answer to a subtraction problem is the *difference*. Write the subtraction problem 7 – 5 = 2 on the board. Ask students to name the difference. Then write the addition problem 7 + (–5) = 2 on the board. Ask students to name the *sum*. Have students compare the two sentences.

Key Concept

Foundational Skills and Concepts After students have read through the Key Concept box, have them try these exercises.

1. Rewrite 15 – 34 as an addition expression. 15 + (–34)
2. Which number, 15 or –34, has the greater absolute value? –34
3. What is the sign of the difference of 15 – 34? negative

Additional *Example 1*

Find the difference of –6 and –4. Use algebra tiles.

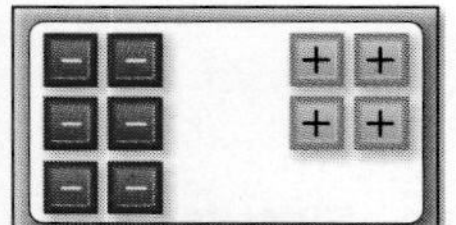

Place six red tiles to represent –6. Then place four yellow tiles to represent adding four.

1. Write the subtraction expression. –6 – (–4)
2. To subtract integers, add the opposite. Write the addition expression. –6 + 4 This is the new expression.
3. Use six negative tiles to represent the first number.
4. Use four positive tiles to represent the second number.
5. You can make 4 zero pairs.

6. There are two negative tiles left.

7. Write the difference. –6 – (–4) = –2

Example 1

Find the difference of 2 and 5. Use algebra tiles.

1. Write the subtraction expression. 2 − 5
2. To subtract integers, add the opposite. Write the addition expression. 2 + (−5) This is the new expression.
3. Use two positive algebra tiles to represent the first number.
4. Use five negative algebra tiles to represent the second number.
5. You can make 2 zero pairs.
6. There are three negative algebra tiles left.
7. Write the difference.

   2 + (−5) = −3

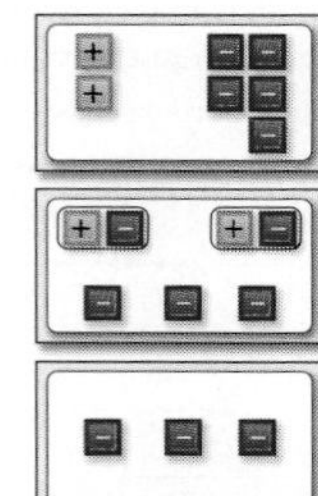

Place five red tiles to represent −5. Then place two yellow tiles to represent adding two.

YOUR TURN!

Find the difference of 3 and 2. Use algebra tiles.

1. Write the subtraction expression. __3 − 2__
2. To subtract integers, add the opposite. Write the addition expression. __3 + (−2)__ This is the new expression.
3. Use __three positive__ algebra tiles to represent the first number.
4. Use __two negative__ algebra tiles to represent the second number.
5. You can make __2__ zero pairs.
6. There is __1 positive__ algebra tile(s) left.
7. Write the difference.

   3 + (−2) = __1__

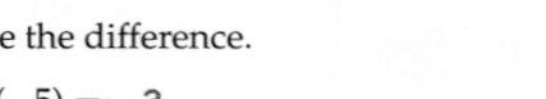

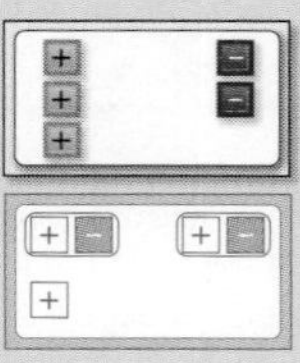

Intervention Strategy

Kinesthetic/Logical Learners

Use Manipulatives

1. Begin this lesson by using concrete materials. Model some subtraction sentences with negative integers using two-color counters. Show how to use the opposite of the second number to rewrite the sentence as an addition expression. Flip over the counters for the second number to show adding the opposite. Have students write the numeric forms of these models on paper.
2. Ask students to practice explaining to one another how to use a number line to demonstrate absolute value and opposites. Encourage correct vocabulary and clear language.

Example 2

Find the difference of −1 and 3. Use the number line.

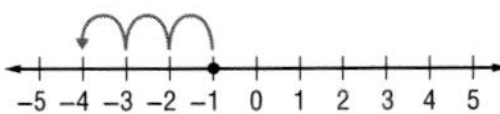

1. Write the subtraction expression.
   −1 − 3
2. To subtract integers, add the opposite.
   Write the addition expression. −1 + (−3)
   This is the new expression.
3. Graph the first number.
4. Start at −1.
5. Since 3 is a negative integer, move left 3 spaces.
6. Write the difference. −1 + (−3) = − 4

YOUR TURN!

Find the difference of −1 and 2. Use the number line.

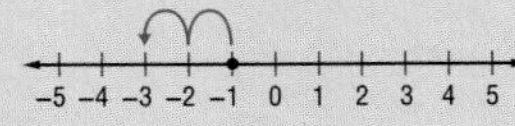

1. Write the subtraction expression. −1 − 2
2. To subtract integers, add the opposite.
   Write the addition expression. −1 + (− 2)
   This is the new expression.
3. Graph the first number.
4. Start at −1.
5. Since 2 is a negative integer, move left 2 spaces.
6. Write the difference. −1 + (−2) = −3

Additional Example 2

Find the difference of −3 and 5. Use the number line.

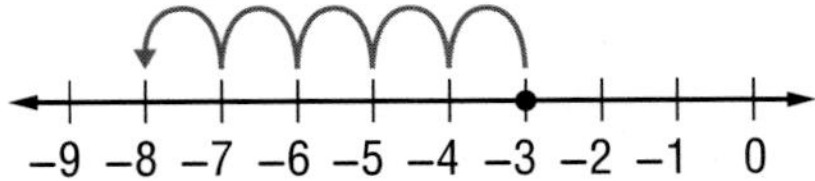

1. Write the subtraction expression. −3 − 5
2. To subtract integers, add the opposite.
   Write the addition expression. −3 + (−5)
   This is the new expression.
3. Graph the first number.
4. Start at −3.
5. Since −5 is a negative integer, move left 5 spaces.
6. Write the difference. −3 − 5 = −8

English Learner Strategy

Guiding Questions Write −12 and 10 on the board. Then ask the following questions to ensure that students understand the concept.

- Imagine these two numbers on a number line.
- How many units from 0 is −12? This is the absolute value of −12.
- How many units from 0 is 10? This is the absolute value of 10.
- Which number is more units from 0? This is the number with the greater absolute value.
- What is the absolute value of −12?
- What is the absolute value of 10?

Additional *Example 3*

Which number has the greater absolute value?

–5 or 6

1. –5 is 5 units from 0.
   So, |–5| = 5.
2. 6 is 6 units from 0.
   So, |6| = 6.
3. Which integer has the greater absolute value?
   6

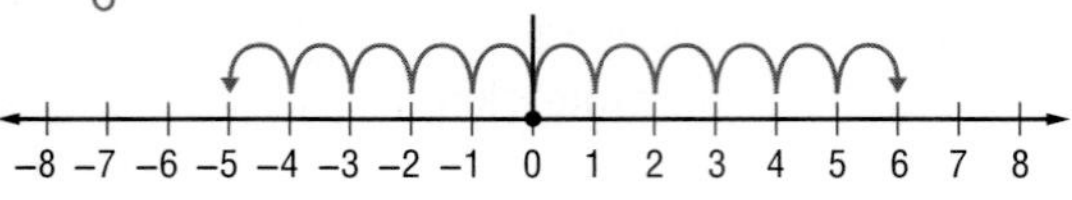

Using Manipulatives

Algebra Tiles When presenting the subtraction of integers, use concrete materials such as algebra tiles to model positive and negative integers.

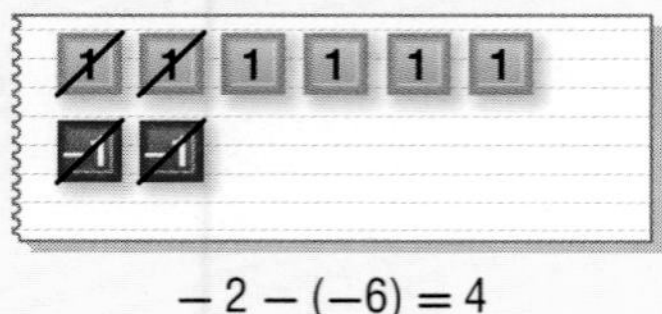

$$-2-(-6)=4$$
$$-2+6=4$$

Pattern Blocks Use different pattern blocks to represent positive and negative numbers in subtraction sentences.

Thermometer Use a thermometer to model subtraction sentences and find differences.

Money Use money to model subtraction. Owing someone money is the same as subtracting/adding a negative number.

On-Hand Manipulatives Use two types of everyday objects as counters, such as beans and coins. Beans could represent negative integers, while coins represent positive integers.

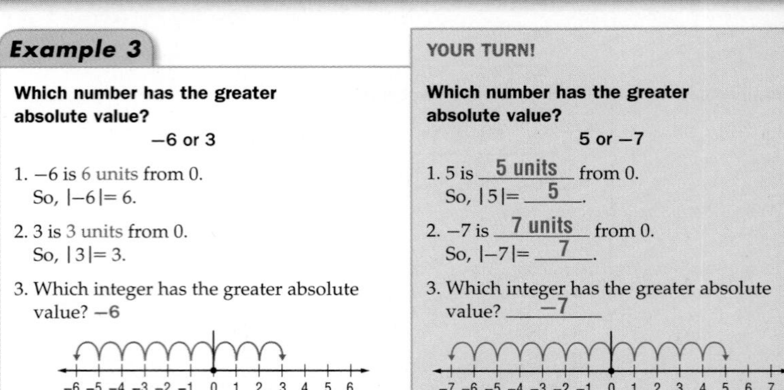

Example 3

Which number has the greater absolute value?

–6 or 3

1. –6 is 6 units from 0.
   So, |–6| = 6.
2. 3 is 3 units from 0.
   So, |3| = 3.
3. Which integer has the greater absolute value? –6

–6 –5 –4 –3 –2 –1 0 1 2 3 4 5 6

YOUR TURN!

Which number has the greater absolute value?

5 or –7

1. 5 is 5 units from 0.
   So, |5| = 5.
2. –7 is 7 units from 0.
   So, |–7| = 7.
3. Which integer has the greater absolute value? –7

–7 –6 –5 –4 –3 –2 –1 0 1 2 3 4 5 6 7

Who is Correct?

Find the difference of –1 and 5. Use algebra tiles.

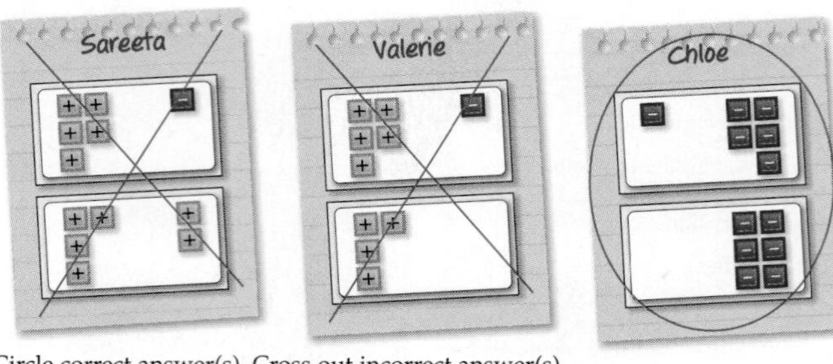

Circle correct answer(s). Cross out incorrect answer(s).

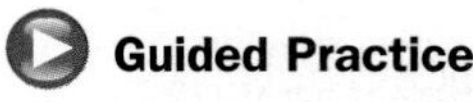

Guided Practice

Find each difference. Use algebra tiles.

1. 9 – 3 = 6

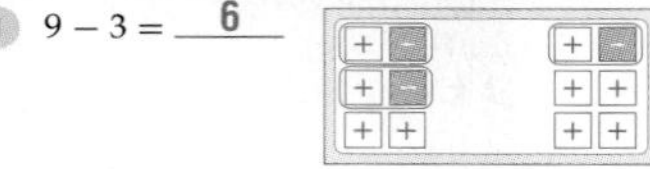

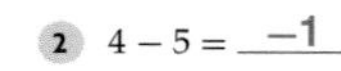

2. 4 – 5 = –1

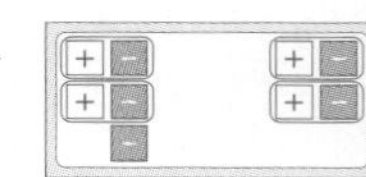

Who *is Correct?*

Diagnostic Teaching

- Sareeta's work is incorrect. She added the opposite of 1.
- Valerie's work is incorrect. She added 5 instead of –5.
- Chloe's work is correct. She subtracted correctly by adding –5.

Remind students to add the opposite of the number after the minus sign.

Step by Step Practice

3 Find the difference of −6 and −3. Use the number line.

Step 1 Write the subtraction expression. $-6 - (-3)$

Step 2 To subtract integers, add the opposite.
Write the addition expression. $-6 + 3$
This is the new expression.

Step 3 Graph the first number.

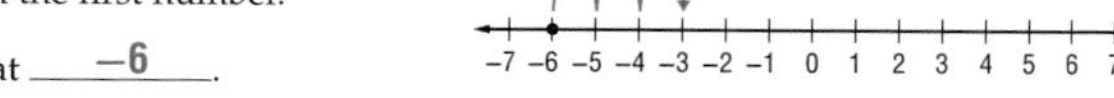

Step 4 Start at -6.

Step 5 Since 3 is a positive integer, move right 3 spaces.

Step 6 Write the difference. $-6 + 3 = -3$

Find each difference. Use the number line.

4 $6 - (-4)$

Write the addition expession. 6 + 4

Start at 6 and move right 4 spaces. 6 + 4 = 10

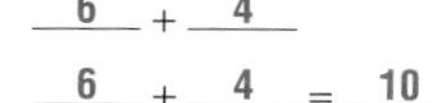

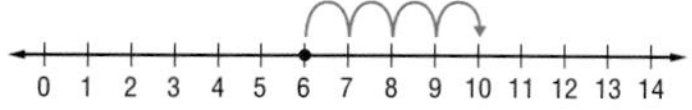

5 $-3 - 1 =$ -4

6 $-6 - (-7) =$ 1

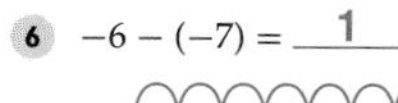

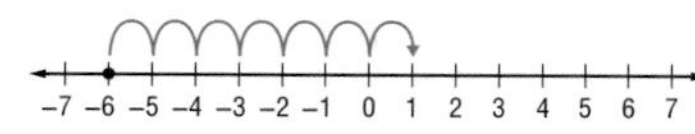

Which number has the greater absolute value?

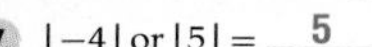

7 $|-4|$ or $|5| =$ 5

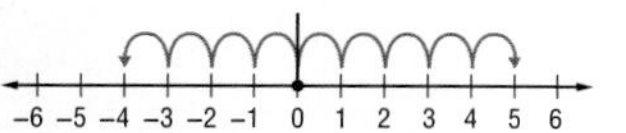

8 $|2|$ or $|-3| =$ -3

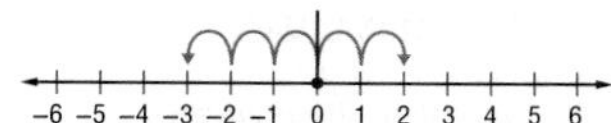

Are They Getting It?

Check students' understanding of subtracting integers by writing these problems on the board. Ask students to point out wrong answers and explain why they are wrong.

1. $-12 - (-2) = -10$
   This is correct.

2. The difference of −17 and 6 is −11.
   This is incorrect. $-17 - 6 = -17 + (-6) = -23$

3. $|-11|$ has a greater absolute value than $|5|$.
   This is correct.

Note This!

Separate Symbols and Signs Notice that in the problems two operation signs are not placed side by side. If a negative number in an expression follows either a subtraction sign or an addition sign, place the negative number in parentheses.

Step by Step Problem-Solving Practice

Problem-Solving Strategies

- ☐ Draw a diagram.
- ☐ Use logical reasoning.
- ☑ Make a table.
- ☐ Solve a simpler problem.
- ☐ Act it out.

Solve.

9 FINANCES Sue bought a stock for \$7 a share. The first month the stock gained \$11. The next month the stock lost \$5. How much is her stock worth now?

Understand Read the problem. Write what you know.

The stock was bought for \$7.

The stock then gained \$11 and lost \$5 in value.

Plan Pick a strategy. One strategy is to make a table.

Solve Follow the changes in the stock's value using the table. $\$7 + \$11 + (-\$5) =$ \$13

Check You can use a number line to check your answers.

Change (\$)	Stock Value
	\$7
+11	\$18
−5	\$13

10 WEATHER The low temperature one winter was 10 degrees below 0°F. In summer, the high temperature was 90°F. What is the change in temperature from winter to summer?

Check off each step.

✔ Understand: I underlined key words.

✔ Plan: To solve the problem I will, draw a diagram

✔ Solve: The answer is $90 - (-10) = 90 + 10 = 100$; There is a 100 degree difference

✔ Check: I checked my answer by subtracting 10 from 100 to get 90

11 MINIATURE GOLF Rico and his friend Carla played miniature golf. If Rico scored a −4 and Carla scored a −1, what was the difference of their scores?

$-4 - (-1) = -4 + 1 = -3$

Intervention Strategy

Kinesthetic/Interpersonal Learners

Absolute Birthdays Have each student write a four-digit number where the first two numbers are the month of his or her birth and the last two digits are the day of the month of his or her birth. Below the number on their papers, students should make a table like the one shown below. Each student should rotate around the classroom calculating *x* with other students. For each calculation, make a tally mark in the appropriate column. Students can check tables to make sure all tables in the class match.

Let $x = \lvert \text{my number} - \text{other student's number} \rvert$			
$0 \le x \le 100$	$100 < x \le 350$	$351 < x \le 600$	$601 < x$

2 **Reflect** Is the statement true or false? "The absolute value of a number depends on its direction from zero." Explain.

The statement is false. The absolute value depends on the distance from 0, not the direction, because distance is always a positive number.

Skills, Concepts, and Problem Solving

Find each difference. Use algebra tiles.

13 $-4 - (-6) =$ 2

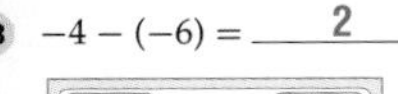

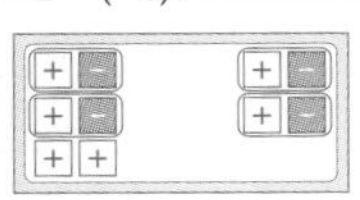

14 $-5 - 4 =$ -9

Find each difference. Use the number line.

15 $-10 - (-11) =$ 1

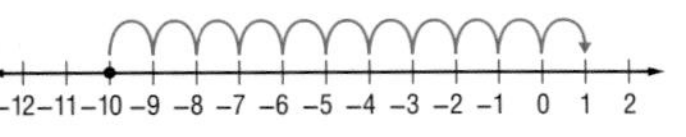

16 $-6 - 5 =$ -11

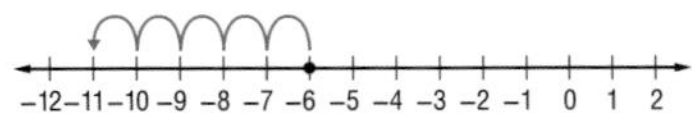

Find each difference.

17 $-8 - (-2) =$ -6

18 $-3 - 9 =$ -12

19 $15 - 5 =$ 10

20 $11 - (-7) =$ 18

Which number has the greater absolute value?

21 $|-9|$ or $|9|$ same

22 $|-8|$ or $|-12|$ -12

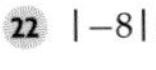

Solve.

23 CLIMBING In gym class, Greta climbed 13 feet up the rock wall. She descended 5 feet. How high up is Greta on the rock wall?

$13 - (+5) = 13 - 5 = 8$ feet

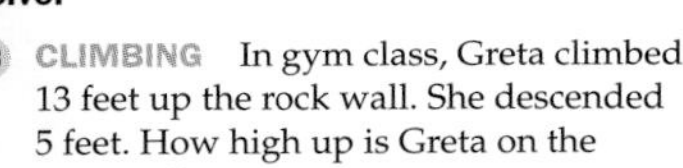

GO ON

Math Challenge

Larger Numbers Have students work in pairs. Each student should write a subtraction problem using one integer greater than 200 and one integer less than –300. Have students solve their own problems and then trade papers, solve their partner's problem, and compare answers.

Odd/Even Assignments

Exercises 13–24 are structured so that students practice the same concepts whether they are assigned the odd or even problems.

In-Class Assignment

Have students complete Exercises 13, 16, 20, 21, 24, and 28 to ensure that they understand the concept.

Additional Answer

Exercise 28 Answers will vary. Sample answer: Positive means something good in everyday situations, while negative means something bad. In math, positive means that a number is greater than zero. A negative number is less than zero.

See It, Do It, Say It, Write It

Step 1 Write several subtraction sentences on the board using negative integers. Ask students to find the difference for each sentence.

Step 2 Ask students to model the problems using a number line or counters.

Step 3 Have students share their models in small groups or with the class.

Step 4 Have students work in pairs. Tell them to write a word problem to represent a subtraction sentence. Include the solution and a model that represents the situation.

Looking Ahead: Pre-teach

Add and Subtract Groups of Integers In the next lesson, students will learn about adding and subtracting groups of integers. Use the Associative Property of Addition to simplify these calculations.

Example

Simplify 8 – (–6) + (–5) – 3.

Rewrite the subtraction as addition. Use the Associative Property of Addition. Then find the sum from left to right.

$8 + (6) + (-5) + (-3) =$
$(8 + 6) + ((-5) + (-3)) = 14 + (-8) = 6$

Simplify.

1. –3 – 4 + (–2) – 5 –14
2. 9 – (–7) – 1 + (–8) 7
3. 5 + (–6) – 2 + (–7) –10

24 FOOTBALL Jack ran the ball two times in last week's high school football game. On his first run he was tackled for a 4 yard loss. On his second run he was tackled for a 9 yard loss. How many yards were lost?

–4 + (–9) = –13; –13 yards

Vocabulary Check **Write the vocabulary word that completes each sentence.**

25 Subtraction is used to compare two numbers.

26 Opposites are numbers that are the same distance from zero in opposite directions.

27 The absolute value of a number is the distance the number is from zero on a number line.

28 Writing in Math How are the words positive and negative used differently in math than in everyday situations?

See TE margin.

Spiral Review

What is the opposite of each number? Use it to show the Inverse Property of Addition. (Lesson 8-1, p. 318)

29 –18 18; –18 + 18 = 0

30 4 –4; 4 + (–4) = 0

31 –31 31; –31 + 31 = 0

32 17 –17; 17 + (–17) = 0

Solve. (Lesson 8-1, p. 318)

33 COMPUTERS Francisco had 11 folders on his desktop. He added 4 folders to his desktop. How many folders are on his desktop now?

11 + 4 = 15; 15 folders

34 MUSIC Mora removed 8 songs from her MP3 player on Thursday. On Friday she removed 3 more songs. How many songs did she remove from her MP3 player?

–8 + (–3) = –11; –11 songs

STOP

Ticket Out the Door

Subtraction Sentences Ask students to write five subtraction problems using all different numbers so that the problems have differences of 0, 1, 2, 5, and 10. Each problem should use one positive number and one negative number. Students should hand in their problems as they exit the classroom.

Progress Check 1 (Lessons 8-1 and 8-2)

nd each sum. Use the number line.

$-3 + (-6) =$ __−9__

2 $8 + (-2) =$ __6__

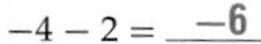

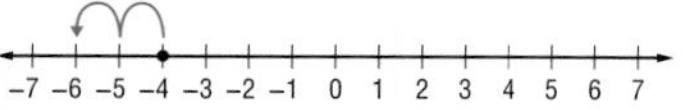

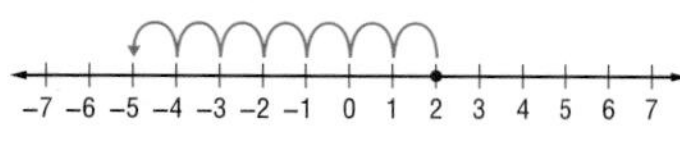

nd each sum.

$6 + (-9) =$ __−3__

4 $-2 + -7 =$ __−9__

hat is the opposite of each number? Use it to show the Inverse
operty of Addition.

-10 __10; (−10) + 10 = 0__ 6 -8 __8; (−8) + 8 = 0__ 7 6 __(−6); 6 + (−6) = 0__

nd each difference. Use the number line.

$-4 - 2 =$ __−6__

9 $2 - 7 =$ __−5__

nd the difference.

$-4 - 5 =$ __−9__

11 $-3 - (-7) =$ __4__

hat number has the greater absolute value?

$|-5|$ or $|5|$ __both are the same__

13 $|4|$ or $|-6|$ __−6__

14 $|-7|$ or $|-14|$ __−14__

lve.

HEALTH Every 10 steps burns 5 Calories. Every apple adds 35 Calories. If Paulina ate 1 apple and took 10 steps, how many Calories did she gain?

__−5 + 35 = 30; 30 Calories__

Chapter 8 Progress Check 333

Progress Check 1

Chapter 8

Formative Assessment

Use the Progress Check to assess students' mastery of the previous lessons. Have students review the lesson indicated for the problems they answered incorrectly.

Odd/Even Assignments

Exercises are structured so that students practice the same concepts whether they are assigned the odd or even problems.

Common Error *Alert*

Use Diagrams Students should try to make a transition between using a diagram to solve the problems to solving the problems abstractly.

Exercise 3 If students look at Exercise 3 and see the 6 and the 9 (not taking into account the negative sign) they can refer to a number line to visualize the answer.

Exercise 15 Encourage students to break down the information in Exercise 15 into pieces. Ask: Does the word "burn" indicate negative or positive?

Data-Driven Decision Making

Students missing Exercises . . .	Have trouble with . . .	Should review and practice . . .
1-4	finding sums with and without models.	SSG Lesson 8-1, p. 318 CRM Skills Practice, p. A158
5-7	stating opposites and showing the Inverse Property of Addition.	SSG Lesson 8-1, p. 318 CRM Skills Practice, p. A158
8-11	finding differences with and without models.	SSG Lesson 8-2, p. 325 CRM Skills Practice, p. A162
12-14	comparing absolute values.	SSG Lesson 8-2, p. 325 CRM Skills Practice, p. A162
15	solving a word problem involving integers.	CRM Problem-Solving Practice, pp. A159 and A163

Lesson 8-3 Lesson Notes

Lesson Planner

Objective Add and subtract groups of integers.

Vocabulary **Associative Property of Addition**

Materials/Manipulatives pattern blocks, algebra tiles, two-color counters, connecting cubes, money, plastic cups, red and black markers, number cubes

Chapter Resource Masters

- CRM Vocabulary and English Language Development (p. A165)
- CRM Skills Practice (p. A166)
- CRM Problem-Solving Practice (p. A167)
- CRM Homework Practice (p. A168)

1 Introduce

Vocabulary

Simplify Model how to use the Associative Property of Addition to regroup numbers to simplify.

$$\begin{aligned} -12 - (-15) - 8 &= -12 + 15 + (-8) \\ &= -12 + (-8) + 15 \\ &= (-12 + (-8)) + 15 \\ &= -20 + 15 \\ &= -5 \end{aligned}$$

Follow this process with several more addition and subtraction sentences.

2 Teach

Key Concept

Foundational Skills and Concepts After students have read through the Key Concept box, have them try these exercises.

1. $((-17) + 43) + 18 = (-17) + (43 + 18)$ is an example of which property? Associative Property of Addition
2. Rewrite the subtraction expression as an addition expression: $23 - 9 - (-18)$. Then simplify. $23 + (-9) + 18 = 32$

Lesson 8-3 Add and Subtract Groups of Integers

KEY Concept

To add and subtract integers, begin by rewriting each subtraction as addition. Then add from left to right.

$$\begin{aligned} &5 - 6 + 2 \\ &= 5 + (-6) + 2 \\ &= -1 + 2 \\ &= 1 \end{aligned}$$

You can also use mental math to work the problem.

Use the **Associative Property of Addition** to make solving problems easier. The order in which you group numbers does not change the answer.

$(3 + 6) + (-6) = 3 + (6 + (-6))$ — Group the 6 and −6 together.

Follow the rules for subtraction and rewrite each subtraction expression as an addition expression. When there are parentheses in a problem, perform the operations in the parentheses *first*. Then add or subtract from left to right.

$$\begin{aligned} &21 - 8 + (7 - (-2)) + (-5) \\ &= 21 + (-8) + (7 + 2) + (-5) \\ &= 21 + (-8) + 9 (-5) \\ &= 13 + 9 + (-5) \\ &= 22 + (-5) \\ &= 17 \end{aligned}$$

VOCABULARY

Associative Property of Addition the way addends are grouped does not change the sum
Example: $(4 + 5) + 2 = 4 + (5 + 2)$

Example 1

Use the Associative Property of Addition to find the missing number.

$(4 + 13) + 7 = 4 + (\_\_\_\_ + 7)$

1. The numbers are in the same order.
2. Did the parentheses move to different numbers? yes
3. Write the missing number.
   $4 + (13 + 7)$

Additional Example 1

Use the Associative Property of Addition to find the missing number.

$(3 + 8) + 9 = 3 + (\_\_\_ + 9)$

1. The numbers are in the same order.
2. Did the parentheses move to different numbers? yes
3. Write the missing number. $3 + (8 + 9)$

YOUR TURN!

Use the Associative Property of Addition to find the missing number.

(2 + 15) + 5 = 2 + (_____ + 5)

1. Are the numbers in the same order? yes
2. Did the parentheses move to different numbers? yes
3. Write the missing number.

   2 + (15 + 5)

Example 2

Simplify 5 + (−6) − 7 + 3 − (−2).

1. Rewrite each subtraction as addition.

   5 + (−6) − 7 + 3 − (−2) = 5 + (−6) + (−7) + 3 + 2

2. Find the sum from left to right.

   = 5 + (−6) + (−7) + 3 + 2

   = (−1) + (−7) + 3 + 2

   = (−8) + 3 + 2

   = (−5) + 2

   = (−3)

YOUR TURN!

Simplify 4 + (−3) − 2 + 5 − (−1).

1. Rewrite each subtraction as addition.

   4 + (−3) − 2 + 5 − (−1) = 4 + (−3) + (−2) + 5 + 1

2. Find the sum from left to right.

   = 4 + (−3) + (−2) + 5 + 1

   = 1 + (−2) + 5 + 1

   = (−1) + 5 + 1

   = 4 + 1

   = 5

GO ON

Intervention Strategy

Kinesthetic/Visual Learners

Create a Number Line Have students create a large number line that extends the length of one side of the classroom with zero in the center. Use students as plotted points to demonstrate adding and subtracting integers. Write addition and subtraction expressions on the board. Invite student volunteers to physically show how to simplify the expressions by writing them on the board and acting them out on the number line to prove their answers are correct.

Additional *Example 2*

Simplify 7 + (–5) – 9 + 8 – (–6).

1. Rewrite each subtraction as addition.

7 + (–5) – 9 + 8 – (–6) =

7 + (–5) + (–9) + 8 + 6

2. Find the sum from left to right.

(7 + (–5)) + (–9) + 8 + 6

= (2 + (–9)) + 8 + 6

= (–7 + 8) + 6

= (1 + 6)

= 7

Math Coach Notes

Simplify Expressions Teach the process of simplifying expressions as a manner of manipulating or rewriting them as equivalent. More easily workable expressions will help students recognize and utilize properties. As students become more proficient, they will be able to transfer this practice to equations and variables.

Additional **Example 3**

Simplify $14 - 4 + (7 - (-5)) + (-3)$.

1. Rewrite each subtraction as addition.
$14 - 4 + (7 - (-5)) + (-3) =$
$14 + (-4) + (7 + 5) + (-3)$

2. Simplify the expression in the parentheses.
$14 + (-4) + (7 + 5) + (-3) =$
$14 + (-4) + 12 + (-3)$

3. Simplify from left to right.
$= (14 + (-4)) + 12 + (-3)$
$= (10 + 12) + (-3)$
$= (22 + (-3))$
$= 19$

Math Coach Notes

Strategy Begin this lesson by adding and subtracting lesser integers. Have students practice rewriting subtraction expressions as addition until they become comfortable with the process. Slowly introduce greater integers and more negative signs in the examples.

Intervention Strategy

Kinesthetic/ Visual/ Logical Learners

Model Expressions Have students work in pairs. Give each group a plastic cup filled with two kinds of pattern blocks or two-colored counters. Ask students to use the blocks or counters to model addition and subtraction expressions with integers. Then write the numeric forms of the modeled expressions on a sheet of paper. Challenge students to vary their operations and signs and explain how to simplify each expression.

Example 3

Simplify $6 + 5 - (3 - (-4)) + (-7)$.

1. Rewrite each subtraction as addition.
$6 + 5 - (3 - (-4)) + (-7) = 6 + 5 - (3 + 4) + (-7)$
2. Simplify the expression in the parentheses.
$6 + 5 - (3 + 4) + (-7) = 6 + 5 - 7 + (-7)$
3. Simplify from left to right. $= 6 + 5 - 7 + (-7)$
$= 11 - 7 + (-7)$
$= 4 + (-7)$
$= -3$

YOUR TURN!

Simplify $10 - 7 - (5 - (-6)) + (-4)$.

1. Rewrite each subtraction as addition.
$10 - 7 - (5 - (-6)) + (-4) = 10 + (\underline{-7}) - (5 + \underline{6}) + (-4)$
2. Simplify the expression in the parentheses.
$10 + (\underline{-7}) - (5 + \underline{6}) + (-4) = 10 + (\underline{-7}) - \underline{11} + (-4)$
3. Simplify from left to right. $= 10 + (\underline{-7}) - \underline{11} + (-4)$
$= \underline{3} - 11 + (-4)$
$= \underline{-8} + (-4)$
$= \underline{-12}$

Who is Correct?

Simplify $9 + (-8) - 5 + 7 - (-3)$.

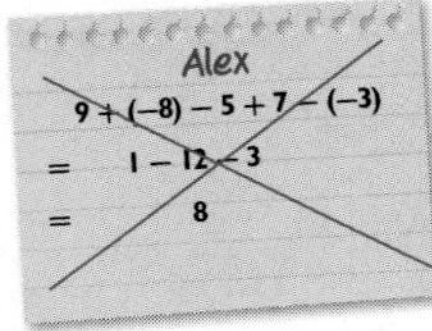

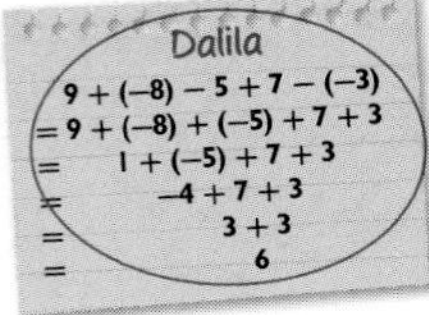

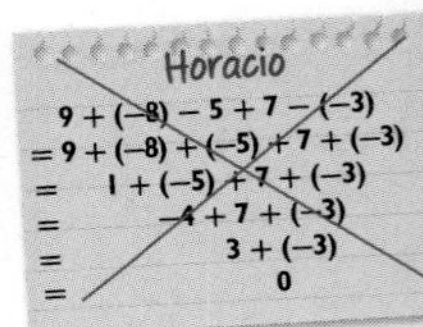

Circle correct answer(s). Cross out incorrect answer(s).

336 Chapter 8 Integer Operations

Who *is Correct?*

Diagnostic Teaching

- Alex's work is not correct. He tried to do too many steps at one time and did not add the opposite of –3.
- Dalila's work is correct. She simplified and computed correctly.
- Horacio's work is incorrect. He did not add the opposite of –3.

Remind students to begin at the left and change all subtraction to adding the opposite. Then simplify one step at a time.

Guided Practice

se the Associative Property of Addition to find the missing number.

$(9 + 12) + 8 = 9 + (\underline{12} + 8)$

Are the numbers in the same order? yes

Did the parentheses move to surround different numbers? yes

tep by Step Practice

Simplify $6 + (-7) + 8 - 4 - (-3)$.

Step 1 Rewrite each subtraction as addition.

$6 + (-7) + 8 - 4 - (-3) = \underline{6 + (-7) + 8 + (-4) + 3}$

Step 2 Find the sum from left to right.

$6 + (-7) + 8 + (-4) + 3 =$

$= \underline{-1} + 8 + (-4) + 3$

$= \underline{7} + (-4) + 3$

$= \underline{3} + 3$

$= \underline{6}$

mplify.

$-8 + (-3) - (-15)$ rewritten sentence: $\underline{-8 + (-3) + 15}$

sum: $\underline{4}$

$7 - (-4) - (-3) = \underline{14}$

5 $-1 + 5 - (-11) = \underline{15}$

$11 - 5 - 13 + 5 = \underline{-2}$

7 $-3 - (-5) - (-9) - 6 = \underline{5}$

$18 - 2 + (9 + (-4)) + (-9) = \underline{12}$

9 $22 + 9 - (5 - (-2)) + 12 = \underline{36}$

Are They Getting It?

Check students' understanding of integer operations by writing these problems on the board. Have students state which are correct and which are not correct. Make certain they provide reasons. Encourage them to use drawings or examples in their explanations.

1. Using the Associative Property of Addition, $(-15) + ((-36) - 8) = (-15 + (-36)) + (-8)$. This is correct.
2. $14 - 8 + (-9) = 3$ This is incorrect. $14 - 8 + (-9) = 14 + (-8) + (-9) = 14 + (-17) = -3$
3. $-52 - 35 - (-47) + 15 = -119$ This is incorrect. $-52 - 35 - (-47) + 15 = -52 + (-35) + 47 + 15 = -87 + 62 = -25$

3 Practice

Using Manipulatives

Algebra Tiles When presenting the addition or subtraction of integers, use concrete materials such as algebra tiles to model positive and negative integers.

$-5 - (-7) = 2$

Connecting Cubes Use two different colors of connecting cubes to model and find the sums of addition sentences with integers.

On-Hand Manipulatives Use a thermometer that shows only one measurement scale, such as Fahrenheit, to help students create and solve addition and subtraction sentences with positive and negative integers.

Common Error *Alert*

Exercises 4–9 If students have difficulty with Exercises 4–9, they might be overwhelmed by the signs and parentheses. Focus on rewriting the expressions one number at a time. Model reading the problem aloud and then emphasizing the phrase "plus the opposite" before rewriting every number that follows a subtraction sign. For Exercise 4, say: "7 plus the opposite of –4 plus the opposite of –3," and then write the new expression. Sometimes having students say it out loud while they calculate or work through the process can aid in comprehension and accuracy.

Math Coach Notes

Study Tip Encourage students to create addition and subtraction expressions of their own. Have them practice explaining how to simplify their expressions to a family member or classmate. Tell students that by explaining the steps to someone else they are reinforcing the process for themselves and gaining confidence in their proficiency.

English Learner Strategy

Guiding Questions Write 5 – 6 – (–3) on a piece of paper. Then ask the following questions to ensure that students understand the concept.

- Which of these numbers are positive? Which are negative?
- What is the opposite of –3? Locate this number on a number line.
- Explain how to rewrite this subtraction expression as an addition expression.
- Explain whether it matters in which order you add the integers.
- Explain how to use tiles to simplify this expression.

Note This!

Spacing Problems Encourage students to leave enough space between numbers and signs, especially when subtracting negative numbers. It is easy for negative signs and subtraction signs to run together, resulting in computational errors. Writing problems clearly and with enough space between numbers can help. Also try placing parentheses around all negative numbers in expressions to keep the signs and operators clearly marked.

Step by Step Problem-Solving Practice

Problem-Solving Strategies
- ☑ Draw a diagram.
- ☐ Use logical reasoning.
- ☐ Guess and check.
- ☐ Solve a simpler problem.
- ☐ Use an equation.

Solve.

10 WEATHER On a summer day in the morning, the temperature in Death Valley, California was about 84° F. By the afternoon, the temperature increased by 27° F. In the evening, the temperature dropped 23° F. What was the temperature in the evening?

Understand The temperature in the morning was __84°F__.
The temperature increased __27°__ in the afternoon.
The temperature dropped __23°__ in the evening.

Plan Pick a strategy. One strategy is to draw a diagram.
Make a number line to represent a thermometer.

Solve Use the number line to find the change in temperature.

80° 85° 90° 95° 100° 105° 110° 115°

Begin at 84°F, increase 27°, and then decrease 23°.
84 + 27 − 23 = __84 + 27 + (−23) = 88__

Check Does the answer make sense? Look over your solution. Did you answer the question?

11 TRANSPORTATION A bus picked up 15 people at the first stop and 10 people at the second stop. Then, 5 people got off the bus at the third stop. Finally, 8 more people got off at the fourth stop. How many people are on the bus now?
Check off each step.

__✓__ Understand: I underlined key words.

__✓__ Plan: To solve the problem, I will __use an equation__

__✓__ Solve: The answer is __15 + 10 − 5 − 8 = 12; There are 12 people still on the bu__

__✓__ Check: I checked my answer by __reviewing my addition and subtraction__

12 FINANCES Elizabeth bought stock for $200. The first week, the stock fell $55. The second week, the stock rose $30. What is the stock worth now? Write an integer that represents the stock's loss or gain.
__200 − 55 + 30 = 175; $175; −$25__

338 Chapter 8 Integer Operations

Intervention Strategy

Auditory/Logical/Interpersonal Learners

Simplify Expressions Ask students to work in small groups or pairs. Recite several expressions and tell students to write them on a sheet of paper. Tell students to practice explaining how to simplify the expressions to one another. Have them practice using calculators to prove their answers are correct. Once each student in the group has simplified and checked his or her expressions, create new expressions together for the class to simplify.

Reflect Explain how the Associative Property of Addition helps you to add integers.

Sample answer: It makes solving problems easier because the order in which you group numbers does not change the answer.

Skills, Concepts, and Problem Solving

e the Associative Property of Addition to find the missing number.

$(15 + 18) + 12 = 15 + (\underline{18} + 12)$

15 $\underline{11} + (14 + 13) = (11 + 14) + 13$

$(101 + 13) + 9 = \underline{101} + (13 + 9)$

17 $\underline{93} + (15 + 12) = (93 + 15) + 12$

mplify.

$8 + (-12) - 7 + 9 = \underline{-2}$

19 $-15 - (-11) + 10 + (-12) = \underline{-6}$

$7 + (-5) - 16 - (-3) = \underline{-11}$

21 $-2 + (-7) + 13 - (-8) = \underline{12}$

$14 - 4 + (8 + (-5)) + (-8) = \underline{5}$

23 $10 - 4 + (6 - 15) + 21 = \underline{18}$

$12 + 8 + (3 - 10) - 17 = \underline{-4}$

25 $-9 - 11 + (7 - (-2)) + (-12) = \underline{-23}$

lve.

ROLLER COASTER A roller coaster climbs a 129-foot hill and then descends 100 feet. If the roller coaster climbs back up 40 feet, what is its elevation?

$129 + (-100) + 40 = 69$; 69 feet

TRAVEL A crop-dusting plane flies at an altitude of 630 feet. It then descends 227 feet when it turns on the duster. When it is done, the plane ascends 180 feet. What altitude is the plane flying then?

$630 + (-227) + 180 = 583$; 583 ft

GO ON

Math Challenge

Signed Cubes Have students create integer number cubes. Ask them to use a red marking tool to write the negative integers and a black marking tool to label the positive integers. Students can choose to mix the kinds of numbers on the same cube or make one with all positive integers and the other with all negative integers. Have students roll the number cubes to create expressions to simplify. For more proficient students, challenge them to include many numbers and signs in their expressions.

Odd/Even Assignments

Exercises 14–28 are structured so that students practice the same concepts whether they are assigned the odd or even problems.

In-Class Assignment

Have students complete Exercises 14, 20, 23, 26, and 30 to ensure that they understand the concept.

Intervention Strategy

Linguistic/Interpersonal Learners

Write Word Problems Ask students to work in small groups. Tell them to write word problems that require a series of integers to be added or subtracted. Encourage students to use positive and negative numbers. Have them include the simplified answer and a model to represent the situation. Students should work together as a group to make the problems as clear as possible and to anticipate any possible errors other students might make when trying to solve their word problems. Ask groups to present their work and encourage classmates to try their word problems.

Additional Answer

Exercise 30 Sample answer: Absolute value stands for how far a number is from zero. The number with the greater absolute value will be farther from zero. When the signs are different, the integer with the larger absolute value will determine the sign of the difference. You subtract the integers and take the sign of the integer with the greater absolute value. Examples: $|-6| < |8|$, $|-7| < |-8|$, $|8| < |9|$.

See It, Do It, Say It, Write It

Step 1 Write several addition and subtraction expressions with negative numbers on the board. Ask students to simplify each expression.

Step 2 Ask students to explain to a partner how they simplified each expression and identify which properties were used.

Step 3 Write an addition or subtraction expression using negative integers on the board. Have students work in pairs. Tell them to write a word problem to represent the expression. Include the solution and a model that represents the situation. Have students share their word problems in small groups or with the class.

Looking Ahead: Pre-teach

Multiply Integers In the next lesson, students will learn about multiplying integers. All of the multiplication properties for whole numbers apply to integers.

Example

The Zero Property of Multiplication states any number times zero is ______, so $-8 \times 0 =$ ___. zero; 0

Have students find the product of each pair of integers.

1. Using the Identity Property of Multiplication, $-12 \times 1 =$ ___. -12
2. Using the Zero Property of Multiplication, $-6 \times 0 =$ ___. 0

28 HIKING A backpacker starts her hike at 307 feet below sea level and then descends 253 feet more below sea level. If the backpacker hikes back up 178 feet, how far below sea level is the backpacker?

$-307 + (-253) + 178 = -382$; 382 ft below sea level

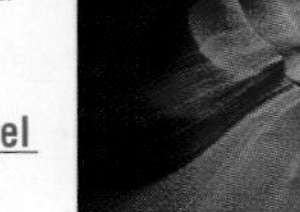

HIKING A backpacker begins her hike 307 feet below sea lev…

Vocabulary Check Write the vocabulary word that completes each sentence.

29 The Associative Property of Addition states that the grouping of the addends does not change the sum.

30 Writing in Math Explain how absolute value helps you add integers. Give at least three examples.

See TE margin.

Spiral Review

What is the opposite of each number? Use it to show the Inverse Property of Addition. (Lesson 8-1, p. 318)

31 9 -9; $9 + (-9) = 0$

32 -7 7; $-7 + 7 = 0$

33 -18 18; $-18 + 18 = 0$

34 23 -23; $23 + (-23) = 0$

Which number has the greater absolute value? (Lesson 8-2, p. 325)

35 $|9|$ or $|8|$ 9

36 $|-3|$ or $|-4|$ -4

37 $|-6|$ or $|6|$ same

38 $|1|$ or $|-2|$ -2

Solve.

39 PARTY Fifteen of Tremaine's friends came to his birthday party. Eight of his friends left the party. How many of Tremaine's friends are there now? (Lesson 8-1, p. 318)

$15 + (-8) = 7$; 7 of Tremaine's friends are there now.

40 EXERCISING While exercising, Oscar burned 325 Calories. After he exercised, he ate a granola bar that had 430 Calories. What is his net gain of Calories? (Lesson 8-2, p. 325)

$-325 + 430 = 105$; 105 Calories

STO…

340 **Chapter 8** Integer Operations

Ticket Out the Door

Weather Report Write the following on the board.

The low temperature on Monday was –17°F, and the high temperature was 6°F. The low temperature on Wednesday was –8°F, and the high temperature was 13°F. Find the temperature difference for each day. Which day had the greater change in temperature?

Ask students to write and simplify an expression for each day. Students will hand in their papers as they exit the classroom.

Monday: $6 - (-17) = 23$°F; Wednesday: $13 - (-8) = 21$°F; Monday had the greater change in temperature.

Lesson 8-4

Multiply Integers

KEY Concept

When you multiply integers, the numbers that you are multiplying are called **factors**. The answer is the **product**. To find the product, multiply the absolute values of the numbers and then determine the correct sign of the answer.

If the signs are the same, then the sign of the product is positive.

$$2 \times 4 = 8 \text{ and } -2 \times (-4) = 8$$

If the signs are different, then the sign of the product is negative.

$$-2 \times 4 = -8 \text{ and } 2 \times (-4) = -8$$

Multiplication is repeated addition. It can be shown on a number line.

$$3 \times (-2) = (-2) + (-2) + (-2) = -6$$

−2 −2 −2

−12 −11 −10 −9 −8 −7 −6 −5 −4 −3 −2 −1 0 1 2

3 groups of −2

All of the multiplication properties for whole numbers apply to integers.

Properties of Multiplication

Property	States that. . .	Example
Zero	any number times zero equals zero	$-5 \times 0 = 0$
Identity	any number times 1 equals that number	$-5 \times 1 = -5$
Commutative	the order in which the numbers are multiplied does not change the product	$-2 \times 5 = 5 \times (-2)$
Associative	the product stays the same when you change the grouping of the numbers	$(2 \times (-3)) \times 3 = 2 \times (-3 \times 3)$

VOCABULARY

Associative Property of Multiplication
the way in which numbers are grouped does not change the product

Commutative Property of Multiplication
the order in which numbers are multiplied does not change the product

factor
a number that divides into a whole number with a remainder of zero

Identity Property of Multiplication
any number times 1 equals that number

product
the answer or result to a multiplication problem; it also refers to expressing a number as the product of its factors

Zero Property of Multiplication
any number times zero equals zero

GO ON

Intervention Strategy

Kinesthetic/Interpersonal Learners

Speed Products Students get into groups of 4 to 5. Each group needs a standard deck of playing cards with the face cards removed. Deal out all the cards face down so that each group member has a stack. Explain that the red cards represent negative numbers and the black cards represent positive numbers. Choose two people to begin by turning up the top cards on their stacks. The first player (not the one turning up a card) to announce the correct product of these two factors gets the two cards to add to his or her stack. Rotate around the group clockwise, each time two players turn up two cards. The object of the game is to collect all of the cards. Once a person is out of cards, that player is out of the game.

Lesson Notes

Lesson 8-4

Lesson Planner

Objective Multiply integers.

Vocabulary **Associative Property of Multiplication**, **Commutative Property of Multiplication**, **factor**, **Identity Property of Multiplication**, **product**, **Zero Property of Multiplication**

Materials/Manipulatives algebra tiles, geoboards, playing cards, index cards, hundreds chart

Chapter Resource Masters

- CRM Vocabulary and English Language Development (p. A169)
- CRM Skills Practice (p. A170)
- CRM Problem-Solving Practice (p. A171)
- CRM Homework Practice (p. A172)

1 Introduce

Vocabulary

Write Examples Write the following examples on the board. Model the terms for students.

multiplication	**9** × **7** = **63** 9 + 9 + 9 + 9 + 9 + 9 + 9 = 63
factors	**7** and **9** are factors of 63. What are other factors of 63?
product	the answer to a multiplication problem 9 × 7 = **63**

2 Teach

Key Concept

Foundational Skills and Concepts After students have read through the Key Concept box, have them try these exercises.

1. Which property is modeled by $6 \times 0 = 0$? Zero Property of Multiplication
2. Which property states that $4 \times (-6) = -24$ and $-6 \times 4 = -24$? Commutative Property of Multiplication

Additional ***Example 1***

Find 2 × (–5). Use a number line.

1. Identify the first number in the expression. 2
   This is the number of times the group is repeated.
2. Identify the second number in the expression. –5
   This is the group size.
3. Draw a number line. Mark off 2 groups of –5.

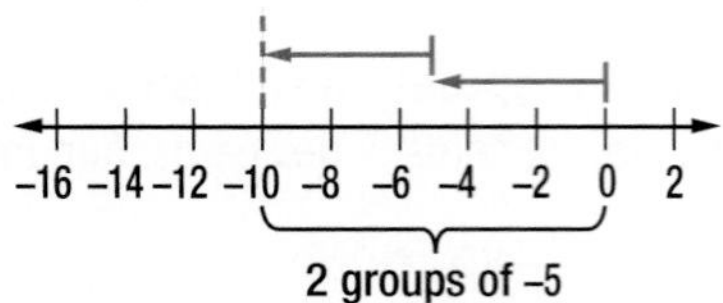

4. The signs are different, so the product is negative.
5. Write the product. –10

Additional ***Example 2***

Find –4 × (–3) by multiplying absolute values.

1. Find the absolute value of each.
   $|-4| = 4$ and $|-3| = 3$
2. Multiply the absolute values of the numbers.
   $4 \times 3 = 12$
3. The signs are the same, so the product is positive.
4. Write the product. 12

Example 1

Find 3 × (–6). Use a number line.

1. Identify the first number in the expression. 3
   This is the number of times the group is repeated.
2. Identify the second number in the expression. –6
   This is the group size.
3. Draw a number line. Mark off 3 groups of –6.

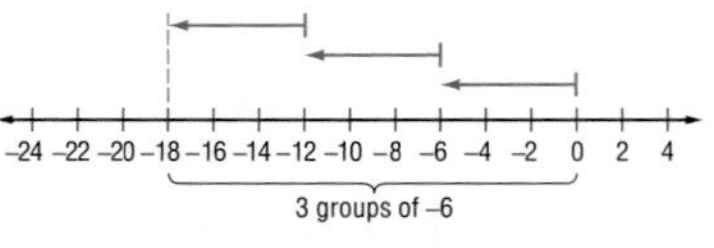

4. The signs are different, so the product is negative.
5. Write the product. –18

YOUR TURN!

Find 4 × (–3). Use a number line.

1. Identify the first number in the expression. __4__
   This is the number of times the group is repeated.
2. Identify the second number in the expression. __–3__
   This is the group size.
3. Draw a number line. Mark off 4 groups of –3.

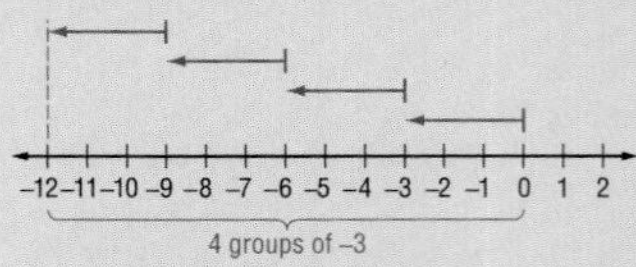

4. The signs are __different__, so the product is __negative__.
5. Write the product. __–12__

Example 2

Find 5 × (–4) by multiplying absolute values.

1. Find the absolute value of each.
   $|5| = 5$ and $|-4| = 4$
2. Multiply the absolute values of the numbers.
   $5 \times 4 = 20$
3. The signs are different, so the product is negative.
4. Write the product. –20

YOUR TURN!

Find –9 × (–3) by multiplying absolute values.

1. Find the absolute value of each.
   $|-9| =$ __9__ and $|-3| =$ __3__
2. Multiply the absolute values of the numbers.
   __9__ × __3__ = __27__
3. The signs are the same, so the product is __positive__.
4. Write the product. __27__

Are They Getting It?

Check students' understanding of multiplying integers by writing these problems on the board. Have students state which are correct and which are not correct.

1. $-5 \times (-2) = -10$ This is incorrect. The sign of the product should be positive.
2. $-3 \times 6 = -18$ This is correct.
3. $8 \times (-5) = -40$ This is correct.

Example 3

Simplify. Name the property.

$(2 \times (-5)) \times 1 = 2 \times (-5 \times 1)$ Associative Property

$= 2 \times (-5 \times 1)$ Identity Property

$= 2 \times (-5)$

$= -10$

YOUR TURN!

Simplify. Name the property.

$(-8 \times 0) = (0 \times (-8))$ Commutative Property

$= (0 \times (-8))$ Zero Property

$= 0$

Who is Correct?

Find 3 × (−5).

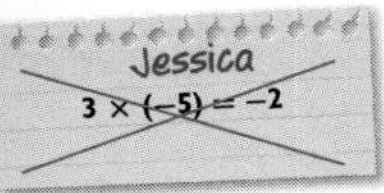

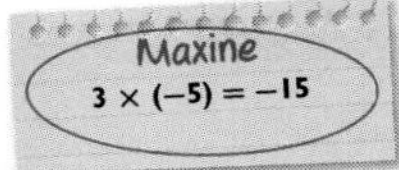

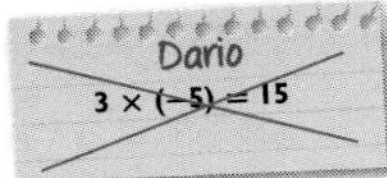

Circle correct answer(s). Cross out incorrect answer(s).

Guided Practice

Find each product. Use a number line.

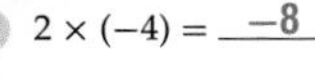

1 $2 \times (-4) =$ −8

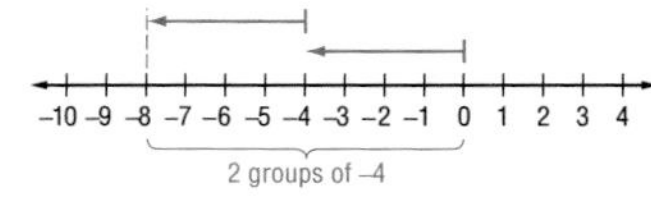

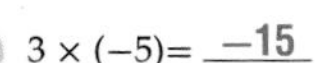

2 $3 \times (-5) =$ −15

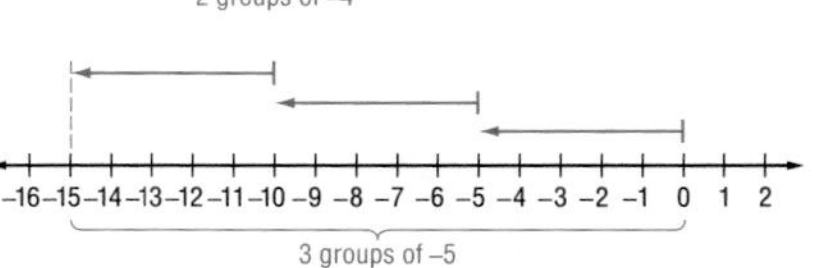

GO ON

Additional *Example 3*

Simplify. Name the property.

$5 \times (-1) \times 7 = 5 \times 7 \times (-1)$ Commutative Property of Multiplication

$= 35 \times (-1)$ Identity Property of Multiplication

$= -35$

3 Practice

Using Manipulatives

Geoboards When presenting Examples 1 and 2, use concrete materials such as geoboards to determine the products. Determine the correct sign for the product based on the signs of the factors.

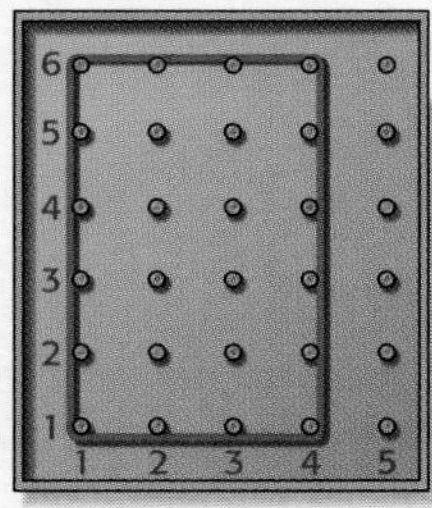

$-6 \times -4 = 24$

Algebra Tiles Use algebra tiles to form arrays or use as counters for multiplication sentences.

On-Hand Manipulatives Use a hundreds chart to practice and solve multiplication sentences. Students will need to determine the correct sign for the product based on the signs of the factors.

Who *is Correct?*

Diagnostic Teaching

- Jessica's work is incorrect. She subtracted instead of multiplied.
- Maxine's work is correct. She multiplied and used the signs correctly.
- Dario's work is incorrect. He multiplied correctly but has the incorrect sign.

Remind students that when multiplying integers, the signs have to be different for the product to be negative.

Intervention Strategy — Logical Learner

Multiplication

If students are having difficulty understanding multiplication, lead them to "discovering" the rules by finding a pattern.

$4 \times 2 = 8$	$4 \times -2 = -8$
$3 \times 2 = 6$	$3 \times -2 = -6$
$2 \times 2 = 4$	$2 \times -2 = -4$
$1 \times 2 = 2$	$1 \times -2 = -2$
$-1 \times 2 = -2$	$-1 \times -2 = 2$
$-2 \times 2 = -4$	$-2 \times -2 = 4$
$-3 \times 2 = -6$	$-3 \times -2 = 6$
$-4 \times 2 = -8$	$-4 \times -2 = 8$
Students can discover that the product of a negative and a positive is negative.	Students can discover that the product of a negative and a negative is positive.

Note This!

Equations of Signs A good visual to have students include in their notebooks is equations using the signs of factors and the product, without numbers. The following is what the students should write:

$(+) \times (+) = (+)$

$(+) \times (-) = (-)$

$(-) \times (-) = (+)$

$(-) \times (+) = (-)$

Step by Step Practice

3 Find $(-6) \times (-4)$ by multiplying absolute values.

Step 1 Find the absolute value of each. $|-6| = 6$ and $|-4| = 4$

Step 2 Multiply the absolute values of the numbers.
6 × 4 = 24

Step 3 The signs are the same, so the product is positive.

Step 4 Write the product. 24

Find each product by multiplying absolute values.

4 $-9 \times (-3) =$ 27 sign: positive

5 $4 \times (-5) =$ −20

6 $6 \times 2 =$ 12

7 $-8 \times 4 =$ −32

8 $-3 \times (-7) =$ 21

Step by Step Problem-Solving Practice

Problem-Solving Strategies
- ☑ Draw a diagram.
- ☐ Use logical reasoning.
- ☐ Guess and check.
- ☐ Solve a simpler problem.
- ☐ Work backward.

Solve.

9 FINANCES Chandra's stock lost $2 each month for 3 months. How much has the stock lost in value?

Understand Read the problem. Write what you know. It lost a value of $2 a month for 3 months.

Plan Pick a strategy. One strategy is to draw a number line to represent the value of the stock.

Solve Use the number line to find the change in value.
Draw a number line.
Mark off 3 groups of −2.
The stock has lost $6 in value.

Check Add the numbers in a different order. Your sum should match your answer.

344 Chapter 8 Integer Operations

Intervention Strategy — Visual Learners

Flash Cards Team students up to make a set of flash cards that they can use to practice multiplication facts of integers. Using the index cards, have one student make cards for the facts for 1, 3, 6, 9, 10, and 12. Have the other student make cards for the facts for 2, 4, 5, 7, 8, and 11. For each fact, three cards need to be made: positive × positive; positive × negative or negative × positive; and negative × negative. After the cards are made you can allow time in class for the partners to practice quizzing each other using the complete set of cards for 1 through 12.

EXERCISE After finishing his workout, Tony's heart rate decreased by 2 beats per minute for each of the next 4 minutes. How much did Tony's heart rate drop in 4 minutes?
Check off each step.

✔ Understand: I underlined key words.

✔ Plan: To solve the problem, I will solve an equation.

✔ Solve: The answer is $-2 \times 4 = -8$; Tony's heart rate dropped eight beats.

✔ Check: I checked my answer by using the Commutative Property.

FOOTBALL The football team lost 7 yards on 3 plays in a row. How many yards did they lose altogether?

$-7 \times 3 = -21$; the football team lost 21 yards altogether.

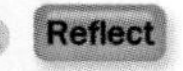

Reflect Explain how you multiply integers. Give two examples.

See TE margin

Skills, Concepts, and Problem Solving

nd each product. Use a number line.

$7 \times (-1) =$ -7

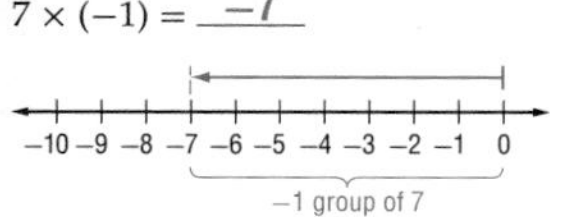

14 $-4 \times 2 =$ -8

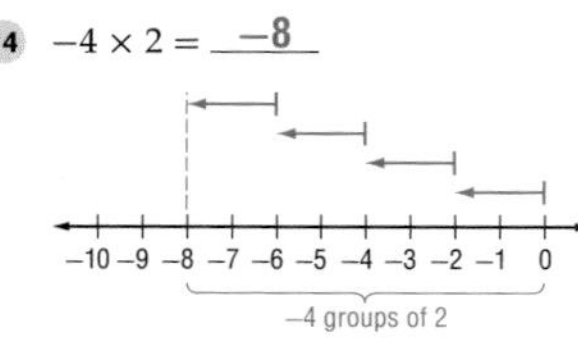

nd each product by multiplying absolute values.

$3 \times (-2) =$ -6 16 $-9 \times 1 =$ -9 17 $-8 \times (-5) =$ 40

$2 \times (-7) =$ -14 19 $3 \times 8 =$ 24 20 $-6 \times (-5) =$ 30

nd the missing number. Name the property.

$(4 \times 5) \times (-5) = 4 \times (\underline{5} \times (-5))$ Associative Property of Multiplication

$-9 \times \underline{0} = 0$ Zero Property of Multiplication

GO ON

Math Challenge

Writing Problems Have students write a page of 20 multiplication problems where each problem has one factor that is an integer –12 through 12 and the other factor is greater than 15 or less than –15. Problems should be written neatly with enough room to do multiplication below each problem. Students should make a separate answer sheet for their 20 problems. Collect these problems and answers and consider using them as quizzes for advanced students.

Additional Answer

Exercise 12 Multiply the absolute value of the numbers and write the sign. Determine the sign by the following rules: When the factor signs are different, the product sign is negative. When the factor signs are the same, the product sign is positive.

Examples:
$-8 \times (-7) = 56$
$9 \times (-8) = -72$

Odd/Even Assignments

Exercises 13–24 are structured so that students practice the same concepts whether they are assigned the odd or even problems.

In-Class Assignment

Have students complete Exercises 13, 17, 18, 21, 23, and 27 to ensure that they understand the concept.

Common Error *Alert*

Multi-Step Problem If students struggle with Exercises 23 and 24, they might not comprehend the reading clues that indicate the signs for the integers represented in the situation. Have students read the problems aloud and translate the given integers using their own words. Encourage students to draw a diagram, create a chart or table, or act out the situations to aid comprehension. When students find a solution, ask them to reread the problem to check the answer for reasonableness and completeness.

4 Assess

See It, Do It, Say It, Write It

Step 1 Write several multiplication expressions on the board using positive and negative integers.

Step 2 Ask students to find the product for each expression.

Step 3 Ask students to explain in pairs how to model the sentences using a number line or counters.

Step 4 Have students work in pairs to write a word problem to represent one of the multiplication sentences on the board. Include the solution and a model that represents the situation. Have students share their word problems in small groups or with the class.

Looking Ahead: Pre-teach

Divide Integers In the next lesson, students will learn how to divide integers. Division is the inverse operation for multiplication. The sign rules are the same as the rules for multiplication.

Example

Find $-15 \div 3$.

The signs are different so the quotient will be negative. Divide by the absolute values of the numbers.
$15 \div 3 = 5$ so the quotient is -5.

Have students find each quotient.

1. $-36 \div -12$ 3
2. $-42 \div 7$ -6
3. $56 \div -8$ -7

Solve.

23. SCHOOL The number of students in the ninth-grade class has decreased by 12 students each of the last three years. By the end of the third year, how many fewer students are in the ninth grade?
$-12 \times 3 = -36$; There are 36 fewer students.

24. WEATHER The temperature was 68°F in the evening. It dropped 3°F every hour over a 4-hour period. What was the temperature in the morning?
$4 \times (-3) = -12$; The temperature dropped 12°, 68°F − 12°F = 56°F.

Vocabulary Check. **Write the vocabulary word that completes each sentence.**

25. The Identity Property of Multiplication states that any number times 1 equals that number.

26. Multiplication can also be thought of as repeated addition.

27. Writing in Math Chet worked the problem to the right. What mistake did he make?

$-8 \times (-4) = -32$

The mistake was made using the signs. The signs of the two numbers are the same, so the product should have a positive value.

Spiral Review

Find each sum. (Lesson 8-1, p. 318)

28. $11 + (-8) =$ 3

29. $-9 + (-7) =$ -16

Find each difference. (Lesson 8-2, p. 325)

30. $-14 - (-5) =$ -9

31. $-7 - (-3) =$ -4

Solve. (Lesson 8-3, p. 334)

32. Keisha flew her remote control airplane 47 feet in the air. She then made the airplane descend 28 feet. Then she made the airplane ascend 19 feet. What is the airplane's elevation now?
$47 + (-28) + 19 = 38$; 38 feet

STOP

Ticket Out the Door

Multiple Problems, Same Product Instruct students to write eight multiplication problems that have a product of 24. Students should only use four different sets of factors. As they exit the classroom, have them tell you one of their problems and then hand in their papers.

Chapter 8

Progress Check 2 (Lessons 8-3 and 8-4)

se the Associative Property of Addition to find the missing number.

1. $(170 + (-14)) + (-52) =$ <u>170</u> $+ (-14 + (-52))$
2. $-77 + (-6 + (-17)) = (-77 +$ <u>(-6)</u>$) + (-17)$
3. $(14 + (-93)) + 70 = 14 + ((-93) +$ <u>70</u>$)$
4. $(7 + (-13)) + 56 = 7 + ($<u>(-13)</u> $+ 56)$

implify.

5. $-5 + (-7) - (-11) - 15 =$ <u>-16</u>
6. $9 - 13 + (-17 - (-12)) + 4 =$ <u>-5</u>
7. $(5 - (-13)) + 4 - (-8) + 12 =$ <u>42</u>
8. $(8 - (-4)) + 16 - (-5) + 19 =$ <u>52</u>

ind each product. Use a number line.

9. $3 \times (-3) =$ <u>-9</u>
10. $4 \times (-2) =$ <u>-8</u>

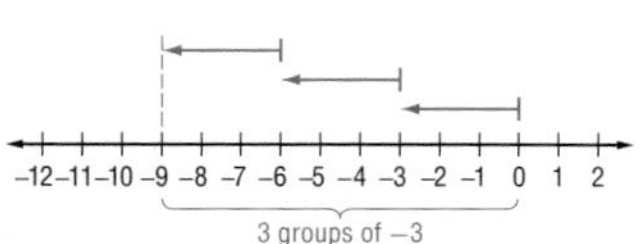

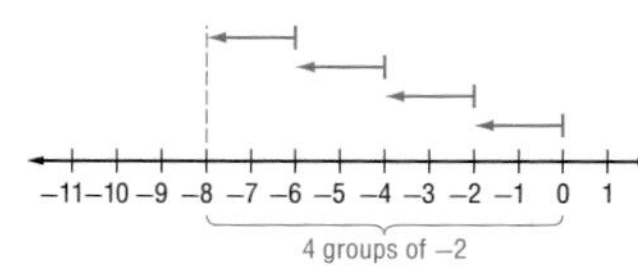

ind each product by multiplying absolute values.

11. $-3 \times (-4) =$ <u>12</u>
12. $1 \times (-8) =$ <u>-8</u>
13. $-2 \times 5 =$ <u>-10</u>
14. $-7 \times -8 =$ <u>56</u>

nd the missing number. Name the property.

15. $-3 \times 1 =$ <u>-3</u> <u>Identity Property of Multiplication</u>
16. $5 \times (-7) =$ <u>-7</u> $\times 5$ <u>Commutative Property of Multiplication</u>

olve.

17. **TRAVEL** Jamil hiked down the North Rim of the Grand Canyon until he was at an elevation of 1,325 meters below sea level. He stopped to rest, and then hiked down 583 meters more. What elevation is he at if he hiked 477 meters up?

<u>$-1{,}325 + (-583) + 477 = -1{,}431$; 1,431 meters below sea level</u>

Progress Check 2

Chapter 8

Formative Assessment

Use the Progress Check to assess students' mastery of the previous lessons. Have students review the lesson indicated for the problems they answered incorrectly.

Odd/Even Assignments

Exercises are structured so that students practice the same concepts whether they are assigned the odd or even problems.

Common Error *Alert*

Exercise 17 Students should extract the information from the word problem and write a number sentence before solving the problem. They should verify their answer is reasonable.

Data-Driven Decision Making

Students missing Exercises . . .	Have trouble with . . .	Should review and practice . . .
1-4	using the Associative Property of Addition to find the missing number.	SSG Lesson 8-3, p. 334 CRM Skills Practice, p. A166
5-8	adding and subtracting groups of integers.	SSG Lesson 8-3, p. 334 CRM Skills Practice, p. A166
9-14	finding products using number lines and by multiplying absolute values.	SSG Lesson 8-4, p. 341 CRM Skills Practice, p. A170
15-16	using properties involving integers.	SSG Lesson 8-4, p. 341 CRM Skills Practice, p. A170
17	solving a word problem that involves addition and subtraction of integers.	CRM Problem-Solving Practice, pp. A167 and A171

Lesson 8-5 Lesson Notes

Lesson Planner

Objective Divide integers.

Vocabulary **dividend**, **divisor**, **quotient**

Materials/Manipulatives fraction circles, geoboards, hundreds charts, algebra tiles

Chapter Resource Masters

- CRM Vocabulary and English Language Development (p. A173)
- CRM Skills Practice (p. A174)
- CRM Problem-Solving Practice (p. A175)
- CRM Homework Practice (p. A176)

Vocabulary

Division Formats Write several division expressions on the board. Vary the formats of the expressions as shown below. Ask student volunteers to find each quotient. Then ask other volunteers to identify each part of the sentences, using the terms *dividend, divisor,* and *quotient.*

horizontal format $45 \div 9 = 5$

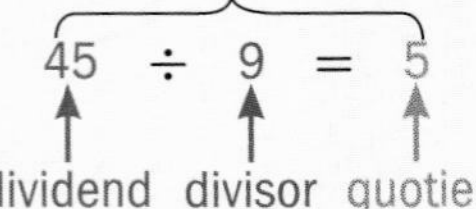

vertical format $9\overline{)45}$ with quotient 5

fractional format $\frac{45}{9} = 5$

Key Concept

Foundational Skills and Concepts After students have read through the Key Concept box, have them try these exercises.

1. When is a quotient negative? when the dividend and divisor have unlike signs
2. What is the sign of the quotient of $-39 \div (-3)$? positive

Lesson 8-5 Divide Integers

KEY Concept

Division is the inverse operation for multiplication. You use the multiplication facts whenever you divide. The sign rules are the same as the rules for multiplication.

If the signs are the same, then the **quotient** is positive. If the signs are different, then the quotient is negative.

Sample Table		
Division	Signs	Answer
$6 \div 3$	same	2
$-6 \div (-3)$	same	2
$-6 \div 3$	different	-2
$6 \div (-3)$	different	-2

VOCABULARY

dividend
the number that is being divided
divisor → $4\overline{)8}$ ← dividend, 2 ← quotient

divisor
the number by which the dividend is being divided
Example: In $3\overline{)9}$, 3 is the divisor.

quotient
the answer or result of a division problem

Division by zero is impossible. For example, $3 \div 0$ is undefined.

Example 1

Find $18 \div (-6)$ by dividing by absolute values.

1. Find the absolute value of each.
   $|18| = 18$ and $|-6| = 6$
2. Divide the absolute values of the numbers.
   $18 \div 6 = 3$
3. The signs are different. The quotient will be negative.
4. Write the quotient with a negative sign. -3

YOUR TURN!

Find $-36 \div 9$ by dividing by absolute values.

1. Find the absolute value of each. $|-36| = 36$ and $|9| = 9$
2. Divide the absolute values of the numbers. 36 ÷ 9 = 4
3. The signs are different. The quotient will be negative.
4. Write the quotient. -4

Additional Example 1

Find $-50 \div (-5)$ by dividing by absolute values.

1. Find the absolute value of each.
   $|-50| = 50$ and $|-5| = 5$
2. Divide the absolute values of the numbers. $50 \div 5 = 10$
3. The signs are the same. The quotient will be positive.
4. Write the quotient with the sign. 10

Who is Correct?

Simplify $-30 \div (-5)$.

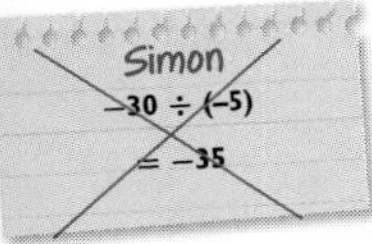

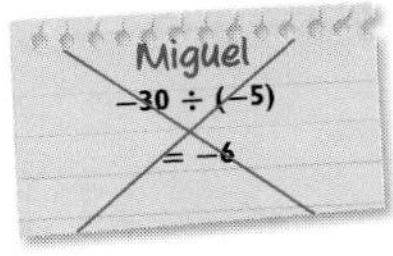

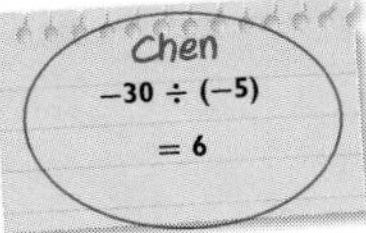

Circle correct answer(s). Cross out incorrect answer(s).

Guided Practice

Find each quotient.

1. $5 \div 1 =$ 5
2. $-5 \div 1 =$ −5
3. $-5 \div (-1) =$ 5
4. $5 \div (-1) =$ −5
5. $12 \div (-2) =$ −6
6. $-12 \div (-2) =$ 6
7. $-12 \div 2 =$ −6
8. $12 \div 2 =$ 6

Step by Step Practice

9. Find $-16 \div 4$.

Step 1 Find the absolute value of each.
$|-16| = 16$ and $|4| = 4$

Step 2 Divide the absolute values of the numbers.
16 ÷ 4 = 4

Step 3 The signs are different. The quotient will be negative.

Step 4 Write the quotient. −4

Check the sign to make sure it is correct.
$(-) \div (+) = (-)$

GO ON

Who *is Correct?*

Diagnostic Teaching

- Simon's work is incorrect. He added instead of divided.
- Miguel's work is incorrect. The signs are the same, so the quotient should be positive.
- Chen's work is correct. He divided and wrote the quotient correctly.

Remind students that when the signs of the dividend and divisor are the same, the quotient is positive.

3 Practice

Using Manipulatives

Geoboards When presenting Example 1, use concrete materials such as geoboards to determine the quotients. Determine the correct sign for the quotient based on the signs of the dividend and divisor.

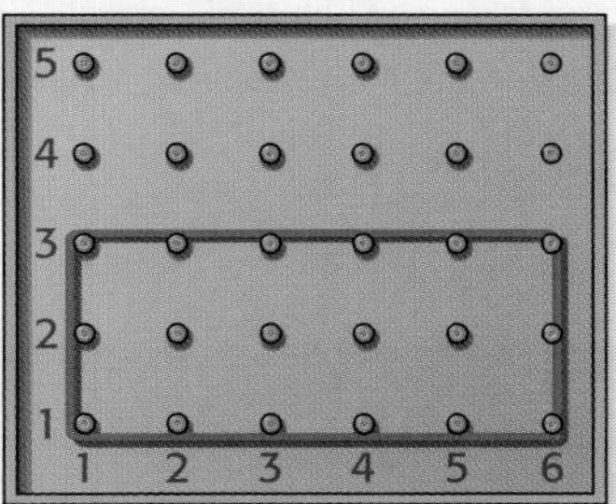

$-18 \div (-6) = 3$

Algebra Tiles Use algebra tiles to form arrays or use as counters to create division sentences.

On-Hand Manipulatives Use a hundreds chart to practice and solve division sentences. Students will need to determine the correct sign for the product based on the signs of the factors. (Find the Hundreds Chart with the *Patterns and Grids*.)

Intervention Strategy

Interpersonal Learners

Listing Fact Families For each multiplication fact previously learned, there are four multiplication facts with integral factors and four related division problems. Arrange students into groups so that there are twelve groups in the class. Assign each group a number from 1 to 12. Groups should have a table that contains all multiplication and division facts with integral factors. Each table should contain 84 factors. You can display the tables around the classroom when each group has finished.

Common Error *Alert*

Exercises 11–22 If students have difficulty with Exercises 11-22, encourage them to review the fact families. Tell students to focus on the absolute values of the integers in the problems to identify the missing term. Practice basic multiplication and division facts using flashcards and identify the other members of the fact family. Then review the rules for determining the correct sign for the product or quotient.

Find each quotient.

10 $30 \div (-3)$

signs: (+) ÷ (–) = (–)

quotient: –10

11 $24 \div (-8) =$ –3

12 $-12 \div 3 =$ –4

13 $-16 \div (-4) =$ 4

14 $15 \div 3 =$ 5

15 $-18 \div 3 =$ –6

16 $33 \div (-11) =$ –3

17 $-20 \div (-2) =$ 10

18 $-25 \div (-5) =$ 5

19 $36 \div (-9) =$ –4

20 $-42 \div (-6) =$ 7

21 $-32 \div (-4) =$ 8

22 $45 \div (-5) =$ –9

Step by Step Problem-Solving Practice

Problem-Solving Strategies
- ☑ Use a model.
- ☐ Use logical reasoning.
- ☐ Make a table.
- ☐ Guess and check.
- ☐ Solve a simpler problem.

Solve.

23 FINANCES Mr. Murphy lost \$240 in the last 4 months on his stocks. If he lost the same amount each month, what was his loss per month?

Understand Read the problem. Write what you know.
Mr. Murphy lost \$240 in a 4-month period of time.

Plan Pick a strategy. One strategy is to use a model.
Draw a fraction bar worth a total of \$240.
Divide it into 4 equal parts.
How much is each part worth?

\$60	\$60	\$60	\$60

Solve Divide \$240 by 4. \$240 ÷ 4 = \$60
So, Mr. Murphy lost \$60 per month.

Check Multiply to check your answer.
\$60 × 4 = \$240

350 Chapter 8 Integer Operations

Are They Getting It?

Check students' understanding of dividing integers by writing these problems on the board. Ask students to point out wrong answers and explain why they are wrong.

1. $-32 \div (-4) = -8$ This is incorrect. The signs are the same, so the answer is positive.
2. $-42 \div 6 = -7$ This is correct.
3. $72 \div (-9) = 8$ This is incorrect. The signs are not the same so the quotient should be negative. $72 \div (-9) = -8$

24 FOOTBALL A football team lost 33 yards in 3 plays. If the team lost the same number of yards each play, what was the loss per play? Check off each step.

✔ Understand: I underlined key words.

✔ Plan: To solve the problem, I will use a model.

✔ Solve: The answer is $-33 \div 3 = -11$; The average loss per play was 11 yards.

✔ Check: I checked my answer by using multiplication.

25 WEATHER The temperature dropped a total of 40 degrees in 5 hours. How much did the temperature drop per hour if the temperature dropped the same amount each hour?

$-40 \div 5 = -8$; The temperature dropped an average of 8 degrees per hour.

26 Reflect Explain how to divide integers.

Determine the sign. Divide the absolute values of the numbers and write the correct sign.

Skills, Concepts, and Problem Solving

Find each quotient.

27 $-8 \div 4 =$ -2

28 $9 \div (-3) =$ -3

29 $-10 \div (-2) =$ 5

30 $-12 \div (-6) =$ 2

31 $-22 \div 2 =$ -11

32 $-40 \div (-8) =$ 5

33 $-28 \div -4 =$ 7

34 $-14 \div (-7) =$ 2

35 $27 \div (-9) =$ -3

36 $54 \div (-6) =$ -9

37 $-72 \div 8 =$ -9

38 $-60 \div (-6) =$ 10

39 $48 \div (-6) =$ -8

40 $-56 \div (-7) =$ 8

GO ON

Math Challenge

Generating Problems Have students write five division problems that have single-digit divisors (both positive and negative) and three digit dividends. Students can discuss amongst themselves how to generate problems that do not have remainders. Students need to realize that to write division problems that do not have remainders, they should work backward; multiply the desired quotient by the single-digit divisor to find the dividend.

Odd/Even Assignments

Exercises 27–42 are structured so that students practice the same concepts whether they are assigned the odd or even problems.

In-Class Assignment

Have students complete Exercises 27, 32, 37, 41, and 45 to ensure that they understand the concept.

Common Error Alert

Multi-Step Problem If students struggle with word problems, they might not be able to organize the given information into useful chunks. Have students start by reading the entire problem aloud, then reread for smaller pieces of information. For each piece of data, show students how to draw a diagram or model to make the information more tangible. Tell students to summarize each piece of information in their own words and identify what they need to know to answer the question. Encourage students to try a variety of strategies to solve for the answer. Then ask students to review the problem again to check their solution for reasonableness and completeness.

4 Assess

See It, Do It, Say It, Write It

Step 1 Write several division expressions on the board using positive and negative integers. Vary the formats of the expressions.

Step 2 Ask students to find the quotient for each expression and then label each part of the division sentences.

Step 3 Ask students to explain in pairs how to model the sentences using concrete materials. Have students build a model for one of the sentences on the board.

Step 4 Write a new division expression on the board. Have students work in pairs to write a word problem to represent the expression. Ask students to include the quotient and a model that represents the situation. Have students share their word problems in small groups or with the class.

Looking Ahead: Pre-teach

Exponents In the next lesson, students will learn about powers and how to calculate using exponents. The expression below is a power and means to use the base a as a factor n times.

$$a^n = \underbrace{a \times a \times \ldots \times a}_{n \text{ times}}$$

Example

Simplify 3^4

$3^4 = 3 \times 3 \times 3 \times 3 = 81$

Have students try the following problems.

Simplify.

1. 5^2 25
2. 2^6 64
3. 4^3 64
4. 1^{15} 1

Solve.

41 MONEY Blake wants to save $100. If he wants to save the money in 10 weeks, how much should he save each week?

100 ÷ 10 = 10; Blake needs to save $10 per week.

42 WEATHER The temperature at the base of the mountain is 78°F. At the top of the mountain, which is 5,000 feet high, the temperature is 53°F. Rodney is hiking up to the peak of the mountain. How many degrees will the temperature decrease for every 200 feet he travels?

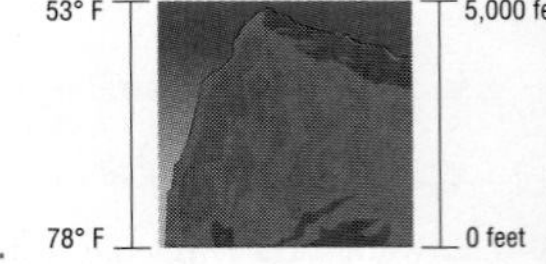

5,000 ÷ 200 = 25 and 78 − 53 = 25, 25 ÷ 25 = 1;

Every 200 feet that Rodney hikes up the mountain, the temperature will decrease 1°F.

Vocabulary Check **Write the vocabulary word that completes each sentence.**

43 The dividend is the number being divided.

44 A(n) quotient is the answer or result of a division problem.

45 **Writing in Math** Johanna worked the problem at the right. What mistake did she make?

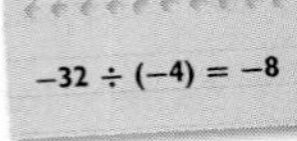

She used the wrong sign. The signs of the dividend and divisor are the same, so the quotient is positive.

Spiral Review

Find each product. (Lesson 8-4, p. 341)

46 $-2 \times 4 =$ −8

47 $-7 \times (-1) =$ 7

48 $5 \times (-3) =$ −15

49 $-4 \times (-6) =$ 24

50 $6 \times 6 =$ 36

51 $-10 \times 5 =$ −50

Solve. (Lesson 8-4, p. 341)

52 CROSS COUNTRY After finishing a race, Jasmine's heart rate decreased by 3 beats per minute for each of the next 5 minutes. How much did Jasmine's heart rate drop in 5 minutes?

−3 × 5 = −15; Jasmine's heart rate dropped 15 beats.

352 Chapter 8 Integer Operations

Ticket Out the Door

Inverse Operations As students approach the door to exit, state a multiplication fact using integers. The student in return needs to state a division fact that is part of the fact family. For example, you can say −7 × 8 = −56 and the student can say −56 ÷ 8 = −7.

Lesson 8-6 Exponents

KEY Concept

When an integer has an **exponent**, multiply the integer by itself the number of times shown by the exponent.

This is the base. — 4^3 — This is the exponent.

$4^3 = 4 \times 4 \times 4 = 64$

The **base** is the number used as a factor. The **exponent** indicates how many times the base is used as a factor.

Numbers expressed using exponents are called **powers**. Numbers raised to the second or third power have special names.

Powers	Words
3^4	3 to the fourth power
5^2	5 to the second power or 5 **squared**
6^3	6 to the third power or 6 **cubed**

VOCABULARY

base
the number used as the factor in an expression involving exponents
Example: In 2^5, the base is 2.

cubed
the product in which a number is a factor three times; two cubed is 8 because $2 \times 2 \times 2 = 8$

exponent
the number of times a base is multiplied by itself
Example: In 2^5, 5 is the exponent.

squared
a number multiplied by itself; 4×4, or 4^2

Any number (except 0) to the zero power is equal to 1. For example, $^0 = 1$. Any number to the first power is always equal to itself. For example, $5^1 = 5$.

Example 1

Write $7 \times 7 \times 7$ using an exponent.

1. The base is 7.
2. The exponent is 3.
3. Write $7 \times 7 \times 7$ using an exponent.
   $7 \times 7 \times 7 = 7^3$

YOUR TURN!

Write $6 \times 6 \times 6 \times 6$ using an exponent.

1. The base is 6.
2. The exponent is 4.
3. Write $6 \times 6 \times 6 \times 6$ using an exponent.
   $6 \times 6 \times 6 \times 6 = 6^4$

GO ON

Additional *Example 1*

Write $9 \times 9 \times 9 \times 9 \times 9$ using an exponent.

1. The base is 9.
2. The exponent is 5.
3. Write $9 \times 9 \times 9 \times 9 \times 9$ using an exponent.
   $9 \times 9 \times 9 \times 9 \times 9 = 9^5$

Lesson Notes

Lesson 8-6

Lesson Planner

Objective Recognize and use exponents.

Vocabulary **base**, **cubed**, **exponent**, **squared**

Materials/Manipulatives counters, pattern blocks, index cards, scissors

Chapter Resource Masters

- CRM Vocabulary and English Language Development (p. A177)
- CRM Skills Practice (p. A178)
- CRM Problem-Solving Practice (p. A179)
- CRM Homework Practice (p. A180)

1 Introduce

Vocabulary

Multiplication Terms Write $-5 \times -5 \times -5 \times -5$ on the board. Explain which number is the *base* and which is the *exponent*. Write $7 \times 7 \times 7 \times 7$ on the board. Have one student identify the base and one student identify the exponent.

2 Teach

Key Concept

Foundational Skills and Concepts After students have read through the Key Concept box, have them try these exercises.

1. Write 3^5 as repeated mutiplication. $3 \times 3 \times 3 \times 3 \times 3$
2. What is the base of 4^3? 4
3. How do you read 2^{10}? 2 to the tenth power
4. How do you read 15^3? 15 cubed or 15 to the third power
5. How do you read 20^2? 20 squared or 20 to the second power

Additional *Example 2*

Write 7^3 as repeated multiplication. Solve.

1. The base is 7.
2. The exponent is 3, so multiply the base 3 times.
3. Write 7^3 as repeated multiplication.
   $7^3 = 7 \times 7 \times 7$
4. Multiply.
   $7^3 = 343$

Additional *Example 3*

Evaluate the expression $(-2)^5$.

1. The base is –2.
2. The exponent is 5.
3. Write $(-2)^5$ as repeated multiplication.
   $(-2) \times (-2) \times (-2) \times (-2) \times (-2)$
4. The sign of the product is negative because the exponent is odd.
5. Multiply. $(-2)^5 = -32$.

Example 2

Write 3^4 as repeated multiplication. Solve.

1. The base is 3.
2. The exponent is 4, so multiply the base 4 times.
3. Write 3^4 as repeated multiplication.
   $3^4 = 3 \times 3 \times 3 \times 3$
4. Multiply. $3^4 = 81$

YOUR TURN!

Write 5^3 as repeated multiplication. Solve.

1. The base is 5.
2. The exponent is 3, so multiply the base 3 times.
3. Write 5^3 as repeated multiplication.
   $5^3 = 5 \times 5 \times 5$
4. Multiply. $5^3 = 125$

Example 3

Evaluate the expression $(-4)^3$.

1. The base is –4.
2. The exponent is 3.
3. Write $(-4)^3$ as repeated multiplication.
   $(-4) \times (-4) \times (-4)$
4. The sign of the product is negative because the exponent is odd.
5. Multiply. $(-4)^3 = -64$

YOUR TURN!

Evaluate the expression $(-5)^3$.

1. What is the base? –5
2. What is the exponent? 3
3. Write $(-5)^3$ as repeated multiplication.
   $(-5) \times (-5) \times (-5)$
4. The sign of the product is negative because the exponent is odd.
5. Multiply. $(-5)^3 = -125$

Who is Correct?

Evaluate the expression 6^2.

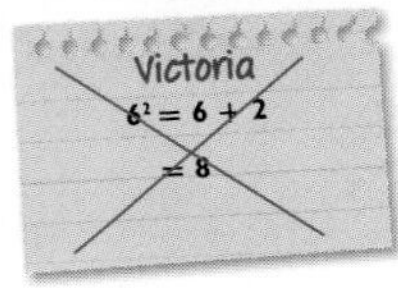

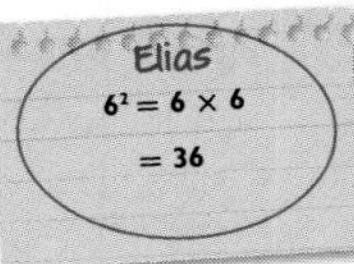

Circle correct answer(s). Cross out incorrect answer(s).

Who *is Correct?*

Diagnostic Teaching

- Victoria is not correct. The exponent tells how many times to multiply the base times itself, so $6^2 = 6 \times 6$, not 6×2.
- Leon is not correct. He added the exponent and the base, and should have multiplied the base times itself the number of times as the exponent indicates.
- Elias wrote 36. This is correct.

Remind students that the base is the factor. The exponent tells how many times the base is multiplied by itself.

Guided Practice

Write each expression using an exponent.

1. $3 \times 3 \times 3 \times 3 =$ 3^4 base = 3 exponent = 4
2. $2 \times 2 \times 2 =$ 2^3 base = 2 exponent = 3

Write each expression as repeated multiplication.

3. 5^3
   base = 5
   exponent = 3
   multiply the base 3 times
   $5 \times 5 \times 5$
4. 8^5
   base = 8
   exponent = 5
   multiply the base 5 times
   $8 \times 8 \times 8 \times 8 \times 8$

Write the expression in word form.

5. 7^2 seven to the second power, or seven squared
6. 5^3 five to the third power, or five cubed

Step by Step Practice

7. Evaluate the expression 5^3.

   Step 1 The base is 5.

   Step 2 The exponent is 3.

   The exponent is 3, so multiply the base 3 times.

   Step 3 Multiply to find the value of the expression. $5 \times 5 \times 5 = 125$

Evaluate each expression.

8. 10^2 base: 10
   exponent: 2
   $10^2 =$ 10 $\times$ 10 $=$ 100

9. $(-7)^3$ $(-7) \times (-7) \times (-7) = -343$
10. $(-9)^3$ $(-9) \times (-9) \times (-9) = -729$

Lesson 8-6 Exponents 355

3 Practice

Using Manipulatives

Counters Model the base using counters (any object of which you have many). Build from that model using the previous base as the new base a number of times to match the exponent. Two examples are shown at the bottom of this page.

The number of times you repeat the previous base at each step is determined by the base.

The number of steps you make matches the exponent. For 6^4, model 6, then in each step repeat the previous base 4 times. There will be 4 steps in all.

Blocks When dealing with exponents of 2 or 3, you can use blocks to build squares for exponents of 2 and cubes for exponents of 3. The square or cube should have edges the length given by the base. The power is equal to the number of blocks used to build the figure.

2^5

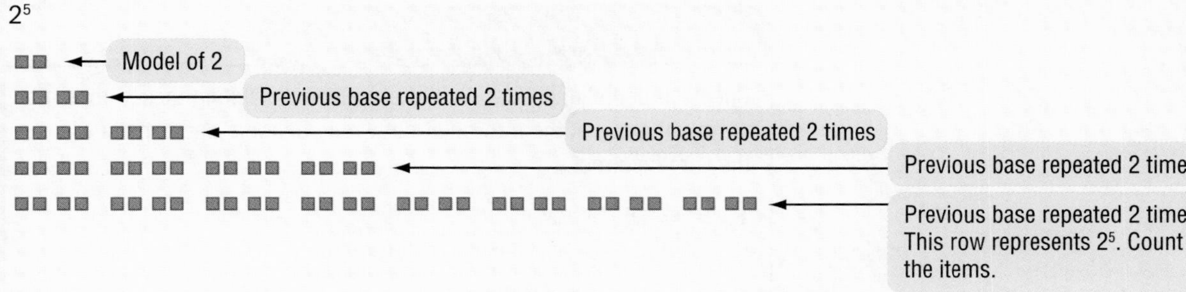

3^3

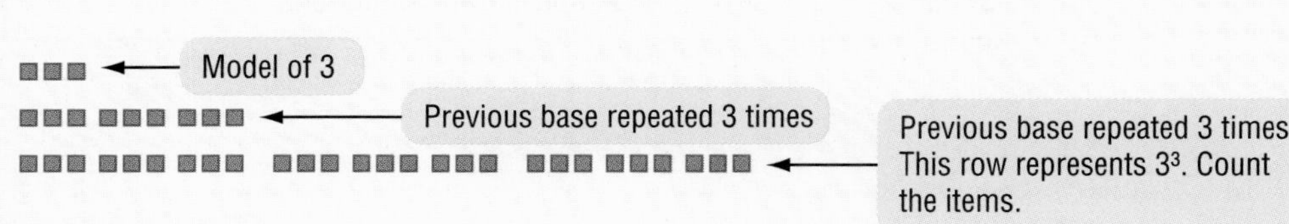

Intervention Strategy

Kinesthetic/ Visual/ Interpersonal Learners

Integer Cards

Materials needed: blank index cards, 1 pair of scissors per group

Have students work in small groups. Tell them to label four index cards with one operation sign (+, −, ×, ÷) each. Cut the fifth index card into a small square and write the number 2 on it with a black writing tool. Take another stack of index cards. Write the numbers 1 to 10 in red marker on separate cards. Then write the same numbers on another set of index cards in black marker. Explain that the cards with red numbers represent negative integers and the cards with the black numbers represent positive integers. Have students shuffle their cards and draw three or four cards. Use the drawn cards and operation cards to create expressions. Tell students to assign the squared exponent to one of the number cards. Ask students to write and simplify their expressions on a sheet of paper. Encourage students to manipulate the numbers and operation cards so that the simplified results are integers and not fractions or decimals. Allow time for groups to share a few of their expressions with the class.

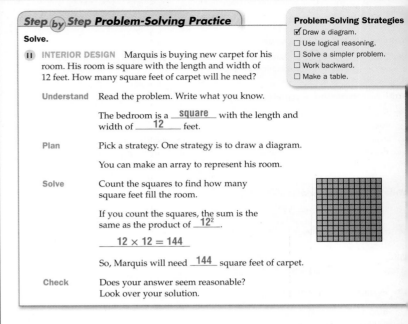

Step by Step Problem-Solving Practice

Problem-Solving Strategies
- ☑ Draw a diagram.
- ☐ Use logical reasoning.
- ☐ Solve a simpler problem.
- ☐ Work backward.
- ☐ Make a table.

Solve.

11 INTERIOR DESIGN Marquis is buying new carpet for his room. His room is square with the length and width of 12 feet. How many square feet of carpet will he need?

Understand Read the problem. Write what you know.

The bedroom is a __square__ with the length and width of __12__ feet.

Plan Pick a strategy. One strategy is to draw a diagram.

You can make an array to represent his room.

Solve Count the squares to find how many square feet fill the room.

If you count the squares, the sum is the same as the product of __12^2__.

__$12 \times 12 = 144$__

So, Marquis will need __144__ square feet of carpet.

Check Does your answer seem reasonable? Look over your solution.

12 HEALTH Sumi has been training for a 5k run. She ran 3 miles, 3 times a week for 3 weeks. Find the total number of miles Sumi ran by solving an expression.

Check off each step.

✔ Understand: I underlined key words.

✔ Plan: To solve the problem, I will __make a table__.

✔ Solve: The answer is __$3^3 = 27$; 27 miles__.

✔ Check: I checked my answer by __checking my work on a calculator__

Are They Getting It?

Check students' understanding of exponents by writing these problems on the board. Ask them to point out wrong answers and explain why they are incorrect.

1. $5^3 = 15$ This is incorrect. The exponent tells how many times to use the base as a factor. The exponent is not one of the factors.
2. The power for $8 \times 8 \times 8 \times 8$ is 8^4. This is correct.
3. 2^5, $2 \times 2 \times 2 \times 2 \times 2$, and 32 are equivalent. This is correct.

13 SCIENCE Derrick is conducting an experiment growing mold. He measures the area it covers daily. Complete the table showing the mold's growth.

Dimensions	1 × 1	2 × 2	3 × 3	4 × 4	5 × 5	6 × 6	7 × 7	8 × 8	9 × 9	10 × 10
Exponential Form	1^2	2^2	3^2	4^2	5^2	6^2	7^2	8^2	9^2	10^2
Area	1	4	9	16	25	36	49	64	81	100

14 **Reflect** Define an exponent. Explain why you would use an exponent.

An exponent tells how many times a base is multiplied by itself.

It is a shortcut and saves space.

Skills, Concepts, and Problem Solving

Write each expression using an exponent.

15 5 × 5 × 5 5^3

16 3 × 3 × 3 × 3 × 3 3^5

17 7 × 7 × 7 × 7 × 7 7^5

18 9 × 9 × 9 × 9 9^4

Write each expression as repeated multiplication. Solve.

19 3^3 3 × 3 × 3 = 27

20 7^3 7 × 7 × 7 = 343

21 8^4 8 × 8 × 8 × 8 = 4,096

22 6^4 6 × 6 × 6 × 6 = 1,296

23 $(-10)^3$ (−10) × (−10) × (−10) = −1,000

24 $(-2)^4$ (−2) × (−2) × (−2) × (−2) = 16

Write the expression in word form.

25 4^3 four to the third power or four cubed

26 9^2 nine to the second power or nine squared

GO ON

Odd/Even Assignments

Exercises 15–33 are structured so that students practice the same concepts whether they are assigned the odd or even problems.

In-Class Assignment

Have students complete Exercises 15, 19, 23, 25, 30, and 36 to ensure that they understand the concept.

Math Challenge

Different Powers, Same Number Different powers may represent the same number. For example 3^4 and 9^2 both represent 81. Have students find other pairs of powers that have this relationship. After several pairs are found, students may be able to determine a pattern and then may be able to generate many pairs with this relationship.

See It, Do It, Say It, Write It

Step 1 Write several powers in expanded form on the board. Ask students to write the power for each expression and the product.

Step 2 Ask students to write three powers that are different than those presented in Step 1. Then they should show the expanded form for each power and the product.

Step 3 Send each student to the board to showcase one of their powers from Step 2. Do not allow more than one student to present the same power unless all three problems that a student wrote have already been presented. As each power is presented, students should pay attention and note which powers were expanded or simplified incorrectly.

Step 4 Students should write any problem presented with errors on their own papers and correct the mistakes explaining where the error took place. If no problems were presented with errors, write several problems on the board yourself with a few of them having errors so that the students are sure to have some powers to correct.

Looking Ahead: Pre-teach

Order of Operations In the next lesson, students will learn about the order of operations. The rules for the order of operations follow.

1. Simplify operations with parentheses.
2. Simplify powers.
3. Multiply or divide from left to right.
4. Add or subtract from left to right.

Example
Simplify $3 \times 2^3 \div (5 - 6)$.
Using the order of operations:

$3 \times 2^3 \div (5 - 6) = 3 \times 2^3 \div (-1)$	Parentheses first.
$= 3 \times 8 \div (-1)$	Powers next.
$= 24 \div (-1)$	Multiply.
$= -24$	Divide.

Evaluate each expression.

27 $8^2 =$ 64

28 $5^2 =$ 25

29 $4^4 =$ 256

30 $7^3 =$ 343

31 $(-12)^3 =$ −1,728

32 $(-3)^5 =$ −243

Solve.

33 MARCHING BAND The high school marching band lined up in 8 rows. There were 8 band members in each row. How many total band members are lined up? Write an expression using exponents, and then evaluate the expression.
8^2; 64 band members

Vocabulary Check **Write the vocabulary word that completes each sentence.**

34 The base is the number used as the factor in an expression involving exponents.

35 The exponent tells you how many times a base is multiplied by itself.

36 **Writing in Math** Austin was asked to evaluate the expression 7^3. He wrote $7 \times 3 = 21$. What did he do wrong?
The expression should be $7^3 = 7 \times 7 \times 7 = 343$. He did not use the exponent correctly. The exponent 3 tells you to multiply the base 7 three times.

Spiral Review

Find each quotient. (Lesson 8-5, p. 348)

37 $40 \div (-8) =$ −5

38 $-24 \div (-4) =$ 6

39 $-15 \div (-5) =$ 3

40 $-63 \div 7 =$ −9

Solve. (Lesson 8-5, p. 348)

41 SOCCER The high school soccer team has lost by a total of 12 points over the last 4 games. If the team lost by the same number of points each game, what integer represents the change in their score each game?
$-12 \div 4 = -3$; −3 points

STOP

Ticket Out the Door

Squared Birthday Tell students that when they were 1 year old, 4 years old, and 9 years old their ages were perfect squares. When they were 1 year old and 8 years old their ages were perfect cubes. Have students think about at what next age their ages will be a perfect square and perfect cube. From there have them write the sentences below completed on their papers.

I am <current age>. In the year <20XX> my age will be a perfect square and in the year <20XX> my age will be a perfect cube.

Students should turn in their papers as they exit the classroom.

358 Chapter 8 Integer Operations

Lesson 8-7 Order of Operations

KEY Concept

You must follow the **order of operations** to evaluate mathematical expressions correctly.

Order of Operations	Symbol
1. Simplify grouping symbols.	(parentheses)
2. Simplify exponents.	base → 2^5 ← exponent
3. Multiply and divide in order from left to right.	× ÷
4. Add and subtract in order from left to right.	+ −

VOCABULARY

base (of a power) the number used as the factor Example: In 2^5, 2 is the base.

exponent the number of times a *base* is multiplied by itself Example: In 2^5, 5 is the exponent.

order of operations rules that tell what operation to perform first when evaluating expressions
(1) Simplify grouping symbols.
(2) Simplify exponents.
(3) Multiply and divide in order from left to right.
(4) Add and subtract in order from left to right.

ometimes parentheses are used to set a number apart from ther operations. If there is no operation to be performed ıside the parentheses, check for **exponents**.

Example 1

Find the value of 3 + (12 + 6) ÷ 3.

1. Simplify grouping symbols. $3 + (12 + 6) \div 3 =$
2. Multiply and divide in order from left to right. $= 3 + 18 \div 3$
3. Add and subtract in order from left to right. $= 3 + 6$
$= 9$

YOUR TURN!

Find the value of 7 + (5 − 3) × 4.

1. Simplify grouping symbols. $7 + (5 - 3) \times 4 =$
2. Multiply and divide in order from left to right. $= 7 +$ __2__ $\times 4$
3. Add and subtract in order from left to right. $= 7 +$ __8__
$=$ __15__

Lesson 8-7 Order of Operations 359

Additional *Example 1*

Find the value of 13 × (5 – 2) + 4².

1. Simplify grouping symbols. $13 \times (5 - 2) + 4^2 =$
2. Simplify exponents. $= 13 \times (3) + 4^2$
3. Multiply and divide in order from left to right. $= 13 \times 3 + 16$
4. Add and subtract in order from left to right. $= 39 + 16$
$= 55$

Lesson Notes

Lesson 8-7

Lesson Planner

Objective Use the order of operations to simplify expressions.

Vocabulary **base (of a power)**, **exponent**, **order of operations**

Materials/Manipulatives algebra tiles, colored pencils or markers

Chapter Resource Masters

- CRM Vocabulary and English Language Development (p. A181)
- CRM Skills Practice (p. A182)
- CRM Problem-Solving Practice (p. A183)
- CRM Homework Practice (p. A184)

Vocabulary

Access Vocabulary Write 6 + 8 ÷ 2 on the board. Give students time to calculate the problem having them show each step of their work on their papers. Then announce that the answer is 10. Many students will not have gotten that answer, but rather 7. Emphasize the need for an order of operations so that those calculating math problems arrive at the same answer.

Key Concept

Foundational Skills and Concepts After students have read through the Key Concept box, have them try these exercises.

1. When simplifying an expression, what is the first symbol you should look for? parentheses
2. When multiplying and dividing, in what direction do you work? left to right
3. In the expression, 24 + 16 ÷ 2 × 2, what operation is done first? division

Additional *Example 2*

Find the value of $9 \times 3 + (5 + 3)^2 \div 4$.

$9 \times 3 + (5 + 3)^2 \div 4$	Simplify grouping symbols.
$= 9 \times 3 + 8^2 \div 4$	Simplify exponents.
$= 9 \times 3 + 64 \div 4$	Multiply and divide in order from left to right.
$= 27 + 16$	Add and subtract in order from left to right.
$= 43$	

3 Practice

Using Manipulatives

Algebra Tiles Use unit blocks to give students a visual concept of the order of operations. First show the problem using the unit cubes.

$6 + (4 - 1)^2 \div 3$

6 + (4 − 1)² ÷ 3

Next show the simplified answer after each operation until the expression is simplified.

On-Hand Manipulatives Students can use colored markers to guide them through using the order of operations. Have students assign a color to Steps 1 – 4. Then before calculating they should circle or highlight the operations using the colors that correspond to the steps.

Example 2

Find the value of $6^2 - (7 - 3) \times 3 + 9$.

1. Simplify grouping symbols.	$6^2 - (7 - 3) \times 3 + 9$
2. Simplify exponents.	$= 6^2 - 4 \times 3 + 9$
3. Multiply and divide in order from left to right.	$= 36 - 4 \times 3 + 9$
4. Add and subtract in order from left to right.	$= 36 - 12 + 9$
	$= 33$

From left to right, subtraction comes first in this problem.

YOUR TURN!

Find the value of $7 - 2 + (9 - 5)^2 \div 2$.

1. Simplify grouping symbols.	$7 - 2 + (9 - 5)^2 \div 2$
2. Simplify exponents.	$= 7 - 2 + \underline{4^2} \div 2$
3. Divide in order from left to right.	$= 7 - 2 + \underline{16} \div 2$
4. Add and subtract in order from left to right.	$= 7 - 2 + \underline{8}$
	$= \underline{13}$

Who is Correct?

Find the value of $10 \div 2 + (2 + 2)^2 \times 2$.

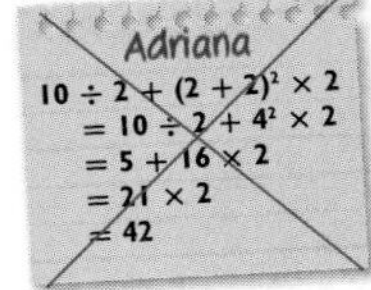

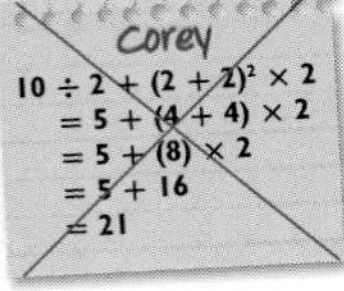

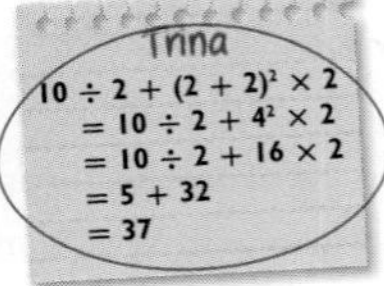

Circle correct answer(s). Cross out incorrect answer(s).

Guided Practice

Name the step that should be performed first in each expression.

1. $9 + 5^3 \div 5 + 2 \times 6$ exponent
2. $8 + 2 \div 2 \times 5 - 1$ division
3. $4 \times 6 + (30 - 3) \div 3^2$ subtraction
4. $26 \div 1 - (1 + 7) \times 2$ addition

Who *is Correct?*

Diagnostic Teaching

- Adriana's answer is incorrect. She did not follow the order of operations. She added prior to multiplying.
- Corey's answer is incorrect. He did not follow the order of operations. He simplified from left to right.
- Trina's answer is correct. She followed the order of operations.

Step by Step Practice

5. Find the value of $14 - 6 \times (2 - 1)^2 - 5 + 2$.

Step 1 Use the order of operations. Simplify the grouping symbols.
$14 - 6 \times (2 - 1)^2 - 5 + 2 = 14 - 6 \times (\underline{\ 1\ })^2 - 5 + 2$

Step 2 Simplify the exponent.
$14 - 6 \times 1^2 - 5 + 2 = 14 - 6 \times \underline{\ 1\ } - 5 + 2$

Step 3 Multiply and divide.
$14 - 6 \times 1 - 5 + 2 = 14 - \underline{\ 6\ } - 5 + 2$

Step 4 Add and subtract.
$14 - 6 - 5 + 2 = \underline{\ 8\ } - 5 + 2$
$= \underline{\ 3\ } + 2$
$= \underline{\ 5\ }$

Find the value of each expression.

6. $9 - (1 + 8) + 3 \times 3^2 = 9 - \underline{\ 9\ } + 3 \times 3^2$
$= 9 - \underline{\ 9\ } + 3 \times \underline{\ 9\ }$
$= 9 - \underline{\ 9\ } + \underline{\ 27\ }$
$= \underline{\ 0\ } + \underline{\ 27\ }$
$= \underline{\ 27\ }$

7. $8 \div 2 + (5 \times 2)^2 - 7 = 8 \div 2 + (\underline{\ 10\ })^2 - 7$
$= 8 \div 2 + \underline{\ 100\ } - 7$
$= \underline{\ 4\ } + \underline{\ 100\ } - 7$
$= \underline{\ 104\ } - 7$
$= \underline{\ 97\ }$

8. $20 - 4 \div 4 \times 2 + (7 - 4) = \underline{\ 21\ }$

9. $(4 - 3)^2 \times 50 \div 5 - (3 + 6) = \underline{\ 1\ }$

10. $40 \div (9 - 7)^2 + 6 \times 5 = \underline{\ 40\ }$

11. $50 \div (7 + 3) \times 4 \div 2 = \underline{\ 10\ }$

12. $(28 - 7) \div (6 + 1) + 8 = \underline{\ 11\ }$

13. $(4 \times 5) \div (12 - 7) + 3 = \underline{\ 7\ }$

GO ON

Note This!

Reference List Students should write the order of operations clearly and completely in their notebooks. If they are using color to help them with order, the different steps should be written in those colors.

Are They Getting It?

Check students' understanding of the order of operations by writing these problems on the board. Have students point out wrong answers and explain why they are wrong. Encourage students to use a diagram in their explanations.

1. $4 \times 3^2 \div (1 - 7) \times 2 = -3$ This is incorrect. Multiplication and division should be done from left to right. The answer is –12.
2. $3 \times (1 + 40 \div (-5)) + 5^2 = 4$. This is correct.
3. $2^3 \times 4 \div (2^4 \div 4) - 9 \times 4 = -28$. This is correct.

English Learner Strategy

Rules in Native Language Students that are not native English speakers should write in their notebooks the rules for the order of operations in English and then a direction below or beside them using their native language. Give each English Learner student a problem to simplify and have them use the rules written in their native language. If they make an error, help them clarify the rules so their translations are not the cause of the errors.

Step by Step Problem-Solving Practice

Problem-Solving Strategies
- ☐ Draw a diagram.
- ☐ Look for a pattern.
- ☐ Guess and check.
- ☐ Act it out.
- ☑ Solve a simpler problem.
- ☐ Work backward.

14 NUTRITION Marcos has 2 baskets that each hold 12 oranges. He has 6 more baskets that each hold 10 oranges. Write and simplify an expression to find how many oranges Marcos has in all.

Understand Read the problem. Write what you know. There are baskets with __12__ oranges each and baskets with __10__ oranges each.

Plan Pick a strategy. One strategy is to solve a simpler problem. In this case, solving a simpler problem means to work on smaller parts of the expression, one at a time.

Solve Write an expression for the total number of oranges.

__2__ × 12 + __6__ × 10
2 baskets of 12 — 6 baskets of 10

Simplify the expression using the order of operations.

__2__ × 12 + __6__ × 10
= __24__ + __60__ Multiply.
= __84__ Add.

Marcos has __84__ oranges.

Check You can use addition to check.
12 + 12 + 10 + 10 + 10 + 10 + 10 + 10 = __84__

Write and simplify an expression to solve each problem.

15 NATURE Brandy likes to watch birds. She saw a green heron make 2 nests. Three green herons each made 4 nests. Five nests were damaged during a storm. How many nests were left? Check off each step.

__✔__ Understand: I underlined key words.

__✔__ Plan: To solve the problem, I will __write an expression__

__✔__ Solve: The answer is __2 + (3 × 4) − 5 = 2 + 12 − 5 = 14 − 5 = 9; 9 nests__

__✔__ Check: I checked my answer by __using a calculator__

362 **Chapter 8** Integer Operations

Intervention Strategy — Auditory Learners

Many use the memory device *Please Excuse My Dear Aunt Sally* as a way to remember the order of operations. If this memory device does not help your students, have them come up with different words that have meaning for them. For example, maybe a student has an aunt Stacy and she is Dingy. That student's memory device could be *Please Excuse My Dingy Aunt Stacy*. The possibilities are endless.

16 COLLECTIONS April bought 3 packs of comic books. Each pack had 5 comic books. She gave 7 comic books to her brother. Then she bought 2 more packs of comic books with 18 books in each. How many comic books does April have now?

$(3 \times 5) - 7 + (2 \times 18) = 15 - 7 + 36 = 8 + 36 = 44$; 44 books

17 PHOTOGRAPHY Marlene was looking through her photo album. She looked at 6 pages with 4 photos each. She removed 2 photos. She then looked at 10 pages with 8 photos each. She removed 6 photos. How many photos were left in the album?

$(6 \times 4) - 2 + (10 \times 8) - 6 = 24 - 2 + (10 \times 8) - 6 = 24 - 2 + 80 - 6 =$
$22 + 80 - 6 = 102 - 6 = 96$; 96 photos

18 **Reflect** Explain why $16 \div 2 + 6$ has a different value than $16 \div (2 + 6)$.

Answers will vary. Sample answer: $16 \div 2 + 6 = 14$ and $16 \div (2 + 6) = 2$; without parentheses, division is performed first. With parentheses, addition is performed first.

Skills, Concepts, and Problem Solving

Name the step that should be performed first in each expression.

19 $2 \times (3 - 6)^2 + 9 \div 3$ subtraction

20 $3 \times 2 + (4 \div 2) - 2^2$ division

21 $4 + (6 - 2 \times 7) \div 2^2$ multiplication

22 $(7 - 2^2 \times 4) - 8 \div 1$ exponent

Find the value of each expression.

23 $10 + 8 \div 2 - (10 + 2) =$ 2

24 $50 \div 5 + 3 \times 2^2 - (8 - 2) =$ 16

25 $(9 - 6)^2 + 8 \div 4 + 5 \times 6 =$ 41

26 $16 - 4^2 \times 0 + 18 - 15 =$ 19

27 $(50 \div 10) \times 7 - 3^2 =$ 26

28 $(14 - 6) \div 2^2 \times 9 =$ 18

29 $(4 \times 3) - (13 + 5) \div 6 =$ 9

30 $4^2 \div 8 \times (9 + 3) \div 6 =$ 4

GO ON

Math Challenge

Stump the Teacher Have students make up problems that include all the operations plus parentheses and exponents. They should write problems that they think are hard and might stump a teacher. Their problems should include answers. Then have students get into groups of three to write a letter to a math teacher in the school asking them to help them verify their answers to the three problems. Answers should not be included in the letter, but rather students should ask the teacher to return the letter with their answers to the problems. Then students can compare their answers to the answers returned and determine if the problems they wrote were actually *stumper* problems.

Odd/Even Assignments

Exercises 19–32 are structured so that students practice the same concepts whether they are assigned the odd or even problems.

In-Class Assignment

Have students complete Exercises 19, 25, 29, 32, and 35 to ensure that they understand the concept.

4 Assess

See It, Do It, Say It, Write It

Step 1 Write the following problem on the board. Have students simplify the expression.
$45 + 5^2 \div 5 \div 3 - (-7) \times 3$

Step 2 Tell students that parentheses are missing from the problem. The answer should be 15. Ask students to determine where parentheses can be added to the problem so that the answer is 15.

Step 3 Ask students to work in pairs or small groups. Have each student show their group members their modified expression and explain why their answer is now 15.

Step 4 Have students work alone to write an expression that is missing parentheses that will not yield the desired answer. Then have students get back into their groups from Step 3 and study each other's problems to determine where the parentheses need to be placed.

Write and simplify an expression to solve each problem.

31 BOOKS Ramona borrowed 2 stacks of books with 8 books each. She then returned 9 books. Then Ramona borrowed 2 stacks of 5 books each. How many books does Ramona have now?

$(2 \times 8) - 9 + (2 \times 5) = 16 - 9 + 10 = 7 + 10 = 17$; 17 books

32 COLLECTIONS Don had 100 collector cards. He sold 5 packs of baseball cards with 10 cards each. He then bought 3 packs of football cards with 12 cards each. Then Don sold 25 hockey cards. How many cards does Don have left?

$100 - (5 \times 10) + (3 \times 12) - 25 = 100 - 50 + 36 - 25 = 50 + 36 - 25 =$
$86 - 25 = 61$; 61 cards

Vocabulary Check **Write the vocabulary word that completes each sentence.**

33 A(n) ___exponent___ is the number of times a base is multiplied by itself.

34 The ___order of operations___ is a set of rules that tells what operation to perform first when evaluating an expression.

35 Writing in Math Does $30 - (10 - 5)$ equal $(30 - 10) - 5$? Explain.

No; $30 - (10 - 5) = 25$ and $(30 - 10) - 5 = 15$; the parentheses change the order in which the expressions are simplified.

Spiral Review

Simplify. (Lesson 8-3, p. 334)

36 $5 + (-13) + 7 + 3$ ___2___

37 $-9 - (-4) + 14 + (-6)$ ___3___

38 $11 + (-5 + (-12)) - (-7)$ ___1___

39 $7 + (-15 - (-13)) - 10$ ___−5___

Solve. (Lesson 8-6, p. 353)

40 FOOD The number of Calories in an average slice of cheese pizza can be written as 4^4. Find the product of 4^4.

256 Calories

Ticket Out the Door

The Next Operation Write $((70 \div 7)^2 + 15) \div 5$. Students should get in a group with three other students to simplify the expression. When they have a result, each student should take one step to simplify the expression and write it on a scrap piece of paper. All group members should approach the door together and hand in their scrap papers in the order that expression is simplified according to the order of operations.

The first paper should be $(10^2 + 15) \div 5$.

The second paper should be $(100 + 15) \div 5$.

The third paper should be $115 \div 5$.

The fourth paper should be 23.

Chapter 8

Progress Check 3 (Lessons 8-5, 8-6, and 8-7)

nd each quotient.

4 ÷ (−1) = -4

2 −15 ÷ (−3) = 5

−42 ÷ (−7) = 6

4 −24 ÷ 3 = -8

45 ÷ (−9) = -5

6 −56 ÷ (−8) = 7

aluate the expression.

4^3 = 64

8 7^2 = 49

8^3 = 512

10 6^3 = 216

$(-5)^4$ = 625

12 $(-7)^4$ = 2,401

nd the value of each expression.

18 + 16 ÷ 4 × (5 − 2) + 7 = 37

14 10 − (2 − 1) + 16 ÷ 2 × (4 + 3) = 65

28 ÷ 2^2 × 8 + 4 ÷ 2 = 58

16 54 ÷ 3^2 × 7 − (6 × 4) ÷ 3 = 34

lve.

WEATHER The temperature dropped a total of 35 degrees in 7 hours. How much did the temperature drop per hour if the temperature dropped by the same amount each hour?

−35 ÷ 7 = −5; The temperature dropped an average of 5 degrees per hour.

SCHOOL SUPPLIES Cole had 32 markers. He sold 2 boxes of markers with 4 markers each. He then bought 2 packs of markers with 6 markers each. Then Cole gave 8 markers to his sister. How many markers does Cole have left?

32 − (2 × 4) + (2 × 6) − 8 = 32 − 8 + 12 − 8 = 24 + 4 = 28; 28 markers

Chapter 8 Progress Check 365

Progress Check 3

Chapter 8

Formative Assessment

Use the Progress Check to assess students' mastery of the previous lessons. Have students review the lesson indicated for the problems they answered incorrectly.

Odd/Even Assignments

Exercises are structured so that students practice the same concepts whether they are assigned the odd or even problems.

Common Error Alert

Exercises 13–16 Be sure students pay attention to the order of operations and do not just work problems from left to right.

Data-Driven Decision Making

Students missing Exercises . . .	Have trouble with . . .	Should review and practice . . .
1-6	finding quotients of integers.	SSG Lesson 8-5, p. 348 CRM Skills Practice, p. A174
7-12	evaluating expressions with exponents.	SSG Lesson 8-6, p. 353 CRM Skills Practice, p. A178
13-16	simplifying expressions according to the order of operations.	SSG Lesson 8-7, p. 359 CRM Skills Practice, p. A182
17-18	solving word problems involving operations with integers.	CRM Problem-Solving Practice, pp. A175, A179, and A183

Chapter 8 Study Guide
Formative Assessment

Vocabulary and Concept Check

If students have difficulty answering Exercises 1–8, remind them that they can use the page references to refresh their memories about the vocabulary terms.

Vocabulary Review Strategies

Vocabulary Table Have students fold a sheet of notebook paper vertically. On the left side, they should list the vocabulary terms. On the right side, they should provide a definition or summary for each of the terms, including examples or summaries when appropriate. For example, when listing *order of operations,* the students should actually list out the rules sequentially.

Lesson Review

Each example walks the students through the main concepts of this chapter, which include the following:

- adding integers (demonstrated through the use of number lines)
- subtracting integers (demonstrated through the use of number lines)
- comparing absolute values (demonstrated through the use of number lines)
- adding and subtracting groups of integers
- multiplying integers (by multiplying absolute values)
- multiplying several integers (utilizing order of operations)
- dividing integers (by dividing absolute values)
- using exponents
- using order of operations on a mixture of integer operations

If the given examples are not sufficient to review the questions, remind students that the page references tell them where to review that topic in their textbooks.

Find **Extra Practice** for these concepts in the Practice Worksheets, pages A157–A184.

Chapter 8 Study Guide

Vocabulary and Concept Check

absolute value, *p. 325*
Associative Property of Addition, *p. 334*
base, *p. 353*
cubed, *p. 353*
divisor, *p. 348*
exponent, *p. 353*
Inverse Property of Addition, *p. 318*
order of operations, *p. 359*
quotient, *p. 348*
squared, *p. 353*

Write the vocabulary word that completes each sentence. Not a[ll] vocabulary terms will be used.

1. The order of operations is a set of rules that tells which operation to perform first in evaluating an expression.
2. The exponent indicates the number times the base is multiplied by itself.
3. Write the name of the property shown below. $5 + (-5) = 0$ Inverse Property of Addition
4. The absolute value is the distance betwe[en] a number and 0 on a number line.
5. The quotient is the answer or resul[t] of a division problem.
6. Write the name of the property shown below. $(3 \times (-5)) \times 2 = 3 \times (2 \times (-5))$ Associative Property of Multiplication
7. The number used as the factor in an expression involving exponents is called the base.
8. A number multiplied by itself; 4×4, or 4^2 is squared.

Lesson Review

8-1 Add Integers (pp. 318–324)

Find each sum.

9. $-1 + 6 =$ 5
10. $3 + (-7) =$ −4
11. $-7 + (-2) =$ −9
12. $8 + (-4) =$ 4
13. $9 + 3 =$ 12
14. $7 + (-10) =$ −3

Example 1

Find the sum of 5 and −2. Use a number line.

1. Graph the first number.
2. Start at 5.
3. Since 2 is a negative integer, move left 2 spaces.

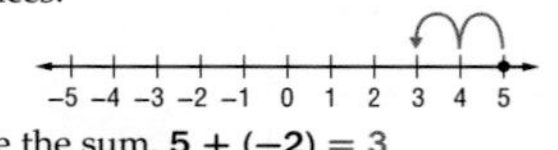

4. Write the sum. $5 + (-2) = 3$

Classroom Management

Pair and Share Pair a student who has a good grasp of the material with another student who needs extra support. Have the student pairs take turns giving each other questions that they write (based upon the examples in the Study Guide). After answering the questions, if necessary, have the author of the questions explain the strategy and answer to the other student.

-2 Subtract Integers (pp. 325–332)

ind each difference.

5 $-5 - 2 =$ __−7__

6 $1 - (-3) =$ __4__

7 $6 - 8 =$ __−2__

8 $-3 - (-8) =$ __5__

hich number has the greater bsolute value?

9 $|6|$ or $|-9|$ __−9__

0 $|-5|$ or $|-3|$ __−5__

Example 2

Which number has the greater absolute value?

$|-4|$ or $|2|$

1. -4 is 4 units from 0. So, $|-4| = 4$.
2. 2 is 2 units from 0. So, $|2| = 2$.
3. Which integer has the greater absolute value? -4

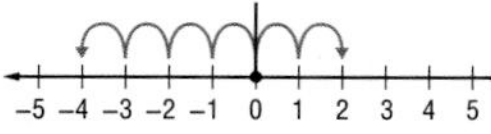

-3 Add and Subtract Groups of Integers (pp. 334–340)

implify.

1 $8 + (-2) - 2 + 7 - (-9)$ __20__

2 $14 + (-8) + 5 - (-4) - 3$ __12__

3 $21 + 5 - (-3) - 6 + 6$ __29__

4 $8 - 4 + (5 - (-3)) + (-9)$ __3__

5 $2 + 5 + (9 - 17) + (-6)$ __−7__

Example 3

Simplify $-4 + (-9) - 3 + 6 - (-1)$.

1. Rewrite the subtraction as addition.

$-4 + (-9) - 3 + 6 - (-1) = -4 + (-9) + (-3) + 6 + 1$

2. Find the sum from left to right.

$$\begin{aligned} & -4 + (-9) + (-3) + 6 + 1 \\ = & -13 + (-3) + 6 + 1 \\ = & -16 + 6 + 1 \\ = & -10 + 1 \\ = & -9 \end{aligned}$$

Intervention Strategy Visual Learners

Use of Number Lines Have students use number lines any time they are in need of more visualization with the various operations involving integers.

Dinah Zike's Foldables®

Review Remind students to complete and refer to their Foldables as they progress through the Chapter 8 Study Guide. Have students share and compare their completed Foldables with a partner. You may also choose to have them use their Foldable as a study aid in preparing for the Chapter Test. (For complete instructions, see Chapter Resource Masters, p. A154.)

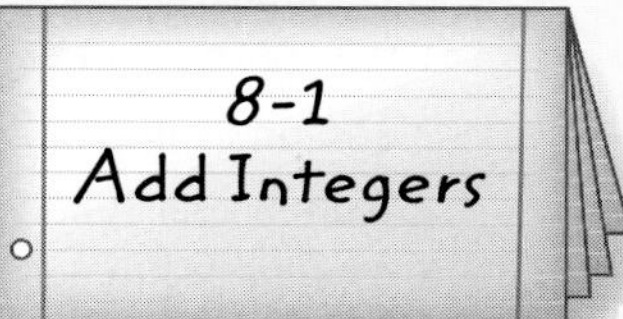

Common Error Alert

Rewrite as Addition Remind students when calculating a problem that requires subtracting a negative integer to rewrite it as an addition expression.

Note This!

Create a Checklist Help students create a study checklist. The checklist should include all of the following items:

- Notes from class
- Sketches, drawings, or number lines in their notebooks
- Foldables
- Vocabulary terms and definitions
- Lesson Examples
- Written assignments and quizzes
- Chapter 8 Study Guide

8-4 Multiply Integers
(pp. 341–346)

Find each product.

26 $8 \times (-3) =$ -24

27 $-9 \times (-2) =$ 18

28 $-2 \times (-15) =$ 30

29 $12 \times (-6) =$ -72

Example 4

Find $-7 \times (-4)$ by multiplying absolute values.

1. Find the absolute value of each.
   $|-7| = 7$ and $|-4| = 4$
2. Multiply the absolute values of the numbers.
   $7 \times 4 = 28$
3. The signs are the same, so the product is positive.
4. Write the product with the sign. 28

8-5 Divide Integers (pp. 348–352)

Find each quotient.

30 $-44 \div (-11) =$ 4

31 $-12 \div (-6) =$ 2

32 $-35 \div 7 =$ -5

33 $36 \div (-12) =$ -3

Example 5

Find $27 \div (-3)$ by dividing absolute values.

1. Find the absolute value of each.
   $|27| = 27$ and $|-3| = 3$
2. Divide the absolute values of the numbers.
   $27 \div 3 = 9$
3. The signs are different.
   The quotient will be negative.
4. Write the quotient with a negative sign. -9

8-6 Exponents (pp. 353–358)

Write each expression using an exponent.

34 $4 \times 4 \times 4 \times 4 \times 4 =$ 4^5

35 $9 \times 9 \times 9 =$ 9^3

Example 6

Write $5 \times 5 \times 5$ using an exponent.

1. The base is 5.
2. The exponent is 3.
3. Write $5 \times 5 \times 5$ using an exponent.
   $5 \times 5 \times 5 = 5^3$

368 Chapter 8 Study Guide

Intervention Strategy Kinesthetic Learners

Use of Counters For those students who benefit from "hands-on" mathematical techniques, provide them with the opportunity to use counters for integer addition and subtraction exercises.

Write each expression as repeated multiplication. Solve.

6 3^3 $3 \times 3 \times 3 = 27$

7 6^4 $6 \times 6 \times 6 \times 6 = 1{,}296$

8 3^5 $3 \times 3 \times 3 \times 3 \times 3 = 243$

9 $(-9)^4$ $(-9) \times (-9) \times (-9) \times (-9) = 6{,}561$

10 $(-8)^3$ $(-8) \times (-8) \times (-8) = -512$

Example 7

Write 7^3 as repeated multiplication. Solve.

1. The base is 7.
2. The exponent is 3, so multiply the base 3 times.
3. Write 7^3 as repeated multiplication.
   $7^3 = 7 \times 7 \times 7$
4. Multiply.
   $7^3 = 343$

8-7 Order of Operations (pp. 359–364)

Simplify.

11 $9 \div 3 \times (15 \div 3) =$ 15

12 $8 + (2 \times 4) \times 3^3 \div 9 =$ 32

13 $6 + (3 \times 5) \div 5 + 22 =$ 31

14 $12 \div 4 + (2 \times 3)^2 =$ 39

Example 8

Find the value of $2 + (13 - 7)^2 \div 4$.

1. Simplify grouping symbols. $2 + (13 - 7)^2 \div 4$
2. Simplify exponents. $= 2 + 6^2 \div 4$
3. Multiply and divide in order from left to right. $= 2 + 36 \div 4$
4. Add and subtract in order from left to right. $= 2 + 9$
   $= 11$

Math Coach Notes

Test-Taking Tip Have students define the Identity Property of Multiplication. Have them demonstrate the property by showing examples.

Common Error *Alert*

Order of Operations If students are struggling with problems that use the order of operations, have them jot down a list of the order of operations on the corner of their paper. Then, in an effort to reduce the risk of careless mistakes, have students rewrite the expression step-by-step referring to their lists.

Ticket Out the Door

Write Word Problems Divide the class into two groups. Have each student in the first group create a word problem that demonstrates a real-world application of the use of addition or subtraction of integers. Similarly, have each student in the second group create a word problem that demonstrates a real-world application of the use of multiplication or division of integers. Groups should exchange the problems and solve them before handing them to you as they exit the classroom.

Chapter 8

Chapter Test

Chapter Resource Masters

Additional forms of the Chapter 8 Tests are available.

Test Format	Where to Find it
Chapter 8 Test	Math Online glencoe.com
Blackline Masters	Assessment Masters, p. 118

Customize and create multiple versions of your chapter tests and their answer keys. All of these questions from the chapter tests are available on ExamView® Assessment Suite.

Online Assessment and Reporting
glencoe.com

This online assessment tool allows teachers to track student progress with easily accessible comprehensive reports available for every student. Assess students using any internet-ready computer.

Alternative Assessment

Use Portfolios Ask students to write examples of each type of problem from this chapter in their portfolios. Ask them to include a number line, a drawing of counters, or a sketch with the examples, where appropriate and/or needed. Also, have the students find the answer to each example in their portfolios. Emphasize that they show all of the work required to arrive at their answer.

Chapter 8

Chapter Test

Find each sum.

1. $-5 + (-2) =$ **−7**
2. $(-3) + 6 =$ **3**
3. What is the opposite of 8? Use it to show the Inverse Property of Addition.
   −8; 8 + (−8) = 0

Find each difference.

4. $-1 - (-4) =$ **3**
5. $-3 - (-1) =$ **−2**

Which number has the greater absolute value?

6. $|-12|$ or $|-9|$ = **−12**
7. $|-3|$ or $|2|$ = **−3**

Write each expression using an exponent.

8. $4 \times 4 \times 4 \times 4 \times 4 =$ **4^5**
9. $7 \times 7 \times 7 \times 7 =$ **7^4**

Evaluate each expression.

10. $8^3 =$ **512**
11. $5^4 =$ **625**

Simplify.

12. $(5 - 1)^2 + (17 - 5) \div 3 =$ **20**
13. $3^2 + (28 \div 7) \times 12 \div 8 =$ **15**

Find each product.

14. $2 \times (-5) =$ **−10**
15. $-6 \times (-3) =$ **18**

370 Chapter 8 Test

English Learner Strategy

Assessment Allow students time to look over the assessment. Have the students take a close look at all the problem directions and the word problems.

Most of the directions are not very complicated; however, be sure the students are aware of the *Inverse Property of Addition,* which is referred to in the test. If students are having trouble remembering the property, provide an opportunity for them to clarify the definition by referring them to the appropriate page in their text where it is located.

d each quotient.

-72 ÷ 9 = __−8__

17 −36 ÷ (−4) = __9__

ve.

FOOTBALL On the first play of their drive, the Tigers started from their own 30-yard line and gained 5 yards. On the second play of their drive, they lost 2 yards. On the third play, the Tigers gained 8 yards. On what yard line were they?

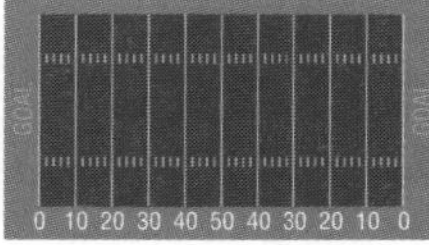

$5 + (-2) + 8 = 11$, $11 + 30 = 41$; 41-yard line

HEALTH Missy went to the dentist. The cost was $128. She expected her dental insurance to pay $80. Missy wrote the dentist a check for $48. Later, Missy found out that her insurance actually paid $88. Assuming Missy had no prior balance on her account, what was her balance after both payments were received?

$128 - 88 - 48 = -8$; She had an account balance of −$8. In other words, the dentist owed her $8.

rect the mistakes.

WEATHER The weather forecaster on channel 15 said, "It is currently 27°F. Overnight there is a cold front expected, and the temperature will drop by approximately 40°F. That will bring us to a low temperature of 13°F." What is wrong with this prediction?

27°F − 40°F = −13°F; The temperature will be 13°F *below* zero.

MONEY Jake purchased a credit card at his cafeteria for $25. He bought food that totaled $6.25. Jake told his mom that he had a balance of $6.25. What is wrong with Jake's answer?

He spent $6.25, but the credit he had remaining was actually $25 − $6.25 = $18.75.

Math Coach Notes

Test-Taking Tip Have students circle or highlight the numbers in the word problems that are to be used in the calculation(s), and cross out any numbers that are insignificant to finding a solution.

Data-Driven Decision Making

Students missing Exercises . . .	Have trouble with . . .	Should review and practice . . .
1–3	finding sums of integers, demonstrating the Inverse Property of Addition.	SSG Lesson 8-1, p. 318 CRM Skills Practice, p. A158
4–7	finding differences of integers and finding and comparing absolute values.	SSG Lesson 8-2, p. 325 CRM Skills Practice, p. A162
8–11	using exponents.	SSG Lesson 8-6, p. 353 CRM Skills Practice, p. A178
12–13	simplifying expressions.	SSG Lesson 8-7, p. 359 CRM Skills Practice, p. A182
14–17	multiplying and dividing integers.	SSG Lessons 8-4 and 8-5, pp. 341 and 348 CRM Skills Practice, p. A170 and A174
18–21	solving word problems involving integer operations.	CRM Problem-Solving Practice, pp. A163 and A167

Test Practice

Diagnose Student Errors

Survey student responses for each item. Class trends may indicate common errors and misconceptions.

1. A multiplied base and exponent
B only multiplied base twice
(C) correct
D multiplied base four times

2. A misinterpreted change in direction
(B) correct
C misinterpreted depth below sea level
D misinterpreted change in direction

3. (A) correct
B misinterpreted operations, forgot to subtract from paycheck
C guess
D misinterpreted operations, added all the numbers together

4. A added without considering negative
(B) correct
C subtracted absolute values
D guess

5. (A) correct
B guess
C misinterpreted operation
D misinterpreted operation

6. A added incorrectly
B incorrect sign
(C) correct
D added incorrectly

7. (A) correct
B division error, $-45 \div 3 = -15$
C calculation error
D guess

8. A incorrect order
(B) correct
C incorrect order
D incorrect order

9. (A) correct
B incorrect exponent used
C incorrect exponent used
D incorrect exponent used

Test Practice

Choose the best answer and fill in the corresponding circle on the sheet at right.

1 Evaluate the expression 7^3.

A 21 (C) 343
B 49 D 2,401

2 Irina went scuba diving in the ocean. She dove to 55 feet below sea level to explore a cave. Then she climbed 19 feet to take pictures of some jellyfish. Where is Irina in relation to sea level?

A −74 feet C 36 feet
(B) −36 feet D 74 feet

3 Joaquin owed his brother $15. He also owed his mother $22 and his best friend $9. If he earns $65 next week, how much money will he have left after he pays what he owes?

(A) $19 C $49
B $46 D $111

4 Find the sum of −12 and 3.

A −15 C 9
(B) −9 D 15

5 Due to a construction project, a small restaurant loses $4,000 per day in business. If this pattern continues for the next 3 days, how much money will this restaurant lose?

(A) −$12,000 C −$8,000
B −$10,000 D −$4,000

6 Simplify $11 - 4 - 10 + 7$.

A −10 (C) 4
B −4 D 10

7 A football team lost 45 yards on 3 play If the team lost the same number of yards on each play, which integer show the yards lost per play?

(A) −15 yards C −10 yards
B −12 yards D −8 yards

8 Use the order of operations to solve this problem.

$4^3 - (36 \div 9) \times 10 \div 5$ ______

A 50 C 72
(B) 56 D 120

372 **Chapter 8** Test Practice

10. A subtracted both values
(B) correct
C misinterpreted 'gain' and 'loss'
D added all values

11. A picked first operation from left to right
B picked last operation from left to right
C did not consider exponent in parentheses
(D) correct

12. (A) correct
B miscalculated
C miscalculated
D wrong sign

9 Ms. Brooks garden has 7 rows of vegetables in her garden. Each row has 7 vegetable plants. How many total vegetable plants does Ms. Brooks have in her garden? Write an expression using exponents, then evaluate the expression.

(A) $7^2 = 49$ C $7^4 = 2{,}401$
B $7^3 = 343$ D $7^5 = 16{,}807$

10 Hugo bought a stock for $9 a share. The first month the stock gained $3. The next month the stock lost $5. How much is his stock worth?

A $1 C $8
(B) $7 D $17

11 Name the step that should be performed first in the expression.

$$(20 - 3^2 \times 2) + 14 \div 2$$

A subtraction C division
B multiplication (D) exponent

12 The temperature was 35°F in the evening. It dropped 2°F every hour over a 6-hour period. How many degrees did the temperature change in the 6-hour period?

(A) −12°F C 8°F
B −4°F D 12°F

ANSWER SHEET

Directions: Fill in the circle of each correct answer.

1	A	B	●	D
2	A	●	C	D
3	●	B	C	D
4	A	●	C	D
5	●	B	C	D
6	A	B	●	D
7	●	B	C	D
8	A	●	C	D
9	●	B	C	D
10	A	●	C	D
11	A	B	C	●
12	●	B	C	D

Success Strategy
Align your answers to the correct circles. Make sure you are filling in the correct bubble for each question. Hold your place as you read the questions with your finger, your pen, or a sheet of paper.

Diagnosing Student Errors and Misconceptions

Corrections When working on the Test Practice problems, have students show their work on a separate sheet of notebook paper that can be used later as a reference as needed. After the class has completed the Test Practice problems, have them trade papers (without their names showing). Go over all the correct responses and have the students score each other's responses. Collect the papers and redistribute them to their owners. Have students correct missed problems.

Polls Take an informal poll of how many students missed each question. Tell them to refer to their work and try to find and correct any mistakes made. You should explain any questions that are continuing to confuse a number of students at this point.

Eliminate Wrong Answers If students are not able to successfully eliminate wrong answer choices, it would be helpful for you to point out the following:

Exercise 9 Have students think about the situation. Answers C and D are not reasonable. A person will not plant 2,400 or 16,800 vegetables in a garden. Answer B is even a fairly large number when you consider planting in a garden.

Exercise 10 Have students think about the situation. Answer D is not reasonable. The problem states that the stock gained and lost, so there is no way that the price could be greater than $9, the price he originally paid. Answer A is not reasonable because the loss of $5 would put the stock at $4, and the problem tells of a gain. The value of the stock has to be greater than $4.

Chapter 9

Chapter Overview

Chapter-at-a-Glance

Lesson	Math Objective	State/Local Standards
9-1 Algebraic Expressions (pp. 376-382)	Use variables to write expressions.	
9-2 Translating Verbal Phrases into Mathematical Symbols (pp. 383-390)	Use variables to write expressions and represent unknown quantities.	
Progress Check (p. 391)		
9-3 Simplify Expressions (pp. 392-398)	Simplify algebraic expressions.	
9-4 Evaluate Algebraic Expressions (pp. 399-404)	Write, simplify, and evaluate numerical expressions.	
Progress Check (p. 405)		

Content-at-a-Glance

The diagram below summarizes and unpacks Chapter 9 content.

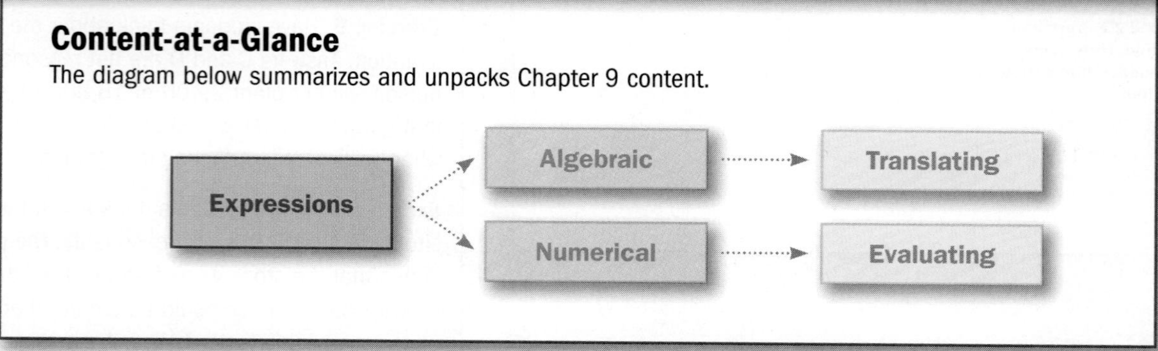

Online Assessment and Reporting
glencoe.com

Chapter Assessment Manager

Diagnostic Diagnose students' readiness.

	Student Study Guide/ Teacher Edition	Assessment Masters	Technology
Course Placement Test		1	ExamView® Assessment Suite
Book 3 Pretest		101	ExamView® Assessment Suite
Chapter 9 Pretest		126	ExamView® Assessment Suite
Quiz/Preview	SSG 375		Math Online glencoe.com StudentWorks™ Plus

Formative Identify students' misconceptions of content knowledge.

	Student Study Guide/ Teacher Edition	Assessment Masters	Technology
Progress Checks	SSG 391, 405		Math Online glencoe.com StudentWorks™ Plus
Vocabulary Review	SSG 406		Math Online glencoe.com
Lesson Assessments			ExamView® Assessment Suite
Are They Getting It?	TE 378, 385, 394, 401		Math Online glencoe.com

Summative Determine student success in learning concepts in the lesson, chapter, or book.

	Student Study Guide/ Teacher Edition	Assessment Masters	Technology
Chapter 9 Test	SSG 410	129	ExamView® Assessment Suite
Test Practice	SSG 412	132	ExamView® Assessment Suite
Alternative Assessment	TE 410	135	
See It, Do It, Say It, Write It	TE 382, 390, 398, 404		
Book 3 Test		148	ExamView® Assessment Suite

Back-mapping and Vertical Alignment **McGraw-Hill's *Math Triumphs*** intervention program was conceived and developed with the final result in mind: student success in grade-level mathematics, including Algebra 1 and beyond. The authors, using the **NCTM Focal Points and Focal Connections** as their guide, developed this brand-new series by backmapping from grade-level and Algebra 1 concepts, and vertically aligning the topics so that they build upon prior skills and concepts and serve as a foundation for future topics.

Chapter Resource Manager

	Lesson 9-1	Lesson 9-2	Lesson 9-3	Lesson 9-4
Concept	Algebraic Expressions	Translating Verbal Phrases into Mathematical Symbols	Simplify Expressions	Evaluate Algebraic Expressions
Objective	Use variables to write expressions.	Use variables to write expressions and represent unknown quantities.	Simplify algebraic expressions.	Write, simplify, and evaluate numerical expressions.
Math Vocabulary	algebraic expression coefficient constant term variable	algebraic expression coefficient constant term	like terms simplify term	algebraic expression evaluate order of operations value
Lesson Resources	**Materials** • Colored pencils • Construction paper **Manipulatives** • Algebra tiles **Other Resources** CRM Vocabulary and English Language Development CRM Skills Practice CRM Problem-Solving Practice CRM Homework Practice	**Materials** • Construction paper • Colored markers • Index cards **Manipulatives** • Algebra tiles • Base-ten blocks **Other Resources** CRM Vocabulary and English Language Development CRM Skills Practice CRM Problem-Solving Practice CRM Homework Practice	**Materials** • Colored pencils • Construction paper • Highlighters **Manipulatives** • Algebra tiles • Base-ten blocks • Bingo chips **Other Resources** CRM Vocabulary and English Language Development CRM Skills Practice CRM Problem-Solving Practice CRM Homework Practice	**Materials** • Colored pencils • Index cards **Manipulatives** • Two-Color Counters **Other Resources** CRM Vocabulary and English Language Development CRM Skills Practice CRM Problem-Solving Practice CRM Homework Practice
Technology	Math Online glencoe.com StudentWorks™ Plus ExamView® Assessment Suite	Math Online glencoe.com StudentWorks™ Plus ExamView® Assessment Suite	Math Online glencoe.com StudentWorks™ Plus ExamView® Assessment Suite	Math Online glencoe.com StudentWorks™ Plus ExamView® Assessment Suite

Intervention Strategy

Expressions

Students working cooperatively to translate verbal and numerical expressions will help them be more successful when solving word problems.

Step 1: Have students brainstorm and list all of the words and phrases they can think of that represent the four operations.

Step 2: Divide students into eight groups. Assign two groups for each of the four operations.

Step 3: Each group will write a verbal phrase with one unknown for each of the other groups. On a separate paper they can write the translations. For example, the addition groups would write the phrase "the sum of some number and 3". Each group will receive seven phrases to translate. Students can share their work with the class, particularly different or unique phrases.

Step 4: Repeat this activity by having each group write an algebraic expression for each of the other groups to translate into words. Students will write the answers on another paper. Students can write difficult or interesting expressions or translations on the board to share with the class.

Step 5: This activity can be extended by increasing the number of variables from one to two in each verbal phrase and expression. For example, the addition groups would write the phrase "some number plus another number has a sum of fifteen".

Chapter 9

Chapter Notes

Real-World Applications

Money and Games At the amusement center, Jimmy had only a 10-dollar bill in his pocket when he located his favorite golf arcade game. For every three holes, it cost $0.25 to play. If he used the expression *4d* to find the number of quarters he could exchange his 10-dollar bill for, how many quarters would he receive? He could exchange $10 for 40 quarters.

Intervention Strategy

Coins and Bills

Step 1 Divide students into groups of four.

Step 2 Tell students to pretend they just received a 5-dollar bill. The 5-dollar bills will need to be exchanged for 4 sets of coins—only quarters, only dimes, only nickels, or only pennies.

Step 3 Each group should write and solve an expression describing all four situations.

Step 4 Students should present their findings to the class and compare expressions, variables, and solutions.

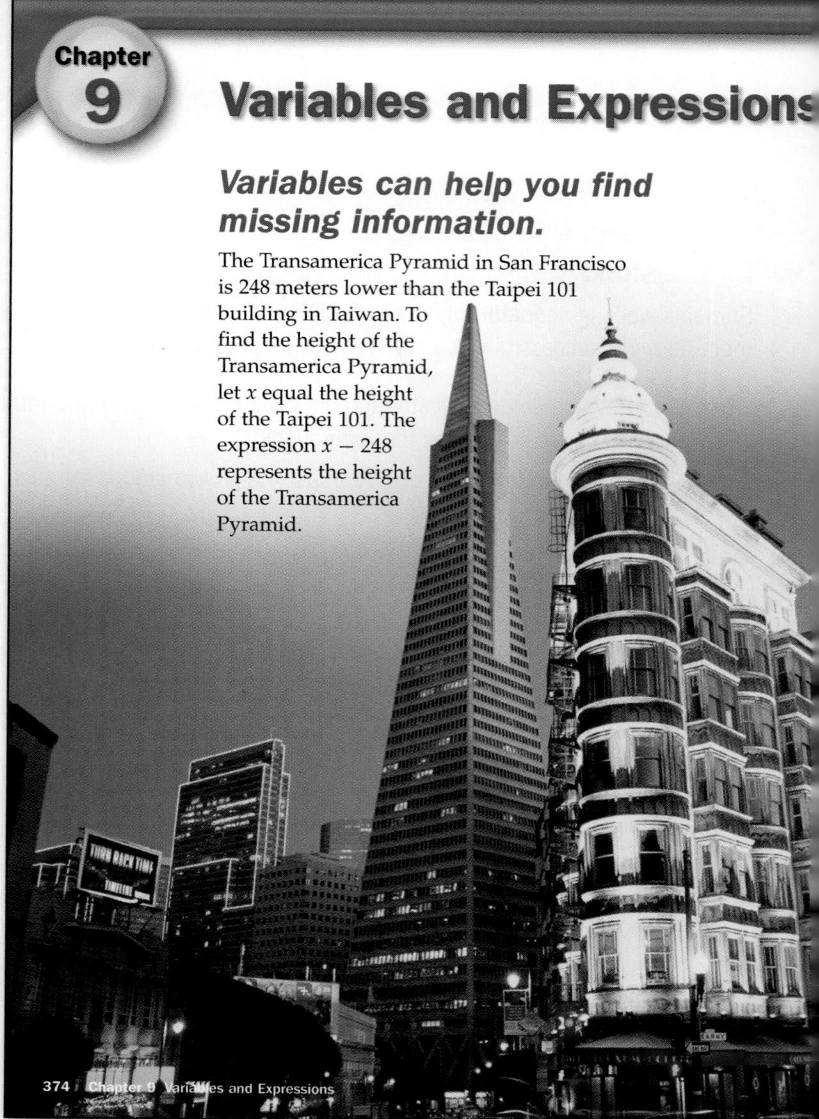

Chapter 9
Variables and Expressions
Variables can help you find missing information.
The Transamerica Pyramid in San Francisco is 248 meters lower than the Taipei 101 building in Taiwan. To find the height of the Transamerica Pyramid, let x equal the height of the Taipei 101. The expression $x - 248$ represents the height of the Transamerica Pyramid.
374 Chapter 9 Variables and Expressions

Key Vocabulary

Find interactive definitions in 13 languages in the **eGlossary** at glencoe.com.

English **Espanol** *Introduce the most important vocabulary terms from Chapter 9.*

algebraic expression **expresión algebraica**
a combination of variables, numbers, and at least one operation (p. 376)

coefficient **coeficiente**
the numerical factor of a term that contains a variable (p. 376)

constant **constante**
a value that does not change (p. 376)

like terms **términos semejantes**
terms that contain the same variables (p. 392)

term **término**
each of the quantities connected by plus or minus signs in an algebraic expression (p. 376)

variable **variable**
a symbol, usually a letter, used to represent a number (p. 376)

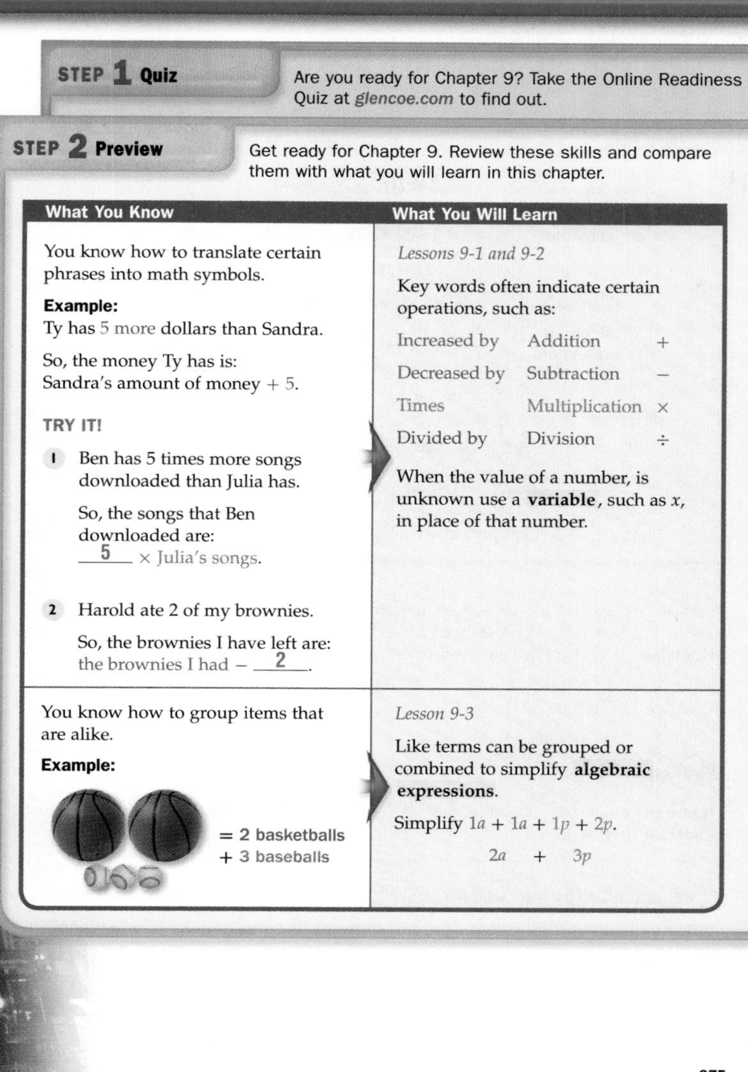

STEP 1 Quiz

Are you ready for Chapter 9? Take the Online Readiness Quiz at *glencoe.com* to find out.

STEP 2 Preview

Get ready for Chapter 9. Review these skills and compare them with what you will learn in this chapter.

What You Know	What You Will Learn
You know how to translate certain phrases into math symbols. **Example:** Ty has 5 more dollars than Sandra. So, the money Ty has is: Sandra's amount of money + 5. **TRY IT!** 1 Ben has 5 times more songs downloaded than Julia has. So, the songs that Ben downloaded are: __5__ × Julia's songs. 2 Harold ate 2 of my brownies. So, the brownies I have left are: the brownies I had − __2__.	*Lessons 9-1 and 9-2* Key words often indicate certain operations, such as: Increased by — Addition — + Decreased by — Subtraction — − Times — Multiplication — × Divided by — Division — ÷ When the value of a number, is unknown use a **variable**, such as x, in place of that number.
You know how to group items that are alike. **Example:** = 2 basketballs + 3 baseballs	*Lesson 9-3* Like terms can be grouped or combined to simplify **algebraic expressions**. Simplify $1a + 1a + 1p + 2p$. $2a + 3p$

375

Step 1 Quiz

Pretest/Prescribe Students can take the Online Readiness Quiz or the Diagnostic Pretest in the Assessment Masters.

Step 2 Preview

Use this pre-chapter activity to activate students' prior knowledge, build confidence, and help students preview the lessons.

Dinah Zike's Foldables®

Guide students through the directions on p. A185 in the Chapter Resource Masters to create their own Foldable graphic organizer for use with this chapter.

Home Connections

- Ask students to find situations in their homes that would use $3x$, $6x$, and $10x$ in expressions. For example, $12x$ could be used to represent the number of eggs contained in any number of egg cartons.

Vocabulary Preview

- As students complete the Chapter Preview, have them make a list of important terms throughout the chapter.
- Have students use the list of vocabulary words along with any additional unfamiliar and/or important words throughout the chapter. Using index cards, have students write a vocabulary term on one side of each card. On the opposite side, students should write 3–5 synonyms or antonyms for the term. Be sure to identify on the card if they are synonyms or antonyms.
- Once students are finished, pair them so they may trade cards and challenge each other to identify the terms being described.

Mc Graw Hill Professional Development

Targeted professional development has been articulated throughout **McGraw-Hill's *Math Triumphs*** intervention program. **The McGraw-Hill Professional Development Video Library** provides short videos that support the **NCTM Focal Points and Focal Connections**. For more information, visit glencoe.com.

Lesson 9-1

Lesson Notes

Lesson Planner

Objective Use variables to write expressions.

Vocabulary **algebraic expression**, **coefficient**, **constant**, **term**, **variable**

Materials/Manipulatives algebra tiles, colored pencils, construction paper

Chapter Resource Masters

- CRM Vocabulary and English Language Development (p. A188)
- CRM Skills Practice (p. A189)
- CRM Problem-Solving Practice (p. A190)
- CRM Homework Practice (p. A191)

Vocabulary

Nonexamples Talk about the part of an expression that is not defined in this lesson, the operation sign. Explain that in an expression the operation sign can be an addition sign, a subtraction sign, a multiplication sign, or a division sign.

Key Concept

Foundational Skills and Concepts After students have read through the Key Concept box, have them try these exercises.

1. What separates the terms in the example expression? addition sign
2. What is another name for the addition sign? operation sign
3. What parts of the expression can be represented by a number? the constant and the coefficient

Lesson 9-1

Algebraic Expressions

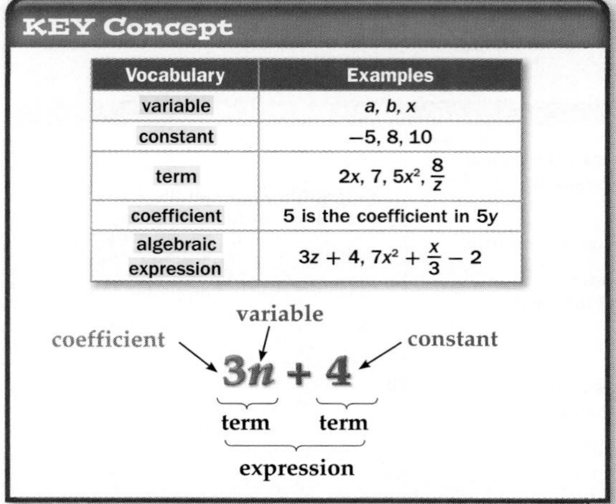
KEY Concept

Vocabulary	Examples
variable	*a*, *b*, *x*
constant	−5, 8, 10
term	$2x$, 7, $5x^2$, $\frac{8}{z}$
coefficient	5 is the coefficient in $5y$
algebraic expression	$3z + 4$, $7x^2 + \frac{x}{3} - 2$

VOCABULARY

algebraic expression a combination of variables, numbers, and at least one operation

coefficient the numerical factor of a term that contains a variable

constant a value that does not change

term each of the quantities connected by plus or minus signs in an algebraic expression

variable a symbol, usually a letter, used to represent a number

Terms are separated by + or − signs. Constants are terms that do not have a variable. A constant includes the sign that is written before it. The constant is +4 in the expression above.

Example 1

Name the coefficient, variable, and constant in $8t + 2$.

1. The coefficient is the number 8 because it is multiplied by the variable *t*.
2. The variable is the letter *t*.
3. The constant is the number 2.

YOUR TURN!

Name the coefficient, variable, and constant in $7x - 5$.

1. The coefficient is the number 7 because it is multiplied by the variable.
2. The variable is the letter *x*.
3. The constant is the number −5.

376 Chapter 9 Variables and Expressions

Additional Example 1

Name the coefficient, variable, and constant in $6 + 5x$.

1. The coefficient is the number 5 because it is multiplied by the variable *x*.
2. The variable is the letter *x*.
3. The constant is the number 6.

Example 2

Write three different algebraic expressions that have the constant term 9 and the variable *h*.

1. Write the variable with the constant term.
   $h + 9$
2. Write a coefficient before the variable.
   $3h + 9$
3. Write one more expression that has a constant term 9 and a variable *h*.
   $9 + 2h$ The order of the terms does not matter.

YOUR TURN!

Write three different algebraic expressions that have the constant term 5 and the variable *a*.

1. Write the variable with the constant term.
   Sample answer: $a + 5$
2. Write a coefficient before the variable.
   Sample answer: $6a + 5$
3. Write one more expression that has a constant term 5 and a variable *a*.
   Sample answer: $\frac{a}{3} + 5$

Who is Correct?

Write an algebraic expression that has the constant term 2, a variable *n*, and the coefficient 8.

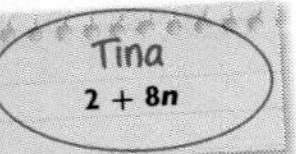

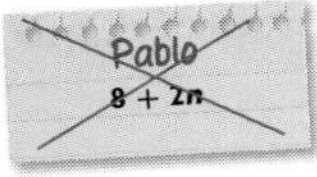

Circle correct answer(s). Cross out incorrect answer(s).

Remember that constant terms do not have a variable. Their values do not change.

Guided Practice Sample answers are given.

1. Write three different algebraic expressions that have the constant term 1 and the variable *h*.

   $h + 1$ $5h + 1$ $\frac{7}{h} + 1$

2. Write three different algebraic expressions that have the constant term 5 and the variable *a*.

   $a + 5$ $8a + 5$ $\frac{a}{9} + 5$

GO ON

Who *is Correct?*

Diagnostic Teaching

- Tina's answer is correct.
- Pablo's answer is incorrect. He wrote the constant term 8 and the coefficient 2.
- Carson's answer is correct.

Additional Example 2

Write three different algebraic expressions that have the constant term −7 and the variable *y*.

1. Write the variable with the constant term.
   $y - 7$
2. Write a coefficient before the variable.
   $3y - 7$
3. Write one more expression that has a constant term −7 and a variable *y*.
   $-7 + 2y$

Using Manipulatives

Algebra Tiles When presenting Additional Example 2, use algebra tiles to give students a visual concept of writing an expression. First, show the constant term −7 using the unit tiles with the red side up, which indicates a negative number. Next, show the variable y using the variable tile with the green side up, which indicates a positive value.

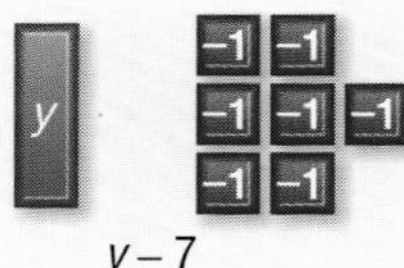

$y - 7$

On-Hand Manipulatives Cut out small different-colored squares of construction paper to place as models for expressions.

Math Coach Notes
Strategies

1. When determining expressions and identifying the parts, create a labeling code to visually identify the parts. The example below uses shapes to identify the parts. Make sure that the labeling code is understandable.

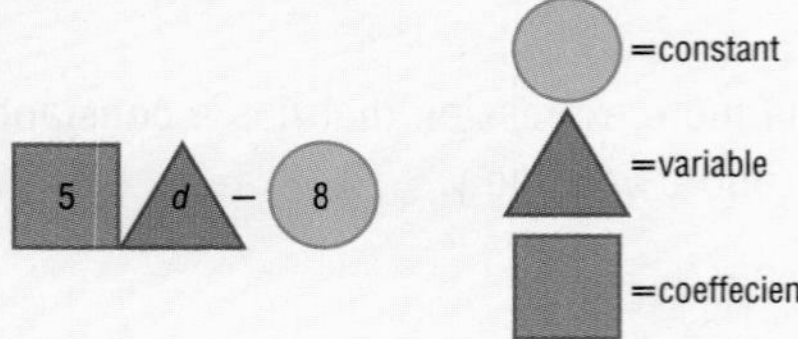

2. Write this example on the board to help students visually identify the parts of an expression. Have students create their own labeling code. Invite students to share their codes with the class so that students can pick the labels they like best and use them.

Step by Step Practice

3 Name the coefficient, variable, and constant in $-12 + k$.

Step 1 Determine the coefficient.
The coefficient is the number multiplied by the variable.
The coefficient is 1.

Step 2 Determine the variable.
The variable is the letter *k*.

Step 3 Determine the constant.
The constant is the number −12.

Name the coefficient, variable, and constant in each expression.

4 $9n + 5$
coefficient: 9
variable: *n*
constant: 5

5 $d + 12$
coefficient: 1
variable: *d*
constant: 12

6 $-2x + 9$
coefficient: −2
variable: *x*
constant: 9

7 $-6 + v$
coefficient: 1
variable: *v*
constant: −6

8 $-2 + 6n$
coefficient: 6
variable: *n*
constant: −2

9 $7x + (-7)$
coefficient: 7
variable: *x*
constant: −7

10 $3w^2 + (-5)$
coefficient: 3
variable: *w*
constant: −5

11 $4h + 9$
coefficient: 4
variable: *h*
constant: 9

378 **Chapter 9** Variables and Expressions

Are They Getting It?

Check students' understanding of expressions by writing these problems on the board. Ask students to point out the wrong answers and explain why they are wrong.

1. $8 + 3x$
variable: *x*
constant: 3
coefficient: 8
This is incorrect. The constant and the coefficient are switched.

2. $\frac{m}{5} + 12$
variable: *m*
constant: 12
coefficient: $\frac{1}{5}$
This is correct.

Step by Step Problem-Solving Practice

Problem-Solving Strategies
- ☐ Draw a diagram.
- ☐ Look for a pattern.
- ☐ Guess and check.
- ☑ Use logical reasoning.
- ☐ Solve a simpler problem.

Solve.

2 HEIGHT Doris was 42 inches tall on her birthday. She grew the next year. Write an expression for Doris's new height in inches.

Understand Read the problem. Write what you know.

Doris's height is expressed by the constant term __42__.

Plan Pick a strategy. One strategy is to use logical reasoning.

Determine the operation that should be used in the expression.

The phrase "grew" indicates __addition__.

Doris's height should be greater after one year.

Select a variable to represent the number of inches that Doris grew. __Sample answer: h__

Solve Write the expression.

__$42 + h$__

Check Does the expression make sense? Doris's height next year will be greater than the height on her birthday.

3 MONEY Percy saved $86. He spent m amount of money on comic books. Write an expression for the amount of money Percy has left.

Check off each step.

__✔__ Understand: I underlined key words.

__✔__ Plan: To solve the problem, I will __use logical reasoning__.

__✔__ Solve: The answer is __$86 - m$__.

__✔__ Check: I checked my answer by __using subtraction because Percy's savings will be less after he spent money on comic books__.

Intervention Strategy Naturalist Learners

Natural Expressions Use a picture of a tree to provide students an analogy for naming individual parts of an expression. Draw a tree on the board with roots, a trunk, and branches. Then write an expression next to it. In a class discussion, ask students to identify the object on the board. Write their response below the object. Next ask them to identify the parts of the tree as you list their responses on the board beside each part. Make a connection between the tree and the expression and between the parts of the tree and the parts of the expression.

English Learner Strategy

Prior Knowledge Use a highlighter or colored pencil to highlight, circle, or underline key words in word problems. Hold a class discussion in which you ask for volunteers to define each term and give examples.

Math Coach Notes

Study Strategies As students get sent home with more and more homework, they need to use their time as efficiently as possible. Each student needs to make a study-friendly atmosphere in a location at home to do his or her homework. The location should be quiet, have good lighting, and be used only for studying.

Symbols When students are asked to find a quantity that satisfies a number of conditions, you are introducing the students to symbols. A successful method is to let a symbol stand for the unknown quantity in the given situation. These equations can be manipulated using principles and properties to find the solution.

Common Error *Alert*

Operation Words If students are having difficulty translating word problems into numerical expressions, have them review key words that tell which operation to use. Reassure them that there can be more than one key word for every operation. Suggest that students create a comprehensive list of key words for each operation.

Odd/Even Assignments

Exercises 18–35 are structured so that students practice the same concepts whether they are assigned the odd or even problems.

In-Class Assignment

Have students complete Exercises 19, 24, 29, 33, and 40 to ensure that they understand the concept.

Solve.

14 PETS Akiko feeds her fish x teaspoons of fish food each day. Write an expression for the amount of food, in teaspoons, Akiko feeds her fish in 7 days. $7x$

EATING OUT Dustin took his friend out for lunch. He ordered the soup and salad special. His friend ordered a turkey sandwich. They both ordered regular milkshakes.

Finer Diner
Soup and Salad Special $6.00
Sandwiches (Turkey or Ham) $5.00
Milkshakes Large $4.00
Regular

15 Dustin could not read the cost of a regular milkshake. Write an expression for the total price of the meal.

Sample answers: $6 + 5 + 2m$

or $6 + 5 + m + m$

16 Write an expression for the total cost of t sandwiches and two large milkshakes.

Sample answer: $5t + 2(4)$

17  **Reflect** List key words that tell you which operation to use when writing an expression.

Answers may vary. Sample answer: *more than* means to add, *less than* means to subtract, *times* means to multiply, *divided by* means to divide

Skills, Concepts, and Problem Solving Sample answers are given.

18 Write three different expressions that have the constant term -15 and the variable d.

$-15 + d$ $-15 + 7d$ $d - 15$

19 Write three different expressions that have the constant term 6 and the variable q.

$q + 6$ $3q + 6$ $6 - q$

380 Chapter 9 Variables and Expressions

Intervention Strategy Interpersonal Learners

Cooperative Learning Arrange students into groups of four. Tell them that one person in the group will write an expression and the other three will identify the parts. Have each one of the three students pick a variable, constant, or coefficient to identify. Instruct students to rotate roles and repeat the activity until each student has participated in each role.

Name the coefficient, variable, and constant in each expression.

20 $-17 + z$

coefficient: 1

variable: z

constant: -17

21 $16p + 5$

coefficient: 16

variable: p

constant: 5

22 $3h + 7$

coefficient: 3

variable: h

constant: 7

23 $-4 + s$

coefficient: 1

variable: s

constant: -4

24 $y - 1$

coefficient: 1

variable: y

constant: -1

25 $3k + 7$

coefficient: 3

variable: k

constant: 7

26 $-b + 4$

coefficient: -1

variable: b

constant: 4

27 $12 - 7z$

coefficient: -7

variable: z

constant: 12

28 $5a^2 - 7$

coefficient: 5

variable: a

constant: -7

29 $6 + 3d^2$

coefficient: 3

variable: d

constant: 6

30 $c^2 + 9$

coefficient: 1

variable: c

constant: 9

31 $9 - x^2$

coefficient: -1

variable: x

constant: 9

GO ON

Note This!

Write the Words Suggest that students write a mathematical expression in their notes, then write the expression in words. Encourage them to use a variety of words to describe the expression. For example, instead of always using "times" for multiplication, they can use "multiplied by" or "of."

Common Error *Alert*

Negative Coefficients Review Exercises 26 and 27. Be sure students understand that the minus sign translates to a negative coefficient.

Math Challenge

Translate Expressions to Word Problems Arrange students into pairs and have one student write a number sentence that has multiple operations. Have the other student identify the parts of each expression and write a word problem that represents the number sentence created by his or her partner. Share the word problems with the class to check for understanding and correctness.

4 Assess

See It, Do It, Say It, Write It

Step 1 Write five expressions on the board. Vary the attributes of the parts.

Step 2 Have students identify the parts of each expression.

Step 3 Arrange the students in pairs and have them explain to each other how they identified the parts of each expression.

Step 4 Have one student in each pair verbally describe an expression while the other student writes the expression described. Students should verify each other's work. Repeat the activity, reversing roles.

Looking Ahead: Pre-teach

Translate Verbal Expressions In the next lesson, students will learn how to translate verbal phrases into mathematical symbols.

Example

Translate "six less than a number *m*" to an expression.

1. The phrase "less than" indicates subtraction (–).
2. The phrase "six" is represented by a constant term, 6.
3. The phrase "number" is represented by a variable, *m*.

The expression is $m - 6$.

Have students translate each phrase to an expression.

1. the sum of *a* and 5 $a + 5$
2. *x* divided by 6 $x \div 6$
3. 12 decreased by *y* $12 - y$

Solve.

32 PRODUCE Gabrielle's orange tree has 72 oranges. She gave an equal number of oranges to each of her cousins. Write an expression for the number of oranges Gabrielle gave each cousin.

Sample answers: $72 \div c$ or $\frac{72}{c}$

33 MOVIES Kendrick had 48 DVDs in his collection. He bought more DVDs. Write an expression for the total number of DVDs in Kendrick's collection.

Sample answer: $48 + d$

34 BAKING Gavin promised to bring cupcakes for Christine's party. Christine wants to have enough cupcakes so each party guest can eat two. Write an expression for the number of cupcakes Gavin must bring.

Sample answer: $2p$

35 MOVIES Esteban and Lucas (both 14 years old) are taking their younger sisters (who are under 13) to a movie. They have *x* younger sisters. Write an expression for the total cost of admission.

Sample answers: $2 \times 8 + 5x$ or $8 + 8 + 5x$

Vocabulary Check **Write the vocabulary word that completes each sentence.**

36 A(n) variable is a symbol, usually a letter, used to represent a number.

37 A(n) coefficient is the numerical factor of a term that contains a variable.

38 A value that does not change is a constant.

39 A(n) algebraic expression is a combination of variables, numbers, and at least one operation.

40 Writing in Math What is the coefficient in the expression $y + 14$? Explain.

1; The term *y* can also be written as 1*y*, due to the Identity Property of Multiplication.

STOP

382 Chapter 9 Variables and Expressions

Ticket Out the Door

Identify and Exit Have students line up at the door in single file. As each student approaches the door, have him or her identify one part of an expression including the possible operations. Continue until all students have exited the classroom.

Lesson 9-2

Translating Verbal Phrases into Mathematical Symbols

KEY Concept

You can look for certain words in problems to help you determine which operations to use. Below are the most common of these words.

Addition +	Subtraction −	Multiplication ×	Division ÷
sum	difference	product	quotient
more than	less than	times	divided by
increased by	decreased by	twice	separate into equal groups
plus	minus	double	

VOCABULARY

algebraic expression
a combination of variables, numbers, and at least one operation

coefficient
the numerical factor of a term that contains a variable

constant
a value that does not change

term
each of the quantities connected by plus or minus signs in an algebraic expression

When you need to write an expression that includes division, use a fraction. For example, write ÷ 3 as $\frac{1}{3}$.

Example 1

Translate "seven more than a number *n*" to an expression.

1. The words "more than" tell you to use addition (+).
2. The word "seven" indicates that the constant term is 7.
3. The words "a number *n*" tell you to use the variable *n*.

seven more than a number *n*
7 + *n*

The expression is $7 + n$.

YOUR TURN!

Translate "a number *x* decreased by 5" to an expression.

1. The words "decreased by" tell you to use subtraction.
2. The constant term is 5.
3. The words "a number *x*" tell you to use the variable *x*.

a number *x* decreased by 5
x − 5

The expression is $x - 5$.

GO ON

Additional Example 1

Translate "a number *h* decreased by six" to an expression.

1. The words "decreased by" tell you to use subtraction (–).
2. The word "six" indicates that the constant term is 6.
3. The words "a number h" tell you to use the variable *h*.

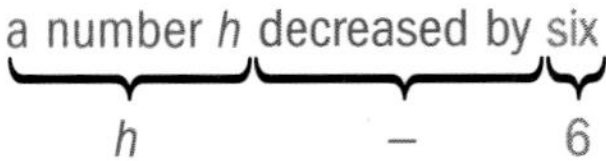

The expression is $h - 6$.

Lesson Notes

Lesson 9-2

Lesson Planner

Objective Use variables to write expressions and represent unknown quantities.

Vocabulary **algebraic expression**, **coefficient**, **constant**, **term**

Materials/Manipulatives algebra tiles, base-ten blocks, construction paper, colored markers, index cards

Chapter Resource Masters

- CRM Vocabulary and English Language Development (p. A192)
- CRM Skills Practice (p. A193)
- CRM Problem-Solving Practice (p. A194)
- CRM Homework Practice (p. A195)

Vocabulary

Access Vocabulary Because these terms are not new for this lesson, write each term on the board and have the students, in their own words, write the definition for each term. Review their definitions for errors.

2 Teach

Key Concept

Foundational Skills and Concepts After students have read through the Key Concept box, have them try these exercises.

1. Are any of the words familiar to you? Check students' work.
2. Are any of the words unfamiliar to you? Check students' work.
3. Can you add any words to the list? Check students' work.
4. Give an everyday example using two of the words/phrases in the table. Check students' work. Sample answers: I divided my time between working and studying. I am twice as old as my sister.

Additional **Example 2**

Write an expression to represent the following situation.

Kathryn has nine more games than Molly.

1. The words "more games than" tell you to use addition (+).
2. The word "nine" indicates that the constant term is 9.
3. The words "more games than Molly" tell you to use the variable g.

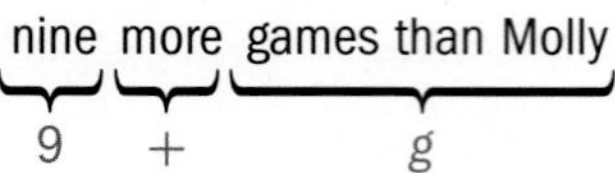

The expression is $9 + g$.

Using Manipulatives

Algebra Tiles When presenting Additional Example 2, use algebra tiles to give students a visual concept of translating verbal phrases into mathematical symbols. The algebra tiles are red on one side, which represents negative, and yellow on the other side, which represents positive.

Kathryn has nine more games than Molly.

$9 \quad + \quad g$

Base-Ten Blocks Demonstrate translating verbal phrases into mathematical symbols using base-ten blocks. Use the base-ten blocks in a similar manner as the algebra tiles.

On-Hand Manipulatives Cut out small, different-colored squares of construction paper to place as models for expressions.

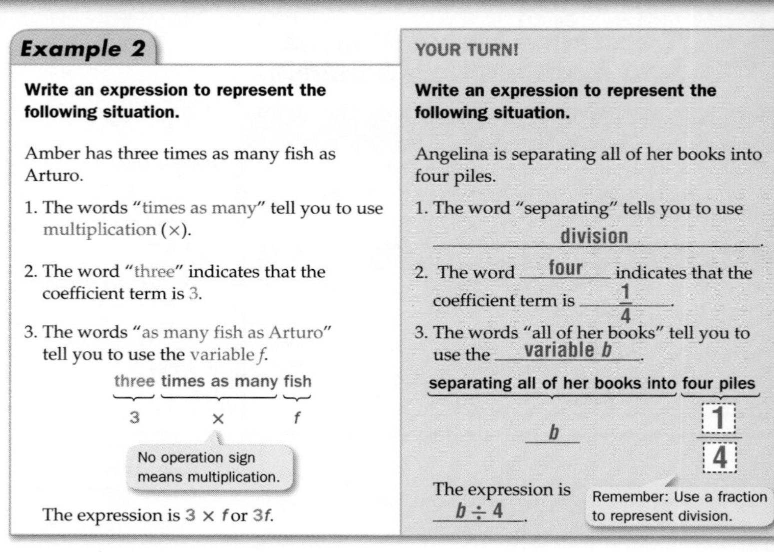

Example 2

Write an expression to represent the following situation.

Amber has three times as many fish as Arturo.

1. The words "times as many" tell you to use multiplication (×).
2. The word "three" indicates that the coefficient term is 3.
3. The words "as many fish as Arturo" tell you to use the variable f.

three times as many fish
3 × f

No operation sign means multiplication.

The expression is $3 \times f$ or $3f$.

YOUR TURN!

Write an expression to represent the following situation.

Angelina is separating all of her books into four piles.

1. The word "separating" tells you to use division.
2. The word four indicates that the coefficient term is $\frac{1}{4}$.
3. The words "all of her books" tell you to use the variable b.

separating all of her books into four piles

b $\frac{1}{4}$

The expression is $b \div 4$.

Remember: Use a fraction to represent division.

Who is Correct?

Translate "a number minus four" to an expression.

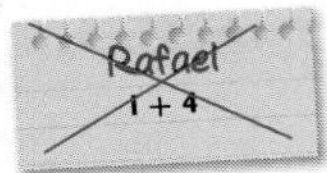

Circle correct answer(s). Cross out incorrect answer(s).

Guided Practice

For each phrase, name the operation.

1. n decreased by 13 subtraction
2. the sum of a and 8 addition
3. 8 divided by w division
4. twice the amount of y multiplication

384 **Chapter 9** Variables and Expressions

Who *is Correct?*

Diagnostic Teaching

- Mitchell's answer is incorrect. His expression means "four minus a number."
- Rafael's answer is incorrect. He added 1 and 4.
- Natasha's answer is correct.

Remind students to look for key words that indicate operations when translating phrases.

or each phrase, name the operation.

7 more than x

addition

6 the quotient of s and 9

division

ranslate each phrase to an expression.

five times a number

operation: multiplication

constant term: none

coefficient: 5

variable: n

five times a number

$5 \quad \times \quad n$

expression: $5 \times n$ or $5n$

8 twenty more than a number

operation: addition

constant term: 20

coefficient: 1

variable: n

twenty more than a number

$20 \quad + \quad n$

expression: $n + 20$ or $20 + n$

eleven less than 3 times a number

operations: subtraction, multiplication

variable: n

expression: $3n - 11$

10 two times the sum of a number and 15

operations: multiplication, addition

variable: n

expression: $2(n + 15)$

6 divided by a number

$6 \div n$ or $\frac{6}{n}$

12 a number divided by 10

$n \div 10$ or $\frac{n}{10}$

3 four less than 2 times a number

$2n - 4$

14 three times the sum of x and 10

$3(x + 10)$

5 six times the quotient of y and 7

$6 \times \frac{y}{7}$ or $6(y \div 7)$

16 the sum of 12 divided by a number and 8

$\frac{12}{n} + 8$ or $(12 \div n) + 8$

GO ON

Are They Getting It?

Check students' understanding of translating verbal phrases into symbols by writing these problems on the board. Ask students to point out the wrong answers and explain why they are wrong.

1. seven times a number
   operation(s): multiplication
   variable: n
   expression: $7 \times n$

   This is correct.

2. a number divided by ten
   operation(s): division
   variable: n
   expression: $10 \div n$

   This is incorrect. You cannot switch the order of the numbers when dividing.

Math Coach Notes

Strategies

1. When translating verbal phrases into mathematical symbols, create a labeling code to visually identify the parts that need to be translated. Use the example below to color code the parts to translate. Make sure that your labeling code is understandable.

   nine less than four times a number

   operation = blue
   constant term = red
   coefficient = green
   variable = orange

   nine less than four times a number

2. Write this example on the board to help students visually identify the parts of an expression. Have students create their own verbal phrases to translate.

Common Error *Alert*

Re-Wording Phrases If students are having difficulty translating verbal phrases to mathematical symbols, give them a phrase and let them reword it in their own words. Then write the phrase in mathematical symbols. Have them compare their own word phrases with other students' phrases. You must caution students that their reworded phrases cannot change the meaning of the original phrase.

Note This!

Study Strategies Encourage students to rewrite the verbal phrase on their paper for editing. Under the verbal translation, write the translated mathematical expression so that the translated symbol is directly below its verbal equivalent. The expression will originally be very spaced out. After the translation, rewrite the expression using normal spacing between the parts.

Math Coach Notes

Symbols When students are translating verbal phrases into mathematical expressions, a symbol or variable is used to represent a number. Instruct the students that the symbol or variable represents a number and therefore can be added, subtracted, multiplied, or divided.

Step by Step Practice

Write an expression to represent the following situation.

17 Latitia has four fewer magazines than Arleta.

Step 1 The word "fewer" tells you to use subtraction.

Step 2 The word "four" indicates that the constant term is 4.

Step 3 The words "fewer magazines" tell you to use m for the variable.

Step 4 Write the expression. $m - 4$

Write an expression to represent each situation.

18 Charlotte separated her postcards into 3 equal stacks.

Which word(s) tell you the operation to use?
separated into equal stacks

operation: division

variable: Sample answer: p

expression: $p \div 3$

19 Joe's puppy weighed 3 pounds more than it did last month.
$p + 3$

20 The blueberry muffin has twice as many Calories as the bran muffin.
$2c$

21 Angelina has 5 times as many songs on her MP3 player as Tom.
$5s$

22 Each box contains the same number of bagels.

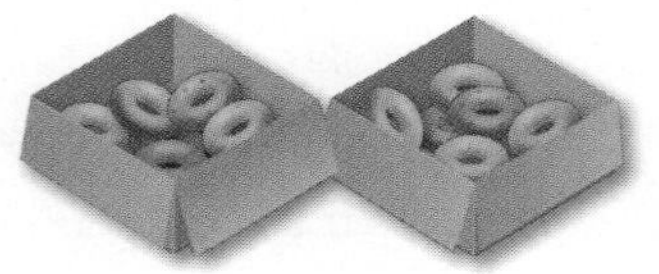

This is the total number of bagels. $2b$

Intervention Strategy Linguistic Learners

Write Stories Arrange the students into pairs. Instruct them to write a story using the operational words found in the Key Concept box at the beginning of the lesson. Make sure students know the story should meet all the criteria required by their language-arts teacher for an assignment. Have the students volunteer to read their story to the class.

Step by Step Problem-Solving Practice

Solve.

3 GEOMETRY The perimeter of a triangle is the sum of the lengths of its sides. One side length is 12 feet. Another side length is 9 feet. Write an expression for the perimeter of the triangle.

Problem-Solving Strategies
- ☑ Draw a diagram.
- ☐ Look for a pattern.
- ☐ Guess and check.
- ☐ Solve a simpler problem.
- ☐ Work backward.

Understand Read the problem. Write what you know.

The perimeter of a triangle is the __sum__ of the lengths of __3__ sides.

One side is __12__ feet.

One side is __9__ feet.

One side is __unknown__.

Plan Pick a strategy. One strategy is to draw a diagram.

Sketch the triangle. Choose a variable for the length of the unknown side.

The operation to use is __addition__.

12 x 9

Solve Write the expression for the perimeter.

__$12 + 9 + x$ or $21 + x$__

Check Does the expression make sense? The perimeter of the triangle should be greater than the length of the two known sides combined.

4 FITNESS Alberto runs 4 miles each day. Write an expression for the number of miles Alberto runs in d days.
Check off each step.

✓ Understand: I underlined key words.

✓ Plan: To solve the problem, I will __draw a diagram__.

✓ Solve: The answer is __$4d$__.

✓ Check: I checked my answer by __making sure the number of miles is 4 times the variable__.

GO ON

Intervention Strategy Visual Learners

Use Diagrams Help students determine if they are visual learners. A visual learner is one who would be more likely to look at a picture to figure out how to assemble a bicycle than to read the step-by-step instructions. When students are deciding which problem-solving strategy to use, encourage the visual learners to draw a diagram. This will allow the students to assign each useable part of the word problem to the diagram. Have the students compare diagrams from the same problem to check for differences and similarities.

English Learner Stragegy

Vocabulary Sentences Have students write a one-sentence summary that explains either the definition of a term used in this section or how to translate verbal phrases to math expressions. Have students read the sentence aloud and explain it to you as needed so that you can ensure that they understand the concept accurately.

Common Error *Alert*

Check Your Answer If students are solving a word problem using the step-by-step strategy and they frequently leave out the final step, explain that this step is important for two reasons. The first is to make sure the answer is correct. The second is to help the students' number sense in how they check for correctness.

Note This!

Use Color The use of color can enhance a student's retention of material. Offer students colored markers to use to make a list of commonly used words for operations. Next to each word, have students write whether the word implies addition, subtraction, multiplication, or division. All words that relate to addition, including the word *addition,* should be one color. Choose different colors for the other three operations.

Odd/Even Assignments

Exercises 28–61 are structured so that students practice the same concepts whether they are assigned the odd or even problems.

In-Class Assignment

Have students complete Exercises 28, 33, 39, 45, 48, 55, 58, and 64 to ensure that they understand the concept.

25 SAFETY Paquito's dad is taking Paquito and his friends on a hot-air balloon ride. The weight limit is 900 pounds. Paquito's dad weighs 250 pounds. Paquito weighs 74 pounds. Jim weighs 87 pounds. Larisa weighs b pounds. Write an expression for their combined weights in pounds. $250 + 74 + 87 + b$

26 FAMILY Paul is 23 years younger than his mother. Write an expression for Paul's age. $a - 23$

27 **Reflect** Do the expressions $5 - r$ and $r - 5$ have the same value? Explain and give an example.

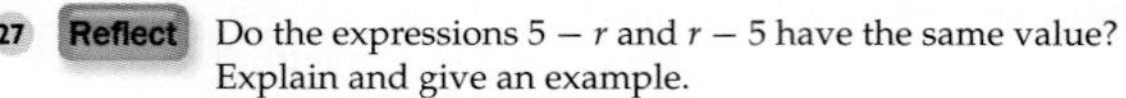

No; the order in which you subtract affects the answer. The Commutative Property does not hold true for subtraction. Let $r = 1$. $5 - 1 = 4$ and $1 - 5 = -4$

Skills, Concepts, and Problem Solving

For each phrase, name the operation.

28 the product of h and 9
multiplication

29 the quotient of e and 5
division

30 a number minus 6
subtraction

31 a number plus 10
addition

32 13 less than a number
subtraction

33 the sum of a number and 7
addition

34 24 split into 3 equal groups
division

35 4 groups of 5 each
multiplication

Translate each phrase to an expression.

36 45 | minus | x
45 | $-$ | x
expression: $45 - x$

37 a number | plus | 61
n | $+$ | 61
expression: $n + 61$

38 14 | groups of | a number
14 | $\times$ | n
expression: $14 \times n$ or $14n$

39 b | divided by | 7
b | $\div$ | 7
expression: $b \div 7$ or $\frac{b}{7}$

Math Challenge

Hear and Write Another way for students to translate phrases is to listen to a word problem as it is read aloud. Arrange students into pairs and have them write a word problem that can be translated into an expression. Have each pair read their problem to another pair. The other pair should write and solve the problem. Tell students that they may need to read the problem a few times for understanding and clarity. Rotate pairs so that each pair gets to read and solve the word problems. Allow students who struggle with auditory learning to write down the problem as it is read aloud.

Translate each phrase to an expression.

40 7 divided by a number n

$7 \div n$ or $\frac{7}{n}$

41 2 times c

$2 \times c$ or $2c$

42 3 less than m

$m - 3$

43 e increased by 32

$e + 32$

44 the quotient of 9 and y

$9 \div y$ or $\frac{9}{y}$

45 12 decreased by w

$12 - w$

46 the sum of w and 50

$w + 50$

47 20 groups of x each

$20x$

48 14 more than h

$14 + h$

49 the quotient of 36 and x

$36 \div x$ or $\frac{36}{x}$

50 n less than 45

$45 - n$

51 62 plus a number

$62 + n$

Write an expression to represent each situation.

52 FOOD A party-sized sandwich feeds 18 students. Write an expression for the number of sandwiches needed for s students.

$s \div 18$ or $\frac{s}{18}$

53 ANIMALS Read the photo caption to the right. Write an expression for the speed of the antelope.

$c - 9$

ANIMALS A cheetah can run 9 miles per hour faster than an antelope.

54 GAMES Sabrina scored 63 points fewer than Ayana playing a board game. Ayana scored p points. Write an expression for the number of points Sabrina scored.

$p - 63$

55 MONEY Xavier has \$18, Nela has \$24, and Joan has d dollars. Write an expression for the sum of money Xavier, Nela, and Joan have altogether.

$18 + 24 + d$

GO ON

Intervention Strategy

Linguistic/Intrapersonal Learners

Shuffled Expressions Using index cards, have students write a verbal phrase for one part of an expression on one side of the card and its equivalent mathematical symbol on the reverse side. Collect the cards and shuffle them. In front of the class, select four to five cards to construct a verbal phrase. Students can translate this phrase to math symbols. Turn the cards over so that students can verify their written expressions. As a class, discuss any discrepancies between the cards and the class members' answers.

Math Coach Notes

Use Properties When students are translating verbal phrases to mathematical symbols, instruct them to refer to the Associative and Commutative Properties of Addition and Multiplication. Remind them that the order of the terms does matter when subtracting and dividing.

Note This!

Vocabulary Check When students are asked to answer a vocabulary-check section, they should try to answer each problem from memory. The vocabulary words that they could not answer should be highlighted in their notes from the beginning of the lesson and referred to when doing homework and studying for tests.

Common Error *Alert*

Less Than If the phrase *less than* is confusing to students, then point out that this phrase indicates that you must change the order the symbols are written to the reverse of how the words are presented.

Ten less than fifty.

50 − 10

See It, Do It, Say It, Write It

Step 1 Hand out a sheet of word problems to each student. As a class, read through the problems and have students highlight or underline key words that indicate the operation for each problem.

Step 2 On their own, have students translate the word problems into math expressions.

Step 3 Invite students to explain to the class how they identified the parts of each word problem that helped them translate it into an expression.

Step 4 Have students write verbal phrases in their math journals and then translate them into math symbols. Students should also work backward and write a math expression using symbols and then translate it into a word phrase.

Looking Ahead: Pre-teach

Simplify Expressions In the next lesson, students will learn how to write math expressions in simplest form.

Example

Simplify $8 + 10p + 13 + 4p + 6$.

1. Name the like terms.
   Constant terms: 8, 13, 6
   p terms: $10p$ and $4p$
2. Rearrange to group the constant terms and the p terms together.
   $8 + 10p + 13 + 4p + 6 = 8 + 13 + 6 + 10p + 4p$
3. Add the like terms.
   $= (8 + 13 + 6) + 10p + 4p$
   Add the constants.
   $= 27 + (10p + 4p)$
   Add the variables.
   $= 27 + 14p$

Have students name the like terms in each expression.

1. $15 - 5r + 7r + 8$ 15 and 8, $-5r$ and $7r$
2. $3b + 11 - 2b + 14$ $3b$ and $-2b$, 11 and 14
3. $7h + 2h^2 - 18 - 4h + 12$ $7h$ and $-4h$, $2h^2$, -18 and 12

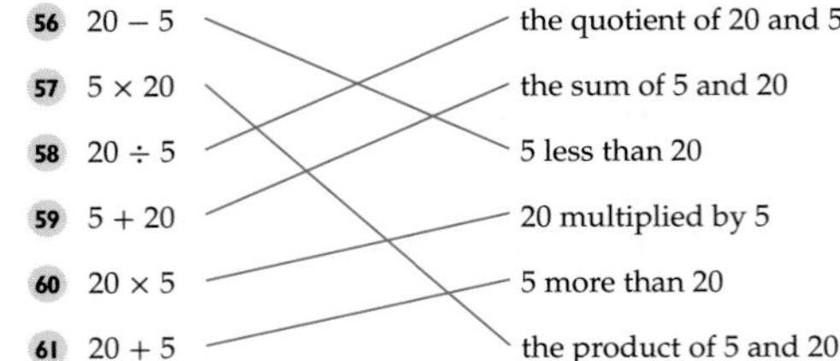

In Exercises 56–61, match the expressions on the left with the phrases on the right.

56 $20 - 5$	the quotient of 20 and 5
57 5×20	the sum of 5 and 20
58 $20 \div 5$	5 less than 20
59 $5 + 20$	20 multiplied by 5
60 20×5	5 more than 20
61 $20 + 5$	the product of 5 and 20

Vocabulary Check **Write the vocabulary word that completes each sentence.**

62 The quantities connected by a plus or minus sign in an algebraic expresion are called ___terms___.

63 A combination of numbers, ___variables___, and at least one operation is called an algebraic expression.

64 **Writing in Math** How do you know when to use a variable when writing an expression?

Answers will vary. Sample answer: Use a variable when one of the terms can have different values (or the value is unknown).

Spiral Review (Lesson 9-1, p. 376)

Name the coefficient, variable, and constant in each expression.

65 $14 + z$
coefficient: 1
variable: z
constant: 14

66 $2x + 25$
coefficient: 2
variable: x
constant: 25

Solve.

67 COLLECTOR CARDS Damon has 18 collector cards. He gave an equal number of cards to his three friends. Write an expression for the number of cards Damon gave each friend.

Sample answer: $18 \div c$ or $\frac{18}{c}$

390 Chapter 9 Variables and Expressions

Ticket Out the Door

One Word Have students line up at the door in single file. As each student approaches the door, name an operation. The student must give you one word that translates to that operation.

Chapter 9

Progress Check 1 (Lessons 9-1 and 9-2)

1 Write three different expressions that have the constant term 7 and the variable f.

Answers will vary. Sample answer: $f + 7$, $2f + 7$, $\frac{f}{8} + 7$, $7 - f$.

or each phrase, name the operation.

2 the sum of 4 and y addition

3 5 times p multiplication

ame the coefficient, variable, and constant in each expression.

4 $w - 8$

coefficient: 1

variable: w

constant: -8

5 $8k + 6$

coefficient: 8

variable: k

constant: 6

ranslate each phrase to an expression.

6 a number n divided by 9

$n \div 9$ or $\frac{n}{9}$

7 13 less than h

$h - 13$

rite an expression to represent each situation.

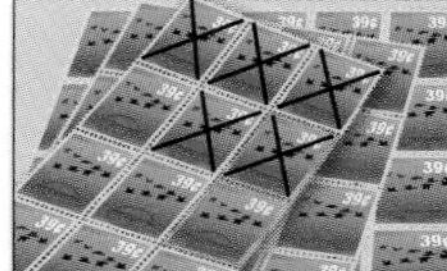

8 Trish has 6 times as many pencils as Betty. $6p$

9 Monica has 5 fewer stamps than Sasha. $s - 5$

olve.

0 **BUSINESS** Sherita made 47 glasses of lemonade. She sold x glasses of lemonade. Write an expression to represent how many glasses of lemonade Sherita has left.

$47 - x$

1 **CRAFTS** Gigi made 28 bracelets. She separated the bracelets into p piles. Write an expression to represent the number of bracelets in each pile.

$28 \div p$ or $\frac{28}{p}$

Progress Check 1

Chapter 9

Formative Assessment

Use the Progress Check to assess students' mastery of the previous lessons. Have students review the lesson indicated for the problems they answered incorrectly.

Odd/Even Assignments

Exercises are structured so that students practice the same concepts whether they are assigned the odd or even problems.

Common Error Alert

Create a Chart If students are having difficulties translating word phrases into expressions, then have them remake a chart of words associated with various operations.

Exercise 4 Students may write the coefficient as 0 or none. They should rewrite the expression as $1w - 8$ to see that the coefficient is 1.

Exercise 9 Students may get distracted by the image of the stamps. The number of sheets of stamps is unknown and is therefore the variable in the expression.

Data-Driven Decision Making

Students missing Exercises . . .	Have trouble with . . .	Should review and practice . . .
1	writing an expression.	SSG Lesson 9-1, p. 376 CRM Skills Practice, p. A189
2-3	identifying an operation from a word phrase.	SSG Lesson 9-2, p. 383 CRM Skills Practice, p. A193
4-5	identifying the variable, constant, and coefficient.	SSG Lesson 9-1, p. 376 CRM Skills Practice, p. A189
6-9	translating a word phrase into an expression.	SSG Lesson 9-2, p. 383 CRM Skills Practice, p. A193
10-11	writing an expression given a word problem.	CRM Problem-Solving Practice, pp. A190 and A194

Lesson 9-3

Lesson Notes

Lesson Planner

Objective Simplify algebraic expressions.

Vocabulary **like terms**, **simplify**, **term**

Materials/Manipulatives algebra tiles, base-ten blocks, colored pencils, construction paper, bingo chips, highlighters

Chapter Resource Masters

- CRM Vocabulary and English Language Development (p. A196)
- CRM Skills Practice (p. A197)
- CRM Problem-Solving Practice (p. A198)
- CRM Homework Practice (p. A199)

1 Introduce

Vocabulary

Access Vocabulary Have students recall the definition for the word *term*. Write the words *like terms* and *simplify* on the board and ask students to volunteer to explain the meanings in their own words. Compare students' definitions as a class until a definition can be agreed upon. Have the students compare the class definition with the definition found in the text.

2 Teach

Key Concept

Foundational Skills and Concepts After students have read through the Key Concept box, have them try these exercises.

1. What does the word *combine* mean to you? Check students' work.
2. Does there have to be a *variable* or *exponent* to be like terms? Possible answer: No; constants are like terms.
3. If the bases of the exponents are different, can you combine the terms? no

Lesson 9-3

Simplify Expressions

KEY Concept

Recall that **terms** can be a number, a variable, or a combination of numbers and variables. Terms can be positive or negative, and they can have exponents.

Examples of Like Terms	Why They Are Like Terms
6 and 13	They are both constants.
x and $3x$	Both contain the variable x and the exponent 1. (Remember that when no exponent is shown, it is really a 1.)
$2x^2$ and $5x^2$	Both contain the variable x and the exponent 2.

Like terms can be combined, or **simplified**.

$x + 3x = 1x + 3x$ *Add the coefficients of terms with like variables: $1 + 3 = 4$.*

$= 4x$

Unlike terms cannot be combined. For example, in $2y + 4x$ the terms cannot be combined because the variables are different.

VOCABULARY

like terms
terms that contain the same variables

simplify
to combine like terms

term
each of the quantities connected by plus or minus signs in an algebraic expression

When grouping and simplifying like terms, use the Associative and Commutative Properties of Addition and the Distributive Property of Multiplication.

Example 1

Simplify $3x + 2y + 2x$ by using a model.

1. Let ♥ represent x and ☆ represent y.
2. Draw a model to represent the expression.

♥♥♥ + ☆☆ + ♥♥
$3x$ $2y$ $2x$
= ♥♥♥♥♥ + ☆☆
$5x$ $2y$

3. Write the result. $3x + 2y + 2x = 5x + 2y$

YOUR TURN!

Simplify $c + 3t + 2c$ by using a model.

1. Let ● represent c and ▲ represent t.
2. Draw a model to represent the expression.

○ + △△△ + ○○
c + $3t$ + $2c$

3. Write the result. $3c + 3t$

392 Chapter 9 Variables and Expressions

Additional Example 1

Simplify $4m + 2b + m$ by using a model.

1. Let ☺ represent m and ☾ represent b.
2. Draw a model to represent the expression.

☺☺☺☺ + ☾☾ + ☺ = ☺☺☺☺☺ + ☾☾
$4m + 2b + m = 5m + 2b$

3. Write the result.
$4m + 2b + m = 5m + 2b$

Example 2

Simplify $2r^2 + 9r + 13 + 17r + 5r^2$.

1. Name the like terms.
   r^2 terms: $2r^2$ and $5r^2$
   r terms: $9r$ and $17r$
   Constant terms: 13
2. Rearrange to group the like terms together.
   $2r^2 + 9r + 13 + 17r + 5r^2$
   $= 2r^2 + 5r^2 + 9r + 17r + 13$ — Use the Commutative and Associative Properties.
3. Combine all like terms.
   $= (2r^2 + 5r^2) + 9r + 17r + 13$ — Add the r^2 terms.
   $= 7r^2 + (9r + 17r) + 13$ — Add the r terms.
   $= 7r^2 + 26r + 13$

YOUR TURN!

Simplify $13p + 9p^2 - 5p + 7 - 3p^2$.

1. Name the like terms.
   p^2 terms: $9p^2$ and $-3p^2$
   p terms: $13p$ and $-5p$
   constant terms: 7
2. Rearrange to group the terms together.
   $13p + 9p^2 - 5p + 7 - 3p^2$
   $= 9p^2 - 3p^2 + 13p - 5p + 7$
3. Combine all like terms.
   $= (9p^2 - 3p^2) + 13p - 5p + 7$
   $= 6p^2 + (13p - 5p) + 7$
   $= 6p^2 + 8p + 7$

Who is Correct?

Simplify $14u^2 + 6 + 19u + 4 - 3u^2 - 8u$.

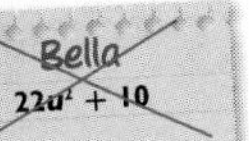

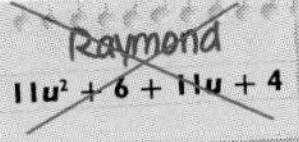

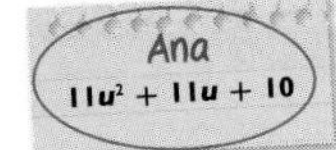

Circle correct answer(s). Cross out incorrect answer(s).

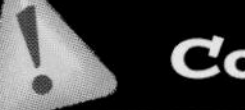

Additional Example 2

Simplify $7h + 8 + 3h + 4 + h$.

1. Name the like terms.
   h terms: $7h$, $3h$, h
   Constant terms: 8, 4
2. Rearrange to group the terms together.
   $7h + 8 + 3h + 4 + h$
   $= (7h + 3h + h) + 8 + 4$
3. Combine all like terms.
   $= 11h + (8 + 4)$
   $= 11h + 12$

Common Error *Alert*

Like Terms If students are having trouble placing the like terms together when simplifying expressions, remind them to use the Commutative Property to switch the order of the terms so that like terms are together. Remind students that the Commutative Property is for addition and multiplication only, not subtraction and division.

Who *is Correct?*

Diagnostic Teaching

- Bella's answer is incorrect. She combined the u terms with the u^2 terms. Those terms are *unlike terms.*
- Raymond's answer is incorrect. He combined the variable terms correctly, but did not combine the constant terms.
- Ana's answer is correct.

Remind students that terms with exponents can be combined only if both the base and the exponent are the same.

3 Practice

Using Manipulatives

Algebra Tiles When presenting Additional Example 2, use algebra tiles to give students a visual concept of combining like terms and simplifying expressions.

$$7h + 8 + 3h + 4 + h$$

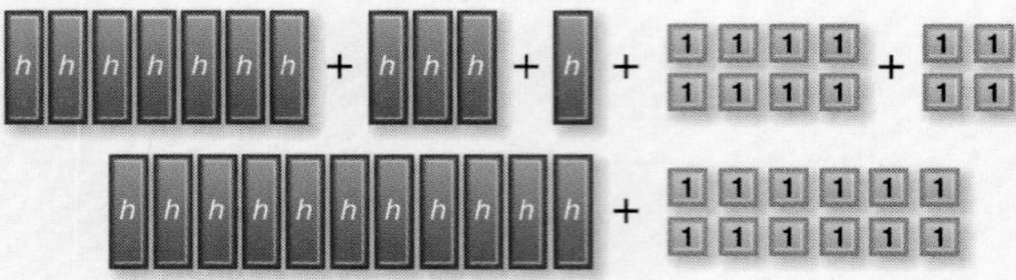

Base-Ten Blocks Demonstrate combining like terms and simplifying expressions using base-ten blocks. Use the base-ten blocks in a similar manner as the algebra tiles.

On-Hand Manipulatives Use colored bingo chips or squares cut out from construction paper as algebra tiles.

Math Coach Notes

Strategies

1. When students are simplifying an expression, emphasize that mistakes are usually made when steps are skipped. Showing every step reduces mistakes and allows a mistake to be found easier.
2. Write an example on the board and show students how to simplify an expression using steps.

Guided Practice

Name the like terms in each expression.

1. $5t - 8 + 6t + 10$
   - $5t$ and $6t$
   - -8 and 10
2. $9 - c + 4 + 7c$
   - $-c$ and $7c$
   - 9 and 4
3. $3d^2 + 12 - d + 7d^2 - 8 + 4d$
   - $3d^2$ and $7d^2$
   - $-d$ and $4d$
   - 12 and -8
4. $-6n - 2n^2 + n + 5 + 8n^2 - 3$
   - $-2n^2$ and $8n^2$
   - $-6n$ and n
   - 5 and -3

Step by Step Practice

5. Simplify $23 + 6u^2 + 18u - 2 + 5u^2 - 9u$.

Step 1 Group the like terms together.

$23 + 6u^2 + 18u - 2 + 5u^2 - 9u$

$= \underline{6u^2 + 5u^2 + 18u - 9u + 23 - 2}$

Step 2 Combine the u^2 terms.

$= \underline{6u^2} + \underline{5u^2} + 18u - 9u + 23 - 2$

$= \underline{11u^2} + 18u - 9u + 23 - 2$

Step 3 Combine the u terms.

$= 11u^2 + \underline{18u} - \underline{9u} + 23 - 2$

$= 11u^2 + \underline{9u} + 23 - 2$

Step 4 Combine the constant terms.

$= 11u^2 + 9u + \underline{23} - \underline{2}$

$= 11u^2 + 9u + \underline{21}$

The simplified expression is $\underline{11u^2 + 9u + 21}$.

394 **Chapter 9** Variables and Expressions

Are They Getting It?

Check students' understanding of simplifying expressions by writing these problems on the board. Ask students to point out the wrong answers and explain why they are wrong.

Name the like terms in each expression.

1. $3b - 4 + b - 6$
   - $3b$ and b
   - 4 and 6

   This is incorrect. The constants are negative.
2. $5 - 4r + 10 + 6r$
   - $-4r$ and $6r$
   - 5 and 10

   This is correct.
3. $4d^2 - 7 + 4d + 8 + d - 6d^2$
   - $4d^2$ and $-6d^2$
   - $4d$
   - -7 and 8

   This is incorrect. The term d can be combined with $4d$, $1d + 4d = 5d$

Simplify each expression by using a model.

6 $7m + 5a + 3m$

Let ♥ represent m and ▲ represent a.

♥♥♥♥♥♥♥ + ▲▲▲▲▲ + ♥♥♥ =
♥♥♥♥♥♥♥♥♥♥ + ▲▲▲▲▲

So, $7m + 5a + 3m = 10m + 5a$.

7 $4b + 6r - 3r$

Let ● represent b and ☆ represent r.

●●●● + ★★★★★★ − ★★★ =
●●●● + ★★★

So, $4b + 6r - 3r = 4b + 3r$.

Simplify each expression. Show your work.

8 $7p + 6 - 2p + 5$

$7p - 2p + 6 + 5$

$= (\underline{7p} - \underline{2p}) + 6 + 5$ Combine the p terms.

$= \underline{5p} + 6 + 5$

$= \underline{5p} + (\underline{6} + \underline{5})$ Combine the constant terms.

$= \underline{5p} + \underline{11}$

9 $25 + 5x - 15 + 12x$

$5x + 12x + 25 - 15$

$= (\underline{5x} + \underline{12x}) + 25 - 15$

$= \underline{17x} + 25 - 15$

$= \underline{17x} + (\underline{25} - \underline{15})$

$= \underline{17x} + \underline{10}$

10 $13 + 12k - 2k^2 - 6k + 5k^2 + 28$

$\underline{3k^2 + 6k + 41}$

11 $8a - 5 + 6a^2 - 7a + 10 - 4a^2$

$\underline{2a^2 + a + 5}$

12 $3y - 5y^2 + 10 + 12y^2 - 6y + 9$

$\underline{7y^2 - 3y + 19}$

13 $12 + b^2 + 5b - 4 - 4b^2 - 8b$

$\underline{-3b^2 - 3b + 8}$

GO ON

Intervention Strategy Kinesthetic Learners

Manipulatives Students who learn best with hands-on activities will benefit from using algebra tiles. At first, make the tiles available for the student to use to simplify expressions. After much practice, instruct the student to simplify expressions without using the tiles, but use the tiles to check answers.

Common Error *Alert*

Like Terms Students may be having difficulty simplifying expressions because they are combining all the variable terms, e.g., $3w^2 + 4w = 7w^2$. Remind them that only terms with exactly the same variable term may be combined. Use an apple and orange analogy. Suppose x means an apple and x^2 means an orange. Three apples ($3x$) and two oranges ($2x^2$) cannot be stated as anything other than three apples and two oranges. On the other hand, three apples ($3x$) and two apples ($2x$) can be stated as five apples ($5x$).

Common Error *Alert*

Coefficients of 1 If students missed Exercise 11, review that when a variable does not appear to have a coefficient, it is actually a coefficient of 1. Explain that the coefficient is multiplied by the variable; therefore it has to be a 1 because of the Multiplication Property of 1. If the coefficient were zero, then the term would equal zero and not be written at all.

Math Coach Notes

Write Vertically When students are simplifying expressions, recommend that they list like terms beneath each other. Once the terms are grouped vertically, have the students combine the like terms.

English Learner Strategy

Content Use a visual image technique to have EL students combine like terms and simplify expressions. After the word problem is read, have EL students close their eyes and picture the items and numbers involved in the problem.

Common Error *Alert*

Common Mistakes The two mistakes students might make are with minus signs before coefficients and with coefficients of 1. To avoid mistakes with the minus signs, you can instruct students to change all subtraction signs to "plus the opposite." To avoid coefficient of 1 mistakes, instruct students to write the coefficients of 1 in place next to the variables.

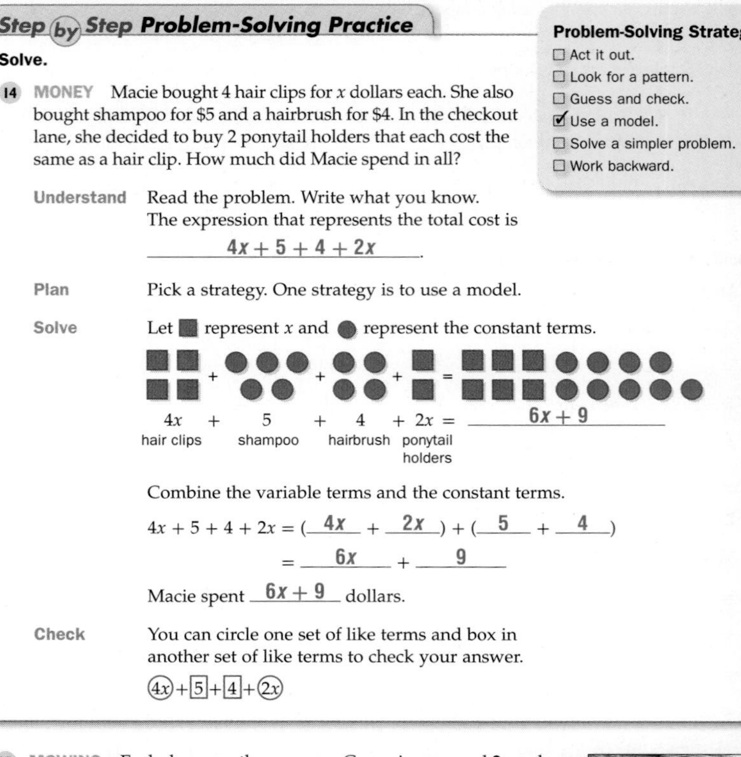

Step by Step Problem-Solving Practice

Problem-Solving Strategies
- ☐ Act it out.
- ☐ Look for a pattern.
- ☐ Guess and check.
- ☑ Use a model.
- ☐ Solve a simpler problem.
- ☐ Work backward.

Solve.

14 MONEY Macie bought 4 hair clips for x dollars each. She also bought shampoo for \$5 and a hairbrush for \$4. In the checkout lane, she decided to buy 2 ponytail holders that each cost the same as a hair clip. How much did Macie spend in all?

Understand Read the problem. Write what you know. The expression that represents the total cost is $4x + 5 + 4 + 2x$.

Plan Pick a strategy. One strategy is to use a model.

Solve Let ■ represent x and ● represent the constant terms.

$4x$ (hair clips) + 5 (shampoo) + 4 (hairbrush) + $2x$ (ponytail holders) = $6x + 9$

Combine the variable terms and the constant terms.

$4x + 5 + 4 + 2x = (4x + 2x) + (5 + 4)$

$= 6x + 9$

Macie spent $6x + 9$ dollars.

Check You can circle one set of like terms and box in another set of like terms to check your answer.

$(4x) + \boxed{5} + \boxed{4} + (2x)$

15 MOWING Each day over the summer, Germaine mowed 2 yards, Kevin mowed 3 yards, and Aiden mowed 1 yard. The expression $2d + 3d + d$ represents the number of yards they mowed in d days. Simplify the expression. Check off each step.

✔ Understand: I underlined key words.

✔ Plan: To solve the problem, I will use a model

✔ Solve: The answer is $6d$

✔ Check: I checked my answer by reviewing my addition

396 Chapter 9 Variables and Expressions

Intervention Strategy — Visual Learners

Color Code Have students use different-colored highlighters to highlight the variables. Use a unique color for each variable. Variables such as x and x^2 need to be highlighted with different colors because they are not like terms. Then have students group their variables according to color. Repeat the process with a variety of expressions.

6 AGES Kimberly is n years old. Elisa is 2 years older than Kimberly. Martin is 3 years older than Elisa. Represent the sum of their ages with the expression $n + (n + 2) + (n + 2 + 3)$. Simplify the expression.

$3n + 7$

7 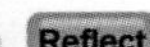 Are $5h^2$ and $-9h^2$ like terms? Explain.

Yes; Both terms have the same variable and same exponent.

Skills, Concepts, and Problem Solving

ame the like terms in each expression.

8 $7s - s^2 + 5s + 9s^2$

$-s^2$ and $9s^2$

$7s$ and $5s$

19 $15 + 4f - 2f - 8$

$4f$ and $-2f$

15 and -8

implify each expression. Show your work.

0 $4x + 7c - 2x$
Let ■ represent x and ☺ represent c.

■■■■ − ■■ + ☻☻☻☻☻☻☻ =

■■ + ☻☻☻☻☻☻☻

So, $4x + 7c - 2x = 2x + 7c$.

21 $5d + 3s + 4s$
Let ◆ represent d and ◣ represent s.

◆◆◆◆◆ + ◣◣◣ + ◣◣◣◣ =

◆◆◆◆◆ + ◣◣◣◣◣◣◣

So, $5d + 3s + 4s = 5d + 7s$.

implify each expression. Show your work.

2 $4g + 8 + 6g + 18g^2 - 10g^2 - 13$

$8g^2 + 10g - 5$

23 $9b^2 - 6b + 2b^2 - 2 + 4b + 12$

$11b^2 - 2b + 10$

4 $3y - 4y^2 + y^2 - y + 5 + 7y^2$

$4y^2 + 2y + 5$

25 $16z + 10 - 9z^2 - 5z - 3 + 6z^2$

$-3z^2 + 11z + 7$

GO ON

Note This!

Operation Effects While taking notes on simplifying expressions, ask students to observe the effect each operation has on the variables. Have them write a sentence summarizing their observations.

Odd/Even Assignments

Exercises 18–26 are structured so that students practice the same concepts whether they are assigned the odd or even problems.

In-Class Assignment

Have students complete Exercises 18, 21, 22, 26, and 29 to ensure that they understand the concept.

Math Challenge

Group Simplifying Another way for students to fully understand how to simplify expressions is to create a word problem from a simplified expression. Arrange the students into pairs and have them write a word problem from a simplified expression. Combine two groups and have one group read their problem to the other group to simplify. Compare their simplified expressions with the original expressions for equality. Have groups volunteer to share their word problems with the class.

Intervention Strategy

Interpersonal Learners

Act It Out When using word problems to simplify expressions, have the students act out the problem for the class. For example, Exercise 26 can be acted out for the class. Have student volunteers play Mrs. Perry and her three children and use fake money for the money used in the word problem. This strategy will also help visual, auditory, and kinesthetic learners.

4 Assess

See It, Do It, Say It, Write It

Step 1 Hand out a sheet of problems with expressions.

Step 2 Have students color code the like terms in each problem.

Step 3 Arrange the students in pairs. Students verify with each other that they have identified the like terms properly.

Step 4 Have students simplify each expression and verify answers with their partners.

Looking Ahead: Pre-teach

Evaluate Algebraic Expressions Explain to students that they will learn how to evaluate expressions with variables.

Example

Evaluate $13x + 7$ when $x = 2$.

$13x + 7$	
$13(2) + 7$	Substitute 2 for x.
$26 + 7$	Multiply.
33	Add.

Have students evaluate each expression.

1. $y + 14$ when $y = 6$ 20
2. $2x + 3$ when $x = 5$ 13
3. $7c - 4$ when $c = 12$ 80

Solve.

26 MONEY Mrs. Perry gives her three children an allowance each week. Jill gets n dollars. Brooke gets twice as much as Jill. Katrina gets \$3 less than Brooke. The expression $n + 2n + (2n - 3)$ represents the total of the three allowances. Simplify the expression. $5n - 3$

Vocabulary Check **Write the vocabulary word that completes each sentence.**

27 Terms that contain the same variables are called like terms.

28 To simplify means to combine like terms.

29 Writing in Math Explain how to combine the like terms in the expression $7x + 5 + 4x$ using the Associative Property and the Commutative Property.

Answers will vary. Sample answer: Use the Commutative Property to switch the addends: $7x + 4x + 5$. Use the Associative Property to group like terms: $(7x + 4x) + 5$. Then add the like terms to get $11x + 5$.

Spiral Review (Lesson 9-2, p. 383)

For each phrase, name the operation.

30 the quotient of z and 3 division

31 a number minus 7 subtraction

32 the sum of a number and 14 addition

33 the product of y and 5 multiplication

Translate each phrase to an expression.

34 y increased by 17 $y + 17$

35 the quotient of 8 and b $8 \div b$ or $\frac{8}{b}$

36 the product of 9 and c $9 \times c$ or $9c$

37 z less than 24 $24 - z$

Solve.

38 BIRTHDAYS Zach is 3 times the age of Sarah. Write an expression for Zach's age. $3a$

Ticket Out the Door

Simplify Terms Write constant and variable terms randomly all over the board. Have student volunteers simplify two like terms and write their simplified term on the board. Have that student erase the original terms they used and line up at the door. Repeat until all the terms are simplified and all students have lined up in single file to exit the classroom.

Lesson 9-4 Evaluate Algebraic Expressions

KEY Concept

To **evaluate** an **algebraic expression**, substitute a **value** for a variable. Then perform the operations.

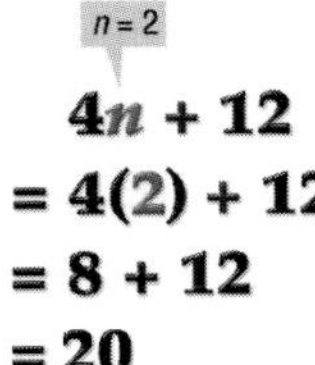

$4n + 12$
$= 4(2) + 12$
$= 8 + 12$
$= 20$

Remember to use the **order of operations** after substituting or replacing the variables with numbers.

VOCABULARY

algebraic expression
a combination of variables, numbers, and at least one operation

evaluate
to find the *value* of an *algebraic expression* by replacing variables with numerals

order of operations
the rules that tell which operation to perform first when more than one operation is used;
(1) Simplify grouping symbols, like parentheses
(2) Simplify exponents.
(3) Multiply and divide in order from left to right.
(4) Add and subtract in order from left to right.

value
the amount of a number

Example 1

Evaluate $5x + 2$ when $x = 4$.

1. Replace x with 4 in the expression.

$5x + 2$
$= 5(4) + 2$

2. Simplify using the order of operations.

$5(4) + 2$ Multiply.
$= 20 + 2$ Add.
$= 22$

YOUR TURN!

Evaluate $y^2 - 8$ when $y = 6$.

1. Replace y with 6 in the expression.

$y^2 - 8$
$= \underline{6^2 - 8}$

2. Simplify using the order of operations.

$6^2 - 8$ Simplify the exponent.
$\underline{36} - 8$ Subtract.
$\underline{28}$

GO ON

Additional Example 1

Evaluate $9d - 4$ when $d = 5$.

1. Replace d with 5 in the expression.

$9d - 4$
$= 9(5) - 4$

2. Simplify using the order of operations.

$9(5) - 4$ Multiply.
$= 45 - 4$ Subtract.
$= 41$

Lesson Notes

Lesson 9-4

Lesson Planner

Objective Write, simplify, and evaluate numerical expressions.

Vocabulary **algebraic expression**, **evaluate**, **order of operations**, **value**

Materials/Manipulatives two-color counters, colored pencils, index cards

Chapter Resource Masters

CRM Vocabulary and English Language Development (p. A200)
CRM Skills Practice (p. A201)
CRM Problem-Solving Practice (p. A202)
CRM Homework Practice (p. A203)

1 Introduce

Vocabulary

Distinguish Between Terms Distinguish between the terms *simplify* and *evaluate*. To *simplify* means to combine like terms in an expression, while *evaluate* means to replace a variable with a number and then simplify it as a numerical expression. An algebraic expression where the value of the variable is unknown *can* be simplified, but *cannot* be evaluated.

2 Teach

Key Concept

Foundational Skills and Concepts After students have read through the Key Concept box, have them try these exercises.

1. What operation does $4n$ represent? multiplication
2. Why is multiplication done before addition? because of the order of operations

Additional *Example 2*

Evaluate $c^2 + 16 - 2t$ when $c = 3$ and $t = 5$.

1. Replace each variable in the expression.

$c^2 + 16 - 2t$
$3^2 + 16 - 2(5)$

2. Simplify using the order of operations.

$= 3^2 + 16 - 2(5)$	Simplify the exponent.
$= 9 + 16 - 2(5)$	Multiply.
$= 9 + 16 - 10$	Add.
$= 25 - 10$	Subtract.
$= 15$	

3 Practice

Using Manipulatives

Two-Color Counters When evaluating operations, use two-color counters to give students a visual representation of the variables. A two-color counter will work with expressions that have 2 or less variables.

On-Hand Manipulatives Demonstrate evaluating expressions using two-color counters. Use classroom objects in a similar manner as the two-color counters.

Example 2

Evaluate $3x - 6 + 5y$ when $x = 7$ and $y = 2$.

1. Replace each variable in the expression.

$3x - 6 + 5y$
$= 3(7) - 6 + 5(2)$

2. Simplify using the order of operations.

$3(7) - 6 + 5(2)$	Multiply.
$= 21 - 6 + 10$	Subtract.
$= 15 + 10$	Add.
$= 25$	

YOUR TURN!

Evaluate $x^2 \div (4y)$ when $x = 8$ and $y = 2$.

1. Replace each variable in the expression.

$x^2 \div (4y)$
$= 8^2 \div (4 \times 2)$

2. Simplify using the order of operations.

$8^2 \div (4 \times 2)$	Simplify the operation in the parentheses.
$= 8^2 \div$ 8	Simplify the exponent.
= 64 ÷ 8	Divide.
= 8	

Who is Correct?

Evaluate the expression $3xy$ when $x = 2$ and $y = 7$.

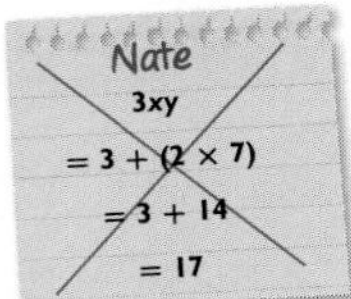

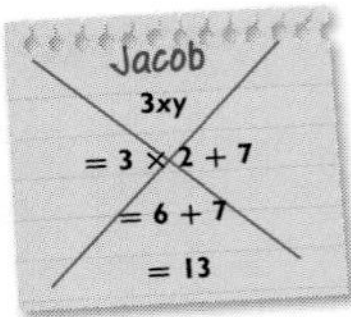

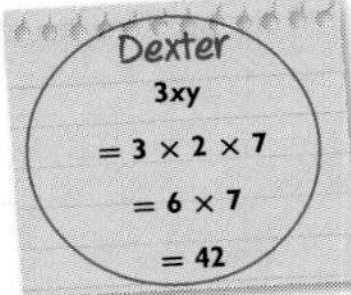

Circle correct answer(s). Cross out incorrect answer(s).

Guided Practice

Evaluate each expression when $x = 4$ and $y = 7$.

1. $8x$ 8 (4) = 32
2. $56 \div y$ 56 ÷ 7 = 8
3. $12 + y$ 12 + 7 = 19
4. $3y + 6$ 3(7) + 6 = 27

400 Chapter 9 Variables and Expressions

Who *is Correct?*

Diagnostic Teaching

- Nate's answer is incorrect. He used the incorrect operation of addition.
- Jacob's answer is incorrect. He used the incorrect operation of addition.
- Dexter's answer is correct.

Remind students that when a coefficient is by a *variable*, such as $3xy$, this indicates the operation of multiplication. So, $3xy$ equals $3 \times x \times y$.

Step by Step Practice

5 Evaluate the expression $7 + 6y \div 8$ when $y = 4$.

Step 1 $6y$ means 6 __times__ y. Replace y with __4__ in the expression.

Step 2 Simplify using the order of operations.

$7 + (6 \times 4) \div 8$ Multiply.

$= 7 +$ __24__ $\div 8$ Divide.

$= 7 +$ __3__ Add.

$=$ __10__

The value of the expression is __10__.

Evaluate each expression when $x = 2$, $y = 5$, and $z = 3$.

6 $5x + 7 - 4$

$= 5 \times$ __2__ $+ 7 - 4$ Multiply.

$=$ __10__ $+ 7 - 4$ Add.

$=$ __17__ $- 4$ Subtract.

$=$ __13__

7 $y^2 - 6z$

$=$ __5^2__ $- 6 \times$ __3__ Simplify the exponent.

$=$ __25__ $- 6 \times$ __3__ Multiply.

$=$ __25__ $-$ __18__ Subtract.

$=$ __7__

8 $7 + 8z \div 12$

__$7 + 8(3) \div 12 = 9$__

9 $9x \div 3 + 6y$

__$9(2) \div 3 + 6(5) = 36$__

Math Coach Notes

Substitute Values for Variables When students are substituting values for variables, they may get confused about what to do next. Show an example.

$3m$ means $3 \times m$

Replace the variable with the value and multiply.

$3m$ can also mean $3(m)$

Replace the variable with the value and use the Distributive Property.

Common Error *Alert*

Sign Alert When evaluating algebraic expressions, students should be careful of the signs within the expression and the sign of the number. For example, evaluate these expressions when $x = -2$.

$x - 4 = -2 - 4 = -6$

$10 - x = 10 - (-2) = 12$

Are They Getting It?

Check students' understanding of evaluating expressions by writing these problems on the board. Ask students to point out the wrong answers and explain why they are wrong.

Evaluate each expression when $x = 2$, $y = 3$, and $z = 4$.

1. $x^2 + 2y - z = 2^2 + 2(3) - 4$
$= 4 + 2(3) - 4$
$= 4 + 6 - 4$
$= 10 - 4$
$= 6$

This is correct.

2. $5x - 2y + z = 5(4) - 2(3) + 2$
$= 20 - 2(3) + 2$
$= 20 - 6 + 2$
$= 14 + 2$
$= 16$

This is incorrect. The values of the variables were not replaced correctly.

English Learner Strategy

Reference Cards Write the problem-solving strategies on index cards. On the front side write a description in English. On the reverse side, have students write a description in their native languages. When students are choosing a problem-solving strategy, display the card when using the strategy. Encourage the students to keep the problem-solving strategies index cards handy for reference.

Note This!

Study Strategies When students are asked to evaluate algebraic expressions, encourage students to combine like terms before evaluating the expression while following the order of operations.

Step by Step Problem-Solving Practice

Problem-Solving Strategies
- ☐ Draw a diagram.
- ☑ Use an equation.
- ☐ Guess and check.
- ☐ Act it out.
- ☐ Solve a simpler problem.

Solve.

10 READING Darnell read 24 pages in a book in one hour. The number of pages in the book is p.

Use the expression $p \div 24$ to find how many hours it will take Darnell to read a 312-page book.

Understand Read the problem. Write what you know.
Darnell is reading a book that is __312__ pages long.
He reads __24__ pages each hour.

Plan Pick a strategy. One strategy is to use an equation.
Let h represent hours. Write an equation using h and the expression $p \div 24$.
number of hours = number of pages ÷ 24
$h = p \div 24$

Solve Replace p with __312__ in the equation. Then simplify.
$h =$ __312__ $\div 24$
$h =$ __13__
It will take Darnell __13__ hours to read a 312-page book.

Check Multiply to check your division.

11 ENTERTAINMENT Silvio wants to buy a CD for $12 and 3 DVDs. Use the expression $12 + 3d$ to find the total cost, where d represents the cost per DVD. Evaluate the expression when $d = \$20$. Check off each step.

__✓__ Understand: I underlined key words.

__✓__ Plan: To solve the problem, I will __use an equation__

__✓__ Solve: The answer is __$72; 12 + 3(20), 12 + 60 = 72__

__✓__ Check: I checked my answer by __checking my multiplication and addition__

Intervention Strategy — Visual Learners

Use Shapes When evaluating algebraic expressions, draw a shape around each variable. Use the same shape for like variables. Rewrite the expression with the shape instead of the variable. The student can then write the replacement value inside the shape and continue to evaluate the expression. For problems with multiple variables, more shapes can be used.

2 FOOD The school cafeteria pays $25 per case for hamburger patties. Write an expression for the cost of c cases. Find the cost of 8 cases. $25c$, $200

3 **Reflect** Does the expression $40 \div k + 3$ have a greater value when $k = 5$ or $k = 8$? Explain.

$k = 5$. When $k = 5$, $40 \div 5 + 3 = 11$.

When $k = 8$, $40 \div 8 + 3 = 8$.

Skills, Concepts, and Problem Solving

valuate each expression when $x = 9$, $y = 6$, and $w = 2$.

4 $4x \div 6 + 7w$

$4(9) \div 6 + 7(2) = 20$

15 $y^2 + 5w$

$6^2 + 5(2) = 46$

6 $x^2 - 7y$

$9^2 - 7(6) = 39$

17 $12w \div 8 + 3x$

$12(2) \div 8 + 3(9) = 30$

valuate each expression when $a = 4$, $b = 7$, and $c = 10$.

8 $b^2 - 2c$

$7^2 - 2(10) = 29$

19 $6c \div 5 + 8a$

$6(10) \div 5 + 8(4) = 44$

0 $5b + 12a \div 6$

$5(7) + 12(4) \div 6 = 43$

21 $c^2 - 9b$

$10^2 - 9(7) = 37$

Math Challenge

Different Expressions, Same Value Choose a number for students to use as their target number. Have students write four different algebraic expressions, each with at least two variables that will evaluate to the target number. They will write the expressions and determine which values will replace their variables.

Intervention Strategy — Visual Learners

Color Code As students write their notes, have them highlight or underline variables in the equation. For expressions with multiple variables, use a different color for each variable.

Odd/Even Assignments

Exercises 14–22 are structured so that students practice the same concepts whether they are assigned the odd or even problems.

In-Class Assignment

Have students complete Exercises 14, 21, 22, and 25 to ensure that they understand the concept.

4 Assess

See It, Do It, Say It, Write It

Step 1 Write an algebraic expression on the board. Show how to represent the expression with a drawing or model. Ask students to use shapes to represent the variable in the expression.

Step 2 Make a list of algebraic expressions on the board. Repeat the process used in Step 1, with students using items to represent the variables. Share solutions in a class discussion.

Step 3 Have students work in pairs. Assign one student to create an algebraic expression and the other to substitute shapes for the variables. Have students share their work with the class. Repeat several times.

Step 4 Have students work alone. Tell them to write and evaluate an algebraic expression. Encourage them to include a picture or a model.

Solve.

22 GAMES Dewayne plays a grammar game in which nouns are worth 5 points, verbs are worth 10 points, and adjectives are worth 15 points. The total score equals the expression $5n + 10v + 15a$, when n represents the number of nouns, v is the number of verbs, and a is the number of adjectives. Find Dewayne's score when $n = 3$, $v = 7$, and $a = 10$.

235 points

Vocabulary Check **Write the vocabulary word that completes each sentence.**

23 The amount of a number is its value.

24 A combination of variables, numbers, and at least one operation is called a(n) algebraic expression.

25 **Writing in Math** Explain how to evaluate $r - 8 \times 2$ when $r = 30$.

Answers may vary. Sample answer: Replace r with 30 in the expression $r - 8 \times 2$, and then simplify the expression using the order of operations.

Spiral Review

Name the coefficient, variable, and constant in each expression. (Lesson 9-1, p. 376)

26 $6a + 3$

coefficient: 6

variable: a

constant: 3

27 $5d - 9$

coefficient: 5

variable: d

constant: -9

Simplify each expression. Show your work. (Lesson 9-3, p. 392)

28 $6a + 7 + 3a + 9a^2 - 5a^2 - 2$

$4a^2 + 9a + 5$

29 $4b - 5b^2 + b + 6 + 8b^2$

$3b^2 + 5b + 6$

Solve. (Lesson 9-2, p. 383)

30 CRAFTS Eva has 120 beads. She makes bracelets that have b beads. Write an expression to find the number of bracelets Eva can make.

$120 \div b$

STOP

Ticket Out the Door

Solve a Problem Write the following on the board:

Evaluate $x^2 + y \times z$ when $x = 2$, $y = 3$, and $z = 4$.

Have students solve the problem. Tell them they must show their work. Students will hand in their papers as they exit the classroom.

$$\begin{aligned} x^2 + y \times z &= 2^2 + 3 \times 4 \\ &= 4 + 3 \times 4 \\ &= 4 + 12 \\ &= 16 \end{aligned}$$

Progress Check 2 (Lessons 9-3 and 9-4)

ame the like terms in each expression.

$2q + 9 - 5 + 9q^2 - 8q + q^2$

$9q^2$ and q^2

$2q$ and $-8q$

9 and −5

2 $7 - 5c + 8c^2 - 3c^2 + 6 + 7c$

$8c^2$ and $-3c^2$

$-5c$ and $7c$

7 and 6

aluate each expression when $y = 3$ and $z = 5$.

$4y + 15$

$4(3) + 15 = 27$

4 $40 \div 2z$

$40 \div 2(5) = 4$

mplify each expression. Show your work.

$7h - h^2 + 5h + 7h^2 - 10$

$6h^2 + 12h - 10$

6 $-9b + 4b^2 - 5 + 2b^2 + 9$

$6b^2 - 9b + 4$

aluate each expression when $x = 2$, $y = 4$, and $z = 8$.

$5y + 3z \div 6$

$5(4) + 3(8) \div 6 = 24$

8 $9z \div 6 - 3x$

$9(8) \div 6 - 3(2) = 6$

lve.

MONEY Santos has x dollars. Tucker has twice as much money as Santos. Mary has 5 dollars less than Santos. The expression $x + 2x + (x - 5)$ represents the total amount of money Santos, Tucker, and Mary have altogether. Simplify the expression.

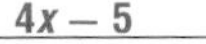

$4x - 5$

UNIFORMS The school band bought uniforms. See the cost of the uniform at right. Write an expression for the cost of u uniforms. Find the cost of 12 uniforms.

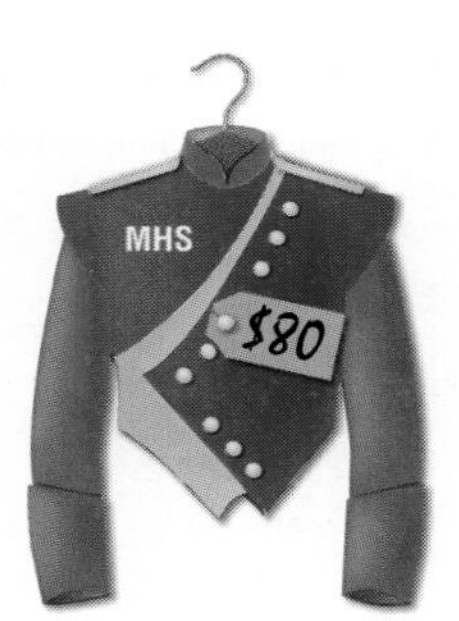

$80u$, \$960

Progress Check 2

Chapter 9

Formative Assessment

Use the Progress Check to assess students' mastery of the previous lessons. Have students review the lesson indicated for the problems they answered incorrectly.

Odd/Even Assignments

Exercises are structured so that students practice the same concepts whether they are assigned the odd or even problems.

Common Error *Alert*

Like Terms If students are having difficulties naming like terms, have them think of terms with similar variables as names of objects. For example, in Exercise 1, they can think of q as apples and q^2 as oranges.

Exercise 5 If students combine h terms with h^2 terms, reinforce that these are different terms. To be like terms, variables must have the same exponent.

Data-Driven Decision Making

Students missing Exercises . . .	Have trouble with . . .	Should review and practice . . .
1–2	identifying like terms in an expression.	SSG Lesson 9-3, p. 392 CRM Skills Practice, p. A197
3–4	evaluating an expression.	SSG Lesson 9-4, p. 399 CRM Skills Practice, p. A201
5–6	simplifying an expression.	SSG Lesson 9-3, p. 392 CRM Skills Practice, p. A197
7–8	evaluating an expression for given values of variables.	SSG Lesson 9-4, p. 399 CRM Skills Practice, p. A201
9–10	solving word problems that contain mathematical expressions.	CRM Problem-Solving Practice, pp. A198 and A202

Chapter 9 Study Guide
Formative Assessment

Vocabulary and Concept Check

If students have difficulty answering Exercises 1–8, remind them that they can use the page references to refresh their memories about the vocabulary terms.

Vocabulary Review Strategies

Color Code Have students use a color-coding system to write expressions. They can use one color for variables, one for constants, and one for coefficients. The more they associate the color with the type of element in each term, the more apt they are to remember that term.

Lesson Review

Each example walks the students through the parts of mathematical expressions. Have students identify parts of the expressions and ensure when students are asked to simplify the expressions, they simplify completely.

Find **Extra Practice** for these concepts in the Practice Worksheets, pages A188–A203.

Classroom Management

Early Finishers Have students who finish the exercises before others create new exercises for each example. They can trade their exercises with other early finishers and check each other's work.

Chapter 9 Study Guide

Vocabulary and Concept Check

algebraic expression, *p. 376*
coefficient, *p. 376*
constant, *p. 376*
evaluate, *p. 399*
like terms, *p. 392*
simplify, *p. 392*
term, *p. 376*

Write the vocabulary word that completes each sentence.

1. To combine like terms is to simplify.
2. A(n) term represents each of the quantities connected by plus or minus signs in an algebraic expression.
3. $4x$ and $3x$ are examples of like terms.
4. To find the value of an algebraic expression by replacing variables with numerals is to evaluate the expression.
5. $7x + 9 - 3y$ is an example of a(n) algebraic expression.
6. A value that does not change is called a(n) constant.

Label each diagram below. Write the correct vocabulary term in each blank.

7. constant or term

$(10) + 3z$

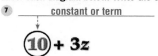

8. coefficient

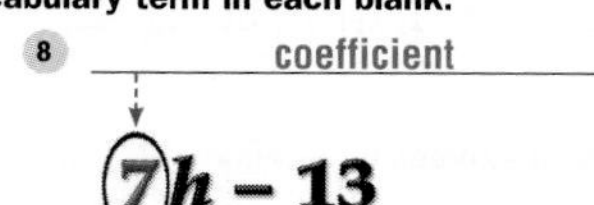

Lesson Review

9-1 Algebraic Expressions (pp. 376–382)

Name the coefficient, variable, and constant in each expression.

9. $11z - 5$

coefficient: 11

variable: z

constant: −5

Example 1

Name the coefficient, variable, and constant in 9y + 4.

1. The coefficient is the number 9 because it is multiplied by the variable y.
2. The variable is the letter y.
3. The constant is the number 4.

406 **Chapter 9** Study Guide

-2 **Translating Verbal Phrases into Mathematical Symbols** (pp. 383–390)

**anslate each phrase into
n expression.**

) n increased by 15

$n + 15$

the product of q and 4

$4q$

9 less than y

$y - 9$

3 g divided by 20

$\frac{g}{20}$

Example 2

Translate "the number y decreased by eleven" to an expression.

1. The words "decreased by" tell you to use subtraction (−).
2. The word "eleven" indicates that the constant term is 11.
3. The words "the number y" tell you to use the variable y.

the number y decreased by eleven

$y \quad - \quad 11$

The expression is $y - 11$.

**rite an expression to represent
ach situation.**

4 The number of fish in the aquarium is decreased by 2.

Sample answer: $f - 2$

5 David has three times as many cards as Steven.

Sample answer: $3c$

Example 3

Write an expression to represent the following situation.

Mollie has nine more marbles than Megan.

1. The word "more" tells you to use addition (+).
2. The word "nine" indicates that the constant term is 9.
3. The words "nine more marbles than Megan" tell you to use the variable m.

nine more marbles

$9 \quad + \quad m$

The expression is $9 + m$ or $m + 9$.

Dinah Zike's Foldables®

Review Remind students to complete and refer to their Foldables as they progress through the Chapter 9 Study Guide. Have students share and compare their completed Foldables with a partner. You may also choose to have them use their Foldable as a study aid in preparing for the Chapter Test. (For complete instructions, see Chapter Resource Masters, p. A185.)

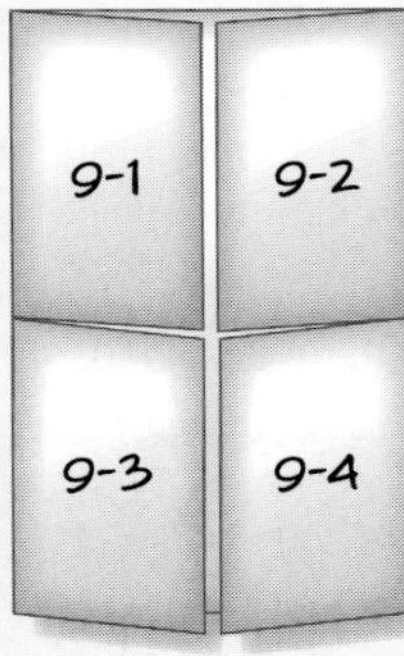

Intervention Strategy — Auditory Learners

Use Correct Vocabulary Encourage students to refer to parts of mathematical expressions by their proper names. Often, these parts are referred to informally. For example, do not allow students to call a coefficient "the number in front of the variable." Persistence of correct vocabulary will help students as they advance into studies of algebraic reasoning.

Common Error *Alert*

Simplifying Steps If students are not simplifying the expressions in Exercise 18–21 correctly, ensure they are showing each step as they simplify each expression. Students often have trouble identifying which sign (positive or negative) goes with the terms they are combining. It may help students to write each subtraction expression as an addition expression in which the opposite of the term is added.

Note This!

Word Wall Help students create a word wall. They should write an expression and label its parts—such as term, coefficient, constant, variable—and its operation. They should pick a value for the variable and simplify the expression.

9-3 Simplify Expressions (pp. 392–398)

Simplify each expression by using a model.

16 $4r + 3v + 2v$

Sample answer: Let ♡ represent r and ⬡ represent v.

♡♡♡♡ + ⬡⬡⬡ + ⬡⬡ =
♡♡♡♡ + ⬡⬡⬡⬡⬡

So, $4r + 3v + 2v = 4r + 5v$.

17 $5s + 2t + s$

Sample answer: Let ○ represent s and ✚ represent t.

○○○○○ + ✚✚ + ○
= ○○○○○○ + ✚✚

So, $5s + 2t + s = 6s + 2t$.

Example 4

Simplify $2x + 3y + x$ by using a model.

1. Let △ represent x and ■ represent y.
2. Draw a model to represent the expression.

△△ + ■■■ + △ = △△△ + ■■■
$2x$ + $3y$ + x = $3x$ + $3y$

3. Write the result.

$2x + 3y + x = 3x + 3y$

Simplify each expression. Show your work.

18 $17 + 15h - 3h^2 - 9h + 7h^2 + 10$

$4h^2 + 6h + 27$

19 $12b - 3 + 11b^2 - 12b + 19 - 7b^2$

$4b^2 + 16$

20 $21 + 3x - x^2 - 7x + x^2 - 10$

$-4x + 11$

21 $35 + 11z^2 - 5z - 4z^2 + 5z - 5$

$7z^2 + 30$

Example 5

Simplify $9z + 16z^2 + 17 - 12z^2 - 3z$.

1. Name the like terms.
   z^2 terms: $16z^2$ and $-12z^2$
   z terms: $9z$ and $-3z$
   Constant terms: 17
2. Rearrange to group the terms together.
   $9z + 16z^2 + 17 - 12z^2 - 3z$
   $= 16z^2 - 12z^2 + 9z - 3z + 17$
3. Combine all like terms.
   $= (16z^2 - 12z^2) + 9z - 3z + 17$
   $= 4z^2 + (9z - 3z) + 17$
   $= 4z^2 + 6z + 17$

9-4 Evaluate Algebraic Expressions (pp. 399–404)

Evaluate each expression when $a = 3$ and $b = 6$.

22 $4a \div 2$

$4(3) \div 2 = 6$

23 $b^2 - 7$

$6^2 - 7 = 29$

24 $8b \div 12$

$8(6) \div 12 = 4$

25 $a^2 + 5$

$3^2 + 5 = 14$

Example 6

Evaluate $8d \div 12$ when $d = 9$.

1. Replace d with 9 in the expression.

$8d \div 12$
$= 8(9) \div 12$

2. Simplify using the order of operations.

$8(9) \div 12$ Multiply.
$= 72 \div 12$ Divide.
$= 6$

Evaluate each expression when $x = 2$, $y = 4$, and $z = 7$.

26 $3z - y + x$

$3(7) - 4 + 2 = 19$

27 $y^2 + 6x$

$4^2 + 6(2) = 28$

28 $8y \div 2 - 2z$

$8(4) \div 2 - 2(7) = 2$

29 $z^2 - 9y$

$7^2 - 9(4) = 13$

30 $5x + 4y \div 8$

$5(2) + 4(4) \div 8 = 12$

Example 7

Evaluate $8n + 7 - 6m$, when $m = 5$ and $n = 9$.

1. Replace the variables in the expression.

$8n + 7 - 6m$
$= 8(9) + 7 - 6(5)$

2. Simplify using the order of operations.

$8(9) + 7 - 6(5)$ Multiply.
$= 72 + 7 - 30$ Add.
$= 79 - 30$ Subtract.
$= 49$

Chapter 9 Study Guide 409

Common Error *Alert*

Substitute Correctly If students are not simplifying the expressions in Exercises 22–30 correctly, have them check to make sure they substituted the correct value for the variables. Ensure they are showing each step when simplifying the expressions and are following the order of operations.

Ticket Out the Door

Write and Evaluate Have students write an expression that contains one variable and at least one operation. Give them constraints for coefficients and exponents on their variables. Each student should use a different variable. Provide students with a list of all possible variables and assign values to the variables. Have students evaluate their expressions for the values of their variables. They should hand their simplified expressions to you as they exit.

Chapter 9

Chapter Test

Chapter Resource Masters

Additional forms of the Chapter 9 Tests are available.

Test Format	Where to Find it
Chapter 9 Test	Math Online glencoe.com
Blackline Masters	Assessment Masters, p. 129

Customize and create multiple versions of your chapter tests and their answer keys. All of these questions from the chapter tests are available on ExamView® Assessment Suite.

Online Assessment and Reporting
glencoe.com

This online assessment tool allows teachers to track student progress with easily accessible comprehensive reports available for every student. Assess students using any internet-ready computer.

Alternative Assessment

Use Portfolios Have students write three expressions in their portfolios. Each expression should contain a unique series of operations. At least one of the expressions should have a variable of degree greater than 1. Have students evaluate their expressions for the given values.

Chapter Test

Name the coefficient, variable, and constant in each expression.

1. $9k - 15$

   coefficient: 9

   variable: k

   constant: -15

2. $t + 5$

   coefficient: 1

   variable: t

   constant: 5

Translate each phrase to an expression.

3. eighteen less than u $u - 18$

4. four more than six times x $6x + 4$

Write an expression to represent each situation.

5. Felisa has ten fewer hair ribbons than Maggie.

   Sample answer: $r - 10$

6. Patrick spent three times as many hours on his research project as Diego.

   Sample answer: $3 \times h$ or $3h$

Name the like terms in each expression.

7. $4x + 11 - 2 + 5x$

   $4x$ and $5x$; 11 and -2

8. $18 - 13d + 6 + 17d$

   $-13d$ and $17d$; 18 and 6

Simplify each expression. Show your work.

9. $15 + 2p + 11p - 18 + 9p^2$

   $9p^2 + 13p - 3$

10. $7j - 13 + 6j^2 - 9j + 11$

    $6j^2 - 2j - 2$

Evaluate each expression when $d = 1$, $b = 4$, and $f = 2$.

11. $5b \div 10 + 6f$

    $5(4) \div 10 + 6(2) = 14$

12. $f^2 \times 3b - 9d$

    $2^2 \times 3(4) - 9(1) = 39$

410 Chapter 9 Test

English Learner Strategy

Assessment Encourage students to highlight key words in each of the word problems on the chapter test. They should find words that identify operations and rewrite the words in their native languages. Translating these words may help them identify the correct operation.

olve.

3 **BAKING** Angela baked 2 dozen cookies. Her brother ate 3 of them. How many cookies did Angela have left?

$12(2) - 3 = 21$

4 **MONEY** Paulo earns \$15 for cutting each lawn. Last week he cut 5 lawns. He also earned \$25 for dog-sitting. What was the total amount of money Paulo earned?

$\$15(5) + \$25 = \$100$

5 **NUMBER SENSE** The perimeter of a quadrilateral is the sum of the lengths of its sides. Write an expression for the perimeter of the quadrilateral.

$12 + 6 + 9 + x$

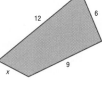

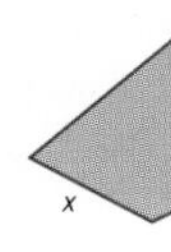

6 **FITNESS** Oscar bikes 15 miles each day. Write an expression for the number of miles Oscar bikes in d days.

$15d$

7 **SHOPPING** Lawana bought 2 bottles of perfume. One bottle was \$54, and the other was \$28. She also bought 2 bars of soap for y dollars each. Write an expression for the total amount she spent.

$\$54 + \$28 + 2y$, or $\$82 + 2y$

8 **AGES** Selma is 5 years older than Reed. Write an expression for Selma's age.

$a + 5$

9 **FOOD** The school cafeteria pays \$54 per case for chicken wings. Each case contains b wings. Write an expression for the cost per chicken wing.

$\frac{\$54}{b}$ or $\$54 \div b$

orrect the mistakes.

0 **PHOTOGRAPHY** Malcolm's photography teacher asked, "If you have photo albums that will each hold 150 pictures, then how many pictures will p photo albums hold?" Malcolm's answer is shown. What mistake did he make?

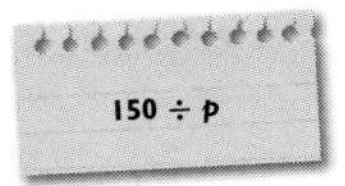

He should have used multiplication instead of division. The number of photos that p albums can hold is actually $150 \times p$, or $150p$.

Math Coach Notes

Reasonable Answers Have students check their work by making sure their answers are reasonable. If students finish early, encourage them to simplify each expression again to ensure they arrive at the same answer.

Data-Driven Decision Making

Students missing Exercises . . .	Have trouble with . . .	Should review and practice . . .
1–2	identifying the variable, constant, and coefficient of an expression.	SSG Lesson 9-1, p. 376 CRM Skills Practice, p. A189
3–6	translating a word phrase into an expression.	SSG Lesson 9-2, p. 383 CRM Skills Practice, p. A193
7–10	identifying and combining like terms in an expression.	SSG Lesson 9-3, p. 392 CRM Skills Practice, p. A197
11–12	evaluating expressions.	SSG Lesson 9-4, p. 399 CRM Skills Practice, p. A201
13–20	writing and solving expressions from word problems.	CRM Problem-Solving Practice, pp. A190, A194, A198, and A202

Chapter 9 Test Practice

Diagnose Student Errors

Survey student responses for each item. Class trends may indicate common errors and misconceptions.

1. A switched order of numbers in the expression
B incorrect operation and coefficent
C switched order of numbers in the expression and incorrect operation
(D) correct

2. A ignored exponent
B incorrect value squared
(C) correct
D wrong order of subtraction

3. (A) correct
B incorrect operations
C used only addition
D multiplied instead of divided

4. (A) correct
B miscalculation
C added 64 and 36 instead of subtracting
D incorrect order of operations

5. A variable
(B) correct
C guess
D constant

6. A miscalculated coefficient on a^2 term
(B) correct
C incorrect sign on *a* term
D miscalculated coefficient on *a* term

7. A found half of perimeter
(B) correct
C guess
D found area, not perimeter

8. A multiplied base times power and added 6 to 5
(B) correct
C guess
D guess

9. (A) correct
B miscalculation
C guess
D guess

10. A misinterpreted Associative Property
B misinterpreted Associative Property
(C) correct
D misinterpreted Associative Property

11. (A) correct
B coefficient
C variable
D guess

Chapter 9 Test Practice

Choose the best answer and fill in the corresponding circle on the sheet at right.

1 Which expression is "three less than twice a number"?

A $3n - 2$ C $3n + 2$
B $3n + 3$ (D) $2n - 3$

2 Which shows $n^2 - 9$ written in word form?

A nine less than a number
B nine squared more than a number
(C) nine less than the square of a number
D a number squared less than nine

3 What is the value of the expression?

$20 \div 5 + 17$

(A) 21 C 42
B 37 D 117

4 Evaluate $8^2 - 3d \times 4$, if $d = 3$.

(A) 28 C 100
B 40 D 220

5 In the expression $4n^2 - 7$, what is the coefficient?

A n C exponent
(B) 4 D -7

6 Simplify the expression below.

$4a - 6a^2 + 10 + 14a^2 - 8a + 9$

A $20a^2 - 4a + 19$
(B) $8a^2 - 4a + 19$
C $8a^2 + 4a + 19$
D $8a^2 - 12a + 19$

7 Find the perimeter of the rectangle if $x = 4$ feet.

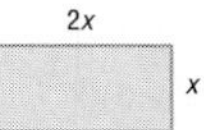

A 12 feet C 28 feet
(B) 24 feet D 32 feet

8 Evaluate $x^2 - 5y$, if $x = 7$ and $y = 6$.

A 3 C 39
(B) 19 D 79

9 What is the value of the expression?

$7 \times (16 - 6) \div 5$

(A) 14 C 35
B 17 D 75

412 Chapter 9 Test Practice

10 If $(5 \times 2) \times 8 = 80$, then what is $5 \times (2 \times 8)$?

A 10 — (C) 80

B 16 — D 88

11 In the expression $3 + 8b^2$, what is the constant?

(A) 3 — C b

B 8 — D exponent

12 Simplify the expression $5x + 9 - 2x - 6 + 4x^2$.

A $11x + 15$ — C $7x + 3$

B $4x^2 + 7x + 3$ — (D) $4x^2 + 3x + 3$

13 Jaleesa sleeps 8.5 hours each night. Which expression represents how many hours she sleeps in z nights?

A 8.5×7 — (C) $8.5z$

B $8.5 + z$ — D $8.5 \div z$

14 Sergio is 2 years older than 3 times Karl's age. If Karl is 5 years old, how old is Sergio?

A 10 — (C) 17

B 11 — D 30

ANSWER SHEET

Directions: Fill in the circle of each correct answer.

	A	B	C	D
1	A	B	C	●
2	A	B	●	D
3	●	B	C	D
4	●	B	C	D
5	A	●	C	D
6	A	●	C	D
7	A	●	C	D
8	A	●	C	D
9	●	B	C	D
10	A	B	●	D
11	●	B	C	D
12	A	B	C	●
13	A	B	●	D
14	A	B	●	D

Success Strategy
Read each problem carefully and look at each answer choice. Eliminate answers you know are wrong. This narrows your choices before solving the problem.

STOP

Diagnosing Student Errors and Misconceptions

Common Errors There are three common errors that students will encounter.

1. They will not remember or use the order of operations correctly. Supervise the student when simplifying until you are sure the student knows the correct order of operations.
2. Students cannot determine if a coefficient or constant is positive or negative. To remedy this, have students rewrite all subtraction operations as addition of the opposite of the term.
3. Students combine coefficients and are off by 1 because they did not remember that a variable without a number in front actually has a coefficient of 1. To correct this mistake, have students make sure that all coefficients are written in place, including 1s.

12. A added all terms and ignored signs and exponents
B added x terms instead of subtracting
C combined all terms, not just like terms
(D) correct

13. A misread number of nights as 7 nights
B incorrect operation
(C) correct
D incorrect operation

14. A miscalculated
B miscalculated
(C) correct
D multiplied all numbers together

Chapter 10

Chapter Overview

Chapter-at-a-Glance

Lesson	Math Objective	State/Local Standards
10-1 Equality (pp. 416-422)	Understand the addition and multiplication properties of equality.	
10-2 Operations with Unknown Quantities (pp. 423-428)	Use variables in expressions and equations.	
Progress Check (p. 429)		
10-3 Solve Equations with Positive Integer Solutions (pp. 430-436)	Solve simple linear equations using addition and subtraction.	
10-4 Solve Equations Using Addition and Subtraction (pp. 437-442)	Use variables in expressions and equations.	
10-5 Solve Equations Using Multiplication and Division (pp. 443-448)	Solve linear equations using multiplication and division with integers.	
Progress Check (p. 449)		

Content-at-a-Glance

The diagram below summarizes and unpacks Chapter 10 content.

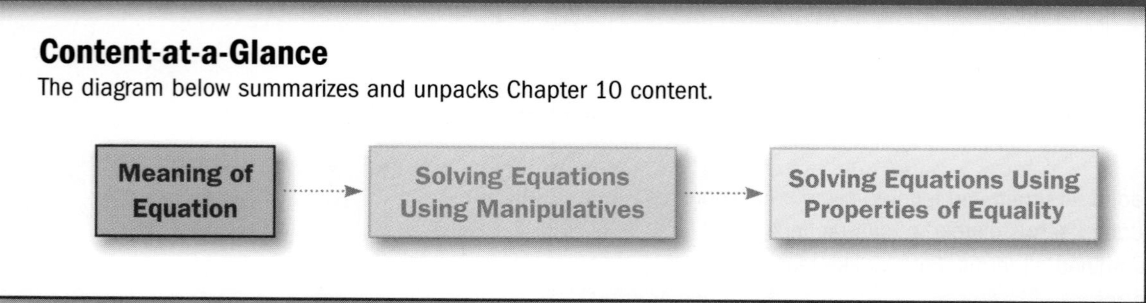

Chapter Assessment Manager

Diagnostic Diagnose students' readiness.

	Student Study Guide/ Teacher Edition	Assessment Masters	Technology
Course Placement Test		1	ExamView® Assessment Suite
Book 3 Pretest		101	ExamView® Assessment Suite
Chapter 10 Pretest		137	ExamView® Assessment Suite
Quiz/Preview	SSG 415		Math Online glencoe.com StudentWorks™ Plus

Formative Identify students' misconceptions of content knowledge.

	Student Study Guide/ Teacher Edition	Assessment Masters	Technology
Progress Checks	SSG 429, 449		Math Online glencoe.com StudentWorks™ Plus
Vocabulary Review	SSG 450		Math Online glencoe.com
Lesson Assessments			ExamView® Assessment Suite
Are They Getting It?	TE 420, 425, 433, 440, 445		Math Online glencoe.com

Summative Determine student success in learning concepts in the lesson, chapter, or book.

	Student Study Guide/ Teacher Edition	Assessment Masters	Technology
Chapter 10 Test	SSG 454	140	ExamView® Assessment Suite
Test Practice	SSG 456	143	ExamView® Assessment Suite
Alternative Assessment	TE 454	146	
See It, Do It, Say It, Write It	TE 422, 428, 436, 442, 448		
Book 3 Test		148	ExamView® Assessment Suite

Back-mapping and Vertical Alignment **McGraw-Hill's *Math Triumphs*** intervention program was conceived and developed with the final result in mind: student success in grade-level mathematics, including Algebra 1 and beyond. The authors, using the **NCTM Focal Points and Focal Connections** as their guide, developed this brand-new series by backmapping from grade-level and Algebra 1 concepts, and vertically aligning the topics so that they build upon prior skills and concepts and serve as a foundation for future topics.

Chapter Resource Manager

	Lesson 10-1	Lesson 10-2	Lesson 10-3	Lesson 10-4
Concept	Equality	Operations with Unknown Quantities	Solve Equations with Positive Integer Solutions	Solve Equations Using Addition and Subtraction
Objective	Understand the addition and multiplication properties of equality.	Use variables in expressions and equations.	Solve simple linear equations using addition and subtraction.	Use variables in expressions and equations.
Math Vocabulary	Addition Property of Equality Division Property of Equality equal equation Multiplication Property of Equality Subtraction Property of Equality	equation inverse operations variable	Addition Property of Equality inverse operations Subtraction Property of Equality variable	Addition Property of Equality Subtraction Property of Equality
Lesson Resources	**Materials** • Balance scale • Construction paper • Colored pencils **Manipulatives** • Algebra tiles • Base-ten blocks • Counters **Other Resources** CRM Vocabulary and English Language Development CRM Skills Practice CRM Problem-Solving Practice CRM Homework Practice	**Materials** • Balance scale • Bingo markers **Manipulatives** • Algebra tiles • Counters **Other Resources** CRM Vocabulary and English Language Development CRM Skills Practice CRM Problem-Solving Practice CRM Homework Practice	**Materials** • Balance scale • Deck of cards **Manipulatives** • Counters • Unit cubes **Other Resources** CRM Vocabulary and English Language Development CRM Skills Practice CRM Problem-Solving Practice CRM Homework Practice	**Materials** • Balance scale • Construction paper **Manipulatives** • Algebra tiles • Counters **Other Resources** CRM Vocabulary and English Language Development CRM Skills Practice CRM Problem-Solving Practice CRM Homework Practice
Technology	Math Online glencoe.com StudentWorks™ Plus ExamView® Assessment Suite	Math Online glencoe.com StudentWorks™ Plus ExamView® Assessment Suite	Math Online glencoe.com StudentWorks™ Plus ExamView® Assessment Suite	Math Online glencoe.com StudentWorks™ Plus ExamView® Assessment Suite

TE Teacher Edition
DVD

Lesson 10-5

Concept	Solve Equations Using Multiplication and Division
Objective	Solve linear equations using multiplication and division with integers.
Math Vocabulary	Division Property of Equality Mutliplication Property of Equality
Lesson Resources	**Materials** • Balance scale • Construction paper • Index cards **Manipulatives** • Algebra tiles • Counters **Other Resources** CRM Vocabulary and English Language Development CRM Skills Practice CRM Problem-Solving Practice CRM Homework Practice
Technology	Math Online glencoe.com StudentWorks™ Plus ExamView® Assessment Suite

Intervention Strategy

Explain Solving Equations

Writing explanations about mathematical concepts, like solving equations, helps students to deepen their understanding of the concept. Explaining their strategy to others builds knowledge and confidence, and expands their skills in problem solving.

Step 1: Have students work in pairs. Assign each pair a one-step equation to solve. Ask students to write how to solve the equation.

Step 2: Tell students to substitute the solution into the original equation to check their answer.

Step 3: Students will come to the board, write their equation, and share their description for problem solving.

Step 4: An alternative to this activity is to have students use a model or draw a picture of how to solve the equation. The model can be recreated on the board as students explain their strategy for problem-solving.

Chapter 10 Chapter Notes

Real-World Applications

Electronics Paul has 4 DVDs. He bought more DVDs. He now has 10 DVDs. How many DVDs did Paul buy? Solve the equation $4 + x = 10$. Subtract 4 from both sides of the equation to undo the addition: $4 - 4 + x = 10 - 4$; $x = 6$. Paul bought 6 DVDs.

Intervention Strategy

Who Has the Solution?

Step 1 Write the equation $x - 3 = 2$ on the board.

Step 2 Give each student an index card with one of the numbers 4, 5, or 6 written on it.

Step 3 Have students go to the board and replace x with the number on the index card. If the result is true, then the number on the card is the solution to the equation.

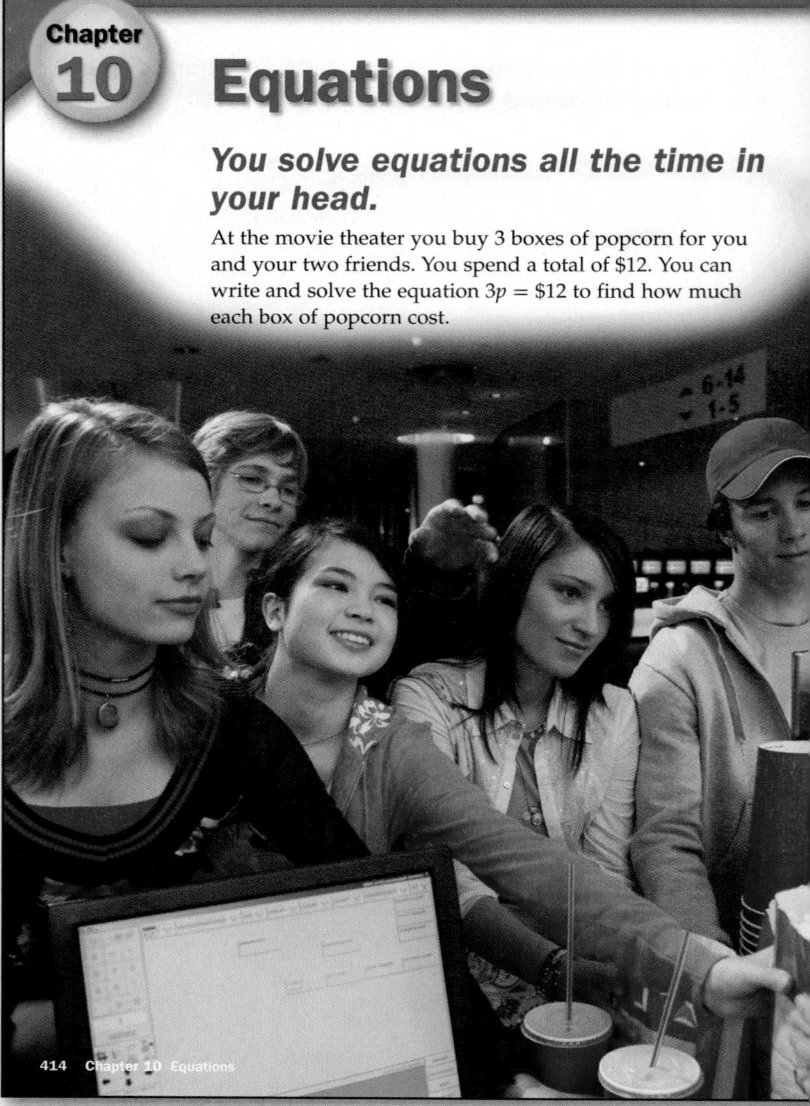

Chapter 10
Equations
You solve equations all the time in your head.
At the movie theater you buy 3 boxes of popcorn for you and your two friends. You spend a total of \$12. You can write and solve the equation 3p = \$12 to find how much each box of popcorn cost.
414 Chapter 10 Equations

Key Vocabulary

Find interactive definitions in 13 languages in the **eGlossary** at glencoe.com.

English **Español** *Introduce the most important vocabulary terms from Chapter 10.*

Addition Property of Equality
propiedad aditiva de la igualdad
adding the same amount to each side of an equation results in a balanced equation (p. 416)

Division Property of Equality
propiedad de igualdad de la división
dividing each side of an equation by the same amount results in a balanced equation (p. 416)

equation **ecuación**
a mathematical sentence that contains an equals sign, = (p. 416)

inverse operations
operaciones inversas
operations which undo each other (p. 423)

Multiplication Property of Equality **propiedad multiplicativa de la igualdad**
multiplying each side of an equation by the same amount results in a balanced equation (p. 416)

Subtraction Property of Equality
propiedad de sustracción de la igualdad
subtracting the same amount from each side of an equation results in a balanced equation (p. 416)

variable **variable**
a symbol, usually a letter, used to represent a number (p. 423)

STEP 1 Quiz

Math Online Are you ready for Chapter 10? Take the Online Readiness Quiz at *glencoe.com* to find out.

STEP 2 Preview

Get ready for Chapter 10. Review these skills and compare them with what you will learn in this chapter.

What You Know	What You Will Learn
You know how to use fact families to show the relationship between numbers. $7 + 9 = 16$; $9 + 7 = 16$; $16 - 7 = 9$; $16 - 9 = 7$	*Lessons 10-2 and 10-3* Addition and subtraction are **inverse operations**. They undo each other. To undo addition, use subtraction. To undo subtraction, use addition.
TRY IT! 1. $8 + 3 = 11$ 2. $3 + 8 = 11$ 3. $11 - 3 = 8$ 4. $11 - 8 = 3$	**Examples:** $5 + y = 8$; $y + 5 - 5 = 8 - 5$; $y = 3$. $b - 4 = 9$; $b - 4 + 4 = 9 + 4$; $b = 13$
You know related multiplication and division facts. There are 3 cartons of eggs. Each carton has 12 eggs. There are 36 eggs in all. $3 \times 12 = 36$. There are 36 eggs in all. Each carton has 12 eggs. There are 3 cartons. $36 \div 12 = 3$	*Lesson 10-5* Multiplication and division are **inverse operations**. They undo each other. Use the inverse operations and the Multiplication or Division Properties of Equality to get the variable alone on one side of the equals sign.
TRY IT! 5. $6 \times 4 = 24$; $24 \div 6 = $ 4. 6. $56 \div 8 = 7$; $7 \times 8 = $ 56	**Examples:** $\frac{z}{9} = 4$; $9 \times \frac{z}{9} = 4 \times 9$; $z = 36$. $8a = 48$; $\frac{8a}{8} = \frac{48}{8}$; $a = 6$

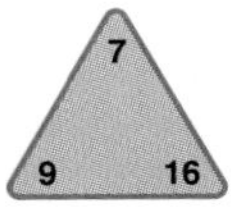

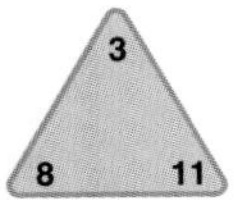

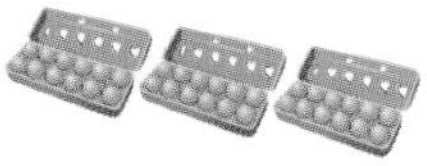

415

Vocabulary Preview

- As students complete the Chapter Preview, have them make a list of important terms throughout the chapter.
- Divide students into pairs. Have each pair compare their lists of terms to make one list. Key words should be included in the list.
- Once the list is final, the pair should prepare to physically act out each term.
- When all groups are finished, they should act out the terms for the class. An option is to have pairs act out the terms for another pair to guess.

Step 1 Quiz

Pretest/Prescribe Students can take the Online Readiness Quiz online or the Diagnostic Pretest in the Assessment Masters.

Step 2 Preview

Use this pre-chapter activity to activate students' prior knowledge, build confidence, and help students preview the lessons.

FOLDABLES® Study Organizer Dinah Zike's Foldables®

Guide students through the directions on p. A204 in the Chapter Resource Masters to create their own Foldable graphic organizer for use with this chapter.

Home Connections

- Make a list of everyday inverse operations such as turning on a light switch/turning off a light switch or putting on socks/taking off socks.

McGraw Hill Professional Development

Targeted professional development has been articulated throughout **McGraw-Hill's *Math Triumphs*** intervention program. **The McGraw-Hill Professional Development Video Library** provides short videos that support the **NCTM Focal Points and Focal Connections**. For more information, visit glencoe.com.

Model Lessons

Instructional Strategies

Lesson 10-1

Lesson Notes

Lesson Planner

Objective Understand the addition and multiplication properties of equality.

Vocabulary **Addition Property of Equality**, **Division Property of Equality**, **equal**, **equation**, **Multiplication Property of Equality**, **Subtraction Property of Equality**

Materials/Manipulatives algebra tiles, balance scale, base-ten blocks, construction paper, colored pencils, counters

Chapter Resource Masters

- CRM Vocabulary and English Language Development (p. A207)
- CRM Skills Practice (p. A208)
- CRM Problem-Solving Practice (p. A209)
- CRM Homework Practice (p. A210)

Vocabulary

Root Words Place two equal amounts of blocks on each side of a balance. Ask students what they observe. Elicit that the sides are *equal. Equality* and *equation* come from the word *equal.* Now, place 5 additional blocks on one side of the balance and not the other. Ask students what can be done to make the sides equal again. Model the *Addition Property of Equality* by adding 5 blocks to the other side. Also model the *Multiplication Property of Equality* using the balance.

Key Concept

Foundational Skills and Concepts After students have read through the Key Concept box, have them try this exercise.

> You have a scale with blue and red cubes that is in balance. What must you do if you remove three blue cubes from the left side of the scale? Remove three blue cubes from the right side of the scale.

Lesson 10-1

Equality

KEY Concept

An **equation** is a mathematical sentence that contains an equals sign. It is like a balance scale that is level.

To keep the scale level, you must do the same thing to each side of the equation.

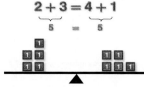

$$\underbrace{2 + 3}_{5} = \underbrace{4 + 1}_{5}$$

Adding 2 to each side of the equation results in a balanced equation.

A true equation is often referred to as a balanced equation.

The equation is balanced because

$$2 + 3 + 2 = 4 + 1 + 2$$
$$7 = 7$$

VOCABULARY

Addition Property of Equality adding the same amount to each side of an equation results in a balanced equation

Division Property of Equality dividing each side of an equation by the same amount results in a balanced equation

equal having the same value

equation a mathematical sentence that contains an equals sign, =

Multiplication Property of Equality multiplying each side of an equation by the same amount results in a balanced equation

Subtraction Property of Equality subtracting the same amount from each side of an equation results in a balanced equation

Example 1

Show that adding 3 to each side of 4 + 6 = 8 + 2 results in a balanced equation.

1. Make a model showing $4 + 6 = 8 + 2$.
   This equation is balanced because $4 + 6 = 10$ and $8 + 2 = 10$.
2. Add 3 to each side of the model.
   This equation is balanced because $(4 + 6) + 3 = 10 + 3 = 13$ and $(8 + 2) + 3 = 10 + 3 = 13$.

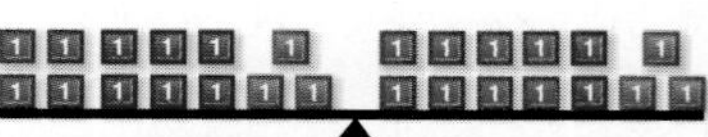

Additional *Example 1*

Show that adding 9 to each side of 1 + 7 = 4 + 4 results in a balanced equation.

1. Make a model showing $1 + 7 = 4 + 4$. This equation is balanced because $1 + 7 = 8$ and $4 + 4 = 8$.
2. Add 9 to each side of the model. This equation is balanced because $(1 + 7) + 9 = 8 + 9 = 17$ and $(4 + 4) + 9 = 8 + 9 = 17$.

YOUR TURN!

Show that adding 4 to each side of 3 + 4 = 5 + 2 results in a balanced equation.

1. Make a model showing 3 + 4 = 5 + 2. This equation is balanced because 3 + 4 = 7 and 5 + 2 = 7.
2. Add 4 to each side of the model. This equation is balanced because (3 + 4) + 4 = 7 + 4 = 11 and (5 + 2) + 4 = 7 + 4 = 11.

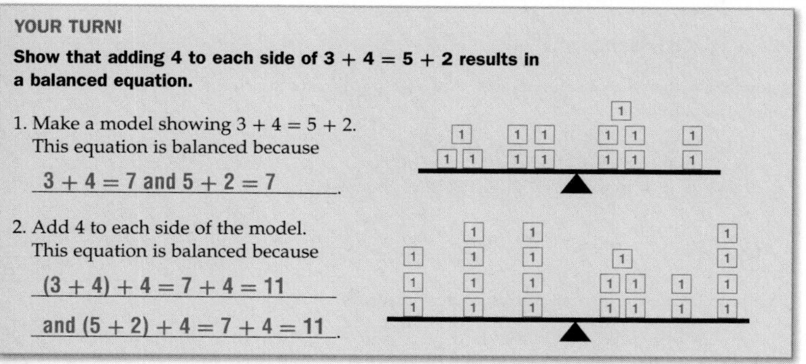

Example 2

Show that multiplying each side by 2 of 4 + 1 = 3 + 2 results in a balanced equation.

1. Make a model showing 4 + 1 = 3 + 2. This equation is balanced because 4 + 1 = 5 and 3 + 2 = 5.

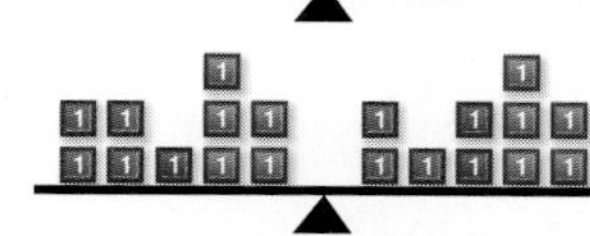

2. Multiply each side of the model by 2. This equation is balanced because (4 + 1) × 2 = 10 and (3 + 2) × 2 = 10.

YOUR TURN!

Show that multiplying each side by 2 of 5 + 3 = 6 + 2 results in a balanced equation.

1. Make a model showing 5 + 3 = 6 + 2. This equation is balanced because 5 + 3 = 8 and 6 + 2 = 8.

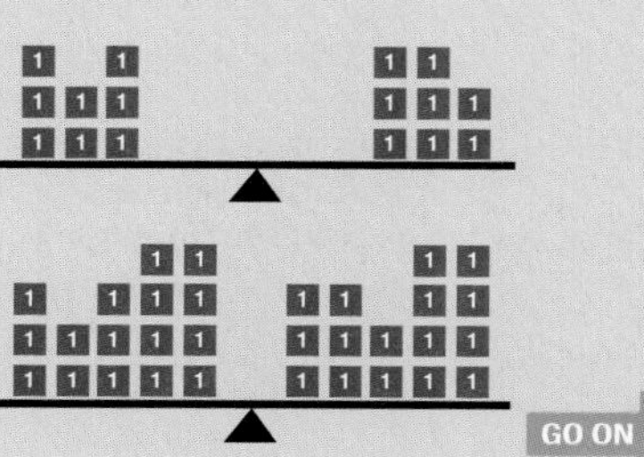

2. Multiply each side of the model by 2. This equation is balanced because (5 + 3) × 2 = 16 and (6 + 2) × 2 = 16.

GO ON

Lesson 10-1 Equality 417

Additional Example 2

Show that multiplying each side by 2 of 4 + 3 = 5 + 2 results in a balanced equation.

1. Make a model showing 4 + 3 = 5 + 2. This equation is balanced because 4 + 3 = 7 and 5 + 2 = 7.

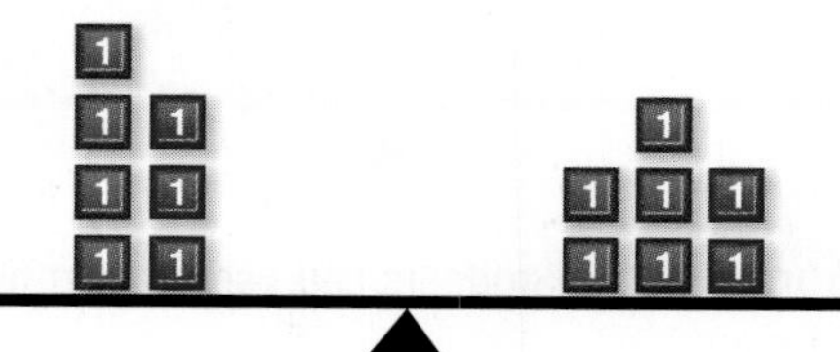

2. Multiply each side of the model by 2. This equation is balanced because (4 + 3) × 2 = 14 and (5 + 2) × 2 = 14.

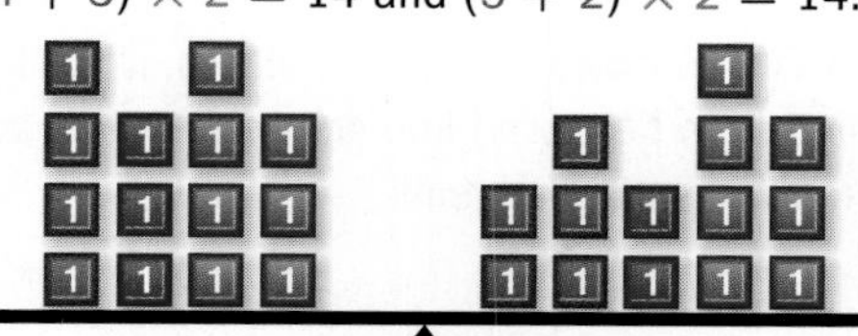

Common Error *Alert*

Modeling Equality If students are having trouble with the concept of equality, fill two different-sized containers with equal amounts of water. Have students guess as to what the relationship is between the two amounts. Prove they are the same amount by pouring them into a like container. Relate this to the idea that things may appear to be unequal when they are actually equal.

Intervention Strategy

Linguistic Learners

Examples of Equality Have students go through magazines and newspapers to find examples of equality (columns of text, headlines, equality in the news, and so on). Discuss in the class the different types of examples that were found.

Note This!

Write Examples As students take notes, encourage them to rewrite the definitions for the equality properties in their own words. Have each student create two examples of each property.

3 Practice

Using Manipulatives

Bucket Balance Use a bucket balance or scale to model problems.

Algebra Tiles Students can use algebra tiles to model equations.

On-Hand Manipulatives Cut different-colored squares from construction paper to use as you would use algebra tiles.

Base-Ten Blocks Base-ten blocks, as well as other counters, can be moved into groups to model addition and multiplication problems.

Math Coach Notes

Strategies

1. A bucket balance or scale is a visual way for students to see balance and equality. Begin with modeling simple equations like $6 = 6$.
2. Begin with simple problems and addition. Then move into expressions that require simplifying before solving.

Who is Correct?

Show that adding 1 to each side of $7 + 9 = 8 + 8$ results in a balanced equation.

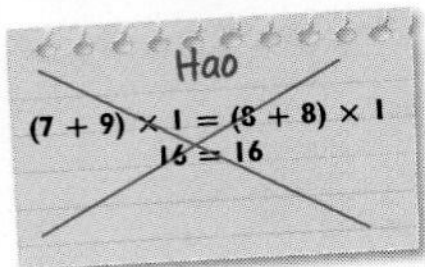
Hao
(7 + 9) × 1 = (8 + 8) × 1
16 = 16

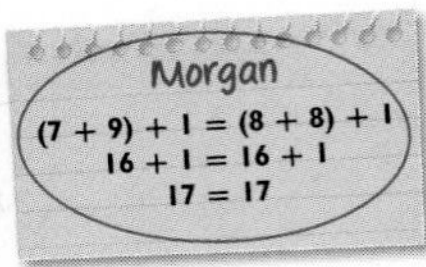
Morgan
(7 + 9) + 1 = (8 + 8) + 1
16 + 1 = 16 + 1
17 = 17

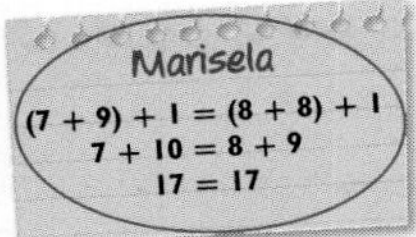
Marisela
(7 + 9) + 1 = (8 + 8) + 1
7 + 10 = 8 + 9
17 = 17

Circle correct answer(s). Cross out incorrect answer(s).

Guided Practice

1. Show that adding 5 to each side of $7 + 2 = 6 + 3$ results in a balanced equation.
   $(7 + 2) + 5 = 9 + 5 = 14$ and
   $(6 + 3) + 5 = 9 + 5 = 14$

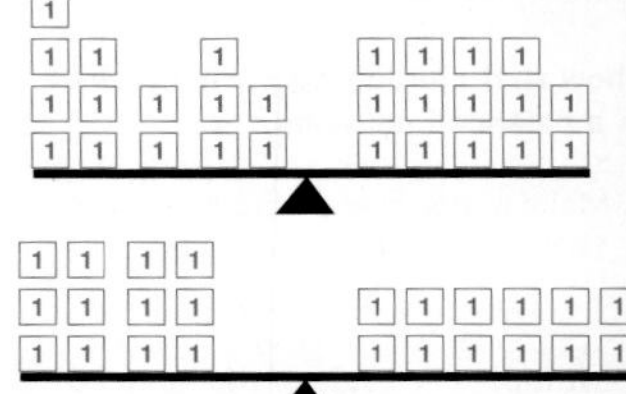

2. Show that multiplying each side by 2 of $2 \times 3 = 6 \times 1$ results in a balanced equation.
   $(2 \times 3) \times 2 = 6 \times 2 = 12$ and
   $(6 \times 1) \times 2 = 6 \times 2 = 12$

Step by Step Practice

3. What number goes in the blank to make $(7 + 4) + 5 =$ ______ $+ (18 - 7)$ a balanced equation?

   Step 1 The expressions inside the parentheses have the same value.
   $7 + 4 =$ <u>18 − 7</u>

   Step 2 Identify and apply the correct property to find the missing number.
   Use the <u>Addition</u> Property of Equality.
   $(7 + 4) + 5 =$ <u>5</u> $+ (18 - 7)$

   Step 3 Check: $(7 + 4) + 5 =$ <u>5</u> $+ (18 - 7)$
   $11 + 5 =$ <u>5</u> $+$ <u>11</u>
   <u>16</u> $=$ <u>16</u> ✓

The left side of the equals sign has the same value as the right side.

418 Chapter 10 Equations

Who *is Correct?*

Diagnostic Teaching

- Hao multiplied by 1 instead of adding 1 to each side of the equation. Hao demonstrated the Multiplication Property of Equality. The question asked him to demonstrate the Addition Property of Equality.
- Morgan wrote $17 = 17$. This is correct.
- Marisela wrote $17 = 17$. This is correct.

Remind students to think about the inverse operation as the operation that will "undo" another operation.

nd the missing number to make each equation balanced.

1 + (20 ÷ 5) = (9 − 5) + ______

Since 20 ÷ 5 = 9 − 5,

1 + (20 ÷ 5) = (9 − 5) + 1

by the Addition Property of Equality.

5 ______ × 18 = (16 + 2) × 5

Since 18 = 16 + 2,

5 × 18 = (16 + 2) × 5

by the Multiplication Property of Equality.

ep by Step Problem-Solving Practice

lve.

MONEY Ronika had 10 dollars. She earned 3 more dollars. Nick had 13 dollars. Then Ronika and Nick earned 4 dollars each. Do Ronika and Nick have the same amount of money now?

Problem-Solving Strategies

- ☐ Look for a pattern.
- ☐ Guess and check.
- ☐ Act it out.
- ☑ Solve a simpler problem.
- ☐ Work backward.

Understand Read the problem. Write what you know.

Ronika has 10 + 3 dollars.

Nick has 13 dollars.

Each earned 4 dollars more.

Plan Pick a strategy. One strategy is to solve a simpler problem. Find the total dollars for each.

Solve Solve the equation for Ronika's money.

10 + 3 + 4 = 17

Solve the equation for Nick's money.

13 + 4 = 17

Do Ronika and Nick have equal amounts of money?

yes

Written as one equation:

Ronika		Nick
(10 + 3) + 4	=	(13 + 4)

Check You can make a model to check your work.

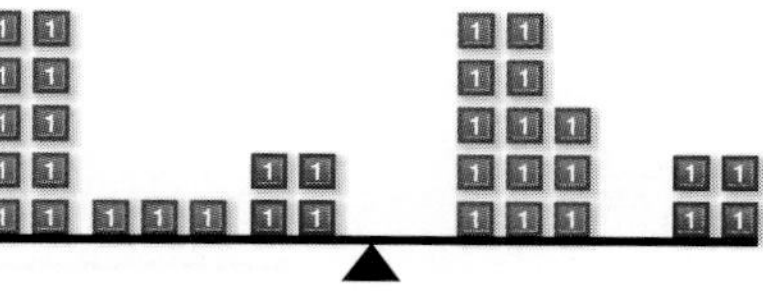

GO ON

Lesson 10-1 Equality 419

English Learner Strategy

Oral Explanations Ask the following questions to help students learn and demonstrate the concepts of equality.

1. Place blocks on the scale to make it equal.
2. Is (4 + 3) = (5 + 2) an equation?
3. Why is the expression on the left equal to the expression on the right? $2 \times (4 + 3) = 2 \times (5 + 2)$
4. Explain how the Addition Property of Equality is similar to the Multiplication Property of Equality.
5. Describe the Addition and Multiplication Properties of Equality.

Math Coach Notes

Properties

The basic component of symbolic manipulation has to do with equations in the form of the Addition and Multiplication Properties of Equality. Students should know how to express the two properties, i.e., the two standards of this lesson, with any four numbers. As the grade level progresses, students should realize that these properties are valid no matter the numbers, even for fractions and variables.

Common Error *Alert*

Multi-Step Problem If a student struggles with Exercise 8, he or she may not be able to translate the use of money into a number sentence. Model these problems using money. Make an equation mat with paper. Place the cost for jeans on one side and the cost for 2 shirts on the other. Remove $5 from each side. Have the student model Exercise 8. Write the equations down on paper to connect the materials with the symbols.

Odd/Even Assignments

Exercises 10–24 are structured so that students practice the same concepts whether they are assigned the odd or even problems.

In-Class Assignment

Have students complete Exercises 10, 11, 17, 18, 22, and 26 to ensure that they understand the concept.

7 HOBBIES Pia had 12 CDs. She bought 2 more. Leigh had 9 CDs. She bought 5 more. Pia and Leigh each received 2 CDs for their birthdays. How many CDs do Pia and Leigh each have?
Check off each step.

✔ Understand: I underlined key words.

✔ Plan: To solve the problem, I will solve a simpler problem

✔ Solve: The answer is $(12 + 2) + 2 = 16$ and $(9 + 5) + 2 = 16$; Pia and Leigh each have 16 CDs

✔ Check: I checked my answer by making a model

8 SHOPPING Jeans are on sale for $24 each. Shirts are on sale for $11 each. Kaya has a coupon for $5 off any purchase. She wants to buy 2 shirts. Will she spend the same amount if she buys 1 pair of jeans? If not, which will cost less?

No; $24 - 5 = 19$ and $(11 + 11) - 5 = 17$

2 shirts will cost less.

9 Reflect How are the Addition and Multiplication Properties of Equality the same?

If you add to or multiply by the same number on each side of an equation, the two sides remain equal.

Skills, Concepts, and Problem Solving

10 Show that adding 7 to each side of $1 + 3 = 2 + 2$ results in a balanced equation.

$(1 + 3) + 7 = 4 + 7 = 11$ and

$(2 + 2) + 7 = 4 + 7 = 11$

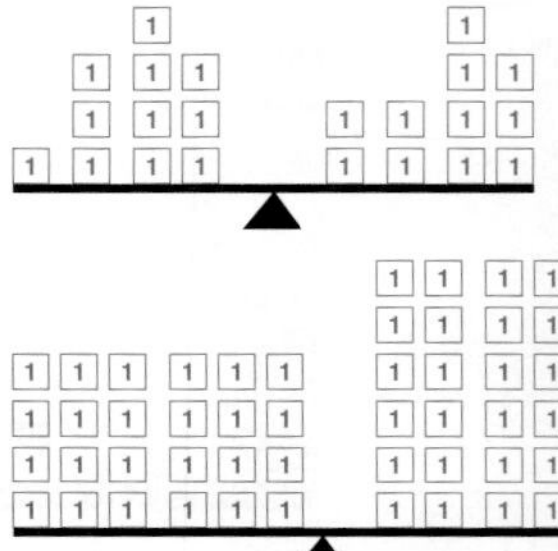

11 Show that multiplying each side by 2 of $3 \times 4 = 2 \times 6$ results in a balanced equation.

$(3 \times 4) \times 2 = 12 \times 2$ or 24 and

$(2 \times 6) \times 2 = 12 \times 2$ or 24

420 Chapter 10 Equations

Are They Getting It?

Check students' understanding of the Addition and Multiplication Properties of Equality by writing these problems on the board. Have students state which are correct and which are incorrect.

1. The model shows that adding 3 to each side of $3 + 2 = 4 + 1$ results in a balanced equation.

This is incorrect because there are 8 tiles on the right and only 5 tiles on the left.

2. This equation models the Addition Property of Equality: $(11 + 2) \times 2 = (12 + 1) \times 2$

This is incorrect. It models the Multiplication Property of Equality because both sides are multiplied by 2.

12 Show that adding 3 to each side of $3 + 3 = 4 + 2$ results in a balanced equation.

$(3 + 3) + 3 = 6 + 3 = 9$ and

$(4 + 2) + 3 = 6 + 3 = 9$

13 Show that multiplying each side by 2 of $3 \times 2 = 6 \times 1$ results in a balanced equation.

$(3 \times 2) \times 2 = 6 \times 2 = 12$ and

$(6 \times 1) \times 2 = 6 \times 2 = 12$

14 Show that adding 4 to each side of $7 + 2 = 5 + 4$ results in a balanced equation.

$(7 + 2) + 4 = 9 + 4 = 13$ and

$(5 + 4) + 4 = 9 + 4 = 13$

15 Show that multiplying each side by 2 of $4 + 3 = 5 + 2$ results in a balanced equation.

$(4 + 3) \times 2 = 7 \times 2 = 14$ and

$(5 + 2) \times 2 = 7 \times 2 = 14$

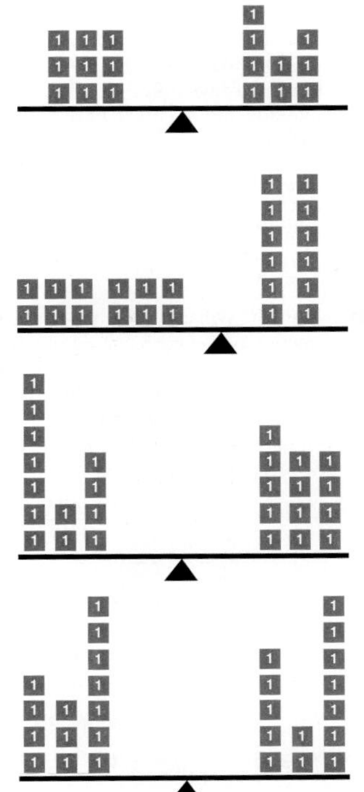

Find the missing number to make each equation balanced.

16 $(15 \times 2) + \underline{10} = 10 + (6 \times 5)$

17 $4 \times (19 - 1) = (13 + 5) \times \underline{4}$

18 $5 + (24 \div 4) = 5 + (2 \times \underline{3})$

19 $8 \times (3 + \underline{2}) = 8 \times (12 - 7)$

20 $3 + (5 \times 2) = 3 + (6 + \underline{4})$

21 $(8 + 6) + 9 = \underline{9} + (20 - 6)$

Note This!

Color Coding Some students will become confused and mix up the two equality properties. Tell these students to go through their notes and highlight examples of the Addition Property of Equality using one color. Then go back and use another color for the Multiplication Property of Equality. When they are solving problems have them highlight the operation sign using the same color as they highlighted that property in their notes.

Math Challenge

Cooperative Equations Divide students into pairs. Each student will write an expression using addition or multiplication. Then students will trade papers. Each student will then write an expression that is equal to the one written.

Example:

Student 1 writes:		Student 2 writes:
$(7 + 1) \times 3$	=	$3 \times (6 + 2)$

4 Assess

See It, Do It, Say It, Write It

Step 1 Write an equation on the board. Add 7 to one side of the equation. Select a student to say what must be done to the other side to make the equation balanced.

Step 2 Repeat step one, but multiply one side of the equation by 3.

Step 3 Write 10 equations on the board. Tell students to rewrite 5 of the equations using the Addition Property of Equality and the other 5 equations using the Multiplication Property of Equality. Students can share their strategies in class.

Step 4 Write 6 new equations on the board that demonstrate both properties. Leave one blank in each equation. Have students use manipulatives such as a balance, algebra tiles, or base-ten blocks to model and find the missing number. Students can share their strategies in class.

Looking Ahead: Pre-teach

Operations with Unknown Quantities In the next lesson, students will learn about operations with unknown quantities. A *variable* represents an unknown quantity. Multiplication and division are *inverse operations.* Addition and subtraction are *inverse operations.* This means these operations undo each other.

Example

What number belongs in the blank to make the equation balanced? Check your answer using the inverse operation. $7 \times$ ____ $= 14$ 2; $14 \div 2 = 7$

Find the value of each variable.

1. $5 \times x = 20$ $x = 4$
2. $7 \times z = 42$ $z = 6$
3. $\frac{y}{12} = 3$ $y = 36$

Solve.

22 WEATHER The graph shows the amount of snowfall in Colorado and Michigan over three days. After Wednesday, did Colorado and Michigan have the same amount of snow? Explain.

Yes; After Wednesday, both Colorado and Michigan had 22 inches of snow.

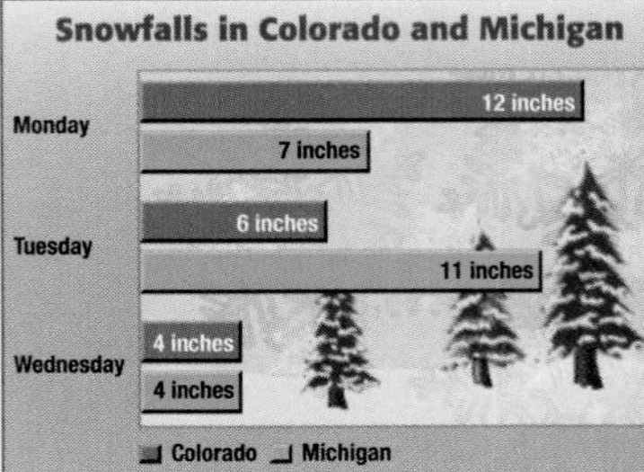

23 MOVIES Will and Morena went to see a movie. Will spent \$3 on a soda, \$6 on popcorn, and \$2 on candy. Morena spent \$4 on a soda and \$7 on candy. If Will and Morena paid \$10 for each of their tickets, did they spend the same amount of money at the movies? Explain.

Yes; $(3 + 6 + 2) + 10 = (4 + 7) + 10$; $11 + 10 = 11 + 10$; $21 = 21$

24 GARDENING Vivian and Tara planted flowers in their backyard. Vivian planted 5 tulips and 4 daisies. Tara planted 5 tulips and 3 daises. If both Vivian and Tara planted 6 daffodils, did they plant the same amount of flowers? Explain.

No, Vivian planted more flowers; Vivian $(5 + 4) + 6 = 9 + 6 = 15$; Tara $(5 + 3) + 6 = 14$

Vocabulary Check **Write the vocabulary word that completes each sentence.**

25 The Multiplication Property of Equality states that multiplying each side of an equation by the same amount results in a balanced equation.

26 Writing in Math Explain the meaning of the equals sign (=).

Answers will vary. Sample answer: The equal sign means that both sides of an equation are equal or have the same value.

422 Chapter 10 Equations

Ticket Out the Door

Fill in the Blanks Write the following on the board:

1. $(10 \times 3) + 5 =$ ____ $+ (28 + 2)$ 5
2. $3 \times (4 +$ ____$) = 3 \times (12 - 6)$ 2
3. $9 + (5 + 5) = (14 - 4) +$ ____ 9

Have students transfer the problems on paper and solve them. They will hand in their answers as they exit the classroom.

Lesson 10-2 Operations with Unknown Quantities

KEY Concept

You can use a letter, a box, or other symbols to represent an unknown amount or quantity.

Expressions	*Equations*
5 + □	10 × □ = 15
8 − □	16 ÷ □ = 4

You can use inverse operations to solve for □.

4 + □ = 7 7 − 4 = 3 4 + 3 = 7 So, □ = 3.

Inverse operations are opposite operations. They undo each other. Addition and subtraction are inverse operations. Multiplication and division are also inverse operations.

You can use a fact triangle to help you solve simple equations.

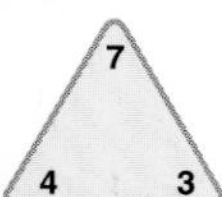

4 + 3 = 7 3 + 4 = 7
7 − 4 = 3 7 − 3 = 4

If you know that 4 + 3 = 7, you can solve the equation 4 + □ = 7.

VOCABULARY

equation
a mathematical sentence that contains an equals sign, =

inverse operations
operations which undo each other; for example, addition and subtraction are inverse operations

variable
a symbol, usually a letter, used to represent a number

To undo addition, use subtraction. To undo subtraction, use addition. To undo multplication, use division. To undo division, use multiplication.

Example 1

Find the value of the □ to make the equation 6 + □ = 9 balanced.

1. Use the inverse operations of addition and subtraction.
 6 + □ = 9, so 9 − 6 = □
 9 − 6 = 3, so □ = 3

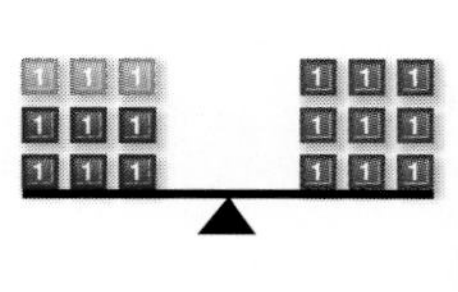

2. Use a model to check your answer.
 Think: What number added to 6 equals 9?
 6 + 3 = 9 The value of □ must be 3.

GO ON

Additional ***Example 1***

Find the value of the □ to make the equation □ + 9 = 16 balanced.

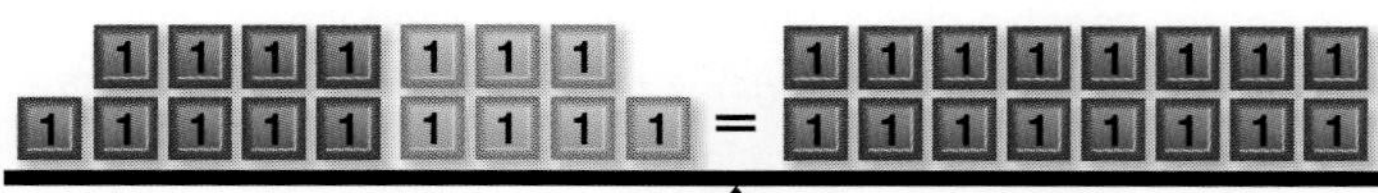

1. Use the inverse operations of addition and subtraction.
 □ + 9 = 16, so 16 − 9 = □ 16 − 9 = 7, so □ = 7
2. Use a model to check your answer.
 Think: What number added to 9 equals 16?

 7 + 9 = 16 The value of □ must be 7.

Lesson Notes

Lesson 10-2

Lesson Planner

Objective Use variables in expressions and equations.

Vocabulary **equation**, **inverse operations**, **variable**

Materials/Manipulatives algebra tiles, bucket balance, counters, bingo markers

Chapter Resource Masters

CRM Vocabulary and English Language Development (p. A211)

CRM Skills Practice (p. A212)

CRM Problem-Solving Practice (p. A213)

CRM Homework Practice (p. A214)

1 Introduce

Vocabulary

Clarify Terms Write 7 + □ = 10 on the board. What number belongs in the box? Replace the box with an *x*. What quantity does the *variable* represent? Talk about *variables*; reinforce that a *variable* represents an unknown number or quantity. Model how to get the *variable* alone. Guide students to see that subtraction will undo addition, so subtraction is the *inverse operation* of addition. *Inverse operations* are the direct opposites of each other. Repeat with a multiplication equation.

2 Teach

Key Concept

Foundational Skills and Concepts After students have read through the Key Concept box, have them try these exercises.

1. If 5 − □ = 2, then □ = ? 3
2. If 24 ÷ □ = 4, then 4 × □ = ? 24
3. The operation to undo addition is _____. subtraction

Additional **Example 2**

Find the value of □ in the equation $5 \times \square = 30$.

1. Use the inverse operations of multiplication and division.

$5 \times \square = 30$, so $30 \div 5 = \square$
$30 \div 5 = 6$, so $\square = 6$

2. Check your answer by substituting 6 for □.

$5 \times \square = 30$
$5 \times 6 = 30$
$30 = 30$ ✓

Math Coach Notes

The Variable Students should be taught from the beginning that a variable represents a value. As a value, a variable can be added, subtracted, multiplied, and divided. Although you may initially start with boxes or lines, use letters for variables to remind students that the variable is much more than a placeholder; it represents an unknown quantity.

Note This!

Questions and Stars As students take notes, encourage them to put question marks by things they do not understand and stars by concepts that are important. Later, they can use their textbooks or ask to clarify information they did not understand. The stars will clue them in to items to which they should pay particular attention.

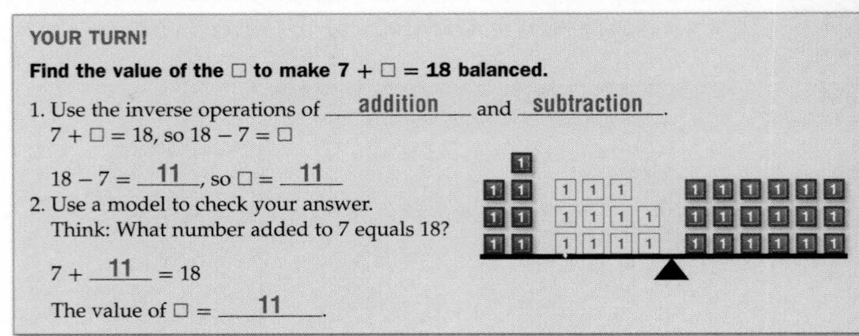
YOUR TURN!

Find the value of the □ to make $7 + \square = 18$ balanced.

1. Use the inverse operations of <u>addition</u> and <u>subtraction</u>.
   $7 + \square = 18$, so $18 - 7 = \square$
   $18 - 7 =$ <u>11</u>, so $\square =$ <u>11</u>
2. Use a model to check your answer.
   Think: What number added to 7 equals 18?
   $7 +$ <u>11</u> $= 18$
   The value of □ = <u>11</u>.

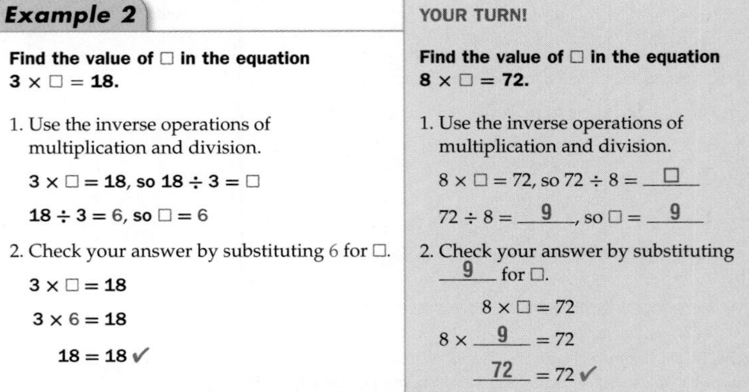
Example 2

Find the value of □ in the equation $3 \times \square = 18$.

1. Use the inverse operations of multiplication and division.
   $3 \times \square = 18$, so $18 \div 3 = \square$
   $18 \div 3 = 6$, so $\square = 6$
2. Check your answer by substituting 6 for □.
   $3 \times \square = 18$
   $3 \times 6 = 18$
   $18 = 18$ ✓

YOUR TURN!

Find the value of □ in the equation $8 \times \square = 72$.

1. Use the inverse operations of multiplication and division.
   $8 \times \square = 72$, so $72 \div 8 =$ <u>□</u>
   $72 \div 8 =$ <u>9</u>, so $\square =$ <u>9</u>
2. Check your answer by substituting <u>9</u> for □.
   $8 \times \square = 72$
   $8 \times$ <u>9</u> $= 72$
   <u>72</u> $= 72$ ✓

Who is Correct?

Find the value of the box in the equation $3 \times \square = 96$.

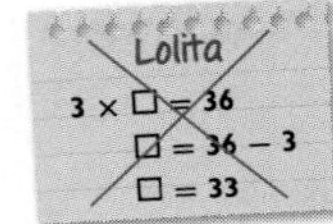

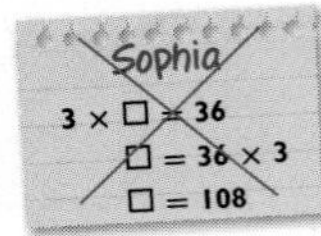

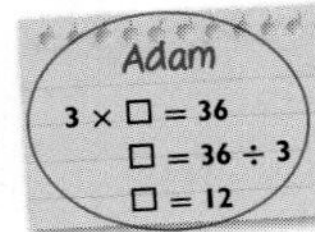

Circle correct answer(s). Cross out incorrect answer(s).

Who *is Correct?*

Diagnostic Teaching

- Lolita wrote □ = 33. This is incorrect. Lolita subtracted 3 from each side to get the variable alone. She should have used the inverse operation of multiplication. If students have solved the problem this way, then review the inverse operations.
- Sophia wrote □ = 108. This is incorrect because she did not use the inverse operation of multiplication. Review the inverse operations.
- Adam wrote □ = 12. This is correct because 3 times 12 equals 36.

Remind students to check their answers by substitution.

Guided Practice

Find the value of each box by modeling the equation.

1. $4 + \square = 10$

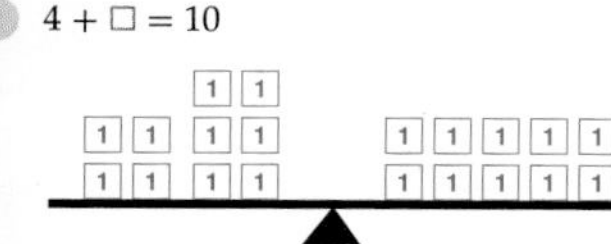

$\square =$ 6

2. $11 - \square = 7$

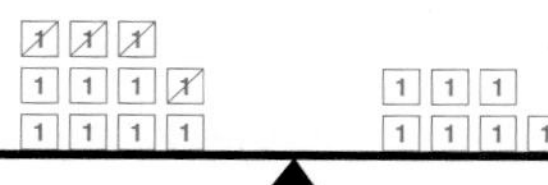

$\square =$ 4

Step by Step Practice

3. Find the value of $\square$ in the equation $\frac{\square}{8} = 4$.

Step 1 $\frac{\square}{8}$ means $\square \div 8$. Use the inverse operations of multiplication and division.

$\square \div 8 = 4$, so $8 \times 4 =$ $\square$

$8 \times 4 =$ 32, so $\square =$ 32

Step 2 Check your answer by substituting 32 for $\square$.

$\frac{\square}{8} = 4$

$\frac{32}{8} = 4$

4 $= 4$ ✓

Find the value for the box in each equation.

4. $\square - 17 = 9$

$\square - 17 = 9$, so $9 +$ 17 $= \square$

$9 +$ 17 $=$ 26, so $\square =$ 26

5. $4 \times \square = 28$

$4 \times \square = 28$, so $28 \div$ 4 $= \square$

$28 \div$ 4 $=$ 7, so $\square =$ 7

6. $\frac{\square}{3} = 9$

$\square =$ 27

7. $13 + \square = 21$

$\square =$ 8

GO ON

Are They Getting It?

Check students' understanding of solving equations to find the unknown quantity. Have them draw diagrams or models to explain. Ask students to point out which answers are wrong and explain the errors.

1. The value of $\square$ in $6 \times \square = 36$ is 6. This is correct because $6 \times 6 = 36$.
2. The inverse operation of subtraction is division. This is incorrect. The inverse operation of subtraction is addition.
3. If $11 + \square = 22$, then $22 - 11 = \square$. This is correct because subtraction is the inverse operation of addition.

3 Practice

Using Manipulatives

Bucket Balance When presenting Example 1, use a bucket balance or scale to model the problem.

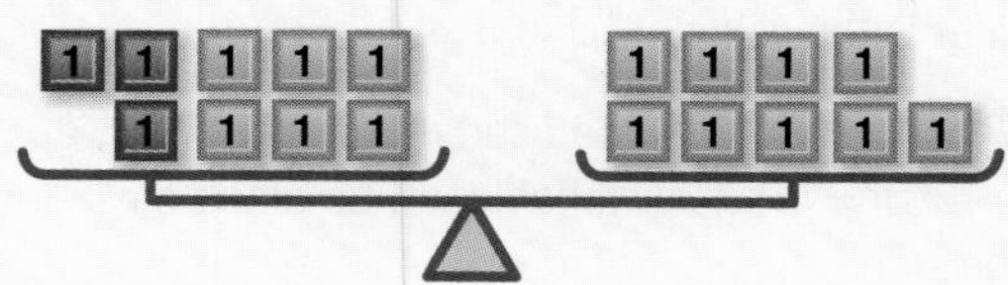

Algebra Tiles Students can use algebra tiles to perform inverse operations and find the value of unknown quantities.

Counters Two-colored counters can be used to represent known and unknown quantities in an equation.

On-Hand Manipulatives Use Bingo markers of different colors in place of algebra tiles or counters.

Math Coach Notes

Strategies

1. Connect this lesson with the previous lesson on equality. Remind students that the values on either side of an equal sign are the same. To find the value of a variable, use inverse operations to get the variable alone on one side of the equal sign.
2. Question students on what operations are in an equation, and what the inverse operation is. As algebraic equations increase in difficulty, students will need to know how to isolate the variable. Start with simple equations and then increase their complexity.

English Learner Strategy

Guiding Questions Put 3 blocks or tiles on the right side of a scale. Put 7 blocks on the left side. Working aloud with students, say:

- Place blocks on one side of the scale to make it equal.
- What is the value of □ in 3 + □ = 7?
- What operation can be used on the equation 3 + □ = 7 so the variable will be alone on one side?
- Explain how to find the value of □ in the equation □ ÷ 4 = 7.
- Describe how to use inverse operations to find the value of an unknown quantity.

Math Coach Notes

Practice Sheets

In mathematics, practice is essential for learning to occur. When it is time to study for a quiz or test, make practice sheets for students to complete. Share the solutions with the class, or make an answer sheet available for students to check their own answers.

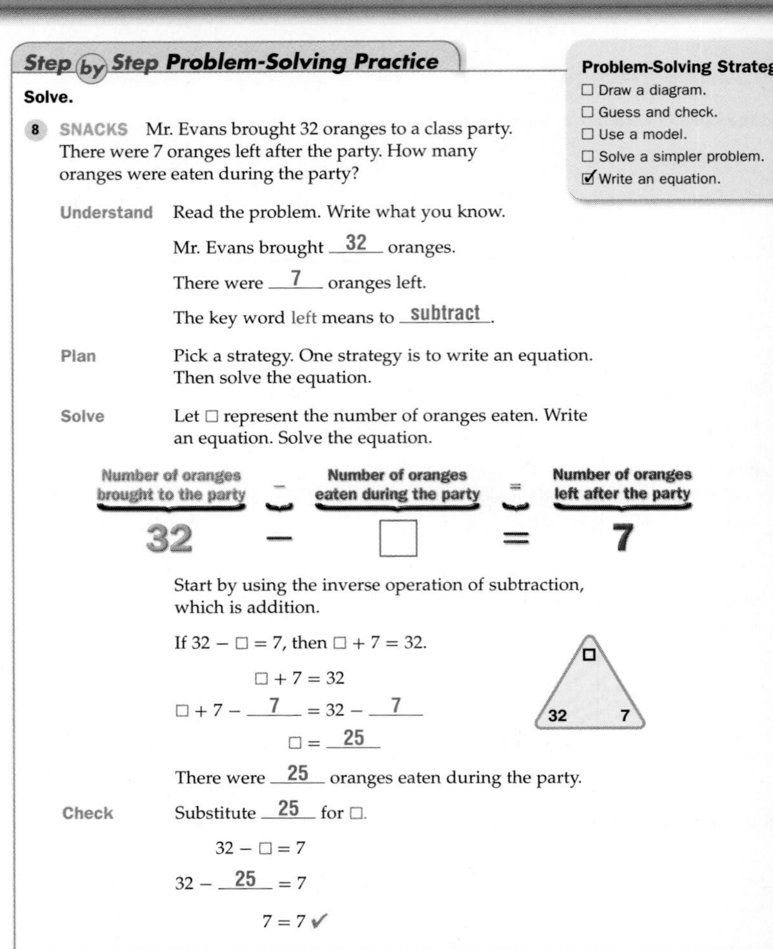

Step by Step Problem-Solving Practice

Problem-Solving Strategies
- ☐ Draw a diagram.
- ☐ Guess and check.
- ☐ Use a model.
- ☐ Solve a simpler problem.
- ☑ Write an equation.

Solve.

8 SNACKS Mr. Evans brought 32 oranges to a class party. There were 7 oranges left after the party. How many oranges were eaten during the party?

Understand Read the problem. Write what you know.

Mr. Evans brought __32__ oranges.

There were __7__ oranges left.

The key word left means to __subtract__.

Plan Pick a strategy. One strategy is to write an equation. Then solve the equation.

Solve Let □ represent the number of oranges eaten. Write an equation. Solve the equation.

Number of oranges brought to the party − Number of oranges eaten during the party = Number of oranges left after the party

32 − □ = 7

Start by using the inverse operation of subtraction, which is addition.

If 32 − □ = 7, then □ + 7 = 32.

□ + 7 = 32

□ + 7 − __7__ = 32 − __7__

□ = __25__

There were __25__ oranges eaten during the party.

Check Substitute __25__ for □.

32 − □ = 7

32 − __25__ = 7

7 = 7 ✓

426 Chapter 10 Equations

Intervention Strategy

Intrapersonal/Visual Learners

Graphic Organizers

1. Use an overhead to project the following:

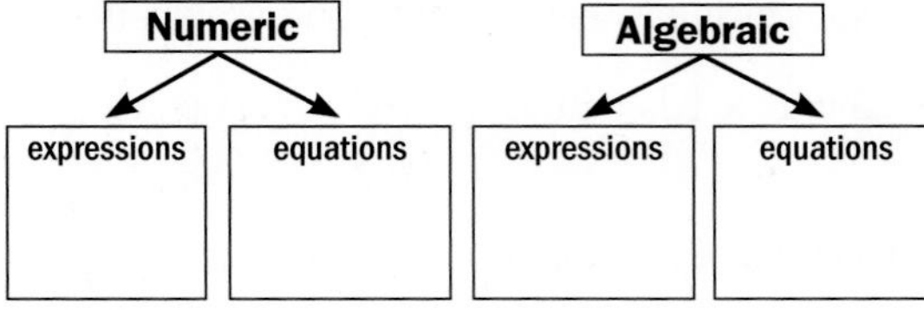

2. Talk about the graphic organizer and discuss the meanings of the different words. Model a numeric equation and expression, as well as an equation and expression that have variables.
3. Tell students to write three examples for each category.
4. Ask them to share their examples. Use this technique to help students connect concepts and words. Encourage them to make their own vocabulary charts or concept maps in other lessons.

ENTERTAINMENT Emmett and Toby went to a baseball game. They bought snacks that cost $7.50. The total cost of the game tickets and snacks was $23.50. How much did the tickets cost? Check off each step.

✔ Understand: I underlined key words.

✔ Plan: To solve the problem, I will write an equation

✔ Solve: The answer is □ + 7.50 = 23.50; 23.50 − 7.50 = 16; □ = $16

✔ Check: I checked my answer by substituting a value for the □

FOOD Terrence is packaging bagels to sell at the fair. He is using boxes that hold 12 bagels each. How many of these boxes will he need to package 192 bagels?

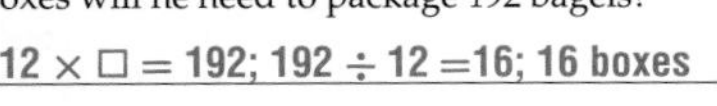

12 × □ = 192; 192 ÷ 12 =16; 16 boxes

ELECTIONS Mrs. Dixon was running for school board. She had 225 campaign buttons to hand out. After one week, she had 36 buttons left. How many buttons did she hand out that week?

36 + □ = 225; 225 − 36 = 189; 189 buttons

2 **Reflect** How do you decide which operation to perform to solve an equation that contains a variable?

Answers may vary. Sample answer: Look at the operation shown in the equation. Use the inverse operation of that operation.

Skills, Concepts, and Problem Solving

ind the value of each box by modeling the equation.

3 2 × □ = 14

14 6 + □ = 13

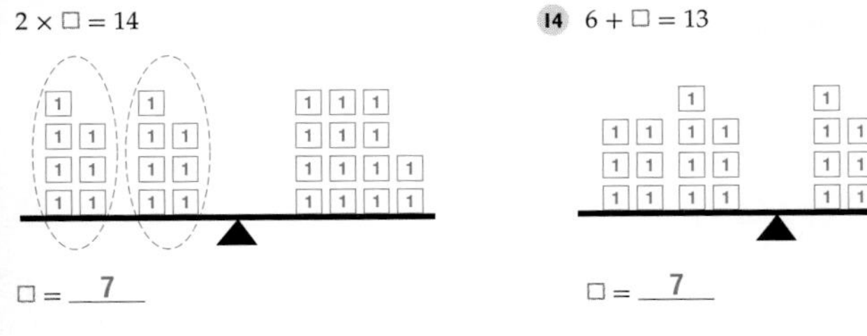

□ = 7

□ = 7

GO ON

Common Error *Alert*

Multi-Step Problem If a student struggles with Exercise 10, he or she may not understand what operation the word problem represents. Ask the student to reread the problem and then rephrase it in his or her own words. This problem could also be modeled with base-ten blocks using division. Either way would be correct.

Odd/Even Assignments

Exercises 13–20 are structured so that students practice the same concepts whether they are assigned the odd or even problems.

In-Class Assignment

Have students complete Exercises 13, 16, 20, and 22 to ensure that they understand the concept.

Math Challenge

Secret Words Give each student a card with a secret word that has about five letters. Each letter in the word represents its place in the alphabet. For example, a "j" is worth 10 because it is the tenth letter of the alphabet. Students write the number that represents each letter. Next, students take each number (in order) and use that value to represent □ in an equation. For instance, for "j" students might write 8 × □ = 80; the value of the variable is 10. Once they have written their equations in order, they will trade with their partners and solve the equations. Whoever gets the other student's secret word first wins.

Example:

For the secret word "jack," the numbers are 10, 1, 3, and 11.
The four equations might be:
1) 8 × □ = 80 2) 9 ÷ □ = 9
3) □ + 15 = 18 4) 1 + □ = 12

See It, Do It, Say It, Write It

Step 1 Write four algebraic equations on the board using each of the four operations.

Step 2 Ask students what the inverse operations are for each. Then solve.

Step 3 Students work in pairs or alone with algebra tiles and equation mats. Have them model several equations. Have them use the models to find the unknown quantities.

Step 4 Ask students to describe what a variable is. Have them write the steps they would take to solve two equations that you have written on the board.

Looking Ahead: Pre-Teach

Equations In the next lesson, students will learn about solving equations with positive integer solutions.

Example

Solve $x + 7 = 16$.

Subtract 7 from each side of the equation so that x is isolated on one side of the equals sign.

$$\begin{array}{r} x + 7 = 16 \\ -7 = -7 \\ \hline x = 9 \end{array}$$

Solve each equation.

1. $n - 8 = 10$ $n = 18$
2. $y + 4 = 12$ $y = 8$
3. $b - 1 = 7$ $b = 8$

Find the value of the box in each equation.

15. $2 \times \square = 16$ $\square =$ 8
16. $\square - 12 = 8$ $\square =$ 20
17. $19 + \square = 27$ $\square =$ 8
18. $\frac{\square}{4} = 5$ $\square =$ 20

Write an equation to represent each situation. Then answer the question.

19. FUNDRAISING Lance is a student of Ms. Williams' class. Lance sold 39 items from the school's fundraising catalog. How many items did the rest of his class sell?
$39 + \square = 205; 205 - 39 = 166;$ 166 items

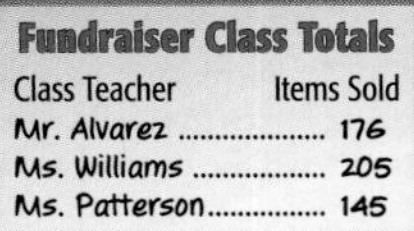

Fundraiser Class Totals

Class Teacher	Items Sold
Mr. Alvarez	176
Ms. Williams	205
Ms. Patterson	145

20. JOBS José earned $8 per hour last week. His total earnings were $200. How many hours did José work last week?
$8 \times \square = 200; 200 \div 8 = 25;$ 25 hours

Vocabulary Check **Write the vocabulary word or term that completes each sentence.**

21. A variable is a symbol, usually a letter, used to represent a number.

22. Writing in Math Explain why multiplication and division are inverse operations. Include an example.
Answers will vary. Sample answer: Multiplication and division are inverse operations because they undo each other. $4 \times 5 = 20$ and $20 \div 5 = 4$

Spiral Review (Lesson 10-1, p. 416)

23. Show that adding 2 to each side of $21 - 4 = 12 + 5$ results in a balanced equation.

$(21 - 4) + 2 = (12 + 5) + 2$

$17 + 2 = 17 + 2$

$19 = 19$

STO

428 Chapter 10 Equations

Ticket Out the Door

Exit Questions Write the following on the board:

1. Give an example of a variable. Define it. Answers will vary. A variable represents a number or quantity.
2. Name the four operations and their inverse operations. Addition is subtraction, subtraction is addition, multiplication is division, and division is multiplication.
3. Use a drawing or a diagram to show how to solve the equation: $13 - \square = 7$. Drawings will vary.

Students hand in their papers as they exit the classroom.

Chapter 10 Progress Check 1 (Lessons 10-1 and 10-2)

Show that adding 6 to each side of $1 + 4 = 2 + 3$ results in a balanced equation.

$(1 + 4) + 6 = (2 + 3) + 6$

$5 + 6 = 5 + 6$

$11 = 11$

2 Show that multiplying by 2 on each side of $1 \times 4 = 2 \times 2$ results in a balanced equation.

$2 \times (1 \times 4) = 2 \times (2 \times 2)$

$2 \times 4 = 2 \times 4$

$8 = 8$

d the missing number to make each equation balanced.

$(12 \times 3) + \underline{5} = 5 + (9 \times 4)$

4 $2 \times (16 - 7) = (6 + 3) \times \underline{2}$

$7 + (32 \div 4) = 7 + (\underline{2} \times 4)$

6 $9 \times (5 + \underline{6}) = 9 \times (18 - 7)$

d the value of each box by modeling the equation.

$9 - \square = 4$ $\square = \underline{5}$

8 $2 + \square = 10$ $\square = \underline{8}$

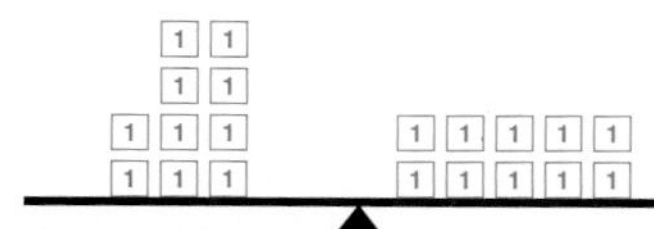

d the value of the box in each equation.

$\frac{\square}{4} = 7$ $\square = \underline{28}$

10 $15 + \square = 34$ $\square = \underline{19}$

$50 - \square = 13$ $\square = \underline{37}$

12 $9 \times \square = 108$ $\square = \underline{12}$

ite an equation to represent each situation. Then answer question.

MONEY Renee earned $9 per hour last week. Her total earnings were $207. How many hours did Renee work last week?

$9 \times \square = 207$; $207 \div 9 = 23$; 23 hours

AGES Tyrell is 14 years old. The difference between his age and his younger sister's age is 4 years. How old is his younger sister?

$14 - \square = 4$; $4 + 10 = 14$; 10 years old

Chapter 10 Progress Check 429

Progress Check 1

Chapter 10

Formative Assessment

Use the Progress Check to assess students' mastery of the previous lessons. Have students review the lesson indicated for the problems they answered incorrectly.

Odd/Even Assignments

Exercises are structured so that students practice the same concepts whether they are assigned the odd or even problems.

Common Error Alert

Use Models If students cannot visualize how to use the equation balance models, provide students with hands-on manipulatives that they can use to model the equations. You can give them counters and an equation mat and have them physically add tiles to both sides or remove tiles from both sides.

Exercise 14 Ensure students write an equation before trying to find the solution. Remind them that the process of solving is more important than the solution. They can use their mental math skills to check their work.

Data-Driven Decision Making

Students missing Exercises . . .	Have trouble with . . .	Should review and practice . . .
1-6	verifying the operations performed to each side of an equation results in a balanced equation.	SSG Lesson 10-1, p. 416 CRM Skills Practice, p. A208
7-8	solving an equation by using a model.	SSG Lesson 10-1, p. 416 CRM Skills Practice, p. A208
9-12	solving an equation.	SSG Lesson 10-2, p. 423 CRM Skills Practice, p. A212
13-14	solving word problems by writing an equation.	CRM Problem-Solving Practice, pp. A209 and A213

Lesson 10-3

Lesson Notes

Lesson Planner

Objective Solve simple linear equations using addition and subtraction.

Vocabulary **Addition Property of Equality**, **inverse operations**, **Subtraction Property of Equality**, **variable**

Materials/Manipulatives counters, deck of cards, bucket balance, unit cubes

Chapter Resource Masters

- CRM Vocabulary and English Language Development (p. A215)
- CRM Skills Practice (p. A216)
- CRM Problem-Solving Practice (p. A217)
- CRM Homework Practice (p. A218)

Vocabulary

Equations Review the term *equation*. Remind students that the values on each side must be equal for it to be a true sentence. Use simple equations to illustrate this point. Then replace one of the terms with a variable and discuss how the sentence is still an equation, just with an unknown value.

Key Concept

Foundational Skills and Concepts After students have read through the Key Concept box, have them try these exercises.

1. Suppose you solved $p + 19 = 30$ and got $p = 11$. Explain how to check if your answer is correct. Replace the variable with your answer. If the sentence is true, your answer is correct.
2. Explain how to use the Addition Property of Equality to solve $t - 8 = 12$. Add 8 to both sides of the equation to get the variable alone.

Lesson 10-3

Solve Equations with Positive Integer Solutions

KEY Concept

When you solve an equation, you find the value of the variable in an equation. In other words, you find out what value could be used for the variable to make the equation balanced.

To find the value of x in the equation $x + 4 = 7$, you need x (the variable) to be on one side of the equation by itself.

The **Addition and Subtraction Properties of Equality** allow you to add or subtract the same amount from each side of the equals sign without making the equation unbalanced. Subtracting 4 from each side of $x + 4 = 7$ makes both sides of the equation equal.

$$x + 4 = 7$$
$$x + 4 - 4 = 7 - 4$$
$$x = 3$$

To leave x by itself, subtract 4 from each side.

A model can show the same process.

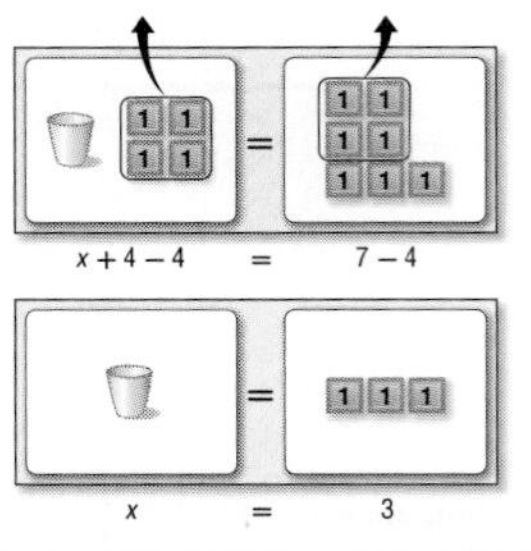

VOCABULARY

Addition Property of Equality adding the same amount to each side of an equation results in a balanced equation

inverse operations operations which undo each other; for example, addition and subtraction are inverse operations

Subtraction Property of Equality subtracting the same amount from each side of an equation results in a balanced equation

variable a symbol, usually a letter, used to represent a number

Remember, the goal is to find the value for the variable that will make the equation balanced.

430 **Chapter 10** Equations

Intervention Strategy — Visual Learners

Write the following equations on the board. Have students work in pairs. Distribute two-color counters to each group. Ask students to use the counters to create a model to solve each equation. They should draw the models they create and write the value of each variable on a piece of paper. Tell students to insert their answers into the equations to check their work. Then have pairs share their findings with other groups.

$x + 7 = 13$	$x = 6$
$a - 9 = 6$	$a = 15$
$c - 3 = 8$	$c = 11$
$y + 8 = 17$	$y = 9$
$m - 5 = 19$	$m = 24$

Example 1

Use a model to solve $x + 3 = 8$.

1. Model the equation.

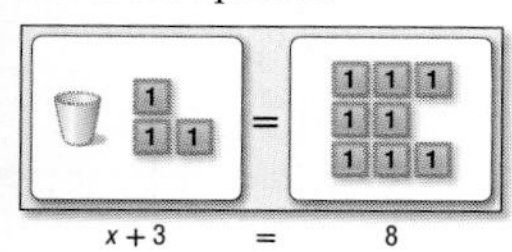

2. Remove 3 tiles from each side to get the cup by itself.

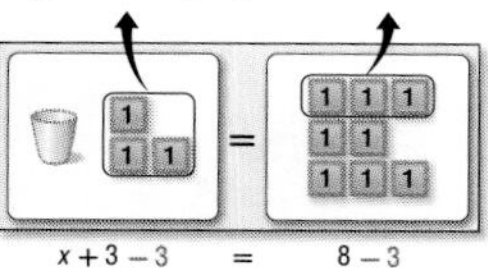

3. There are 5 tiles remaining on the right side, so $x = 5$.

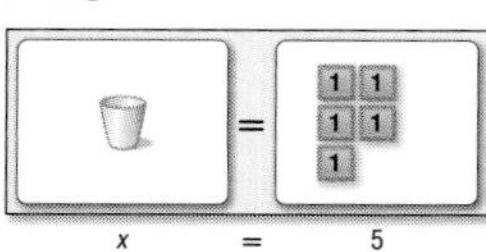

YOUR TURN!

Use a model to solve $x + 5 = 9$.

1. Model the equation.

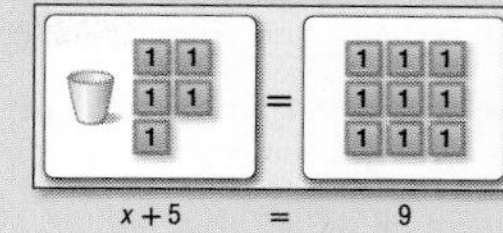

2. Remove __5__ tiles from each side to get the cup by itself.

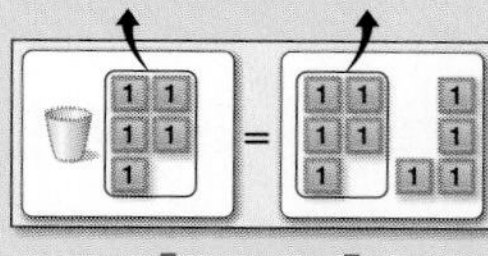

$x + 5$ __−5__ $= 9$ __−5__

3. There are __4__ tiles remaining on the right side, so $x =$ __4__.

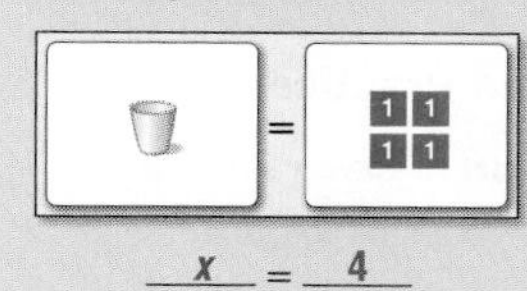

__x__ = __4__

Example 2

Solve $m + 6 = 13$.

1. The side of the equation with the variable has addition, so use subtraction. $m + 6 = 13$
2. To get m by itself, subtract 6 from each side. $m + 6 - 6 = 13 - 6$
3. There are 7 on the right side, so $m = 7$. $m = 7$

Additional Example 1

Use a model to solve $x + 8 = 14$.

1. Model the equation.

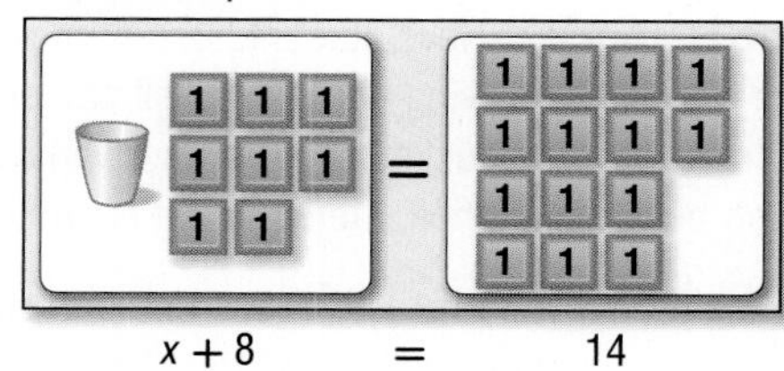

$x + 8 = 14$

2. Remove 8 tiles from each side to get the cup by itself.

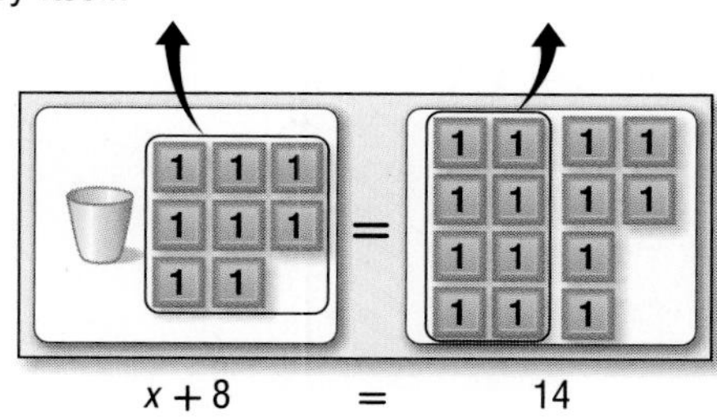

$x + 8 = 14$

$x + 8 - 8 = 14 - 8$

3. There are 6 tiles remaining on the right side. So $x = 6$.

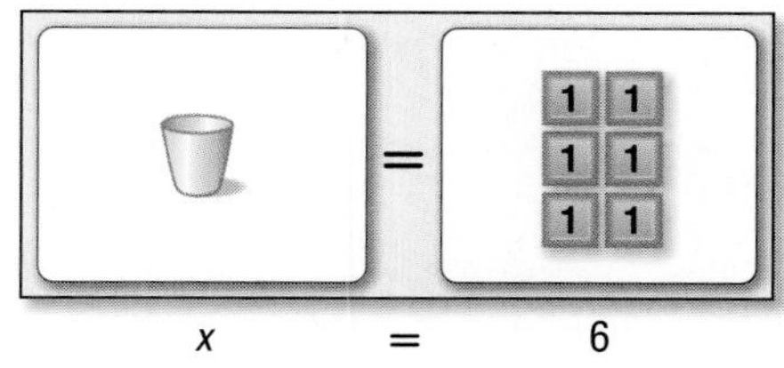

$x = 6$

Intervention Strategy

Interpersonal/Visual Learners

Write the following equations on the board. Ask students to work in small groups to write situations for each equation. Tell students to solve the equations for the variables. Have groups share their situations and challenge the class to choose which equation each situation matches.

$j - 42 = 19$	$j = 61$
$u + 19 = 42$	$u = 23$
$r - 19 = 42$	$r = 61$
$w + 42 = 61$	$w = 19$

Additional Example 2

Solve $y - 7 = 6$.

1. The side of the equation with the variable has subtraction, so use addition.
   $y - 7 = 6$
2. To get y by itself, add 7 to each side.
   $y - 7 + 7 = 6 + 7$
3. There are 13 on the right side, so
   $y = 13$.

3 Practice

Using Manipulatives

Bucket Balance Have students use a bucket balance to practice solving equations. Tell students to use counters in each bucket to solve for a variable. When the buckets balance, the equation is equal.

On-Hand Manipulatives Use unit cubes to model equations with a variable. Have students use unit cubes of one color to represent known values and a different color to represent the variable.

YOUR TURN!

Solve $z - 3 = 1$.

1. The side of the equation with the variable has subtraction, so use <u>addition</u>. $z - 3 = 1$
2. To get z by itself, <u>add 3</u> to each side. $z - 3$ <u>$+3$</u> $= 1$ <u>$+3$</u>
3. There are <u>4</u> on the right side, so $z =$ <u>4</u>. $z =$ <u>4</u>

Who is Correct?

Solve $p - 3 = 8$.

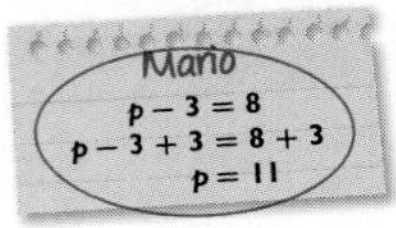
Mario
p − 3 = 8
p − 3 + 3 = 8 + 3
p = 11

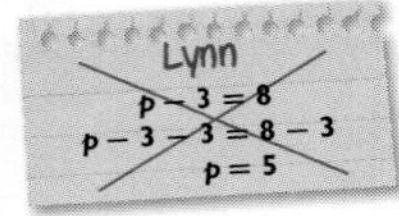
Lynn
p − 3 = 8
p − 3 − 3 = 8 − 3
p = 5

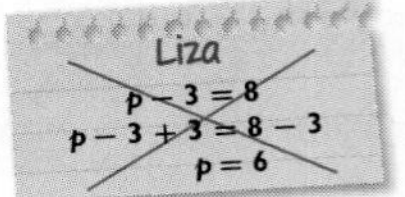
Liza
p − 3 = 8
p − 3 + 3 = 8 − 3
p = 6

Circle the correct answer(s). Cross out incorrect answer(s).

Guided Practice

1. **Use a model to solve $x + 4 = 8$.**

Step 1 Model the equation.

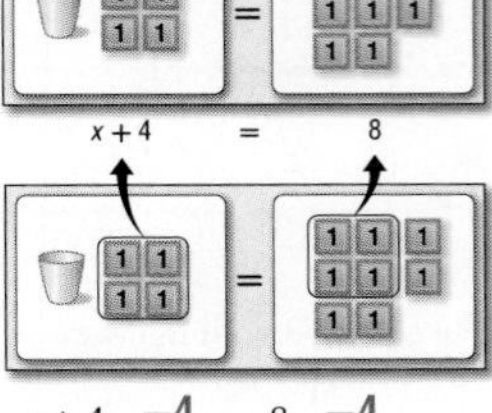
x + 4 = 8

Step 2 Remove <u>4</u> tiles from each side of the mat.

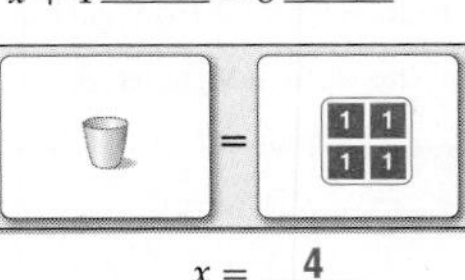

$x + 4$ <u>-4</u> $= 8$ <u>-4</u>

Step 3 There are now <u>4</u> tiles on the right side, so $x =$ <u>4</u>.

$x =$ <u>4</u>

432 **Chapter 10** Equations

Who *is Correct?*

Diagnostic Teaching

- Mario is correct. He used inverse operations correctly.
- Lynn is incorrect. She subtracted instead of added on both sides of the equation.
- Liza is incorrect. She added on one side, but subtracted on the other side of the equation.

Remind students that they should always perform the same operation on both sides of the equation.

2 **Draw a model to solve $x + 5 = 11$.**

Step 1 Model the equation.

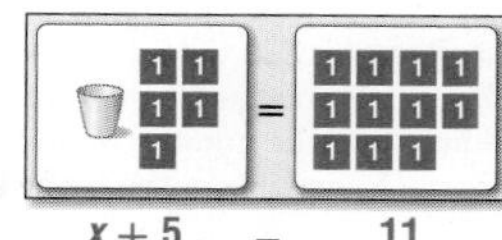

$x + 5$ = 11

Step 2 Remove 5 tiles from each side of the mat.

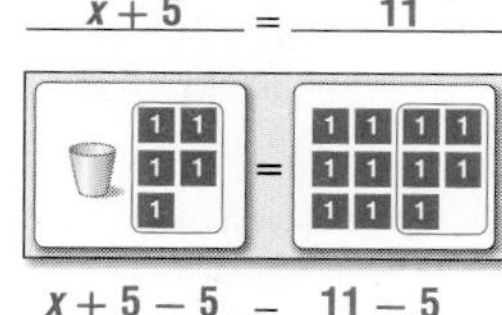

$x + 5 - 5$ = $11 - 5$

Step 3 There are now 6 tiles remaining on the right side, so $x =$ 6.

Step by Step Practice

3 Solve $y - 9 = 12$.

Step 1 The side of the equation with the variable has subtraction, so use addition. $y - 9 = 12$

Step 2 To get y by itself, add 9 to each side. $y - 9 + 9 = 12 + 9$

Step 3 There are now 21 on the right side, so $y =$ 21. $y = 21$

Solve for x.

4 $d - 3 = 7$

$d - 3 + 3 = 7 + 3$

$d = 10$

5 $m + 10 = 17$

$m + 10 - 10 = 17 - 10$

$m = 7$

6 $r + 15 = 31$

$r + 15 - 15 = 31 - 15$

$r = 16$

7 $a - 13 = 20$

$a - 13 + 13 = 20 + 13$

$a = 33$

GO ON

Are They Getting It?

Check students' understanding of solving equations by writing these problems on the board. Ask them to point out incorrect answers and explain their reasoning.

1. $d = 32$ in the equation $d + 12 = 21$. This is incorrect. $d = 9$
2. To check if $s = 15$, replace s with 15 in the equation $s - 8 = 7$. The equation balances. This is correct.
3. To solve $x - 14 = 5$, use the Subtraction Property of Equality to subtract 14 from both sides. This is incorrect. Use the Addition Property of Equality to add 14 to both sides. $x = 19$

Math Coach Notes

Step-by-Step Use Exercises 4–7 to emphasize the importance of writing out each step when solving for a variable. Students may want to skip steps using mental math, but calculation errors are easier to catch when every step is itemized. Include checking the answer by inserting it into the original equation as the final step of the process.

Note This!

Translating Words into Equations

Writing equations to represent situations can be very challenging for students. Learning where to put the known values and which operation is required takes practice. Have students restate each piece of given information in their own words. Tell them to try a few different equations to decide which one best represents the information they know. Once they determine an equation and a solution, have them reread the situation to make sure their answer matches.

Step by Step Problem-Solving Practice

Problem-Solving Strategies

- ☐ Draw a diagram.
- ☐ Look for a pattern.
- ☐ Act it out.
- ☐ Solve a simpler problem.
- ☑ Write an equation.

8 PARTY Jennifer had to fold 58 invitations for her birthday party. She has 32 left to fold. Write an equation to find the number of invitations Jennifer has already folded. Solve the equation.

Understand Read the problem. Write what you know.
Jennifer had 58 invitations to fold.
She has 32 invitations left to fold.

Plan Pick a strategy. One strategy is to write an equation. Then solve the equation.
You know the total number of invitations to fold is 58.

Solve Let p stand for the number of invitations Jennifer has already folded.

invitations folded + invitations left to fold = total number to fold

$$p + 32 = 58$$
$$p + 32 - 32 = 58 - 32$$
$$p = 26$$

Jennifer has already folded 26 invitations.

Check Add the invitations she has folded to those she has left to fold.

9 FUNDRAISER Bernardo had 75 wristbands to sell for the soccer team's fundraiser. He has 27 left to sell. Write an equation to find w, the number of wristbands Bernardo has sold. Solve the equation.

✔ Understand: I underlined key words.

✔ Plan: To solve the problem, I will write an equation

✔ Solve: The answer is $w + 27 = 75$; 48 wristbands

✔ Check: I checked my answer by using the inverse operation

English Learner Strategy

Giving Context Use Exercise 9 to discuss wristbands. Have students brainstorm different reasons people wear wristbands and their functions. Examples could include admission to multiple-day events like concerts, social events where the wristbands distinguish different groups based on age or location, advertising or marketing for companies or fundraising causes, identification for school groups, etc. Ask students to discuss whether they have ever worn a wristband for a particular event or cause and to describe the function of the wristband for that occasion.

10 HOMEWORK Evita has 54 addition and subtraction equations to complete for her math homework. There are 29 addition equations to complete. Write an equation to find e, the number of subtraction equations she has to complete.

$e + 29 = 54$; 25 equations

11 **Reflect** Is 18 the solution to $d - 27 = 45$? Explain.

No; add 27 to both sides of the equation, $d - 27 + 27 = 45 + 27$; $d = 72$

Solve each equation. Use models.

12 $z + 2 = 5$

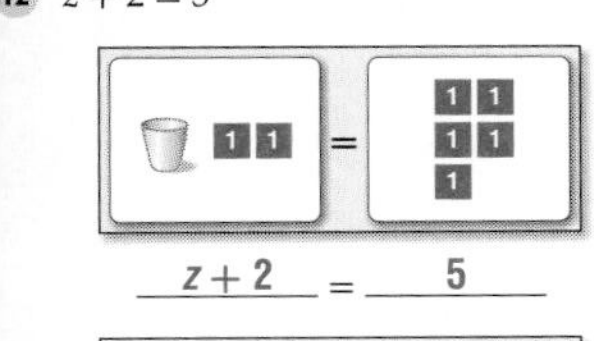

$z + 2$ = 5

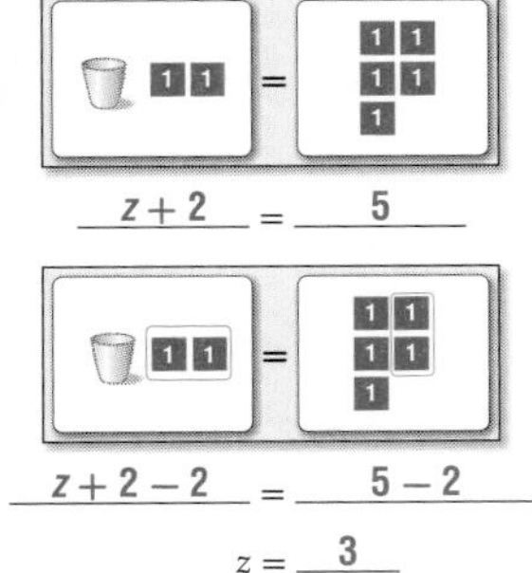

$z + 2 - 2$ = $5 - 2$

z = 3

13 $a + 3 = 8$

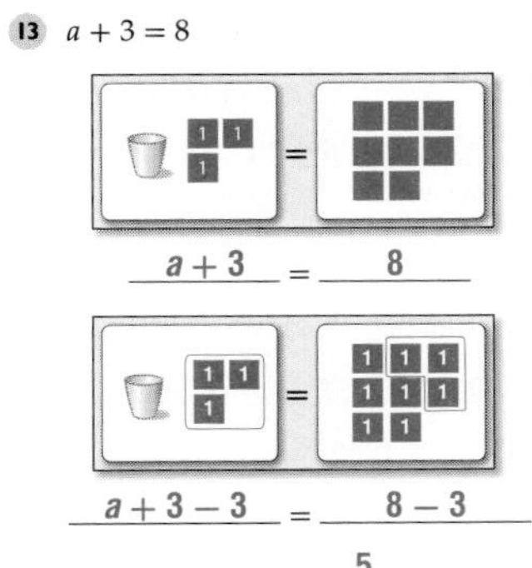

$a + 3$ = 8

$a + 3 - 3$ = $8 - 3$

a = 5

Skills, Concepts, and Problem Solving

Solve each equation.

14 $x + 6 = 13$ x = 7

15 $v - 11 = 8$ v = 19

16 $s - 9 = 15$ s = 24

17 $f + 10 = 18$ f = 8

18 $t - 12 = 7$ t = 19

19 $n + 4 = 17$ n = 13

20 $r + 7 = 12$ r = 5

21 $y - 5 = 22$ y = 27

22 $h - 3 = 7$ h = 10

Odd/Even Assignments

Exercises 14–24 are structured so that students practice the same concepts whether they are assigned the odd or even problems.

In-Class Assignment

Have students complete Exercises 14, 15, 23, and 27 to ensure that they understand the concept.

Math Challenge

Creating Equations Use the numbered cards from a deck of playing cards to create equations. Draw two cards from the deck. Name a variable. Write an addition equation with the first number drawn on the same side as the variable and the second number drawn on the opposite side as the equals sign. Then write a subtraction equation using the same numbers. Solve each equation for the variable and check that each solution is correct.

4 Assess

See It, Do It, Say It, Write It

Step 1 Write the equation $n - 19 = 42$ on the board.

Step 2 Tell students to create a model for this equation and then solve for the variable. Students should include proof that their answer is correct.

Step 3 Have students work in pairs. Ask them to share their models and explain how they determined the solution.

Step 4 Students should work alone to write an evaluation of the equation, including how they proved their solution is correct.

Looking Ahead: Pre-Teach

Solve Equations Using Addition and Subtraction In the next lesson, students will learn about solving equations using addition and subtraction. The focus will be on equations that involve negative integers.

Example

Solve $x + 13 = 3$.

Subtract 13 from each side of the equation so that x is isolated on one side of the equals sign.

$$\begin{array}{r} x + 13 = 3 \\ -13 = -13 \\ \hline x = -10 \end{array}$$

Solve each equation.

1. $k + 5 = -9$ $k = -14$
2. $m - 2 = -5$ $m = -3$
3. $d + 11 = -19$ $d = -30$

23 MOVIES Dawn put money in her purse before she left for the movies. She spent $7 on her movie ticket. She now has $16 in her purse. Write and solve an equation to find t, the amount of money she had in her purse before she bought the movie ticket.

$t - 7 = 16$; $t = \$23$

24 RUNNING Shantel and Carol ran 32 miles this week. Carol ran 17 miles. Write and solve an equation to find m, the number of miles Shantel ran.

$m + 17 = 32$; $m = 15$ miles

Vocabulary Check **Write the vocabulary word that completes each sentence.**

25 Inverse operations are operations which undo each other.

26 The Subtraction Property of Equality states that subtracting the same amount from each side of an equation results in a balanced equation.

27 Writing in Math How do the Addition and Subtraction Properties of Equality help to solve equations while keeping them balanced?

Adding or subtracting the same amount from each side of the equation forms a balanced equation.

Spiral Review

Find the missing number to make each equation balanced. (Lesson 10-1, p. 416)

28 $(10 \times 2) +$ 3 $= 3 + (4 \times 5)$

29 $3 \times (17 - 9) = (5 + 3) \times$ 3

Find the value of the box in each equation. (Lesson 10-2, p. 423)

30 $3 \times \square = 27$ 9

31 $\square - 15 = 12$ 27

Solve. (Lesson 10-1, p. 416)

32 COLLECTOR CARDS Dave had 13 baseball cards. He bought 4 more. Jimmy had 10 baseball cards. He bought 7 more. If Dave and Jimmy both bought 5 more baseball cards, how many do they each have?

Dave and Jimmy have the same amount of baseball cards; $(13 + 4) + 5 = 17 + 5 = 22$ and $(10 + 7) + 5 = 17 + 5 = 22$

STOP

436 Chapter 10 Equations

Ticket Out the Door

Solving Simple Equations Write the following situation on the board. As students approach the classroom door to exit, alternate asking them to give the equation that matches the situation or the solution.

Gwen read 17 pages of her history chapter. She now has 13 pages left to read. Write and solve an equation to find p, the number of pages in the history chapter.

$p - 17 = 13$; 30 pages

Solve Equations Using Addition and Subtraction

KEY Concept

Addition and subtraction are **inverse operations**.

Inverse Operations	Example	Definition
addition and subtraction	$7 + 8 = 15$, so $15 - 7 = 8$ and $15 - 8 = 7$	When $a + b = c$, then $c - a = b$ and $c - b = a$

You can use inverse operations to help solve equations. Solving an equation means to find the value of the variable that makes both sides of an equation equal.

To solve an equation, you must isolate the variable on one side of the equals sign. To do this, use inverse operations and the **Addition or Subtraction Properties of Equality**.

VOCABULARY

Addition Property of Equality adding the same amount to each side of an equation results in a balanced equation

Subtraction Property of Equality subtracting the same amount from each side of an equation results in a balanced equation

Example 1

Use a model to solve $a + 5 = 3$.

1. Model the equation.

To model subtraction use red algebra tiles.

2. Use the Subtraction Property of Equality to isolate the variable. Place 5 red negative algebra tiles on each side of the mat.

3. Create zero pairs with yellow and red tiles. Remove 5 zero pairs from the left side and 3 zero pairs from the right side.

4. There are two negative algebra tiles on the right side. So, $a = -2$. The solution is -2.

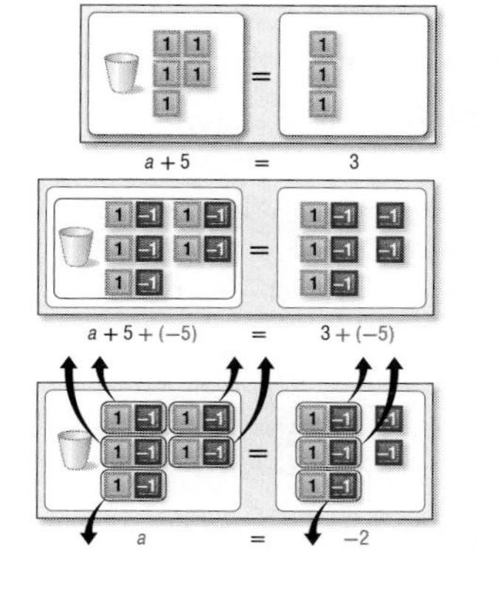

Lesson Notes

Lesson 10-4

Lesson Planner

Objective Use variables in expressions and equations.

Vocabulary **Addition Property of Equality**, **Subtraction Property of Equality**

Materials/Manipulatives algebra tiles, balance scale, counters, construction paper

Chapter Resource Masters

- CRM Vocabulary and English Language Development (p. A219)
- CRM Skills Practice (p. A220)
- CRM Problem-Solving Practice (p. A221)
- CRM Homework Practice (p. A222)

Vocabulary

Access Vocabulary Have students give the definitions for the words *variable* and *inverse operations* in their own words. Write the word *Addition Property of Equality* on the board and ask students to volunteer to explain what they think it means (in their own words). Use the balance bucket to demonstrate this property.

Key Concept

Foundational Skills and Concepts After students have read through the Key Concept box, have them try these exercises.

1. What is the inverse operation of addition? subtraction
2. What does it mean to isolate the variable? Possible answer: get the variable by itself, with a coefficient of one, on one side of the equation.

Additional **Example 1**

Use a model to solve $c + 8 = 5$.

1. Model the equation.

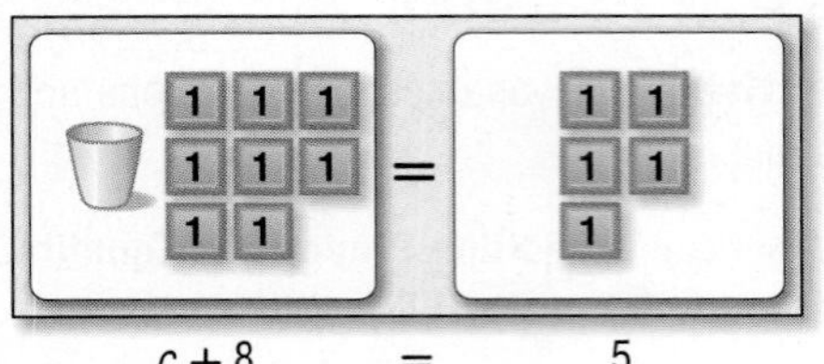

$c + 8 \quad = \quad 5$

2. Use the Subtraction Property of Equality to isolate the variable. Place 8 red negative algebra tiles to each side of the mat.

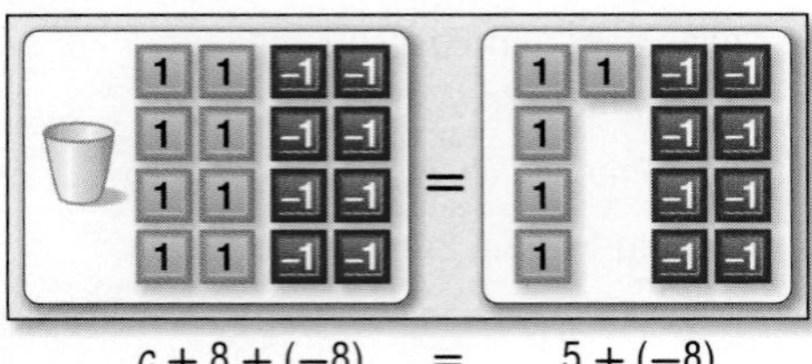

$c + 8 + (-8) \quad = \quad 5 + (-8)$

3. Create zero pairs with yellow and red tiles. Remove 8 zero pairs from the left side and 5 zero pairs from the right side.

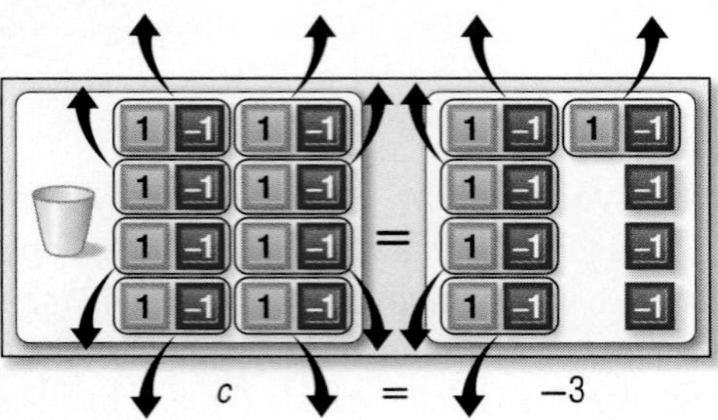

$c \quad = \quad -3$

4. There are three negative algebra tiles on the right side.
So, $c = -3$. The solution is -3.

Additional **Example 2**

Solve $x - 8 = -12$.

1. The expression $x - 8$ can be rewritten as $x + (-8)$.

2. The opposite of -8 is $+8$, since $(-8) + (+8) = 0$.

3. Add 8 to each side of the equation.

$$\begin{aligned} x + (-8) &= -12 \\ +8 \quad &\quad +8 \\ \hline x + 0 &= -4 \\ x &= -4 \end{aligned}$$

YOUR TURN!

Use a model to solve $z - 4 = -3$.

1. Model the equation.

To model addition, use yellow algebra tiles.

2. Use the Addition Property of Equality to isolate the variable. Place <u>4</u> yellow algebra tiles to each side of the mat to make <u>4</u> zero pairs on the left side.

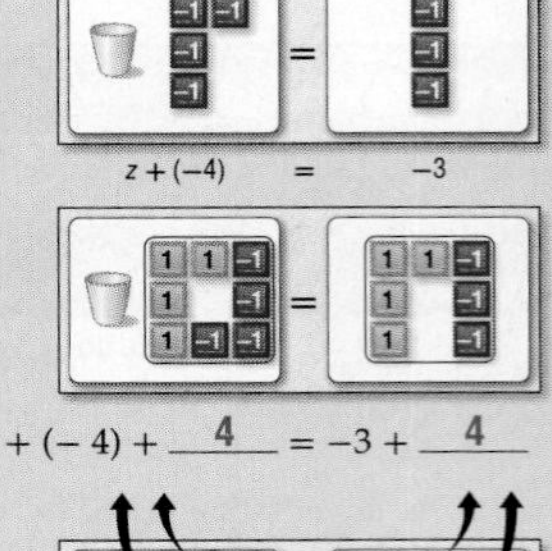

$z + (-4) = -3$

$z + (-4) + \underline{4} = -3 + \underline{4}$

3. Create zero pairs with yellow and red tiles. Remove <u>4</u> zero pairs from the left side and <u>3</u> zero pairs from the right side.

4. There is one yellow algebra tile on the right side. So, $z =$ <u>1</u>. The solution is <u>1</u>.

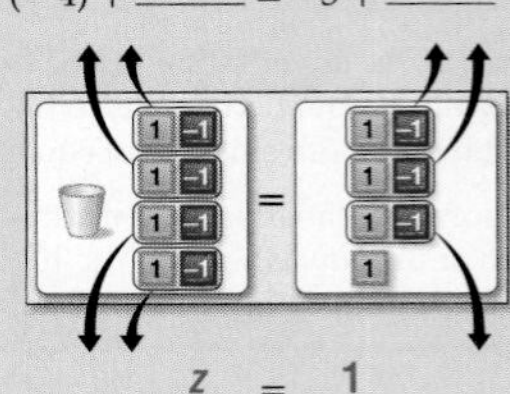

$\underline{z} = \underline{1}$

Example 2

Solve $x - 2 = -4$.

1. The expression $x - 2$ can be rewritten as $x + (-2)$.
2. The opposite of -2 is $+2$, since $(-2) + (+2) = 0$.
3. Add 2 to each side of the equation.

$$\begin{aligned} x + (-2) &= -4 \\ +2 \quad &\quad +2 \\ \hline x + 0 &= -2 \\ x &= -2 \end{aligned}$$

YOUR TURN!

Solve $a + 3 = -1$.

1. The opposite of $+3$ is <u>-3</u>, since <u>$+3 + (-3)$</u> $= 0$.
2. <u>Subtract 3</u> from each side of the equation.

$$\begin{aligned} a + 3 &= -1 \\ -3 \quad &\quad -3 \\ \hline a \ \underline{+0} &= \underline{-4} \\ a &= \underline{-4} \end{aligned}$$

Intervention Strategy — Linguistic Learners

Translate and Solve Have students translate an equation into a word phrase. Have students solve the equation using words. Then have students write their own verbal linear equation. Students should translate their verbal equation into a numerical equation and solve it. Students may also benefit from starting with an equation and translating it into a word phrase.

Who is Correct?

Solve $h - 13 = 15$.

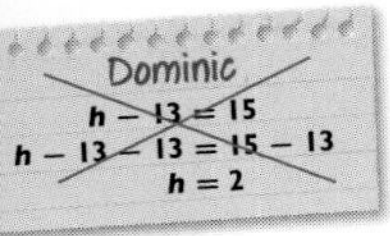
Dominic
h − 13 = 15
h − 13 − 13 = 15 − 13
h = 2

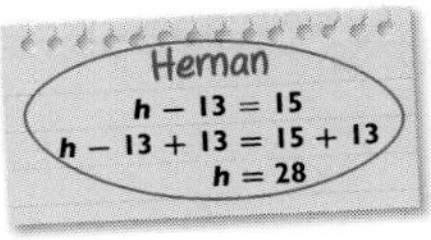
Hernan
h − 13 = 15
h − 13 + 13 = 15 + 13
h = 28

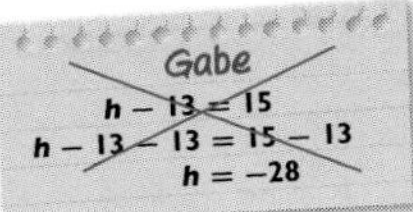
Gabe
h − 13 = 15
h − 13 − 13 = 15 − 13
h = −28

Circle correct answer(s). Cross out incorrect answer(s).

Guided Practice

Use a model to solve $x + 3 = -4$.

Step 1 Model the equation.

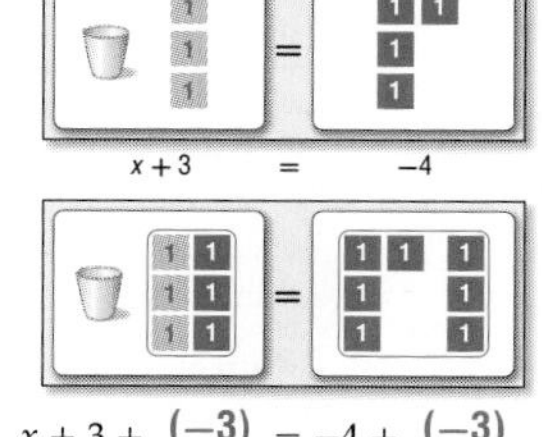

$x + 3 = -4$

Step 2 Add 3 red negative algebra tiles to each side of the mat.

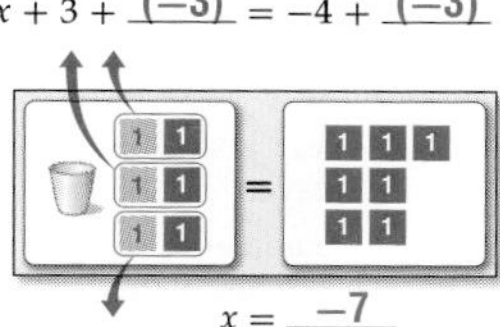

$x + 3 + \underline{(-3)} = -4 + \underline{(-3)}$

Step 3 Remove __3__ zero pairs from the left side of the mat. There are __7__ red negative algebra tiles on the right side.

$x = \underline{-7}$

Step by Step Practice

Solve $w + 3 = -7$.

Step 1 The opposite of 3 is __−3__, since __3 + (−3)__ = 0.

Step 2 Subtract __3__ from each side of the equation.

$w + 3 = -7$

$w + 3 - \underline{3} = -7 - \underline{3}$

$w = \underline{-10}$

GO ON

Lesson 10-4 Solve Equations Using Addition and Subtraction 439

Who *is Correct?*

Diagnostic Teaching

- Dominic's answer is incorrect. He did not *add* the inverse of −13.
- Hernan's answer is correct.
- Gabe's answer is incorrect. He did not add the inverse of −13. He also subtracted incorrectly.

Remind students to isolate the variable by writing out each step.

3 Practice

Using Manipulatives

Bucket Balance Use a bucket balance to give students a visual concept of the equality when they are solving equations using addition and subtraction. Show the buckets balanced when performing the inverse operation.

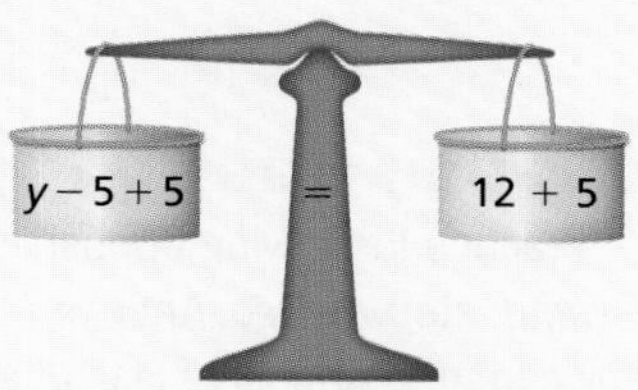
y − 5 + 5
=
12 + 5

Algebra Tiles You can also demonstrate equality with algebra tiles.

On-Hand Manipulatives Use different-colored squares of construction paper as you would algebra tiles.

Note This!

Study Strategies As students attempt to solve equations, they may switch the steps necessary to undo addition and subtraction. Reinforce the concept that addition undoes subtraction, and subtraction undoes addition.

Common Error *Alert*

Properties of Equality When solving equations using addition and subtraction, students should be aware of the properties of equality. Emphasize to students that the main objective when solving an equation is to isolate the variable with a coefficient of 1. The value on the other side of the equals sign is the solution to the equation.

English Learner Strategy

Opposites Practice identifying opposites, such as *black* and *white*, *stop* and *go*. After you have practiced many common opposites, include addition and subtraction in the list. Students should remember that *addition* and *subtraction* are opposites just like *stop* and *go* are opposites.

Math Coach Notes

Check Answers

1. After performing the inverse operation, have students work the problem backward for clarity and understanding.
   $11 + x = 22$
   After solving the problem, the answer is $x = 11$.
2. Substitute 11 for x to check the answer.
   $11 + 11 = 22$
3. Reinforce the importance of the check step. Explain to students that they should not miss any answers because checking their answers should be part of finding the solution.

Solve each equation.

3. $d + 11 = 4$
   $d + 11 - \underline{11} = 4 - \underline{11}$
   $d = \underline{-7}$

4. $v + 4 = -13$
   $v + 4 - \underline{4} = -13 - \underline{4}$
   $v = \underline{-17}$

5. $t - 8 = -22$
   $t - 8 + \underline{8} = -22 + \underline{8}$
   $t = \underline{-14}$

6. $f - 19 = -7$
   $f - 19 + \underline{19} = -7 + 19$
   $f = \underline{12}$

Step by Step Problem-Solving Practice

Problem-Solving Strategies
- ☐ Draw a diagram.
- ☐ Guess and check.
- ☐ Use a model.
- ☐ Solve a simpler problem.
- ☑ Write an equation.

Solve.

7. MUSIC Frank's MP3 player holds 75 songs. He has space for 26 more songs. How many songs are already on Frank's MP3 player?

Understand Read the problem. Write what you know.
Frank's player holds __75__ songs. He can add __26__ more songs.

Plan Pick a strategy. One strategy is to write an equation. Then solve the equation.
You know the total number of songs the MP3 player holds is 75.

Solve Let s = the number of songs already on the MP3 player. Write an equation. Solve the equation.

number of songs already on player	plus	26	equals	75
s	$+$	26	$=$	75
		-26	$=$	-26
			$s =$	49

Frank has __49__ songs on his MP3 player.

Check Does the answer make sense? The number of songs already on the player plus 26 should equal 75.
$\underline{49} + 26 = 75$
$\underline{75} = 75$ ✓

Are They Getting It?

Check students' understanding of solving equations using addition and subtraction by writing these problems on the board. Ask students to point out the wrong answers, and explain why they are wrong.

1. $x - 14 = -6$
   inverse operation: __addition__
   Add __14__ to each side of the equation.
   $x - 14 = -6$
   $+14 \quad +14$
   $x = 8$
   This is correct.

2. $9 + x = -5$
   inverse operation: __subtraction__
   Add __−9__ to each side of the equation.
   $9 + x = -5$
   $-9 \quad -9$
   $x + 0 = -4$
   $x = -4$
   This is incorrect. The inverse operation is correct, but the sum on the right side is incorrect.

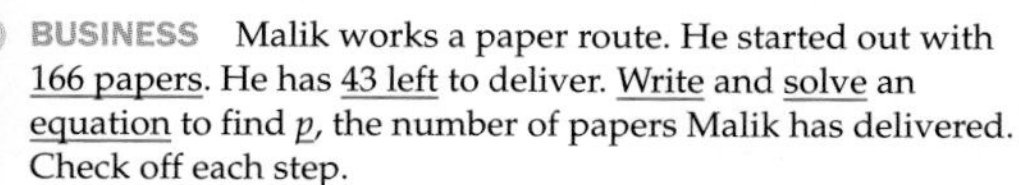

9 BUSINESS Malik works a paper route. He started out with 166 papers. He has 43 left to deliver. Write and solve an equation to find p, the number of papers Malik has delivered. Check off each step.

✓ Understand: I underlined key words.

✓ Plan: To solve the problem, I will write an equation.

✓ Solve: The answer is $43 + p = 166$; 123 newspapers.

✓ Check: I checked my answer by adding 43 and 123 to get 166.

10 PARADES Last year's Labor Day parade had 114 participants, which is 27 less than this year's parade. Write and solve an equation to find p, the number of participants in this year's parade.

$p - 27 = 114$; 141 participants

11 **Reflect** Is 9 the solution to the equation $w + 7 = 16$? Explain.

Yes; substitute 9 for w and then solve: $9 + 7 = 16$; $16 = 16$.

Skills, Concepts, and Problem Solving

Solve each equation.

12 $n + 10 = 4$

$n =$ −6

13 $f - 3 = -18$

$f =$ −15

14 $w + 25 = 7$

$w =$ −18

15 $q + 19 = 6$

$q =$ −13

16 $z - 12 = -3$

$z =$ 9

17 $c - 24 = -9$

$c =$ 15

18 $d + 18 = 11$

$d =$ −7

19 $f + 9 = -21$

$f =$ −30

20 $a - 5 = -17$

$a =$ −12

21 $x + 7 = -26$

$x =$ −33

Math Challenge

Writing Equations Have students number their papers from 0 to 10 and from 0 to −10. For each number written have students write an equation that requires addition or subtraction to solve so the solution corresponds to the number written. Students should try not to use the same numbers in more than one equation. For example, on the line numbered 8, the equation $x + 4 = 12$ can be written and for the line numbered −7, the equation $x + 2 = -5$ can be written.

Note This!

Similarities and Differences While taking notes, students will encounter equations using either addition or subtraction. Ask students to track any similarities or differences between addition and subtraction equations. Have students create a chart of similarities and differences in their notes.

Odd/Even Assignments

Exercises 12–22 are structured so that students practice the same concepts whether they are assigned the odd or even problems.

In-Class Assignment

Have students complete Exercises 12, 17, 22, and 25 to ensure that they understand the concept.

See It, Do It, Say It, Write It

Step 1 Write an equation on the board. Model how to identify the operation and its inverse. Do this several times with equations using addition and subtraction.

Step 2 Have students work in pairs. Assign one student to create an equation, while the other identifies the operation and its inverse. Together the students can solve and check their equations. Have students share their work with the class. Repeat several times.

Step 3 Ask students to show how to identify the operation and solve an equation. Give them a list of equations on the board. Repeat with students identifying the operations and solving. Share solutions in a class discussion.

Step 4 Have students work alone. Tell them to solve a variable equation. Tell them to include a picture or a model and a step-by-step plan of the work they did to solve the problem.

Looking Ahead: Pre-teach

Solve Equations Using Multiplication and Division Students will learn how to solve equations using multiplication and division.

Example

Solve $5 \times d = 30$.

$$5 \times d = 30$$
$$\frac{5 \times d}{5} = \frac{30}{5}$$
$$d = 6$$

Solve the following equations.

1. $\frac{b}{7} = 5$ $b = 35$
2. $3x = 27$ $x = 9$
3. $24 = 4y$ $y = 6$

22 TEMPERATURE On a typical summer day in Death Valley, California, the high temperature is 30°F higher than the low temperature, which is 85°F. What is the typical high temperature? Write and solve an equation to find the high temperature, t.

$t - 30 = 85$; $t = 115$°F

Vocabulary Check **Write the vocabulary word that completes each sentence.**

23 The Addition Property of Equality states that adding the same amount to both sides of an equation keeps the equation balanced.

24 Addition and subtraction are inverse operations because they undo each other.

25 Writing in Math Explain how to solve the equation $9 + t = 4$.

Answers will vary. Sample answer: Add −9 to both sides of the equation.

$9 + (-9) + t = 4 + (-9)$; $t = -5$

Spiral Review

Find the value of the box in each equation. (Lesson 10-2, p. 423)

26 $14 + \square = 23$ $\square = 9$

27 $3 \times \square = 21$ $\square = 7$

28 $\square - 17 = 8$ $\square = 25$

Solve each equation. (Lesson 10-3, p. 430)

29 $b + 2 = 7$ $b = 5$

30 $w - 4 = 9$ $w = 13$

31 $c + 7 = 13$ $c = 6$

Solve. (Lesson 10-3, p. 430)

32 MONEY Destiny went to the amusement park with her friend. She started out with $38. When she left the amusement park she had $7 left. Write and solve an equation to find m, the amount of money spent at the amusement park.

$m + 7 = 38$; $31

STOP

Ticket Out the Door

Creating Equations As each student approaches the door to exit the classroom, state a first step to solving an equation, such as add 5 to each side. The student should respond with an equation that would be solved using that first step. An answer for the above step is $x - 5 = 24$.

Lesson 10-5

Solve Equations Using Multiplication and Division

KEY Concept

Multiplication and division are **inverse operations**.

Inverse Operations	Example	Definition
multiplication and division	$4 \times 3 = 12$, so $12 \div 4 = 3$ and $12 \div 3 = 4$	When $a \times b = c$, then $c \div a = b$ and $c \div b = a$.

Solving an equation with multiplication or division is similar to solving equations with addition and subtraction. Use inverse operations and the **Multiplication or Division Properties of Equality** to get the variable alone on one side of the equals sign.

VOCABULARY

Division Property of Equality
dividing each side of an equation by the same amount results in a balanced equation

Multiplication Property of Equality
multiplying each side of an equation by the same amount results in a balanced equation

Example 1

Solve $9y = -36$.

1. The side of the equation with the variable is $9y$. The operation is multiplication. The inverse operation is division.
2. The Division Property of Equality states that dividing each side of the equation by the same amount keeps the equation balanced. Divide each side of the equation by 9.

$$\frac{9y}{9} = \frac{-36}{9}$$
$$y = -4$$

$9 \div 9$, or $\frac{9}{9}$, is an equivalent form of one.

3. Check your answer by substituting -4 for y.

$$9y = -36$$
$$9(-4) = -36$$
$$-36 = -36 \checkmark$$

Both sides of the equation are the same, so the solution is correct.

YOUR TURN!

Solve $7b = 42$.

1. The operation is multiplication.
   The inverse operation is division.
2. Divide each side of the equation by 7.

$$\frac{7b}{7} = \frac{42}{7}$$
$$b = 6$$

3. Check your answer.

$$7b = 42$$
$$7 \times 6 = 42$$
$$42 = 42 \checkmark$$

Both sides of the equation are the same, so the solution is correct.

GO ON

Additional Example 1

Solve $6x = -36$.

1. The side of the equation with the variable is $6x$. The operation is multiplication. The inverse operation is division.
2. The Division Property of Equality states that dividing each side of the equation by the same amount keeps the equation balanced. Divide each side of the equation by 6.

$$6x = -36$$
$$\frac{6x}{6} = -\frac{36}{6}$$
$$x = -6$$

3. Check your answer by substituting -6 for x.

$$6x = 36$$
$$6(-6) = 36$$
$$-36 = -36 \checkmark$$

Both sides of the equation are the same, so the solution is correct.

Lesson Notes

Lesson 10-5

Lesson Planner

Objective Solve linear equations using multiplication and division with integers.

Vocabulary **Division Property of Equality**, **Multiplication Property of Equality**

Materials/Manipulatives algebra tiles, balance scale, counters, construction paper, index cards

Chapter Resource Masters

- CRM Vocabulary and English Language Development (p. A223)
- CRM Skills Practice (p. A224)
- CRM Problem-Solving Practice (p. A225)
- CRM Homework Practice (p. A226)

1 Introduce

Vocabulary

Access Vocabulary Have students recall the definitions for the words *variable* and *inverse operations*. Write *Multiplication Property of Equality* on the board and ask students to volunteer to explain the meaning in their own words using their prior knowledge of properties. Compare students' definitions and discuss how this property is similar to other properties practiced in this chapter.

2 Teach

Key Concept

Foundational Skills and Concepts After students have read through the Key Concept box, have them try these exercises.

1. What does *balanced equation* mean in the definition of the Multiplication Property of Equality? Possible answer: The values on either side of the equation are equal.
2. What should happen when you check your solution? Possible answer: The values on either side of the equation should be equal.

Additional Example 2

Solve $5 = \frac{b}{-4}$.

1. The side of the equation with the variable is $\frac{b}{-4}$. The operation is division. The inverse operation is multiplication.
2. The Multiplication Property of Equality states that multiplying each side of the equation by the same amount keeps the equation balanced. Multiply each side of the equation by −4.

$$-4 \times 5 = -4 \times \frac{b}{-4}$$

$$-4 \times 5 = \frac{-4}{-4}b$$

$$-20 = b$$

3. Check your answer by substituting −20 for *b*.

$$5 = \frac{b}{-4}$$

$$5 = \frac{-20}{-4}$$

$$-5 = -5 \checkmark$$

Both sides of the equation are the same, so the solution is correct.

Math Coach Notes

Terminology With the introduction of multiplication as an operation in the equations students solve in this lesson, a review of coefficients is in order. Students struggle to remember that there is actually a coefficient of 1 on any variable that does not have a number next to it in a term.

The importance of the coefficient of 1 is that students need to understand the concept of isolating the variable. This isolation is not simply the variable terms, but rather it means that the variable term needs to be the only term on one side of the equals sign, and the term must have a coefficient of 1.

Example 2

Solve $\frac{c}{3} = 9$.

1. The side of the equation with the variable is $\frac{c}{3}$. The operation is division. The inverse operation is multiplication.
2. The Multiplication Property of Equality states that multiplying each side of the equation by the same amount keeps the equation balanced. Multiply each side of the equation by 3.

$$3 \times \frac{c}{3} = 3 \times 9$$

$3 \times \frac{c}{3} = \frac{3c}{3}$. $\frac{3}{3}$ is an equivalent form of one.

$$\frac{3c}{3} = 3 \times 9$$

$$c = 27$$

3. Check your answer by substituting 27 for *c*.

$$\frac{c}{3} = 9$$

$$\frac{27}{3} = 9$$

$$9 = 9 \checkmark$$

Both sides of the equation are the same, so the solution is correct.

YOUR TURN!

Solve $\frac{x}{-8} = 5$.

1. The operation is division.
   The inverse operation is multiplication.
2. Multiply each side of the equation by −8.

$$-8 \times \frac{x}{-8} = -8 \times 5$$

$$\frac{-8}{-8}x = -8 \times 5$$

$$x = -40$$

3. Check your answer.

$$\frac{x}{-8} = 5$$

$$\frac{-40}{-8} = 5$$

$$5 = 5 \checkmark$$

Both sides of the equation are the same, so the solution is correct.

Who is Correct?

Solve the equation $2f = 80$.

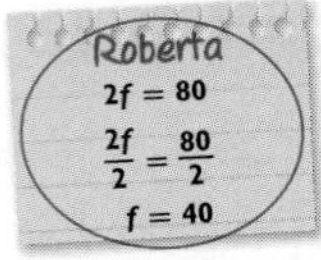

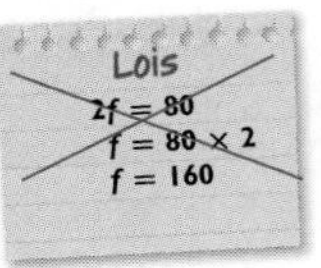

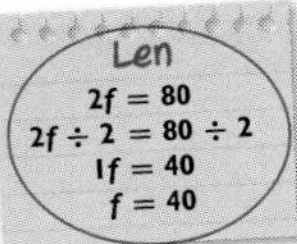

Circle correct answer(s). Cross out incorrect answer(s).

Who is Correct?

Diagnostic Teaching

- Roberta's answer is correct.
- Lois' answer is incorrect. She did not perform the correct inverse operation.
- Len's answer is correct.

Remind students that the inverse operation of multiplication is division, and the inverse operation of division is multiplication.

Guided Practice

Solve each equation.

1. $4k = 20$
   inverse operation: division
   Divide each side of the equation by 4.
   $k =$ 5

2. $\frac{w}{-2} = 7$
   inverse operation: multiplication
   Multiply each side of the equation by −2.
   $w =$ −14

Step by Step Practice

3. Solve $\frac{v}{-7} = 8$.

Step 1 The operation is division.
The inverse operation is multiplication.

$$\frac{v}{-7} = 8$$
$$-7 \times \frac{v}{-7} = -7 \times 8$$
$$v = -56$$

Step 2 Multiply each side of the equation by −7.

$$\frac{-56}{-7} = 8$$

Step 3 Check your answer.

$$8 = 8 \checkmark$$

Solve each equation.

4. $\frac{d}{5} = 3$
   $d =$ 15

5. $-6u = 24$
   $u =$ −4

6. $7f = 63$
   $f =$ 9

7. $\frac{t}{-4} = 12$
   $t =$ −48

8. $\frac{b}{-8} = 7$
   $b =$ −56

9. $3y = -27$
   $y =$ −9

GO ON

3 Practice

Using Manipulatives

Bucket Balance Use a bucket balance to give students a visual concept of an equation and how to solve it using multiplication and division. Show the buckets balanced when performing the inverse operation.

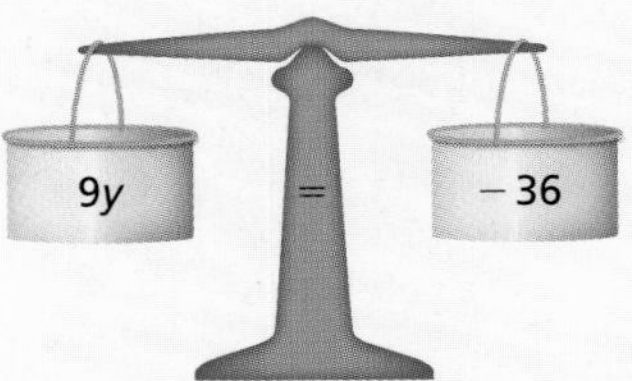

Algebra Tiles Also demonstrate equality with algebra tiles.

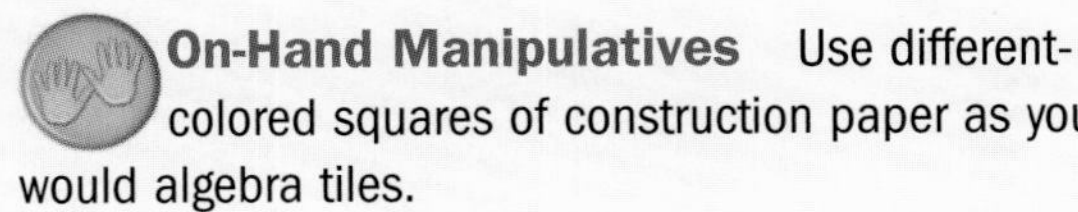

On-Hand Manipulatives Use different-colored squares of construction paper as you would algebra tiles.

Math Coach Notes

Equation-Solving Strategies When students begin to solve equations, have them write the operation being performed directly underneath the original operation. Once the operation is complete, the coefficient on the variable is 1, because any number divided by itself equals 1, or any number times its reciprocal equals 1.

Are They Getting It?

Check students' understanding of solving equations using multiplication and division by writing these problems on the board. Ask students to point out wrong answers, and explain why they are wrong.

1. $\frac{x}{7} = 5$

inverse operation: multiplication
Multiply each side of the equation by 5.

$$\frac{x}{7} = 5$$
$$5 \times \frac{x}{7} = 5 \times 5$$
$$35x = 25$$

This is incorrect. The inverse operation is correct, but the value to multiply by is incorrect. Both sides should be multiplied by 7.

2. $8x = 32$

inverse operation: division
Divide each side of the equation by 8.

$$8x = 32$$
$$\frac{8x}{8} = \frac{32}{8}$$
$$x = 4$$

This is correct.

Math Coach Notes

Tips for Students

1. Write each step of your solution so that you can review it and it is clear and understandable.

   $4x = 12$

   $x = 3$

2. Substitute 3 for x to see if the problem makes sense.

   $4 \times 3 = 12$

3. Reinforce the importance of the "check" step.

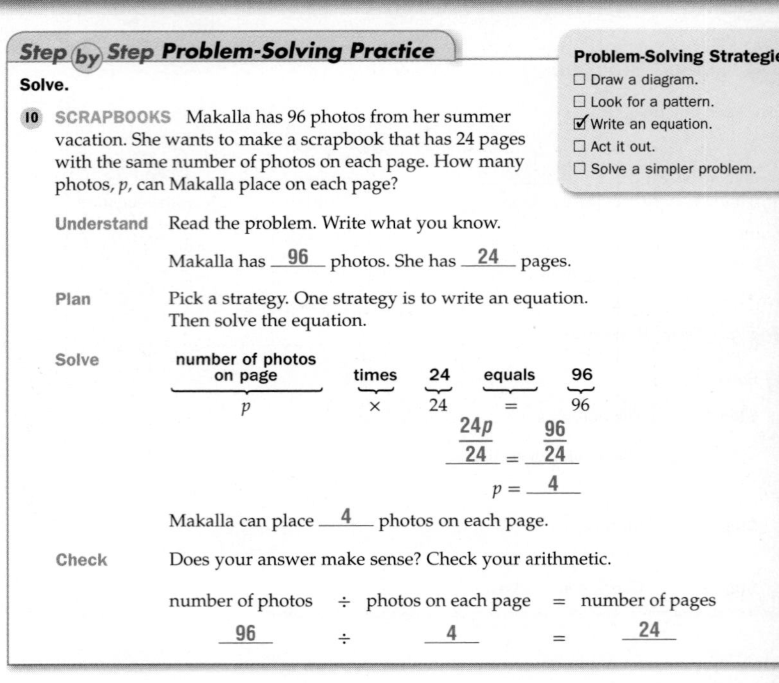

Step by Step Problem-Solving Practice

Problem-Solving Strategies

- ☐ Draw a diagram.
- ☐ Look for a pattern.
- ☑ Write an equation.
- ☐ Act it out.
- ☐ Solve a simpler problem.

Solve.

10 SCRAPBOOKS Makalla has 96 photos from her summer vacation. She wants to make a scrapbook that has 24 pages with the same number of photos on each page. How many photos, p, can Makalla place on each page?

Understand Read the problem. Write what you know.

Makalla has <u>96</u> photos. She has <u>24</u> pages.

Plan Pick a strategy. One strategy is to write an equation. Then solve the equation.

Solve

number of photos on page	times	24	equals	96
p	$\times$	24	$=$	96

$$\frac{24p}{24} = \frac{96}{24}$$

$$p = 4$$

Makalla can place <u>4</u> photos on each page.

Check Does your answer make sense? Check your arithmetic.

number of photos	÷	photos on each page	=	number of pages
96	÷	4	=	24

11 FINANCE Kendra's mom bought her a new television. Kendra plans to pay back her mom <u>$27 per month</u> for the next <u>6 months</u>. Write and solve an equation to <u>find x</u>, the <u>total amount</u> Kendra will pay her mom.

Check off each step.

✔ Understand: I underlined key words.

✔ Plan: To solve the problem, I will <u>write an equation</u>.

✔ Solve: The answer is $\frac{x}{6} = 27$; $x = \$162$.

✔ Check: I checked my answer by <u>dividing 162 by 27</u>.

Intervention Strategy — Kinesthetic Learners

Solve with Manipulatives Students may have trouble visualizing the multiplication and division equations. Prompt students to use counters, buttons, and other items to represent the equation, and then solve using the manipulative. Students should model the equation, and then draw a picture of the model. Next, the students should solve the equation, and then check the answer.

12 FOOD Jocelyn's father bought 5 smoothies. He paid \$20. Write and solve an equation to find c, the cost of one smoothie.

$5c = 20$; $c = \$4$

13 TRAVEL Three friends traveled 300 miles on a boating trip. Each of the three steered the boat an equal number of miles. How many miles did each steer the boat? Write and solve an equation to find m, the number of miles each steered the boat.

$3m = 300$; $m = 100$ miles

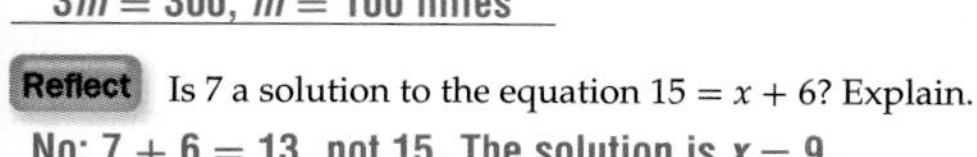

4 **Reflect** Is 7 a solution to the equation $15 = x + 6$? Explain.

No; $7 + 6 = 13$, not 15. The solution is $x = 9$.

Skills, Concepts, and Problem Solving

olve each equation.

5 $\frac{a}{8} = -7$ $a = -56$

16 $-9c = 27$ $c = -3$

7 $\frac{y}{6} = 5$ $y = 30$

18 $5b = 45$ $b = 9$

9 $-7z = 35$ $z = -5$

20 $\frac{x}{4} = -9$ $x = -36$

1 $6f = 66$ $f = 11$

22 $\frac{w}{10} = 8$ $w = 80$

3 $\frac{v}{-3} = 12$ $v = -36$

24 $-9g = -54$ $g = 6$

olve.

5 MEASUREMENT The formula for the area of a parallelogram shown is $A = bh$. Use the formula to write an equation. Find the height of the parallelogram in centimeters by solving for h.

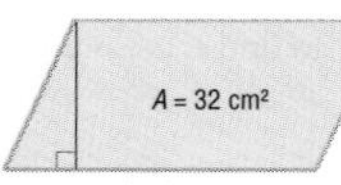

$32 = 8h$; 4 cm

GO ON

English Learner Strategy

Inverse Cards Write the word *multiplication* on one side of an index card with the sign of the inverse operation (division) on the other side. When EL students are choosing the inverse, allow them to use the index card for reference.

Odd/Even Assignments

Exercises 15–27 are structured so that students practice the same concepts whether they are assigned the odd or even problems.

In-Class Assignment

Have students complete Exercises 15, 16, 25, and 29 to ensure that they understand the concept.

Math Challenge

Five Equations Ask students to write and solve five equations that use multiplication or division. One equation needs to have a positive coefficient on the variable. One equation needs to have a fractional coefficient. One equation needs to have the variable divided by a negative number. One equation needs to have a fractional answer. The last equation needs to have an answer of 1.

See It, Do It, Say It, Write It

Step 1 Write an equation on the board. Model how to identify the operation and its inverse. Do this several times with equations using multiplication and division.

Step 2 Ask students to show how to identify the operation and solve an equation. Give them a list of equations on the board. Repeat with students identifying the operations and solving.

Step 3 Have students work in pairs. Assign one student to create a model of an equation using tiles or counters. The other student needs to state the equation, write it down, and solve it. Have students repeat, exchanging roles each time.

Step 4 As a class, discuss a situation that can be solved using an equation. Have students work alone to write the equation and solve it. You can tell about another situation or allow a student volunteer to tell of a situation.

26 BALLOONS Mrs. Washington is bringing balloons to a picnic. She wants to divide the balloons into groups so that each of the 13 students gets 6 balloons. Write and solve an equation for b, the number of balloons Mrs. Washington needs to bring to the picnic.

$\frac{b}{13} = 6$; 78 balloons

27 WORK Adela makes \$6.00 an hour babysitting. She made a total of \$72 last week. Write and solve an equation for h, the number of hours Adela spent babysitting.

$\$6h = \$72$; $h = 12$ hours

Vocabulary Check **Write the vocabulary word that completes each sentence.**

28 The **Multiplication** Property of Equality states that multiplying each side of an equation by the same amount keeps the equation balanced.

29 **Writing in Math** Explain how to solve the equation $5x = 35$.

Divide each side of the equation by 5: $\frac{5x}{5} = \frac{35}{5}$; $x = 7$.

Spiral Review

Solve each equation. (Lesson 10-4, p. 437)

30 $a + 12 = 9$

$a = -3$

31 $m - 7 = -15$

$m = -8$

32 $t - 18 = -4$

$t = 14$

33 $k + 16 = 11$

$k = -5$

34 SCHOOL There are 494 students enrolled in Sunnyvale Middle School. Today 58 students were absent. Write and solve an equation to find s, the number of students who attended school today. (Lesson 10-2, p. 423)

$s + 58 = 494$; 436 students

STOP

Ticket Out the Door

State the Operations Have students line up at the door in single file. As each student reaches the door to exit, state an equation such as $5x = 30$ or $\frac{x}{2} = 14$. Each student needs to tell the operation to use to solve the equation.

Chapter 10

Progress Check 2

Chapter 10 **Progress Check 2** (Lessons 10-4 and 10-5)

Solve each equation.

1 $x + 7 = 15$

$x =$ 8

2 $a + 9 = -5$

$a =$ −14

3 $6b = 42$

$b =$ 7

4 $\frac{y}{8} = -3$

$y =$ −24

5 $z + 6 = 17$

$z =$ 11

6 $c + 11 = 5$

$c =$ −6

7 $\frac{q}{7} = 6$

$q =$ 42

8 $-8b = 72$

$b =$ −9

9 $g - 13 = -25$

$g =$ −12

10 $m - 6 = -18$

$m =$ −12

11 $\frac{d}{-9} = 5$

$d =$ −45

12 $-4n = -28$

$n =$ 7

Solve.

13 **DANCES** Marisa bought punch for a school dance. Write and solve an equation to find g, the number of gallons Marisa should buy to make 80 cups of punch. (*Hint:* 1 gallon = 16 cups)

$16g = 80$; $g = 5$ gallons

14 **HIKING** Larry hiked 15 kilometers below sea level. He stopped to take a break and then finished his hike. At the end of his hike he was 27 kilometers below sea level. Write and solve an equation to find k, the number of kilometers Larry hiked after his break.

$-15 + k = -27$; $k = -12$ kilometers

15 **COMMUNITY SERVICE** Gilberto volunteers at the local hospital. He must distribute 5 baskets of bread to 12 tables. How many baskets of bread does he need in all?

$\frac{t}{5} = 12$; $t = 60$ baskets of bread

Chapter 10 Progress Check 449

Formative Assessment

Use the Progress Check to assess students' mastery of the previous lessons. Have students review the lesson indicated for the problems they answered incorrectly.

Odd/Even Assignments

Exercises are structured so that students practice the same concepts whether they are assigned the odd or even problems.

Data-Driven Decision Making

Students missing Exercises . . .	Have trouble with . . .	Should review and practice . . .
1-2, 5-6, 9–10	solving addition and subtraction equations.	SSG Lessons 10-3 and 10-4, pp. 430 and 437 CRM Skills Practice, pp. A216 and A220
3-4, 7-8, 11–12	solving multiplication and division equations.	SSG Lesson 10-5, p. 443 CRM Skills Practice, p. A224
13–15	writing an equation given a word problem, then solving the word problem.	CRM Problem-Solving Practice, pp. A217, A221, and A225

Chapter 10

Study Guide

Formative Assessment

Vocabulary and Concept Check

If students have difficulty answering Exercises 1–6, remind them that they can use the page references to refresh their memories about the vocabulary terms.

Vocabulary Review Strategies

Vocabulary Pictures Have students draw a picture of each vocabulary word. They can show an equation on a bucket balance, they can show an equation and draw arrows to show a method of solving, and they can draw counters to show a zero pair when working with negative integers.

Lesson Review

Have students read each example and then try the practice problems next to each example. For extra support, have them explain the example to a partner.

Find **Extra Practice** for these concepts in the Practice Worksheets, pages A207–A226.

Classroom Management

Groups Have students work in groups as they complete each lesson's review. Have pairs or individuals within the group solve different problems and then share their work with the others in the group.

Chapter 10

Study Guide

Vocabulary and Concept Check

Addition Property of Equality, *p. 416*
equation, *p. 416*
inverse operations, *p. 423*
Multiplication Property of Equality, *p. 416*
Subtraction Property of Equality, *p. 416*
variable, *p. 423*

Write the vocabulary word that completes each sentence.

1. The <u>Subtraction Property of Equality</u> states that subtracting the same amount from each side of an equation results in a balanced equation.
2. A(n) <u>equation</u> is a mathematical sentence that contains an equals sign, =.
3. Addition and subtraction are <u>inverse operations</u>.
4. The <u>Multiplication Property of Equality</u> states that multiplying each side of an equation by the same amount results in a balanced equation.

Write the correct property in each blank.

5. <u>Division Property of Equality</u>
$(a + 5) \div 4 = 20 \div 4$
6. <u>Addition Property of Equality</u>
$(1 + 7) + 2 = (4 + 4) + 2$

Lesson Review

10-1 Equality (pp. 416–422)

7. Show that adding 9 to each side of $5 + 3 = 2 + 6$ results in a balanced equation.
$(5 + 3) + 9 = (2 + 6) + 9$
$8 + 9 = 8 + 9$
$17 = 17$

8. Show that multiplying by 2 on each side of $5 \times 9 = 3 \times 15$ results in a balanced equation.
$2 \times (5 \times 9) = 2 \times (3 \times 15)$
$2 \times 45 = 2 \times 45$
$90 = 90$

Example 1

Show that adding 4 to each side of $3 + 2 = 4 + 1$ results in a balanced equation.

1. Make a model showing $3 + 2 = 4 + 1$. This equation is balanced because $3 + 2 = 5$ and $4 + 1 = 5$.

2. Add 4 to each side of the model. This equation is balanced because $(3 + 2) + 4 = 5 + 4 = 9$ and $(4 + 1) + 4 = 5 + 4 = 9$.

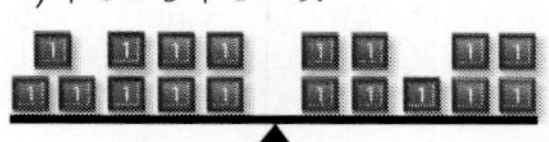

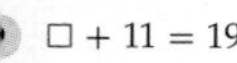

0-2 Operations with Unknown Quantities (pp. 423–428)

ind the value of the box each equation.

□ + 11 = 19
□ = 8

□ − 3 = 31
□ = 34

□ + 10 = 50
□ = 40

□ − 21 = 24
□ = 45

Example 2

Find the value of the box in the equation □ − 6 = 2.

1. Use the inverse operations of addition and subtraction.

   □ − 6 = 2, so 2 + 6 = □   2 + 6 = 8, so □ = 8

2. Use a model to check your answer.

   Think: What number minus 6 equals 2?
   8 − 6 = 2

   The value of □ must be 8.

nd the value of the box in ach equation.

$\frac{\square}{7} = 4$
□ = 28

□ × 5 = 45
□ = 9

$\frac{\square}{2} = 12$
□ = 24

□ × 8 = 56
□ = 7

Example 3

Find the value of the box in the equation 4 × □ = 24.

1. Use the inverse operations of multiplication and division.

   4 × □ = 24, so 24 ÷ 4 = □
   24 ÷ 4 = 6, so □ = 6

2. Check your answer by substituting 6 for □.

   4 × □ = 24
   4 × 6 = 24
   24 = 24 ✓

Dinah Zike's Foldables®

Review Remind students to complete and refer to their Foldables as they progress through the Chapter 10 Study Guide. Have students share and compare their completed Foldables with a partner. You may also choose to have them use their Foldable as a study aid in preparing for the Chapter Test. (For complete instructions, see Chapter Resource Masters, p. A204.)

10-1 Equality

Note This!

Write the Process Have students explain what must be done to each side of an equation before they actually perform the step. Have them write out the process under each equation in their notes and use it as a study checklist.

Intervention Strategy — Kinesthetic Learners

Use Manipulatives Allow students to use counters or a bucket balance and unit blocks to model the equations. Being able to manipulate the parts of the equation serves as a good review of the material.

Common Error Alert

Check If students are not solving the equations in this chapter correctly, ensure they are checking their work by substituting their answers into the original equations.

Fact Families If students are having trouble solving equations because they are not correctly applying inverse operations, have them recall and practice fact families. Write several expressions on the board, then have students solve and complete the fact family for each.

Examples

$3 + 5 = 8$ $\quad 8 - 5 = 3$

$3 \times 5 = 15$ $\quad 15 \div 5 = 3$

10-3 Solve Equations with Positive Integer Solutions

(pp. 430–436)

Solve each equation.

17. $t + 5 = 12$
$t =$ 7

18. $u - 8 = 16$
$u =$ 24

19. $v + 13 = 27$
$v =$ 14

20. $w - 10 = 19$
$w =$ 29

Example 4

Use a model to solve $x + 4 = 7$.

1. Model the equation.

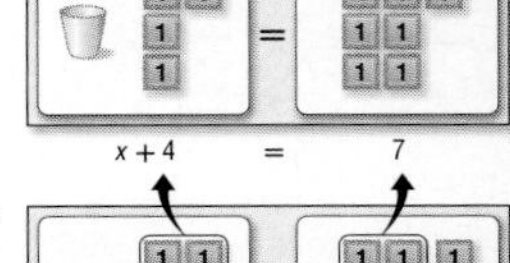

2. Remove 4 tiles from each side to get the cup by itself.

3. There are 3 tiles remaining on the right side, so $x = 3$.

$x = 3$

10-4 Solve Equations Using Addition and Subtraction

(pp. 437–442)

Solve each equation.

21. $z + 7 = 2$
$z =$ −5

22. $m + 3 = -8$
$m =$ −11

23. $b + 9 = 3$
$b =$ −6

24. $c + 11 = -9$
$c =$ −20

Example 5

Use a model to solve $a + 6 = 2$.

1. Model the equation.

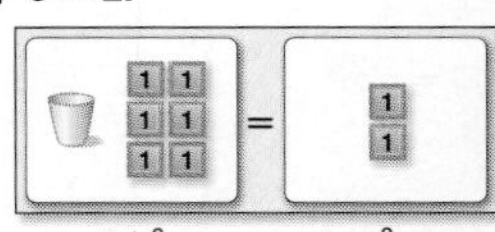

2. Add 6 red negative algebra tiles to each side of the mat.

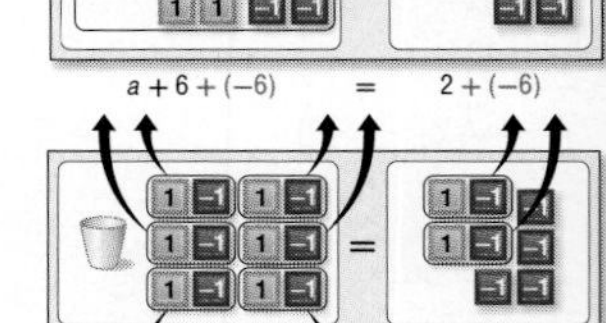

3. Remove 6 zero pairs from the left side and 2 zero pairs from the right side.

$a = -4$

4. So, $a = -4$. The solution is -4.

lve each equation.

$a - 2 = -6$

$a =$ __−4__

$t - 6 = -11$

$t =$ __−5__

$d - 5 = -14$

$d =$ __−9__

$z - 12 = -19$

$z =$ __−7__

Example 6

Solve $z - 5 = -12$.

1. The expression $z - 5$ can be rewritten as $z + (-5)$.
2. The opposite of −5 is +5.
3. Add 5 to each side of the equation.

$$\begin{array}{rcl} z + (-5) & = & -12 \\ +5 & & +5 \\ \hline z + 0 & = & -7 \\ z & = & -7 \end{array}$$

0-5 Solve Equations Using ultiplication and Division

443–448)

ve each equation.

$\frac{x}{3} = 3$

__$x = 9$__

$\frac{y}{-5} = 6$

__$y = -30$__

$8z = 48$

__$z = 6$__

$-7a = 56$

__$a = -8$__

Example 7

Solve $\frac{x}{2} = 6$.

1. The operation is division.
   The inverse operation is multiplication.
2. Multiply each side of the equation by 2.

$$2 \times \frac{x}{2} = 2 \times 6$$
$$\frac{2x}{2} = 12$$
$$x = 12$$

3. Check you answer by substituting 12 for x.

$$\frac{x}{2} = 6$$
$$\frac{12}{2} = 6$$
$$6 = 6 \checkmark$$

Both sides of the equation are the same, so the solution is correct.

Ticket Out the Door

Solve and Exit Write four equations on the board. The four equations should each involve a different operation. Have students solve each equation, showing each step they used to find the solution. They should hand their solutions to you as they exit.

Chapter 10 Chapter Test

Chapter Resource Masters

Additional forms of the Chapter 10 Tests are available.

Test Format	Where to Find it
Chapter 10 Test	Math Online glencoe.com
Blackline Masters	Assessment Masters, p. 140

Customize and create multiple versions of your chapter tests and their answer keys. All of these questions from the chapter tests are available on ExamView® Assessment Suite.

Online Assessment and Reporting
glencoe.com

This online assessment tool allows teachers to track student progress with easily accessible comprehensive reports available for every student. Assess students using any internet-ready computer.

Alternative Assessment

Use Portfolios Ask students to write examples of equations that include each operation in their portfolios. Have students solve their equations and name the inverse operation used to find the value of each unknown.

Chapter Test

1 Show that multiplying by 3 on each side of $2 \times 6 = 4 \times 3$ results in a balanced equation.

$(2 \times 6) \times 3 = (4 \times 3) \times 3$

$12 \times 3 = 12 \times 3$

$36 = 36$

2 Show that adding 6 to each side of $15 + 10 = 5 + 20$ results in a balanced equation.

$(15 + 10) + 6 = (5 + 20) + 6$

$25 + 6 = 25 + 6$

$31 = 31$

Find the missing numbers to make each equation balanced.

3 $(7 + 1) \times 16 =$ 16 $\times (4 + 4)$

4 15 $+ (3 \times 6) = (2 \times 9) + 15$

5 12 $+ (12 \times 2) = (3 \times 8) + 12$

6 $(6 + 4) \times 4 =$ 4 $\times (3 + 8)$

Find the value of the box in each equation.

7 $\square - 14 = 8$

$\square =$ 22

8 $9 \times \square = 72$

$\square =$ 8

9 $\square + 71 = 82$

$\square =$ 11

10 $\frac{\square}{9} = 6$

$\square =$ 54

Complete each sentence below.

11 The inverse operation of subtraction is addition.

12 The inverse operation of multiplication is division.

Solve each equation.

13 $18 + n = 35$

$n =$ 17

14 $d - 12 = 22$

$d =$ 34

15 $\frac{q}{6} = 7$

$q =$ 42

16 $-9k = 63$

$k =$ −7

454 Chapter 10 Test

English Learner Strategy

Assessment Point out certain words in the word problems for students to define before beginning the chapter test. If there are any words students do not understand, provide a dictionary or a translation manual in the student's native language so that the words in the problems do not interfere with the student showing knowledge of the mathematics.

Vrite an equation to represent each situation. Then answer he question.

7 **FIELD TRIPS** Gabriel's class took a field trip to an art museum. There are 28 students in his class. The tickets cost \$196 in all. What was the price of each ticket?

$28t = 196$; $t = \$7$

8 **BAKING** Jude is making pecan pies. He has 12 cups of pecans. His mother brings him more pecans. He has 18 cups in all. How many cups did his mother bring him?

$12 + x = 18$; $x = 6$ cups

9 **SCIENCE** Mr. Morris has 90 test tubes. He must distribute 6 test tubes to each lab station in his classroom. How many lab stations are there?

$6x = 90$; $x = 15$ lab stations

0 **SCIENCE** The boiling point of Cobalt (Co) is 2,870°C. The boiling point of Iron (Fe) is 2,750°C. What is the difference in the two boiling points of these elements?

$2{,}870°C - 2{,}750°C = x$; $x = 120°C$

olve.

1 **GEOGRAPHY** The distance from Loganville to Palmetto is 147 miles. This is 17 more miles than the distance from Loganville to Carrollton. Write and solve an equation to find the distance, *d*, in miles from Loganville to Carrollton.

$d + 17 = 147$; $d = 130$ miles

orrect the mistakes.

2 **VOLUNTEERING** Emma's youth group had 32 participants at the senior-center holiday party. That was four times as many participants, *p*, as last year. Emma wrote an equation to find the number of participants last year. What mistake did she make?

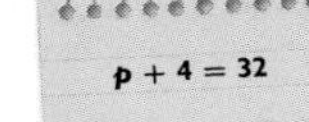

The mistake is that her equation says that the 32 participants are four more than p, rather than four times p; $4p = 32$.

Math Coach Notes

Context Ensure students read each problem carefully. They should verify that their answers make sense in context. Have them ask themselves questions such as "Can a person really eat 15 apples?"

Data-Driven Decision Making

Students missing Exercises . . .	Have trouble with . . .	Should review and practice . . .
1–2	verifying the validity of equations.	SSG Lesson 10-1, p. 416 CRM Skills Practice, p. A208
3–10	finding the missing value in an equation.	SSG Lessons 10-2, 10-3, 10-4, and 10-5; pp. 423, 430, 437, and 443 CRM Skills Practice, pp. A212, A216, A220, and A224
11–16	solving equations and naming inverse operations.	SSG Lessons 10-2, 10-3, 10-4, and 10-5; pp. 423, 430, 437, and 443 CRM Skills Practice, pp. A212, A216, A220, and A224
17–22	solving word problems using mathematical equations.	CRM Problem-Solving Practice, pp. A209, A213, A217, A221, and A225

Test Practice

Diagnose Student Errors

Survey student responses for each item. Class trends may indicate common errors and misconceptions.

1. A guess
B guess
(C) correct
D guess

2. A balanced equation, but not what Emanuel swam
(B) correct
C not a balanced equation
D not a balanced equation

3. A used correct numbers, guessed at operation
(B) correct
C student assumed division rather than writing a multiplication equation
D set up equation incorrectly

4. (A) correct
B wrong operation
C want sum, not difference
D guess

5. (A) correct
B guess
C guess
D misinterpreted operation, added numbers together

6. A used incorrect inverse operation
B guess
C guess
(D) correct

7. A used incorrect inverse operation
B guess
C guess
(D) correct

8. A guess
(B) correct
C did not rename when subtracting
D incorrect inverse operation

Test Practice

Select the best answer and fill in the corresponding circle on the sheet at right.

1 Find the missing number to make the equation balanced.

$(3 \times 8) + \_\_\_ = 7 + (4 \times 6)$

A 3
B 5
(C) 7
D 9

2 Emanuel swam 7 laps on Wednesday. On Thursday he swam 3 laps. Andres swam 5 laps on Wednesday. On Thursday he swam 5 laps. On Friday Emanuel and Andres both swam 4 laps. Which equation represents a balanced equation?

A $(7 + 5) + 4 = (7 + 5) + 4$
(B) $(7 + 3) + 4 = (5 + 5) + 4$
C $(7 + 4) + 5 = (5 + 4) + 5$
D $(3 + 5) + 7 = (5 + 3) + 5$

3 Gina's dad gave her $40 to take some friends to the movies. If movie tickets cost $8 per student, which equation will help Gina figure out how many friends she can take? Let n equal the number of students going to the movies.

A $\$8 - n = \$40$
(B) $\$8 \times n = \$40$
C $\$8 \div n = \$40$
D $\$40 - n = \$8$

4 Laura and Orlando baked a total of 10 pies. Laura baked 3 of the pies on her own. Which equation is used to find the number of pies Orlando baked?

(A) $3 + e = 10$
B $3 \times e = 10$
C $e - 3 = 10$
D $10 \div e = 3$

5 Tyler can walk 4 miles an hour. How many miles can he walk in 3 hours?

(A) 12 miles
B 9 miles
C 8 miles
D 7 miles

6 Solve for z in the equation.

$\frac{z}{6} = 5$

A 11
B 20
C 24
(D) 30

7 Find the value of the box in the equation.

$\square - 15 = 29$

A 14
B 24
C 34
(D) 44

456 **Chapter 10** Test Practice

9. A incorrect operation
B incorrect operation
(C) correct
D incorrect operation

10. A guess
B guess
C guess
(D) correct

11. A sides not equal
(B) correct
C sides not equal
D sides not equal

8. Solve for x in the equation.

$$24 + x = 40$$

A $x = 8$ C $x = 26$

(B) $x = 16$ D $x = 64$

9. Santiago bought 6 pizzas for his birthday party. He paid $72. Which equation can be used to find p, the cost of each pizza?

A $6 + p = 72$ (C) $6p = 72$

B $6 - p = 72$ D $\frac{p}{6} = 72$

10. Solve for b in the equation.

$$9b = 63$$

A $b = 4$ C $b = 6$

B $b = 5$ (D) $b = 7$

11. Which operation keeps the scale balanced?

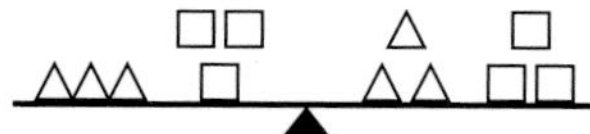

A Add two triangle blocks to the right side.

(B) Add two square blocks to both sides.

C Add two square blocks to the left side.

D Add two square blocks to the right side.

ANSWER SHEET

Directions: Fill in the circle of each correct answer.

1	A	B	**C**	D
2	A	**B**	C	D
3	A	**B**	C	D
4	**A**	B	C	D
5	**A**	B	C	D
6	A	B	C	**D**
7	A	B	C	**D**
8	A	**B**	C	D
9	A	B	**C**	D
10	A	B	C	**D**
11	A	**B**	C	D

Success Strategy

Read the directions carefully. This will help you avoid careless errors. Also, review your answers when you are done. Make sure that you have answered all of the questions and have not mismarked the answer sheet.

Diagnosing Student Errors and Misconceptions

Types of Errors Student errors most likely fall into two classifications: computational errors or use of the wrong operation. If a student missed several problems due to computational errors, determine if the student rushed and made careless mistakes or if the student is lacking basic computational skills. If the student missed several problems due to improper operations, further coverage on vocabulary and concepts of the four operations is in order.

Polls An informal class poll can help you determine if further class instruction is needed on understanding operations, or if individualized or small group intervention is needed.

Common Error *Alert*

Eliminate Wrong Answers If students missed several problems due to computational errors, be sure that students have their graded work to review. Explain that without work shown, the point at which the mistake was made cannot be identified. Have the student try to locate the mistake, but offer assistance for each problem in which the mistake cannot be located.

Index

Red type denotes items only in the Teacher Edition.

D

F

G

H

T

Image Credits

Teacher Edition

Cover Alamy; **iv** (1 7 8)File Photo, (2 3) The McGraw-Hill Companies, (4 5 6)Doug Martin; **ix** PunchStock; **vi, vii** CORBIS; **viii** PunchStock; **x** Robert Glusic/CORBIS; **xi** PunchStock; **xii** Joe Sohm/Getty Images; **xiii** PunchStock; **xiv** Douglas Peebles/Alamy; **xv** CORBIS; **143** Getty Images; **158** Hugh Threlfall/Alamy; **225** The McGraw-Hill Companies.

Student Edition

Book 1

All coins photographed by United States Mint.
All bills photographed by Michael Houghton/StudiOhio.
Cover Alamy; **iv** (1 7 8) File Photo, (2 3) The McGraw-Hill Companies, (4 5 6) Doug Martin; **vi, vii** CORBIS; **viii** PunchStock; **2–3** Jupiterimages; **10** PictureQuest; **15** SuperStock; **16** Alamy; **24, 26** PunchStock; **34** PictureQuest; **35** Getty Images; **44–45** Andersen Ross/Getty Images; **45** (inset)Mark Ransom; **50** Getty Images; **52** CORBIS; **56** Jupiterimages; **57** Getty Images; **58** Charles Smith/CORBIS; **72** Jill Braaten/The McGraw-Hill Companies; **73** **(t)** Millard H. Sharp/Photo Researchers, Inc., **(b)**Steve Maslowski/Visuals Unlimited; **86** Chase Jarvis/Getty Images; **100–101** Miles Ertman/Masterfile; **115** PunchStock; **123** Peter Cade/Getty Images; **130** PunchStock.

Book 2

All coins photographed by United States Mint.
All bills photographed by Michael Houghton/StudiOhio.
Cover Alamy; **iv** (1 7 8) File Photo, (2 3) The McGraw-Hill Companies, (4 5 6) Doug Martin; **vi** PunchStock; **vii** Robert Glusic/CORBIS; **viii** PunchStock; **140-141** (bkgd)Jim Lane/Alamy; **141** (inset)Ryan McVay/Getty Images; **142** Ken Cavanagh/The McGraw-Hill Companies; **143** Getty Images; **145** (bl)G.K. & Vikki Hart/Getty Images, (others)Alamy; **146** Jules Frazier/Getty Images; **147** Mark Ransom/RansomStudios; **148** (l)PunchStock, (r)CORBIS; **157, 159** PunchStock; **160** Getty Images; **161** PunchStock; **162, 169** Siede Preis/Getty Images; **172** (l)PunchStock, (r)Eric Misko/The McGraw-Hill Companies; **175** Jupiterimages; **178-179** Michael A. Keller/CORBIS; **184** (t)Getty Images, (b)Fotosearch; **191** (t)PunchStock, (b)Kevin Cavanagh/The McGraw-Hill Companies; **193** Getty Images; **200** Alamy; **204** Zigy Kaluzny/Getty Images; **205** iStockphoto; **206, 207** Sandra Ivany/Getty Images; **212** Getty Images; **214** PunchStock; **222** Helene Rogers/Alamy; **227** PunchStock; **229** CORBIS; **230** Getty Images; **240-241** Les Gibbon/Alamy; **245** PunchStock; **246** Ryan McVay/Getty Images; **252** Ken Cavanagh/The McGraw-Hill Companies; **253** Alamy; **255** Getty Images; **260** Judith Collins/Alamy; **262** Getty Images; **268** (t)Getty Images, (b)PunchStock; **269** GK & Vikki Hart/Getty Images; **275** Bob Pool/Getty Images.

Book 3

All coins photographed by United States Mint.
All bills photographed by Michael Houghton/StudiOhio.
Cover Alamy; **iv** (1 7 8) File Photo, (2 3) The McGraw-Hill Companies, (4 5 6) Doug Martin; **vi** Joe Sohm/Getty Images; **vii** PunchStock; **viii** Alamy; **ix** CORBIS; **278-279** NASA; **293** CORBIS; **300** PunchStock; **305** SuperStock; **316-317** Javier Pierini/Getty Images; **322** Steve Bronstein/Getty Images; **330** Getty Images; **331** Jupiterimages; **338** PictureQuest; **340** SuperStock; **345** David Young-Wolff/PhotoEdit; **347** CORBIS; **356** Getty Images; **358** Masterfile; **362** SuperStock; 364 John A. Rizzo/Getty Images; **374-375** Ray Kachatorian/Getty Images; **375** (t)Ryan McVay/Getty Images, (b) Getty Images; **388** CORBIS; **389** Martin Harvey/Peter Arnold, Inc.; **396** Patrick Olear/PhotoEdit; **398** Alamy; **402** Andersen Ross/Age Fotostock; **414–415** Erik Dreyer/Getty Images; **420** Janis Christie/Getty Images; **427** Jupiterimages; **434** Getty Images; **442** Zia Soleil/Getty Images; **447** Keith Thomas/PictureQuest.

Chapter Resource Masters

Chapter Resource Masters

NAME ______________________ DATE ______________

Chapter 1

Foldables Study Organizer

Dinah Zike's Foldables

Make this Foldable to help you organize information about fractions.

1. Begin with one sheet of 11″ × 17″ paper. Fold the short sides toward the middle.

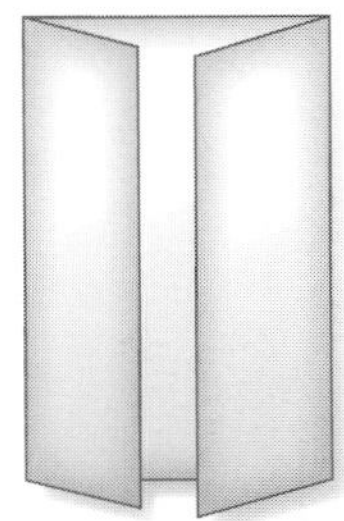

2. Fold the top to the bottom. Open. Cut along the second fold to make four tabs.

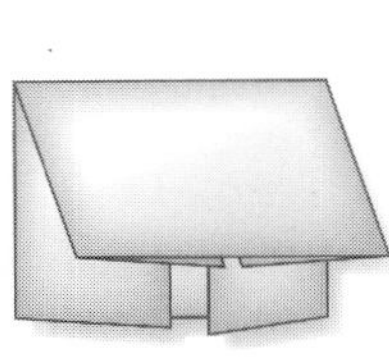

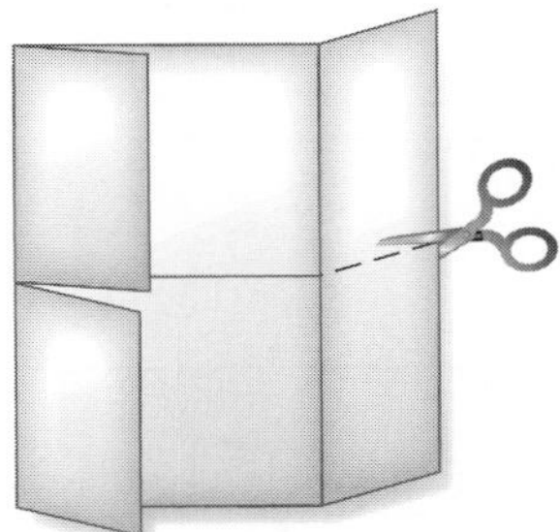

3. Label each of the tabs as shown.

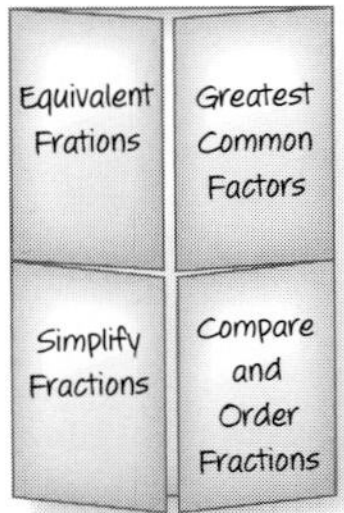

TAKING NOTES
As you read through the chapter, write key terms, their definitions, and examples on the tabs of your Foldable.

USING YOUR FOLDABLE
As you study, open each tab of your Foldable and read the definitions and examples that you have written. Check yourself by looking at the front of the tab.

USING YOUR FOLDABLE
Work with a partner. Take turns saying a term or definition. If you give a definition, your partner must say the term. If you say a term, your partner must give the definition.

NAME ________________________ DATE ____________

Chapter 1

Games and Puzzles

Equivalent Fractions

DIRECTIONS

- Player 1 spins spinner A.
- Player 2 spins spinner B.
- Create a fraction using the number from spinner A as the numerator of the fraction and the number from spinner B as the denominator of the fraction.
- Each player writes the fraction and an equivalent fraction in the first column of their table. Players check each other's work.
- Repeat four more times.
- Each player orders their fractions in the second row of their table from least to greatest.
- **Who Wins**? The player that correctly orders their fractions first.

What You Need

- Equivalent Fractions Spinners
- Equivalent Fractions Tables
- Pencil

Number of Players

2

Player A:					
Fraction					
Equivalent Fraction					

Fractions from least to greatest: ____________________

Player B:					
Fraction					
Equivalent Fraction					

Fractions from least to greatest: ____________________

NAME ________________________________ DATE ________________

Equivalent Fractions Spinners

Spinner A

Spinner B

NAME ______________________________ DATE ______________

Vocabulary and English Language Development

Activate Prior Knowledge

Sara, Carmen, and Josh each ate a whole pizza, which they each cut differently. Their pizzas are shown below. Write equivalent forms of one to express the amount eaten by each person.

1 $\frac{\square}{\square} = 1$

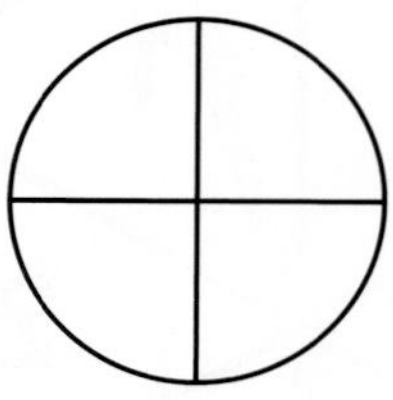

2 $\frac{\square}{\square} = 1$

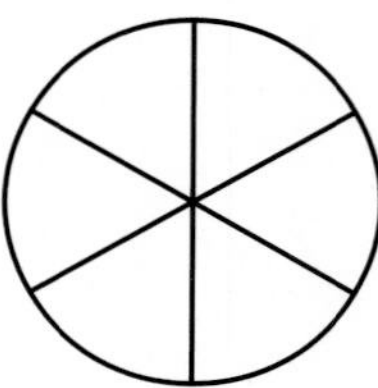

3 $\frac{\square}{\square} = 1$

Definition Review

Equivalent fractions are fractions that name the same number.
An **equivalent form of one** is any nonzero number divided by itself.

Fill in the blank with *equivalent fractions*, or *equivalent forms of one*.

4 $\frac{3}{8}$ and $\frac{6}{16}$ are ______________________________.

5 $\frac{7}{7}$ and $\frac{8}{8}$ are ______________________________.

Application

- Work with a partner.
- Make a model for each fraction.
- Tell whether each pair of fractions is equivalent or not.

- $\frac{4}{5}$ ______________________________ $\frac{6}{10}$
- $\frac{1}{2}$ ______________________________ $\frac{4}{8}$
- $\frac{5}{10}$ ______________________________ $\frac{4}{5}$
- $\frac{4}{6}$ ______________________________ $\frac{2}{3}$
- $\frac{3}{9}$ ______________________________ $\frac{2}{6}$

NAME ______________________ DATE ______________

Lesson 1-1

Skills Practice

Chapter 1

Complete each model to name an equivalent fraction.

1. $\frac{2}{3} = \frac{6}{\square}$

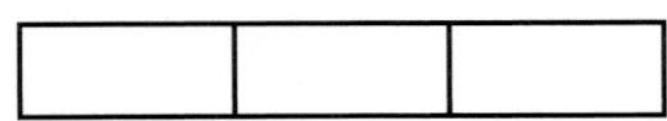

2. $\frac{3}{4} = \frac{\square}{12}$

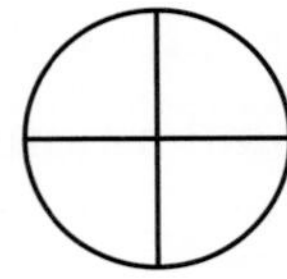

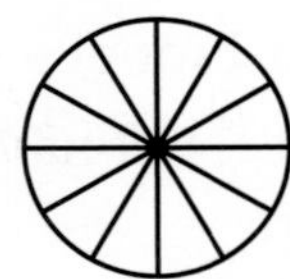

3. $\frac{4}{5} = \frac{\square}{10}$

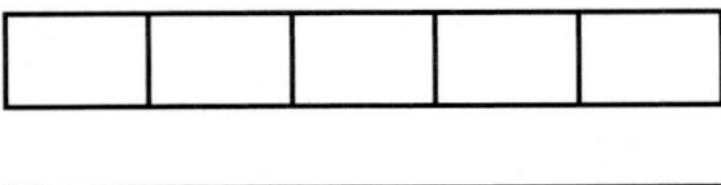

4. $\frac{1}{3} = \frac{2}{\square}$

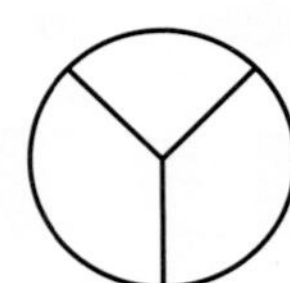

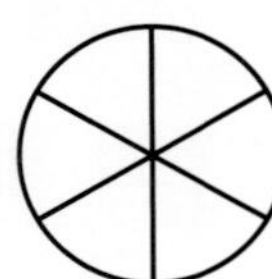

Complete to name an equivalent fraction.

5. $\frac{3}{8} = \frac{6}{\square}$

6. $\frac{2}{9} = \frac{\square}{18}$

7. $\frac{1}{7} = \frac{3}{\square}$

8. $\frac{4}{10} = \frac{12}{\square}$

9. $\frac{2}{5} = \frac{\square}{25}$

10. $\frac{5}{11} = \frac{\square}{66}$

11. $\frac{5}{12} = \frac{10}{\square}$

12. $\frac{7}{9} = \frac{28}{\square}$

13. $\frac{3}{4} = \frac{\square}{16}$

14. $\frac{8}{15} = \frac{24}{\square}$

NAME _______________ DATE _______________

Lesson 1-1 Problem-Solving Practice

Solve.

1 **KNITTING** Rachel and Lionel each knit a scarf 60 inches long. The scarves are shown below.

What fraction of Rachel's scarf is white? _______________

What fraction of Lionel's scarf is white? _______________

Do Rachel and Lionel have equal amounts of white in their scarves? Explain.

____

2 **LUNCH** John cut his 12-inch submarine sandwich into 12 equal pieces. He ate 2 pieces. Juanita cut her 12-inch submarine sandwich into 6 equal pieces. She ate the same amount as John. How many pieces of her sandwich did Juanita eat? _______________

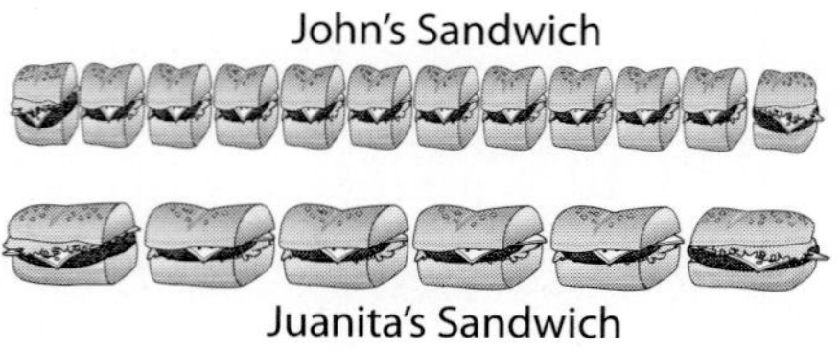

3 **DESSERT** Sylvia made a blueberry pie and cut it into 6 pieces. Thelma made a blueberry pie and cut it into 12 pieces. How many pieces of Thelma's pie equal 2 pieces of Sylvia's pie? _______________

4 **BASEBALL** Anton and Julian both pitched in Friday's little league game. Anton threw 20 pitches of which 18 were strikes. Julian threw 40 pitches of which 36 were strikes. Who threw the greater fraction of strikes in Friday's game?

____

NAME ______________________ DATE ______________

Lesson 1-1

Homework Practice

Complete to name an equivalent fraction.

1. $\frac{2}{3} = \frac{6}{\square}$

2. $\frac{3}{7} = \frac{15}{\square}$

3. $\frac{10}{17} = \frac{20}{\square}$

4. $\frac{4}{5} = \frac{\square}{20}$

Name two equivalent fractions for each fraction.

5. $\frac{1}{9}$ ______________

6. $\frac{3}{5}$ ______________

7. $\frac{5}{7}$ ______________

8. $\frac{2}{3}$ ______________

9. $\frac{7}{8}$ ______________

10. $\frac{1}{4}$ ______________

11. $\frac{7}{11}$ ______________

12. $\frac{3}{10}$ ______________

Solve.

13. **CRAFTS** Keisha had two pieces of ribbon of equal length. She cut each ribbon into equal parts. She cut the first piece of ribbon into 15 parts. Nine parts of the first piece are the same length as 3 parts of the second piece. Into how many parts did she cut the second piece of ribbon? ______________

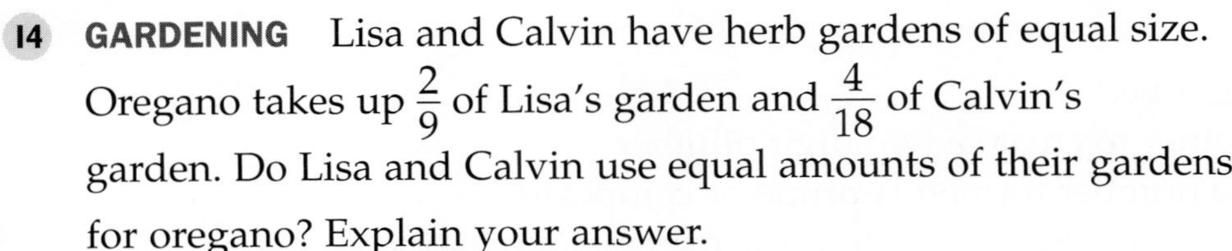

14. **GARDENING** Lisa and Calvin have herb gardens of equal size. Oregano takes up $\frac{2}{9}$ of Lisa's garden and $\frac{4}{18}$ of Calvin's garden. Do Lisa and Calvin use equal amounts of their gardens for oregano? Explain your answer.

____

Write the vocabulary word that completes each sentence.

15. The amount of a number is its ______________.

16. Fractions that name the same number are called ______________.

NAME ______________________________ DATE ______________

Lesson 1-2

Vocabulary and English Language Development

Activate Prior Knowledge

Name two equivalent fractions for each fraction.

1. $\frac{2}{5}$ ______________________

2. $\frac{3}{7}$ ______________________

3. $\frac{5}{9}$ ______________________

4. $\frac{4}{4}$ ______________________

Definition Review

Fill in the blanks.

5. A number greater than 1 with more than two factors is called a ______________ number.

6. A whole number that has exactly two factors, 1 and the number itself, is called a ______________ number.

Application

Follow the directions below.

- Students work in pairs.
- Each student rolls a number cube.
- Slide the number cubes together to create a two digit number.
- Decide together whether the number formed is prime or composite.
- If the number is composite, use a factor tree to find the prime factorization of the number.
- Switch the position of the number cubes to make another two digit number.
- Determine if it is prime or composite. Write the prime factorization if it is composite.
- Repeat as time permits.

NAME ______________________ DATE ______________

Lesson 1-2

Skills Practice

Find the GCF of each set of numbers by listing factor pairs.

1 45 and 50

45	50
______	______
______	______
______	______

The GCF of 45 and 50 is ______.

2 12 and 18

12	18
______	______
______	______
______	______

The GCF of 12 and 18 is ______.

Find the GCF of each set of numbers by making a list.

3 18 and 24

18: ______________________

24: ______________________

The GCF of 18 and 24 is ______.

4 26 and 39

26: ______________________

39: ______________________

The GCF of 26 and 39 is ______.

5 24, 36, and 48

24: ______________________

36: ______________________

48: ______________________

The GCF of 24, 36, and 48 is ______.

6 18, 27, and 45

18: ______________________

27: ______________________

45: ______________________

The GCF of 18, 27, and 45 is ______.

Find the GCF of each set of numbers by using prime factors.

7

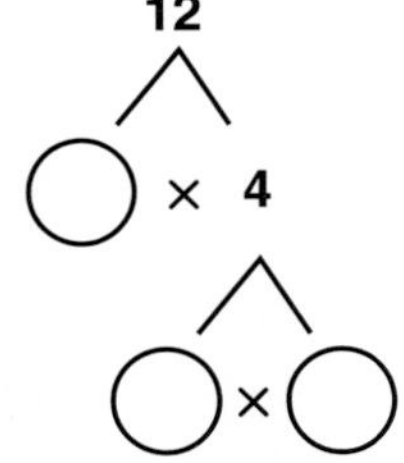

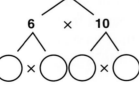

60

6 × 10

× ×

______

8

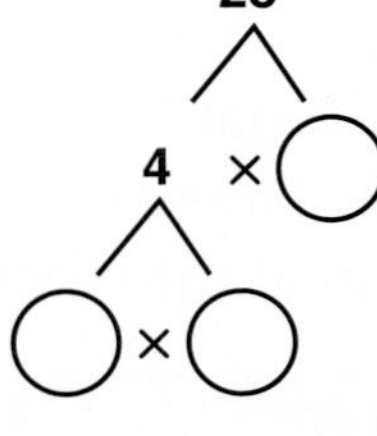

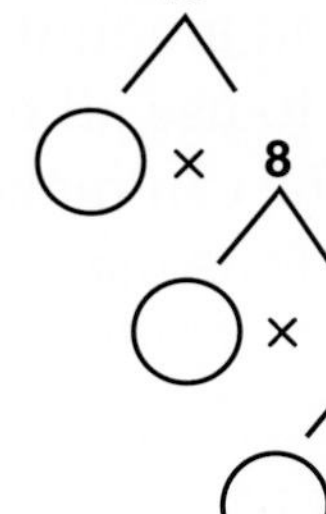

______

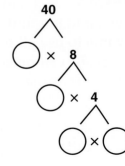

Lesson 1-2

NAME ______________________ DATE ______________

Problem-Solving Practice

Solve.

1 **FLORIST** Quincy works at a floral shop. He is cutting ribbons for bouquets of flowers from a 70-inch piece of ribbon and a 63-inch piece of ribbon. He wants to use all of the available ribbon. If all of the pieces are to be the same length, what is the length of the longest ribbon he can make? ______________

2 **GARDENING** Tobias is cutting wooden tomato stakes for his garden. One piece of wood measures 96 inches and the other measures 160 inches. He wants to make all of the stakes the same length, and he does not want any wood to go to waste. What is the length of the longest stake he can make? ______________

3 **BOOKS** Zie wants to place his books on shelves. He wants each shelf to contain only one kind of book, but he insists that each shelf contain the same number of books. The circle graph shows how many books of each type he has. What is the greatest number of books that can be on each shelf? ______________

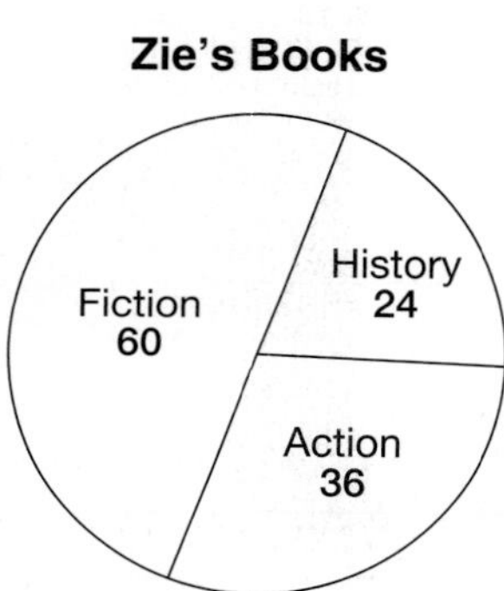

4 **TREATS** Mrs. Lawton is making treat bags for camp leaders. The type and amount of treats she has are shown in the table. She wants to use all the treats. What is the greatest number of treat bags she can make if all the bags are made exactly the same and she puts as many of each treat into each bag as possible? ______________

Item	Quantity
Gum	42
Hard Candy	35
Cookies	56

NAME ______________________ DATE ______________

Homework Practice

Find the GCF of each set of numbers.

1. 16 and 40 ________
2. 12 and 22 ________
3. 66 and 99 ________
4. 25 and 40 ________
5. 40 and 48 ________
6. 27 and 90 ________
7. 42 and 60 ________
8. 12, 20, and 60 ________

Find the GCF of each set of numbers by using prime factors.

9.

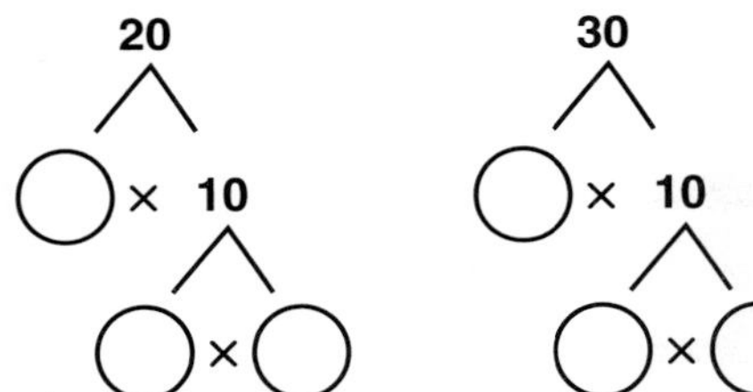

____

10.

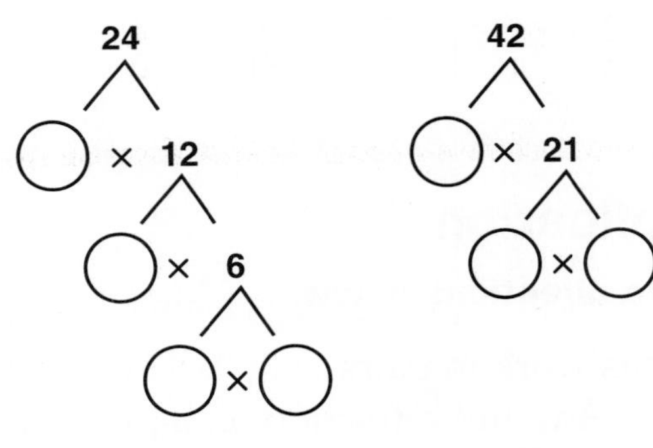

____

11.

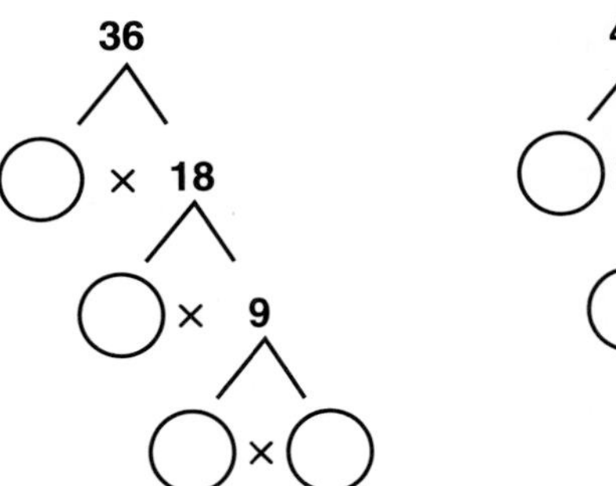

____

12.

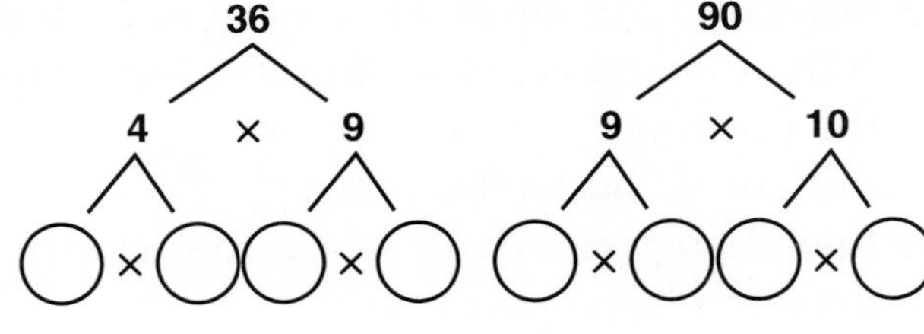

____

Lesson 1-3

NAME ________________________________ DATE ______________

Vocabulary and English Language Development

Activate Prior Knowledge

1. List the names of ten friends or family members. Out of the people you listed, what fraction of them has a dog as a pet? Write your answer in simplest form.

____

____

Definition Review

2. When a fraction is in ______________ form, the GCF of the numerator and denominator is 1.

3. Circle the fractions that are in simplest form.

$\frac{1}{2}$ $\frac{2}{6}$ $\frac{3}{4}$ $\frac{5}{11}$ $\frac{5}{15}$ $\frac{4}{9}$

Application

Follow the directions below.

- Students work in pairs.
- Student *A* writes a fraction on a piece of paper. Numbers used for the numerator and denominator should be whole numbers greater than or equal to one but less than or equal to 100. The numerator of the fraction should be less than or equal to the denominator of the fraction.
- Student *B* identifies whether or not the fraction is in simplest form. If the fraction is not in simplest form, student *B* should simplify the fraction.
- Student *A* checks the answer.
- Interchange roles and repeat the activity.
- Repeat as time permits.

NAME ______________________ DATE ______________

Lesson 1-3

Skills Practice

Write each fraction in simplest form. Use models.

1

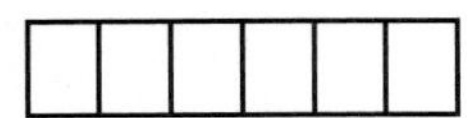

$\frac{4}{6} = \frac{\square}{\square}$

2

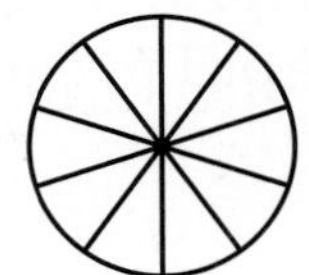 

$\frac{6}{10} = \frac{\square}{\square}$

3

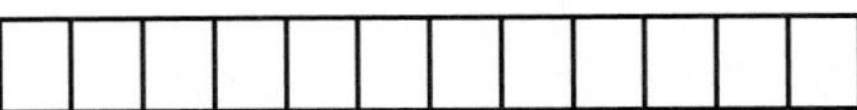

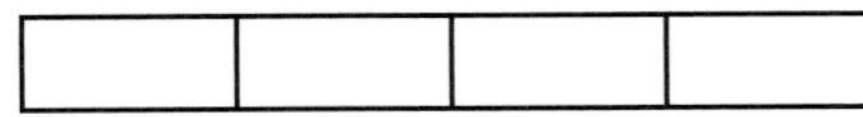

$\frac{9}{12} = \frac{\square}{\square}$

4

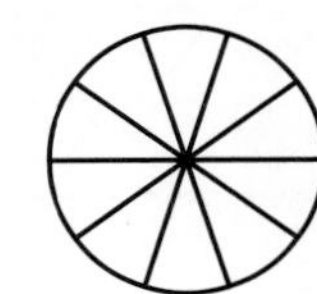 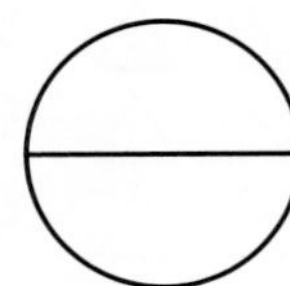

$\frac{5}{10} = \frac{\square}{\square}$

Write each fraction in simplest form. Divide by the GCF.

5 $\frac{9}{15} =$ __________

6 $\frac{6}{14} =$ __________

7 $\frac{18}{24} =$ __________

8 $\frac{50}{100} =$ __________

9 $\frac{5}{25} =$ __________

10 $\frac{18}{27} =$ __________

Write each fraction in simplest form. Use prime factorization.

11 $\frac{12}{24} =$ __________

12 $\frac{8}{32} =$ __________

13 $\frac{27}{81} =$ __________

14 $\frac{10}{45} =$ __________

15 $\frac{12}{28} =$ __________

16 $\frac{22}{55} =$ __________

NAME ______________________ DATE ______________

Problem-Solving Practice

Solve.

1 **RAIN** During the month of April, it rained on 8 days. What is the fraction of days it rained in April in simplest form? (Hint: There are 30 days in April.) ______

2 **BRACELETS** Laurie is making a bracelet using heart-shaped and triangle-shaped beads. She wants to use all of the beads shown below. In simplest form, what fraction of the beads are triangles? ______

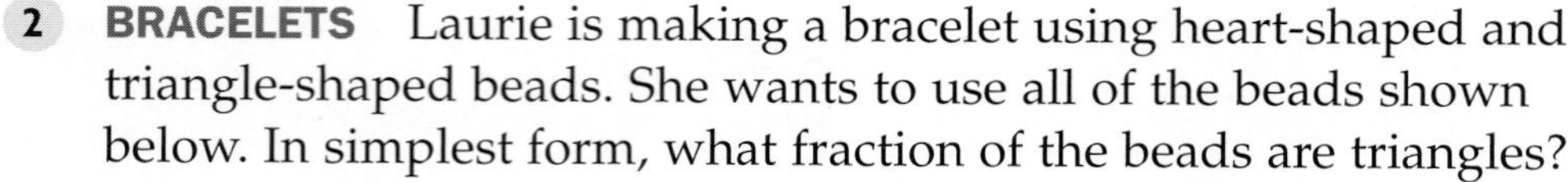

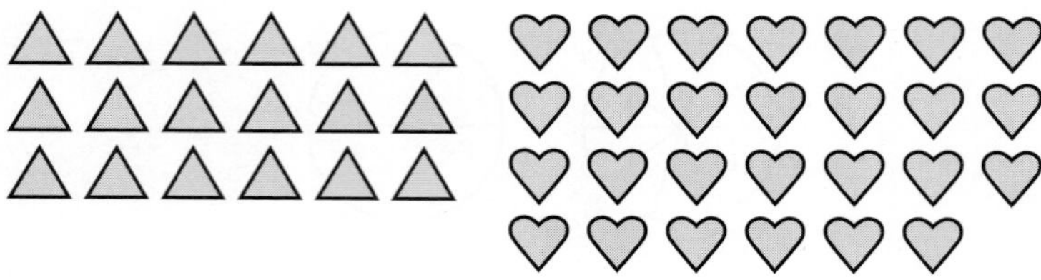

3 **BOOKS** Hector divided the books he read last year into four categories. In simplest form, what fraction of the books are mystery books? ______

Book Categories	
Category	**Number**
Mystery	8
Science Fiction	12
History	4
Biography	4

4 **BASEBALL** A baseball pitcher threw a total of 75 pitches in a ballgame. Forty of those pitches were strikes. In simplest form, what fraction of the pitches were strikes? ______

5 **MUSIC** The school orchestra contains 32 musicians. There are 10 musicians in the brass section. In simplest form, what fraction of the orchestra is the brass section? ______

6 **TESTS** A math test has a total of 24 questions. Darla got 21 questions correct. In simplest form, what fraction of the questions did Darla answer correctly? ______

NAME ______________________________ DATE ______________

Lesson 1-3

Homework Practice

Write each fraction in simplest form. Use models.

1 $\frac{3}{12} =$

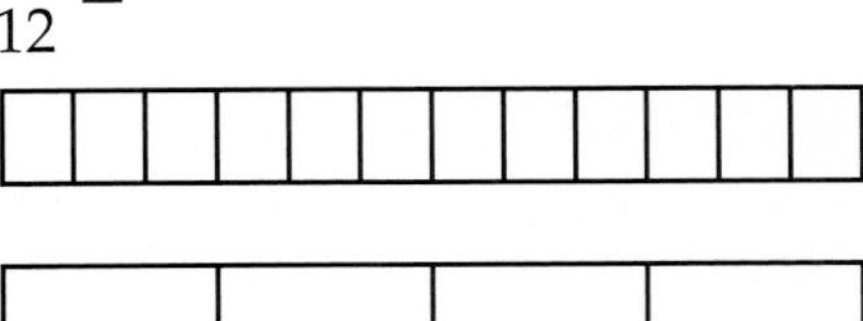

2 $\frac{8}{10} =$

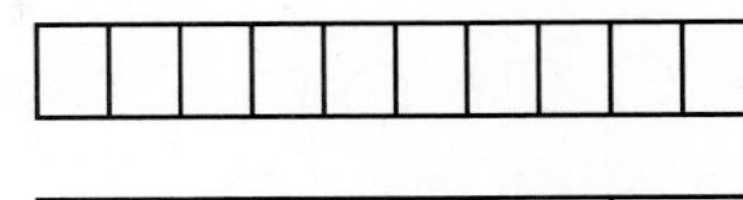

Write each fraction in simplest form. Divide by the GCF.

3 $\frac{5}{50} =$ ________

4 $\frac{8}{36} =$ ________

5 $\frac{12}{70} =$ ________

6 $\frac{18}{42} =$ ________

Write each fraction in simplest form. Use prime factorization.

7 $\frac{15}{100} =$ ________

8 $\frac{20}{30} =$ ________

9 $\frac{54}{81} =$ ________

10 $\frac{8}{44} =$ ________

Solve.

11 **PHOTOGRAPHS** Millie took 36 pictures using her digital camera. She deleted 8 pictures. In simplest form, what fraction of the pictures did Millie keep? ________

12 **SURVEY** A supermarket surveyed 100 people about their favorite brand of orange juice. Thirty-five people said *Sunshine State* orange juice is their favorite brand. In simplest form, what fraction of the people surveyed did ***not*** say *Sunshine State* orange juice was their favorite brand? ________

Write the vocabulary word that completes each sentence.

13 The form of a fraction when the GCF of the numerator and the denominator is 1 is called ____________________.

14 The ____________________ is the greatest of the common factors of two or more numbers.

NAME _______________ DATE _______________

Lesson 1-4

Vocabulary and English Language Development

Activate Prior Knowledge

Use the designs to answer the questions.

* ○ □ * □ □ * ○ □ * ○ □ *	Design A
* ○ □ * ○ □ ○ * ○ □ * ○	Design B
□ ○ * * ○ □ ○ * *	Design C

1 What fraction of the symbols in Design A is circles? _______________

2 What fraction of the symbols in Design B is stars? _______________

3 What fraction of the symbols in Design C is squares? _______________

Definition Review

Fill in the blanks.

4 The same denominator used in two or more fractions is the _______________.

5 The _______________ is the least common multiple of the denominators of two or more fractions.

Application

Use a ruler to cut 4 strips of paper, each 12 inches long. Divide each strip of paper into equal parts to show the fractions below. Then write the fractions in order from least to greatest.

$\frac{1}{2}$

$\frac{1}{3}$

$\frac{1}{12}$

$\frac{1}{4}$

NAME ______________________________ DATE ______________

Lesson 1-4

Skills Practice

Use <, =, or > to compare the fractions. Shade the models given.

1. $\frac{2}{5} \bigcirc \frac{5}{8}$

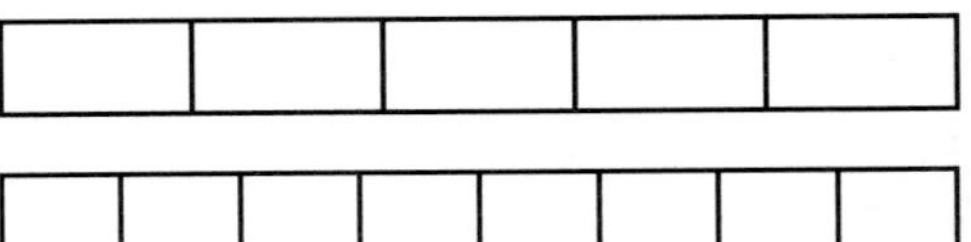

2. $\frac{4}{8} \bigcirc \frac{1}{3}$

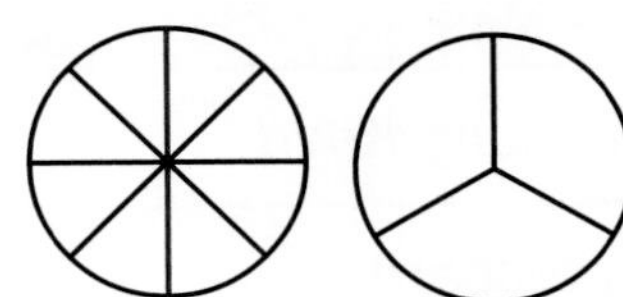

Use <, =, or > to compare the fractions.

3. $\frac{3}{4} \bigcirc \frac{7}{8}$

4. $\frac{1}{3} \bigcirc \frac{2}{9}$

5. $\frac{2}{9} \bigcirc \frac{4}{15}$

6. $\frac{2}{3} \bigcirc \frac{4}{6}$

7. $\frac{8}{14} \bigcirc \frac{5}{7}$

8. $\frac{1}{2} \bigcirc \frac{7}{11}$

Order the fractions from least to greatest.

9. $\frac{1}{3}$, $\frac{1}{6}$, and $\frac{1}{7}$ ______________

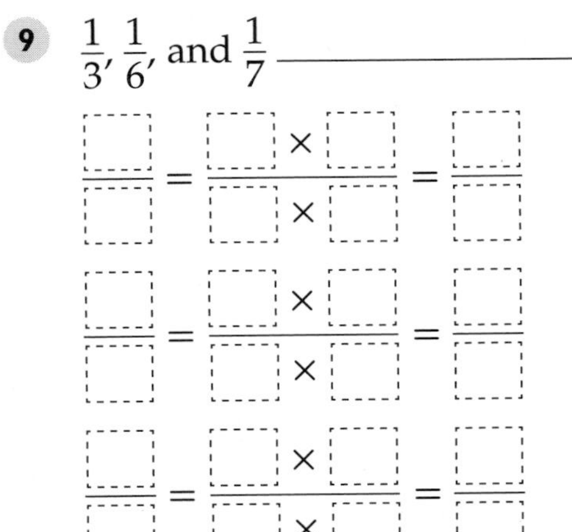

10. $\frac{2}{9}$, $\frac{1}{6}$, and $\frac{1}{2}$ ______________

11. $\frac{3}{4}$, $\frac{1}{2}$, and $\frac{7}{8}$ ______________

12. $\frac{5}{7}$, $\frac{3}{5}$, and $\frac{1}{2}$ ______________

Lesson 1-4

NAME ______________________ DATE ______________

Problem-Solving Practice

Solve.

1 **MUSIC** Chris listened to three songs. The lengths of the songs are shown in the table below. Which song has the greatest length? ______

Songs	
Name	**Length (min.)**
The Long Road	$3\frac{5}{6}$
Skateboard	$3\frac{3}{4}$
Climb High	$3\frac{1}{2}$

2 **SHOPPING** Maria bought $\frac{1}{2}$ pound of white potatoes, $\frac{3}{4}$ pound of red potatoes, and $\frac{7}{8}$ pounds of sweet potatoes. Which kind of potato weighed the least? ______

3 **HARVEST** Three friends went to a farm to pick strawberries. The table shows the amount each person picked. Who picked the greatest amount of strawberries? ______

Strawberries Picked	
Name	**Weight (lbs.)**
Lionel	$1\frac{7}{8}$
Duncan	$1\frac{5}{6}$
Jorge	$1\frac{3}{4}$

4 **PIZZA** Three friends each ordered a small cheese pizza for lunch. Carolina ate $\frac{4}{9}$ of her pizza. Sharona ate $\frac{3}{4}$ of her pizza. Leona ate $\frac{1}{3}$ of her pizza. Who ate the least amount of pizza? ______

5 **GARDENING** Manuel plants a vegetable garden every spring. Tomato plants use $\frac{1}{3}$ of the garden space. Pepper plants use $\frac{1}{6}$ of the garden space. Squash plants use $\frac{1}{2}$ of the garden space. Which vegetable takes up the greatest amount of space in the garden? ______

6 **BASKETBALL** Melanie and Alicia both played in last week's basketball game. Melanie threw 10 foul shots and made 6 of them. Alicia threw 8 foul shots and made 6 of them. Who made the greater fraction of foul shots? ______

Homework Practice

Use <, =, or > to compare the fractions. Shade the models given.

1 $\frac{2}{9} \bigcirc \frac{4}{12}$

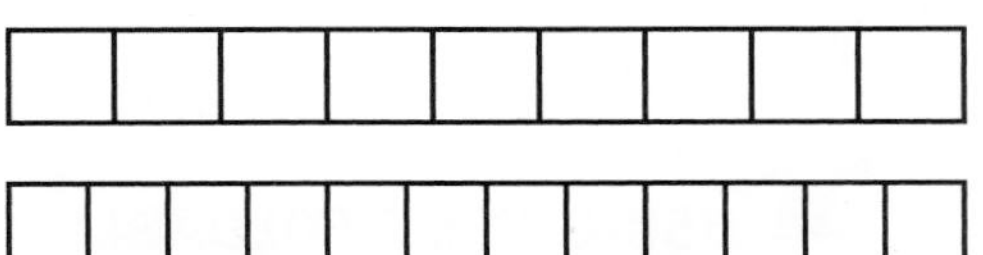

2 $\frac{5}{6} \bigcirc \frac{5}{8}$

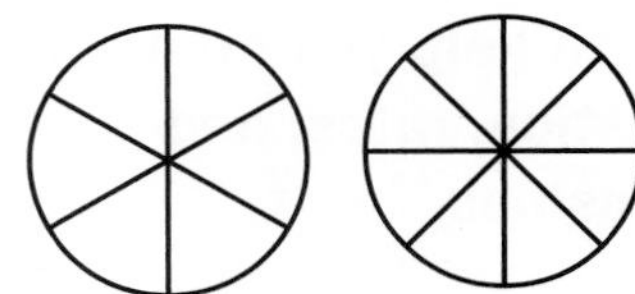

Order the fractions from least to greatest.

3 $\frac{5}{14}$ and $\frac{1}{3}$ ________

4 $\frac{5}{8}, \frac{1}{4},$ and $\frac{4}{5}$ ________

5 $\frac{1}{6}, \frac{2}{3},$ and $\frac{3}{8}$ ________

6 $\frac{5}{9}, \frac{2}{3}, \frac{1}{2},$ and $\frac{4}{5}$ ________

Solve.

7 **STRAWBERRIES** Marinda picked $\frac{5}{7}$ of a pail of strawberries. Kyle picked $\frac{4}{5}$ of a pail of strawberries. Who picked more strawberries? ________

8 **PETS** Amelia has two dogs, Daisy and Rover. Daisy weighs $12\frac{5}{8}$ pounds and Rover weighs $12\frac{3}{4}$ pounds. Which dog weighs more?

9 **OFFICE** The lengths of three paper clips are $1\frac{3}{4}$ inches, $1\frac{1}{8}$ inches, and $1\frac{1}{2}$ inches. Write the lengths in order from least to greatest.

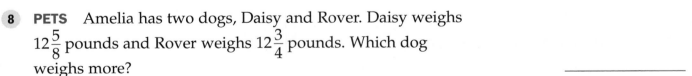

____

NAME ______________________ DATE ______________

Chapter 2 Foldables Study Organizer

Dinah Zike's Foldables

Make this Foldable to help you organize information about ratios, rates, and proportional relationships.

1. Begin with a sheet of notebook paper. Fold lengthwise to the holes.

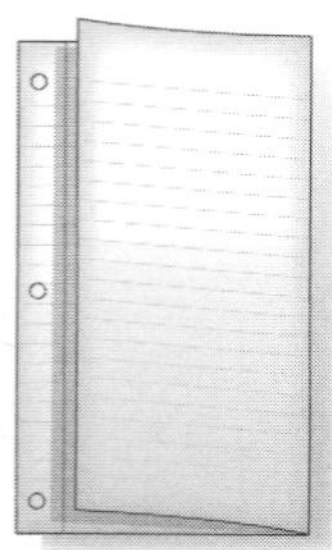

2. Make equal cuts to form 6 tabs.

3. Label the major topics as shown.

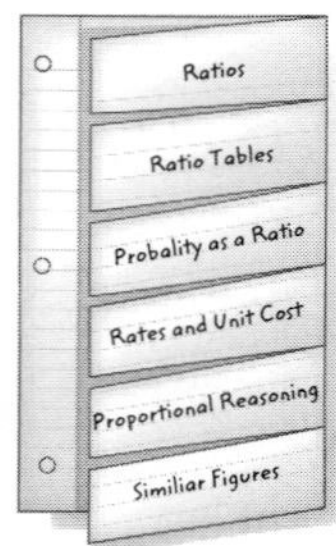

TAKING NOTES

As you read through the chapter, use your Foldable to organize your notes about ratios, rates, and proportional relationships.

USING YOUR FOLDABLE

As you study, select one term or concept from each lesson and write its definition behind the appropriate tab. Give an example of the term or concept to the right of its definition.

USING YOUR FOLDABLE

Work with a partner. Take turns asking each other to define terms on your Foldables.

NAME ______________________ DATE ______________

Chapter 2

Games and Puzzles

Ratio Race

DIRECTIONS

- The first player spins the spinner 2 times.
- Both players write a ratio using the two digits.
- Each player has 20 seconds to write as many equivalent ratios as possible.
- The player with the greatest number of correct ratios wins the round.
- Play continues with the other player taking a turn spinning the spinner twice.
- The first player to win 5 rounds wins the game.

What You Need

- 1–9 Spinner
- Watch with a Second Hand

Number of Players

2

NAME _______________ DATE _______________

Ratio Race Spinner

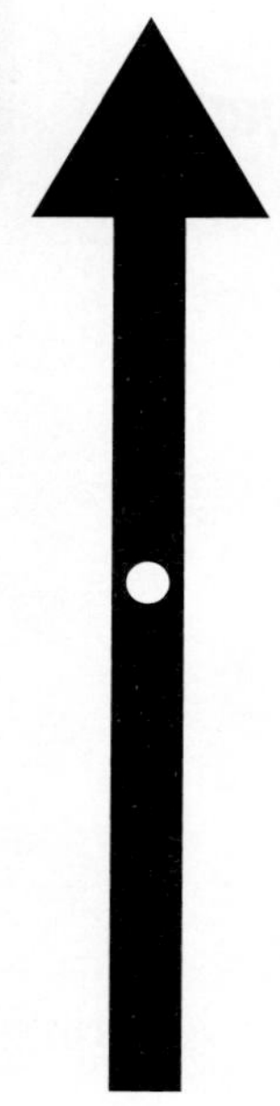

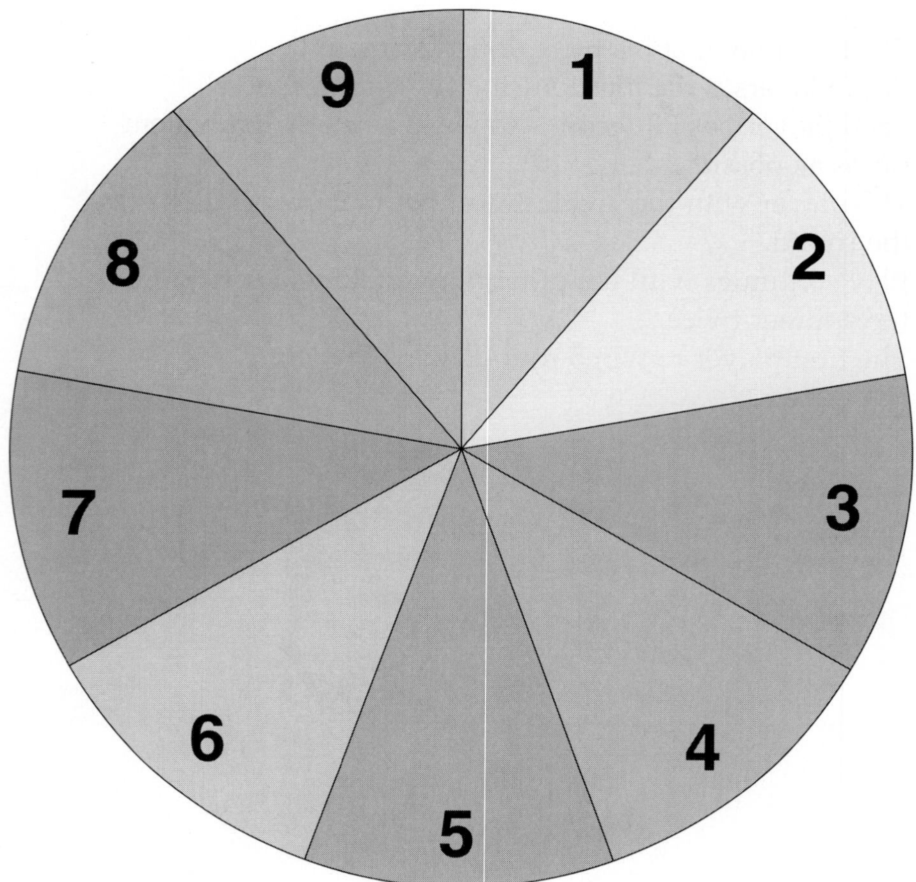

Lesson 2-1

NAME ______________________ DATE ______________

Vocabulary and English Language Development

Activate Prior Knowledge

1 How many members are in your family? ______________

2 How many are males? ______________

3 How many are females? ______________

4 Write the fractions $\frac{\text{males}}{\text{females}}$, $\frac{\text{males}}{\text{total}}$, $\frac{\text{females}}{\text{total}}$. ______________

Definition Review

A **ratio** is a comparison of two quantities by division.

Match each group with the correct ratio.

5 The ratio of ladybugs to butterflies is 2 to 5.

6 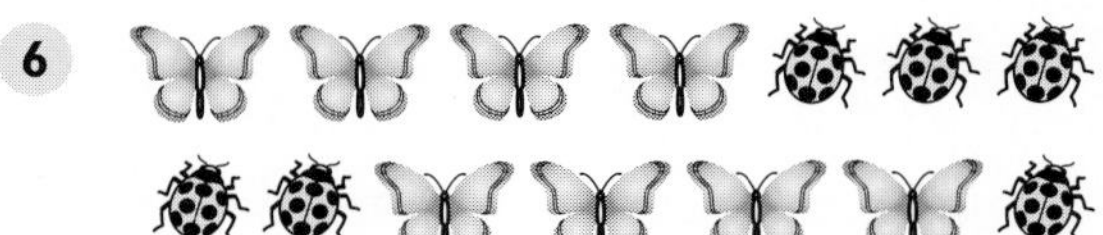 The ratio of ladybugs to butterflies is 2 to 3.

7 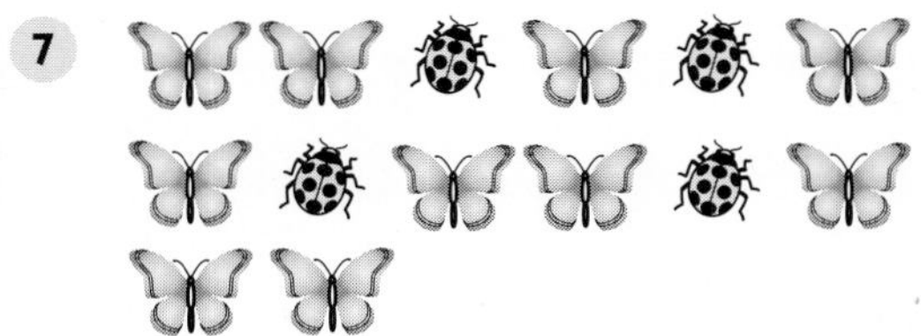 The ratio of ladybugs to butterflies is 3 to 4.

Application

Finding Ratios

- Students initially work individually.
- Students observe their classmates to find the following ratios:
  - The ratio of girls to boys in the class.
  - The ratio of boys to the total number of students in the class.
  - The ratio of students wearing red to students wearing blue.
  - The ratio of students with blond hair to students with black hair.
  - The ratio of students who do not have brown hair to the total number of students in the class.
- When everyone is done, the students compare their results and discuss any inconsistencies.

NAME ______________________ DATE ______________

Lesson 2-1

Skills Practice

Use the diagram to write each ratio as a fraction in simplest form.

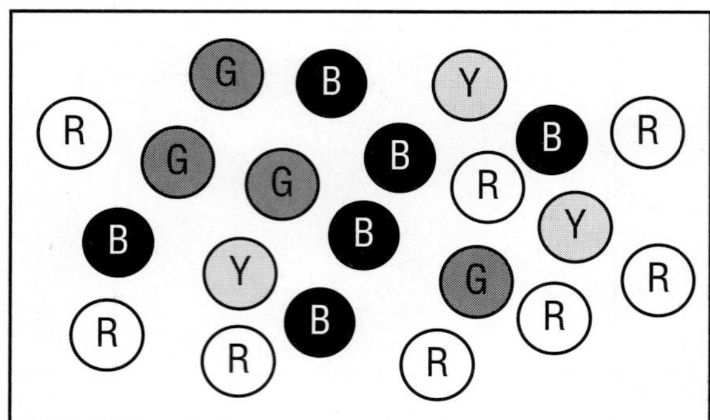

1 The number of yellow marbles to the number of red marbles is ____________.

2 The number of black marbles to the number of red marbles is ____________.

3 The number of green marbles to the number of yellow marbles is ____________.

4 The number of yellow marbles to the number of black marbles is ____________.

Write each ratio as a fraction in simplest form.

5 A computer lab has 5 printers and 20 computers. Write the ratio of printers to computers.

$$\frac{\square}{\square} = \frac{\square \div \square}{\square \div \square} = \frac{\square}{\square}$$

6 In 22 minutes, Margo ran 4 miles. Write the ratio of minutes to miles. ____________

Write the ratio of length to width for each rectangle as a fraction in simplest form.

7 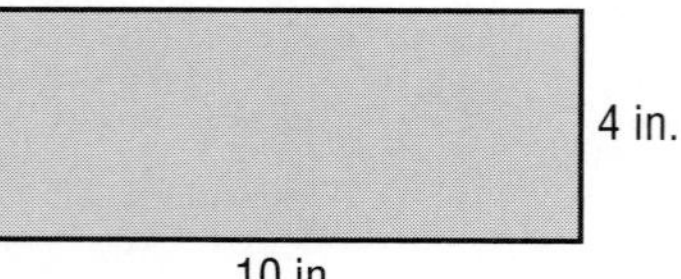

____

8 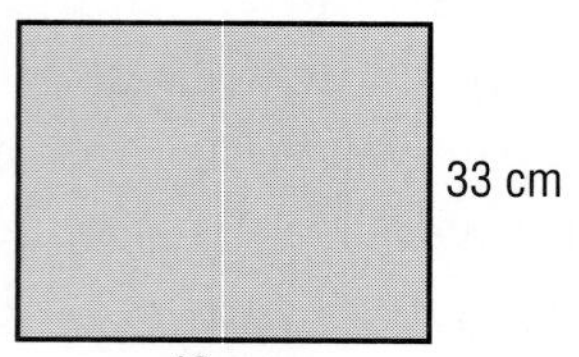

____

NAME ______________________ DATE ____________

Problem-Solving Practice

Solve.

1 **GARDENING** The dimensions of a flower garden are 15 feet long by 5 feet wide. Write the ratio of width to length as a fraction in simplest form. ____________

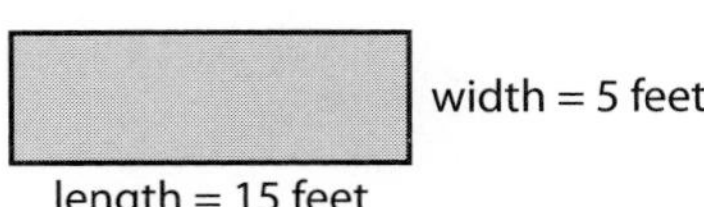

2 **HOBBIES** A jewelry-making kit contains 15 blue beads, 25 red beads, 10 yellow beads, and 30 black beads. Write the ratio of red beads to black beads in simplest form. ____________

3 **ELECTIONS** Carlos, Leona, and Kim ran for class president. The table below shows the number of votes each student received. Write the ratio of votes Carlos received to the total number of votes in simplest form. ____________

Votes Counted for Class President	
Carlos	𝍸 𝍸 𝍸 𝍸 II
Leona	𝍸 𝍸 𝍸 𝍸 I
Kim	𝍸 𝍸 III

4 **WEATHER** During the first 28 days of April, it rained on 8 days. If it rains the last two days of April, what will be the ratio of the number of rainy days in the month to the total number of days in the month? Write your answer in simplest form. ____________

5 **BASEBALL** A baseball team won 40 of the 60 games they played. Write the ratio of games won to the number of games played in simplest form. ____________

Lesson 2-1

NAME ____________________ DATE ____________

Homework Practice

Use the diagram to write each ratio as a fraction in simplest form.

1. baseballs and tennis balls to the total number of balls ____________

2. footballs and basketballs to tennis balls and baseballs ____________

3. baseballs to the total number of balls ____________

4. footballs to basketballs ____________

Write each ratio as a fraction in simplest form.

5. Michele ran 3 out of 7 days this week. ____________

6. A bowl of fruit contains 8 apples and 4 oranges. ____________

Solve.

7. **SWIMMING** The dimensions of a rectangular swimming pool are 44 feet long by 20 feet wide. Write the ratio of the pool's width to length as a fraction in simplest form. ____________

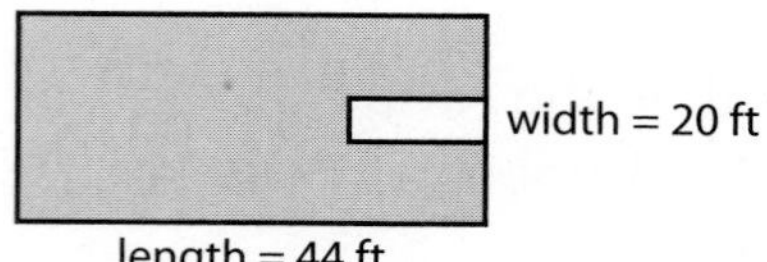

Write the vocabulary word(s) that completes each sentence.

8. A ____________ is a comparison of two quantities by division.

Lesson 2-2

NAME ____________________ DATE ____________

Vocabulary and English Language Development

Chapter 2

Activate Prior Knowledge

Match each ratio in the first column with its simplified form in the second column.

1 $\frac{4}{10}$ ____________ a 7

2 $\frac{21}{3}$ ____________ b $\frac{4}{3}$

3 $\frac{16}{12}$ ____________ c $\frac{2}{5}$

4 $\frac{8}{8}$ ____________ d 1

Definition Review

Fill in the blanks.

5 ____________ ratios are ratios that have the same value.

6 A ____________ is a table with columns filled with pairs of numbers that have the same ratio.

7 Equivalent forms of ____________ are different expressions that represent the same number.

Application

- Students work in pairs.
- Student 1 creates a ratio table omitting the entries in one of the columns.
- Student 2 attempts to determine the missing values and explains to student 1 how the solution was found.
- Students now interchange roles and repeat the activity.
- Repeat as time permits.

Lesson 2-2

NAME ______________________ DATE ____________

Skills Practice

Use the ratio table to solve each exercise.

1. The directions say to mix 3 capfuls of red paint for every capful of yellow paint. How many capfuls of yellow paint should be mixed with 27 capfuls of red paint?

   Use equivalent forms of one.

   $$\frac{3 \times \square = \square}{1 \times \square = \square} \quad \frac{9 \times \square = \square}{3 \times \square = \square}$$

Red paint	3	9	
Yellow paint	1	3	

   You need ______ capfuls of yellow paint.

2. Lori needs 6 large apples to make a pie. How many apples would she need to make 8 pies?

   Use equivalent forms of one.

   $$\frac{6 \times \square = \square}{1 \times \square = \square} \quad \frac{12 \times \square = \square}{2 \times \square = \square} \quad \frac{24 \times \square = \square}{4 \times \square = \square}$$

Number of Apples	6	12		
Number of Pies	1	2		

   Lori would need ______ apples.

Complete the ratio tables.

3.

Numerator	16	32		
Denominator	4	8		

4.

Numerator	3	9		
Denominator	1	3		

5.

Numerator	81	27		
Denominator	54	18		

6.

Numerator	32	16		
Denominator	80	40		

NAME ______________________ DATE ____________

Lesson 2-2

Problem-Solving Practice

Solve.

1 **RESTAURANTS** Mateo receives one free sandwich after buying 10 drinks. How many drinks must he buy to receive 8 free sandwiches? ____________

Number of Drinks	10	20		
Number of Sandwiches	1	2		

2 **PIZZA** Pro Pizza says that one of its family size pizzas will feed 6 people. How many family size pizzas are needed to feed 48 people? ____________

Number of Pizzas	1	2		
Number of People	6	12		

3 **CORN ON THE COBB** The sign at the grocery store says that 24 ears of corn cost $8. How much does 6 ears of corn cost? ____________

Ears of Corn	24		
Cost ($)	8		

4 **MILEAGE** Rico drove 200 miles on 12 gallons of gas. How far can he drive on 3 gallons of gas? ____________

Miles	200		
Gallons of Gas	12	6	

5 **TRAVEL** Eight people can fit into each shuttle van. How many shuttle vans are needed to transport 64 people to the airport? ____________

People	8	16		
Shuttle Vans Needed	1	2		

Lesson **2-2**

NAME ______________________ DATE ______________

Homework Practice

Use the ratio tables to solve each exercise.

1. **GARAGE SALE** The sign at the garage sale said 12 paper back books could be purchased for $8. How much would 3 paper back books cost? ____________

Number of Paper Back Books	12	6	
Cost ($)	8	4	

2. **SUDOKU** Cammy can complete 3 Sudoku puzzles in 2 hours. How many puzzles can she complete in 8 hours? ____________

Sudoku Puzzles	3	6	
Hours	2	4	

3. **EXERCISE** Mark jogged 12 miles in 80 minutes. If he jogged at the same speed the whole time, how far did he jog after 20 minutes? ____________

Miles	12	6	
Minutes	80		

Complete the ratio tables.

4.

Numerator	5	10		
Denominator	2	4		

5.

Numerator	14	28		
Denominator	10	20		

6.

Numerator	48	24		
Denominator	80	40		

Write the vocabulary word that completes each sentence.

7. Different expressions that represent the same number are called

______________________.

8. A ______________ is a comparison of two quantities by division.

Lesson 2-3

NAME ______________________ DATE ______________

Vocabulary and English Language Development

Activate Prior Knowledge

You and your friends are playing a board game using the spinner below. Answer the questions about the spinner.

1 How many numbers are there? ____________

2 How many of the numbers are even? ____________

3 How many of the numbers are greater than 5? ____________

4 How many of the numbers are *not* divisible by 4? ____________

Definition Review

Fill in the blanks.

5 ____________ is the chance that some event will occur.

6 A ____________ is a comparison of two quantities by division.

7 ____________ are the possible results of a probability event.

8 List the outcomes of spinning the spinner above.

____

9 How many of the outcomes are even numbers? ____________

Application

Follow the directions for the activity.

- Work in pairs. Each pair needs one number cube.
- What is the probability of getting a 3 when you roll a 6-sided number cube with the numbers 1–6? ____________
- Roll a number cube 36 times and record the result each time.
- What is the ratio of the number of times a 3 was rolled to the total number of times the number cube was rolled? ____________________________
- Is this ratio equal to the probability you listed above? Is it close? Discuss.

NAME ______________________ DATE ____________

Skills Practice

Use the spinner to find each probability. Write the probability as a fraction in simplest form.

1. P(multiple of 3) ____________
2. P(number greater than 8) ____________

Use the bag of marbles to find each probability. Write the probability as a fraction in simplest form.

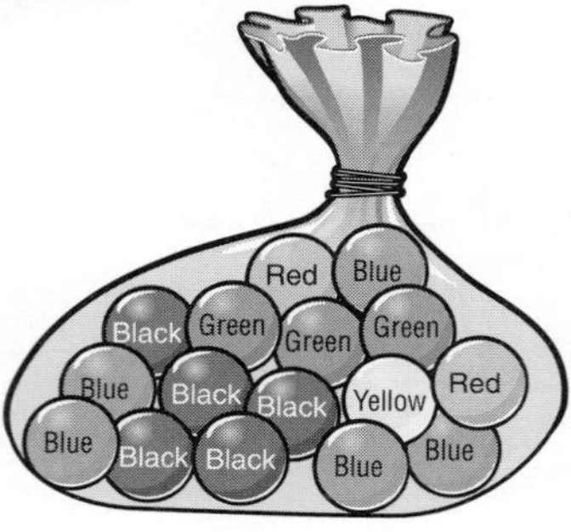

3. P(red) ____________
4. P(blue or green) ____________
5. P(*not* black) ____________
6. P(yellow) ____________

Find each probability using a number cube. Write the probability as a fraction in simplest form.

7. P(even number) ____________
8. P(not an even number) ____________
9. P(number greater than 4) ____________
10. P(number less than 2) ____________

Find the probability of each event. Write the probability as a fraction in simplest form.

11. You pick a month with only 28 days. ____________
12. You pick a month with 6 or fewer letters in its name. ____________
13. You pick the letters *A, E, I, O,* or *U* from the alphabet. ____________
14. You pick a letter that comes before *Y* in the alphabet. ____________

NAME _______________ DATE _______________

Lesson 2-3

Problem-Solving Practice

Solve.

1 **SCHOOL** The ratio of girls to the total number of students in a class is $\frac{3}{5}$. If one student is chosen without looking, what is the probability that the student is *not* a girl? _______________

2 **COINS** The bag below contains 4 pennies, 6 nickels, 3 dimes, and 5 quarters. One coin is drawn from the bag without looking. What is the probability that the coin is a penny or a quarter? _______________

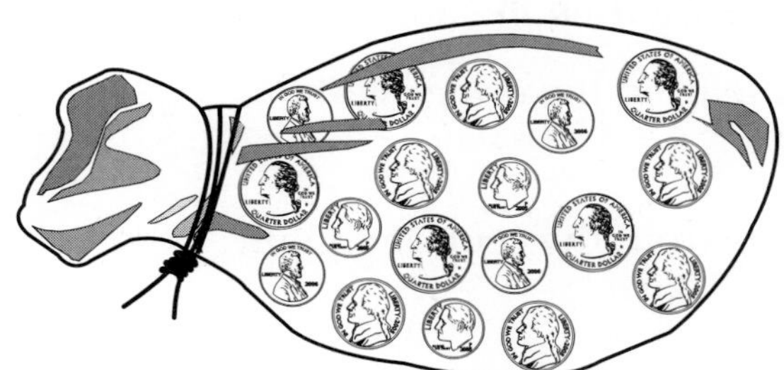

3 **FRUIT** A bag contains 3 oranges, 4 tangerines, 2 pears, and 2 apples. A piece of fruit is chosen without looking. What is the probability that the fruit is not an orange color? _______________

4 **TICKETS** A group of 15 people are attending a baseball game, but they were not able to get seats together. The table below shows the location and number of seats in each row. The tickets are placed in a bag and each person picks one ticket without looking.

Tickets Available	
Row Number	**Number of Tickets**
1	3
5	1
12	2
16	5
27	4

a) What is the probability the first person who picks a ticket gets a seat in row 1? _______________

b) What is the probability the first person who picks a ticket gets a seat in an even numbered row? _______________

c) What is the probability the first person who picks a ticket gets a seat in row 12 or greater? _______________

Chapter 2

Lesson 2-3

NAME ______________________ DATE ____________

Homework Practice

Use the spinner to find each probability. Write the probability as a fraction in simplest form.

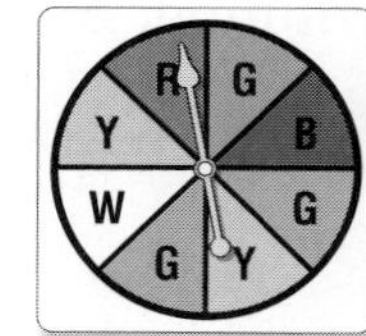

1 P(green or black) ____________

2 P(not yellow) ____________

A cooler contains 6 bottles of water, 3 bottles of tea, 7 bottles of lemonade, and 4 bottles of juice. Write each probability as a fraction in simplest form.

3 What is the probability of choosing one bottle from the cooler without looking and getting a bottle of water? ____________

4 What is the probability of choosing one bottle from the cooler without looking and getting a bottle that is *not* juice? ____________

5 What is the probability of choosing one bottle from the cooler without looking and getting a bottle of tea or a bottle of lemonade? ____________

Find each probability. Write the probability as a fraction in simplest form.

6 12 red jelly beans, 8 black jelly beans, and 4 yellow jelly beans; P(red jelly bean) ____________

7 4 bags of corn chips, 3 bags of pretzels, and 5 bags of popcorn; P(bag that is *not* popcorn) ____________

Solve.

8 **LANGUAGE** Suppose the letters HOLLYWOOD are placed in a bag. A letter is pulled out without looking. What is the probability that the letter is an O? ____________

Write the vocabulary word that completes each sentence.

9 An ____________ is a possible result of a probability event.

10 A ____________ is the comparison of two quantities by division.

11 An ____________ is a set of outcomes.

12 ____________ is the chance that some event will occur.

Lesson 2-4

NAME ______________________ DATE ______________

Vocabulary and English Language Development

Chapter 2

Activate Prior Knowledge

Find each unit cost.

____

2

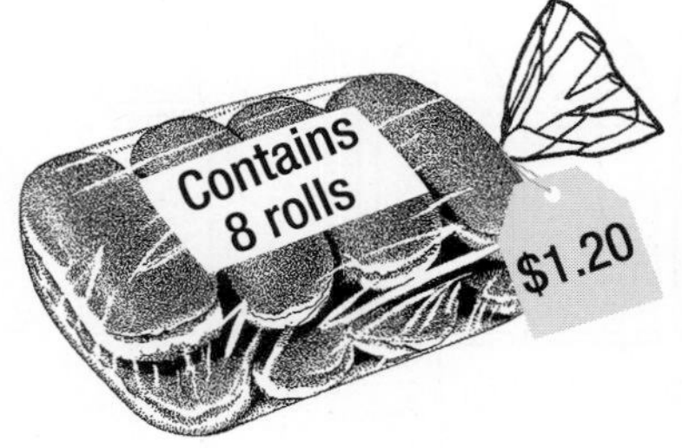

____

Definition Review

Fill in the blanks.

3 A ______________ is a ratio comparing two quantities with different kinds of units.

4 A ______________ is a rate that has a denominator of 1.

5 The cost of a single item is a ______________.

6 **Underline rates that are unit rates.**

18 kilometers in 3 hours

20 miles per hour

60 feet per minute

640 miles in 4 days

7 **Underline costs that are unit costs.**

$0.85 per bottle

$3.15 per dozen

$29.99 per book

$5.00 per 3 pounds

Application

Find unit rates.

- Students work in pairs.
- Student 1 writes a non-unit rate on a piece of paper.
- Student 2 finds the unit rate.
- Students 1 and 2 reverse roles.
- Repeat as time permits.

NAME ______________________ DATE ______________

Lesson 2-4

Skills Practice

Write each rate as a fraction. Find each unit rate.

1 

____

2 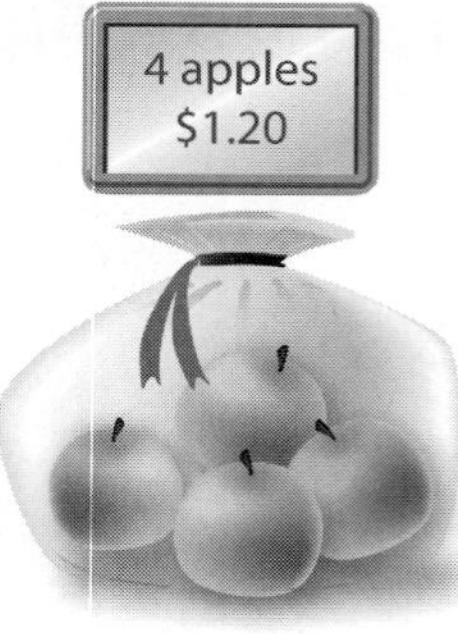

____

3 250 envelopes in 10 minutes

____

4 15 pages in 45 minutes

____

Find each unit rate. Use the unit rate to find the unknown amount.

5 125 miles for 2 hours; ☐ miles for 5 hours ______________

6 64 ounces for 8 people; ☐ ounces for 30 people ______________

7 250 inches in 5 seconds; ☐ inches in 12 seconds ______________

8 $65 for 4 CDs; ☐ dollars for 7 CDs ______________

Which product has the lower unit cost? Round to the nearest cent.

9 a 40-oz bag of dog food for $6.79 or a 24-oz bag of dog food for $3.60

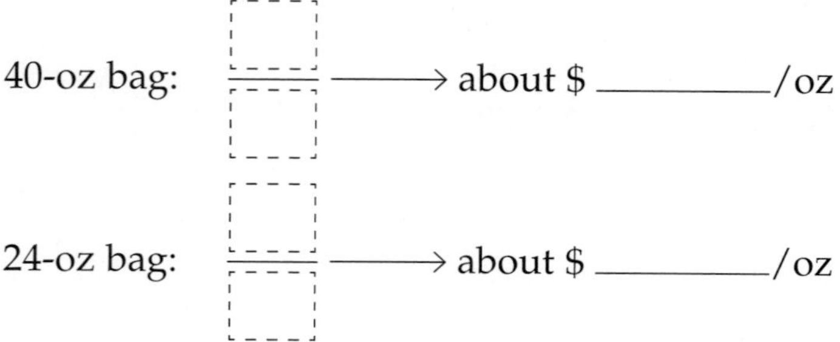

The ________ bag costs less per ounce.

10 a pound of pears for $0.99 or 5 pounds of pears for $4.59 ____________

11 a 16-oz box of cereal for $4.29 or a 12-oz box of cereal for $2.99 ____________

Lesson 2-4

NAME ________________ DATE ________________

Problem-Solving Practice

Solve.

1 **TECHNOLOGY** A laser printer can print 150 pages in 5 minutes. How many pages can the printer print in 22 minutes? ________________

2 **FITNESS** The table below shows the time and distance walked for two different walkers. Which walker had the faster unit rate? Show your work. ________________

Jenna		Theo	
Time	Distance	Time	Distance
120 minutes	8 miles	90 minutes	6.5 miles

3 **FOOD** The diagrams below show the prices of large pizzas at two local restaurants. Which restaurant has the lower unit cost per pizza? ________________

Pizza Shack Specials
Buy 2 large pizzas for $12.99 and get 1 large pizza

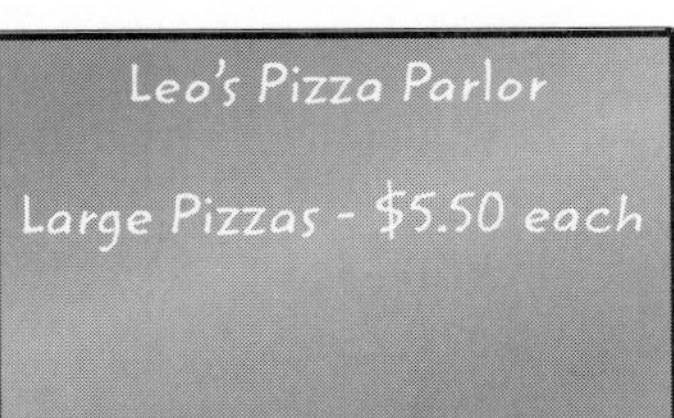

4 **AMUSEMENT PARKS** A Ferris wheel makes 8 revolutions in 2 minutes. How many revolutions does it make in 5 minutes? ________________

5 **PLANTS** A plant grows 4.5 inches in 3 months. At the same rate, how many inches will the plant grow in 8 months? ________________

6 **TRAVEL** A jet aircraft traveled 2,750 miles in 5 hours. Find a unit rate to describe its average speed. ________________

7 **CURRENCY** In Europe, people use euros rather than dollars. You are visiting Europe and want to exchange $400 for euros. The rate of currency exchange is approximately 0.65 euros per $1. How many euros will you receive? ________________

NAME ______________________ DATE ____________

Lesson 2-4

Homework Practice

Write each rate as a fraction. Find each unit rate.

1. 110 miles in 2 hours ______________

2. 36 points scored in 3 games ______________

3. 90 customers served in 4.5 hours ______________

4. 12 pencils in 2 packs ______________

Find each unit rate. Use the unit rate to find the unknown amount.

5. 12 gallons in 5 minutes; ☐ gallons in 7 minutes ______________

6. 140 heartbeats in 2 minutes; ☐ heartbeats in 5 minutes ______________

Which product has the lower unit cost? Round to the nearest cent.

7. a 6-pack of juice for $1.89 or a 12-pack of juice for $4.15 ______________

8. 2 pounds of granola for $2.50 or 5 pounds of granola for $6.30 ______________

9. a box of 30 CDs for $10.99 or a box of 100 CDs for $32.99 ______________

Solve.

10. **TRANSPORTATION** A car travels 144 miles on 6 gallons of gasoline. How many miles can the car travel on 15 gallons of gasoline? ______________

Write the vocabulary word that completes each sentence.

11. The ______________ is the cost of a single item.

12. A ______________ is the comparison of two quantities by division.

13. A ______________ is a ratio comparing two quantities with different kinds of units.

14. A ______________ is a rate that has a denominator of 1.

NAME ______________________ DATE ______________

Lesson 2-5

Vocabulary and English Language Development

Activate Prior Knowledge

Circle the equivalent ratios.

1. $\frac{3}{5}$ $\frac{15}{30}$ $\frac{6}{10}$ $\frac{9}{20}$

2. $\frac{8}{6}$ $\frac{12}{9}$ $\frac{16}{15}$ $\frac{4}{3}$

3. $\frac{7}{15}$ $\frac{4}{8}$ $\frac{1}{2}$ $\frac{2}{6}$

Chapter 2

Definition Review

Fill in the blanks.

4. A ______________ is an equation stating that two ratios or rates are equivalent.

5. To ______________ is to find the product of the numerator of one fraction and the denominator of the other fraction.

Write the equation that results from cross multiplying.

6. $\frac{a}{b} = \frac{c}{d}$

______ = ______

7. $\frac{1}{3} = \frac{m}{n}$

______ = ______

8. $\frac{2}{x} = \frac{5}{y}$

______ = ______

9. $\frac{3}{w} = \frac{y}{4}$

______ = ______

Application

Follow the directions for the activity.

- Work individually.
- Draw a floor plan of the classroom without knowing measurements.
- Drawing must include all walls, windows, doors, and desks.
- Then work in small groups to find the actual measurements of the walls, windows, doors, and desks.
- Determine an appropriate scale and draw a new floor plan of the classroom.
- Compare the original drawing with the second drawing.
- Discuss the importance of using scales and using proportions when creating floor plans, maps, blueprints, and model planes or cars.

Lesson 2-5

NAME ________________ DATE ________

Skills Practice

Find the value of each variable.

1 $\frac{4}{16} = \frac{1}{x}$ $x =$ ________

2 $\frac{n}{25} = \frac{3}{5}$ $n =$ ________

3 $\frac{7}{r} = \frac{14}{20}$ $r =$ ________

4 $\frac{3}{10} = \frac{12}{t}$ $t =$ ________

5 $\frac{6}{8} = \frac{15}{y}$ $y =$ ________

6 $\frac{28}{12} = \frac{f}{3}$ $f =$ ________

7 $\frac{4}{3} = \frac{p}{12}$ $p =$ ________

8 $\frac{1}{7} = \frac{9}{w}$ $w =$ ________

9 $\frac{6}{b} = \frac{24}{52}$ $b =$ ________

10 $\frac{110}{2} = \frac{c}{9}$ $c =$ ________

NAME _______________ DATE _______________

Lesson 2-5

Problem-Solving Practice

Solve.

1 **GROCERY** Felipe bought 6 boxes of crackers at the store. They were on sale for 4 for $5. How much did he spend? _______________

2 **TEMPERATURE** Sarah noticed that it takes 5 minutes for the oven to heat to 100° Fahrenheit. At this rate, how long will it take the oven to heat to 250° Fahrenheit? _______________

3 **PANCAKES** Edgar is making pancakes using the recipe on the back of the pancake mix box. If he wants to make 70 pancakes, how many cups of pancake mix should he use? _______________

4 **CABINETRY** Kalaya is building cabinets in her kitchen. The instructions require that she make 8 drawers for every 2 cabinets. Kalaya wants to make 3 cabinets. How many drawers does Kalaya need to make? _______________

5 **CONSTRUCTION** Federico used 90 planks of wood to build a 150 square foot deck. How many planks of wood will Federico use to build a 225 square foot deck? _______________

6 **GARDENS** Omarr made a scale model of his garden. His actual garden is 20 feet long. What is the width of Omarr's garden? _______________

Lesson 2-5

NAME ________________ DATE ________________

Homework Practice

Find the value of each variable.

1. $\frac{18}{20} = \frac{9}{t}$ $t =$ ________

2. $\frac{8}{s} = \frac{56}{35}$ $s =$ ________

3. $\frac{8}{y} = \frac{10}{25}$ $y =$ ________

4. $\frac{r}{3} = \frac{42}{18}$ $r =$ ________

5. $\frac{18}{24} = \frac{l}{16}$ $l =$ ________

6. $\frac{n}{9} = \frac{30}{45}$ $n =$ ________

Solve.

7. **SNACKS** A can of nuts has 8 peanuts for every 2 cashews. How many cashews are in a can with 100 peanuts? ________

8. **CANDY** A bag of jelly beans has 7 green jelly beans for every 8 red jelly beans. How many red jelly beans are in a bag with 56 green jelly beans? ________

9. **SWIMMING** The swim team has 5 seniors for every 3 freshmen. If there are 18 freshmen on the team, how many seniors are there? ________

10. **CHEMISTRY** Hassan is mixing a solution and needs 30 mL of ammonia for every 2 L of solution. How much ammonia does Hassan need to make 5 L of solution? ________

Write the vocabulary word that completes each sentence.

11. A(n) ________________ is an equation stating that two ratios or rates are equivalent.

12. To ________________ is to find the product of the numerator of one fraction and the denominator of the other fraction.

NAME ______________________________ DATE ______________

Lesson 2-6

Vocabulary and English Language Development

Activate Prior Knowledge

Identify each shape.

1 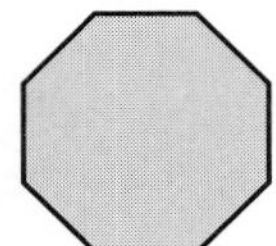

____

2 

____

3 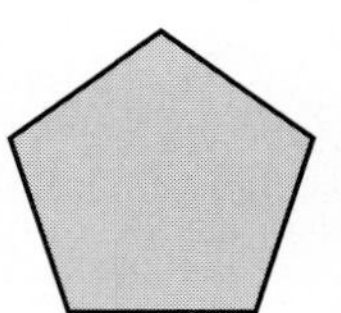

____

Definition Review

Write the vocabulary word that completes the sentence.

4 A ______________________ is an equation stating that two ratios or rates are equivalent.

5 ______________________ are figures that have the same shape but may have different sizes.

Determine whether the shapes are similar.

6 ________  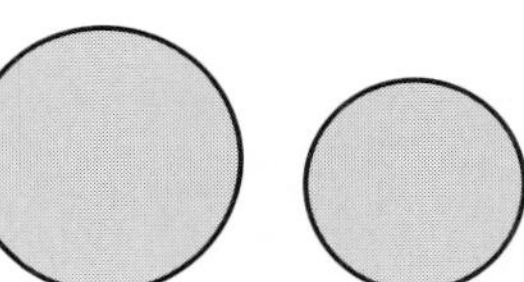

7 ________ 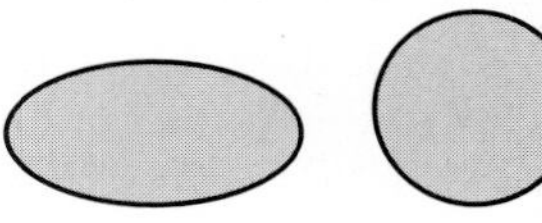

8 ________ 

9 ________ 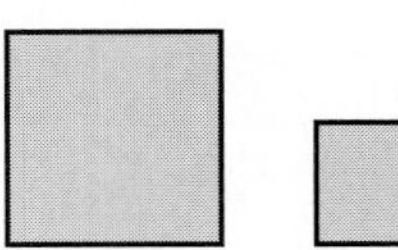

Application

Follow the directions for the activity.

- Ask volunteers to bring in city, state, and country maps.
- Organize the class into groups of 3 to 4 students.
- Provide each group with a map.
- Each group should select a central location on their map.
- Have each student select a destination on their map.
- Instruct students to find the distance from the central location to their destination using the scale.
- Discuss how maps are proportional to actual areas.
- Allow groups to trade maps and repeat the activity as time allows.

Lesson 2-6

NAME _______________ DATE _______________

Skills Practice

Find the value of *x* in each pair of similar figures.

1. $x =$ ______

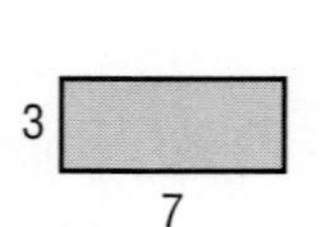

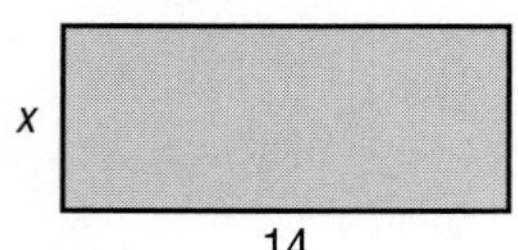

2. $x =$ ______

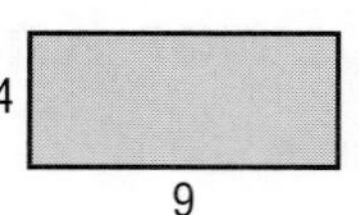

x

10.5

3. $x =$ ______

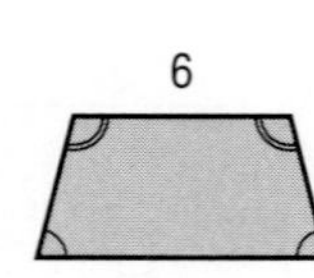

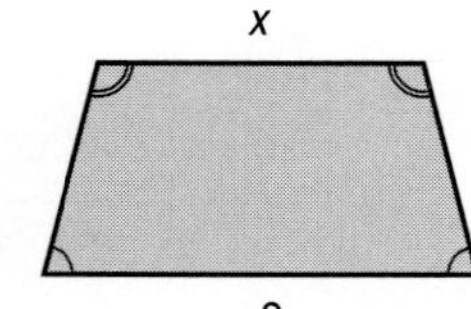

4. $x =$ ______

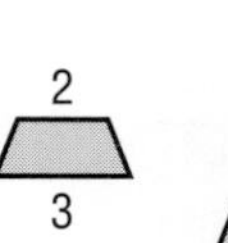

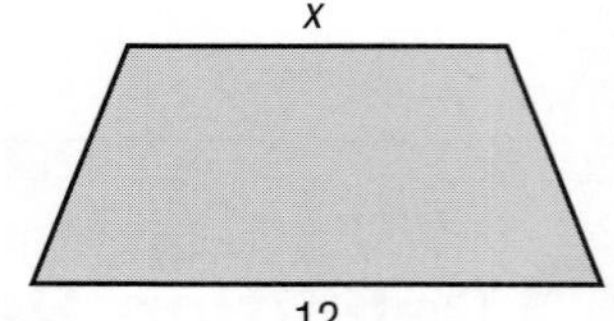

5. $x =$ ______

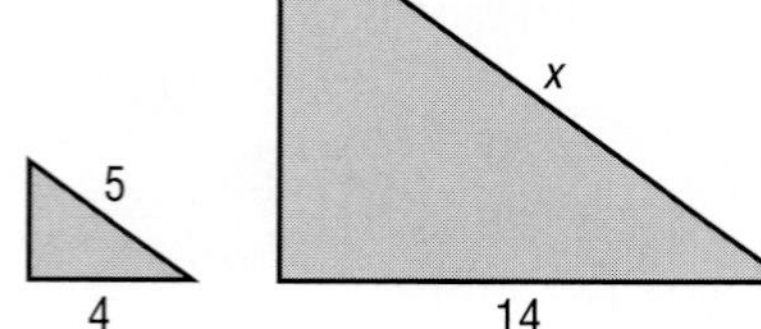

6. $x =$ ______

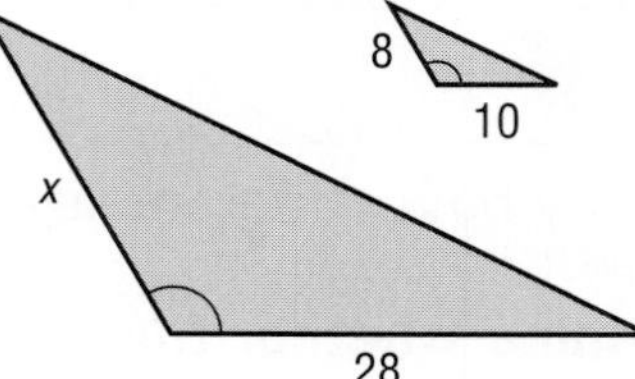

7. $x =$ ______

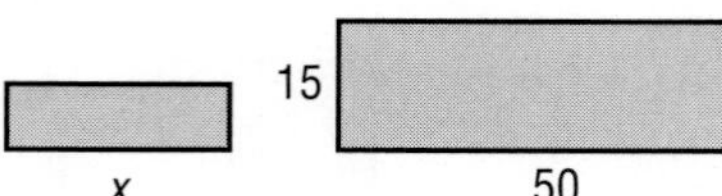

8. $x =$ ______

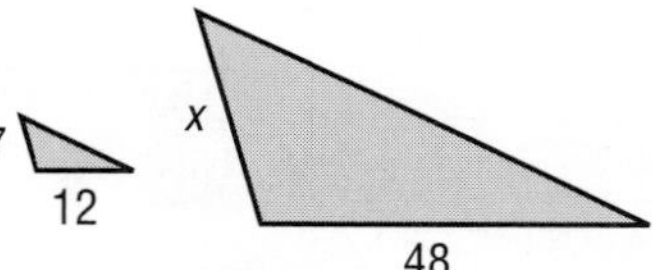

9. $x =$ ______

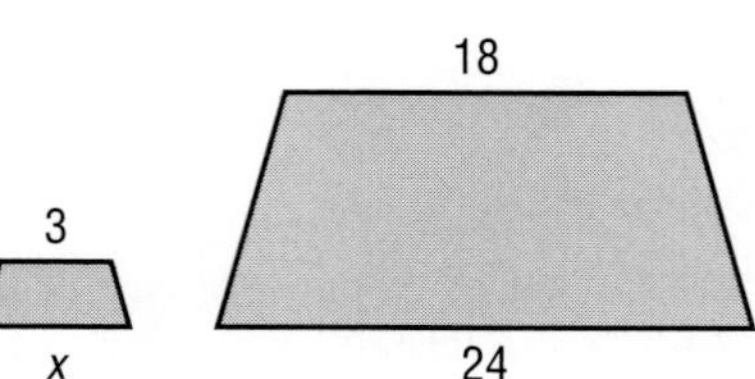

10. $x =$ ______

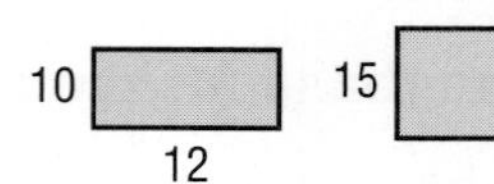

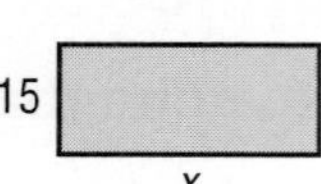

NAME ______________________ DATE ______________

Lesson 2-6

Problem-Solving Practice

Solve.

1 **SPA** Casey is filling her hot tub. The water is coming out at a rate of 3 gallons per minute. Her hot tub can hold 100 gallons. How long will it take for Casey to fill her hot tub? ______________

2 **TECHNOLOGY** Ernesto downloaded a picture from his friend. The picture downloaded at a rate of 90 kilobytes per second. What was the size of the picture? ______________

3 **TYPING** Marvin can type 52 words per minute. His boss gave him a 5-page report to type this morning. Marvin assumes that there are 250 words on each page. How long will it take Marvin to type the report? ______________

4 **UTILITIES** The Rollins family consists of 8 people. Mr. Rollins never has enough hot water for his shower. Their house has a 20-gallon hot water heater which runs out of hot water after 4 showers. Mr. Rollins wants to buy a larger water heater. What is the smallest size water heater he can buy so that everyone can take a hot shower? ______________

5 **HOUSEKEEPING** Felicia can clean 10 hotel rooms in 2 hours. Her boss wants to know how long it will take her to clean all 15 rooms on the 8th floor. How long will it take Felicia to clean all of the rooms? ______________

6 **INCOME** Lakita is saving her money to buy a new computer. She gets paid $112.00 for 8 hours of work. How many hours will Lakita have to work to purchase a new computer? ______________

7 **FISH** Areva's fish tank is gaining 7 parts per million of nitrate every 2 days. Areva was told to change the water when it reaches 28 parts per million of nitrate. How often should Areva expect to change the water? ______________

Chapter 2

Lesson 2-6

NAME ________________________ DATE ____________

Homework Practice

Find the value of *x* in each pair of similar figures.

1 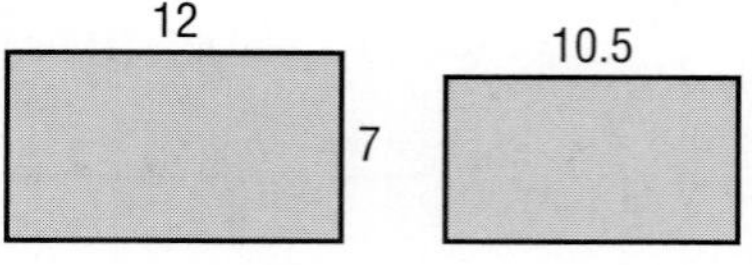

$x =$ ______

2 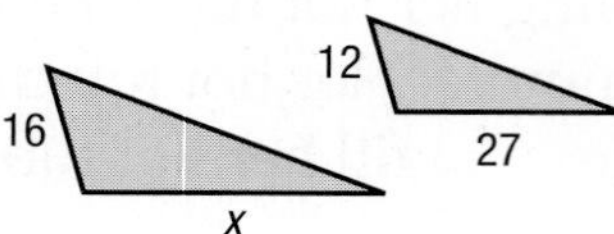

$x =$ ______

3 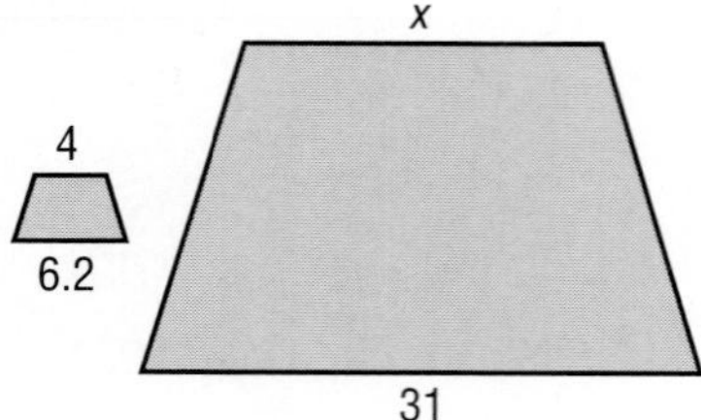

$x =$ ______

4 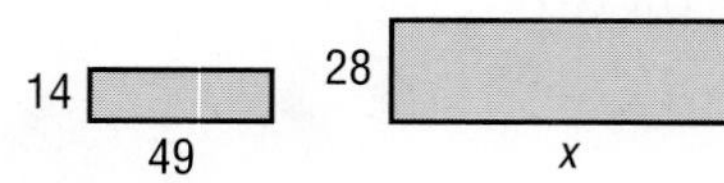

$x =$ ______

5 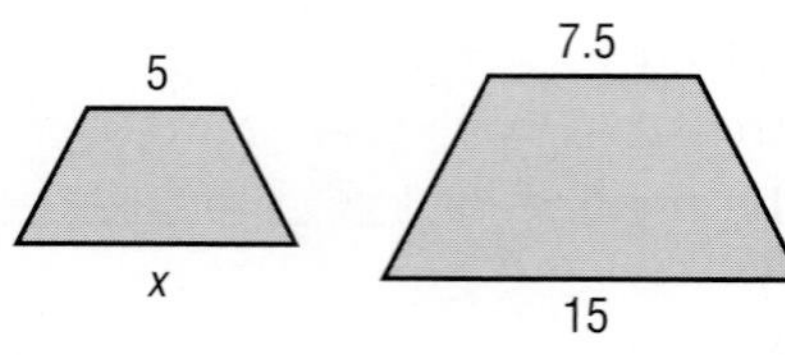

$x =$ ______

6 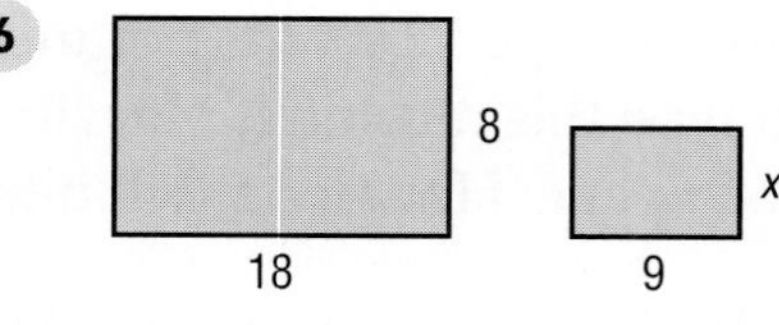

$x =$ ______

7 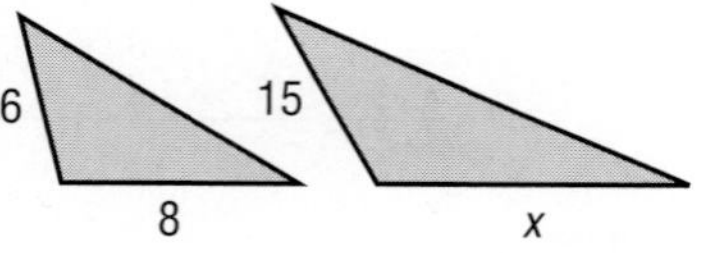

$x =$ ______

8 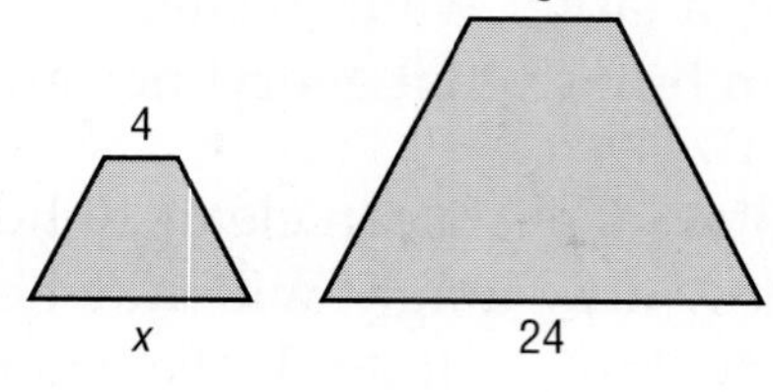

$x =$ ______

Use a proportion to solve each problem.

9 Six oranges cost $3.30. What is the cost of 11 oranges? ______

10 The Min family uses 7 gallons of milk in 2 weeks. How many gallons of milk does the Min family use in 7 weeks? ______

Solve.

11 **LAUNDRY** Rosa needs 3 hours to do 6 loads of laundry. She has 5 loads this week. How long will it take Rosa to do her laundry this week? ______

12 **PHOTOGRAPHS** Paco has $6.00 to buy prints from his camera. The store offers 6 prints for $1.50. How many prints can Paco buy? ______

NAME ______________________ DATE ____________

Foldables Study Organizer

Dinah Zike's Foldables

Make this Foldable to help you organize information about percents.

1. Begin with one sheet of 11″ × 17″ paper. Fold a 2″ tab along the long side of the paper.

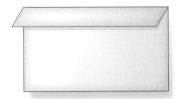

2. Unfold the paper and fold in thirds widthwise.

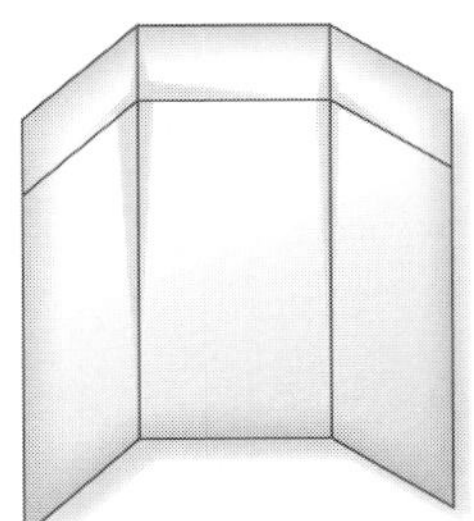

3. Draw lines along the folds and label the head of each column as shown. Label the front of the folded table with the chapter title.

Fraction	Percent	Decimal
$\frac{1}{2}$ →	50% →	0.5

TAKING NOTES
Use your Foldable to list examples of equal sets of fractions, percents, and decimals.

USING YOUR FOLDABLE
Under the columns of your Foldable, write notes about what you learn about percents, fractions, and decimals.

USING YOUR FOLDABLE
Work with a partner. One student should name a percent. The other student should write an example of the equivalent fraction and decimal.

Chapter 3

NAME ______________________ DATE ____________

Games and Puzzles

Ratio Race

DIRECTIONS

- The first player spins the spinner 2 times.
- Both players write a ratio using the two digits.
- Each player has 30 seconds to write as many equivalent ratios as possible.
- The player with the greatest number of correct ratios wins the round.
- Play continues with the other player taking a turn spinning the spinner twice.
- The first player to win 5 rounds wins the game.

What You Need

- Ratio Race Spinner
- Watch with a Second Hand

Number of Players

2

NAME ______________________ DATE ______________

Ratio Race Spinner

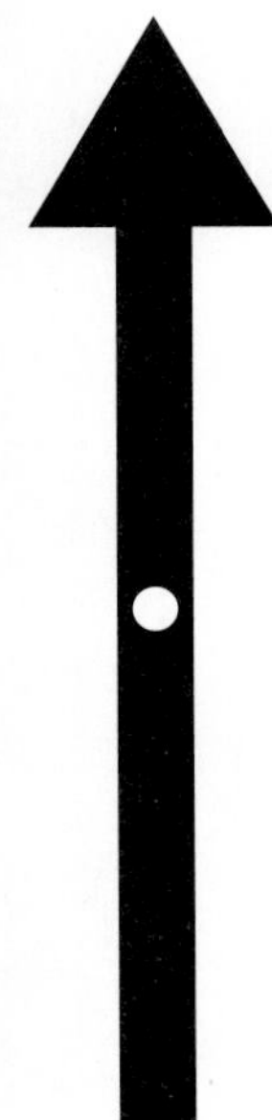

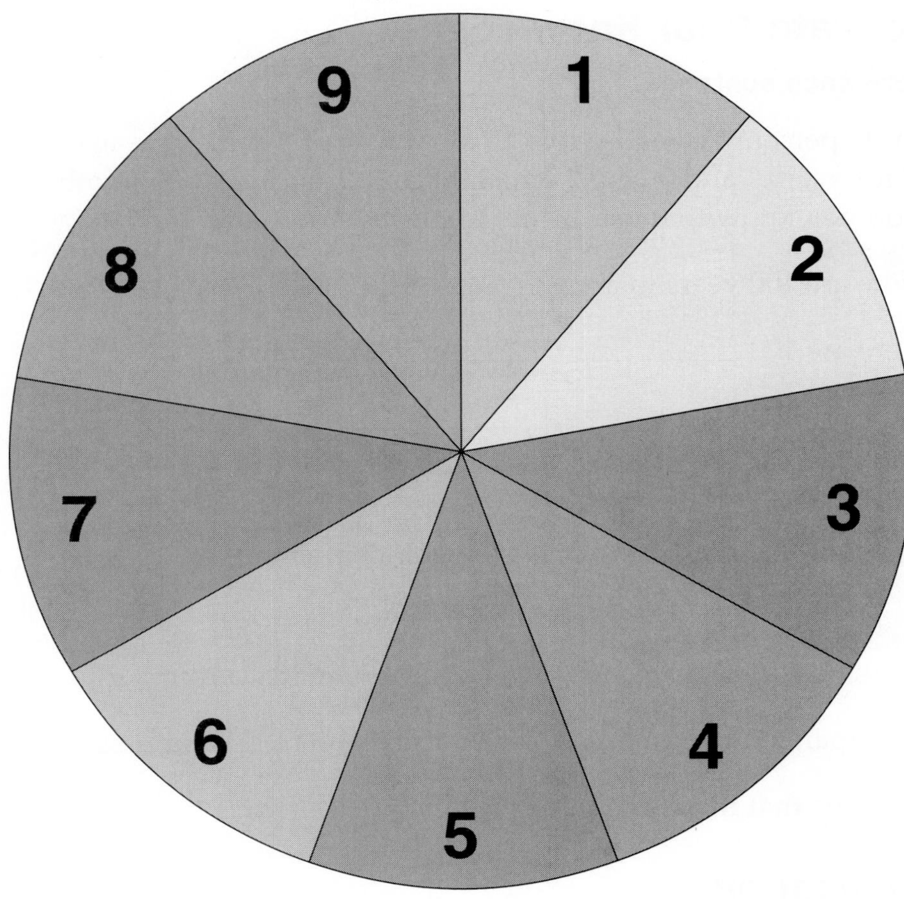

Lesson 3-1

NAME ____________________ DATE ____________

Vocabulary and English Language Development

Activate Prior Knowledge

Complete each sentence.

The word "percent" is made from two parts: "per-" which means "out of" or "for every," and "-cent," which means "hundred." What other words do you know that use "cent" to mean "hundred"?

1 There are 100 years in a ____________.

2 There are 100 ____________ in one dollar.

3 There are 100 ____________ in one meter.

Definition Review

Use the following words to complete each sentence.

equivalent ratio percent

4 A ____________ is a ratio that compares a number to 100.

5 A comparison of two quantities by division is a ____________.

6 Fractions that name the same number are ____________.

Application

Complete each web.

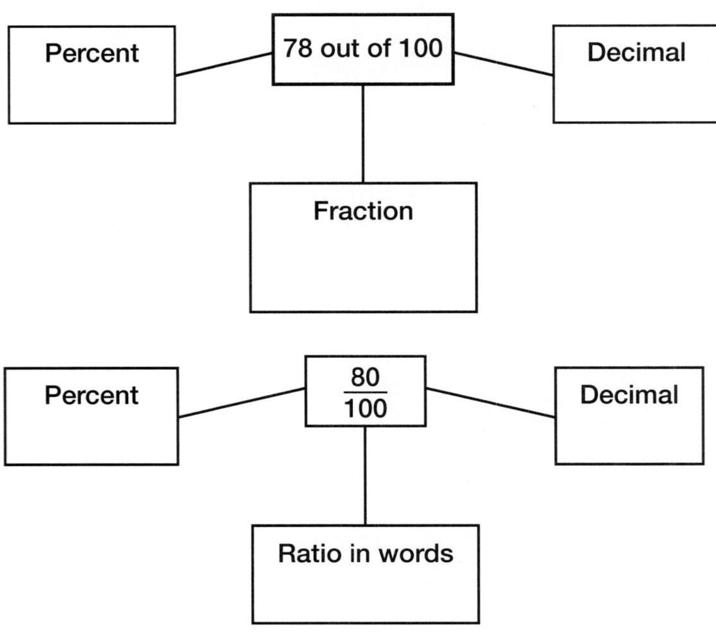

Lesson 3-1

NAME ________________ DATE ________________

Skills Practice

Identify the percent shown in each model.

1 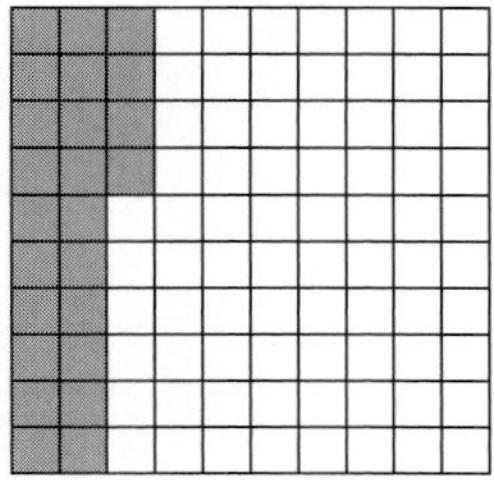 ____________

2 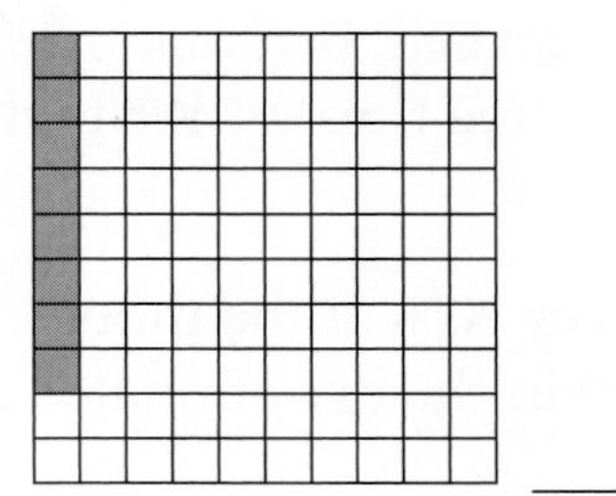 ____________

Chapter 3

Write each ratio as a percent. Then write the ratio as a fraction with 100 in the denominator and as a decimal.

3 garden with 100 flowers; 24 are tulips

percent: ____________

fraction: $\frac{\square}{\square}$

decimal: ____________

4 parking lot with 100 spaces; 7 are empty

percent: ____________

fraction: ____________

decimal: ____________

5 box with 100 golf balls; 83 are white

percent: ____________

fraction: ____________

decimal: ____________

Write each percent as a fraction with 100 in the denominator and as a decimal.

6 85% ____________

7 32% ____________

8 2% ____________

9 105% ____________

10 100% ____________

11 49% ____________

Lesson 3-1

NAME ______________________ DATE ____________

Problem-Solving Practice

Solve.

1. **BASKETBALL** At practice, Ben made 88 out of 100 free throws. Kirk made 90 out of 100 free throws. Write the ratios as percents. ____________

2. **SAVINGS** Jodi saves 20% of the money she earns. Write the percent as a fraction with 100 in the denominator and as a decimal. ____________

3. **TENNIS** Ben has two sets of tennis balls. In the first set, 60% of the tennis balls are yellow. In the second set, 55% of the tennis balls are yellow. Write each percent as a fraction with 100 in the denominator and as a decimal. Which set has more yellow balls? ____________

4. **GAMES** Gary has won 37 out of 100 games he played with his family. His brother Keith has won 41 out of 100 games. Write each ratio as a percent and as a decimal. ____________

5. **PATTERNS** For each pattern, write the ratio of dark squares to the total number of squares as a fraction with 100 in the denominator and as a percent. ____________

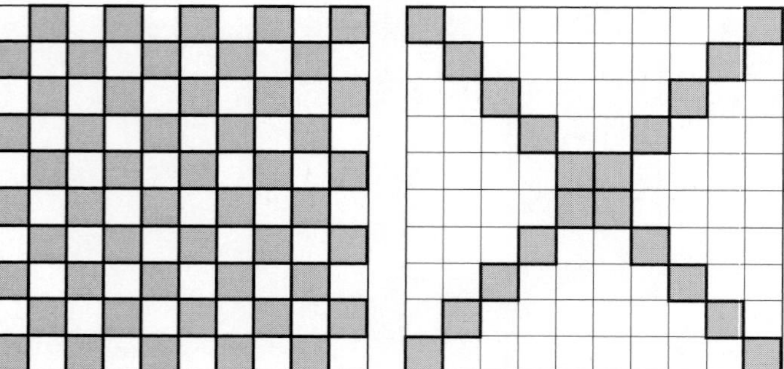

6. **BOOKS** A school librarian asked all 300 students to name their favorite type of book. The responses are shown in the table. Write each percent as a decimal and a fraction with a denominator of 100.

Type of book	Mystery	Fiction	Biography	Nonfiction
Percent of students	15%	44%	7%	34%

____

Lesson 3-1 NAME ______________________ DATE ______________

Homework Practice

Identify the percent shown in each model.

1 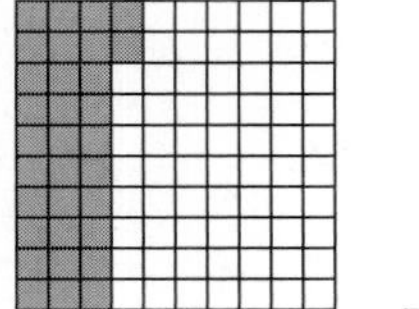 ________

2 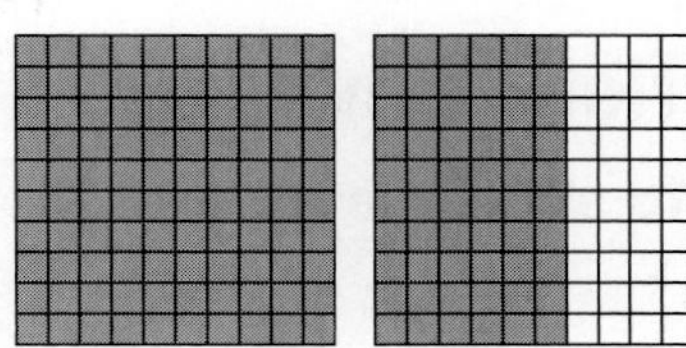 ________

Write each ratio as a percent. Then write the ratio as a fraction with 100 in the denominator and as a decimal.

3 playground with 100 children; 63 are boys

percent: ________

fraction: ________

decimal: ________

4 fruit basket with 100 pieces of fruit; 8 are peaches

percent: ________

fraction: ________

decimal: ________

Write each percent as a fraction with 100 in the denominator and as a decimal.

5 68% ________

6 146% ________

7 3% ________

8 90% ________

Solve.

9 **SAVINGS** Marcos deposited 30% of his money into his savings account. Write the percent as a decimal. ________

10 **PARKING** In section A of the mall parking lot, there are a total of 100 vehicles, of which 54 are minivans. In section B, there are 100 vehicles, of which 90 are minivans. Write each ratio as a percent. ________

Write the vocabulary word that completes the sentence.

11 A ________ is a comparison of two quantities by division.

12 A ________ is a ratio that compares a number to 100.

Chapter 3

NAME _______________ DATE _______________

Lesson 3-2

Vocabulary and English Language Development

Activate Prior Knowledge

Shade each model to show the percent.

1 56%

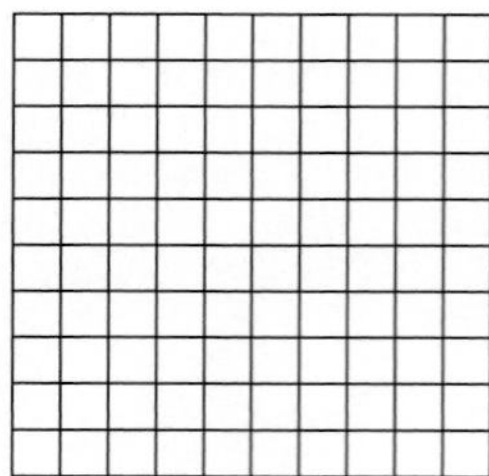

2 12%

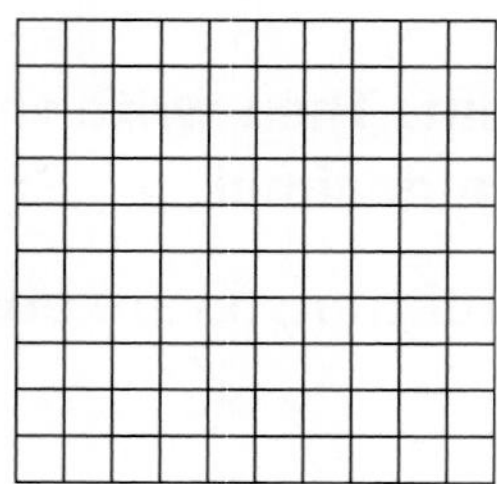

Definition Review

Percent means *"out of one hundred."*

Fill in the blanks.

3 A _______________ is a ratio that compares a number to 100.

4 A _______________ is a number that has digits in the tenths place and beyond.

5 _______________ are fractions that name the same number.

Application

- Students work in groups of 4 or 5. Each student answers *yes* or *no* to the following questions.
  - Do you have any pets?
  - Do you walk to school?
  - Do you have any brothers or sisters?
- Students then work together as a group to find the percent of their group that answered yes to each question.
- If time permits, students can make up their own questions and then share the percents with the rest of the class.

NAME ______________________ DATE ______________

Lesson 3-2

Skills Practice

Write each percent as a fraction or mixed number in simplest form and as a decimal.

1. 40% ____________

2. 5% ____________

3. 15% ____________

4. 350% ____________

5. 166% ____________

6. 75% ____________

Write each fraction as a decimal and as a percent.

7. $\frac{15}{50}$ ____________

8. $\frac{1}{4}$ ____________

9. $\frac{3}{5}$ ____________

10. $\frac{3}{16}$ ____________

11. $\frac{11}{25}$ ____________

12. $\frac{12}{5}$ ____________

13. $\frac{5}{4}$ ____________

14. $\frac{13}{50}$ ____________

15. $\frac{3}{8}$ ____________

16. $\frac{37}{10}$ ____________

Chapter 3

Lesson 3-2

NAME ________________ DATE ________________

Problem-Solving Practice

Solve.

1 **SHOPPING** A store is having a sale as shown on the sign. Write the percent as a fraction in simplest form and a decimal. ________________

2 **FAVORITES** A school survey showed that $\frac{4}{25}$ of the students said that their favorite color was blue. Write the fraction as a percent. ________________

3 **DOGS** 78% of the dogs at the park were black. Write the percent as a fraction in simplest form. Write the percent of dogs as a decimal. ________________

4 **POPULATION** The town gender population is shown in the table. Write each percent as a decimal. ________________

Population	
Women	Men
42%	58%

5 **MUSIC** The table shows student responses to a survey about the students' favorite types of music.

Type of Music	% of Students
Country	12%
Rap	18%
Classical	25%
Rock	45%

a. What percent chose rock? Write the percent as a fraction. ________________

b. What percent chose classical? Write the percent as a fraction. ________________

Lesson 3-2

NAME ______________________ DATE ______________

Homework Practice

Chapter 3

Write each percent as a fraction or mixed number in simplest form and as a decimal.

1. 36% ______________
2. 29% ______________
3. 714% ______________
4. 45% ______________

Write each fraction as a decimal and as a percent.

5. $\frac{7}{10}$ ______________
6. $\frac{3}{4}$ ______________
7. $\frac{1}{8}$ ______________
8. $\frac{32}{10}$ ______________
9. $\frac{14}{5}$ ______________
10. $\frac{13}{20}$ ______________

Solve.

11. **TIPS** A customer at the salon wants to leave a 20% tip. Write the percent as a fraction in simplest form. ______________

12. **PARTY** At the holiday party, 82% of people ate some cake. Write the percent as a fraction in simplest form. ______________

13. **BAKING** While baking cookies, Maggie had to use a measuring cup. For each ingredient, she filled the cup as shown. Which ingredient filled the cup to 75%? ______________

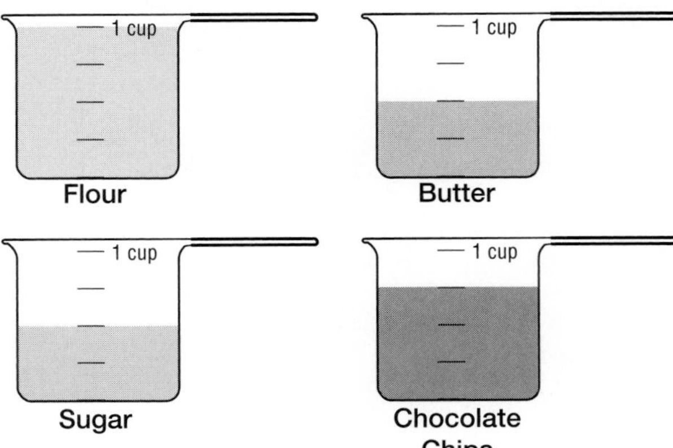

14. **MAIL** Jerod estimates that $\frac{2}{5}$ of the mail he receives is junk mail. Write the fraction as a percent and as a decimal. ______________

NAME ________________________________ DATE ______________

Lesson 3-3

Vocabulary and English Language Development

Activate Prior Knowledge

Write each percent as a fraction or mixed number in simplest form and as a decimal.

	Planet	Percent of Earth Weight	Fraction or Mixed Number	Decimal
1	Mercury	38%		
2	Jupiter	254%		
3	Uranus	80%		

Definition Review

A percent is a ratio that compares a number to 100.

Fill in the blanks.

4 The percent equation is ______________ × ______________ = ______________.

5 The figure shows dark squares and light squares.

■ ■ ■ □ □ □ □

Write this comparison of dark squares to light squares in three different ways:

____

6 A ______________ is a symbol, usually a letter, used to represent a number.

Application

Follow the directions for the activity.

- Students work in pairs.
- The table above can be used to convert weights on other planets to its Earth weight. For example, your weight on Mercury is 38% of what it is on Earth.
- Find your weight on each planet. For example, a person who weighs 80 pounds will be answering the question, *What is 38% of 80?*, when finding their weight on Mercury.

NAME _______________ DATE _______________

Lesson 3-3

Skills Practice

Write each percent as a decimal.

1. 28% _______
2. 65.5% _______
3. 150% _______
4. 125% _______

Who is correct?

5. What percent of 90 is 45? Who is correct? _______

Bob	Opal	Che
n x 45 = 90	n x 90 = 45	n x 90 = 45
n = 2	n = 0.5	n = 0.5
(200%)	(0.5)	(50%)

6. What is 16% of 25? Who is correct? _______

Kristen	Paulina	Marvin
n x 25 = 16	0.16 x 25 = n	n x 16 = 25
n = 0.64	n = 4	n = 1.5625
(64%)	(4)	(1.56)

Solve using the percent equation. Check each answer.

7. What is 125% of 80?

percent × whole = part

_______ × _______ = _______

_______ $= n$

check: _______ × _______ = _______

8. What percent of 6,000 is 36?

percent × whole = part

_______ × _______ = _______

$n =$ _______

_______ = _______

check: _______ × _______ = _______

9. What is 24% of 120? _______
10. 12% of what number is 30? _______
11. 65% of what number is 52? _______
12. 1% of what number is 8? _______
13. What percent of 25 is 18? _______
14. What percent of 40 is 50? _______

Chapter 3

NAME ______________________ DATE ______________

Lesson 3-3

Problem-Solving Practice

Solve.

1 **SCHOOL** At a local high school, 540 of the 1,500 students were on the honor roll. What percent of the students were on the honor roll? ________

2 **TESTING** A test has 60 questions, and 70% of the questions are multiple choice. How many questions are multiple choice? ________

3 **EATING OUT** Kevin's breakfast bill was $14. If he leaves a 20% tip, how much will he leave? ________

4 **BOOKS** Ernesto has a book collection. Twenty-four of the books are science fiction. How many books does he have in his collection if 40% of the collection is science fiction? ________

5 **SCIENCE** A scientist must prepare a 25% alcohol solution. The total amount of the solution must be 2 ounces. How much of the solution is alcohol? ________

6 **BLOCKS** Angel has a set of 30 building blocks. What percent of Angel's building blocks are round on both the top and the bottom? ________

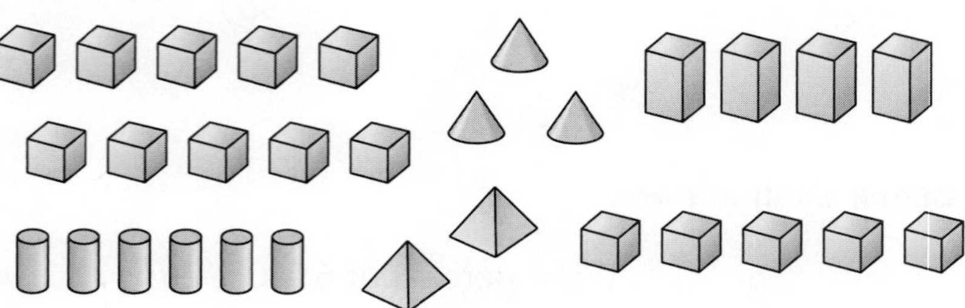

7 **SURVEY** Misu did a survey in his class. He asked each student what sport he or she liked to play the most. The results are displayed in the table. Complete the table, finding the percent of students who chose each sport.

Sport	Number of Students	Percent of Students
Football	3	
Baseball/Softball	8	
Soccer	5	
Basketball	9	

NAME ______________________ DATE ______________

Lesson 3-3 Homework Practice

Write each percent as a decimal.

1. 4% __________
2. 342% __________
3. 175% __________
4. 8.65% __________

Who is correct?

5. What percent of 40 is 7? Who is correct? __________

Crystal
n x 40 = 7
n = 0.175
0.175%

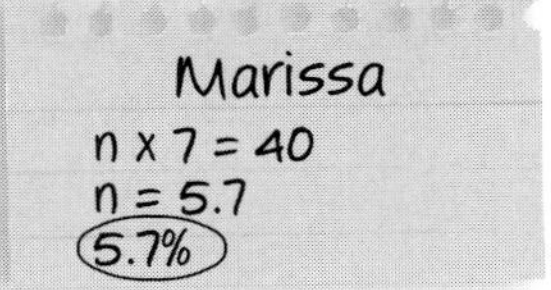

Sabina
n x 40 = 7
n = 0.175
17.5%

Solve using the percent equation. Check each answer.

6. What percent of 20 is 7? __________
7. What is 5% of 90? __________
8. 32% of what number is 40? __________
9. What is 210% of 50? __________
10. 75% of what number is 18? __________
11. What percent of 5,400 is 27? __________

Solve.

12. **BASKETBALL** Rick made 230 free throws, and missed only 23. What percent of his free throws did Rick make? __________

13. **TIPS** Jim and Edith left a tip of $5.50 for their server. This was 20% of the bill. How much was their bill? __________

14. **YEARBOOK** Of the 280 students at the school, 15% are working on the school yearbook. How many students are working on the school yearbook? __________

Lesson 3-4

NAME ______________________________ DATE ______________

Vocabulary and English Language Development

Activate Prior Knowledge

1 Draw a line to connect the question on the left with the correct answer on the right.

Question	Answer
What is 10% of 50?	5
What is 25% of 12?	82
What is 100% of 82?	3

Definition Review

A **circle graph** is used to compare parts of a whole.

Fill in the blanks.

2 In a circle graph, the circle represents the __________ and is separated into parts of a __________.

3 A __________ is a pie-shaped section in a circle graph. The sectors add to __________ %.

Application

- Students divide into 4 groups, Group A, Group B, Group C, or Group D.
- Group A chooses 4 TV shows, then asks all the students which TV show they like best.
  Group B chooses 4 sports, then asks all the students which sport they like best.
  Group C chooses 4 foods, then asks all the students which food they like best.
  Group D chooses 4 pets, then asks all the students which pet they like best.
- Each group finds the percent of students that chose each of their categories. Then they answer the following questions in their group:
  If you put the data in a circle graph…
  …which sector would be the largest? Why?
  …would any of your sectors be the same size? Why?
  …which sector, if any, would take up more than half the circle? Why?
- Each group sketches a circle graph of their data and shares it with the class. The class discusses if the graph looks correct based on the percents shown.

NAME ______________________ DATE ______________

Lesson 3-4

Skills Practice

MUSIC Jenna asked her classmates what color MP3 player they owned. Use the circle graph she created to answer each question.

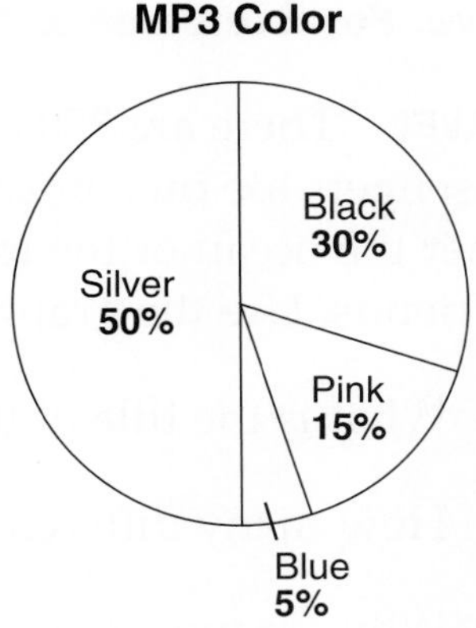

1. How many colors are there? ____________
2. What color do most students have? ____________
3. What color do the fewest students have? ____________
4. What percent of the students have black MP3 players? ____________

INTERNET Arnie asked his neighbors how many people in their house use the Internet every day. Use the circle graph he created to answer each question.

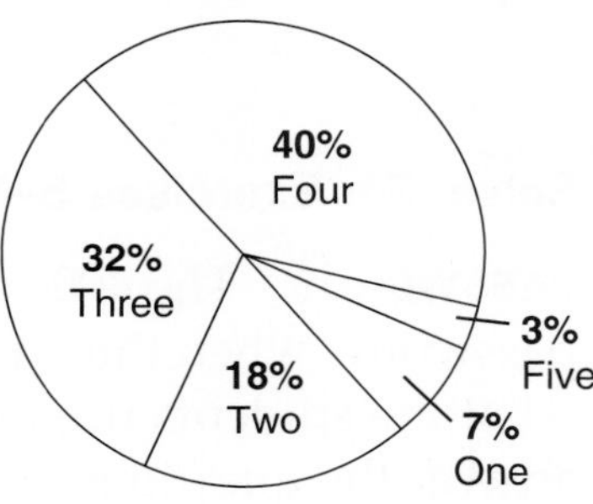

5. Which groups make up 10% of the people Arnie asked?

 ____

6. What percentage of the neighbors said that 4 people in their house use the Internet everyday? ____________

VOTING 200 students voted in the Student Council election. The graph shows the percentage of votes each candidate received.

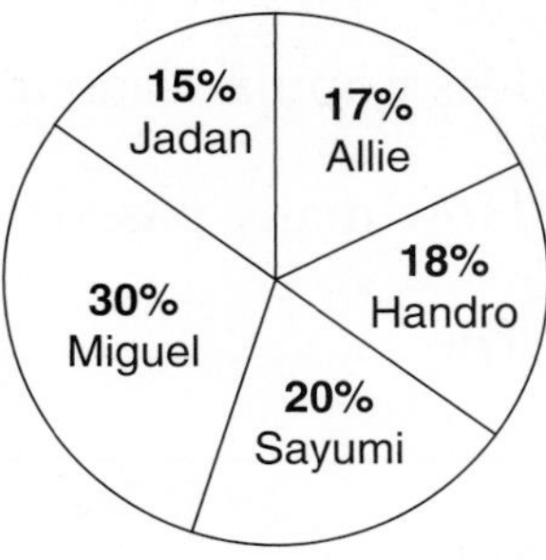

7. What is the title of the graph? ____________
8. Who received the most votes? ____________
9. Who received the least votes? ____________
10. Did any two students receive the same number of votes?

 ____

11. Miguel received twice as many votes as 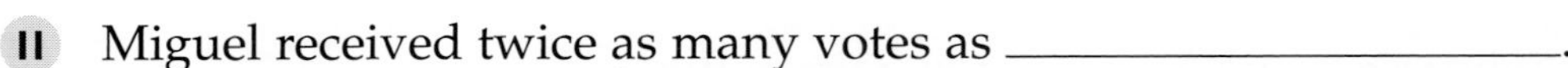.
12. Which three students together received 50% of the votes?

 ____

Chapter 3

NAME _______________ DATE _______________

Lesson 3-4

Problem-Solving Practice

Solve. For Exercises 1–4, use the graph at the right.

TRAVEL There are 250 passengers on an airplane. Some of the passengers are on a business trip, some are going on vacation to either the ocean or the mountains, and some are going to visit family or friends. Use the graph to answer the questions.

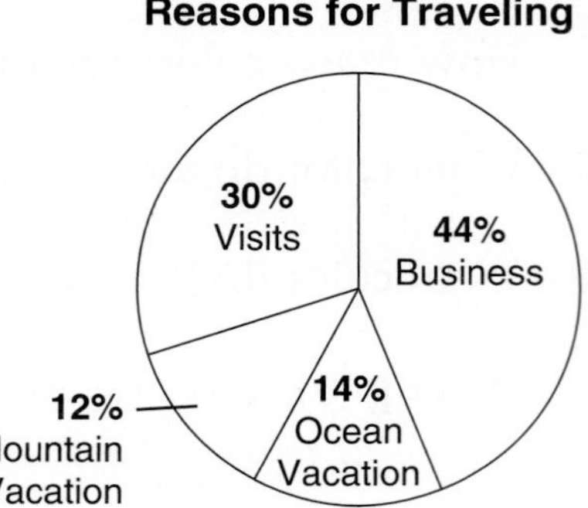

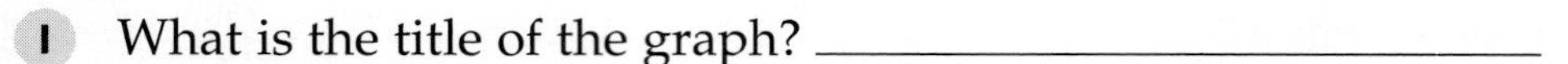

1. What is the title of the graph? _______________

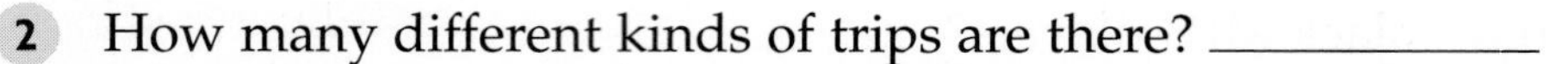

2. How many different kinds of trips are there? _______________
3. Why are most of the passengers traveling? _______________

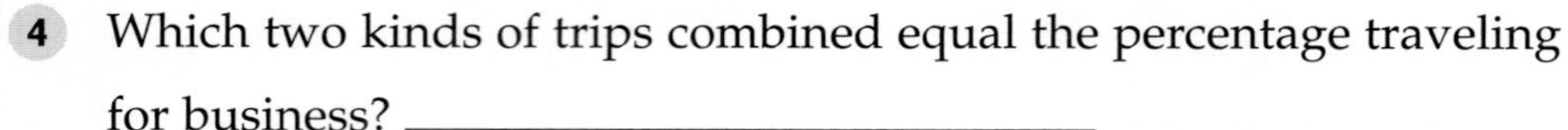

4. Which two kinds of trips combined equal the percentage traveling for business? _______________

Solve. For Exercises 5–10, use the graph at the right.

PASSWORDS The 400 students at Hilltop Middle School use passwords when they use the computer. The circle graph shows what the students use for their passwords. Use the circle graph to answer the questions.

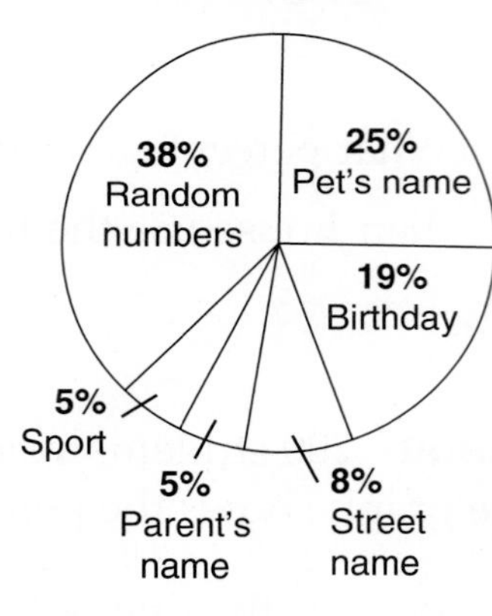

5. What is the most popular type of password?

   ____
6. Which type of password is more popular than a street name but less popular than a pet's name? _______________
7. How many password categories are there? _______________
8. The _______________ category is twice as popular as the _______________ category.
9. Which type of password is less popular than a birthday but more popular than a sport? _______________
10. The number of students who used a pet's name is five times the number who used a _______________ or a _______________.

NAME ______________________ DATE ____________

Homework Practice

Solve. For Exercises 1–4, use the graph at the right.

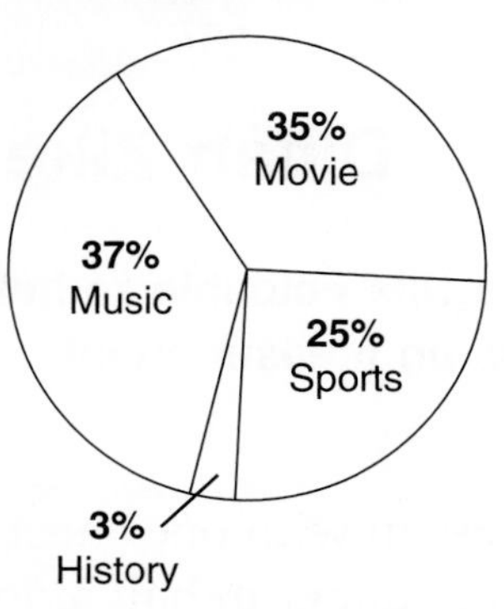

PROM THEME Last week 320 students voted for the theme for the prom. The results are shown in the circle graph. Use the circle graph to answer the questions.

1. What is the title of the graph? ______________
2. How many theme categories are there? ________
3. Which theme do most students prefer? ________
4. Which theme is the least popular? ________

Solve. For Exercises 5–9, use the graph at the right.

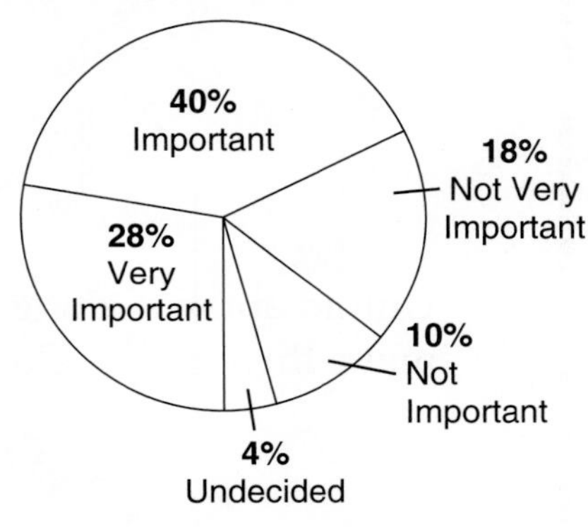

SWIMMING POOL A city surveyed its citizens to see how important building a new swimming pool was to them. The city received 1,200 responses. Use the circle graph to answer the questions.

5. What is the title of the graph?

   ____

6. How many different opinion categories are there? ________
7. Which opinion is more popular than *Not Important* but less popular than *Very Important*? ______________
8. Which two opinions together got more responses than the most popular response? ______________
9. Which two opinions together got the same number of responses as *Very Important*? ______________

Solve. For Exercises 10–12, use the graph at the right.

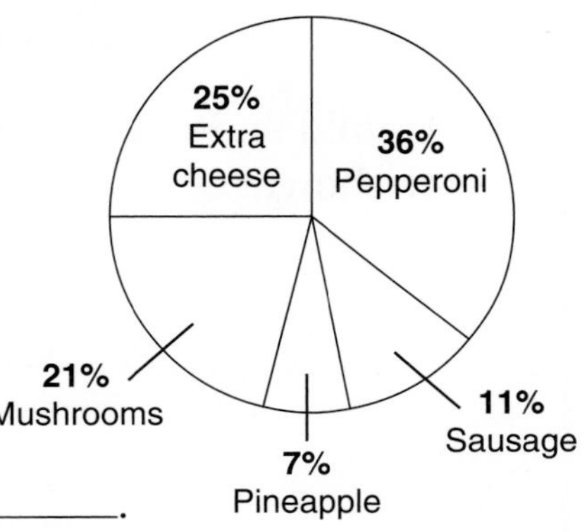

PIZZA Students were surveyed about their favorite pizza topping. The graph shows how many students picked each topping. Use the circle graph to answer the questions.

10. What was the most popular topping? ________
11. What topping was more popular than sausage but less popular than extra cheese? ________
12. Three times as many students picked ________ than ________.

Chapter 3

NAME ________________________________ DATE ____________

Foldables Study Organizer

Dinah Zike's Foldables

Make this Foldable to help you organize your notes on measurement.

1. Begin with one sheet of 11″ × 17″ paper. Fold the paper in half along the length. Then fold in thirds along the width.

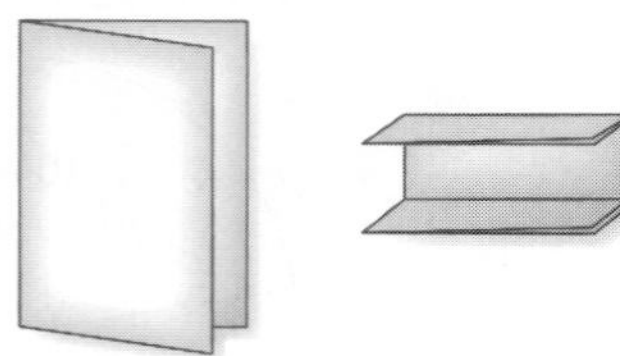

2. Unfold and cut along the two top folds to make three strips. Cut off the first strip.

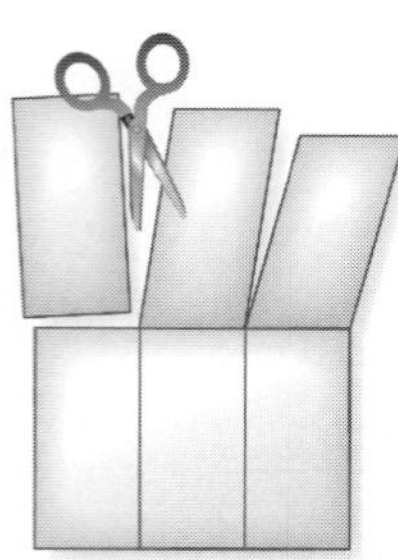

3. Refold the two top strips. Then fold the entire booklet in thirds along the length.

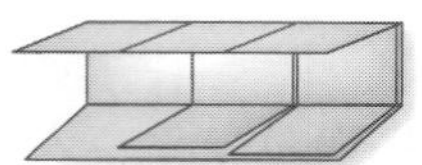

4. Unfold and draw lines along the folds. Label as shown.

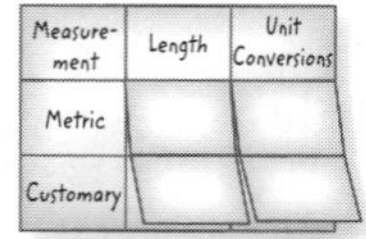

TAKING NOTES
As you read through the chapter, use your Foldable to compare and contrast customary and metric measurements.

USING YOUR FOLDABLE
As you study, take notes, record vocabulary words and definitions, record examples, and show comparisons and contrast in the appropriate sections of your Foldable.

USING YOUR FOLDABLE
Work with a partner. Take turns saying different units of measure. If you say a unit of measure, your partner must state the correct measurement. If you give a measurement, your partner must say the correct unit of measure.

NAME ______________________ DATE ______________

Chapter 4

Games and Puzzles

Get the Greatest Length!

What You Need

- Get the Greatest Length! Spinners
- Get the Greatest Length! Tables

Number of Players

2

GET READY: The players decide who is Player 1 and who is Player 2. They write their names in the correct table.

DIRECTIONS

ROUND 1

- Each player spins both spinners, then uses his or her digits to write the greatest possible number in the kilometer column of his or her table for Round 1.
- The players then fill in the rest of the Round 1 row by converting their length to meters, centimeters, and millimeters.

ROUND 2

- Each player spins both spinners, then uses the digits to write the greatest possible number in the meter column of his or her table for Round 2.
- The players then fill in the rest of the Round 2 row.

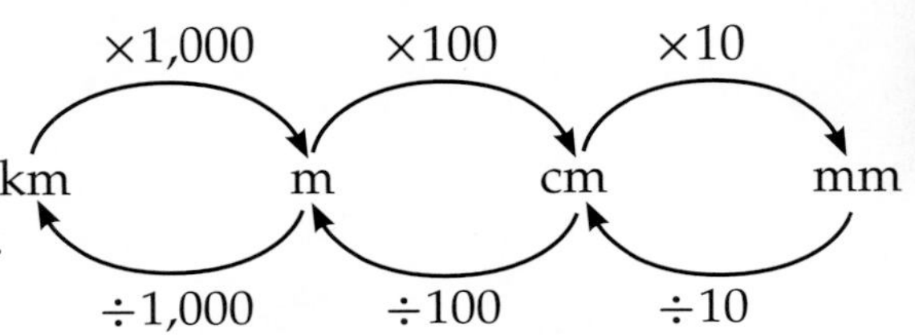

ROUND 3 AND ROUND 4

- The players repeat the directions as above, writing the greatest possible number in the centimeter and millimeter columns.

SCORING

- The player with the greatest number in the kilometer column on the last turn wins.

Player 1 Name:				
	km	m	cm	mm
Round 1				
Round 2				
Round 3				
Round 4				

Player 2 Name:				
	km	m	cm	mm
Round 1				
Round 2				
Round 3				
Round 4				

Chapter 4

NAME ______________________ DATE ______________

Get the Greatest Length! Spinners

Spinner 1

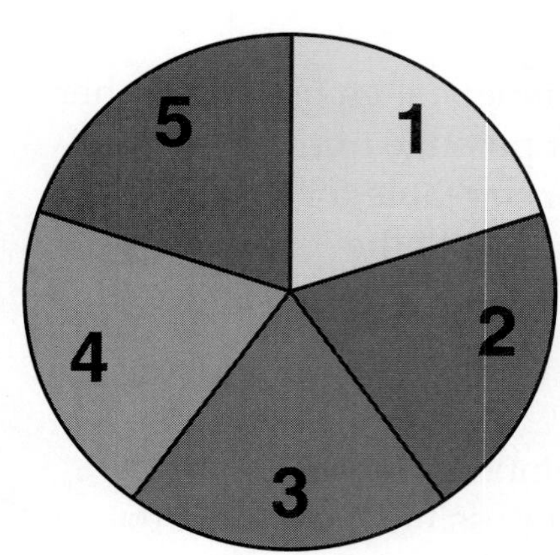

Spinner 2

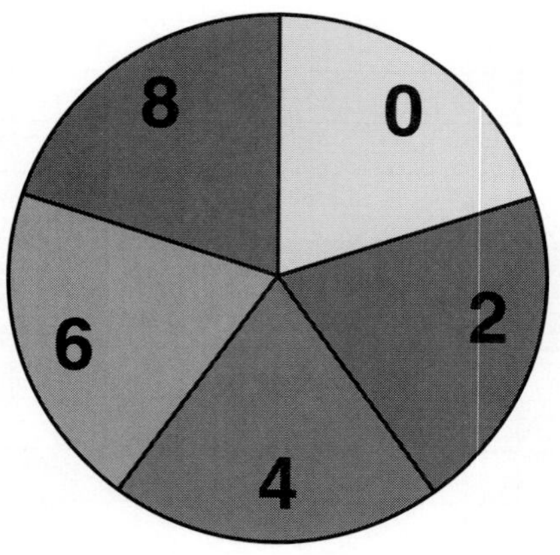

Lesson 4-1

NAME ______________________ DATE ______________

Vocabulary and English Language Development

Activate Prior Knowledge

Label the ruler as indicated.

1 Label the ruler in 1 cm increments.

cm

2 Label the ruler in 10 mm increments.

mm

Chapter 4

Definition Review

A **millimeter** equals one-thousandth of a meter.

A **centimeter** equals one-hundredth of a meter.

A **kilometer** equals one thousand meters.

Fill in the blanks.

3 A ______________ is the base unit of length in the metric system.

4 The ______________ is a decimal system of weights and measures.

5 A centimeter ruler is divided into smaller units called ______________.

6 ______________ is a measurement of the distance between two points.

Application

Follow the directions for the activity.

- Work in pairs.
- Discuss the relationship between millimeters and centimeters.
- Use the rulers you labeled above to complete the table below.

millimeters		20	40	
centimeters	3			9

NAME ______________________ DATE ____________

Skills Practice

Draw a line segment of each length.

1. 8 centimeters

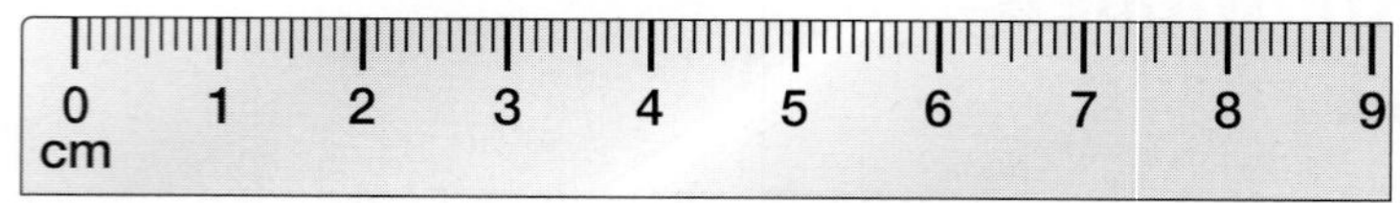

2. 42 millimeters

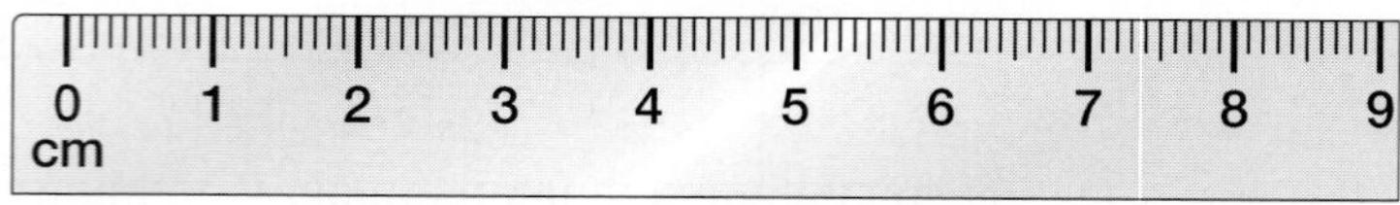

Find the length of each line segment.

3. To the nearest millimeter: ________

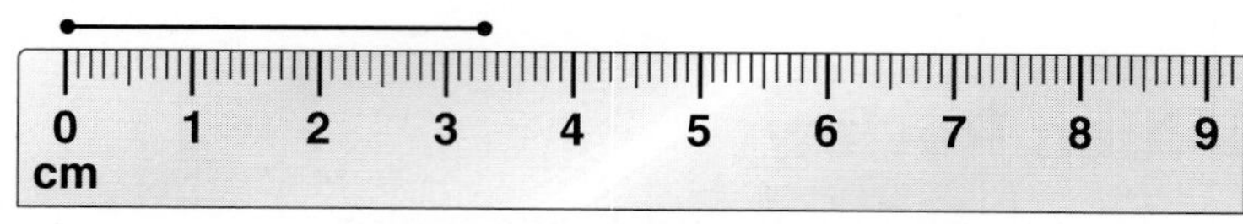

4. To the nearest centimeter: ________

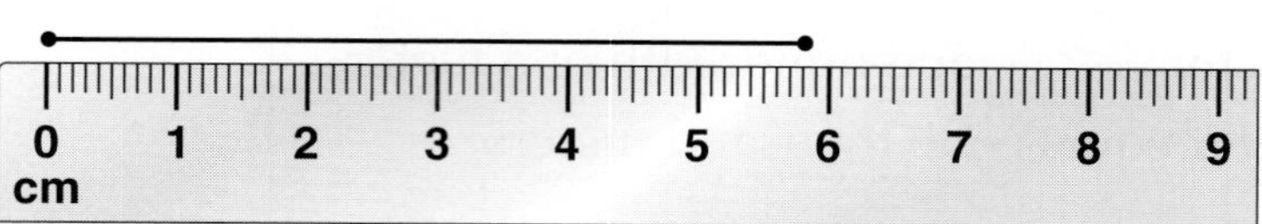

Find the length of the clip to the nearest:

5. millimeter ____________

6. centimeter ____________

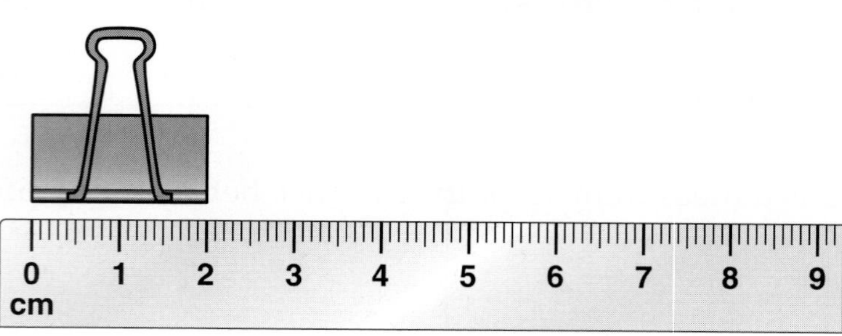

Select the proper unit to measure the length of each object. Write *millimeter*, *centimeter*, *meter*, or *kilometer*.

7. length of a pencil ____________________

8. length of a soccer field ____________________

9. thickness of a piece of gum ____________________

10. length of a dog's tail ____________________

NAME ______________________ DATE ______________

Problem-Solving Practice

Solve.

1 **COOKING** Jake is making a fruit salad. How long is the strawberry to the nearest centimeter? ______

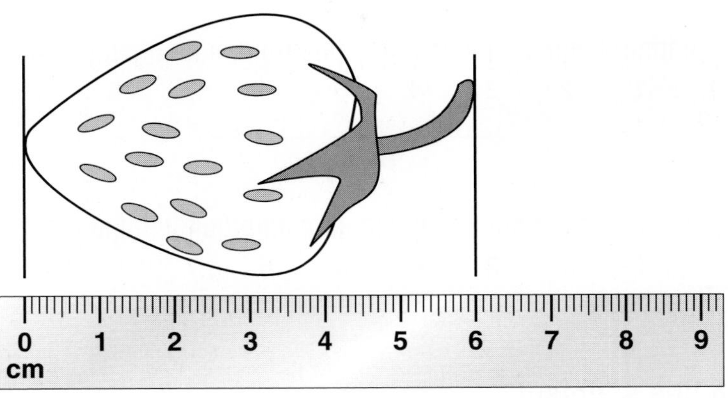

2 **HOUSEHOLD** A standard house key is shown below. What is the length of the key to the nearest centimeter? ______

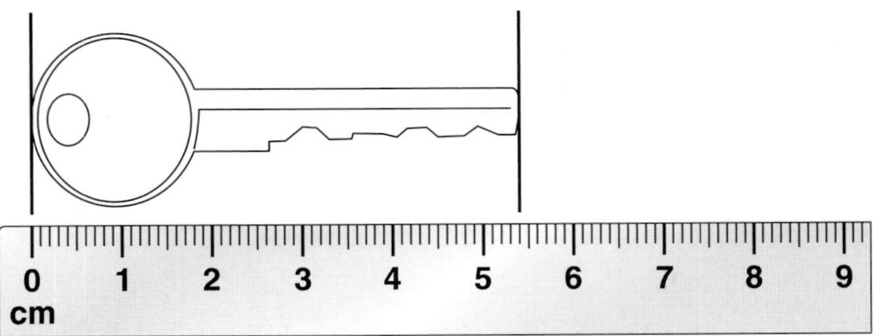

3 **TOOLS** Luisa ordered a metric wrench set for her father's birthday. The largest wrench in the set is shown. What is the size of this wrench to the nearest millimeter? ______

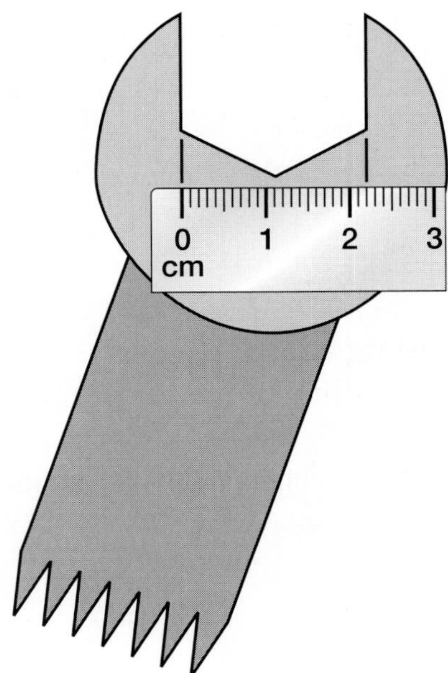

NAME ______________________ DATE ______________

Lesson 4-1

Homework Practice

Draw a line segment of each length.

1. 4 centimeters

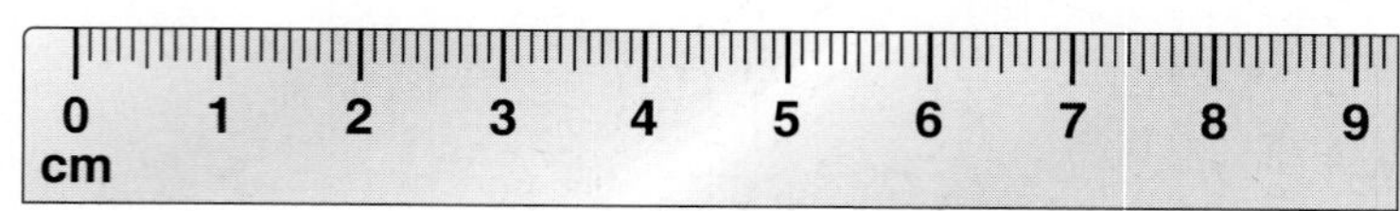

2. 82 millimeters

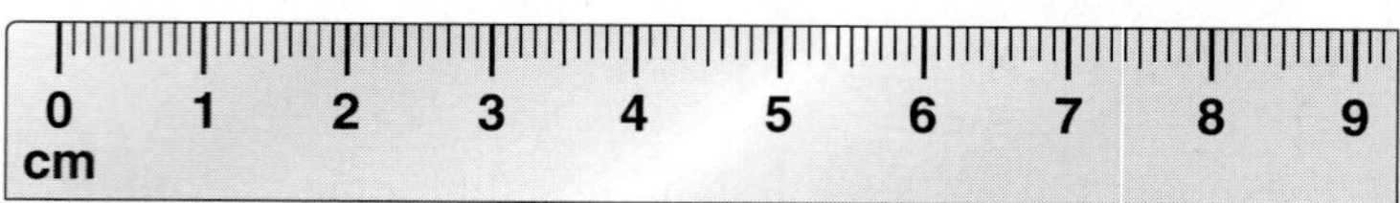

Find the length of each line segment.

3. To the nearest millimeter: ________

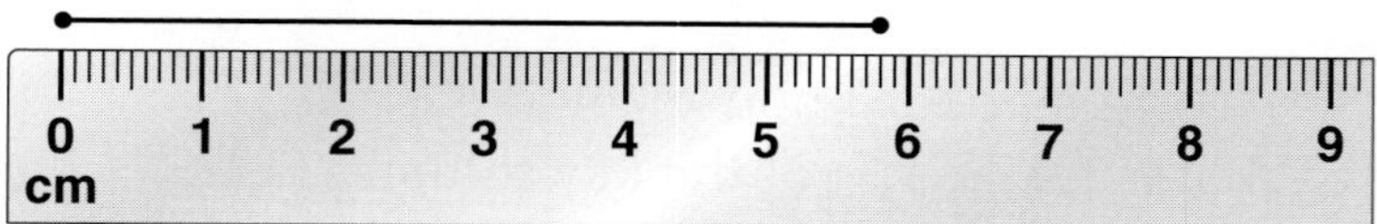

4. To the nearest centimeter: ________

Select the proper unit to measure the length of each object. Write *millimeter*, *centimeter*, *meter*, or *kilometer*.

5. height of a house ________________

6. height of a drinking glass ________________

7. wing of a fly ________________

8. distance from home to work ________________

Solve.

9. **TOOLS** Carlos is building a large dog house. Write the length of the screws he uses in both millimeters and centimeters.

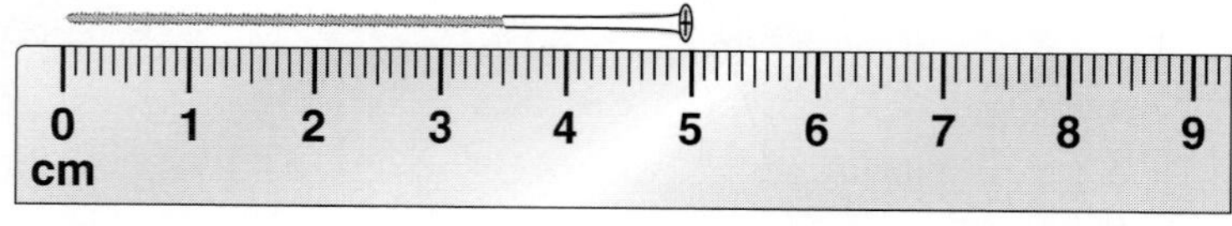

____

Lesson 4-2

NAME ______________________________ DATE ______________

Vocabulary and English Language Development

Activate Prior Knowledge

Complete each sentence using the words *millimeters, centimeters, meters, or kilometers.*

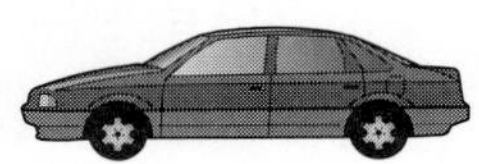

1. The best unit to measure the height of a house is ______________________.
2. The best unit to measure the width of a book is ______________________.
3. The best unit to measure the length of a car is ______________________.
4. The best unit to measure the length of a pencil is ______________________.

Chapter 4

Definition Review

Match each unit of length with its abbreviation.

5 kilometer	mm
6 millimeter	cm
7 centimeter	m
8 meter	km

Application

Follow the directions for the activity.

- Each student needs a metric ruler. Students work in pairs.
- Students should measure the height of a door, the width of their desk, the length of a pencil, and the width of a number cube.
- Students record their measurements in meters, decimeters, centimeters, and millimeters.
- The students then discuss their findings and which unit of measurement would be most appropriate for each item measured.

NAME ______________________ DATE ______________

Lesson 4-2

Skills Practice

Convert using a place-value chart.

1 3 cm = ______________ mm

1000			1	0.1	0.01	0.001
thousands			ones	tenths	hundredths	thousandths
kilo (km)			meters (m)	deci (dm)	centi (cm)	milli (mm)

2 29 mm = ______________ m

1000			1	0.1	0.01	0.001
thousands			ones	tenths	hundredths	thousandths
kilo (km)			meters (m)	deci (dm)	centi (cm)	milli (mm)

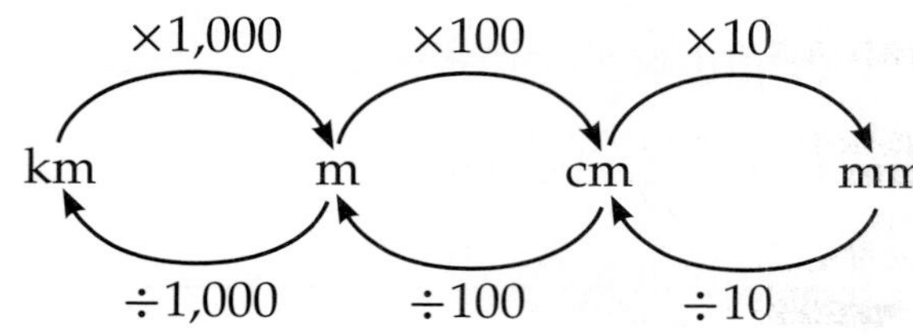

Convert.

3 808 dm = ______________ m

1 dm = ______________ m

Multiply or divide? ______________

808 ______________ 10 = ______________

808 dm = ______________ m

4 2,000 cm = ______________ mm

1 cm = ______________ mm

Multiply or divide? ______________

2,000 ______________ 10 = ______________

2,000 cm = ______________ mm

5 0.09 cm = ______________ dm

6 360 m = ______________ km

7 97.2 m = ______________ mm

8 12 mm = ______________ m

9 0.012 dm = ______________ cm

10 5.1 km = ______________ dm

11 10,000 m = ______________ cm

12 5 dm = ______________ km

13 47.8 cm = ______________ km

14 0.071 mm = ______________ dm

15 0.493 m = ______________ dm

16 0.64 km = ______________ mm

Lesson 4-2

NAME ______________________ DATE ______________

Problem-Solving Practice

Solve.

1 **TABLES** Ms. Lopez wants to buy a dining room table that is 182 centimeters long. How many meters is the length of the table? ____________

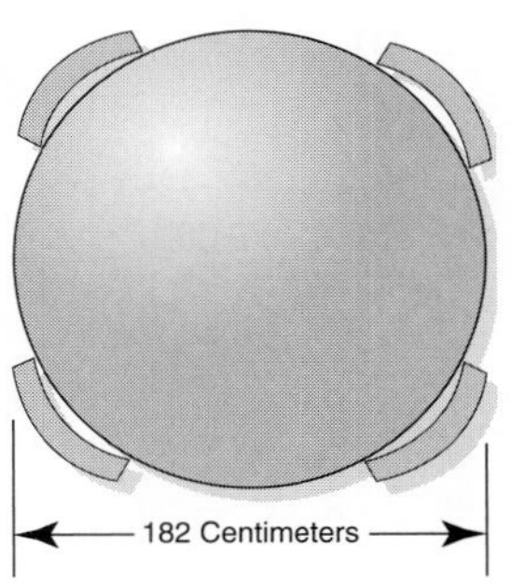

2 **RUNNING** Kathy ran 7.6 kilometers in a marathon. How many meters did Kathy run? ____________

3 **LONG JUMP** At the last track meet, Maya jumped 4.5 meters in the long jump. How many centimeters did Maya jump? ____________

4 **PUZZLES** Lara received a puzzle for her birthday. A puzzle piece had a length of 32 centimeters. How long is the piece in millimeters? ____________

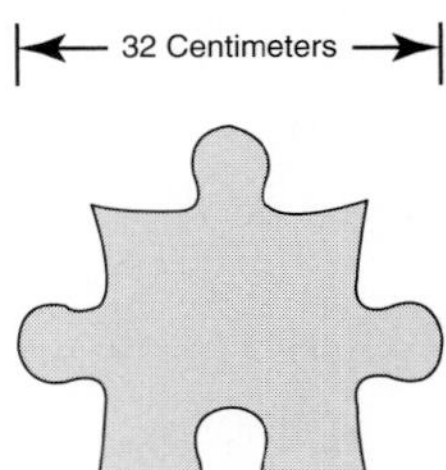

5 **DRIVING** To get to the zoo from Rex's house, his mom must drive 128 kilometers. How many centimeters is it to the zoo? ____________

6 **HOUSES** Mr. Elan is building the house shown in the picture. What will the height of the house be in decimeters? ____________

7 **HEIGHT** Camila is 1,500 millimeters tall. What is Camila's height in meters? ____________

8 **DRIVING** Martin and Brett took turns driving on a trip to the beach. Martin drove 91,000 meters. Brett drove 72 kilometers. How many total kilometers did Martin and Brett drive to the beach? ____________

NAME ____________________ DATE ____________

Lesson 4-2

Homework Practice

Convert using a place-value chart.

1 1.8 km = __________ m

1000			1	0.1	0.01	0.001
thousands			ones	tenths	hundredths	thousandths
			•			
kilo (km)			meters (m)	deci (dm)	centi (cm)	milli (mm)

2 5.12 dm = __________ m

1000			1	0.1	0.01	0.001
thousands			ones	tenths	hundredths	thousandths
			•			
kilo (km)			meters (m)	deci (dm)	centi (cm)	milli (mm)

Convert.

3 2.07 m = __________ mm

4 4,000,000 cm = __________ km

5 0.0007 km = __________ m

6 9,633 mm = __________ dm

7 80 dm = __________ cm

8 0.1 m = __________ dm

9 9 km = __________ cm

10 3,400 cm = __________ m

Solve.

11 **WORMS** In biology class, Mariko's worm was 9.53 centimeters long. How many millimeters long was Mariko's worm? __________ mm

12 **CORN** Each row of corn at the Davis farm is 805 meters long. How many kilometers is each row of corn? __________ km

Write the vocabulary word that completes the sentence.

13 A __________ is an object or number used as a guide to estimate or reference.

14 When you __________, you find an equivalent measure.

NAME ______________________ DATE ____________

Lesson 4-3

Vocabulary and English Language Development

Activate Prior Knowledge

Label the ruler as indicated.

1 Label the ruler in 1-inch increments.

in.

Definition Review

An **inch** is a customary unit of length.

Fill in the blanks.

2 ______________ is a measurement of the distance between two points.

3 Twelve inches equals ________ foot.

4 A ______________ is equal to 5,280 feet or ______________ yards.

5 The ______________ system is a measurement system that includes units such as foot, pound, and quart.

Application

Follow the directions for the activity.

- Work in pairs. Each pair should have an inch ruler.
- Discuss the relationship between inches and feet.
- Name items you would measure in inches, rather than feet.
- Name items you would measure in feet, rather than inches.
- Complete the table.

Inches		24	36	
Feet	1			4

Chapter 4

NAME ______________________ DATE ______________

Lesson 4-3

Skills Practice

Draw a line segment of each length.

1. 3 inches

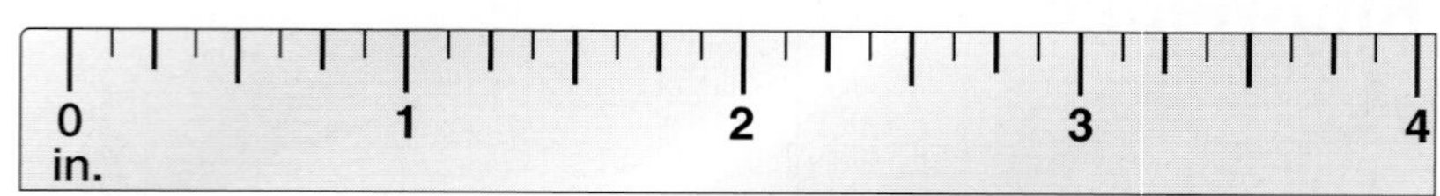

2. $1\frac{1}{2}$ inches

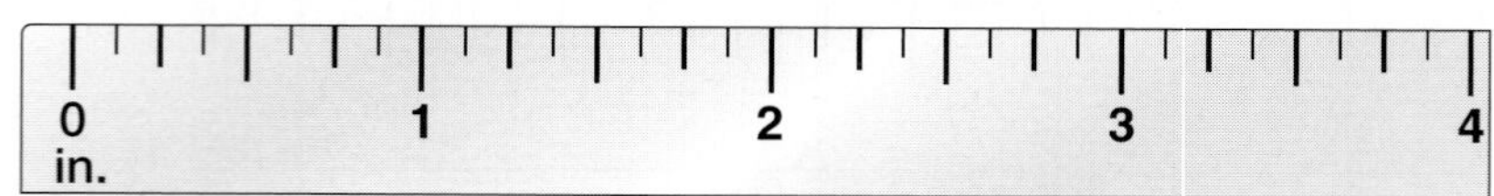

Measure the length of the line segment to the nearest $\frac{1}{2}$ inch.

3.

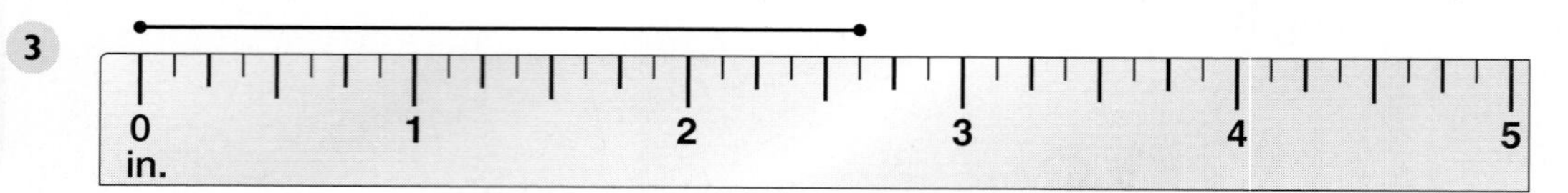

_______ in.

Measure the length of each line segment to the nearest $\frac{1}{4}$ inch.

4.

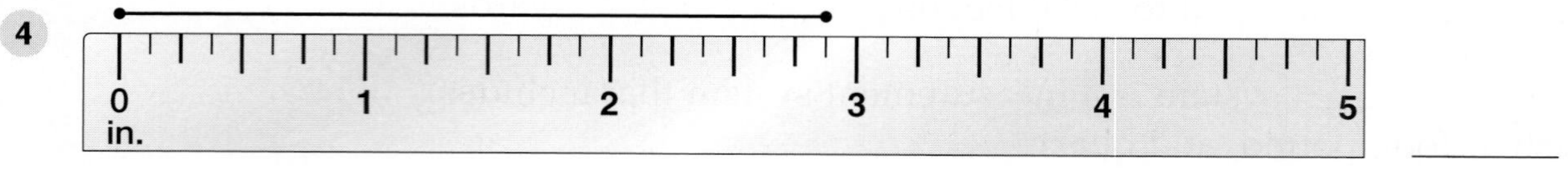

_______ in.

5.

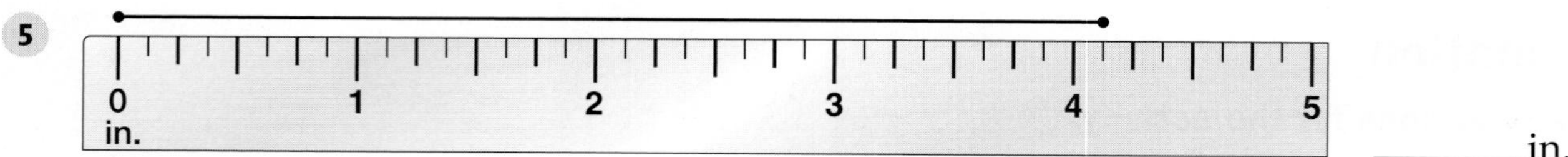

_______ in.

Select the proper unit to measure the length of each object. Write *inch*, *foot*, *yard*, or *mile*.

6. length of a bed ____________

7. height of a cereal bowl ____________

8. length of a dollar bill ____________

9. length of a living room ____________

10. distance traveled in a bus ____________

NAME ______________________ DATE ______________

Lesson 4-3

Problem-Solving Practice

Solve.

1. **SCHOOL** Haro needs a new eraser. What is the length of the eraser to the nearest $\frac{1}{4}$ inch? ________

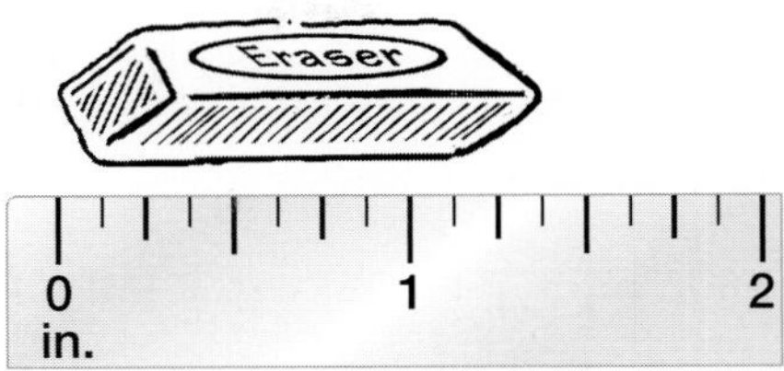

2. **GOLF** A standard golf tee is shown. What is the length of the tee to the nearest inch? ________

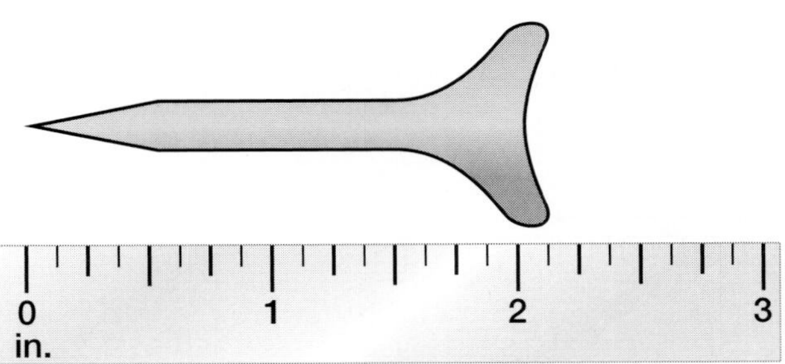

3. **TOOLS** Lindsay wears contact lenses. The case for her lenses is shown. What is the size of the case to the nearest $\frac{1}{2}$ inch? ________

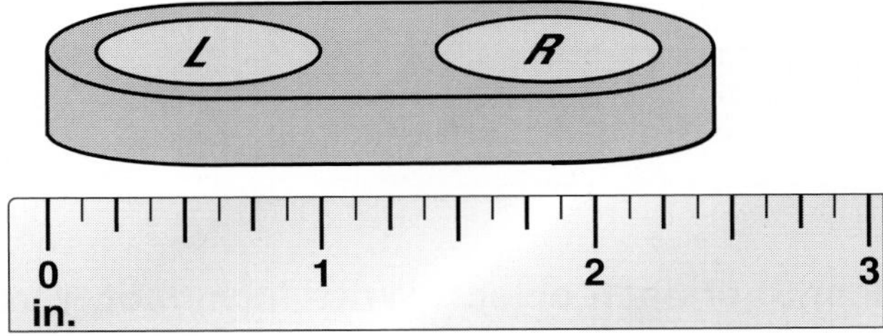

4. **MAIL** An address label is shown. What is the length of the label to the nearest $\frac{1}{2}$ inch? ________

Chapter 4

NAME ______________________ DATE ____________

Lesson 4-3

Homework Practice

Draw a line segment of each length.

1. $2\frac{1}{4}$ inches

2. $3\frac{3}{4}$ inches

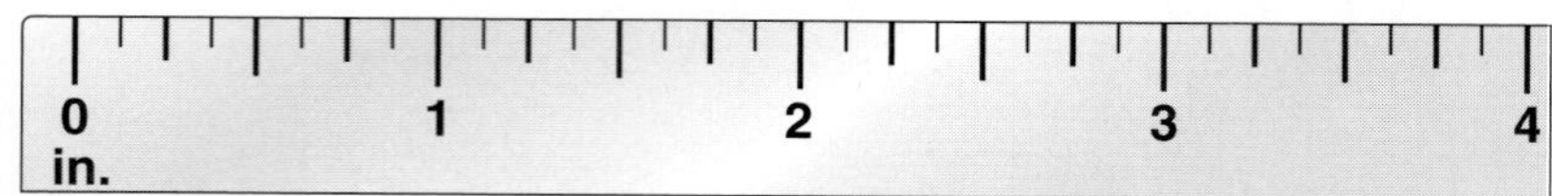

Measure the length of each line segment to the nearest $\frac{1}{4}$ inch and $\frac{1}{2}$ inch.

3. Top line segment to the nearest $\frac{1}{2}$ inch: __________

4. Bottom line segment to the nearest $\frac{1}{4}$ inch: __________

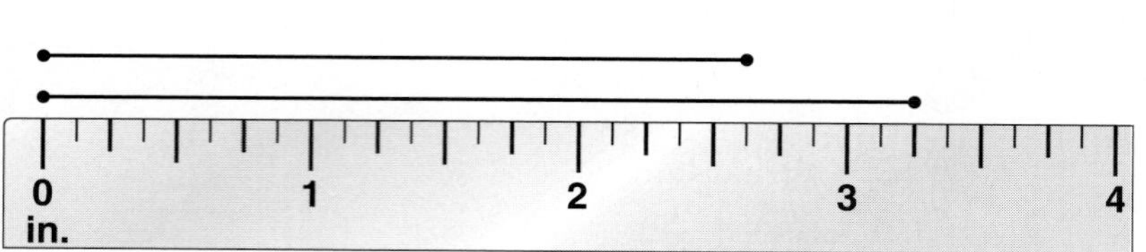

5. Top line segment to the nearest $\frac{1}{2}$ inch: __________

6. Bottom line segment to the nearest $\frac{1}{4}$ inch: __________

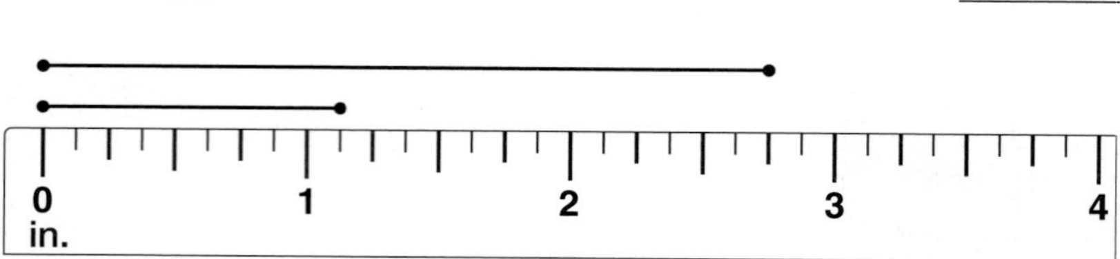

Select the proper unit to measure the length of each object. Write *inch, foot, yard,* or *mile*.

7. tree height __________

8. distance from school to the mall __________

Solve.

9. **TOOLS** Lean takes a vitamin every morning. What is the length of the vitamin to the nearest inch?

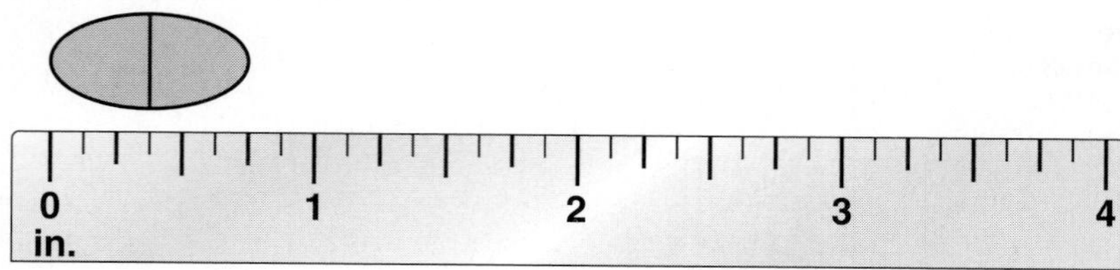

____

NAME _______________________________ DATE _______________

Lesson 4-4

Vocabulary and English Language Development

Activate Prior Knowledge

List three examples of when you use the customary system of measurements for length, height, width, or distance in your daily life.

1 _______________________________

2 _______________________________

3 _______________________________

Chapter 4

Definition Review

Complete each sentence using the words *multiply* or *divide.*

4 To **convert** a larger unit to a smaller unit, you should _______________.

5 To **convert** a smaller unit to a larger unit, you should _______________.

Complete each sentence using the words *larger* or *smaller.*

6 A foot is _______________ than an inch.

7 A mile is _______________ than a yard.

8 An inch is _______________ than a foot.

9 A yard is _______________ than a mile.

Application

Follow the directions for the activity.

- Students each try to find items around the classroom that can be used as a benchmark for an inch, foot, and yard.
- Students should check the measurement of their benchmark items to see if they are appropriate.
- Students share their items with the rest of the class.
- Students discuss how many different items were found and which items are closest to each unit of measurement.
- Students discuss why we might need to use benchmarks. They also discuss when approximate measurements are acceptable to use, and when we need to use exact measurements.

Lesson 4-4

NAME ______________________ DATE ____________

Skills Practice

Convert using a table.

1. 84 in. = ___ ft

Feet							
Inches	12	24	36	48	60	72	84

2. 5 mi = ________ ft

Miles					
Feet	5,280	10,560	15,840	21,120	26,400

Convert.

3. 3 mi = __________ ft
   1 mi = ________ ft
   Multiply or divide? __________
   3 ____ 5,280 = __________
   3 mi = __________ ft

4. 72 in. = __________ yd
   1 yd = ________ in.
   Multiply or divide? __________
   72 ____ 36 = __________
   72 in. = __________ yd

5. 6 mi = ________________ ft

6. 6 mi = ________________ yd

7. 180 in. = ________________ yd

8. 11 ft = ________________ in.

9. 6 yd = ________________ in.

10. 108 in. = ________________ ft

11. 17,600 yd = ________________ mi

12. 3 mi = ________________ yd

13. 52,800 ft = ________________ mi

14. 15 yd = ________________ ft

15. 4 ft = ________________ in.

16. 3 yd = ________________ in.

17. 27 ft = ________________ yd

18. 144 in. = ________________ ft

19. 2.5 mi = ________________ yd

20. 3,520 yd = ________________ mi

NAME ______________________ DATE ______________

Lesson 4-4

Problem-Solving Practice

Solve.

1 **FENCE** The Anoki family is building a fence based on the picture below. What is the perimeter of the fence in yards? (Hint: the perimeter is found by adding the lengths of all the sides.) ______________

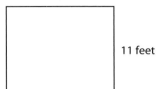

2 **HEIGHT** Alonso was 54 inches tall when he was 10 years old. He grew a total of 0.5 foot over the next three years. How many feet tall was Alonso at the age of 13? ______________

3 **SCHOOL** Mallory's school is 2,640 feet from her house. How many miles does Mallory walk to school each day? ______________

4 **FOOTBALL** Jonah threw a football 22 yards at the first football game of the season. How many feet did Jonah throw the football? ______________

5 **CONCERTS** The line to buy concert tickets became as long as 1 mile. How many feet long was the line? ______________

6 **RUNNING** The track team runs 2 miles at every practice. How many feet do they run? ______________

7 **RIBBON** The manager of a craft store ordered 200 yards of ribbon. How many inches of ribbon did she order? ______________

Chapter 4

Lesson **4-4**

NAME ______________________ DATE ______________

Homework Practice

Convert using a table.

1. 10,560 yd = ______________ mi

Miles						
Yards	1,760	3,520	5,280	7,040	8,800	10,560

2. 144 in. = ______________ yd

Yards				
Inches	36	72	108	144

3. 26,400 ft = ______________ mi

Miles					
Feet	5,280	10,560	15,840	21,120	26,400

Convert.

4. 5.5 mi = ______________ ft
5. 20 ft = ______________ in.
6. 7 yd = ______________ in.
7. 288 in. = ______________ yd
8. 21,120 ft = ______________ mi
9. 8 mi = ______________ yd
10. 72 in. = ______________ ft
11. 3 mi = ______________ yd

Solve.

12. **ARCHEOLOGY** On a dig, Kenyi found a bone after digging 10 feet into the ground. How many inches into the ground did Kenyi dig? ______________

13. **WALKING** Ms. Patton's class walked along a trail in the park. The trail was 880 yards long. How many miles long was the trail? ______________

Write the vocabulary word(s) that completes the sentence.

14. A ______________ is an object or number used as a guide to estimate or reference.

15. The ______________ is a measurement system that includes units such as foot, pound, and quart.

16. To ______________ is to find an equivalent measure.

NAME _______________ DATE _______________

Foldables Study Organizer

Dinah Zike's Foldables

Make this Foldable to help you organize your notes on two-dimensional figures.

1. Begin with one sheet of $8\frac{1}{2}'' \times 11''$ constuction paper and two sheets of notebook paper. Fold the construction paper in half lengthwise. Label the chapter title on the outside.

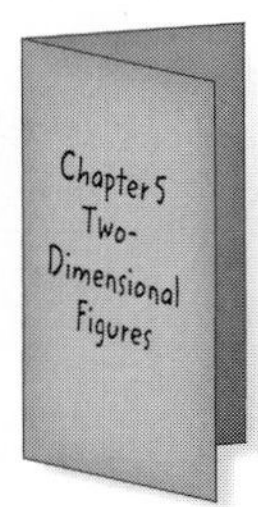

2. Fold the sheets of notebook paper in half lengthwise. Then fold top to bottom twice.

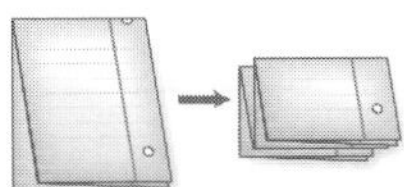

3. Open the notebook paper. Cut along the second folds to make four tabs.

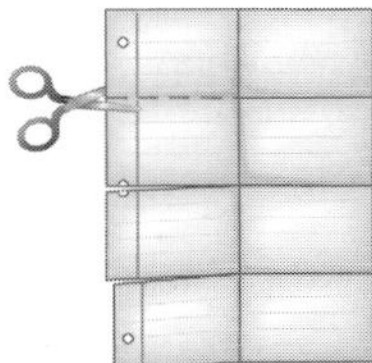

4. Glue the uncut notebook paper side by side onto the construction paper. Label each tab as shown.

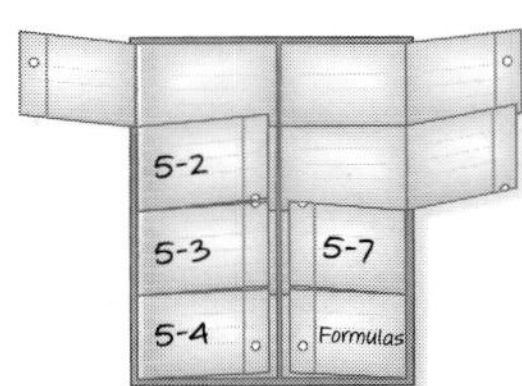

TAKING NOTES
As you read through the chapter, use your Foldable to organize your notes about measuring two-dimensional figures.

USING YOUR FOLDABLE
As you study, use your Foldable to record formulas, key concepts, and procedures under the appropriate tabs. Also give your own examples of the key concepts presented in each lesson.

USING YOUR FOLDABLE
Trade Foldables with a partner. Check each other's Foldable. Does your partner have the same concepts and formulas as you? If not, provide the correct information.

Chapter 5

NAME ______________________ DATE ______________

Games and Puzzles

Finding Area

DIRECTIONS

- Each player writes his or her name in the Area Table.
- Cut out the Area Cards, shuffle the cards, and place them face down.
- Each player turns a card face up.
- Players work together to find the areas of the two figures.
- The players record the areas of their figures in the Area Table.
- The game repeats for two more rounds with the unturned cards. Players then total their three areas. The player with the greater total area wins.

What You Need

- Area Table
- Area Cards

Number of Players

2

Area Table		
	Player Name:	**Player Name:**
	Area	**Area**
Round 1		
Round 2		
Round 3		

Total		

NAME ______________________________ DATE ______________

Area Cards

5 ft

8 ft

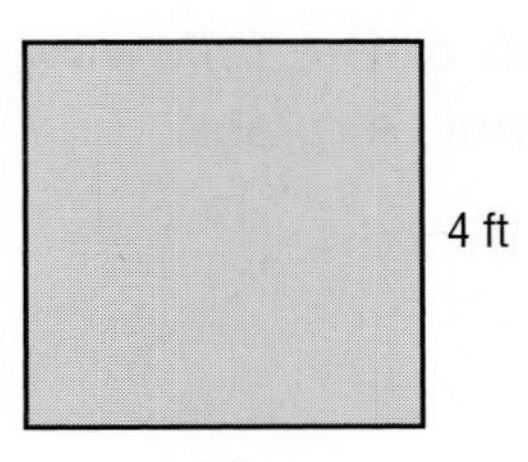

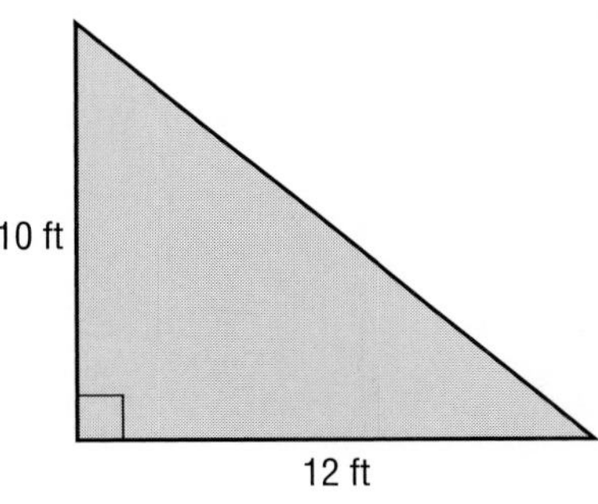

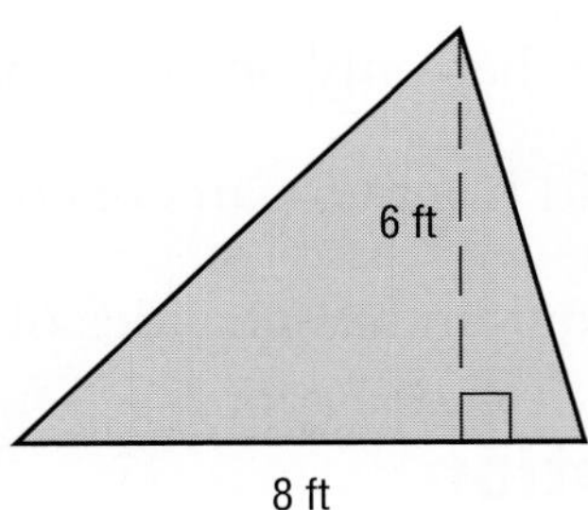

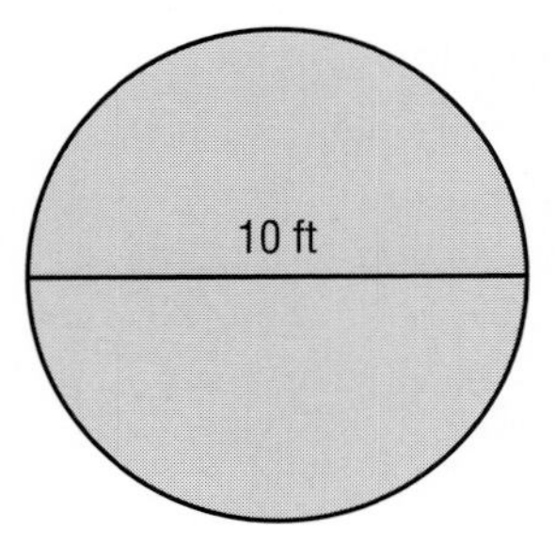

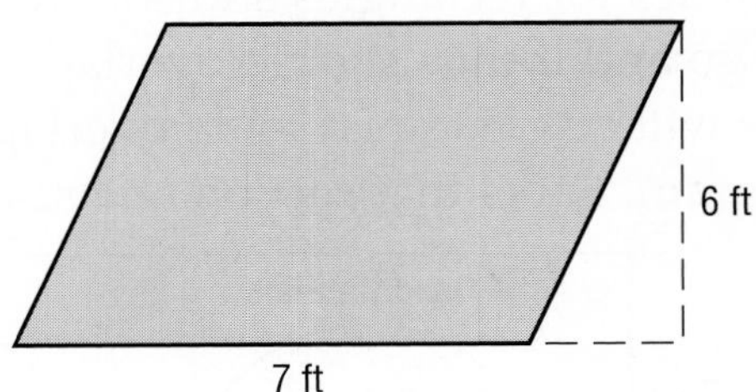

Lesson 5-1

NAME ______________________ DATE ____________

Vocabulary and English Language Development

Activate Prior Knowledge

Determine if each of the following figures can be drawn. If it can, draw it. If it cannot, explain.

1. A square with 5 sides.

2. A rectangle with 2 sides that are 15 millimeters long.

Definition Review

Determine if each statement is *true* or *false*.

3. A rhombus is a parallelogram. ________

4. A square is a rectangle. ________

5. A rectangle has only one right angle. ________

6. A trapezoid has two pairs of congruent sides. ________

7. A parallelogram has no sides of equal length. ________

Application

Create a Venn diagram for quadrilaterals.

- Work in discussion groups of 2 or 3.
- Draw a large rectangle and label it *quadrilaterals.*
- Within the rectangle, draw a circle and label it *trapezoids.*
- Draw another circle and label it *parallelograms.* Use the definitions to discuss why the circles should not overlap.
- Draw circles for rectangles and squares. Discuss where these circles should go and if they should overlap.
- Squares will be contained in an overlapping section of two circles in the diagram. Label that section *squares.*

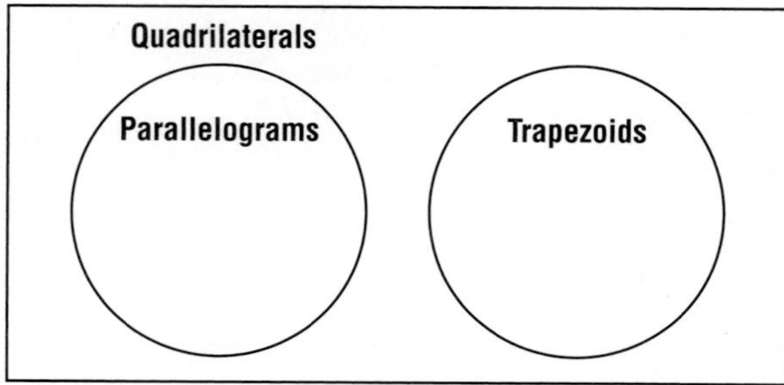

NAME ______________________ DATE ______________

Lesson 5-1

Skills Practice

Classify each quadrilateral in as many ways as possible.

1

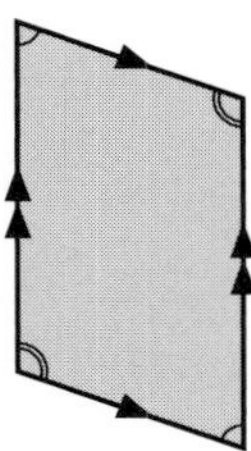

1. Are opposite sides parallel? __________
2. Are the angles right angles? __________
3. Are all four sides congruent? __________
4. The figure is a ______________.

2

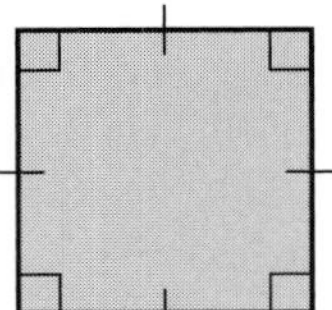

1. Are opposite sides parallel? __________
2. Are all four angles right angles? __________
3. Are all sides equal? __________
4. The figure is a ______________________________.

Identify each figure.

3 The figure has ______________ sides.

All angles are ______________ angles.

The opposite ______________ are equal and parallel.

The figure is a(n) ______________.

4 The figure has ______________ sides.

The figure is a(n) ______________.

There is exactly one pair of ______________ sides.

The figure is a ______________.

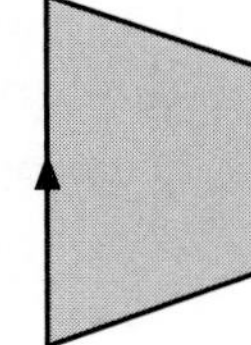

Chapter 5

NAME ______________________ DATE ____________

Problem-Solving Practice

Solve.

1. **FLAGS** The state flag of Texas is shown. The three sections of the flag have opposite sides that are parallel, and the angles are all right angles. What name describes these sections? ____________

2. **FLOOR TILES** Alonso is installing tile in his kitchen. He is using tiles shaped like the one at right. The tile has opposite sides that are parallel, and all four sides are equal. What quadrilateral figure describes the shape of the tile? ____________

3. **RACING** An auto race is often ended with the waving of a checkered flag. The figures on the flag have four equal sides and four right angles. What type of quadrilateral is found on the checkered flag? ____________

4. **BOXES** Erina hung a suggestion box in the school's cafeteria. The side of the box has exacly one pair of parallel sides. What type of quadrilateral does the side of the suggestion box form? ____________

5. **BIRDS** Sondra built a bird house. Each side of the roof is a figure with 4 right angles. The opposite sides of the figure are parallel and congruent. What quadrilateral describes the figure? ____________

6. **ARCHITECTURE** Architects often use a T-square, shown here, to draw lines on a drafting table. The "T" part of its name comes from its design, which looks like the letter T. Explain how this tool can be used to draw a square.

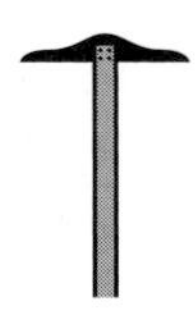

____

____

NAME ______________________ DATE ____________

Lesson 5-1

Homework Practice

1 Circle the parallelograms.

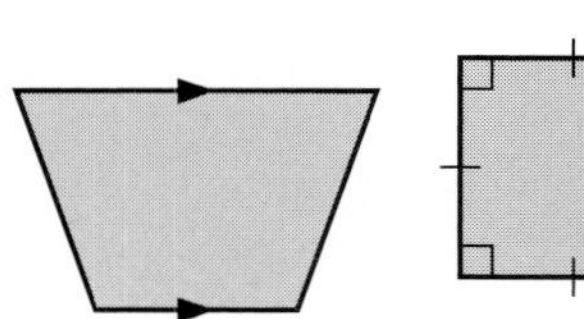

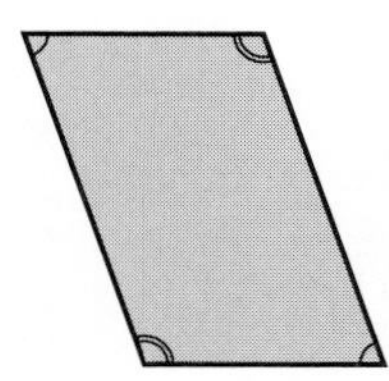

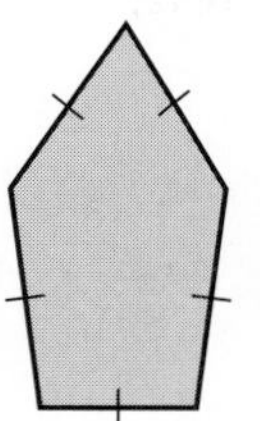

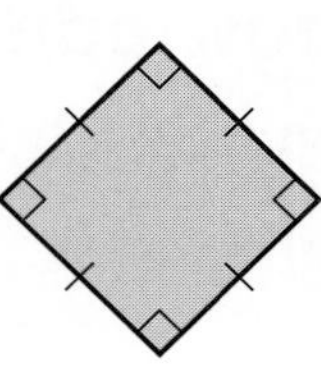

Identify each figure.

2 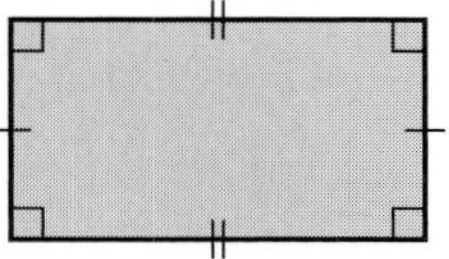

____

3 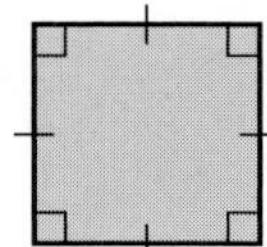

____

4 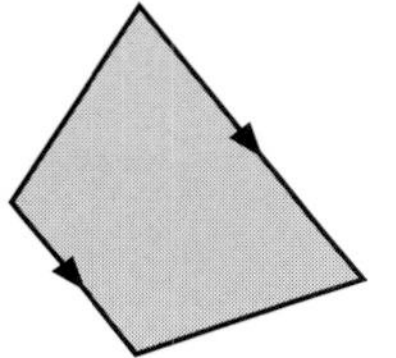

____

5 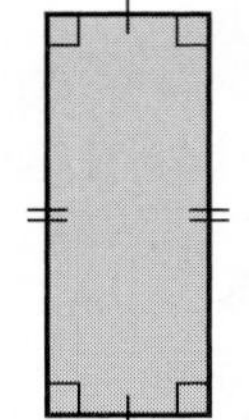

____

6 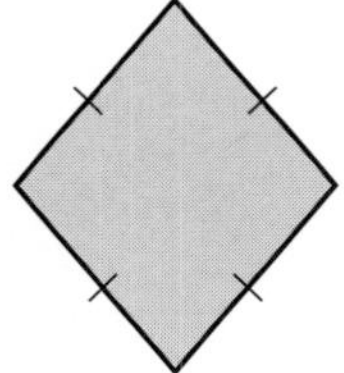

____

7 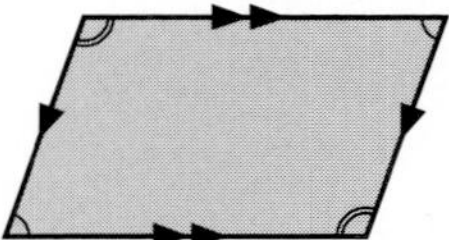

____

Solve.

8 The front side window in Mr. Benson's car has one pair of parallel sides. What quadrilateral describes the window? ______________

Write the vocabulary word that completes the sentence.

9 A ______________ is a quadrilateral with one pair of opposite sides parallel.

NAME ______________________ DATE ______________

Lesson 5-2

Vocabulary and English Language Development

Activate Prior Knowledge

Draw an example of each figure.

1. a trapezoid with two right angles
2. a rhombus

Definition Review

Determine if each statement is *true* or *false*.

3. A right triangle has a right angle. ________
4. An isosceles triangle has at least two congruent sides. ________
5. An equilateral triangle has three congruent sides. ________
6. An acute triangle has three angles less than 90°. ________
7. An obtuse angle measures less than 90°. ________

Application

Create triangles from quadrilaterals.

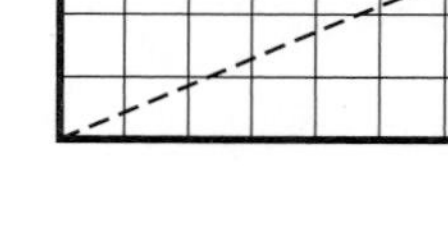

- Work in discussion groups of 2. Use grid paper and a pencil.
- In a quadrilateral, a line connecting two opposite corners is called a diagonal. A diagonal is shown in the rectangle. It divides the rectangle into two triangles. Classify the triangles by sides and by angles. The triangles are ____________________.
- Draw a square. Draw a diagonal. Classify the triangles by sides and by angles. The triangles are ____________________.
- Draw a parallelogram that is neither a rectangle nor a rhombus. Draw a diagonal that joins the acute angles. Classify the triangles by sides and by angles. The triangles are ____________________. Erase the diagonal and draw the diagonal that joins the obtuse angles. Classify the triangles by sides and by angles. The triangles are ____________________.
- Predict what kind of triangles will be formed by the diagonals of a rhombus. Discuss your prediction with your partner. Then check if you were correct by drawing a rhombus and its diagonals.

Lesson 5-2

NAME ______________________ DATE ______________

Skills Practice

Name the triangle by its sides.

1 The triangle has __________ congruent sides.

The triangle is a(n) ______________________.

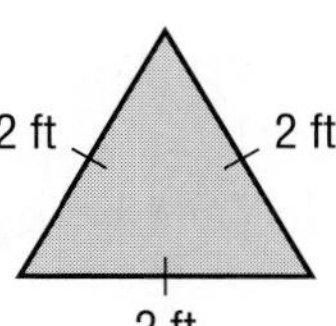

Name the triangle by its angles.

2 There are __________ angles less than 90°.

There are __________ angles greater than 90°.

There is __________ right angle.

The triangle is a(n) ______________________.

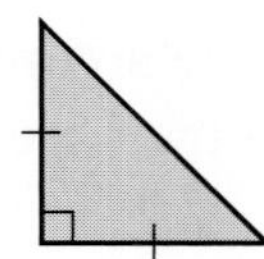

Name each triangle by its angles and sides.

3 number of congruent sides __________

number of acute angles __________

number of right angles __________

number of obtuse angles __________

The triangle is a(n) ______________________ triangle.

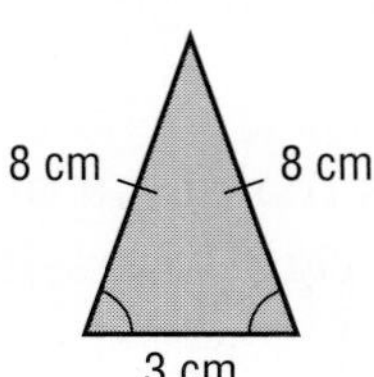

Chapter 5

4 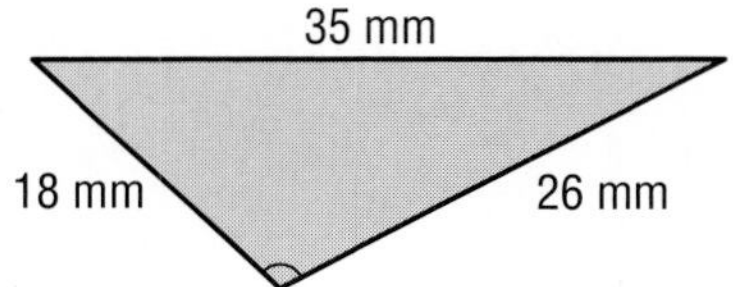

____

5 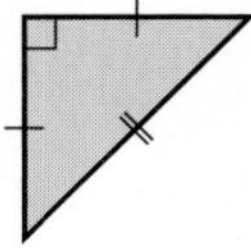

____

6 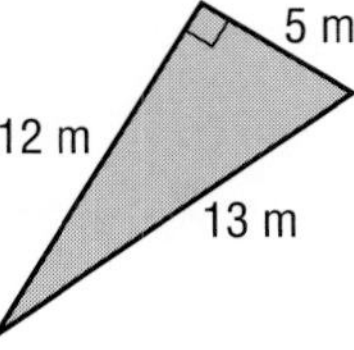

____

7 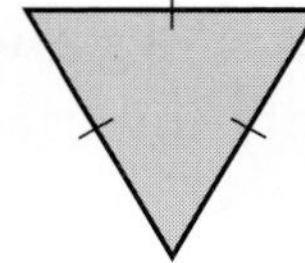

____

NAME ______________________ DATE ______________

Lesson 5-2

Problem-Solving Practice

Solve.

1. **INSTRUMENTS** A harp is a stringed instrument that may come in many sizes, but is generally the same shape. Classify the triangle by its angles.

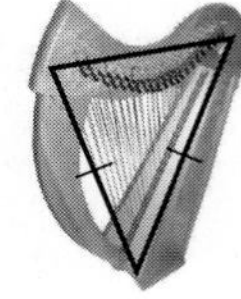

____

2. **TREES** A tree in Arnie's yard is in the shape of a triangle. Classify the triangle by its sides and by its angles.

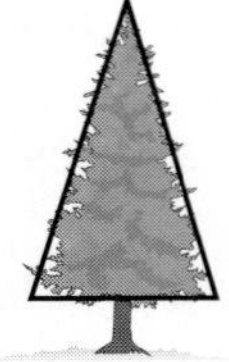

____

____

3. **PROPERTY** Ms. Plum bought a piece of land in the shape of a triangle. The land has a 90° angle and no two sides are the same length. Classify the triangle by its angles and its sides.

____

____

4. **QUILTING** Myre is making a quilt with a design like the one at the right. Classify the triangles by angles.

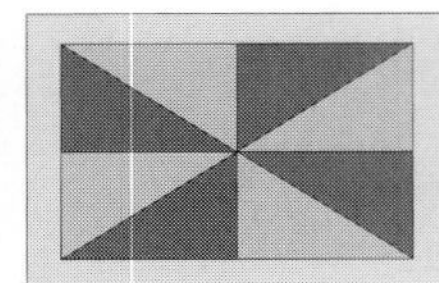

____

5. **PAINTING** Kilam is painting a border on his walls like the one at the right. Classify the triangles by their angles.

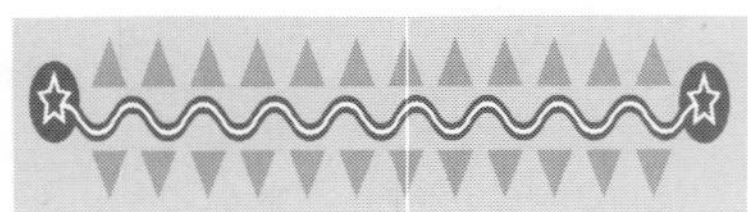

____

6. **FURNITURE** The bases of the table are in the shape of a triangle. The largest angle in the triangle is greater than 90°. What kind of triangles are the bases?

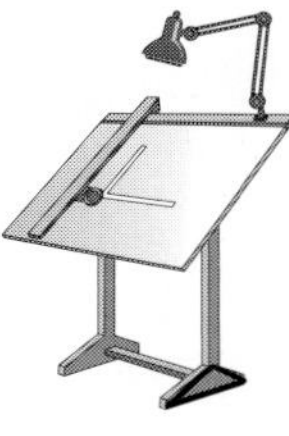

____

7. **ROOFS** The roof of the entry way shown is in the shape of a triangle. Classify the triangle by its angles.

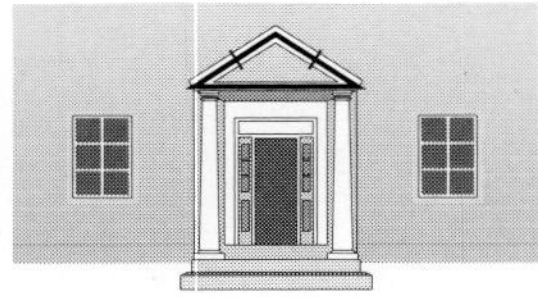

____

8. **CONSTRUCTION** Caroline's house is being built. She notices the framework of the roof is a triangle. Classified by its sides, what type of triangle does the roof form?

____

NAME ______________________ DATE ______________

Lesson 5-2

Homework Practice

Name each triangle by its sides.

1 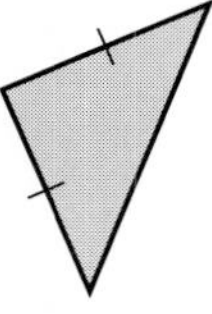

____

2 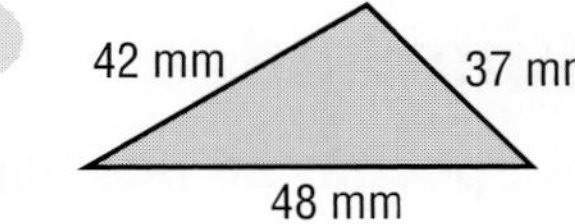

____

Name each triangle by its angles.

3 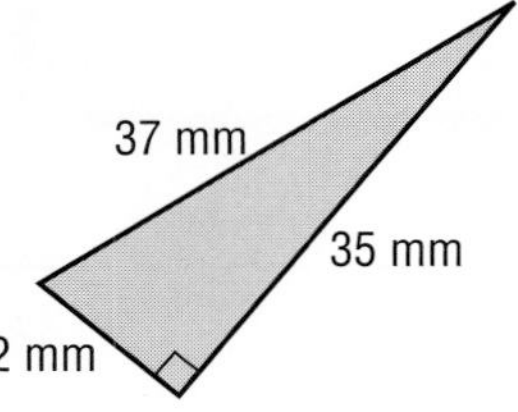

____

4 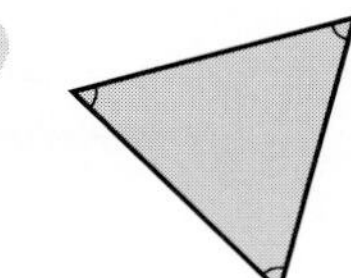

____

Name each triangle by its angles and sides.

5 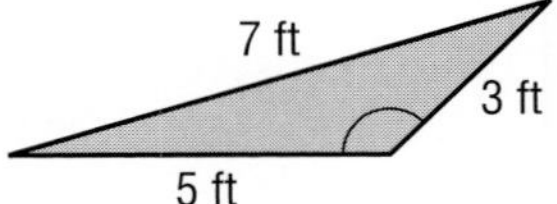

____

6 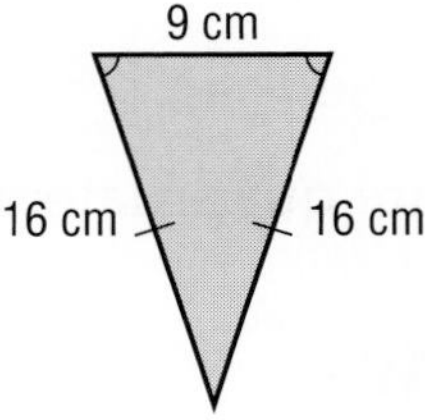

____

Solve.

7 **INSTRUMENTS** The instrument shown is called a triangle. If classified by its sides, what type of triangle is shown? ______________

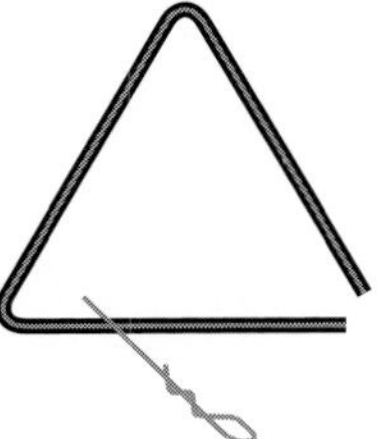

Write the vocabulary word that completes the sentence.

8 A ____________ triangle is a triangle that has no congruent sides.

Chapter 5

Lesson 5-3

NAME ______________________ DATE ______________

Vocabulary and English Language Development

Activate Prior Knowledge

Identify each figure. Be as specific as possible.

1 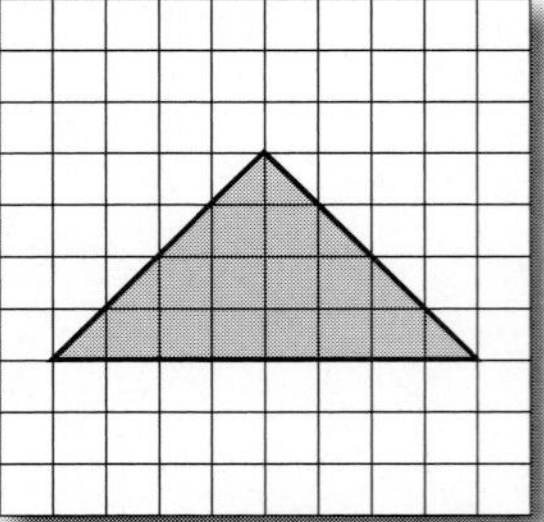

____

2 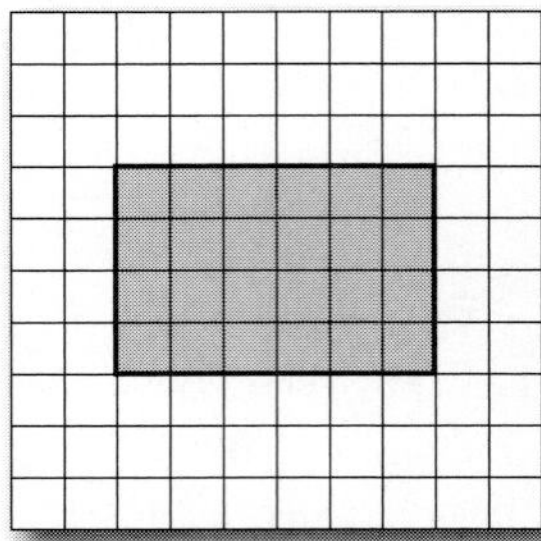

____

3 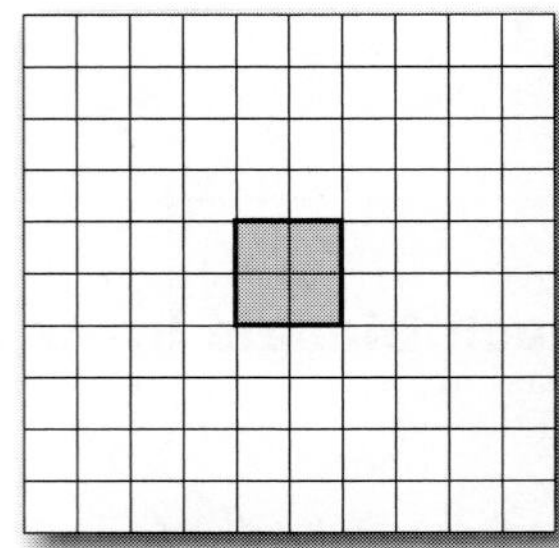

____

4 Identify each figure.

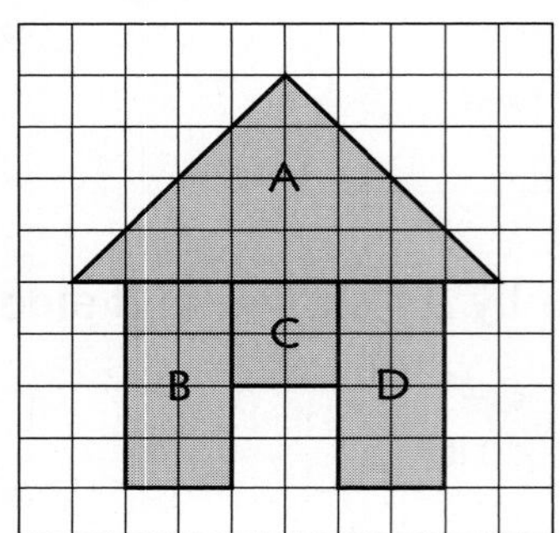

Figure A: ____________

Figure B: ____________

Figure C: ____________

Figure D: ____________

5 Figures ____________ are quadrilaterals.

Definition Review

Fill in the blanks.

6 ____________ is the number of ____________ units needed to cover the surface enclosed by a geometric figure.

7 A ____________ is a unit for measuring area.

Application

Design a logo.

- Work in groups of 2 or 3.
- Each person in the group designs a logo on graph paper using triangles and quadrilaterals.
- The design should cover whole squares or half squares.
- Work together as a group to find the area of each logo.

NAME ______________________ DATE ______________

Lesson 5-3

Skills Practice

Draw a figure that has the given area.

1. 20 square units

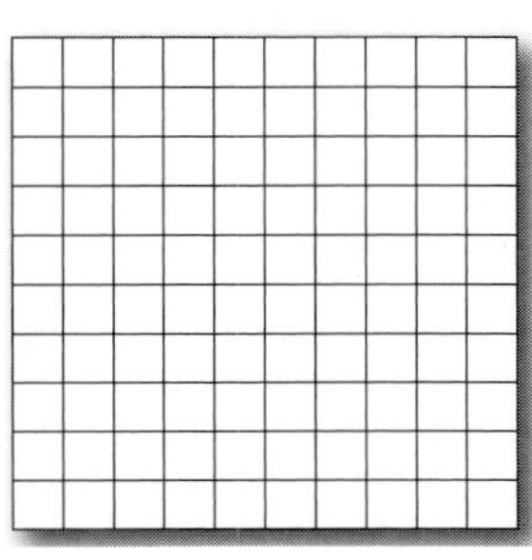

2. 64 square units

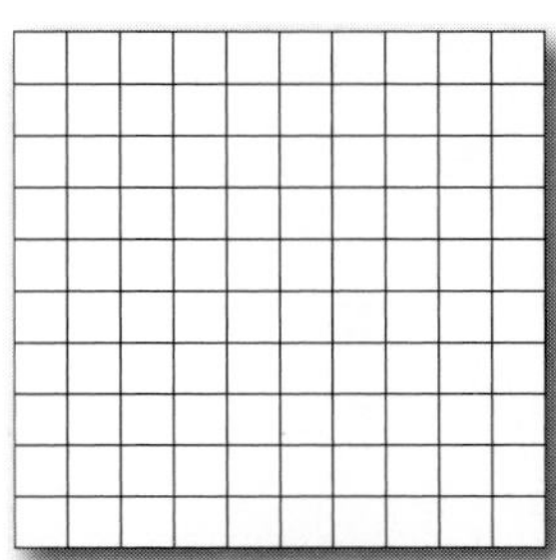

3. 40 square units

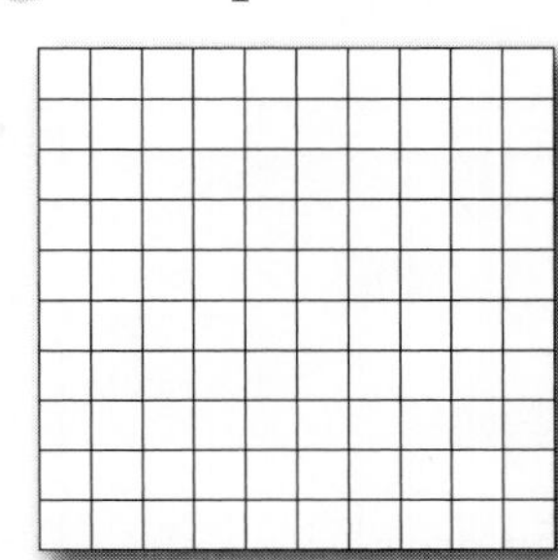

4. 12 square units

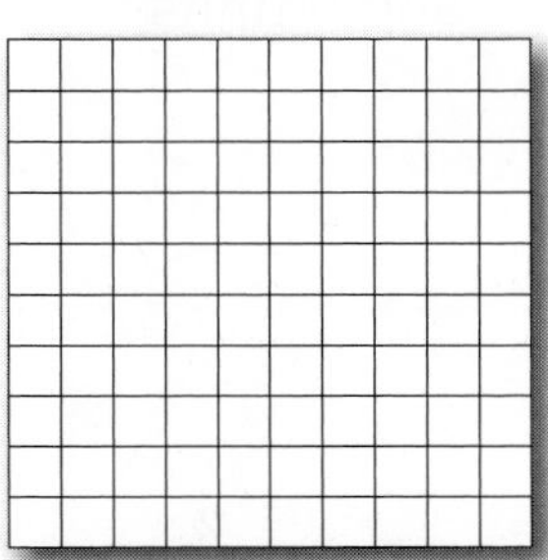

Find the area of each figure.

5.

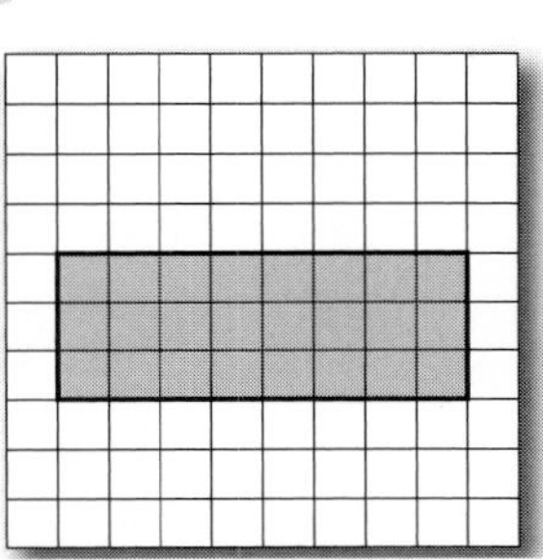

The area of the rectangle is ______ square units.

6.

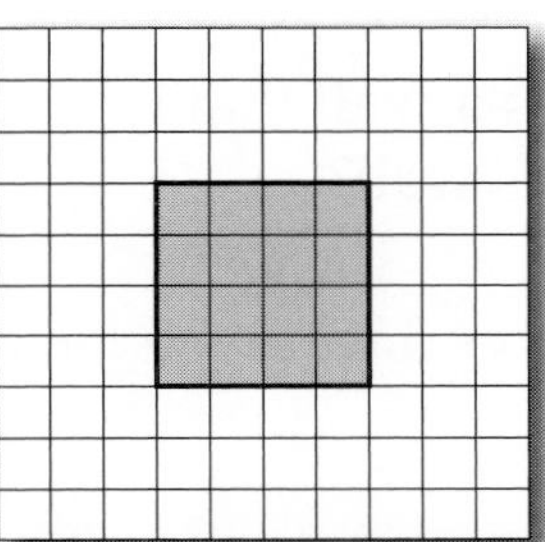

The area of the square is ______ square units.

7.

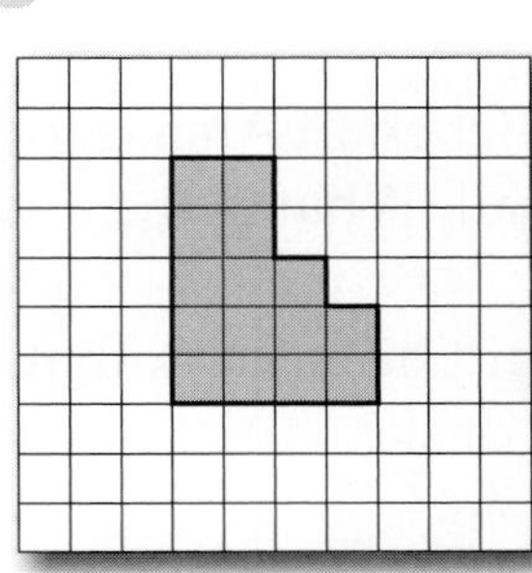

The area of the figure is ______ square units.

8.

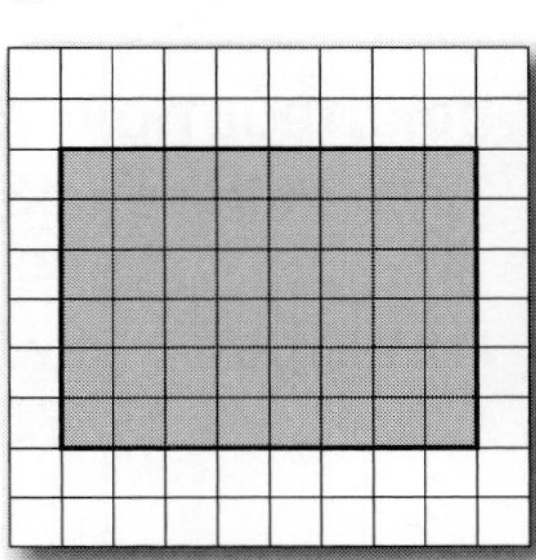

The area of the rectangle is ______ square units.

9.

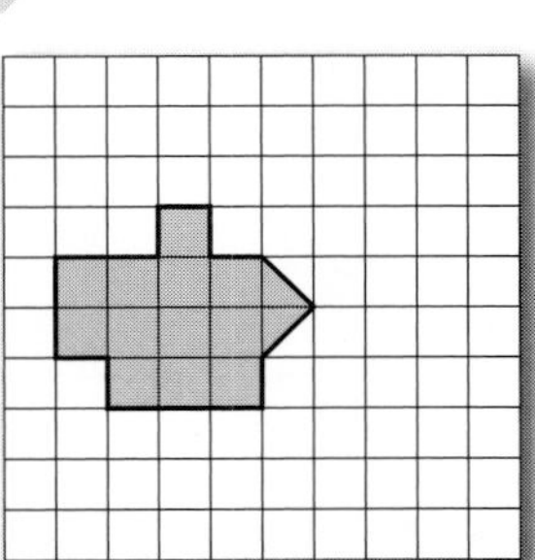

The area of the figure is about ______ square units.

10.

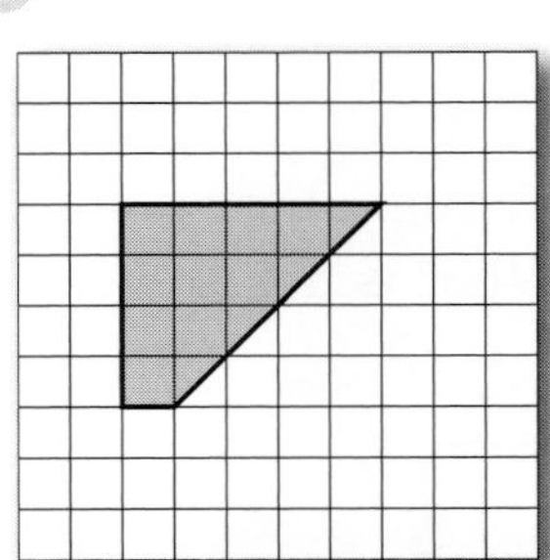

The area of the figure is about ______ square units.

11.

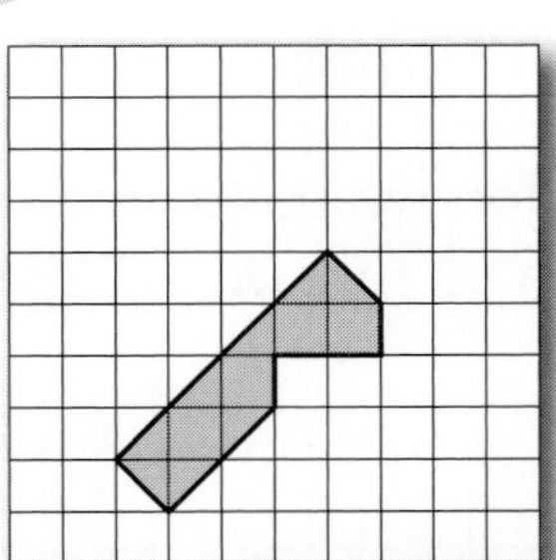

The area of the figure is about ______ square units.

12.

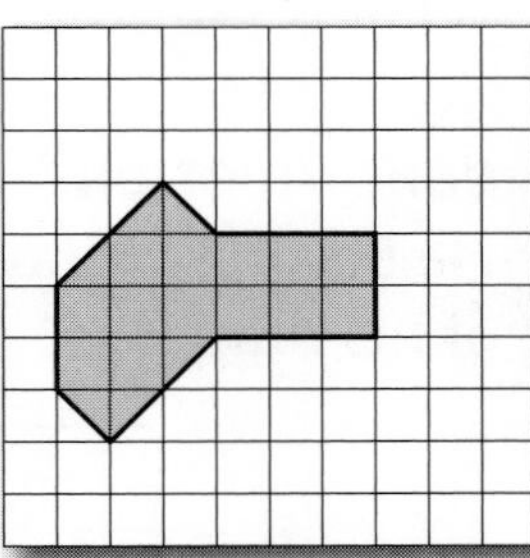

The area of the figure is about ______ square units.

Chapter 5

Lesson 5-3

NAME ______________________ DATE ____________

Problem-Solving Practice

Solve.

1. **GEOMETRY** What is the area of a rectangle that has sides of 6 units and 9 units? ____________

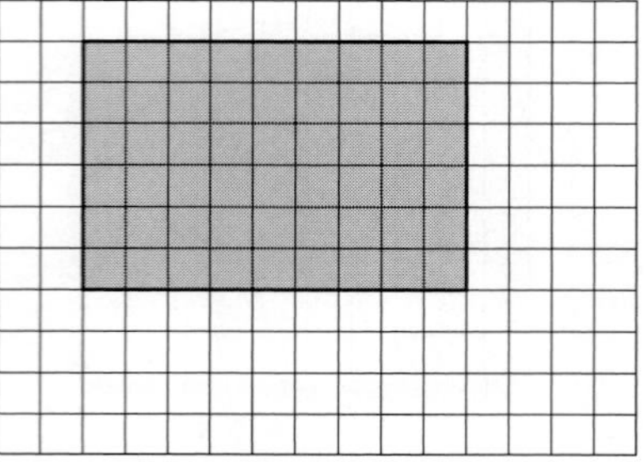

2. **GAMES** Keisha and Halley are playing a game. A rectangular game card measures 2 inches by 3 inches. What is the area of the card? ____________

3. **CONSTRUCTION** The kitchen in Alicia's home has a wall that is 12 feet long and 8 feet tall. What is the area of this wall? ____________

4. **FURNITURE** Mrs. Kincaid has a desk that measures 3 feet by 5 feet. What is the area of this desk? ____________

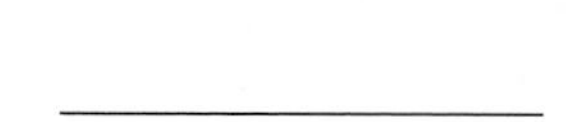

5. **RUGBY** Olivia plays rugby on a field that is 70 meters wide and 100 meters long. What is the area of the rugby field? ____________

6. **GEOMETRY** What is the area of a square that has sides 9 units long? ____________

7. **COOKING** Fidel is cooking brownies. The pan is a rectangle measuring 8 inches on one side and 11 inches on the other side. What is the area of the pan? ____________

8. **CONSTRUCTION** Brandon wants to create a snowman-shaped sign. He began by drawing a picture on grid paper. What is the area of his drawing? ____________

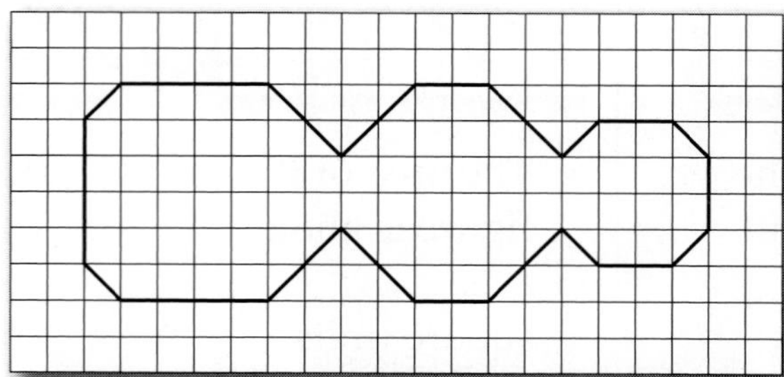

Lesson 5-3

NAME ________________________________ DATE ______________

Homework Practice

Find the area of each figure.

1

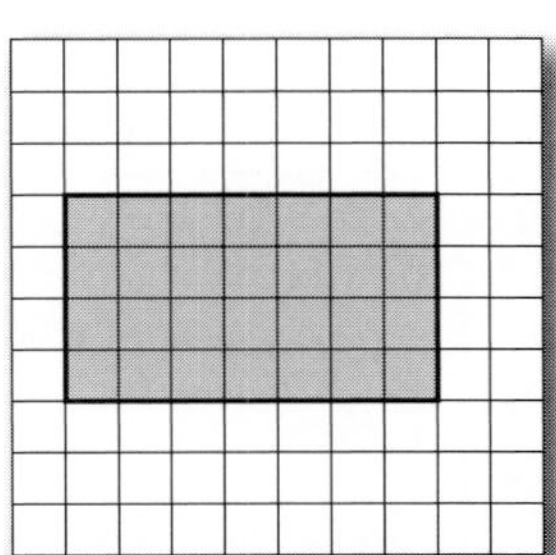

The area of the rectangle is ________ square units.

2

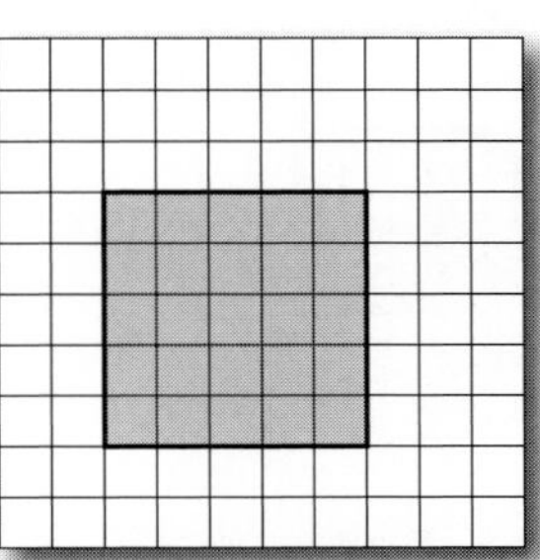

The area of the square is ________ square units.

3

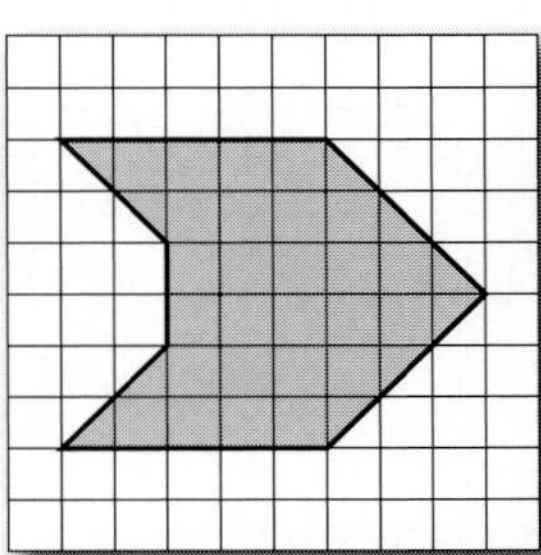

The area of the figure is ________ square units.

4

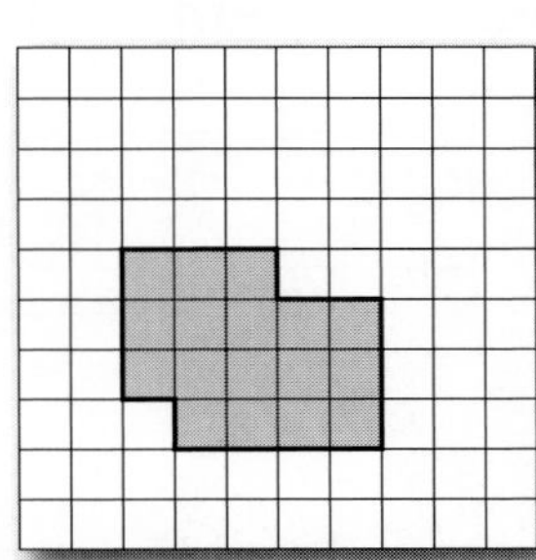

The area of the figure is ________ square units.

Chapter 5

Draw a figure that has the given area.

5 42 square units

6 18 square units

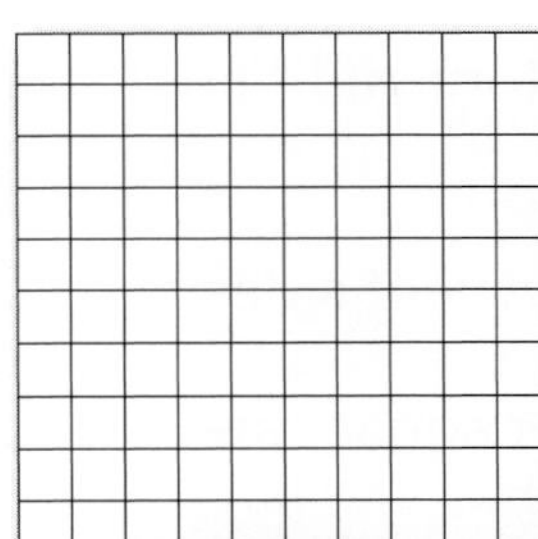

7 10 square units

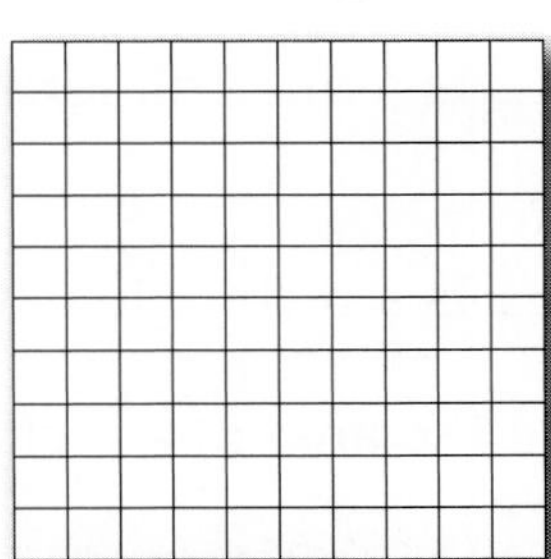

8 49 square units

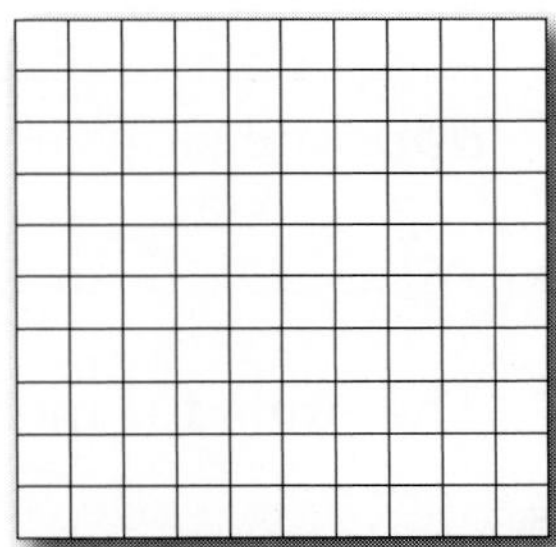

Solve.

9 **CONSTRUCTION** Craig is laying tile on his bathroom floor. The bathroom is a rectangle that measures 10 feet by 6 feet. What is the area of Craig's bathroom floor? ________________

Write the vocabulary word that completes the sentence.

10 The number of square units needed to cover the surface enclosed by a geometric figure is the ____________.

Lesson 5-4

NAME ______________________ DATE ____________

Vocabulary and English Language Development

Activate Prior Knowledge

Find the length, width, and area of each of the following.

1

2 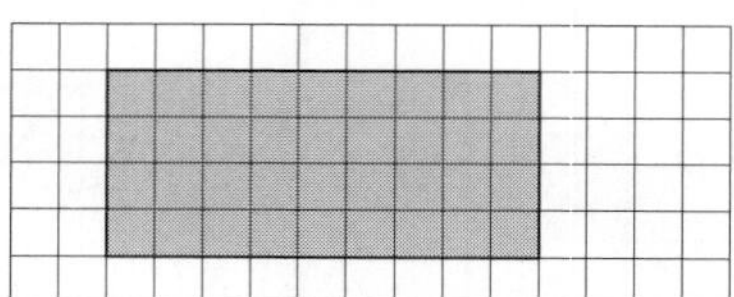

3 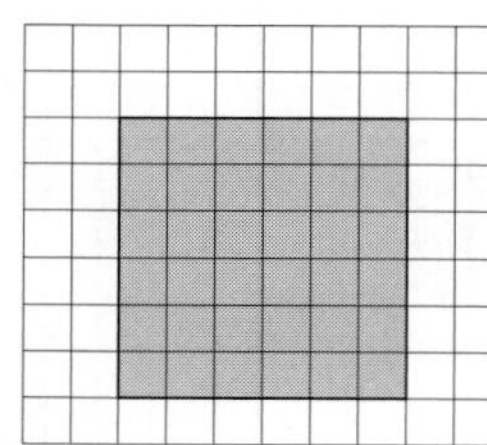

Length = ________
Width = ________
Area = ____________

Length = ________
Width = ________
Area = ____________

Length = ________
Width = ________
Area = ____________

4 When comparing each of the rectangles, the ______________ are the same, but the ______________ and ______________ are different.

Definition Review

Complete each sentence by filling in the blanks.

5 A ______________ is a quadrilateral with four right angles and opposite sides equal.

6 A ______________ is a rectangle with congruent sides.

7 The units for measuring the area of a rectangle or square are ______________.

Application

Create and compare different rectangles with the same area.

- Work in discussion groups of 2 or 3.
- Find the number of squares around the edge of each rectangle in Exercises 1-3 above. ______________
- Which figure has the least number of squares around its edge? ______________
- Draw a 1 by 16 rectangle, an 8 by 2 rectangle, and a 4 by 4 square on graph paper. What is the area of each figure? ______________
- Which figure has the least number of squares around its edge? ______________
- Discuss why squares always have the least number of squares around the edge.

NAME ______________________ DATE ______________

Skills Practice

Draw a rectangle for each given area.

1. 24 cm²

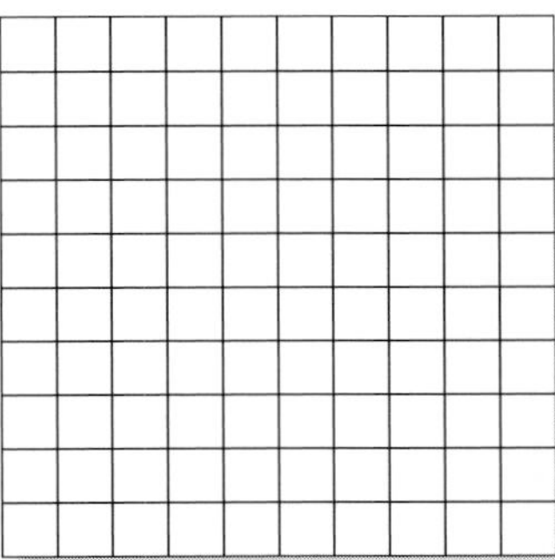

2. 56 in²

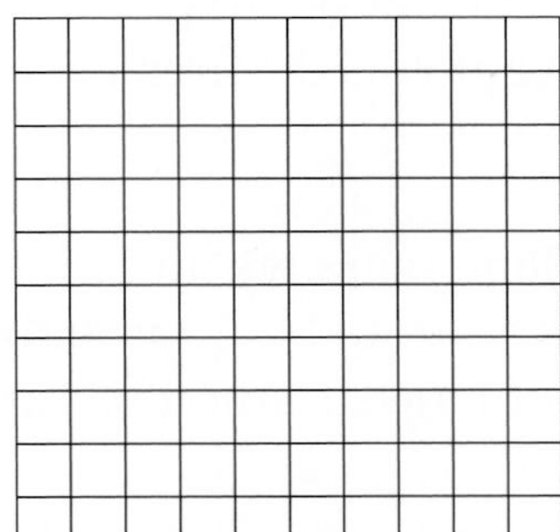

Find the area of each rectangle.

3. $A =$ ______________

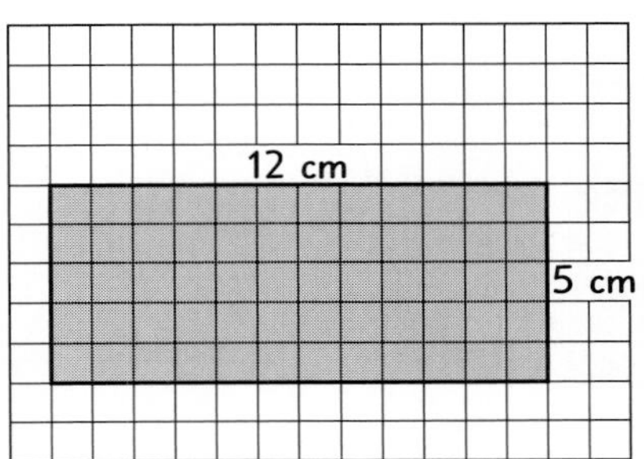

4. $A =$ ______________

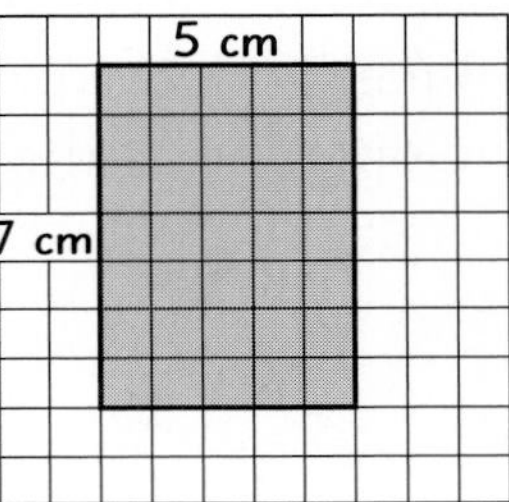

5. $A =$ ______________

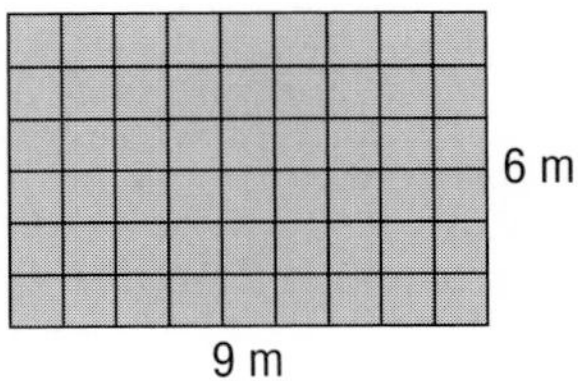

6. $A =$ ______________

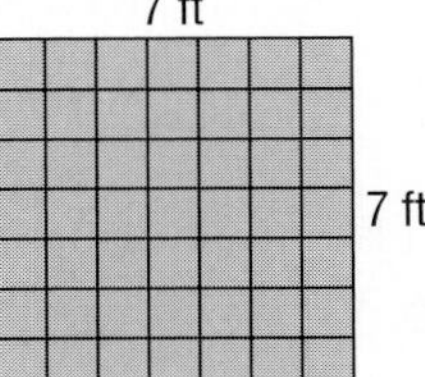

7. $A =$ ______________

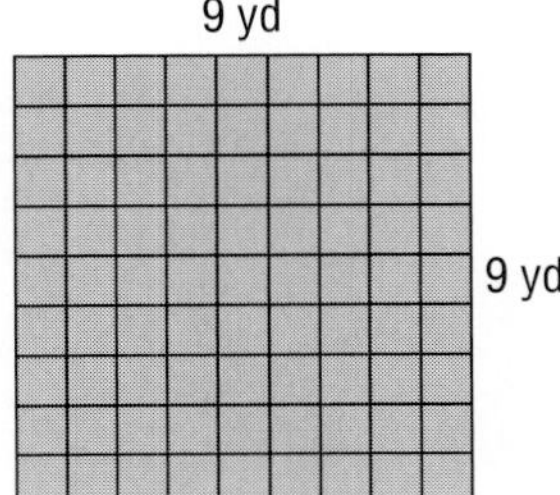

8. $A =$ ______________

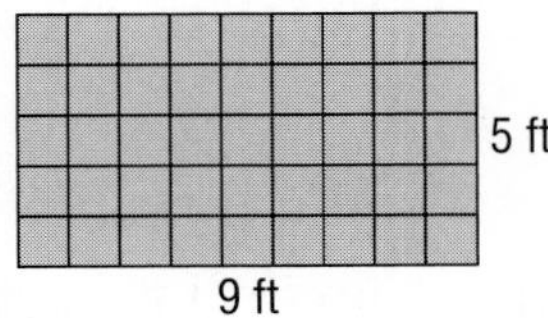

Lesson **5-4** NAME ______________________ DATE ____________

Problem-Solving Practice

Solve.

1 **POSTERS** Mr. Lopez asked his students to create posters for their final projects. The poster boards measured 51 centimeters by 76 centimeters. What was the area of each poster board? ____________

2 **PHOTOGRAPHY** Jane will give an 11 inch by 14 inch framed picture as a gift to her grandmother. What is the area of Jane's framed picture? ____________

3 **CONSTRUCTION** The opening of the doorway in Jake's bedroom is 3 feet wide and 7 feet tall. What is the area of the opening of the doorway? ____________

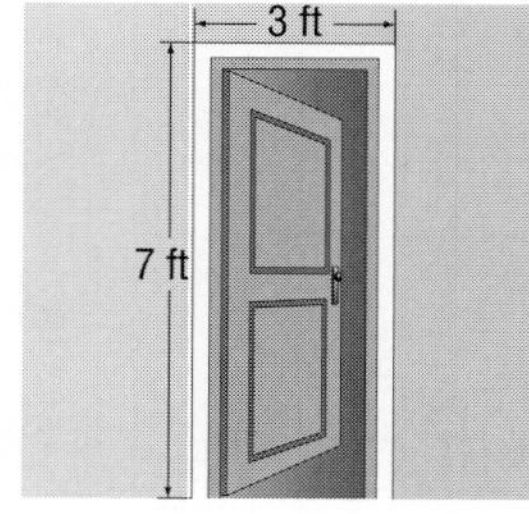

4 **AIRPORT** A small airport has a runway that is 900 meters long and 75 meters wide. What is the area of the runway? ____________

5 **CONSTRUCTION** Malik is building an additional 12 feet by 16 feet bedroom onto his house. What is the area of the new bedroom? ____________

6 **COUNTERTOP** A new kitchen countertop has dimensions of 244 centimeters by 76 centimeters. What is the area of this countertop? ____________

7 **NOTE CARDS** Simon has an oral report for biology class. He made several notes on notecards measuring 3 inches by 5 inches. What is the area of each notecard? ____________

Biology Notes

The femur is the thigh bone.

It is the longest and strongest bone.

NAME ______ DATE ______

Lesson 5-4

Homework Practice

Draw a rectangle for each given area.

1 30 yd^2

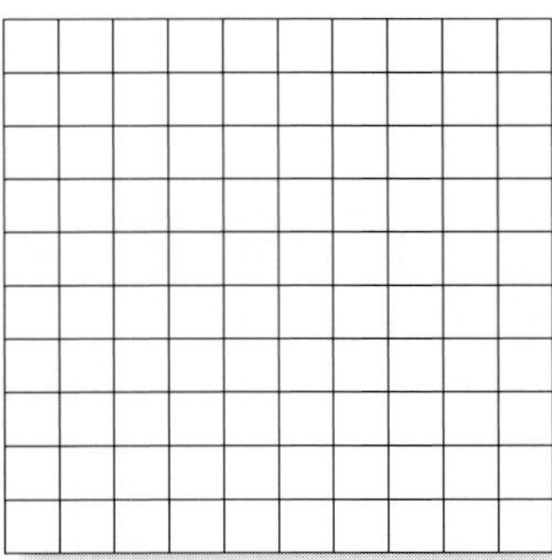

2 8 cm^2

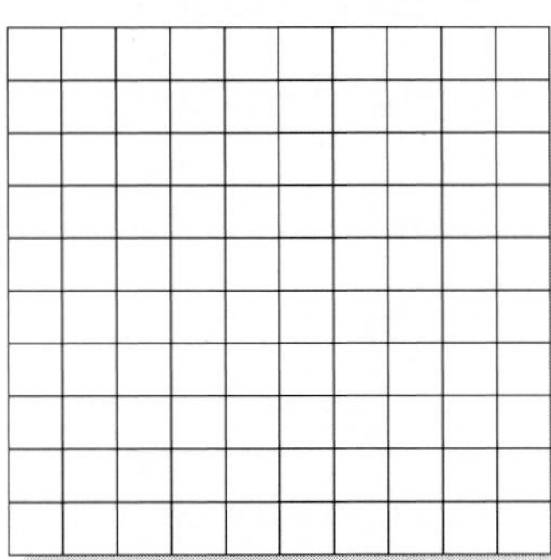

Find the area of each rectangle.

3 $A =$ ______

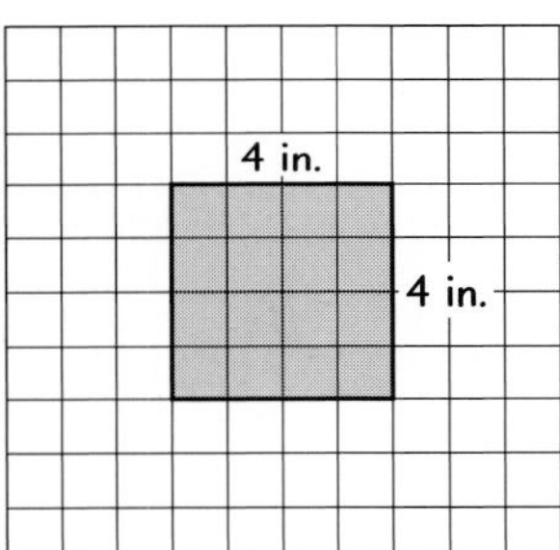

4 $A =$ ______

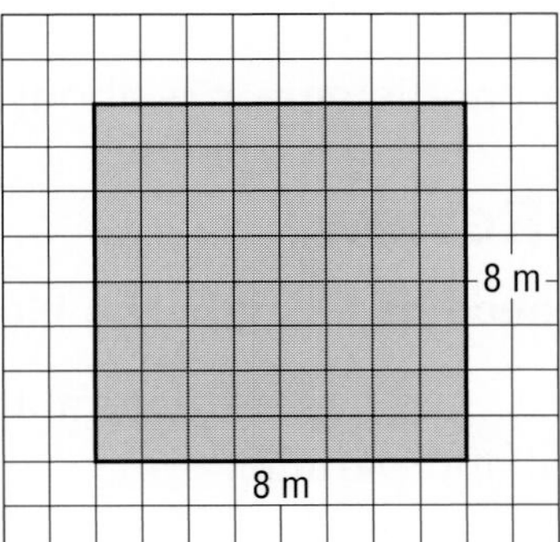

5 $A =$ ______

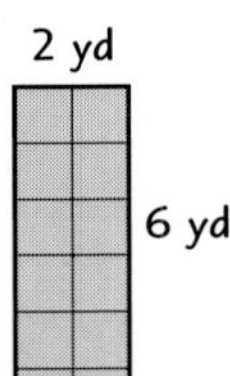

6 $A =$ ______

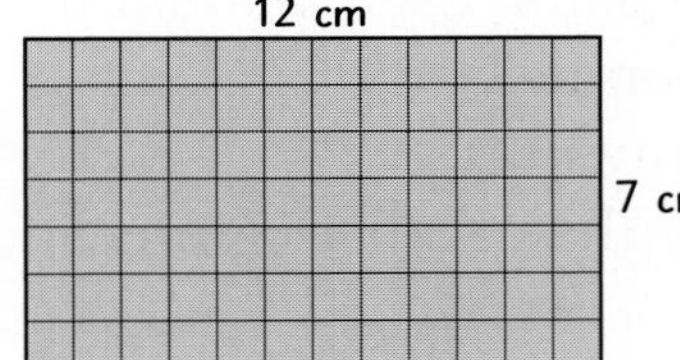

Solve.

7 **RUGS** Lydia bought an area rug for her living room. The rug is a rectangle that measures 42 inches wide by 66 inches long. What is the area of Lydia's rug?

______

Chapter 5

Lesson 5-5

NAME ______________________ DATE ____________

Vocabulary and English Language Development

Activate Prior Knowledge

Estimate the area of the parallelogram.

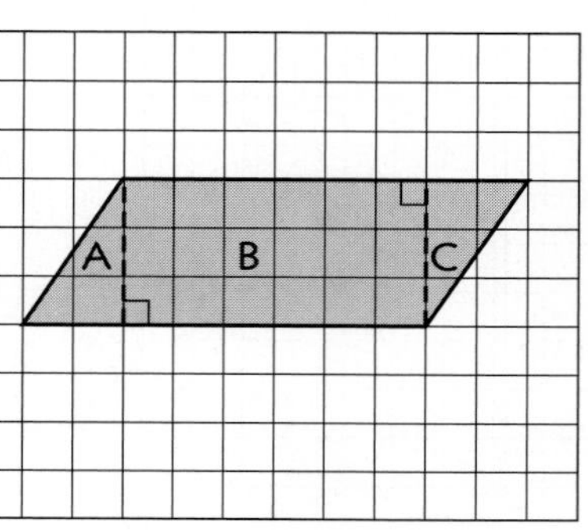

1 Name each figure in the parallelogram.

Figure A is a ______________.

Figure B is a ______________.

Figure C is a ______________.

2 Count the squares covered by each figure to find the areas of figures A, B, and C.

Figure A is about ______________ square units.

Figure B is ______________ square units.

Figure C is about ______________ square units.

3 The area of the parallelogram is about ______________ square units.

Definition Review

Complete the sentence by filling in the blanks.

4 A ______________ is a quadrilateral that has both pairs of ______________ sides congruent and parallel.

Application

Follow the directions for the activity.

- Students work in pairs. Each student uses grid paper, a pencil, and a ruler to draw a parallelogram.
- Students trade drawings.
- Students measure the parallelograms and find their areas. Write down the areas.
- Students then cut out the parallelograms. Using scissors and tape, students cut a triangle from one end of a parallelogram, and tape it to the other end, to form a rectangle.
- Students check one another's shapes to assure they form rectangles. (If rectangles are formed, all four angles must be right angles.)
- Students measure and find the area of the rectangles.
- Students then discuss the relationship between the formula for the area of a rectangle and formula for the area of a parallelogram.
- Repeat activity three times.

NAME ____________________ DATE ____________

Lesson 5-5

Skills Practice

Draw a parallelogram that has the given area.

1 15 cm^2

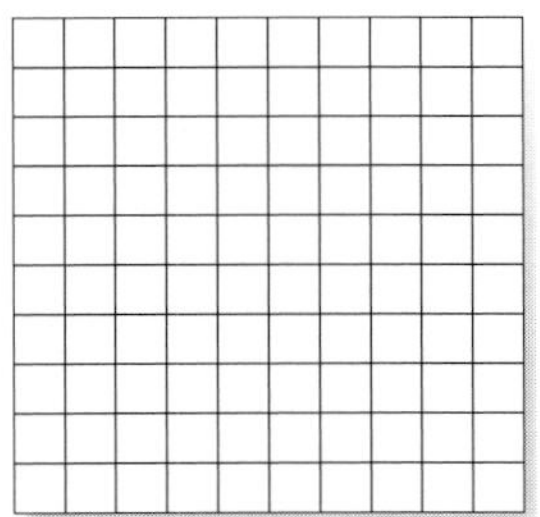

2 32 in^2

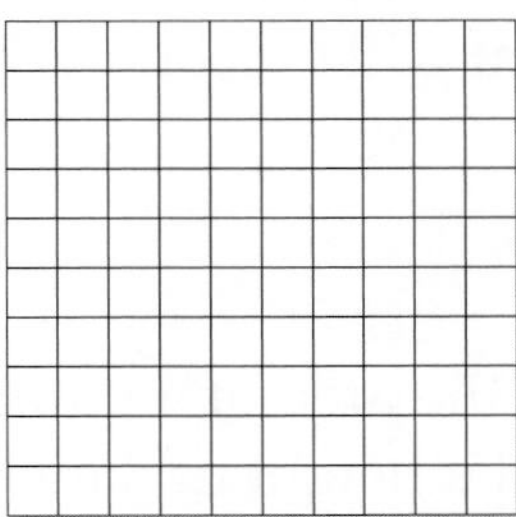

3 7 ft^2

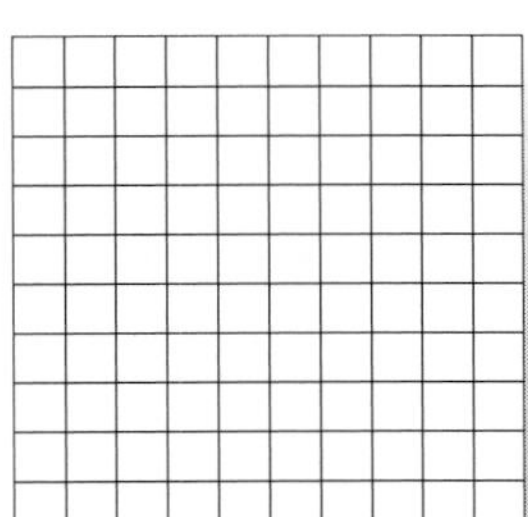

4 18 m^2

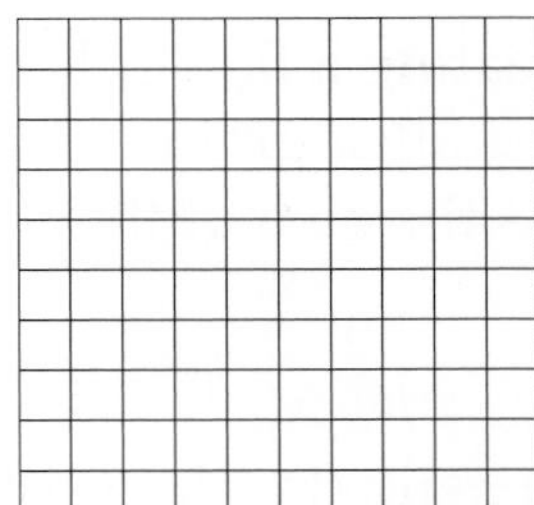

Chapter 5

Find the area of each parallelogram.

5

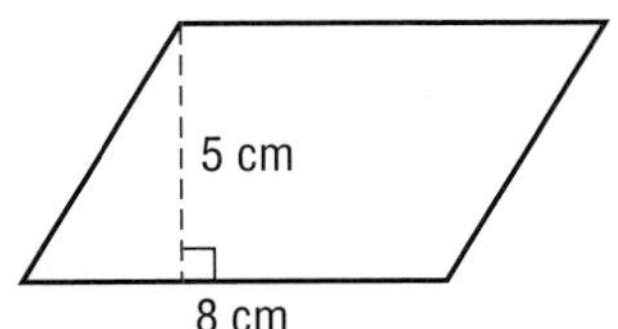

The base of the parallelogram is ____________ and the height is ____________.

$A = b \times h$

$A =$ __________ $\times$ __________

$A =$ ____________

6

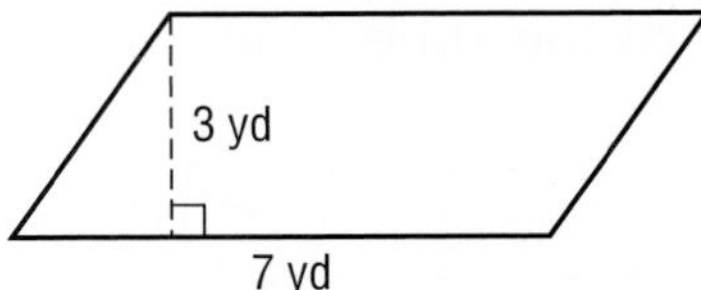

The base of the parallelogram is ____________ and the height is ____________.

$A = b \times h$

$A =$ __________ $\times$ __________

$A =$ ____________

7

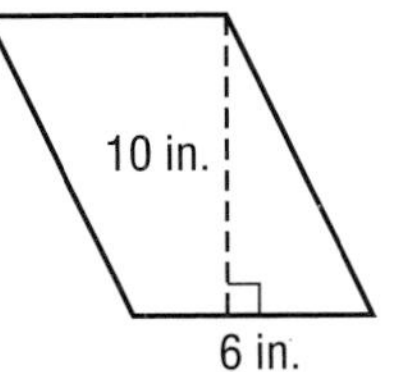

$A =$ ____________

8

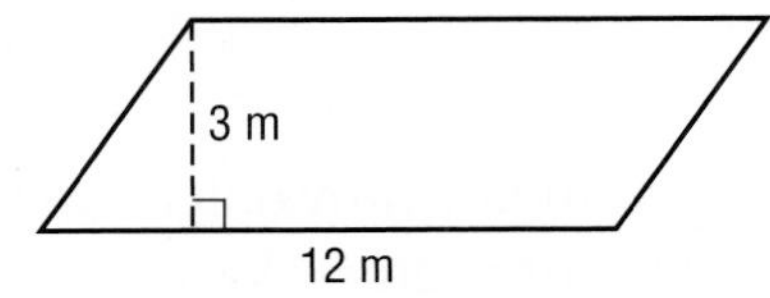

$A =$ ____________

NAME ______________________________ DATE ______________

Lesson 5-5

Problem-Solving Practice

Solve.

1. **PICTURES** While on vacation, Luke bought a wall hanging in the shape of a parallelogram with a base of 18 inches and a height of 24 inches. What is the area of the wall hanging?

2. **GEOMETRY** What is the area of a parallelogram with a base of 11 meters and a height of 8 meters?

3. **STATES** Nodin is creating a flower bed in the shape of a parallelogram. The parallelogram is 5 yards long and 2 yards wide. What is the area of the flower bed?

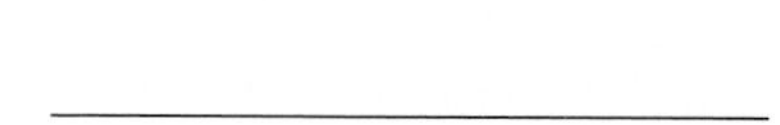

4. **GEOGRAPHY** On the map, the shape of Tennessee is similar to a parallelogram. Approximate the area of Tennessee by using the formula for the area of a parallelogram if the base of the state is about 385 miles and the height of the state is about 110 miles.

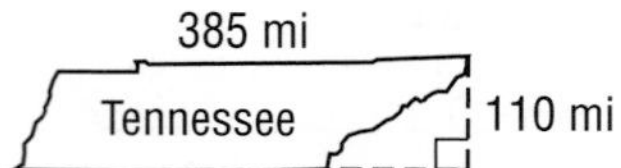

5. **BANNER** For a friend's birthday party, Dario made a banner in the shape of a parallelogram. It had a base of 8 feet and a height of 1 foot. What is the area of the banner?

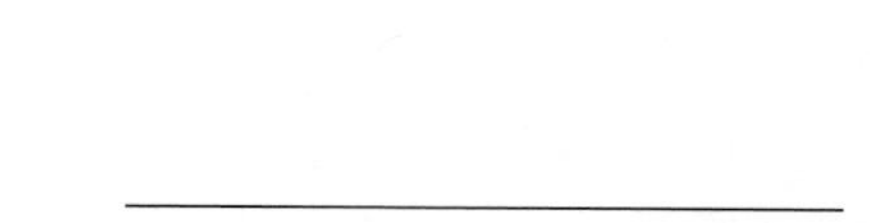

6. **GEOMETRY** A parallelogram has a base of 12 centimeters and a height of 9 centimeters. What is the area of the parallelogram?

____

NAME _______________ DATE _______________

Lesson 5-5

Homework Practice

Draw a parallelogram that has the given area.

1. 20 m^2

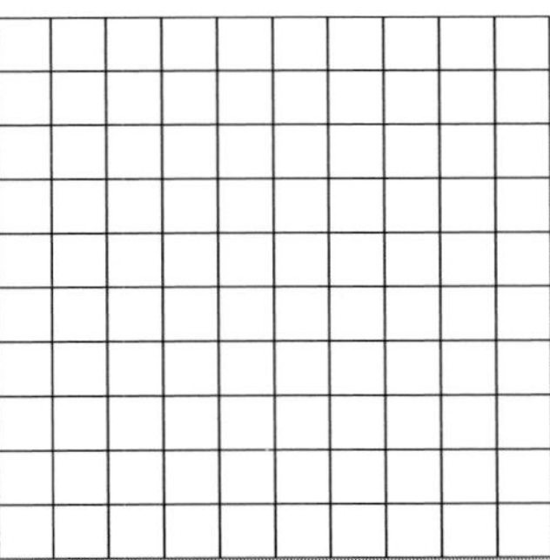

2. 16 yd^2

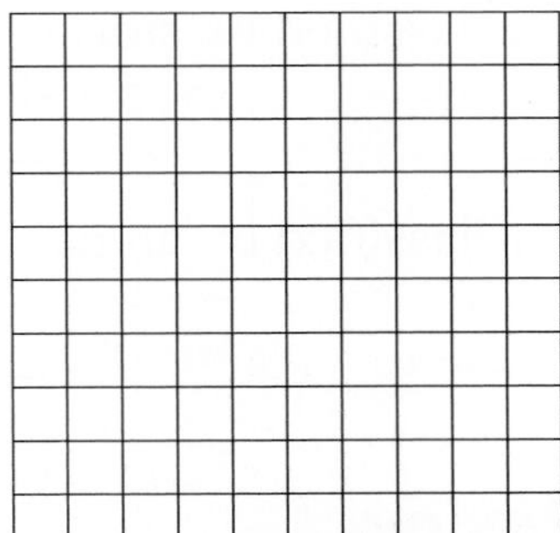

Find the area of each parallelogram.

3.

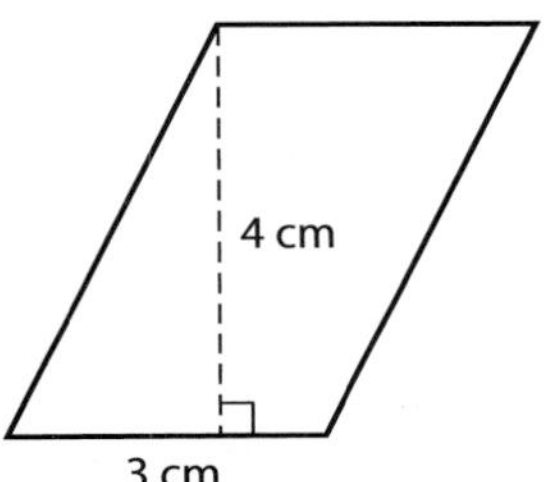

$A =$ _______________

4.

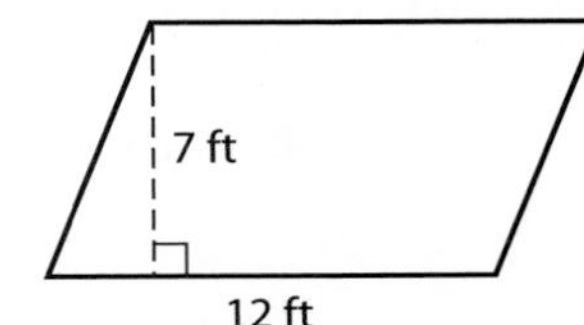

$A =$ _______________

5.

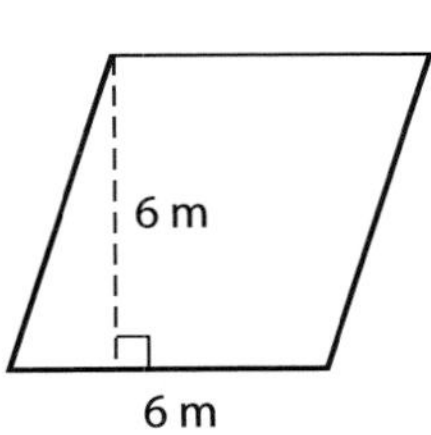

$A =$ _______________

6.

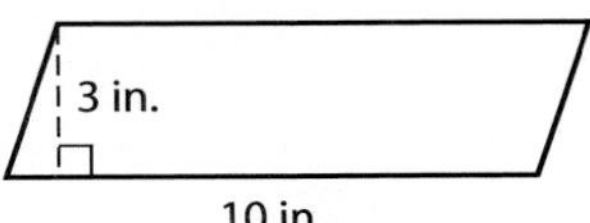

$A =$ _______________.

Solve.

7. **JEWELRY** Ratana made a metal pin for a necklace. The pin was shaped like a parallelogram; it had a base of 2 centimeters and a height of 6 centimeters. What was the area of the pin? _______________

Write the vocabulary word that completes the sentence.

8. _______________ is the number of square units needed to cover the surface enclosed by a geometric figure.

Chapter 5

Lesson 5-6

NAME ______________________ DATE ______________

Vocabulary and English Language Development

Activate Prior Knowledge

1 How are triangles classified by sides?

________________ ________________ ________________

2 How are triangles classified by angles?

________________ ________________ ________________

Definition Review

The formula for finding the area of a triangle is $A = \frac{1}{2}b \times h$.

Draw and label triangles with bases 4 units and heights 3 units.

3 a right triangle

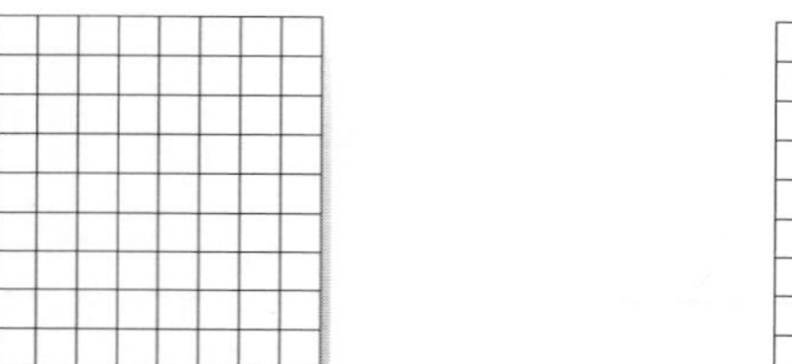

4 an acute triangle

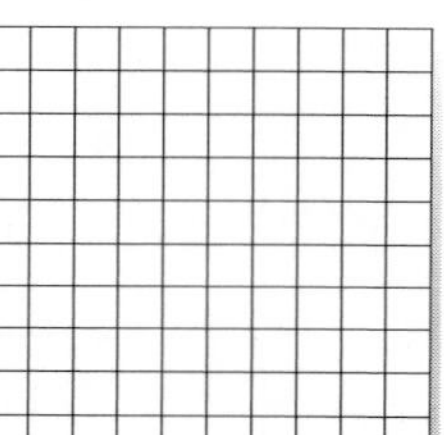

5 an obtuse triangle

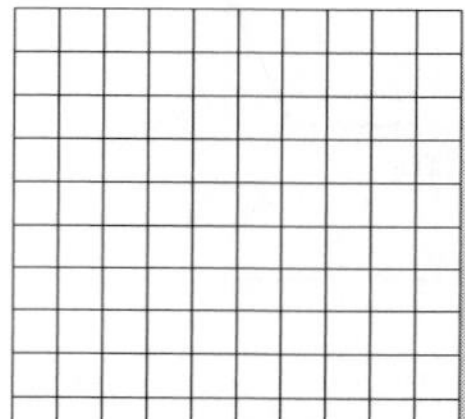

6 What is the area of each of these triangles? ________________

Application

Follow the directions for the activity.

- Students work individually. Use a 3×5 notecard.
- Draw a triangle on the notecard, using one entire side of the card as the base and touching the other as the height.
- Cut out the drawn triangle, and keep the remaining pieces.
- Tape together the remaining pieces to form another triangle. This triangle should be congruent to the one that was cut out.
- Compare your triangles with your classmates and discuss how the area formula for a triangle relates to the area of a rectangle.

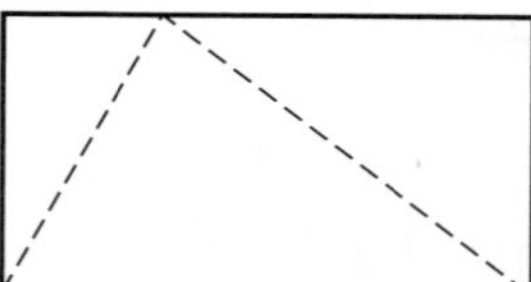

Lesson 5-6

NAME ______________________ DATE ______________

Skills Practice

Draw a triangle that has the given area.

1 16 units^2

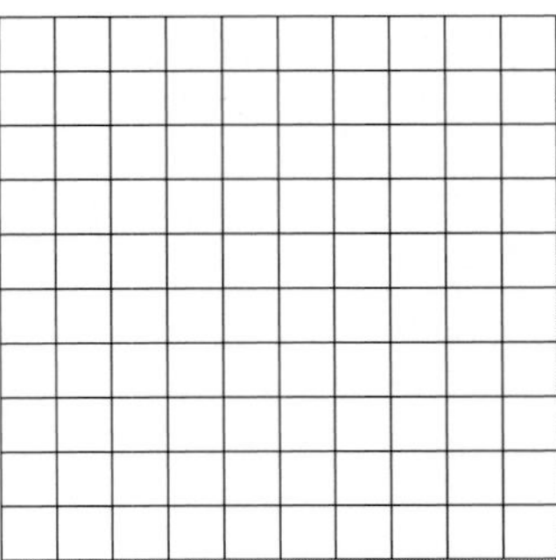

2 24 units^2

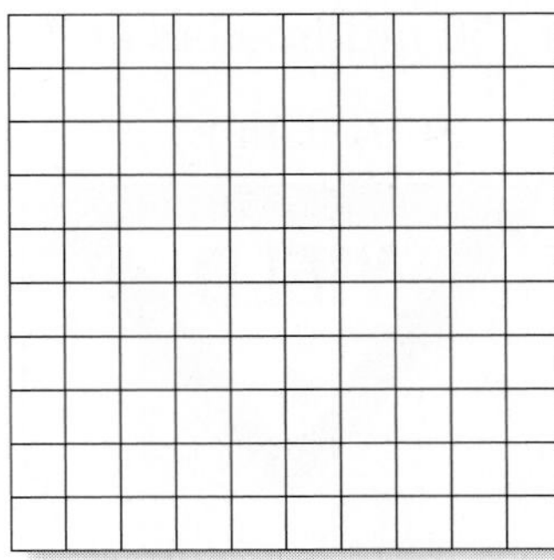

Find the area of each triangle.

3 The base is ______________.

The height is ______________.

$A = \frac{1}{2} \times b \times h$

$A = \frac{1}{2} \times$ __________ $\times$ __________

$A =$ __________

The area of the triangle is ______________.

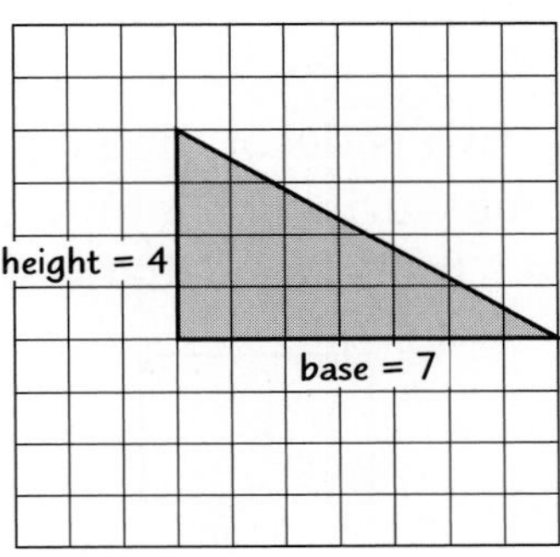

4

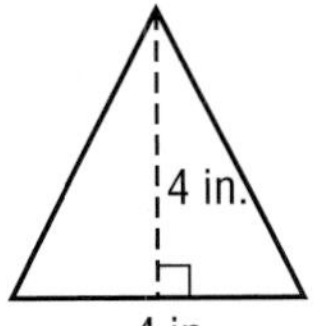

The area of the triangle is

______________________.

5

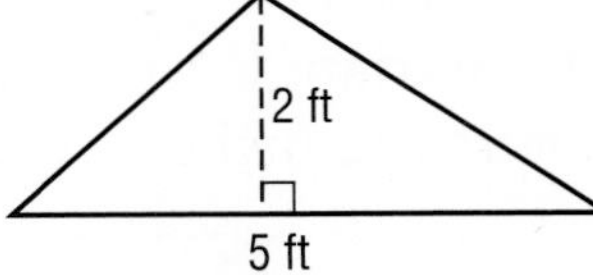

The area of the triangle is

______________________.

6

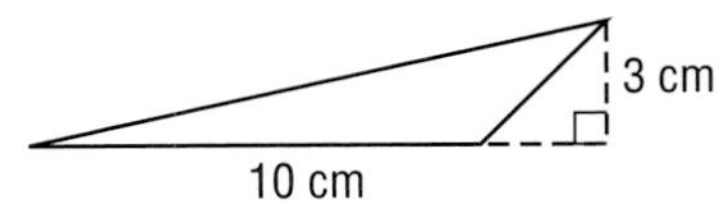

The area of the triangle is

______________________.

7

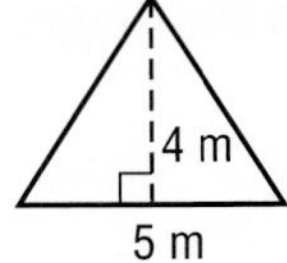

The area of the triangle is

______________________.

Chapter 5

NAME ______________________ DATE ______________

Problem-Solving Practice

Solve.

1 **SIGNS** A yield sign is in the shape of an equilateral triangle (a triangle with three equal sides). What is the area of this yield sign if it has a base of 750 millimeters and a height of 650 millimeters? ______

2 **LOGOS** A company's logo is the shape of a right triangle. The base and height of the logo are each 2 yards long. What is the area of the logo? ______

3 **SCRAPBOOKING** Eva is decorating a page in her scrapbook. She took a rectangle measuring 6 centimeters by 9 centimeters and cut it in half to make 2 triangles. What is the area of each triangle? ______

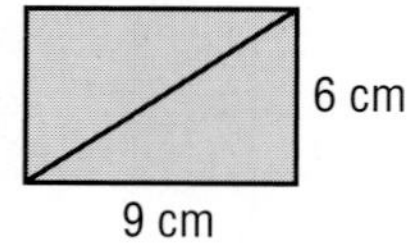

4 **BILLIARDS** The balls in a table game are set inside a triangular shape. The sides of the triangle measure 14 inches and the height of the triangle measures 12 inches. What is the area of the triangle? ______

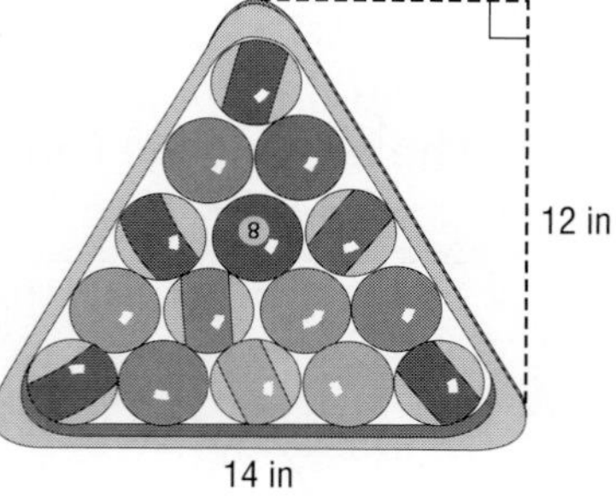

5 **DRAWING** Kyle drew a triangle on his paper. He then measured two sides and found that the base had a length of 6 centimeters and the height of the triangle was 11 centimeters. What is the area of the triangle that Kyle drew? ______

NAME ______________________ DATE ____________

Lesson 5-6

Homework Practice

Draw a triangle that has the area given.

1 $14\ m^2$

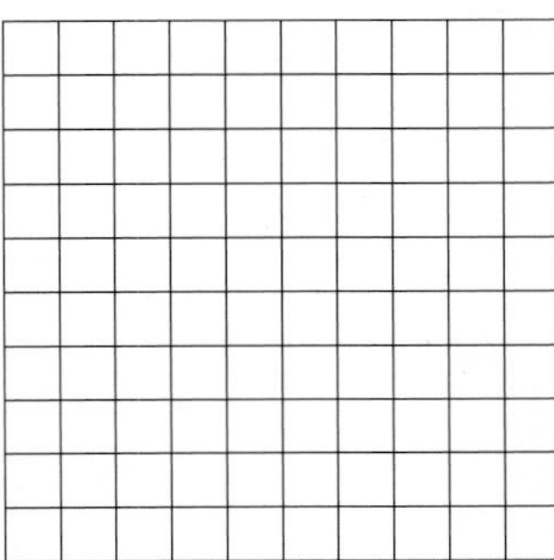

2 $8\ in^2$

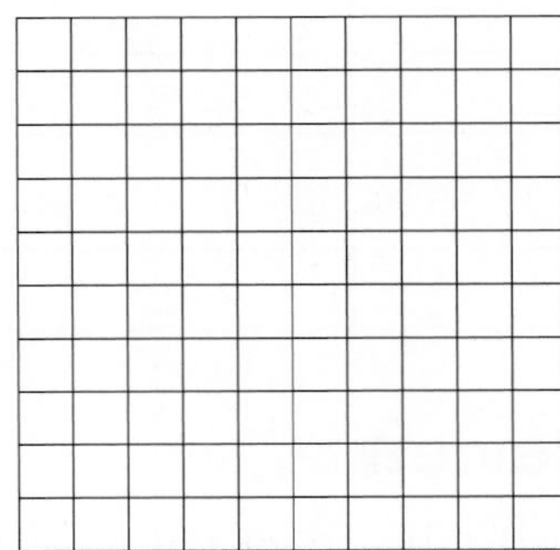

Find the area of each triangle.

3 The base is ____________.

The height is ____________.

The area of the triangle is ____________.

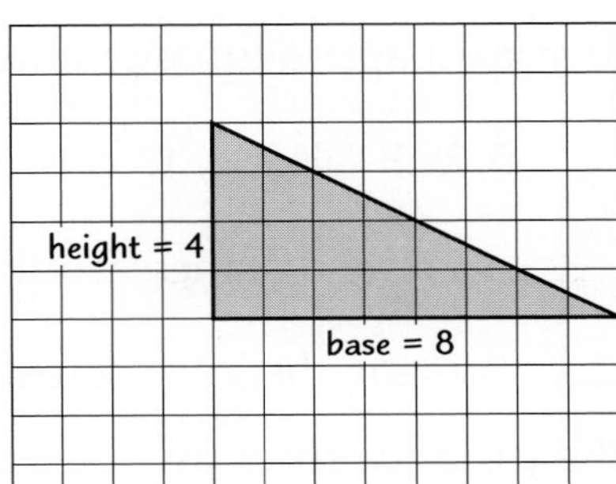

4

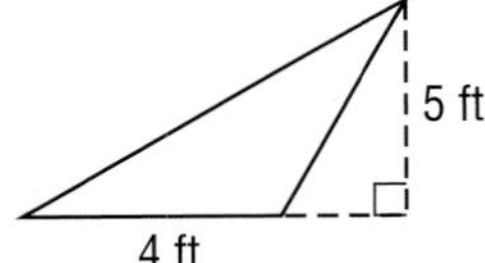

The area of the triangle is ____________.

5

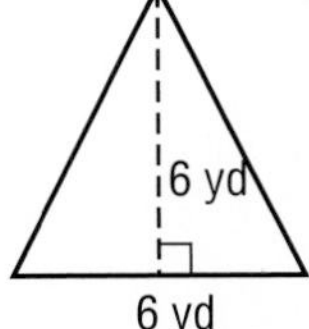

The area of the triangle is ____________.

Solve.

6 **SAILING** In sailing, a pennant is used to signal other boats. This pennant is shaped like a triangle with a base of 2 feet and a height of 4 feet. What is the area of the pennant? ____________

Write the vocabulary word that completes the sentence.

7 A polygon with three sides and three angles is a ____________.

Chapter 5

Lesson 5-7

NAME ______________________ DATE ____________

Vocabulary and English Language Development

Activate Prior Knowledge

List two examples of circles you may need to measure in your daily life.

1 ____

____

2 ____

____

Definition Review

It is not possible to write the exact value of π.
To calculate using π, we use approximate values.

3 Which number is an approximate value for π?

A 2.9 **B** 29.9 **C** 3.14 **D** 31.4

4 ______________ is the distance around a circle.

5 ______________ is the distance across a circle through its center.

6 A radius is the distance from the ______________ of a circle to any point on the circle.

Match to complete each formula.

7 $d =$ ________ πr^2

8 $C =$ ________ $2r$

9 $A =$ ________ πd

Application

Follow the directions for the activity.

- Select a measurement for the radius of a circle. Draw a circle with this radius on grid paper.
- Calculate the circle's diameter and area using this radius.
- Find an approximate area by making a square around the circle and then finding the area of the square. The circle should touch each side of the square.
- Repeat the activity two more times.
- Discuss your findings.

NAME ______________________________ DATE ______________

Skills Practice

Identify the length of the radius and diameter of each circle.

1

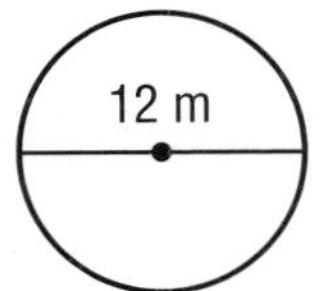

radius: ________ m

diameter: ________ m

2

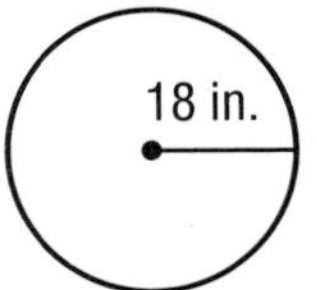

radius: ________ in.

diameter: ________ in.

Find the circumference and area of each circle. Use 3.14 for π.

3

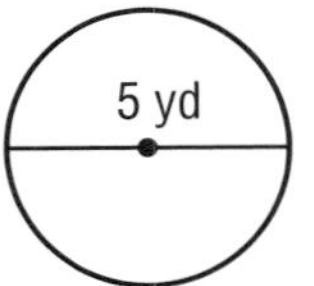

$d =$ ________ yd

$C = \pi d$

$C = 3.14 \times$ ________

$C =$ ________

$r =$ ________ yd

$A = \pi r^2$

$A = 3.14 \times$ ________

$A = 3.14 \times$ ________

$A =$ ________

The circumference of the circle is about ________ yd and the area of the circle is about ________ yd^2.

4

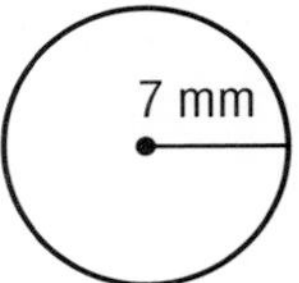

$d =$ ________ mm

$C = \pi d$

$C = 3.14 \times$ ________

$C =$ ________

$r =$ ________ mm

$A = \pi r^2$

$A = 3.14 \times$ ________

$A = 3.14 \times$ ________

$A =$ ________

The circumference of the circle is about ________ mm and the area of the circle is about ________ mm^2.

5

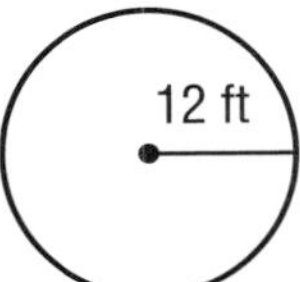

The circumference of the circle is about ________ ft and the area of the circle is about ________ ft^2.

10 m

The circumference of the circle is about ________ m and the area of the circle is about ________ m^2.

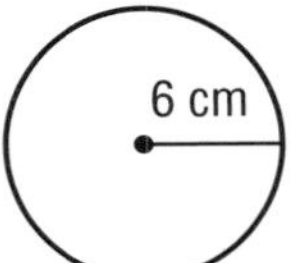

$C \approx$ ____________

$A \approx$ ____________

8

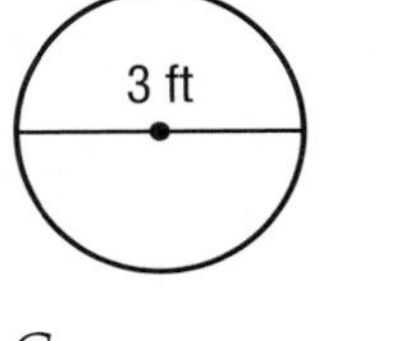

$C \approx$ ____________

$A \approx$ ____________

NAME ______________________ DATE ______________

Lesson 5-7

Problem-Solving Practice

Solve.

1. **HATS** Yori bought a new hat. The diameter of the hat is 7 inches. What is the circumference of the hat? ____________

2. **TABLES** Luke is painting the top of a large circular table. The diameter of the table is 6 feet. What is the area of the table?

3. **EXERCISE** Fiona jogs around the lake every morning. What is the circumference of the lake? ____________

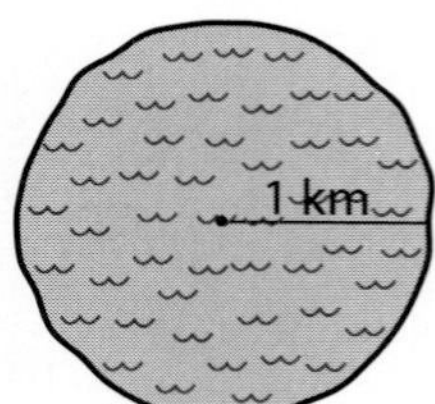

4. **BIOLOGY** Omar is transferring cells to this Petri dish. What is the area of the Petri dish? ____________

5. **WHEELS** Nestor is changing his bicycle wheels so that they have a diameter of 15 inches. What is the circumference of one of his new wheels? ____________

6. **PIZZA** Lani made a pizza with a diameter of 12 inches. What is its area? ____________

NAME ______ DATE ______

Lesson 5-7

Homework Practice

Find the circumference and area of each circle. Use 3.14 for π.

1 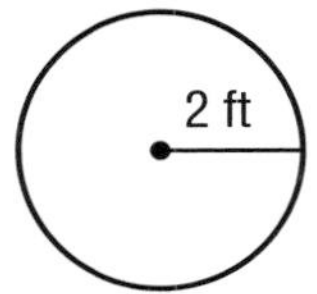

The circumference of the circle is about ______ ft and the area of the circle is about ______ ft^2.

2 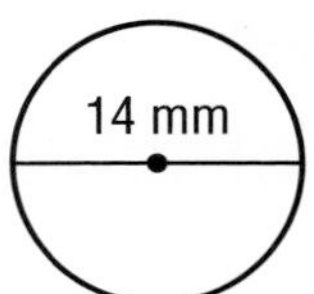

The circumference of the circle is about ______ mm and the area of the circle is about ______ mm^2.

3 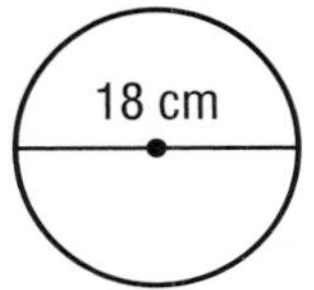

The circumference of the circle is about ______ cm and the area of the circle is about ______ cm^2.

4 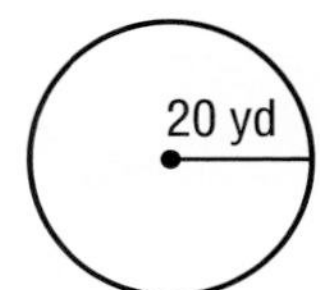

The circumference of the circle is about ______ yd and the area of the circle is about ______ yd^2.

Chapter 5

Solve.

5 **PONDS** Kimoko has a circular fish pond in her backyard. It has a diameter of 7 feet. What is the area of Kimoko's fish pond? ______

6 **RIBBON** Pearl wants to put a ribbon around a basket with a radius of 4 inches. What is the circumference of the basket? ______

Vocabulary Review

Write the vocabulary word(s) that completes the sentence.

7 The value of ______ is approximately 3.14. It is the ratio of the ______ of a circle to the ______ of the same circle.

8 A ______ is the set of all points in a plane that are the same distance from a given point called the ______.

NAME ____________________ DATE ____________

Chapter 6

Foldables Study Organizer

Dinah Zike's Foldables

Make this Foldable to help you organize your notes on three-dimensional figures.

1. Begin with one sheet of 11″ × 17″ paper. Fold the paper in fourths lengthwise.

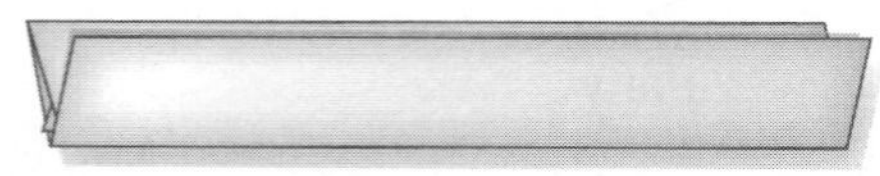

2. Open and fold a 2″ tab along the short side.

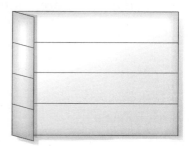

3. Draw lines along the folds and label as shown.

Ch. 6	Rectangular Prisms
Draw Examples	
Find Volume	
Find Surface Area	

TAKING NOTES

As you read through the chapter, use your Foldable to organize your notes about three-dimensional figures.

USING YOUR FOLDABLE

As you study, use your Foldable to draw examples, record formulas, and other information in the cells of the table.

USING YOUR FOLDABLE

Work with a partner. One student draws and labels a figure from the chapter. The second student states a relevant formula. Do this until each student has solved several problems.

NAME ______________________ DATE ______________

Games and Puzzles

Original Thinking

What You Need

- Game Sheet
- Clock or watch

Number of Players

3–4

DIRECTIONS

- All students have exactly two minutes to list on their game sheet every item they can think of that is shaped like a rectangular prism. Students should not let other students see what items they write down.
- When time is up, one student in the group reads the items on their list, one at a time. If no one else thought of that item, the student circles the item. If someone else has the same item, both players cross out that item.
- The next student reads the items that are not yet crossed out on their list, circling the items no one else thought of, and crossing off those that someone else also thought of.
- The remaining students read any remaining items on their list, following the same procedure. The number of items a player has circled is the number of points they have earned for that round.
- Repeat this process for cylinders, spheres, and cones.

- **Who Wins?** The player with the greatest total number of points wins.

Chapter 6

NAME ____________________ DATE ____________

Original Thinking Game Sheet

Rectangular Prisms	Cylinders
Spheres	**Cones**

NAME ______________________ DATE ______________

Lesson 6-1

Vocabulary and English Language Development

Activate Prior Knowledge

Draw each figure.

1 rectangle

2 square

3 trapezoid

4 rhombus

Definition Review

Complete each statement.

5 The flat side of a three-dimensional figure is called a ______________.

6 The line segment where two faces of a three-dimensional figure meet is called an ______________.

7 The point on a three-dimensional figure where three or more edges meet is called a ______________.

Application

Draw a line matching each object below with the figure listed at the right.

rectangular prism

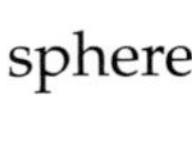

sphere

cone

cube

cylinder

Chapter 6

Lesson 6-1

NAME ______________________ DATE ______________

Skills Practice

Find the number of faces, vertices, and edges.

1
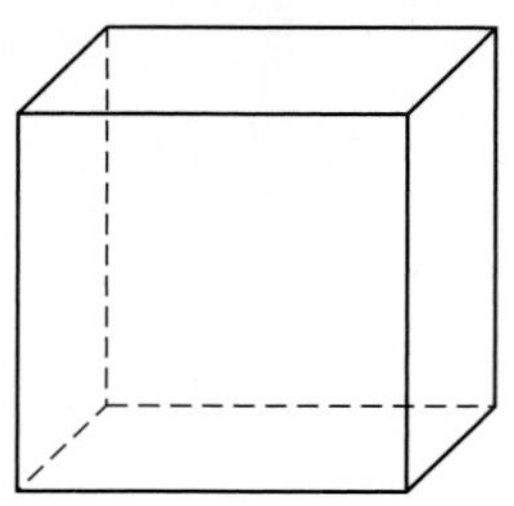

faces ______

vertices ______

edges ______

2
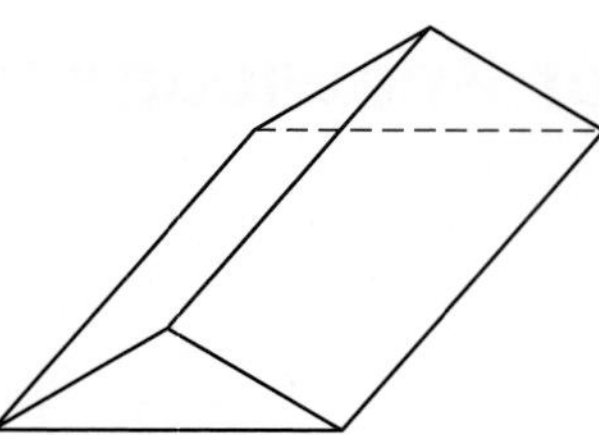

faces ______

vertices ______

edges ______

3
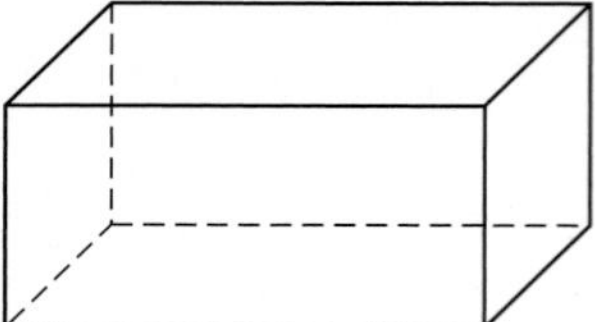

faces ______

vertices ______

edges ______

4
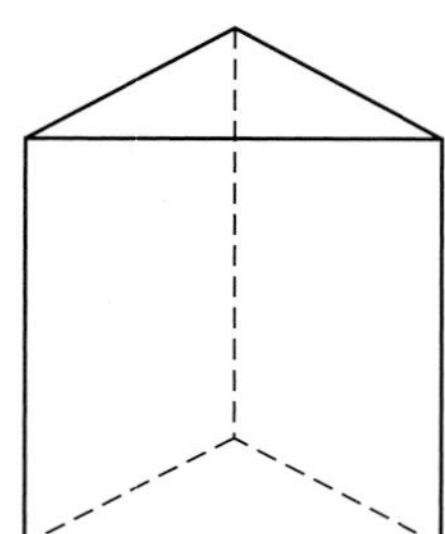

faces ______

vertices ______

edges ______

Identify each three-dimensional figure.

5
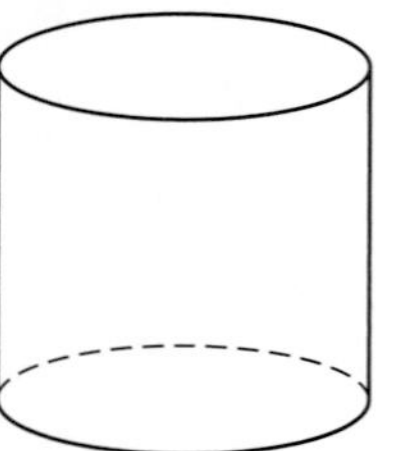

____

6
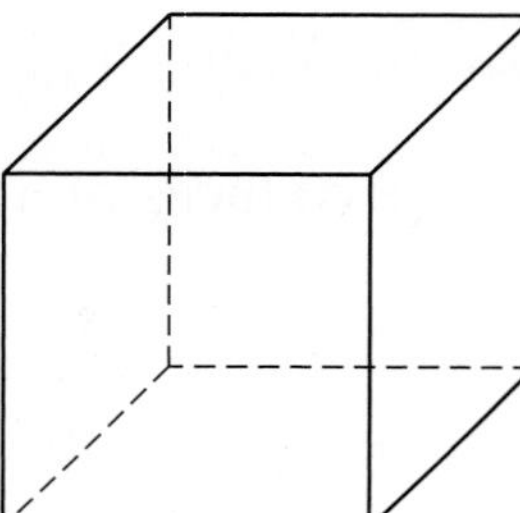

____

7
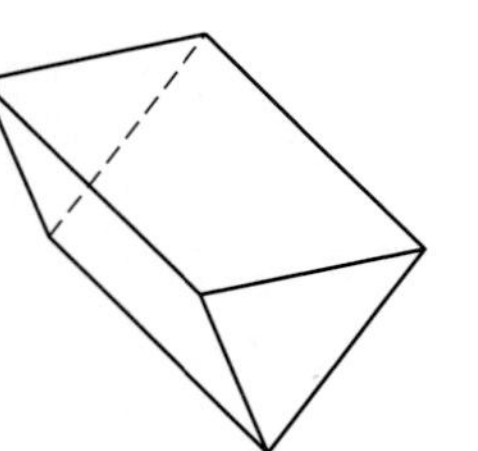

____

8
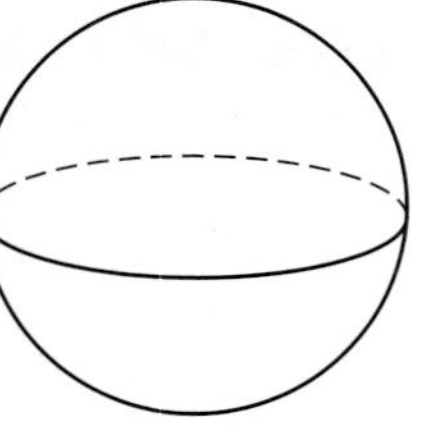

____

9
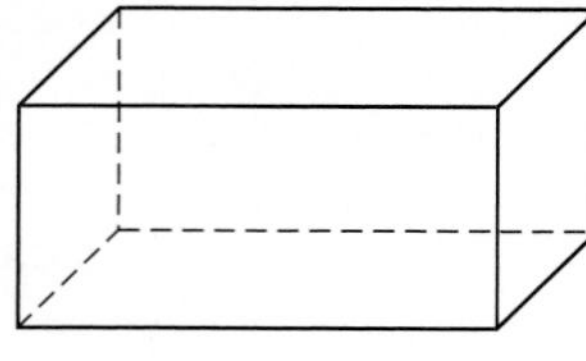

____

10
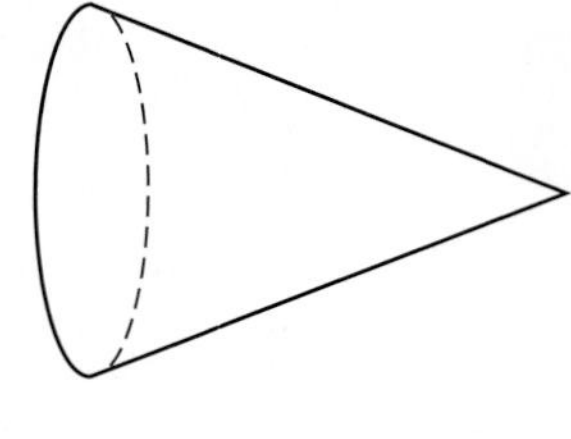

____

NAME ______________________ DATE ______________

Lesson 6-1

Problem-Solving Practice

Solve.

1. **DRAWING** Keela drew the figure below. What figure did Keela draw? ____________

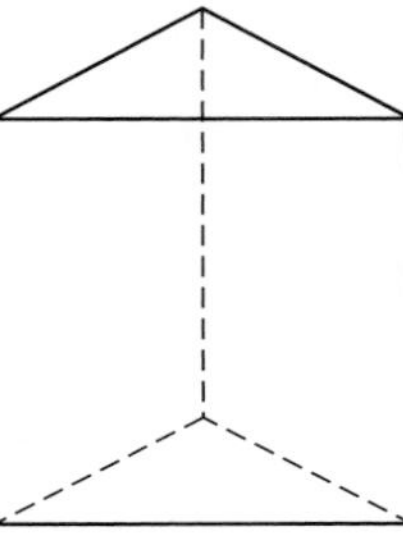

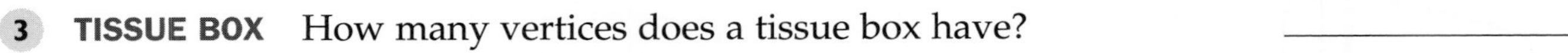

2. **GROCERY STORE** Max was stacking the shelves in the grocery store with cans of tomato sauce. What figure is a can of tomato sauce? ____________

3. **TISSUE BOX** How many vertices does a tissue box have? ____________

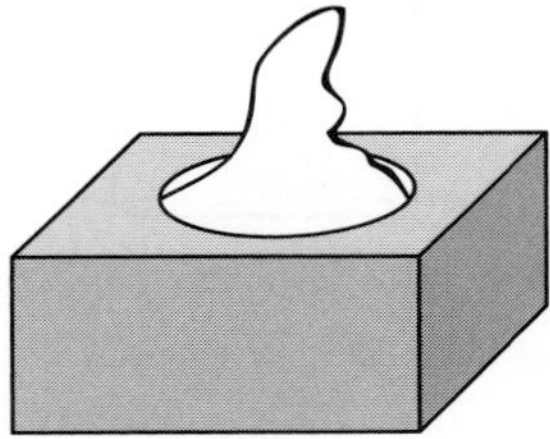

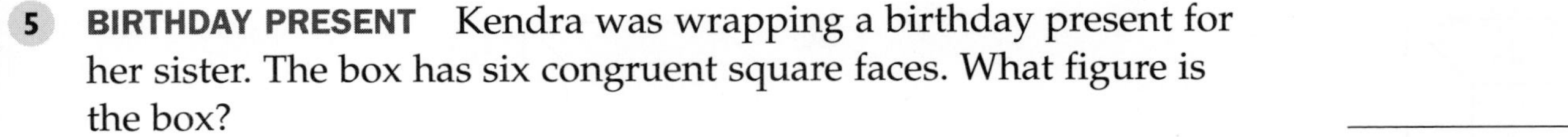

4. **SOCCER** Alexi was playing soccer. What figure is a soccer ball? ____________

5. **BIRTHDAY PRESENT** Kendra was wrapping a birthday present for her sister. The box has six congruent square faces. What figure is the box? ____________

6. **PENCIL BOX** Gary made this pencil box in shop class. How many edges does it have? ____________

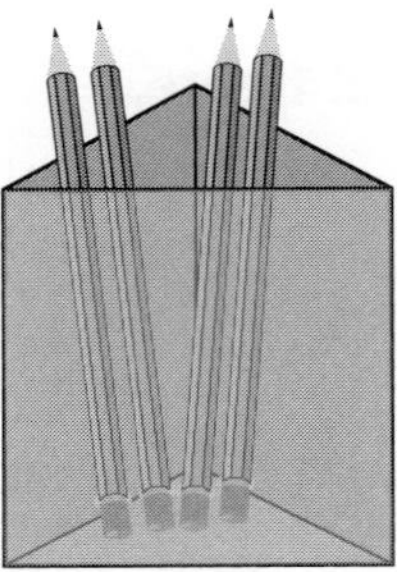

7. **PARTY HAT** Irma made party hats for her friends. Each hat has a circular base and one curved surface from the base to the vertex. What figure are the party hats? ____________

Chapter 6

NAME ______________________________ DATE ______________

Lesson 6-1

Homework Practice

Find the number of faces, vertices, and edges.

1 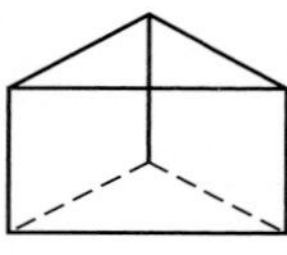

faces ______

vertices ______

edges ______

2 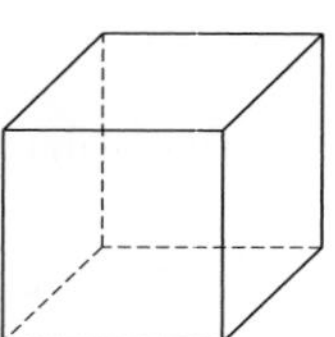

faces ______

vertices ______

edges ______

3

faces ______

vertices ______

edges ______

4

faces ______

vertices ______

edges ______

Identify each three-dimensional figure.

5 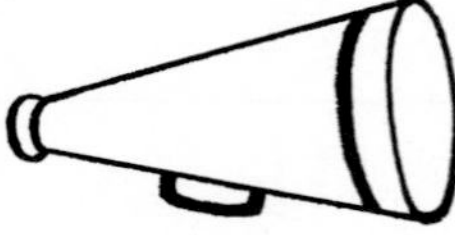

____

6 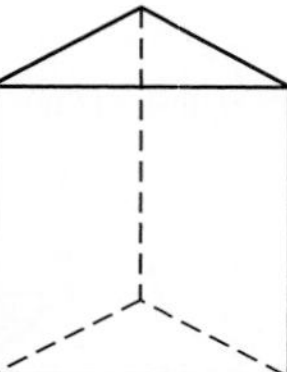

____

7 

____

8 

____

9 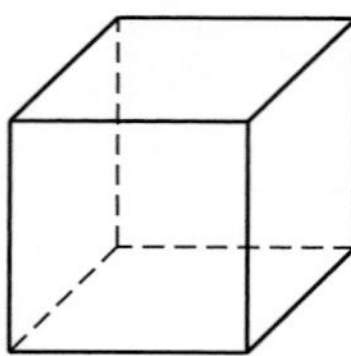

____

10 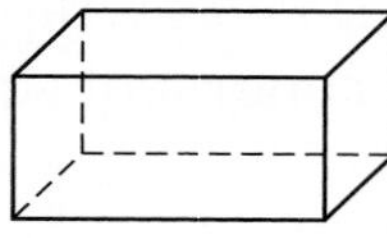

____

Read each description. Identify the three-dimensional figure.

11 The figure has one circular base. ______________

12 The figure has six congruent faces. ______________

13 **LAMP SHADE** Maria's lamp shade has two circular bases and a curved surface connecting them. What shape is the lamp shade? ______________

14 **BUILDING** Ralph works in a building that has two congruent triangular faces and three congruent rectangular faces. What shape is Ralph's building? ______________

Lesson 6-2

NAME ________________________________ DATE ______________

Vocabulary and English Language Development

Activate Prior Knowledge

Find the surface area.

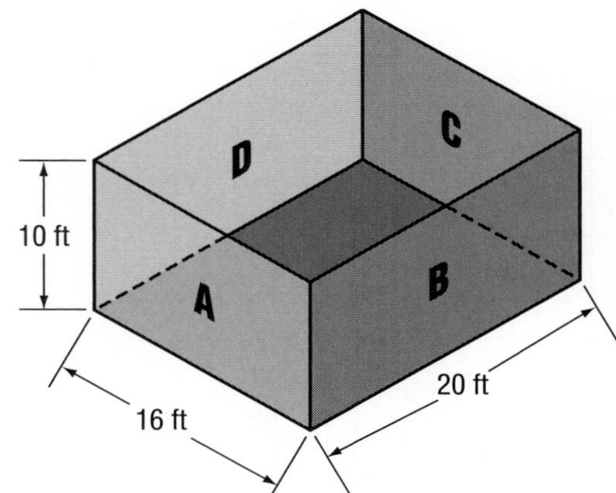

1 Find the area of wall *A*. ____________

2 Which wall has an area equal to wall *A*? ____________

3 Find the area of wall *B*. ____________

4 Which wall has an area equal to wall *B*? ____________

5 Find the area of the ceiling. ____________

6 Aurelia is redecorating this room. She is going to paint all four walls and the ceiling. How much area will she paint in all, *not* including the floor? ____________

Definition Review

Complete each statement.

7 A ____________________ is a two-dimensional figure that can be used to build a three-dimensional figure.

8 ____________________ is the sum of the areas of all the surfaces (faces) of a three-dimensional figure.

Application

Follow the directions to create a cube.

- Students work individually. Each student needs a piece of thick, colored paper.
- Use a pencil and a ruler to draw the net of a cube with side lengths of 10 centimeters.
- Draw tabs which can be used to connect the sides of the cube. Example:
- Using a pair of scissors, cut out the net along exterior sides and tabs.
- Fold along all lines for sides and tabs.
- Using tape, connect tabs to form the cube.

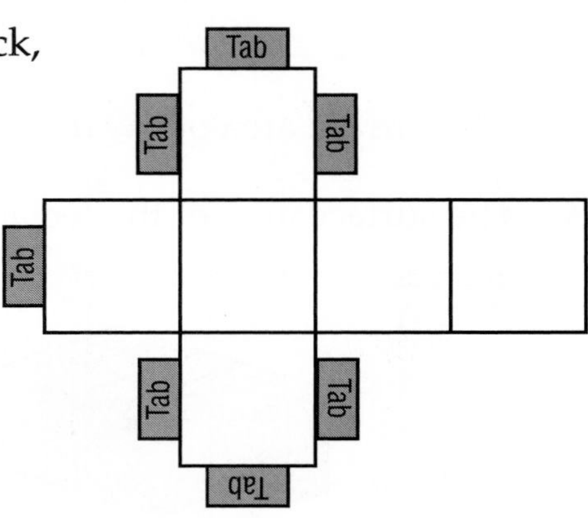

Lesson 6-2

NAME ______________________ DATE ____________

Skills Practice

Draw a net for a rectangular prism with the given length, width, and height.

1 $2 \times 4 \times 8$

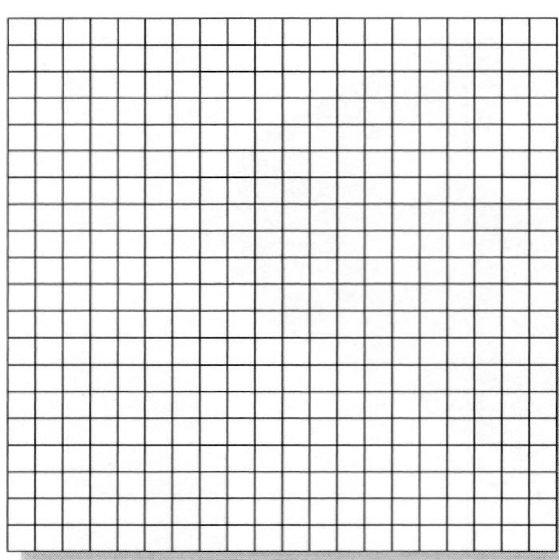

2 $3 \times 3 \times 10$

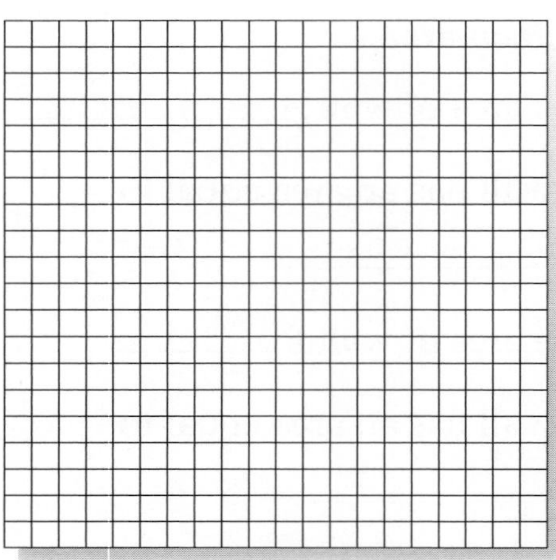

Find the surface area of each rectangular prism.

3 Find the area of faces A and F.

$A = l \times w$

$A =$ ______ $\times$ ______ $=$ ______

Find the area of faces B and D.

$A = l \times w$

$A =$ ______ $\times$ ______ $=$ ______

Find the area of faces C and E.

$A = l \times w$

$A =$ ______ $\times$ ______ $=$ ______

Find the sum of the areas of all faces.

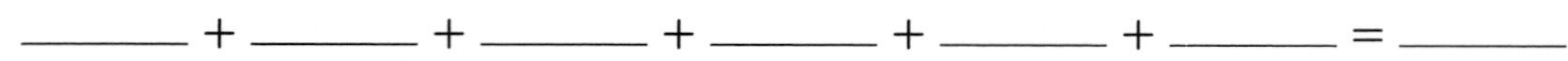

______ + ______ + ______ + ______ + ______ + ______ = ______

The surface area of the rectangular prism is ______ square units.

4 The surface area of the rectangular prism is ______ square units.

5 The surface area of the rectangular prism is ______ square units.

Lesson 6-2

NAME ______________________ DATE ______________

Problem-Solving Practice

Solve.

1 **PANELING** A practice room in a school music department is the shape of a cube. Each wall has length 8 feet. Sound proof panels must be placed on all four walls, the floor, and the ceiling of the room. How much paneling will the room require? ____________

2 **COLORS** Gregory made a color cube with a different color on each side. If each side measures 2 inches, what is the surface area of the cube? Draw a net for the cube.

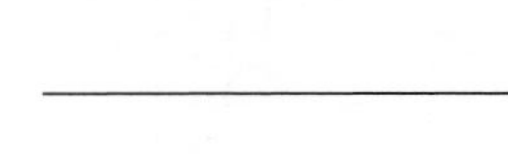

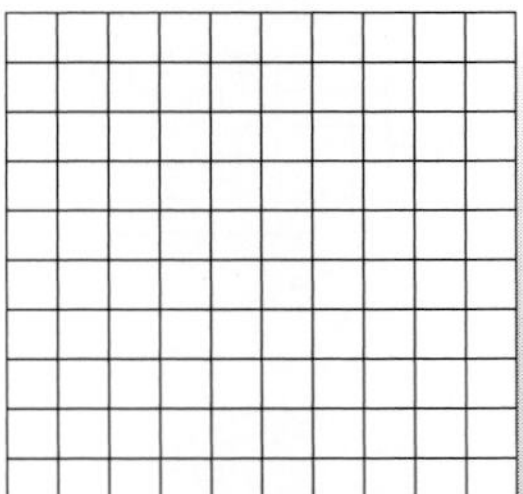

3 **GIFTS** Kenyi placed a rectangular-shaped gift in a box with the dimensions 30 centimeters by 30 centimeters by 5 centimeters. She then wrapped the box with paper. How much wrapping paper did she need?

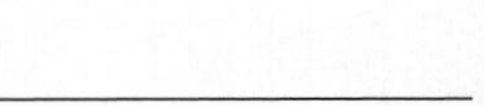

4 **PAINTING** When decorating a room, Nalin painted all the walls as well as the floor and ceiling. The dimensions of the room are 22 feet wide, 20 feet long, and 9 feet high. What surface area did he paint?

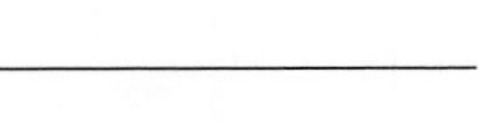

5 **GEOMETRY** What is the surface area of the number cube? ____________

6 **CHEESE** A grocer must wrap a block of cheese with dimensions 3 cm × 10 cm × 15 cm. What is the least amount of plastic wrap the grocer needs to wrap the block of cheese? ____________

7 **RACQUETBALL** When playing racquetball, the entire surface area of the room is used. A racquetball court has a width of 20 feet, a length of 40 feet, and a height of 20 feet. What is the total surface area of the racquetball court? ____________

Chapter 6

Lesson 6-2 Homework Practice

NAME ______________________ DATE ______________

Draw a net for a rectangular prism with the given length, width, and height.

1 $6 \times 2 \times 8$

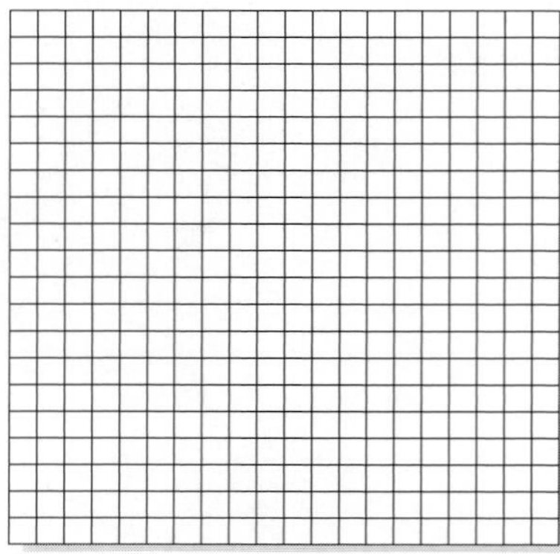

2 $3 \times 3 \times 5$

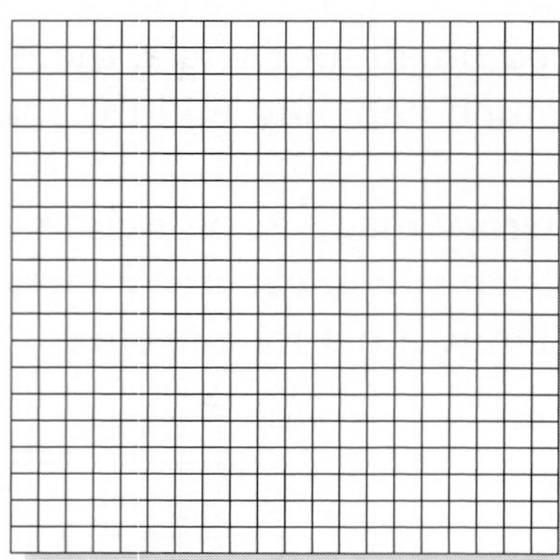

Find the surface area of each rectangular prism.

3

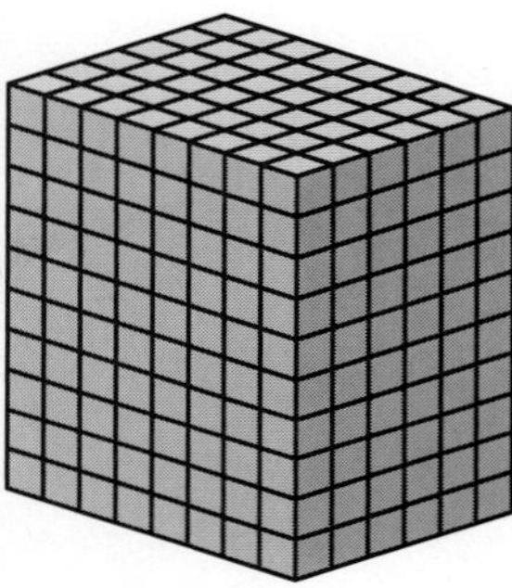

The surface area of the rectangular prism is ____________ square units.

4

The surface area of the rectangular prism is ____________ square units.

Solve.

5 **BLOCKS** Lourdes is playing with building blocks. One block is shaped like a rectangular prism with a length of 14 mm, a width of 40 mm, and a height of 80 mm. What is the surface area of the block?

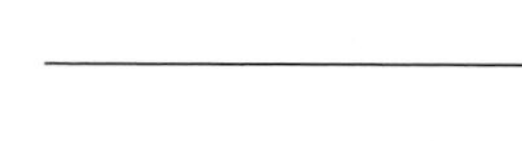

6 **GEOMETRY** A cube has sides of length 7 yards. What is the surface area of the cube?

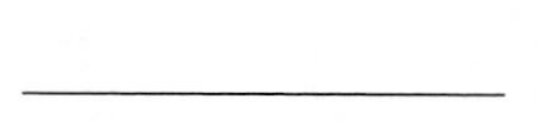

Write the vocabulary term that completes the sentence.

7 The sum of the areas of all the faces of a three-dimensional figure is called ______________.

8 A ______________ is a unit for measuring area.

NAME ______________________ DATE ______________

Lesson 6-3

Vocabulary and English Language Development

Activate Prior Knowledge

1 Draw 2 different rectangular prisms, each with the same surface area.

Definition Review

Complete each statement.

2 The amount of space a three-dimensional figure contains is the ______________ of the figure.

3 A ______________ is used to measure volume. It tells the number of cubes of a given size it will take to fill a three-dimensional figure.

Application

Use blocks or number cubes to create this figure.

4 Count the cubes to find the volume. ______________

5 What is the surface area? ______________

6 Rearrange the cubes to make another rectangular prism. What is te surface area? ______________

7 Did the volume change? ______________

8 Rearrange the cubes to make another rectangular prism. What ishe surface area? ______________

9 Did the volume change? ______________

Chapter 6

NAME ______________________ DATE ______________

Lesson 6-3

Skills Practice

Count the number of cubes in each rectangular prism.

1 

There are ________ cubes in the rectangular prism.

2 

There are ________ cubes in the rectangular prism.

Find the volume of each rectangular prism.

3 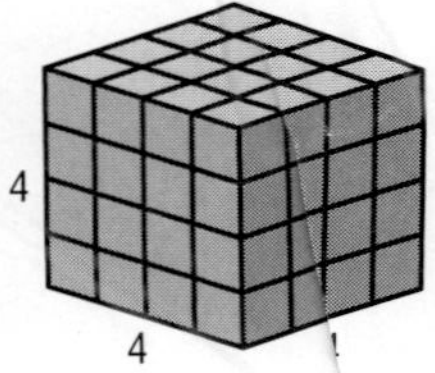

The volume of the rectangular prism is ________ cubic units.

4 

The volume of the rectangular prism is ________ cubic units.

5 

The volume of the rectangular prism is ________ cubic units.

6 

The volume of the rectangular prism is ________ cubic units.

7 

The volume of the rectangular prism is ________ cubic units.

8 

The volume of the rectangular prism is ________ cubic units.

NAME _______________ DATE _______________

Lesson 6-3

Problem-Solving Practice

Solve.

1 **GEOMETRY** What is the volume of the rectangular prism?

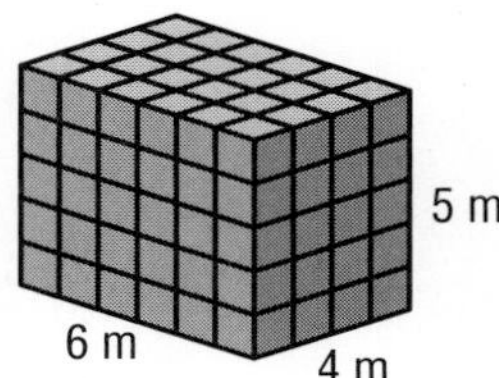

____

2 **APPLIANCES** The size of an appliance is determined by the volume of its interior space. What is the size of a toaster with a width of 5 inches, height of 6 inches, and depth of 7 inches?

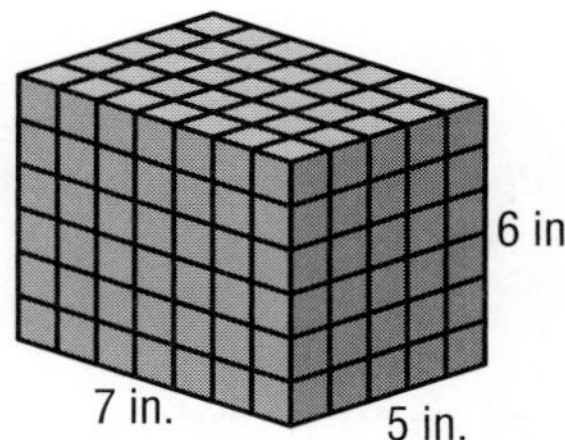

____

3 **TOYS** Macaro is playing with building blocks. He made the structure shown. How many blocks are in Macaro's structure?

____

4 **PACKAGING** A package is 6 inches by 6 inches by 8 inches. What is the volume of the package?

____

5 **GEOMETRY** What is the volume of a cube with sides of length 8 feet?

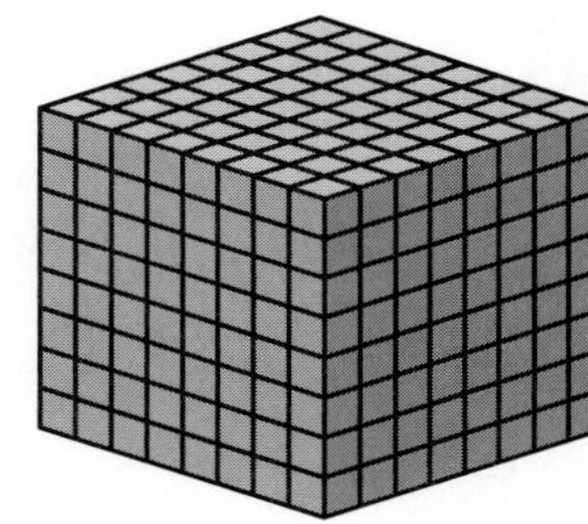

____

Chapter 6

Lesson 6-3

NAME ______________________________ DATE ______________

Homework Practice

How many cubes are in each rectangular prism?

1 

There are _______ cubes in the rectangular prism.

2 

There are _______ cubes in the rectangular prism.

Find the volume of each rectangular prism.

3 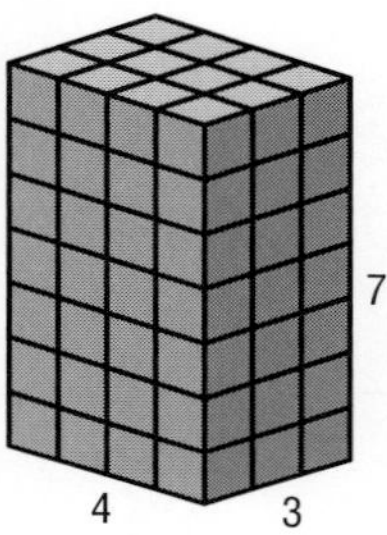

The volume of the rectangular prism is _______ cubic units.

4 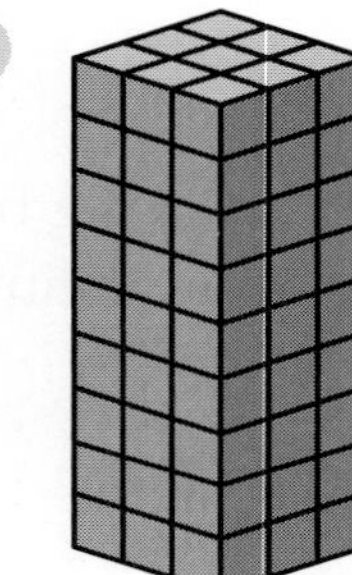

The volume of the rectangular prism is _______ cubic units.

5 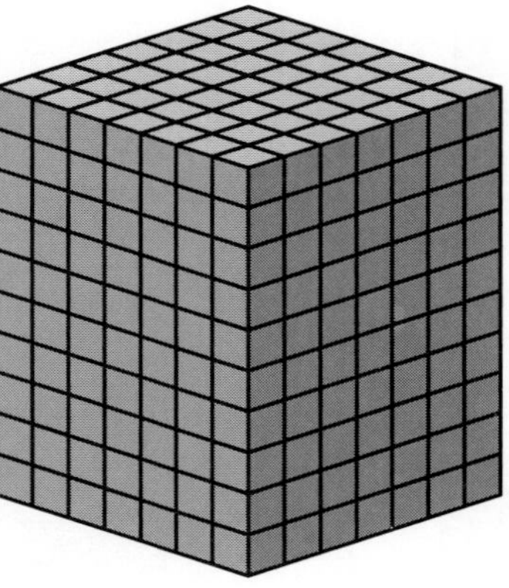

The volume of the rectangular prism is _______ cubic units.

6 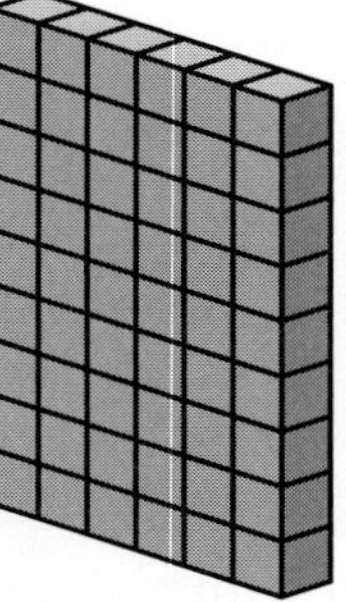

The volume of the rectangular prism is _______ cubic units.

Lesson 6-4

NAME ______________________ DATE ______________

Vocabulary and English Language Development

Activate Prior Knowledge

Find the surface area and volume of the rectangular prism using correct units.

1 What shape can be formed from the net?

____

What is the surface area of the figure?

____

What is the length, width, and height of the figure?

____

What is the volume of the figure?

____

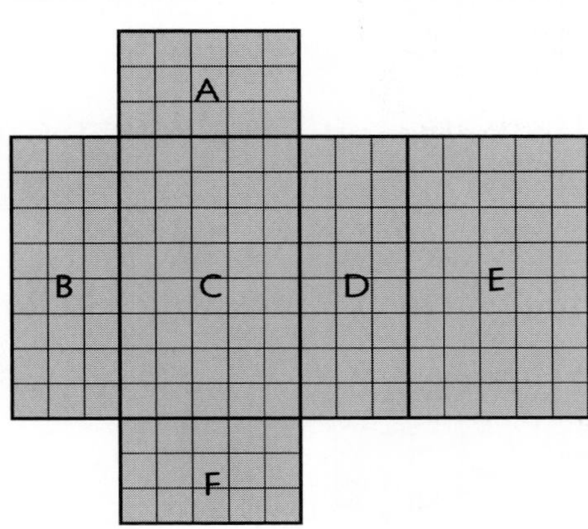

Definition Review

Match each vocabulary word to the description that best fits it.

2 cube ________ A. the amount of space a three-dimensional figure contains

3 volume ________ B. a unit for measuring volume

4 rectangular prism ________ C. solid figure with six rectangular faces

5 cubic unit ________ D. solid figure with six square faces

Chapter 6

Application

Follow the directions to play the game.

- Students play in groups of 3 or 4.
- The first student chooses a rectangular prism in the room, for which the volume can be found. (For example: room itself, a drawer, or a box.)
- Each student examines the prism and estimates its volume. Students write their estimated volumes.
- The first student then uses a ruler, or yard stick, to determine the actual volume of the prism.
- The student with the closest estimate wins the game.
- Repeat the game until all students choose and measure a prism.

NAME ____________________ DATE __________

Lesson 6-4 Skills Practice

Find the number of cubes in each rectangular prism.

1 

There are ________ cubes in the rectangular prism.

2 

There are ________ cubes in the rectangular prism.

Find the volume of each rectangular prism.

3 

$V = \ell \times w \times h$

$V =$ _____ $\times$ _____ $\times$ _____

$V =$ _____

The volume of the rectangular prism is ________ cubic units.

4 

$V = \ell \times w \times h$

$V =$ _____ $\times$ _____ $\times$ _____

$V =$ _____

The volume of the rectangular prism is ________ cubic units.

5 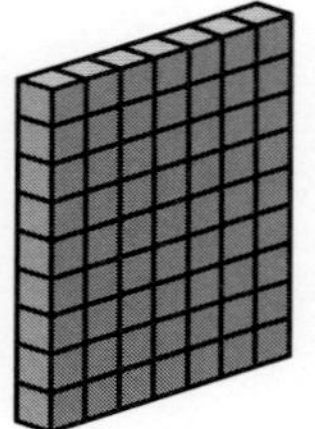

The volume of the rectangular prism is ________ cubic units.

6

The volume of the rectangular prism is ________ cubic units.

7 

The volume of the rectangular prism is ________ cubic units.

8 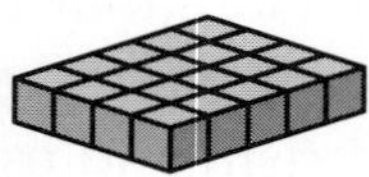

The volume of the rectangular prism is ________ cubic units.

Lesson 6-4

NAME ______________________ DATE ______________

Problem-Solving Practice

Solve.

1 **TOYS** Lina has a toy box in her room. What is the volume of the toy box? ____________

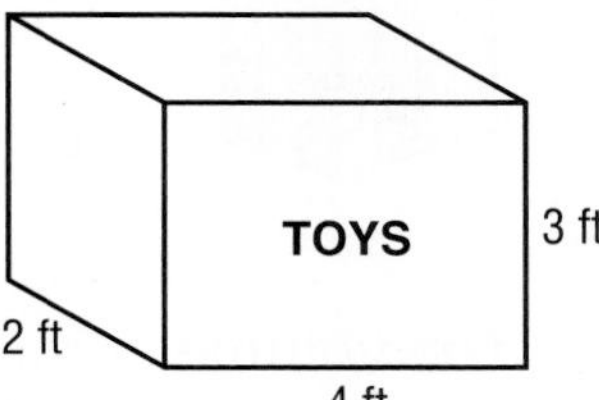

2 **CEREAL** What is the volume of the cereal box? ____________

3 **MOVING TRUCK** The Morris family is moving. To transport some of their belongings to the new house, they rent a moving truck that is 5 feet wide, 8 feet long, and 10 feet tall. What is the volume of the truck? ____________

4 **CLOSET** Robin has a large closet in her bedroom. The closet measures 3 feet by 10 feet, and it is 8 feet tall. What is the volume of Robin's closet? ____________

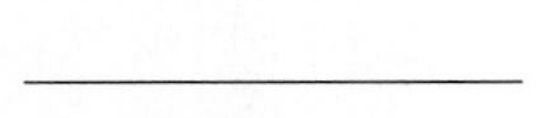

5 **MUSIC BOX** Kenji collects music boxes. Her favorite is one with a length of 3.5 inches, a width of 3.5 inches, and a height of 4 inches. What is the volume of Kenji's favorite music box? ____________

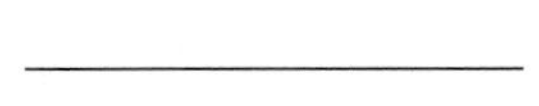

6 **AQUARIUM** The Batista family has pet fish in an aquarium with dimensions of 62 centimeters long, 31 centimeters wide, and 31 centimeters high. What is the volume of their aquarium? ____________

7 **SAND BOX** Scott is playing in his sandbox. He digs a rectangular hole that measures 5 inches wide, 11 inches long, and 1 inch deep. What is the volume of the hole? ____________

Lesson **6-4**

NAME ______________________________ DATE ______________

Homework Practice

Find the volume of each rectangular prism.

1 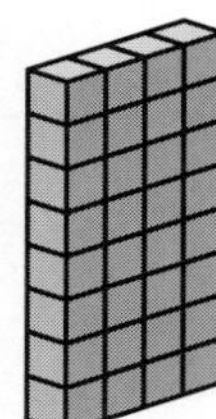

$V = \ell \times w \times h$

$V =$ _____ $\times$ _____ $\times$ _____

$V =$ _____

The volume of the rectangular prism is __________ cubic units.

2 

$V = \ell \times w \times h$

$V =$ _____ $\times$ _____ $\times$ _____

$V =$ _____

The volume of the rectangular prism is __________ cubic units.

Find the volume of each rectangular prism.

3 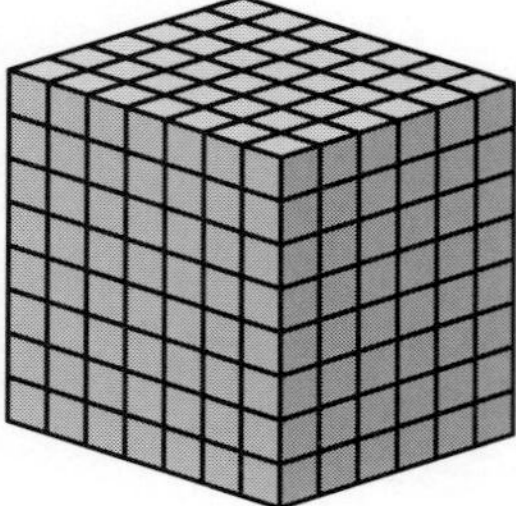

The volume of the rectangular prism is _______ cubic units.

4 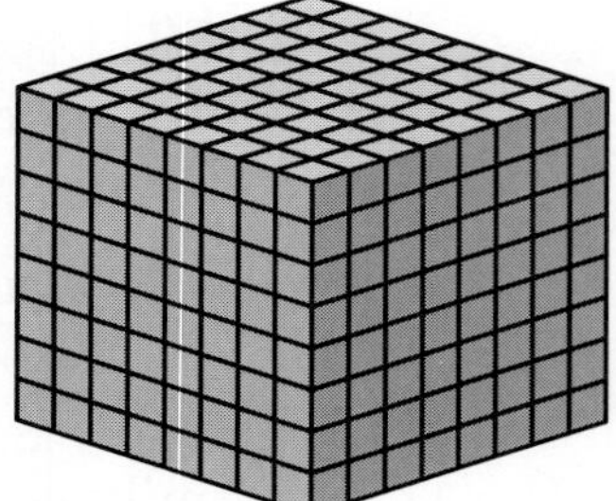

The volume of the cube is _______ cubic units.

5 

The volume of the rectangular prism is _______ cubic units.

6 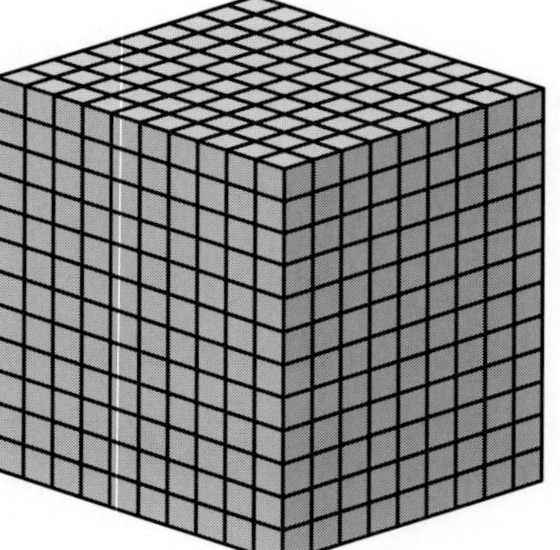

The volume of the rectangular prism is _______ cubic units.

Solve.

7 **COTTON** A bale of cotton is measured by width, length, and height. If the width of the bale is 20 inches, the length is 54 inches, and the height is 33 inches, what is the volume of the cotton bale? __________

NAME ______________________________ DATE ______________

Foldables Study Organizer

Dinah Zike's Foldables

Make this Foldable as a study guide where you will write about whole numbers and integers.

1. Begin with five sheets of notebook paper. Staple the five sheets together to form a booklet.

2. Cut tabs. Make each one 2 lines longer than the one before it.

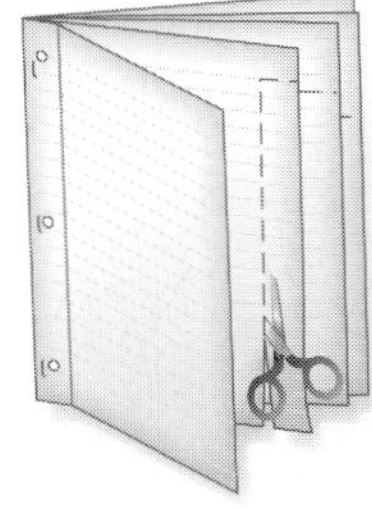

3. Write the chapter title on the cover and label each tab with the lesson number.

TAKING NOTES
As you read through the chapter, use your Foldable to organize your notes about whole numbers and integers.

USING YOUR FOLDABLE
As you study, use your Foldable to write examples, record key concepts, define terms, and take notes. Record what you learn about the parts of each lesson that you find most difficult.

USING YOUR FOLDABLE
Work with a partner. Take turns choosing a number in the millions, then ask your partner to write the number in standard and word form.

NAME ______________________ DATE ______________

Chapter 7

Games and Puzzles

Place-Value War

What You Need
- Number Cube
- Place Value War Game Sheets

Number of Players
2

GET READY: Each player needs a game sheet.

DIRECTIONS

FOR ROUNDS 1–2
- One player rolls the number cube.
- Each player writes the number rolled in one of the blanks on his or her game sheet for Round 1.
- The other player rolls the cube, and each player writes the number rolled in one of the six remaining blanks.
- Play continues until all seven blanks are filled.
- The person with the greater number scores 1 point.
- Repeat.

FOR ROUNDS 3–4
- Play continues as before, but now the person with the smaller number scores 1 point.
- **Who Wins?** The person with the greater number of points is the winner.

Chapter 7

NAME ____________________ DATE ____________

Place Value War Game Sheets

Round 1

____,	____	____	____,	____	____	____
millions	hundred thousands	ten thousands	thousands	hundreds	tens	ones

Round 2

____,	____	____	____,	____	____	____
millions	hundred thousands	ten thousands	thousands	hundreds	tens	ones

Round 3

____,	____	____	____,	____	____	____
millions	hundred thousands	ten thousands	thousands	hundreds	tens	ones

Round 4

____,	____	____	____,	____	____	____
millions	hundred thousands	ten thousands	thousands	hundreds	tens	ones

Lesson 7-1

NAME ______________________ DATE ______________

Vocabulary and English Language Development

Activate Prior Knowledge

Write each number correctly in word form.

1. 800 ______________________

2. 92 ______________________

3. 510 ______________________

Definition Review

4. Complete the **place value** chart by labeling the **place values**.

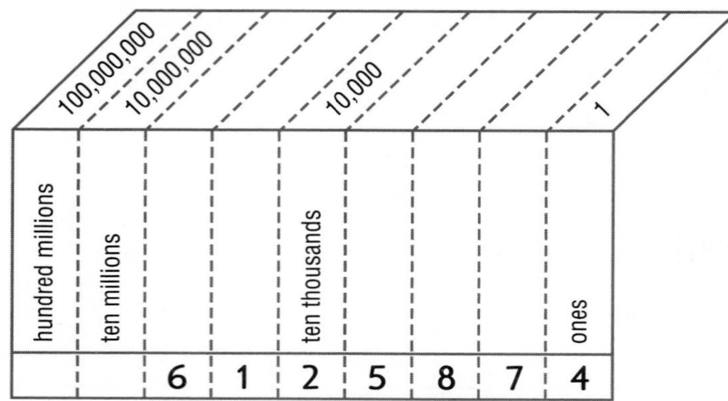

To help you read and write numbers, **place values** are grouped into **periods. Periods** are separated by commas.

Application

Consider the number 1,234,567. Answer the questions.

5. In what **period** are the digits 567? ______________

6. In what **period** are the digits 234? ______________

7. What is used to separate **periods**? ______________

8. What is the **place value** of the 2? ______________

9. What is the **place value** of the 1? ______________

NAME ______________________ DATE ____________

Skills Practice

Use the place-value chart to answer each question. Then write each number in the chart.

1. How many zeros are in 8 million? ____________
2. How many zeros are in 5 thousands? ____________
3. How many zeros are in 2 hundred thousands? ____________

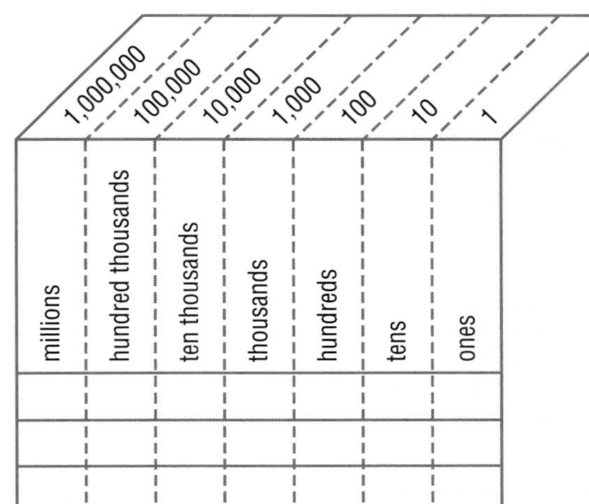

Write each number in word form.

4. 7,050,278 ______ million ______ thousand ______

____

____

5. 246,935 ____

____

6. 5,045,540 ____

____

Write each number in standard form.

7. eight hundred thirty-six million, two hundred fifty ____________
8. five million, two hundred thirty-seven thousand, forty ____________
9. three million, two hundred fifty thousand, two ____________

NAME ______________________ DATE ____________

Lesson 7-1

Problem-Solving Practice

Solve.

1 **PHYSICS** The speed of sound is thirteen thousand, five hundred four inches per second. What is this speed written in standard form?

____

2 **SPACE** The moon is 384,400 kilometers from Earth. Write this distance in word form.

____

3 **WRITING** Juanita wrote 7,025,345 in words on her paper. What mistake did Juanita make if she wrote, "seven million, twenty-five, three hundred forty-five"? ______________________________

____

4 **AREA** Australia is the smallest continent in the world. It has an area of 7,617,930 square kilometers. Write the area of Australia in word form. ______________________________

____

5 **GEOGRAPHY** The table shows the highest points in Asia, Africa, and North America.

Location	Height (in feet)
Kilimanjaro – Africa	19,340
Everest – Asia	29,035
McKinley – North America	20,320

What is the height of Everest in word form? ______________________________

____

Of these three locations, which is the lowest point? ______________________________

____

6 **AGE** Jeremy used a calculator to find his age in minutes. The screen shows 13147200. Write the number in standard form, (with commas), and in word form.

Standard form: ______________________________

Word form: ______________________________

____

Lesson 7-1

NAME ________________ DATE ________________

Homework Practice

What is the missing number in each equation?

1. 2,000,000 + 30,000 + __________ + 400 = 2,035,400

2. 1,000,000 + 700,000 + __________ = 1,703,000

3. 6,000,000 + __________ + 20 + 5 = 6,000,125

Write each number in standard form.

4. twenty million, three hundred fifty thousand, forty __________

5. one hundred twenty-seven million, three hundred fifty-eight __________

6. nine million, four hundred five thousand, seven __________

Write each number in word form.

7. 215,700 __________

8. 5,050,050 __________

Solve.

9. **SCHOOL** In an answer to a math problem, Diego wrote, "two hundred forty thousand, ninety." For the same problem, Tamera wrote, "2 hundred-thousands, 4 ten-thousands, 9 tens." Write each answer in standard form. Did they give the same answer? __________

10. **MONEY** *ABC* Company's check for this year's annual charity donation is shown below. Write the amount of the donation in word form.

____

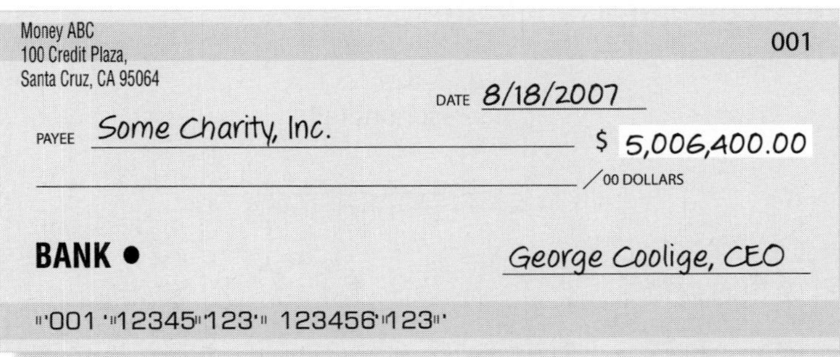

Money ABC
100 Credit Plaza,
Santa Cruz, CA 95064
001
DATE 8/18/2007
PAYEE Some Charity, Inc.
$ 5,006,400.00
/00 DOLLARS
BANK •
George Coolige, CEO
"001 ·"12345"123·" 123456"123"·

Chapter 7

Write the vocabulary word that completes each sentence.

11. A group of three digits in the place-value chart is a __________.

12. The digit 8 in the number 4,178,325 is in the __________ place.

NAME ______________________ DATE ______________

Lesson 7-2

Vocabulary and English Language Development

Activate Prior Knowledge

Examine the list of populations of three metropolitan areas in the United States.

1 What digit is in the hundred thousands place for the population of:

San Franciso: ______________

Washington, DC: ______________

Chicago: ______________

Metropolitan Area Population	
(includes surrounding areas)	
Chicago	9,157,540
San Francisco	7,039,362
Washington, D.C.	7,608,070

Definition Review

Complete the sentences.

3 When comparing two numbers, use the symbols ______________ for **less than**, ______________ for **greater than**, and ______________ for equal to.

4 When **rounding,** all the digits to the right of the ______________ being rounded become zero.

Application

Complete each part of the graphic organizer, rounding as indicated.

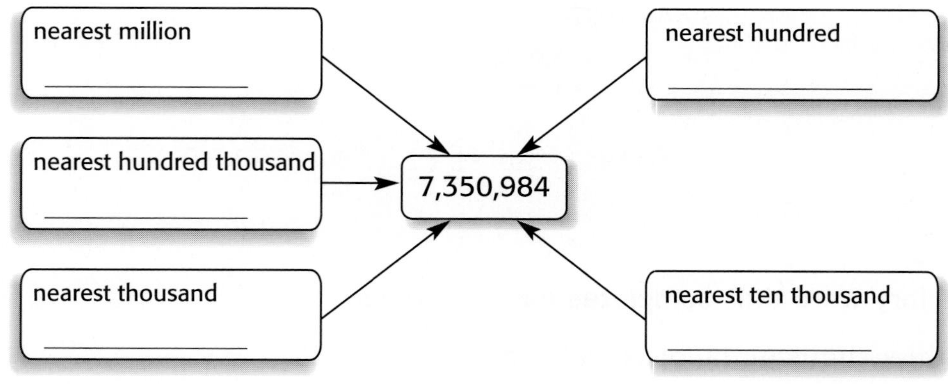

NAME ______________________ DATE ______________

Lesson 7-2

Skills Practice

1 Is 544,229 closer to 500,000 or 600,000? ______________

2 Is 8,621,058 closer to 8,000,000 or 9,000,000? ______________

Round each number to the given place value.

3 682,147; ten thousands

Underline the digit in the ten-thousands place.

Circle the digit in the thousands place.

What is 682,147 rounded to the nearest ten thousand? ______________

4 2,145,300; ten thousands ______________

5 1,270,050; hundred thousands ______________

6 462,385; hundred thousands ______________

Use <, =, or > to complete each statement.

7 2,740,080 __________ 2,816,200

8 2,356,891 __________ 2,396,600

9 509,769 __________ 509,769

10 6,751,395 __________ 6,751,299

11 355,708 __________ 355,807

12 7,859,352 __________ 7,900,610

Write the numbers in order from least to greatest.

13 5,287,000; 4,926,000; 4,910,000 ______________________

14 108,260; 110,500; 110,300 ______________________

15 740,200; 734,128; 742,000 ______________________

16 1,340,000; 1,260,050; 1,304,000 ______________________

Lesson 7-2 NAME ______________________ DATE ____________

Problem-Solving Practice

Solve.

1 **NATURE** A giant panda can eat as much as 30,660 pounds of bamboo in a year. What is this number rounded to the nearest thousand? ____________

2 **AREA** The water area of the United States is 256,645 square miles. What is the area rounded to the nearest hundred thousand? ____________

3 **DISTANCE** The distance from Mercury to the Sun is 57,909,175 km. What is this distance rounded to the nearest million kilometers? ____________

4 **ATTENDANCE** The record attendance for the Los Angeles Coliseum is 134,254. What is the record attendance rounded to the nearest ten thousand? ____________

5 **WEIGHT** The largest land animal is the elephant. The largest elephant on record was an African male elephant weighing 10,886 kilograms. What was his weight rounded to the nearest thousand? ____________

6 **HIGHWAYS** There are 46,837 miles of highway in the National Interstate System. How many miles are in the interstate system rounded to the nearest ten thousand? ____________

7 **AREA** The area of each of the Great Lakes is as follows: Lake Superior 31,698 sq mi, Lake Michigan 22,316 sq miles, Lake Huron 23,011 sq mi, Lake Erie 9,922 sq miles, and Lake Ontario 7,320 sq miles. Round each area to the nearest thousand.

____

____

____

____

____

Lesson 7-2

NAME ______________________ DATE ______________

Homework Practice

Write the hundred thousands that each number is between.

1. 507,288 is between __________ and __________.

2. 942,000 is between __________ and __________.

3. 2,630,005 is between __________ and __________.

Write the number in a place value chart. Round to the given place value.

4. 387,210; ten thousands ____________________

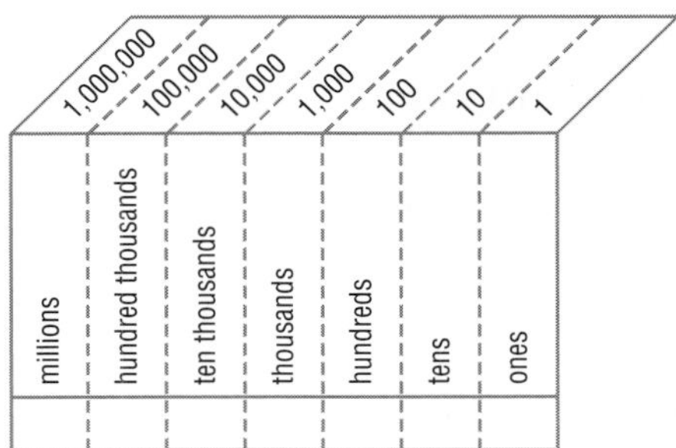

Write *true* or *false* for each sentence.

5. 6,247,000 < 6,420,000 ____________________

6. 237,144 > 300,000 ____________________

7. 42,016,052 < 42,013,087 ____________________

Round to the given place value.

8. 784,271; thousands ____________________

9. 12,604,090; millions ____________________

10. 45,210,000; ten millions ____________________

Solve.

11. **DISTANCE** The distance from Earth to the moon is 238,897 miles, on average. What is this number rounded to the nearest ten thousand? ____________

12. **POPULATIONS** According to the U.S. Census, in the year 2006 there were 6,315,239 males and 6,516,731 females in Illinois. Use <, =, or > to compare the number of males and females. ____________

Chapter 7

Lesson 7-3

NAME ____________________ DATE ____________

Vocabulary and English Language Development

Activate Prior Knowledge

Write the opposite of each action.

1. climbing ____________
2. depositing money ____________
3. taking off ____________
4. walking north ____________

Definition Review

Fill in the blanks.

5. The ____________ are the set of all counting numbers and zero.
6. The ____________ are the whole numbers and their opposites.
7. A ____________ is a number that is greater than zero.
8. A ____________ is a number that is less than zero.

Identify each number as positive or negative.

9. 31 ____________
10. 86 ____________
11. −42 ____________
12. −75 ____________

Application

Follow the directions for the activity.

- Write each integer from −10 through 10 on separate pieces of paper.
- Put the pieces of paper in a bag, hat, or bowl.
- Ask for 5 student volunteers.
- Have each student pick a number from the bag and tell the rest of the class their number.
- The rest of the class then orders the numbers at their desk on a white board.
- Instruct the volunteers to line up in front of the class according to their number from least to greatest.
- Ask the remaining students to verify whether or not the students in front of the class are in the correct order.
- Repeat the steps with each new group of students picking new numbers until each student has had a turn.
- For some variation, instruct some of the groups to line up from greatest to least.

NAME ______________________ DATE ______________

Skills Practice

Graph the integers on a number line. Then write them in order from least to greatest.

1. −2, 1, 5, −4, −3 ______________

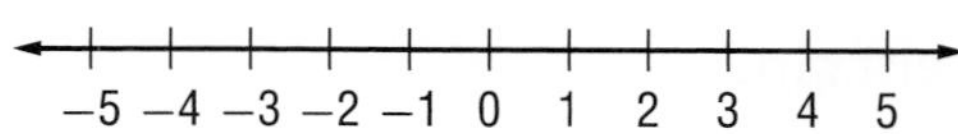

2. −3, −2, 1, −1, 3 ______________

−5 −4 −3 −2 −1 0 1 2 3 4 5

3. 3, −1, 1, 4, −4 ______________

−5 −4 −3 −2 −1 0 1 2 3 4 5

4. 1, −2, 3, −4, 5 ______________

−5 −4 −3 −2 −1 0 1 2 3 4 5

5. −1, 4, −5, −2, 3 ______________

−5 −4 −3 −2 −1 0 1 2 3 4 5

6. −4, −1, 2, −2, −3 ______________

−5 −4 −3 −2 −1 0 1 2 3 4 5

Use <, =, or > to compare each pair of numbers.

7. 3 ◯ −4

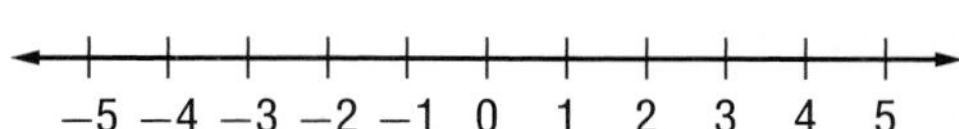

8. −2 ◯ −7

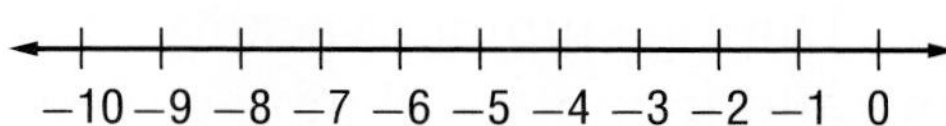

9. −2 ◯ 2

−5 −4 −3 −2 −1 0 1 2 3 4 5

10. 5 ◯ −1

−6 −5 −4 −3 −2 −1 0 1 2 3 4 5 6 7 8

11. −8 ◯ −5

−10 −9 −8 −7 −6 −5 −4 −3 −2 −1 0

12. −1 ◯ −1

−7 −6 −5 −4 −3 −2 −1 0 1 2 3 4 5 6 7

13. Omar lost $5 because of a hole in his pocket. What integer represents the amount he lost? ______________

NAME ______________________ DATE ____________

Lesson 7-3 Problem-Solving Practice

Solve.

1 **FINANCES** Molly withdrew $25 from the bank. What integer represents the amount withdrawn?

2 **TEMPERATURE** The low temperatures for three different cities were −10°F, −12°F, and 13°F. Which temperature was the lowest?

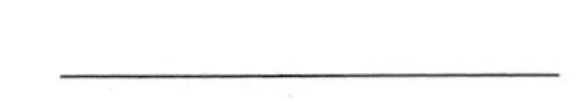

−15 −14 −13 −12 −11 −10 −9 −8 −7 −6 −5 −4 −3 −2 −1 0 1 2 3 4 5 6 7 8 9 10 11 12 13 14 15

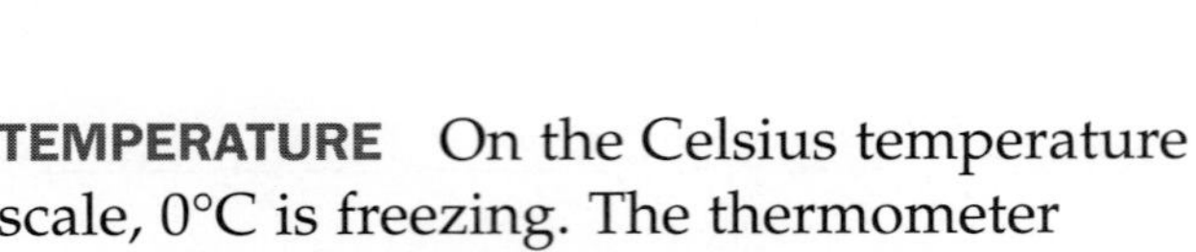

3 **TEMPERATURE** On the Celsius temperature scale, 0°C is freezing. The thermometer shows the current temperature outside. What is the temperature outside?

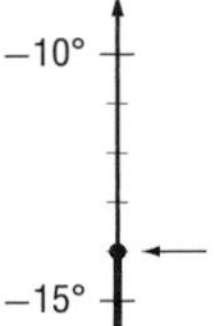

4 **FOOTBALL** A running back was tackled 3 yards behind the line. What integer represents the number of yards gained by the team for that play?

5 **TRAVEL** During summer vacation, Lamar and his family went camping and mountain climbing. The tallest mountain they climbed was 5,746 feet tall. What integer represents the height of the mountain that Lamar climbed with his family?

6 **WEATHER** The temperature at 1:00 PM was 65° F. By 8:00 PM, the temperature had dropped 19° F. What was the temperature at 8:00 P.M.?

7 **BANKING** Jody made a deposit into her checking account of $35. What integer represents the amount of the deposit?

8 **BUILDINGS** Write an integer to represent the sentence. "The elevator is 2 floors below ground level."

Lesson 7-3

NAME ______________________ DATE ______________

Homework Practice

Graph the integers on a number line.

1 4, −1, 3, 1, −2

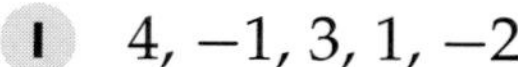

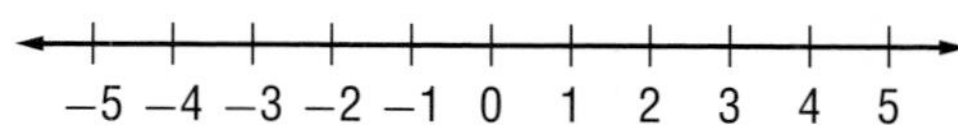

2 3, −3, −4, 1, −1

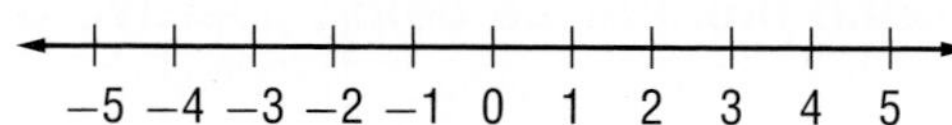

3 1, 2, −5, −2, 4

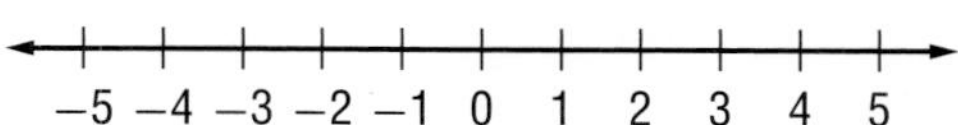

4 0, −5, 3, −4, −2

−5 −4 −3 −2 −1 0 1 2 3 4 5

Write the integers from least to greatest.

5 −15, −21, 12 ______________

6 45, −53, −45 ______________

7 58, −56, −68 ______________

8 −33, 29, 33 ______________

Write the integers from greatest to least.

9 −65, −74, −27 ______________

10 −34, 41, −43 ______________

11 −18, 18, −28 ______________

12 −87, −88, −89 ______________

Use $<$, $=$, or $>$ to compare each number pair.

13 −10 ◯ 10

14 0 ◯ −4

Write an integer to represent each statement.

15 You earned $28 babysitting. ______________

16 A company reported a loss of $300 this quarter. ______________

Solve.

17 **STOCK MARKET** The stock market had a very good day yesterday. It improved by 271 points. What integer represents yesterday's change in the stock market? ______________

18 **BANKING** Sook deposited $500 into his savings account this morning. What integer represents the change in Sook's bank account from this transaction? ______________

Write the vocabulary word that completes the sentence.

19 ______________ are numbers that are the same distance from 0 in opposite directions.

Chapter 7

NAME ______________________ DATE ______________

Lesson 7-4

Vocabulary and English Language Development

Activate Prior Knowledge

Identify each number as being positive or negative.

1 −4 ______________

2 11 ______________

3 5 ______________

4 −8 ______________

5 −17 ______________

6 13 ______________

Definition Review

Fill in the blanks.

7 ______________ are numbers that are the same distance from 0 in opposite directions.

8 The ______________ of a number is the distance between the number and 0 on a number line.

Name the opposite of each number.

9 9 ______________

10 −18 ______________

What is the absolute value of each number?

11 −8 ______________

12 15 ______________

Application

Follow the directions for the activity.

- Create index cards with integers on one side of them. Use integers between −10 and 10. Do not use 0. Make at least enough for each student in the class.
- Put the cards in a bag.
- Students each choose one card without looking.
- Students then have 30 seconds to run around and find another student with the number that is the opposite of their number. No talking is allowed at all. When two people meet, they should hold their papers next to each other to determine if they are opposites.
- Students who found an opposite can sit down. The remaining students repeat the procedure, choosing new cards and having only 20 seconds to find an opposite.
- Repeat one more time, with new cards and 10 seconds.

NAME ______________________ DATE ______________

Lesson 7-4

Skills Practice

Use algebra tiles to model. Form zero pairs to find the sum.

1 -9 and $+9 =$ ______________

2 $+11$ and $11 =$ ______________

3 $+4$ and $-4 =$ ______________

4 -6 and $+6 =$ ______________

Evaluate each expression. Use a number line to model.

5 $|-2|$ ______________

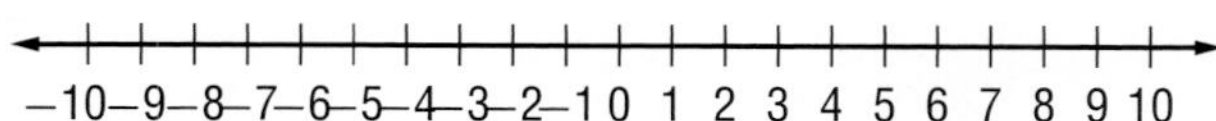

6 $|+7|$ ______________

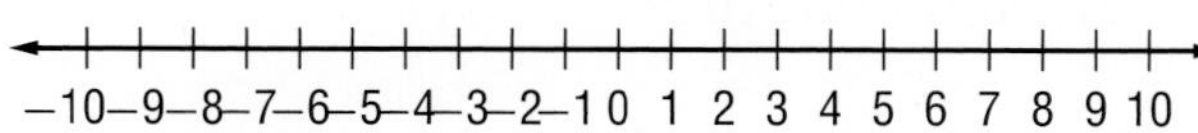

7 $|-8|$ ______________

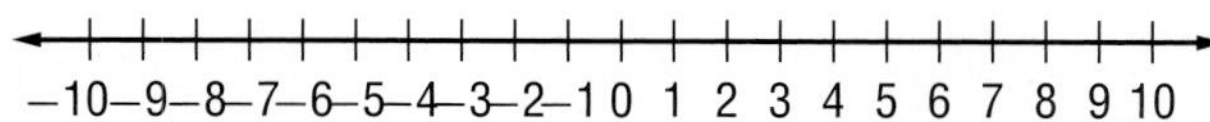

8 $|-10|$ ______________

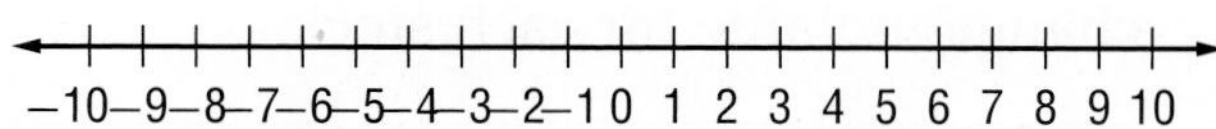

9 $|-3|$ ______________

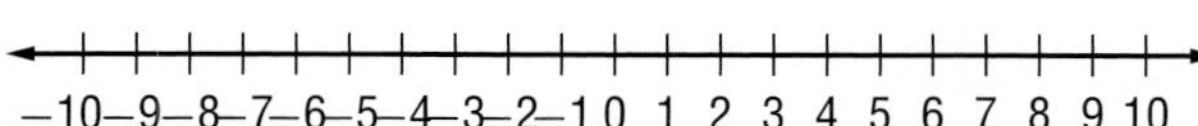

10 $|+9|$ ______________

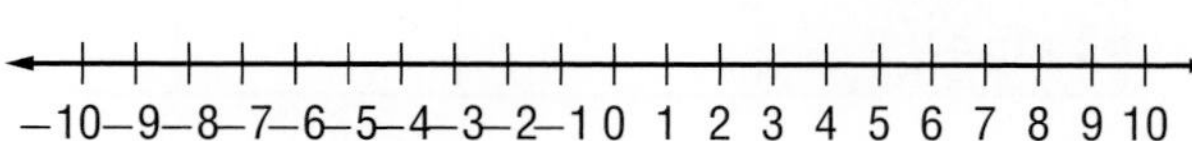

11 $|+5|$ ______________

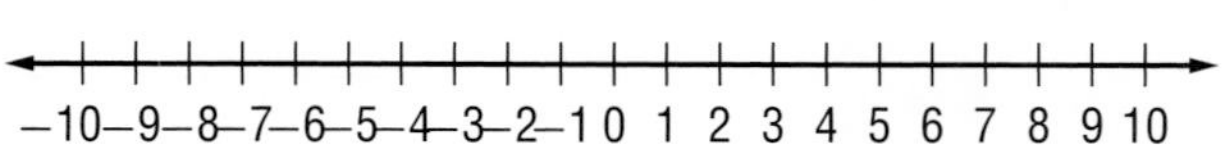

12 $|-6|$ ______________

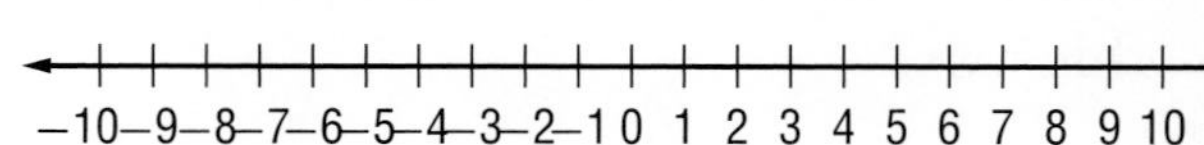

Chapter 7

Write the number that completes each sentence.

13 $13 +$ ______________ $= 0$

14 ______________ $+ -14 = 0$

15 ______________ $+ 22 = 0$

16 $-16 + 16 =$ ______________

17 $-25 +$ ______________ $= 0$

18 ______________ $+ -29 = 0$

19 $-1 +$ ______________ $= 0$

20 ______________ $+ 33 = 0$

Solve.

21 Neil had 3 red algebra tiles on his mat. Then Lucy set 3 yellow algebra tiles on it. How many zero pairs are on Neil's mat?

____

22 What can be done with zero pairs? ______________

NAME ______________________ DATE ______________

Lesson 7-4

Problem-Solving Practice

Solve.

1 **MARINE BIOLOGY** A marine biologist swam down to a depth of –8 feet. What is the absolute value of the distance the marine biologist swam down to? ______________

2 **TEMPERATURE** The record low ever recorded in the state of Alaska was 80° below zero. What integer represents this temperature? ______________

3 **STOCKS** The table shows the change in the value of four stocks sold on the New York Stock Exchange at some point during March of 2008. Complete the table by finding the absolute value of the change in value for each stock.

Change in Value	+\$1.16	–\$1.82	+\$0.14	–\$0.42
Absolute Value				

4 **PAPER ROUTE** Carlos has a paper route. He recently had four families stop delivery of the paper. What integer represents this loss? ______________

5 **HIKING** Milo is hiking down a mountain. In the past hour he has descended 912 feet. What integer represents this distance? What is the absolute value of this distance? ______________

6 **WINTER** Last week, Reagan wrote the high temperature for each day in the table. What day had the lowest temperature? What is the absolute value of this temperature? ______________

Day	Monday	Tuesday	Wednesday	Thursday	Friday
Temperature	–11°	–4°	5°	–13°	–2°

Lesson 7-4

NAME ______________________ DATE __________

Homework Practice

Write the number that completes each sentence.

1. $-11 +$ ______ $= 0$
2. $3 +$ ______ $= 0$
3. $19 +$ ______ $= 0$
4. ______ $+ 41 = 0$
5. $29 +$ ______ $= 0$
6. ______ $+ 63 = 0$

Evaluate each expression. Use a number line to model.

7. $|-6|$ ______

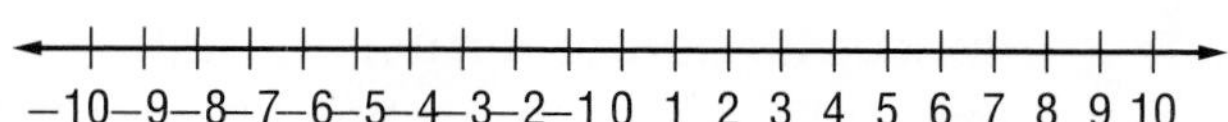

8. $|+7|$ ______

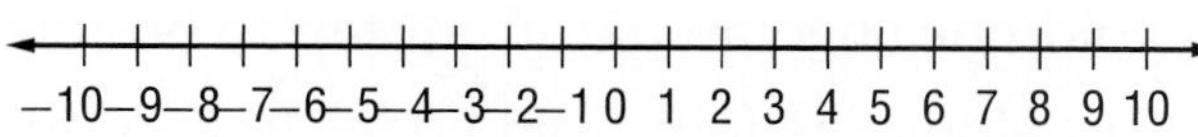

9. $|+5|$ ______

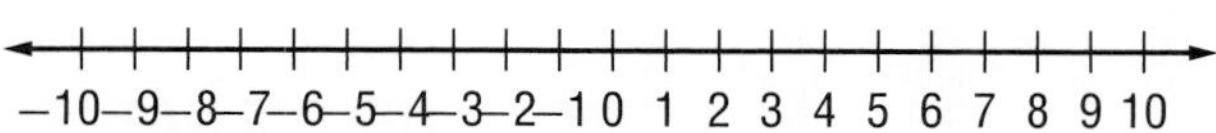

10. $|-4|$ ______

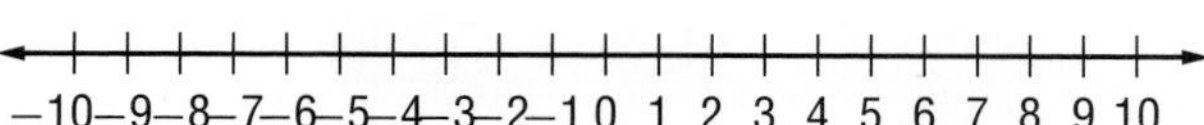

Solve.

11. **ALGEBRA TILES** Ann has 3 red tiles on her mat. Tell what she should do so that the value on her mat is 0. Explain why.

____

____

12. **NATIONAL PARKS** Death Valley National Park is located in California and Nevada. At its lowest point, it is 86 meters below sea level. What integer represents the lowest point in Death Valley?

____

13. **NUMBERS** Wei told her best friend, Carla, that –19 and 19 are the same number since they are the same distance from 0 on the number line. Is Wei correct? Explain?

____

____

14. **WEIGHT** Latrell lost 8 pounds in the past four months. What integer represents his weight loss? What is the absolute value of this number?

____

Write the vocabulary word that completes the sentence.

15. A ______ is the result when one positive number is paired with one negative number.

Chapter 7

NAME ______________________________ DATE ______________

Chapter 8

Foldables Study Organizer

Dinah Zike's Foldables

Make this Foldable to help you organize the information about integers.

1. Begin with two sheets of $8\frac{1}{2}'' \times 11''$ paper. Fold one sheet in half from top to bottom. Cut along the fold from edges to margin.

2. Fold the other sheet in half from top to bottom. Cut along the fold between margins.

3. Insert first sheet through second sheet and align folds.

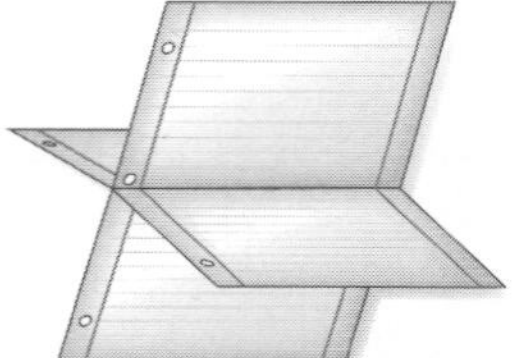

4. Label each inside page with a lesson number and title.

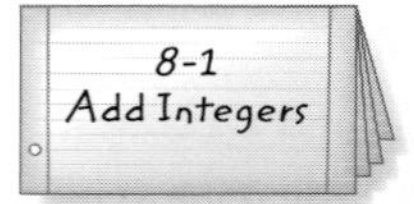

TAKING NOTES

As you read through the chapter, use your Foldable to organize the information you learn about integers.

USING YOUR FOLDABLE

As you study, use your Foldable to write examples, record key concepts, define terms, and take notes. Describe how the subject matter relates to everyday life.

USING YOUR FOLDABLE

Work with a partner. Quiz each other on adding, subtracting, multiplying, and dividing integers. Be sure to give your partner the correct answer if he or she is not correct.

NAME ______________________________ DATE ______________

Games and Puzzles

Falling Off the Ends

DIRECTIONS

Let one number cube represent positive integers and the other represent negative integers.

- Each player places a counter on zero.
- One player rolls both number cubes and adds the numbers shown. If the sum is positive, the player moves his or her counter right the number of spaces indicated by the sum. If the sum is negative, the player moves the counter left the number of spaces indicated by the sum.
- Players take turns rolling the number cubes and moving the counters.

- **Who Wins?** The first player to go off the sheet in either direction wins the game.

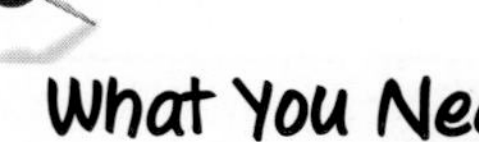

What You Need

- Falling Off the Ends Game Sheets
- 2 Different Colored Number Cubes
- 2 Different Colored Counters

Number of Players

2 or 4

Chapter 8

NAME ______________________________ DATE ______________

Falling off the Ends Game Sheet

−6	−5	−4	−3	−2	−1	0	1	2	3	4	5	6

Falling off the Ends Game Sheet

−6	−5	−4	−3	−2	−1	0	1	2	3	4	5	6

Lesson 8-1

NAME ________________________________ DATE ______________

Vocabulary and English Language Development

Activate Prior Knowledge

Find each sum.

1 $5 + 7 =$ ______

2 $25 + 0 =$ ______

3 $11 + 21 =$ ______

4 $12 + 86 =$ ______

Definition Review

Match each term with its definitiion.

5 ______ Commutative Property of Addition

6 ______ positive number

7 ______ negative number

8 ______ integers

A. a number that is less than zero

B. the whole numbers and their opposites

C. the order in which two numbers are added does not change the sum

D. a number that is greater than zero

Application

Follow the directions for the activity.

- Use masking tape to make a number line from −15 to 15 on the floor.
- Write each integer from −8 through 8 on separate pieces of paper.
- Put the pieces of paper in a bag, hat, or bowl.
- Student 1 picks a number from the bag, finds that number on the number line, and stands on that number.
- Student 2 picks a number from the bag and stands on that number.
- Student 1 adds his or her number to the number of student 2 using the number line. Students sitting in their seats solve the problem on a white board or paper.
- Students then pick new numbers and switch roles. Student 2 will pick the first number and find the sum.
- Repeat the steps with each new pair of students picking new numbers until each student has had a turn.

NAME ______________________ DATE ______________

Lesson 8-1

Skills Practice

Find each sum. Use the number line.

1 $4 + (-2) =$ ______________

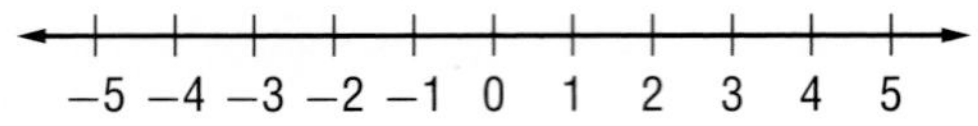

2 $-1 + (-3) =$ ______________

−5 −4 −3 −2 −1 0 1 2 3 4 5

3 $-3 + 7 =$ ______________

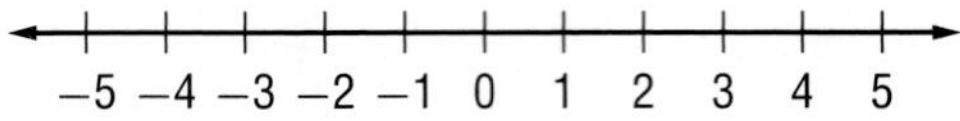

4 $2 + (-3) =$ ______________

−5 −4 −3 −2 −1 0 1 2 3 4 5

5 $-3 + (-3) =$ ______________

−10 −9 −8 −7 −6 −5 −4 −3 −2 −1 0

6 $-2 + 2 =$ ______________

−5 −4 −3 −2 −1 0 1 2 3 4 5

7 $-5 + 2 =$ ______________

−10 −9 −8 −7 −6 −5 −4 −3 −2 −1 0

8 $4 + (-3) =$ ______________

−5 −4 −3 −2 −1 0 1 2 3 4 5

Find each sum.

9 $2 + (-5) =$ ______________

10 $4 + (-4) =$ ______________

11 $16 + (-4) =$ ______________

12 $14 + 0 =$ ______________

13 $(-30) + 5 =$ ______________

14 $(-12) + (-8) =$ ______________

15 $3 + (-2) =$ ______________

16 $1 + (-3) =$ ______________

17 $(-26) + (-4) =$ ______________

18 $17 + (-3) =$ ______________

What is the opposite of each number? Use it to show the Inverse Property of Addition.

19 -1 ______________

20 -2 ______________

21 9 ______________

22 10 ______________

23 6 ______________

24 -7 ______________

25 -12 ______________

26 -8 ______________

NAME ________________ DATE ________________

Lesson 8-1

Problem-Solving Practice

Solve.

1. **FOOTBALL** During last week's game, Nantan rushed for +7 yards and –2 yards. What were Nantan's total rushing yards for the game?

2. **GOLF** During a golf match, Marcel scores +3 (3 over par) on the first hole, and –1 (1 under par) on the second hole. What is Marcel's score after the second hole?

3. **TREASURE HUNT** Sachi is searching for buried treasure. The map says to take 25 steps forward from the tree and then 8 steps backward. How many steps ahead of the tree is the treasure?

4. **ADDING INTEGERS** What addition problem does the number line model?

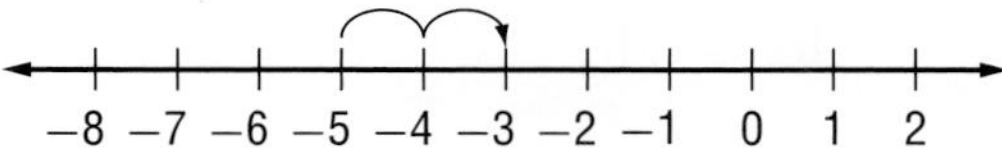

5. **FINANCES** Maggie received $25 for her birthday. She paid her mother back $15 that she borrowed last week. How much money does Maggie have left?

6. **SUBMARINES** A submarine is cruising at a depth of –100 meters. The submarine then rises 22 meters. What is the submarine's new depth?

7. **TEMPERATURE** The table shows the low temperature for the day and the change in temperature for the day. What is the high for the day?

Low Temperature	–4°
Change in Temperature	+15°

Chapter 8

NAME ______________________ DATE ______________

Lesson 8-1

Homework Practice

Find each sum. Use the number line.

1. $-3 + (-5) =$ ________

-10 -9 -8 -7 -6 -5 -4 -3 -2 -1 0

2. $2 + (-6) =$ ________

-8 -7 -6 -5 -4 -3 -2 -1 0 1 2 3

Find each sum. Use algebra tiles.

3. $4 + (-7) =$ ________

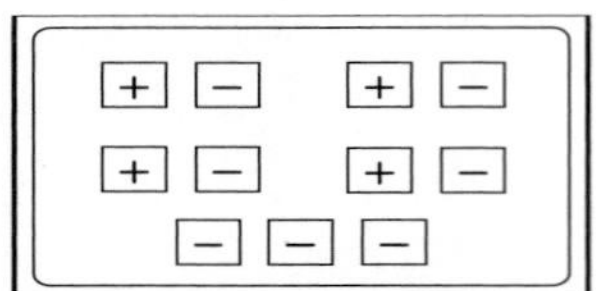

4. $3 + (-9) =$ ________

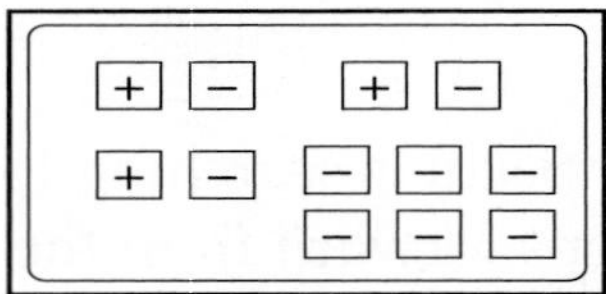

What is the opposite of each number? Use it to show the Inverse Property of Addition.

5. -3 ____________________

6. 4 ____________________

7. 5 ____________________

8. -11 ____________________

Find each sum.

9. $12 + (-9) =$ ________

10. $-2 + (-8) =$ ________

11. $6 + (-10) =$ ________

12. $-8 + 3 =$ ________

Solve.

13. **BUS STOPS** There were 15 passengers on a bus. At the next stop 3 people got off. How many passengers were now on the bus? ________

14. **GAMES** Corey moved 5 spaces forward on his first turn. He then drew a card that said to move backward 3 spaces. How far had Corey advanced from the start? ________

Write the vocabulary word that completes the sentence.

15. The ____________________ states that for any number, the sum of that number and its opposite is zero.

16. The ____________________ states that the order in which two numbers are added does not change the sum.

Lesson 8-2

NAME ____________ DATE ____________

Vocabulary and English Language Development

Activate Prior Knowledge

Find each opposite.

1 $+7$ ______

2 -5 ______

3 -2 ______

4 -4 ______

5 $+6$ ______

6 $+9$ ______

Definition Review

The **absolute value** of a number is the distance between the number and zero on a number line.

Which number has the greater absolute value?

7 -4 or 1 ______

8 9 or -9 ______

9 10 or -16 ______

10 -17 or 23 ______

Application

Follow the directions for the activity.

- Students work in groups of 3 or 4. Each student should have their own index card. Each group should make one additional index card with a plus sign on one side and a minus sign on the other.
- Each student writes an integer from 1 to 10 on one side of their individual card. On the other side, they write the opposite of that number.
- One student places their index card on the table so everyone in the group can see it. They decide which of their numbers to show. Then, they place the index card with the minus sign to the right of their number.
- Another student places their index card to the right of the minus sign. They can use either of their numbers.
- The group reads the subtraction problem out loud. A student then flips the second and third index cards to show the equivalent addition problem. The group reads the addition problem out loud and agrees on an answer.

NAME ______________________ DATE ______________

Lesson 8-2 Skills Practice

Find each difference. Use the number line.

1. 3 − (−4) = ______________

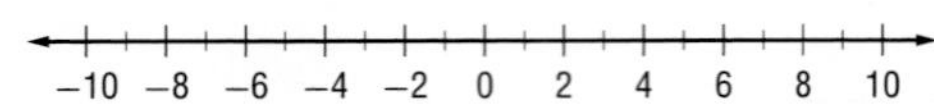

2. 8 − (−1) = ______________

−10 −8 −6 −4 −2 0 2 4 6 8 10

3. −2 − 1 = ______________

−5 −4 −3 −2 −1 0 1 2 3 4 5

4. −4 − (−2) = ______________

−6 −5 −4 −3 −2 −1 0 1 2 3 4 5 6

5. −7 − (−3) = ______________

−10 −8 −6 −4 −2 0 2 4 6 8 10

6. −9 − (−3) = ______________

−10 −8 −6 −4 −2 0 2 4 6 8 10

7. −6 − (−5) = ______________

−10 −8 −6 −4 −2 0 2 4 6 8 10

8. 2 − (−10) = ______________

−15 −12 −9 −6 −3 0 3 6 9 12 15

Find each difference.

9. −5 − (−6) = ______________
10. −4 − (−7) = ______________
11. 10 − (−3) = ______________
12. −1 − 6 = ______________
13. −8 − 4 = ______________
14. 3 − (−3) = ______________
15. 2 − (−3) = ______________
16. −9 − (−7) = ______________
17. 7 − 11 = ______________
18. 1 − 9 = ______________

Which number has the greater absolute value?

19. 8 or −7 ______________
20. −11 or 9 ______________
21. −13 or 10 ______________
22. 5 or −5 ______________
23. 15 or 18 ______________
24. −13 or −1 ______________
25. −2 or 2 ______________
26. −17 or 12 ______________
27. 21 or −21 ______________
28. 15 or 14 ______________

NAME ______________________ DATE ______________

Lesson 8-2

Problem-Solving Practice

Solve.

1. **CONSTRUCTION** Ajay is digging a hole for his bird feeder post. In the morning, he was able to dig an 8 inch hole. During the afternoon it rained and 2 inches of dirt fell back into the hole. How deep is the hole now? ______________

2. **MATH CLASS** Noah and Raphael each solved a subtraction problem on the blackboard. Who solved the problem correctly? ______________

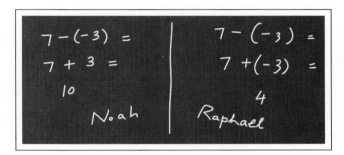

3. **FOOTBALL** The home team needs to gain 23 yards for a touchdown. On the next play, they lose 7 yards. How many yards does the team need now? ______________

4. **SHOPPING** Tobias had $35 in store credit. After using his credit towards the purchase of a pair of jeans, he still owed the store $12. What was the cost of the jeans that Tobias purchased? ______________

5. **TEST** Leticia got her math test back. At the top of the page it said she had 12 points taken away for incorrect answers and received 3 extra points for getting the bonus question correct. How many points were added or subtracted to get Leticia's final score? ______________

6. **MOUNTAIN CLIMBING** Wang is driving to the state capital which is 76 miles away. After driving for an hour he saw the sign below. How many miles has he already driven? ______________

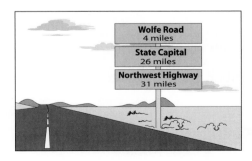

NAME ______________________ DATE ____________

Lesson 8-2 Homework Practice

Find each difference. Use the number line.

1. $-4 - 3 =$ ________

−10 −8 −6 −4 −2 0 2 4 6 8 10

2. $-1 - (-6) =$ ________

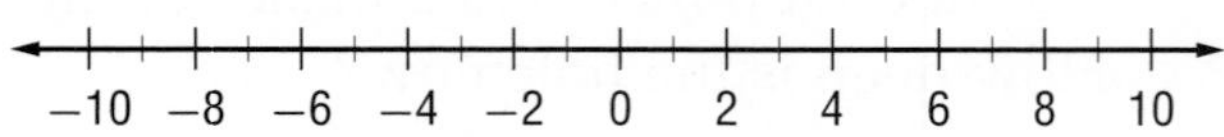

Find each difference. Use algebra tiles.

3. $-8 - 2 =$ ________

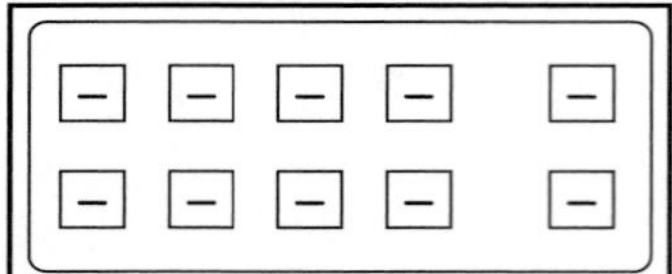

4. $-3 + 5 =$ ________

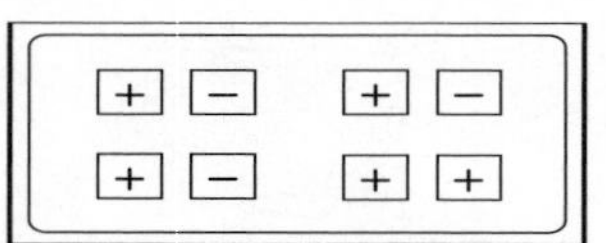

Which number has the greater absolute value?

5. -3 or 2 ________

6. 4 or -4 ________

7. -6 or -9 ________

8. 8 or 1 ________

Find each difference.

9. $6 - (-3) =$ ________

10. $-7 - 1 =$ ________

11. $-12 - (-8) =$ ________

12. $4 - 5 =$ ________

Solve.

13. **WEATHER** On the first day of February in upstate New York, the high temperature was 3° F at 2:00 P.M. Over the next 5 hours, the temperature dropped 10 degrees. What was the temperature at 7:00 P.M? ________

14. **DIVING** Taborri dove in the water to a depth of 13 feet. After two seconds, her depth was only 6 feet. How far had she risen during those two seconds? ________

Write the vocabulary word that completes each sentence.

15. The ________ of a number is the distance between the number and zero on a number line.

16. ________ are numbers that are the same distance from zero in opposite directions.

Lesson 8-3

NAME ______________________ DATE ______________

Vocabulary and English Language Development

Activate Prior Knowledge

List three examples of adding and subtracting integers in daily life.

1 ____

____

2 ____

____

3 ____

____

Definition Review

The **Associative Property of Addition** states that the grouping of addends does not change the sum.

Show how to use the Associative Property of Addition to regroup. The first one is done for you.

4 $(5 + 7) + 3 = 5 + (7 + 3)$

5 $2 + (8 + 11) = (\square + \square) + 11$

6 $(-3) + (3 + 4) = (\square + \square) + 4$

7 $(6 + (-5)) + 5 = \square + (\square + \square)$

Application

Follow the directions for the activity.

- Work in groups of three.
- Each student writes down an integer between −11 and 11.
- Create a word problem using the three integers and solve it.
- Repeat the process a total of four times.
- Trade problems with another group and solve the problems.

NAME ____________________ DATE ____________

Lesson 8-3

Skills Practice

Use the Associative Property of Addition to find the missing number.

1. $(3 + 7) + 1 = 3 + (\_\_\_\_\_\_ + 1)$

2. $(7 + 8) + 9 = 7 + (\_\_\_\_\_\_ + 9)$

3. $(6 + 4) + 9 = \_\_\_\_\_\_ + (4 + 9)$

4. $(10 + 5) + 6 = \_\_\_\_\_\_ + (5 + 6)$

5. $(5 + 2) + 8 = 5 + (\_\_\_\_\_\_ + 8)$

6. $(2 + 6) + 4 = 2 + (\_\_\_\_\_\_ + 4)$

7. $(1 + 5) + 6 = 1 + (5 + \_\_\_\_\_\_)$

8. $(7 + 1) + 9 = 7 + (\_\_\_\_\_\_ + 9)$

9. $(4 + 3) + 2 = \_\_\_\_\_\_ + (3 + 2)$

10. $(4 + 3) + 3 = 4 + (3 + \_\_\_\_\_\_)$

Simplify.

11. $8 - 10 + 2$ rewritten sentence: ____________
sum: ____________

12. $-4 + 13 - 11$ rewritten sentence: ____________
sum: ____________

13. $-6 - 5 + 17$ rewritten sentence: ____________
sum: ____________

14. $12 - (-7) + 8$ rewritten sentence: ____________
sum: ____________

15. $9 - (-8) - 3 = \_\_\_\_\_\_$

16. $3 - 7 + (-3) = \_\_\_\_\_\_$

17. $-10 + (4 - 7) - 9 = \_\_\_\_\_\_$

18. $-5 + 2 - (-10) = \_\_\_\_\_\_$

19. $4 - (-7) + 1 = \_\_\_\_\_\_$

20. $7 - (-5) + (2 - 1) = \_\_\_\_\_\_$

21. $-6 - (-3) - 12 = \_\_\_\_\_\_$

22. $20 - 6 - (-3) + 8 = \_\_\_\_\_\_$

23. $-8 + 5 - 6 = \_\_\_\_\_\_$

24. $2 - 33 + (9 - (-11)) = \_\_\_\_\_\_$

NAME ______________________ DATE ______________

Lesson 8-3

Problem-Solving Practice

Solve.

1 **KITES** Romeo is flying a kite. The height of the kite was 70 feet, but due to wind gusts it fell 12 feet and then rose 10 feet. What is the current height of the kite? ______________

2 **TRAINS** When the train left the station it had 30 passengers on board. At the first stop, 5 passengers got off the train. At the second stop, 9 passengers boarded the train. How many passengers were on the train when it arrived at the third stop? ______________

3 **MATH** Kayla was assigned a math problem to solve. Her work is shown. What mistake did Kayla make?

$$\begin{aligned} & -6 + (8 - (-2)) \\ &= -6 + (8 + (-2)) \\ &= -6 + 6 \\ &= 0 \end{aligned}$$

____

____

____

4 **ANIMALS** A monkey climbed up a tree to a spot 32 feet above the ground. After resting there for a while, he climbed down 12 feet, but then went up another 8 feet. How far is the monkey above the ground now? ______________

5 **SHOPPING** Carlos went shopping and came home with the sales receipt shown below. Unfortunately, as you can see, the total dollars that Carlos spent is missing. How much did Carlos spend? ______________

Sales Receipt		
Shirt	-	\$15
Discount	-	\$5
Hat	-	\$12
Discount	-	\$2
Total		

6 **WEATHER** In the morning, the temperature was 40°F. During the course of the day the temperature fell 13°F and then rose 7°F. What is the final temperature? ______________

Chapter 8

NAME ______________________ DATE ______________

Lesson 8-3 Homework Practice

Use the Associative Property of Addition to find the missing number.

1. $(8 + 4) + 5 =$ ________ $+ (4 + 5)$
2. $(2 + 9) + 11 = 2 + (9 +$ ________ $)$
3. $(3 + 2) + 9 = 3 + ($ ________ $+ 9)$
4. $(1 + 6) + 8 = 1 + ($ ________ $+ 8)$
5. $(6 + 1) + 7 = 6 + ($ ________ $+ 7)$
6. $(7 + 3) + 4 = 7 + (3 +$ ________ $)$
7. $(4 + 12) + 3 =$ ________ $+ (12 + 3)$
8. $(10 + 5) + 4 =$ ________ $+ (5 + 4)$

Simplify.

9. $12 - 6 + (2 - (-7)) =$ ________
10. $28 + 9 - (-2) =$ ________
11. $7 - 12 - (4 + 23) =$ ________
12. $-6 - (-10) + (2 - 5) =$ ________
13. $10 + (-8 + 1) - (-5) =$ ________
14. $8 - 4 + 16 - (-4) =$ ________
15. $-6 - 5 + 14 =$ ________
16. $9 - 15 + (-12) =$ ________
17. $16 + (3 - 8) - 16 =$ ________
18. $14 + (-8) - 3 - 1 =$ ________

Solve.

19. **MOTELS** The Vagabond Motel had 20 rooms occupied on Monday. On Tuesday 13 more rooms were occupied, and on Wednesday the occupants of 4 rooms checked out. How many rooms were still occupied? ________

20. **SWIMMING POOLS** The depth of the water in Martin's swimming pool is 12 feet. He is emptying the pool at a rate of 3 feet per hour. After 4 hours, what is the depth of the water in his pool? ________

Write the vocabulary word that completes the sentence.

21. ________ are numbers that are the same distance from zero in opposite directions.

22. The ________________ states that the way addends are grouped does not change the sum.

Lesson 8-4

NAME ______________________ DATE ____________

Vocabulary and English Language Development

Activate Prior Knowledge

Find each product.

1. $8 \times 3 =$ ________

2. $17 \times 1 =$ ________

3. $6 \times 9 =$ ________

4. $5 \times 0 =$ ________

Definition Review

Write the vocabulary word that completes the sentence.

5. The ____________________ states that any number times zero equals zero.

6. The ____________________ states that any number times 1 equals that number.

Application

Follow the directions for the activity.

- Work with a partner.
- Write 20 integer multiplication problems on the blackboard or a piece of paper.
- Read each problem aloud, one problem at a time.
- If the product is a positive number, both of you should put your thumbs up.
- If the product is zero, both of you should put your thumbs sideways.
- If the product is negative, both of you should put your thumbs down.
- Individually determine the products and compare answers.

Lesson 8-4

NAME ______________________ DATE ____________

Skills Practice

Find the missing number. Name the property.

1. $-8 \times 3 =$ ________ $\times -8$ ______________________

2. $-8 \times$ ________ $= -8$ ______________________

3. $(-8 \times 5) \times (-4) = -8 \times ($________ $\times (-4))$ ______________________

4. $-8 \times 0 =$ ________ ______________________

Find each product. Use a number line.

5. $3 \times (-6) =$ ________

–20 –18 –16 –14 –12 –10 –8 –6 –4 –2 0

6. $4 \times (-3) =$ ________

–20 –18 –16 –14 –12 –10 –8 –6 –4 –2 0

7. $2 \times (-8) =$ ________

–20 –18 –16 –14 –12 –10 –8 –6 –4 –2 0

8. $3 \times (-2) =$ ________

–20 –18 –16 –14 –12 –10 –8 –6 –4 –2 0

Find each product by multiplying absolute values.

9. $-7 \times 3 =$ ________

10. $-10 \times 2 =$ ________

11. $5 \times -5 =$ ________

12. $-8 \times -8 =$ ________

13. $-6 \times 4 =$ ________

14. $2 \times -9 =$ ________

15. $-7 \times -8 =$ ________

16. $12 \times 3 =$ ________

17. $9 \times 5 =$ ________

18. $-4 \times 11 =$ ________

Lesson 8-4

NAME ______________________ DATE ____________

Problem-Solving Practice

Solve.

1 **STOCK MARKET** Pia owns shares of stock in a company. The table below shows how the value of each share of stock has changed over the past three weeks. What is the change in value of one share of stock over these three weeks? ____________

Week	Change in Value
1	Decreased $4
2	Decreased $4
3	Decreased $4

2 **ENVIRONMENT** Haloke records the water level in the lake each week for the city. The water level has dropped 8 inches each week for the past 4 weeks. What has been the total change in the water level for this month? ____________

3 **SCUBA DIVING** Gabe goes scuba diving and descends at a rate of 20 feet per minute. His diving partner times how long his descent takes. The stop watch shows 5 minutes and 0 seconds. What depth did Gabe dive to in the water? ____________

4 **ENGINEERING** Howie is calculating how much power he needs for a machine he is designing. He records devices that give power as positive current, and devices that use power as negative current. He has 5 small pumps in the machine that each use 8 amps of current. What integer will Howie use to record the total current of the pumps? ____________

5 **CARS** The value of Sam's car decreased $1,500 each year for 4 years. By how much did the car decrease in value? ____________

NAME ______________________ DATE ______________

Lesson 8-4

Homework Practice

Find each product. Use a number line.

1. $1 \times (-9) =$ ______

2. $4 \times (-4) =$ ______

3. $3 \times (-3) =$ ______

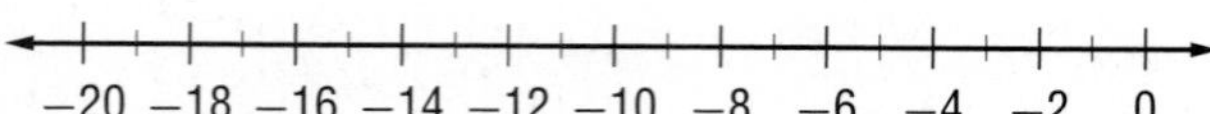

4. $2 \times (-7) =$ ______

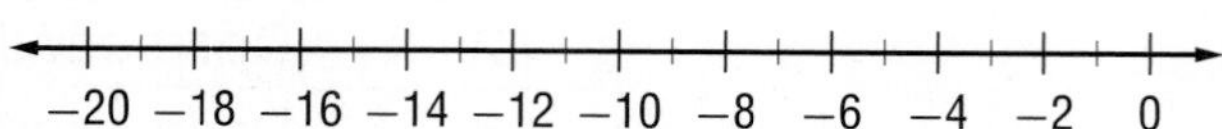

Find each product by multiplying absolute values.

5. $9 \times -7 =$ ______

6. $15 \times 2 =$ ______

7. $-4 \times 8 =$ ______

8. $6 \times -7 =$ ______

9. $-12 \times -3 =$ ______

10. $-8 \times 11 =$ ______

11. $4 \times -5 =$ ______

12. $-2 \times -9 =$ ______

Find the missing number. Name the property.

13. $-3 \times 1 =$ ______ ______________________

14. $-2 \times 6 =$ ______ $\times -2$ ______________________

15. $-8 \times$ ______ $= 0$ ______________________

16. $(-3 \times 4) \times 2 = -3 \times ($______ $\times 2)$ ______________________

Solve.

17. **WEATHER** The daily high temperature has dropped 2° F each day for the past 7 days. What has the change in temperature been for the past week? ______

18. **GOLF** On Saturday, Leon shot −1 (1 under par) for each of the first 3 holes. What is Leon's score after the first 3 holes? ______

Write the vocabulary word that completes the sentence.

19. A ______ is a number that divides into a whole number with a remainder of zero.

20. The answer or result of a multiplication problem is the ______.

NAME ______________________ DATE ______________

Lesson 8-5

Vocabulary and English Language Development

Activate Prior Knowledge

Fill in the blank with *positive* or *negative*.

1 When you multiply two integers with the same sign, the sign of the product is ______________.

2 When you multiply two integers with different signs, the sign of the product is ______________.

Definition Review

Fill in the blank using *divisor*, *quotient*, or *dividend*.

3 The ______________ is the number that is being divided.

4 The ______________ is the number by which the dividend is being divided.

5 The ______________ is the answer to a division problem.

Application

Fill in each blank with the allowable numbers so that each division problem is true. Use all the divisors one time.

- Allowable divisors: −9, −3, 3, and 9
- Allowable dividends: −27 and 9
- Allowable quotients: −3 and 3

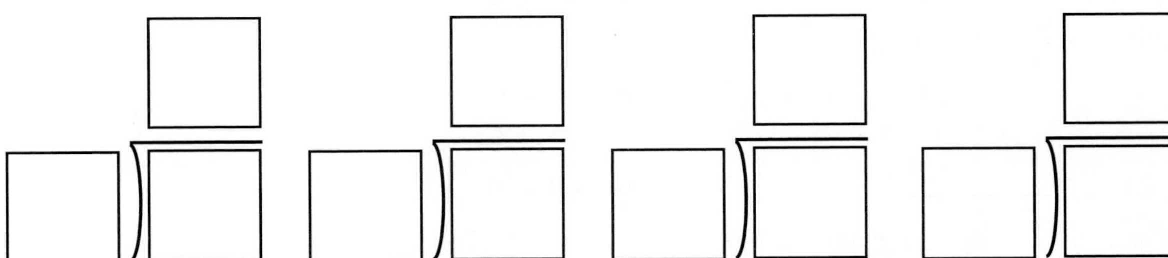

Chapter 8

NAME ________________ DATE ________

Lesson 8-5

Skills Practice

1 Find $10 \div (-2)$.

Step 1 Are the signs the same or different?

____

Step 2 Will the quotient be positive or negative?

____

Step 3 Divide the absolute values of the numbers.

____

Step 4 Write the quotient. ______
Check the sign to make sure it is correct.

____

2 $-20 \div 5$
signs : ______ $\div$ ______ = ______
quotient : ______

3 $-10 \div (-1)$ __________

4 $-10 \div 1$ __________

5 $14 \div (-2)$ __________

6 $49 \div 7$ __________

7 $-55 \div (-5)$ __________

8 $28 \div (-4)$ __________

9 $15 \div (-3)$ __________

10 $-36 \div (-6)$ __________

11 $-9 \div 3$ __________

12 $81 \div (-9)$ __________

13 $56 \div 7$ __________

14 $-42 \div (-6)$ __________

15 $-20 \div (-2)$ __________

16 $60 \div 5$ __________

17 $-36 \div 4$ __________

18 $-16 \div (-4)$ __________

19 $0 \div (-8)$ __________

20 $75 \div 5$ __________

Lesson 8-5

NAME ______________________ DATE ______________

Problem-Solving Practice

Solve.

1 **WEATHER** The temperature dropped 18° F in the last 6 hours. What was the average rate of change in degrees per hour? ______________

2 **RECREATION** Forty-eight people are going canoeing. If each canoe contains 4 people, how many canoes does the group need? ______________

3 **BAKERY** While at Davidson's Bakery, Josefa saw the sign shown below. What does one muffin cost?

4 **SHELVING** Denard is putting up shelving in his bedroom. He wants the length of each of the shelves to be 3 feet long. If he uses the board shown below to make his shelves, how many can he make?

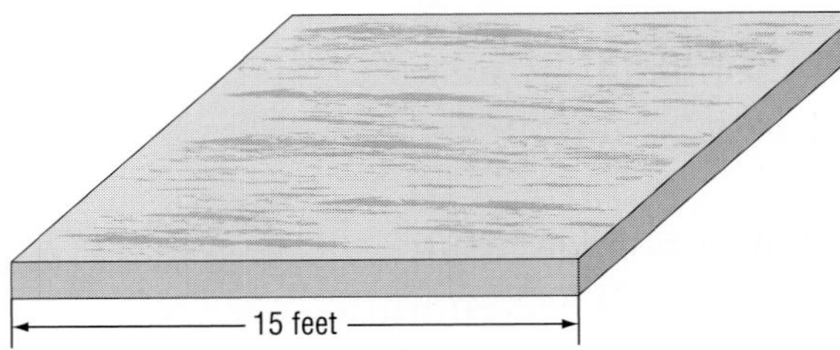

5 **ART** Shayla made an art project by gluing beads to a poster board. On the way home from school, 42 beads fell off her poster board. If it takes Shayla 7 minutes to walk home, what was the average rate of change in beads per minute?

6 **FOOTBALL** A team lost 25 yards on 5 penalties. What was the average loss of yards on each penalty? ______________

Lesson 8-5

NAME ______________________ DATE ____________

Homework Practice

Find each quotient.

1. $-5 \div (-1)$ ____________
2. $-5 \div 1$ ____________
3. $5 \div (-1)$ ____________
4. $5 \div 1$ ____________
5. $6 \div (-2)$ ____________
6. $-18 \div (-3)$ ____________
7. $-35 \div (-7)$ ____________
8. $44 \div 11$ ____________
9. $-54 \div 6$ ____________
10. $50 \div (-2)$ ____________
11. $-25 \div (-5)$ ____________
12. $-70 \div (-10)$ ____________

Solve.

13. **MONEY** A group of 6 friends earned $90 doing yard work. They want to divide the money equally. How much money does each person get? ____________

14. **WEIGHT** Troy's dog lost 27 pounds in 9 months. If he lost the same amount each month, what was his loss per month? ____________

15. **TREES** On a windy day, a tree dropped about 85 leaves in 5 minutes. If about the same number of leaves fell each minute, what was the average number of leaves dropped per minute? ____________

Write the vocabulary word that completes each sentence.

16. A ____________ is a number that is being divided.

17. A ____________ is the number by which the dividend is being divided.

18. The ____________ is the answer or result to a division problem.

Lesson 8-6

NAME ______________________ DATE ______________

Vocabulary and English Language Development

Activate Prior Knowledge

Find each product.

1 $3 \times 12 =$ ______

2 $5 \times 9 =$ ______

3 $2 \times 2 \times 2 =$ ______

4 $3 \times 3 \times 3 \times 3 =$ ______

Definition Review

Identify the base and the exponent of each expression.

5 5^2 base ______, exponent ______

6 3^8 base ______, exponent ______

7 4^3 base ______, exponent ______

8 9^6 base ______, exponent ______

Application

Follow the directions for the activity.

- Work with a partner to find each word in the puzzle. Words can be horizontal, vertical, or diagonal and can be written backward or forward.
- After finding a word, one person uses the word in a sentence and the other writes a math expression that uses it.

BASE CUBED EXPONENT FACTOR POWER
PRODUCT SQUARED

Q	A	D	E	R	A	U	Q	S	P
B	T	C	W	M	T	E	U	B	N
R	T	N	S	A	C	R	E	D	W
C	P	X	E	F	U	E	R	E	P
Q	B	S	W	N	D	W	N	B	E
W	B	R	V	S	O	O	O	U	S
F	A	C	T	O	R	P	D	C	E
G	S	B	U	A	P	S	X	X	N
Q	E	U	A	B	U	S	R	E	A
F	W	R	D	C	P	A	C	X	T

Chapter 8

NAME ______________________ DATE ______________

Lesson 8-6

Skills Practice

Write each expression using an exponent.

1. $5 \times 5 \times 5$ ______

2. $4 \times 4 \times 4 \times 4 \times 4$ ______

3. $8 \times 8 \times 8 \times 8$ ______

4. 3×3 ______

5. $2 \times 2 \times 2 \times 2 \times 2 \times 2$ ______

6. 5 ______

Write each expression as repeated multiplication.

7. 2^3 ______

8. 6^4 ______

9. 1^5 ______

10. 3^5 ______

11. 7^2 ______

12. 8^1 ______

Write the base and exponent in word form.

13. 5^2 ______

14. 7^4 ______

Evaluate the expression.

15. 4^3 ______

16. 2^5 ______

17. 7^2 ______

18. 9^1 ______

19. 2^3 ______

20. 3^4 ______

21. 1^6 ______

22. 8^3 ______

23. 5^4 ______

24. 2^7 ______

NAME ______________________ DATE ______________

Lesson 8-6 Problem-Solving Practice

Solve.

1. **FORESTS** A forester plants trees in the pattern shown below. How many total trees are planted? Write your answer using exponents and then evaluate the expression. ____________

T T T T
T T T T
T T T T
T T T T

2. **MONEY** Milty is saving pennies. In the first week he saved 2 pennies, in the second week he saved 4 pennies, and in the third week he saved 8 pennies. He continued this pattern for seven weeks. How many pennies does he save in the seventh week? Write your answer using exponents and then evaluate the expression. ____________

3. **PATTERNS** Consider what happens when the odd numbers are added.

$$1 + 3 = 4$$
$$1 + 3 + 5 = 9$$
$$1 + 3 + 5 + 7 = 16$$

Write each sum using exponents.
If the pattern continues, what will be the sum of the numbers when there are 9 odd numbers being added? ____________

4. **AREA** The formula for the area of a square is $A = s^2$ where A is the area of the square and s is the length of each side of the square. Find the area of a square with a side length of 9 centimeters. ____________

5. **VOLUME** The formula for the volume of a cube is $V = s^3$ where V is the volume of the cube and s is the length of each side of the cube. Find the volume of a cube with a side length of 4 feet. ____________

Chapter 8

Lesson 8-6

NAME ______________________ DATE ______________

Homework Practice

Write each expression using an exponent.

1. $4 \times 4 \times 4$ __________
2. $7 \times 7 \times 7 \times 7 \times 7$ __________
3. $5 \times 5 \times 5 \times 5 \times 5 \times 5$ __________
4. 9×9 __________

Write each expression as repeated multiplication.

5. 3^2 ______________________
6. 2^4 ______________________
7. 1^5 ______________________

Evaluate each expression.

8. 2^5 __________
9. 3^4 __________
10. 7^2 __________
11. 5^3 __________
12. 1^9 __________
13. 2^8 __________

Solve.

14. **SCHOOL** Mr. Manahon has his choir members stand in rows when they sing. There is the same number of rows as there are choir members in each row. There are 6 rows. How many choir members are in the choir?

Write the vocabulary word that completes the sentence.

15. The ______________ is the number used as the factor in an expression involving exponents.

16. The ______________ indicates the number of times the base is multiplied by itself.

NAME ______________________ DATE ______________

Lesson 8-7

Vocabulary and English Language Development

Activate Prior Knowledge

Find the value of each expression.

1. $5 + 11 =$ ______
2. $19 + (-8) =$ ______
3. $21 - (-7) =$ ______
4. $-5 - 7 =$ ______
5. $8 \times 7 =$ ______
6. $3 \times -7 =$ ______
7. $-24 \div 2 =$ ______
8. $-6 \div -2 =$ ______

Definition Review

9. Write **1st**, **2nd**, **3rd**, and **4th** to put the steps in the correct order.

   ______ Multiply and divide in order from left to right.

   ______ Simplify grouping symbols.

   ______ Add and subtract in order from left to right.

   ______ Simplify exponents.

Application

Follow the directions for the activity.

- Work in groups of 3 or 4.
- One student creates a problem using parentheses, exponents, ×, ÷, +, and –.
- The other students take turns solving a step of the problem.
- The student who created the problem checks if the work is correct.
- Repeat the process, changing roles until every student has a chance to create a problem.

Chapter 8

NAME _______________ DATE _______________

Lesson 8-7 Skills Practice

Name the step that should be performed first in each expression.

1. $8 \times 6 \div (4 + 2) - 4^2$

____

2. $3 \times 6 + 3^2 + 9 \div 3$

____

3. $1 \div 5 - 3 + 2 \times 6$

____

4. $9 - 2 + (12 \times 6) + 9$

____

5. $8 \times 6^2 \div 12 - 2 \times 6$

____

6. $10 \div 2 \times 5 - 1 + 4$

____

Find the value of each expression.

7. $4 \times (2 + 6) - 30 + 4^2$

$= 4 \times$ ______ $- 30 + 4^2$

$= 4 \times$ ______ $- 30 +$ ______

$=$ ______ $- 30 +$ ______

$=$ ______ $+$ ______

$=$ ______

8. $9 + 7 \times 2 - 3^2 + (1 \times 8)$

$= 9 + 7 \times 2 - 3^2 +$ ______

$= 9 + 7 \times 2 -$ ______ $+$ ______

$= 9 +$ ______ $-$ ______ $+$ ______

$=$ ______ $-$ ______ $+$ ______

$=$ ______

9. $7 - 4 \div 2 + 5^2$

______

10. $12 \div 4 \times 2^2 - (3 + 2)$

______

11. $14 \times 2 \div (8 - 4) + 9$

______

12. $10 - (2 + 4) + 2 \times 5$

______

NAME ______________________ DATE ______________

Lesson 8-7 Problem-Solving Practice

Write and simplify an expression to solve each problem.

1 **KITTENS** Carla has 2 cats. Each cat had 5 kittens. She found homes for 7 kittens. How many cats and kittens does Carla have now?

____

____

2 **BAKERY** A baker made 15 loaves of white bread, 12 loaves of wheat bread, and 10 loaves of rye bread. A customer bought 2 loaves of each of the 3 kinds of breads. How many loaves of bread are left?

____

____

3 **COOKIES** Shamika baked 60 oatmeal cookies for a bake sale. She divided the cookies into bags so that there are 5 cookies per bag. At the bake sale she sold 7 bags of cookies. How many bags of cookies does Shamika have left?

____

____

4 **COMPUTERS** Emilio received a $15 discount when he bought an ink-jet printer. He also bought 2 black printer cartridges, 1 color printer cartridge, and 5 packages of paper. His receipt is shown. How much did Emilio spend in all?

____

____

Computer World

Ink-jet printer1	@ $125.00
Discount	–$15.00
Black printer cartridges	2 @ $35.00
Color printer cartridges	1 @ $35.00
Paper	5 @ $5.00

5 **AMUSEMENT PARK** Lalana paid $12 for admission to an amusement park. She rode the roller coaster 3 times and the Ferris wheel 2 times. Each ride cost $2. She also bought a hamburger and 2 waters during the day. How much money did Lalana spend in all?

____

____

Lunch Menu
Hot Dog $2.00
Hamburger $3.00
French Fries $1.00
Lemonade $1.50
Water $1.00

Chapter 8

NAME ______________________ DATE ______________

Lesson 8-7

Homework Practice

Name the step that should be performed first in each expression.

1. $7 + 9 - 2 + 4 \times 4^2$

____

2. $3 \times 18 + (9 - 2) + 3^2 \div 3$

____

3. $9 + (4 \times 2) - 12 \div 3 + 8^2$

____

4. $20 \div 4 \times 2 - 9 \times 2 + 5$

____

Find the value of each expression.

5. $4^2 + 13 + (9 - 1) \times 2$

______

6. $15 \div (2^2 + 1^2) + 5 \times 2$

______

7. $11 + 3 \times 2 + 8 - 8 \div 2$

______

8. $3 + (8 \times 2) - (18 - 3^2) + 1$

______

Write and simplify an expression to solve each problem.

9. **SNACKS** Marla bought 4 boxes of granola bars. Each box contains 6 granola bars. Marla ate 3 granola bars, and she gave her brother 4 granola bars. Marla then bought 2 more boxes of granola bars. How many granola bars does Marla have now?

____

10. **BOOKS** Daniel has 65 books on a book shelf. He divides the books equally among 5 shelves. He then moves 5 books on the top shelf to the bottom shelf. He also buys 3 new books and puts them on the top shelf. How many books are on the top shelf?

____

Write the vocabulary word that completes the sentence.

11. The ______________ of a power is the number used as the factor.

12. A(n) ______________ is the number of times a base is multiplied by itself.

NAME ______________________ DATE ____________

Foldables Study Organizer

Dinah Zike's Foldables

Make this Foldable as a study guide where you will write about variables and expressions.

1. Begin with a sheet of 11″ × 17″ paper. Fold the short sides toward the middle.

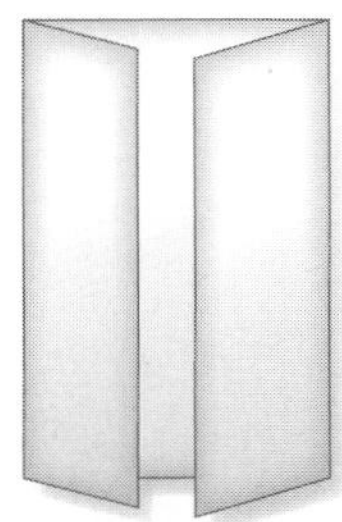

2. Fold the top to the bottom. Open. Cut along the second fold to make four tabs.

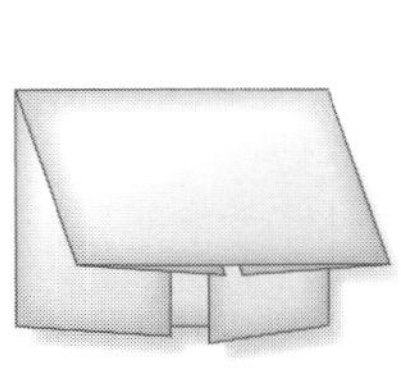

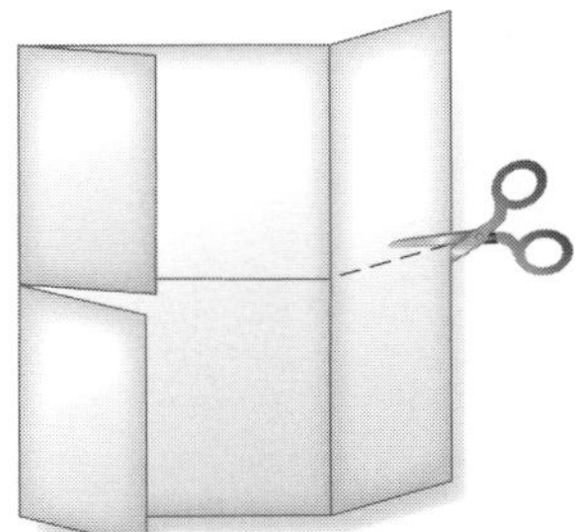

3. Label each of the tabs as shown.

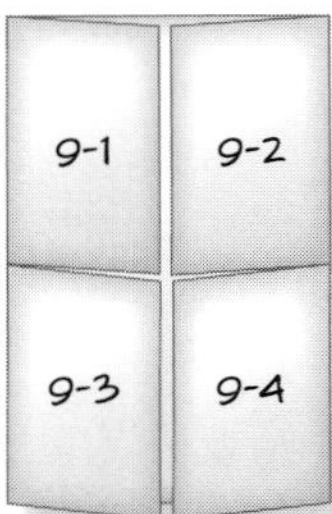

TAKING NOTES

As you read through the chapter, use your Foldable to organize your notes about variables and expressions.

USING YOUR FOLDABLE

As you study, use your Foldable to write examples of algebraic expressions and formulas. Record what you learn about the parts of each lesson that you find most difficult.

USING YOUR FOLDABLE

Trade Foldables with a partner. Check each other's Foldable. Are there differences between you and your partner's work? If so, discuss and correct any errors.

NAME ______________________ DATE ______________

Chapter 9

Games and Puzzles

Order Matters

GET READY: Cut out the Order Matters cards.

DIRECTIONS

- Shuffle the cards. Then spread the cards facedown on the table.
- One player turns over a card and rolls the number cube.
- This player replaces *n* on his or her card with the number rolled and then evaluates the expression. The other player checks their work.
- Switch roles and repeat.
- The player whose expression has the higher value keeps his or her card.
- The other player's card is returned facedown on the table.
- Continue the game until all the cards have been played correctly. Each player adds up the point value on his or her cards. The player with the most points wins.

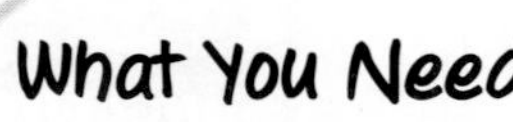

- Order Matters cards
- Number cube
- Scissors
- Pencil and paper

Number of Players

2

NAME ______________________ DATE ______________

Order Matters Cards

$2n$ 1 point	$3n$ 1 point
$4n + 1$ 2 points	$5n - 3$ 2 points
$(4 + 1) \times n$ 3 points	$(5 - 2) \times n$ 3 points
$5 \times n \times (4 - 1)$ 4 points	$6 \times n \times (3 + 2)$ 4 points
$9 \div 3 \times (7 - n)$ 5 points	$8 \div 2 \times (n + 2)$ 5 points

Lesson 9-1

NAME ______________________ DATE ____________

Vocabulary and English Language Development

Activate Prior Knowledge

Use the order of operations to evaluate each expression.

1 $3 \times 5 - 4$

____

2 $7 + 4 \times (-2)$

____

3 $7 + (8 - 10)$

____

4 $5 + 6 \div 3$

____

5 $-3 \times 4 + 1$

____

6 $-24 \div 3 + 5 \times 9$

____

Definition Review

A **constant** is a value that does not change.

An **algebraic expression** is a combination of variables, numbers, and at least one operation.

7 Label the coefficent, the constant, the algebraic expression, and the variable.

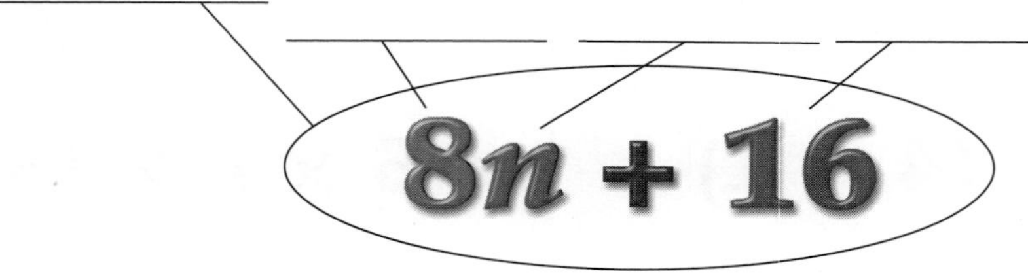

Application

Follow the directions for the activity.

- Divide into groups of 2 or 3 students.
- Each student will write his or her own algebraic expression. Each expression must include two terms, where one of the terms is a constant.
- Students will then trade expressions within their group.
- Students should identify the expression, terms, coefficient, variable, and constant of the expression created by their group members.
- Share two expressions with the rest of the class.
- Write those expressions on the board.
- Review the different parts of each expression.

NAME _______________ DATE _______________

Lesson 9-1

Skills Practice

Write different expressions.

1 Write three different algebraic expressions that have the constant term 7 and the variable f.

_______ _______ _______

2 Write three different algebraic expressions that have the constant term 3 and the variable g.

_______ _______ _______

3 Write three different algebraic expressions that have the constant term -10 and the variable a.

_______ _______ _______

Name the coefficient, variable, and constant in each expression.

4 $3x + 4$ coefficient: _______

variable: _______

constant: _______

5 $7p - 12$ coefficient: _______

variable: _______

constant: _______

6 $5r + 8$ coefficient: _______

variable: _______

constant: _______

7 $13 - 9b$ coefficient: _______

variable: _______

constant: _______

8 $2t + 1$ coefficient: _______

variable: _______

constant: _______

9 $m - 3$ coefficient: _______

variable: _______

constant: _______

10 $-4\ell + 20$ coefficient: _______

variable: _______

constant: _______

11 $-s - 14$ coefficient: _______

variable: _______

constant: _______

12 $3w^2 + 1$ coefficient: _______

variable: _______

constant: _______

13 $2 - 3i$ coefficient: _______

variable: _______

constant: _______

Lesson 9-1

NAME ______________________ DATE ______________

Problem-Solving Practice

Solve.

1 **EARNINGS** Flor earns $9 for every hour she works at the movie theater. Write an expression for how much money Flor earned yesterday. ________

2 **FUEL** Nina's car has some gas in the gas tank. She stops at a gas station and puts 11 gallons of gas in the tank. Write an expression for how much gas is in Nina's tank now. ________

3 **CELL PHONE** Goro made c calls on his cell phone from work last month. He talked for 5 minutes on each call. Write an expression for the total length of time Goro talked on the phone. ________

4 **PENCILS** Sashi gave 12 pencils to her friends. She gave the same number of pencils to each of her friends. Write an expression for the number of pencils Sashi gave each friend. ________

5 **READING** Crystal read some pages in her book. If there are a total of 232 pages, write an expression for the number of pages Crystal has left to read. ________

6 **SCREWS** Bimisi finds some screws on a shelf. He also finds a box of 150 screws in a bag. Write an expression for the number of screws Bimisi finds. ________

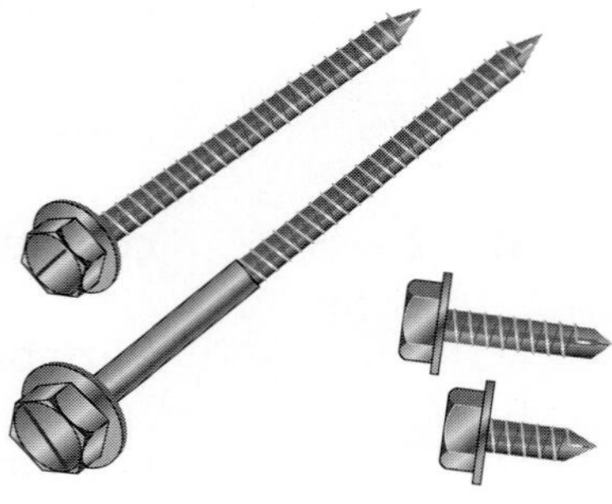

NAME ______________________ DATE ______________

Lesson 9-1 Homework Practice

Write different expressions.

1 Write three different expressions that have the constant term -10 and the variable k.

_____________ _____________ _____________

Name the coefficient, variable, and constant in each expression.

2 $8j - 9$ coefficient: __________

variable: __________

constant: __________

3 $-5 + 10v$ coefficient: __________

variable: __________

constant: __________

4 $3c + 8$ coefficient: __________

variable: __________

constant: __________

5 $-x + 50$ coefficient: __________

variable: __________

constant: __________

6 $-7 - 20f$ coefficient: __________

variable: __________

constant: __________

7 $-2h + 15$ coefficient: __________

variable: __________

constant: __________

8 $12s^2 + 1$ coefficient: __________

variable: __________

constant: __________

9 $m - 6$ coefficient: __________

variable: __________

constant: __________

Solve.

10 **LOADING** Amalia loaded some logs onto her truck. Each log weighs 250 pounds. Write an expression for how much weight Amalia put on her truck. __________

11 **CHEMISTRY** Rohan mixes two solutions. The first solution has a volume of 115 mL. Write an expression for the total volume of the two solutions mixed together. __________

Write the vocabulary word that completes the sentence.

12 A symbol, usually a letter, used to represent a number is called a __________.

13 A __________ is the numerical factor of a term that contains a variable.

Chapter 9

Lesson 9-2

NAME ______________________________ DATE ______________

Vocabulary and English Language Development

Activate Prior Knowledge

Write *increased* or *decreased* to indicate the change in each item.

1 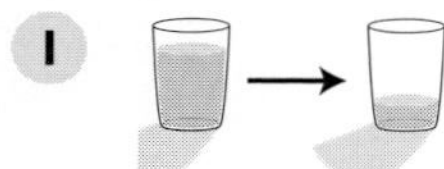

____

2 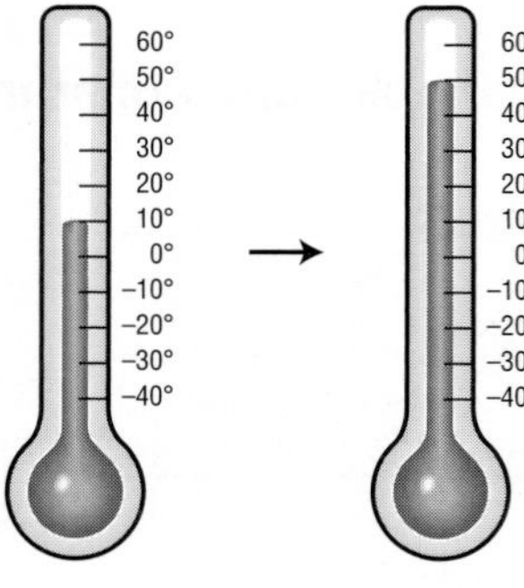

____

3 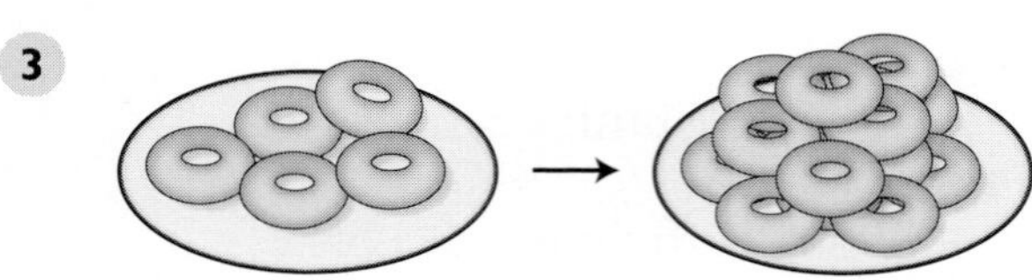

____

Definition Review

Circle the words that tell you to use addition. Draw a rectangle around the words that tell you to use subtraction. Put an X through the words that tell you to use multiplication. Underline the words that tell you to use division.

decreased by   separate into equal groups   times   quotient

product   plus   increased by   twice   divided by

sum   less than   more than   difference   minus

Application

Follow the directions for the activity.

- Divide into groups of 2 or 3 students.
- Each group must solve the following problem.

  Rex has $4. On Sunday, he got 10 times that amount from his grandmother for his birthday. He used half of the gift money to pay back his mother for money he borrowed last month. On Monday, he spent $20 on a new DVD. On Tuesday, he earned $12 for cutting the grass. How much money did Rex have on Tuesday?

- Use play money to solve if needed.
- Discuss the problem and strategies for solving with the class.

NAME ______________________ DATE ______________

Lesson 9-2

Skills Practice

For each phrase, name the operation.

1 the sum of b and 8 ______________

2 r divided by 10 ______________

3 the difference of 22 and p ______________

4 5 times y ______________

5 100 decreased by m ______________

6 24 separated into c equal groups ______________

Translate each phrase to an expression.

7 a number minus 9 ________

8 7 times a number ________

9 the product of 15 and a number ________

10 a number divided by 2 ________

11 42 minus a number ________

12 the sum of a number and 33 ________

13 48 divided by a number ________

14 8 added to a number ________

15 twice a number ________

16 14 less than a number ________

17 22 more than a number ________

18 the quotient of a number and 64 ________

19 take away 1 from a number ________

20 a number divided by 3 ________

Write an expression to represent each situation.

21 Lisa found 15 more shells today.

____

22 Dario earned $6 for each hour of work.

____

23 Tyra gave 3 dolls to her little sister.

____

24 Ting ran 5 miles each day.

____

25 Odina and her friends drove equal parts of their 2,000-mile trip.

____

26 Rajeev bought some CDs that were $16 each.

____

Chapter 9

NAME ______________________ DATE ______________

Lesson 9-2 Problem-Solving Practice

Solve.

1. **EXERCISE** Juwan runs 2 miles every day. Write an expression to represent how far Juwan runs in *d* days. ______________

2. **TRAVEL** Leon has been driving at a constant speed of 60 miles per hour. Write an expression for how long it will take Leon to travel *m* miles. ______________

3. **TRIANGLES** Write an expression for the perimeter of the triangle. ______________

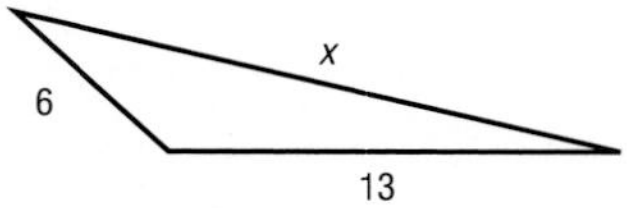

4. **AGES** Celeste is 15 years old. Her sister is 12 years old. Their brother is *y* years old. Write an expression for their combined ages. ______________

5. **READING** Aisha reads 25 pages per hour. Write an expression for how many pages she can read in *h* hours. ______________

6. **TESTS** Sumi scored *t* points fewer than Clara on their biology test. Write an expression to find Sumi's test score if Clara received a 94 on her test. ______________

7. **MAGAZINES** The doctor arranged the 30 magazines equally on *t* tables in the waiting area. Write an expression for the number of magazines on each table. ______________

8. **AGES** Rick is 4 years younger than his sister. Write an expression for Rick's age. ______________

Lesson 9-2

NAME ______________________ DATE ____________

Homework Practice

For each phrase, name the operation.

1. the quotient of t and 3 ________
2. the number 2 plus q ________
3. 5 times f ________
4. 1 increased by m ________
5. the difference between k and 4 ________
6. the product of v and 10 ________
7. 80 divided by r ________
8. a decreased by 9 ________

Translate each phrase to an expression.

9. a number times 18 ________
10. 46 plus a number ________
11. 13 less than a number ________
12. a number divided by 11 ________
13. a number minus 20 ________
14. 53 more than a number ________
15. the quotient of a number and 4 ________
16. 1,000 decreased by a number ________
17. 67 added to a number ________
18. the product of 3 and a number ________

Solve.

19. **PIZZA** An extra large pizza feeds 6 students. Write an expression to find the number of extra large pizzas needed for s students. ________

20. **DRILLS** A factory produces 4 electric drills every minute. Write an expression for how many drills are made in m minutes. ________

Write the vocabulary word that completes the sentence.

21. A ________ is a value that does not change.

22. A(n) ________ is a combination of variables, numbers, and at least one operation.

Chapter 9

Lesson 9-3

NAME ______________________ DATE ______________

Vocabulary and English Language Development

Activate Prior Knowledge

Determine whether the items are similar.

1  

____

2 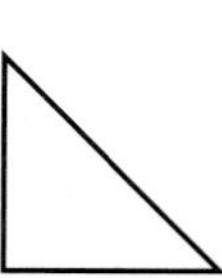 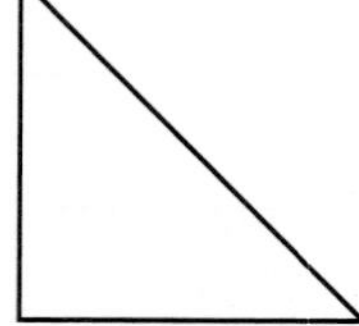

____

3 

____

Definition Review

Draw a line to connect the like terms.

4	$5x$	23
5	$3y^2$	n
6	14	$19x$
7	$-8y$	$-10x^2$
8	$6n$	$4y^2$
9	x^2	$15y$

Application

Follow the directions for the activity.

- Divide into groups of 3 or 4 students.
- Each student will make up like terms that contain constants and variables.
- Students should limit the variables to x and x^2.
- Each group should create an expression using all of the terms created by its members.
- Students then simplify their expressions by combining all of the like terms.
- Share your group's expressions with the rest of the class.
- Did any groups have an expression that was simplified down to 1 term?
- If time allows, combine and simplify the expressions from all of the groups.

NAME ______________________ DATE ____________

Lesson 9-3

Skills Practice

Name the like terms in each expression.

1. $5n + 2 + 13 + n$ ______

2. $12 + 9s^2 - 1 + 8s^2$ ______

3. $4z + 20 - 3z + 10z$ ______

4. $7l + 3l^2 + 8l + l^2 - 6$ ______

5. $3f^2 + 11f + 2 - 4f - 1 + 7f^2$ ______

6. $6g^2 + 15g - 9 + 9g^2$ ______

7. $14y + 9 - 2 + y$ ______

8. $12w + 4 - 2 + 8 + 3$ ______

9. $8h + h + 16 - 6$ ______

10. $12p^2 + 5p - 3p^2 + 18 + 4p - 9$ ______

Simplify each expression. Show your work.

11. $4t + 18 + 10t - 3 + 8$ ______

12. $2g + 5g^2 + 6 + 2g - 6$ ______

13. $8a + 15 - 6 + 3a$ ______

14. $12u^2 + 5u + u - 4 + 3u^2 - 4$ ______

15. $3y^2 + 5y - 2 + 5y + 3$ ______

16. $c^2 + 10c + 7 - 3c + 4c^2 + 3$ ______

Lesson 9-3

NAME ______________________ DATE ____________

Problem-Solving Practice

Solve.

1 **MOVIES** The Gibbons family has several children. When they go to the movies, it usually costs \$4 for each child's ticket, \$2 for each child's popcorn, and \$2 for each child's drink. The expression $4c + 2c + 2c$ represents how much it costs for the Gibbons children to go to the movies. Simplify the expression. ____________

2 **HOUSEWORK** Mr. Hatano needs to clean his house. It usually takes him h hours to dust, $2h$ hours to vacuum, h^2 hours to clean the bathrooms, and $2h$ hours to clean the kitchen. The expression $h + 2h + h^2 + 2h$ represents the number of hours he needs to clean his house. Simplify the expression. ____________

3 **EGGS** Mykia kept track on a chalkboard of how many dozen eggs she used each day last week. Somebody erased her marks from Saturday and Sunday. She knows she always uses twice as many eggs on Sunday as she does on Saturday. She writes the expression $e + 2e + 6 + 4 + 7 + 5 + 6$. Simplify the expression. ____________

4 **RAFFLE** Elise sold x raffle tickets for the school fund-raiser. Jordan sold three times as many tickets as Elise. Sasha sold 22 tickets. Nair sold 15 tickets. The expression $x + 3x + 22 + 15$ represents the number of tickets sold by these four students. Simplify the expression. ____________

5 **CABINETRY** Seth packs 8 screws for each cabinet door and 4 screws for each shelf. In addition, he packs 2 extra screws for each cabinet door order and 1 extra screw for each shelf order. The expression $8d + 2d + 4s + s$ represents the number of screws he packs. Simplify the expression to determine how many screws should be packed based on the number of cabinet doors and shelves. ____________

Lesson 9-3

NAME ______________________ DATE ______________

Homework Practice

Name the like terms in each expression.

1. $7z + 8 - 2 + 4z$

____

2. $9b^2 + 3 + 4b - 3 + b - 6b^2$

____

3. $2a - 4 + 3 - 6a$

____

4. $5h + 10h^2 + 3h^2 + 2h$

____

Simplify each expression. Show your work.

5. $2x + 8x + 5$

____

6. $15 + 3y - y - 9$

____

7. $12a + 5a^2 + 6a - 2a^2 + 3$

____

8. $35g + g^2 - 7 + 7g + 43 + 20g^2$

____

9. $13r + 8r - 16 + 19r^2 - 10r - 4$

____

10. $8n + 9n^2 - 14n + 15n^2$

____

Solve.

11. **NURSES** Kimi manages the nurses in the operating rooms at the local hospital. The expression $n + 2n + n + 2$ represents the number of nurses she needs for every operating room. Simplify the expression to show how many nurses Kimi needs for each operating room. ______________________

Write the vocabulary word that completes the sentence.

12. To ______________ means to combine like terms.

13. A ______________ is a quantity connected by plus or minus signs in an algebraic expression.

Chapter 9

Lesson **9-4**

NAME ______________________________ DATE ______________

Vocabulary and English Language Development

Activate Prior Knowledge

Simplify the expressions following the order of operations.

1. $12 + 8 \div 2$ ________
2. $5 \times 8 + 3$ ________
3. $2 + 7 \times 4$ ________
4. $9 \div 3 - 1 + 6$ ________

Definition Review

When you **evaluate** an **algebraic expression** you find the **value** of the expression by replacing the variables with numerals.

Write the words that explain the order of operations.

To use the order of operations

1. Simplify ____________________ symbols.
2. Simplify ____________________.
3. Multiply and divide in order from ____________________ to ____________________.
4. ____________________ in order from left to right.

Application

Follow the directions for the activity.

- Divide into groups of 5 or 6 students.
- Each student will make up a term using either a, a^2, b, or b^2.
- Each group should create an expression using all of the terms created by its members.
- Groups exchange and simplify each other's expressions.
- They then choose a value for each variable in the expression and evaluate the expression.
- Groups review and share the expression they simplified and evaluated with the rest of the class.

Lesson 9-4

NAME ______________________ DATE ______________

Skills Practice

Evaluate each expression when $x = 2$ and $y = 7$.

1. $x + 5 + y$
2. $3y - 8 + x$
3. $y^2 - x + 20$
4. $5x + 3y - x^2$
5. $xy - 1$
6. $19 + x \div 2 - 2y$
7. $6 + 8y \div 4$
8. $y^2 - 4y + 2x$
9. $2x \div 4 + 6y$
10. $10y - x^2$
11. $18 + 12x \div 6$
12. $5y - 10 + x^2$

Evaluate each expression when $a = 3$, $b = 4$, and $c = 5$.

13. $8a + b^2 - 55 \div c$
14. $3a - b + 6 - a^2$
15. $18 + c + 2a - b$
16. $10b + c^2 - (16 - 7)$
17. $12 - b \div 2 + (b + c)^2$
18. $9b \div 6 + 15 + b^2$
19. $(11c - 10a) \div c + 42$
20. $b + 6c + a^2$
21. $10 - c + 12 - b + 9a$
22. $14 + a^2 - 6 + b \div 2 - 8$

NAME ______________________ DATE ______________

Problem-Solving Practice

Solve.

1. **EARNINGS** Alex gets paid \$5 per hour, plus \$3 per hour in tips, and \$40 per shift. The expression $5h + 3h + 40$ equals how much Alex makes during a shift when h represents the number of hours he works.

   How much will Alex make if he works a 5-hour shift? ______________

2. **ALLOWANCE** For her allowance, Pelipa gets 2 points for taking out the trash, 3 points for doing the dishes, and 1 point for feeding the dog. The expression $2t + 3d + 1f$ equals the total number of points she gets in a week when t represents the number of times she takes out the trash, d represents the number of times she does the dishes, and f represents the number of times she feeds the dog.

   If Pelipa took out the trash once, washed the dishes 3 times, and fed the dog 5 times, how many points did she earn for the week? ______________

3. **GARDENING** Sujit was told to use 10 grams of fertilizer for each tomato plant, 15 grams for each bean plant, and 8 grams for each pepper plant. The expression $10t + 15b + 8p$ equals how much fertilizer should be used when t represents the number of tomato plants, b represents the number of bean plants, and p represents the number of pepper plants.

   How much fertilizer does Sujit need if she has 2 tomato plants, 1 bean plant, and 5 pepper plants? ______________

4. **ELECTRICITY** An air conditioner uses 2 kilowatts of electricity on low and 5 kilowatts on high. The expression $2l + 5h$ equals how much electricity the air conditioner uses when l represents the number of hours on low and h represents the number of hours on high. Leandro ran the air conditioner for 3 hours on low and 6 hours on high yesterday.

   How many kilowatts of electricity did the air conditioner use? ______________

NAME ______________________ DATE ______________

Lesson 9-4

Homework Practice

Evaluate each expression when $x = 2$ and $y = 10$.

1. $17 + x$ ________
2. $x - 1 + y^2$ ________
3. $74 \div x$ ________
4. $y \div x + 3x$ ________
5. $7y + 6 - 3x$ ________
6. $x^2 + 139$ ________
7. $3y \div 5 + 4y \div 5$ ________
8. $11 - y + 6x$ ________

Evaluate each expression when $x = 8$, $y = 9$, and $z = 0$.

9. $x^2 + 3 - 10 + z^2$ ________
10. $5y - 2x + 15 - z$ ________
11. $7z - 4 + 3y$ ________
12. $20 - y + 5x + 6z$ ________
13. $6 + y^2 + 12 - x$ ________
14. $15 + x + y + z + 10y$ ________
15. $4x - z + x \div 2$ ________
16. $4y \div 6 + 7z + x$ ________

Solve.

17. Maria's cat is fed 2 scoops of dry food in the morning, and 1 cup of dry food at night. The expression $2s + c$ equals the number of dry food pieces the cat is fed per day, where s equals the number of pieces in a scoop and c equals the number of pieces in a cup. How many pieces of food does the cat eat per day if a scoop has 30 pieces and a cup has 75 pieces? ________

18. **BAKING** Oya needs 10 minutes to set up, 40 minutes to bake, and 20 minutes to clean up for each loaf of bread. The expression $10b + 40b + 20b$ equals the time it takes for b batches of bread. Oya wants to make 5 batches of bread tomorrow. How many minutes will it take him? ________

Write the vocabulary word that completes the sentence.

19. A(n) ________ is a combination of variables, numbers, and at least one operation.

20. The ________ are rules that tell which operation to perform first when more than one operation is used.

Chapter 9

NAME ______________________ DATE ______________

Chapter 10

Foldables Study Organizer

Dinah Zike's Foldables

Make this Foldable to help you organize the information about equations.

1 Begin with two sheets of $8\frac{1}{2}'' \times 11''$ paper. Fold one sheet in half from top to bottom. Cut along the fold from the edges to the margin.

2 Fold the other sheet in half from top to bottom. Cut along the fold between the margins.

3 Insert the first sheet through the second sheet and align the folds.

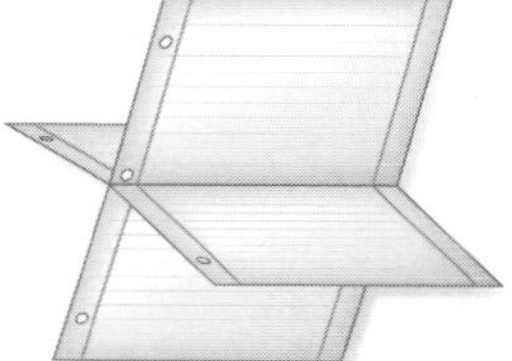

4 Label each inside page with a lesson number and title.

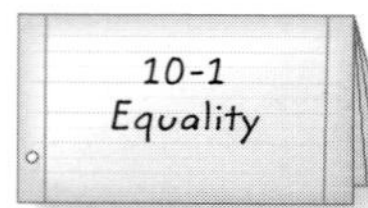

TAKING NOTES

As you read through the chapter, use your Foldable to organize the information you learn about equations.

USING YOUR FOLDABLE

As you study, use your Foldable to write examples, record key concepts, define terms, and take notes. Record what you learn about the parts of each lesson that you find most difficult.

USING YOUR FOLDABLE

Work with a partner. Quiz each other on solving equations using addition, subtraction, multiplication, and division. Be sure to give your partner the correct answer if he or she is not correct.

NAME ______________________ DATE ______________

Chapter 10

Games and Puzzles

Roll a Solution

DIRECTIONS

- Decide who will be Player A and who will be Player B. Both players begin with 5 points.
- Both players solve the equations below and check that they agree on the solutions.
- Take turns rolling a 1–6 number cube. If the number is a solution of…
  … one equation, earn 1 point for that round.
  … two equations, earn 2 points for that round.
- If the number is not a solution, you lose one point for that round.
- Keep track of your points on the score sheet.
- **Who Wins?** The player with the greater score after 10 rounds wins.

What You Need

- Number Cube
- Roll a Solution Score Sheet

Number of Players

2

$x + 4 = 7$	$x + 8 = 12$
$6x = 30$	$x - 1 = 1$
$\frac{x}{12} = 4$	$3x = 18$
$x - 4 = 2$	$9x = 36$

Chapter 10

NAME ____________________ DATE ____________

Roll a Solution Score Sheet

	Player A: ____________	Player B: ____________
	Points	Points
Beginning of Game	5	5
After Round 1		
After Round 2		
After Round 3		
After Round 4		
After Round 5		
After Round 6		
After Round 7		
After Round 8		
After Round 9		
After Round 10		

Lesson 10-1

NAME ________________ DATE ________________

Vocabulary and English Language Development

Activate Prior Knowledge

Use the words *equal* or *unequal* to describe each picture.

1 

____

2 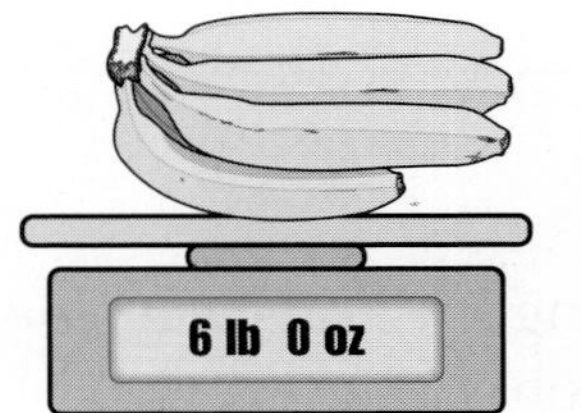

____

Definition Review

Write the vocabulary word that completes each sentence.

3 An ______________ is a mathematical sentence that contains an equals sign, $=$.

4 ______________ means having the same value.

Find the missing number to make each equation true.

5 $12 + 10 =$ ______________ $+ (5 \times 2)$

Since $10 =$ ______________,

$12 + 10 =$ ______________ $+ (5 \times 2)$

by the ______________ Property of Equality.

6 $3 \times 15 =$ ______________ $\times (19 - 4)$

Since $15 =$ ______________,

$3 \times 15 =$ ______________ $\times (19 - 4)$

by the ______________ Property of Equality.

Application

Follow the directions to complete the activity.

- Each pair of students will need 2 dry-wipe boards and markers.
- Student #1 writes an expression using either addition or multiplication.
- Student #2 looks at the expression and writes an equivalent expression.
- Students put the expressions together with an equal sign to create an equation. Students simplify each side to see if the equation is true. Student #2 rewrites his or her expression if both sides are not equal.
- Students switch jobs and continue as time allows.

Chapter 10

NAME ______________________ DATE ______________

Lesson 10-1

Skills Practice

1 Show that adding 4 to each side of $5 + 3 = 6 + 2$ results in a balanced equation.

____

____

2 Show that multiplying by 3 on each side of $3 \times 2 = 6 \times 1$ results in a balanced equation.

____

____

Find the missing number to make each equation balanced.

3 $(8 + 6) + 3 = (10 + 4) +$ ________

4 $(2 \times 5) \times$ ________ $= (10 \times 1) \times 5$

5 $(2 \times$ ________ $) \times 2 = (4 \times 4) \times 2$

6 $(10 + 8) + 1 = ($ ________ $+ 6) + 1$

7 $(21 \div$ ________ $) + 6 = (3 + 4) + 6$

8 $($ ________ $\times 4) \times 3 = 3 \times (10 \times 2)$

9 $(36 \div 4) \times$ ________ $= 7 \times (4 + 5)$

10 ________ $+ (7 - 3) = (2 \times 2) + 4$

11 $(1 \times 9) + 10 =$ ________ $+ (12 - 3)$

12 $($ ________ $\div 6) \times 5 = (2 \times 4) \times 5$

13 $(9 \times$ ________ $) \times 3 = (14 + 4) \times 3$

14 $(15 \div 3) + 1 = 1 + (15 -$ ________ $)$

15 $(40 \div 4) \times 6 = (5 +$ ________ $) \times 6$

16 $(3 \times 9) \times 2 =$ ________ $\times (30 - 3)$

17 $(6 +$ ________ $) + 15 = 15 + (7 + 4)$

18 $9 + (24 - 7) = (20 - 3) +$ ________

NAME ______________________ DATE ____________

Lesson 10-1

Problem-Solving Practice

Solve.

1 **WALKING** Jamal walked 2 miles on Monday and 5 miles on Tuesday. Vito walked 3 miles on Monday and 4 miles on Tuesday. They both walked 4 miles on Wednesday. Did Jamal and Vito walk the same number of miles? Explain.

____

2 **SHOPPING** Brittany bought a jar of peanut butter and a box of crackers. Sharon bought a box of cereal and a pint of milk. They both bought a loaf of bread. Did Brittany and Sharon spend equal amounts of money? Explain.

____

3 **PETS** Benjamin's dog weighs 15 pounds. His cat weighs 8 pounds. Emily's dog weighs 12 pounds. Her cat weighs 10 pounds. They each buy a rabbit that weighs 5 pounds. Is the total weight of Benjamin's pets equal to the total weight of Emily's pets? Explain.

____

4 **PICTURES** Lydia put 1 row of 8 pictures on each of 2 of her bedroom walls. Cecelia put 2 rows of 4 pictures on each of 2 of her bedroom walls. Did Lydia and Cecelia put the same number of pictures on their bedroom walls? Explain.

____

5 **EXERCISE** The bar graph shows the number of miles Sada and Fina ran on each of 3 days. Did Sada and Fina run the same total distance during the 3 days? Explain.

____

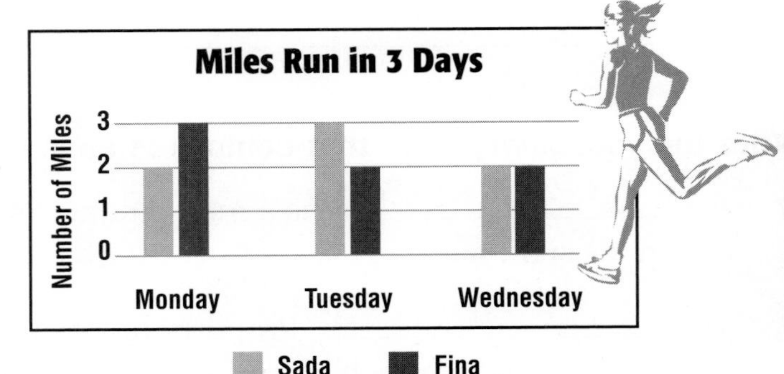

Chapter 10

NAME ______________________________ DATE ______________

Lesson 10-1 Homework Practice

1 Show that adding 3 to each side of $5 + 2 = 6 + 1$ results in a balanced equation.

____

____

2 Show that multiplying 2 on each side of $2 \times 2 = 4 \times 1$ results in a balanced equation.

____

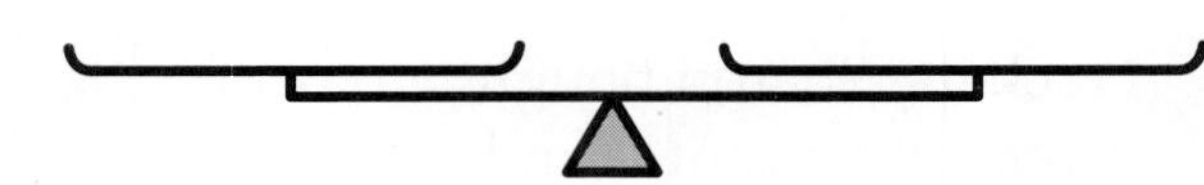

____

Find the missing number to make each equation balanced.

3 $(9 + 5) +$ ______ $= (7 + 7) + 5$

4 $(8 \times 4) \times 3 = ($______ $\times 2) \times 3$

Solve.

5 **SPORTS CARDS** Julian has 10 baseball cards and 15 football cards. Laura has 13 baseball cards and 12 football cards. They each have 8 basketball cards. Do Julian and Laura have the same number of sports cards? Explain.

____

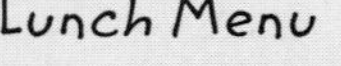

Lunch Menu

Veggie Burger $2.50
Turkey Sandwich $3.00
Tuna fish Sandwich $2.75

Soda $1.00
Bottled Water $0.75
Milk $0.75

Oatmeal cookie $0.50
Fruit Bowl $0.75

6 **LUNCH** Delilah buys a veggie burger and a bottle of water for lunch. Carlos buys a tuna fish sandwich and a carton of milk for lunch. They both buy an oatmeal cookie. Do Delilah and Carlos spend the same amount of money on lunch? Explain.

____

____

Write the vocabulary word that completes each sentence.

7 An ______________ is a mathematical sentence that contains an equals sign, =.

8 The ______________ Property of Equality states that adding the same amount to each side of an equation results in a balanced equation.

Lesson 10-2

NAME ____________ DATE ____________

Vocabulary and English Language Development

Activate Prior Knowledge

Solve.

1 **SAVINGS** Felipe has $12 and wants to buy a skateboard. How much more does Felipe need to save? ______

$55.00

2 **SNACKS** Millie bought 3 of the same granola bar. The total cost was $1.95. Write the price of each granola bar on the price tags.

Definition Review

3 A ____________ is a symbol, usually a letter, used to represent a number.

4 ____________ operations are operations which undo each other.

5 Addition and ____________ are inverse operations.

6 Multiplication and ____________ are inverse operations.

Application

Solve.

- Find the value for the box in each equation.
- Use the key to determine what letters the different values of the box represent.
- Write the letter that the box represents above the question number.
- Use the key to answer the following question.

What area of math deals with representing numbers with letters and solving for the unknown?

___	___	___	___	___	___	___
5	3	1	6	2	4	5

KEY:

A = 50	B = 16	C = 24	E = 82	F = 21	G = 28	I = 32	L = 25
M = 41	O = 85	R = 22	T = 13	V = 61	W = 35	Z = 10	

1 $36 - \square = 8$

$\square =$ ______

2 $\frac{\square}{4} = 4$

$\square =$ ______

3 $\frac{\square}{5} = 5$

$\square =$ ______

4 $\square + 20 = 42$

$\square =$ ______

5 $5 \times \square = 250$

$\square =$ ______

6 $\square - 80 = 2$

$\square =$ ______

Chapter 10

NAME ______________________ DATE ______________

Lesson 10-2

Skills Practice

Find the value of each box by modeling the equation.

1. $3 + \square = 8$

$\square =$ ______

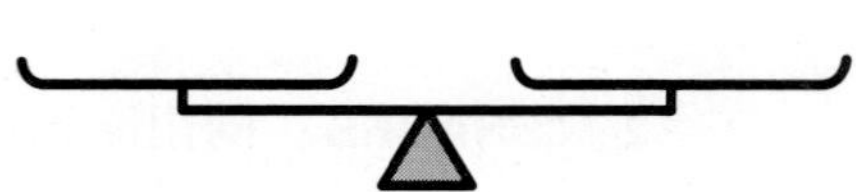

2. $15 - \square = 9$

$\square =$ ______

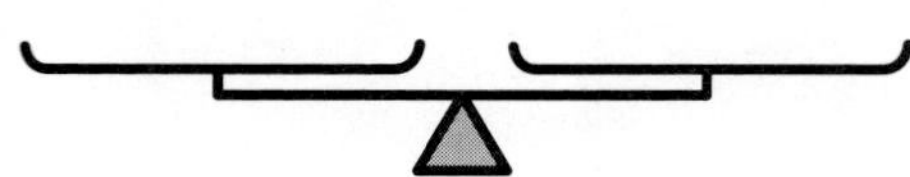

Find the value of the box in each equation.

3. $\square + 12 = 19$

$\square =$ ______

4. $8 \times \square = 24$

$\square =$ ______

5. $20 - \square = 14$

$\square =$ ______

6. $\frac{\square}{3} = 5$

$\square =$ ______

7. $7 + \square = 32$

$\square =$ ______

8. $\square \times 20 = 100$

$\square =$ ______

9. $\square - 14 = 16$

$\square =$ ______

10. $\frac{\square}{5} = 8$

$\square =$ ______

NAME ______________________ DATE ______________

Lesson 10-2

Problem-Solving Practice

Solve.

1 **TRAVEL** Mr. Davis is driving 350 miles to visit his friend. He drives 150 miles the first day of the trip. How many miles does Mr. Davis still need to drive? ____________

2 **TREES** Dion planted 20 fruit trees. He planted 8 apple trees. The rest of the trees were cherry trees. How many cherry trees did he plant? ____________

3 **COOKIES** Melody baked 84 cookies for a bake sale. She divided the cookies equally into 21 bags. How many cookies did Melody put into each bag? ____________

4 **TRAILS** Ruben hiked 2 trails over the weekend. He hiked a total of 22 miles. First Ruben hiked the Canyon Peak trail. What is the name of the second trail he hiked? ____________

Hiking Trails	
Name	**Length (miles)**
Canyon Peak	14
Winding Way	9
Lone Wolf	8
Blue Spring	11

5 **EARNINGS** Ivan worked 16 hours last week and earned $128. How much money did Ivan earn in one hour? ____________

6 **COLLECTIONS** Ally has 74 seashells in her collection. She gives 12 seashells to her sister. How many seashells are in her collection now? ____________

7 **THEATER** Sandra bought 8 tickets to the play *Now is the Time*. All the tickets were in the same section. If Sandra spent $96 on tickets, in what section did she buy the tickets? ____________

Ticket Prices for *Now is the Time*	
Section	**Price**
Lower Level	$15
Middle Level	$14
Upper Level	$12

8 **TENNIS** Jerry bought 6 cans of tennis balls. There are 3 tennis balls in each can. How many tennis balls did Jerry buy? ____________

NAME ______________________ DATE ______________

Lesson 10-2

Homework Practice

Find the value of each box by modeling the equation.

1. $2 \times \square = 12$

$\square =$ ______

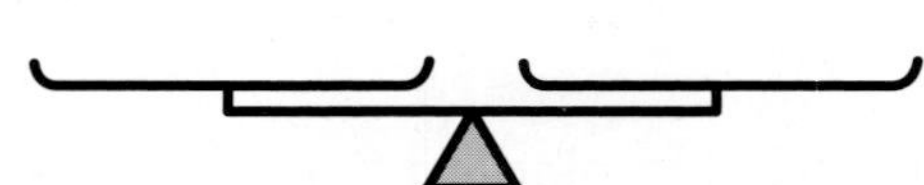

2. $\frac{\square}{4} = 3$

$\square =$ ______

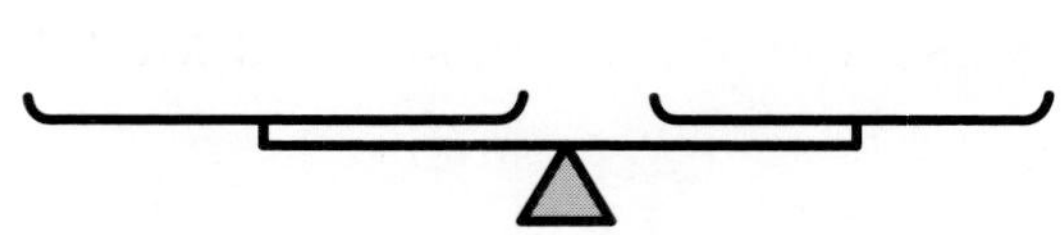

Find the value of the box in each equation.

3. $4 \times \square = 48$

$\square =$ ______

4. $\square + 5 = 17$

$\square =$ ______

5. $\frac{\square}{5} = 5$

$\square =$ ______

6. $16 - \square = 5$

$\square =$ ______

Solve.

7. **TIRES** Reba bought 2 new tires for her bicycle. She spent $30. How much did each tire cost?

8. **FIELD TRIP** Thirty-four students and adults went on a field trip to a museum. Eight adults went on the trip. How many students went?

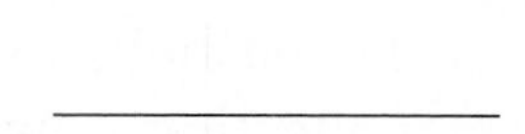

9. **EQUATIONS** Mrs. Ortega wrote the following equation on the board: $6 \times \square = 42$. Jonah said that $\square = 36$. Was Jonah correct? Explain.

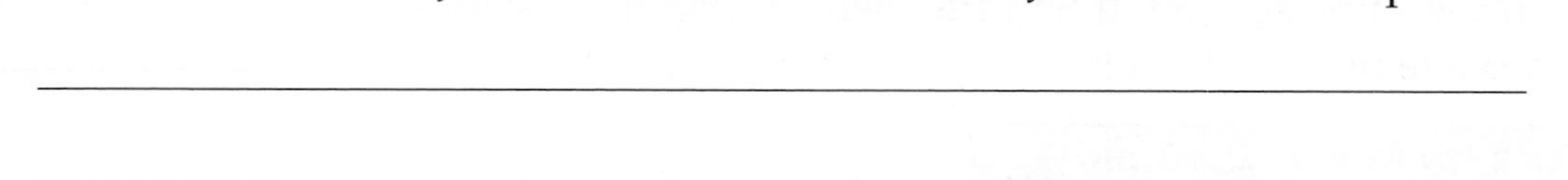

Write the vocabulary word that completes each sentence.

10. A symbol, usually a letter, used to represent a number is a ______________.

11. Operations that undo each other are ______________.

Lesson 10-3

NAME ______________________________ DATE ______________

Vocabulary and English Language Development

Activate Prior Knowledge

Draw a line from each equation to the value of *y* that makes it balanced.

1	$y - 5 = 8$	3
2	$2 \times y = 6$	6
3	$\frac{y}{3} = 9$	13
4	$y + 3 = 9$	27

Definition Review

Fill in the blanks.

5 The ______________________________ states that adding the same amount to each side of an equation results in a balanced equation.

6 The ______________________________ states that subtracting the same amount from each side of an equation results in a balanced equation.

Application

Put on a play.

- Put on a play to model the Subtraction Property of Equality. Use the teacher's desk to represent the equals sign. You can tape a piece of paper with an equals sign to the desk.
- One student stands to the left side of the teacher's desk and holds a piece of paper with an x written on it. A certain number of other students also stand on the left side, while a certain number stand on the right stand. Make the number on the right greater than the number on the left.
- The skit should begin by telling what equation is represented. Then the x student states a reason for wanting to be alone. The students on the same side explain that they cannot leave unless they each have an escort from the other side (or come up with another reason).
- The same number of students from each side of the desk leave the equation and sit down at their seats. The student holding the x is alone on the left side.
- Discuss which equation the remaining students represent.
- Repeat for another equation. Be original with the reasons for leaving the equation. Have fun!
- If time permits, put on a play to model the Addition Property of Equality. One way is to begin with an equation such as $x = 4$.

NAME ______________________ DATE ______________

Lesson 10-3 Skills Practice

Solve for *x*.

1. $x - 6 \quad = 1$

   $x - 6$ ________ $= 1$ ________

   $x =$ ________

2. $x + 4 \quad = 9$

   $x + 4$ ________ $= 9$ ________

   $x =$ ________

3. $x + 11 \quad = 21$

   $x + 11$ ________ $= 21$ ________

   $x =$ ________

4. $x - 18 \quad = 3$

   $x - 18$ ________ $= 3$ ________

   $x =$ ________

Solve each equation.

5. $b + 8 = 30$

   $b =$ ________

6. $g - 7 = 15$

   $g =$ ________

7. $m - 12 = 13$

   $m =$ ________

8. $x + 9 = 10$

   $x =$ ________

9. $v - 13 = 2$

   $v =$ ________

10. $s - 16 = 14$

    $s =$ ________

11. $y + 17 = 25$

    $y =$ ________

12. $w - 12 = 5$

    $w =$ ________

13. $x + 1 = 13$

    $x =$ ________

14. $c + 7 = 13$

    $c =$ ________

15. $a - 4 = 8$

    $a =$ ________

16. $t + 3 = 24$

    $t =$ ________

17. $k + 14 = 23$

    $k =$ ________

18. $k - 1 = 8$

    $k =$ ________

NAME ________________________________ DATE ______________

Lesson 10-3

Problem-Solving Practice

Solve.

1 **YOGA** Write and solve an equation to find *m*, the number of minutes that Kiley practiced yoga. ____________

	Yoga Time
John	30 min
Kiley	?
Total	50 min

2 **MUSIC** Liel and Sara downloaded 8 songs together this week. Sara downloaded 3 songs. Write and solve an equation to find *s*, the number of songs Liel downloaded this week. ____________

3 **FOOD** Eric is serving meals to people at a family dinner. He has already served 4 people. He has 8 people left to serve. Write and solve an equation to find *p*, the number of people Eric is serving at the family dinner. ____________

4 **TICKETS** Jenna and Joey have sold 24 tickets together. Joey has sold 15 tickets. Write and solve an equation to find *t*, the number of tickets Jenna has sold. ____________

5 **VOCABULARY** Marty has to write definitions for science vocabulary words for homework. He has already written definitions for 6 words. He has to write definitions for 10 more words. Write and solve an equation to find *d*, the total number of definitions Marty must write. ____________

6 **BASEBALL HATS** Ricardo bought 2 baseball hats. He now has 22 baseball hats. Write and solve an equation to find *h*, the number of baseball hats Ricardo had before he bought 2 more. ____________

NAME ________________________ DATE ____________

Lesson 10-3

Homework Practice

Solve for *x*.

1. $x + 3 \qquad = 14$

   $x + 3$ ______ $= 14$ ______

   $x =$ ______

2. $x - 5 \qquad = 7$

   $x - 5$ ______ $= 7$ ______

   $x =$ ______

3. $x + 16 \qquad = 32$

   $x + 16$ ______ $= 32$ ______

   $x =$ ______

Solve each equation.

4. $v - 4 = 17$

   $v =$ ______

5. $d + 9 = 19$

   $d =$ ______

6. $a - 18 = 2$

   $a =$ ______

7. $h - 1 = 5$

   $h =$ ______

8. $s + 12 = 24$

   $s =$ ______

9. $y + 6 = 18$

   $y =$ ______

10. $m + 22 = 30$

    $m =$ ______

11. $e - 11 = 21$

    $e =$ ______

Solve.

12. **PAINTING** Rena spent 5 hours painting a picture on Monday and Tuesday. She painted for 2 hours on Tuesday. Write and solve an equation to find *h*, the number of hours Rena painted on Monday. ______

13. **PHOTOGRAPHY** Arno framed some of his digital photos. He gave 4 away as gifts and has 6 left. Write and solve an equation to find *p*, the number of photos Arno framed. ______

Lesson 10-4

NAME ____________________ DATE ____________

Vocabulary and English Language Development

Activate Prior Knowledge

Solve.

1 Sue owes Nabol money. If Sue repays $8, she owes $7 more. Write and solve an equation to find *d*, the amount of the original debt.

2 Sue owes Nabol money. The original debt was $15. After repaying some, Sue still owes $7. Write and solve an equation to find *r*, the amount that was repaid.

Definition Review

Fill in the blanks.

3 The ____________ Property of Equality states that adding the same amount to each side of an equation results in a balanced equation.

4 The Subtraction Property of Equality states that ____________ the same amount from each side of an equation results in a balanced equation.

Application

Follow the directions to solve equations with a physical model.

- Students work in pairs.
- The first student creates an equation with numbers only.
- This student replaces one of the numbers on the left side of the equation with a variable. Rewrite the equation with the variable.
- The first student then represents the equation on a balance scale with blocks. Place a paper bag over the variable on the left side of the scale. (Bag weight may require scale adjustment.)
- The second student begins to solve the equation by removing one block at a time from each side of the scale, keeping the scale balanced.
- This student continues removing blocks until only the bag and its contents remain on the left side of the scale.
- The balanced scale indicates that the blocks on the right must equal those under the bag. This is the solution. Uncover to check.
- Repeat, switching student roles. *(Refer to the example shown.)*

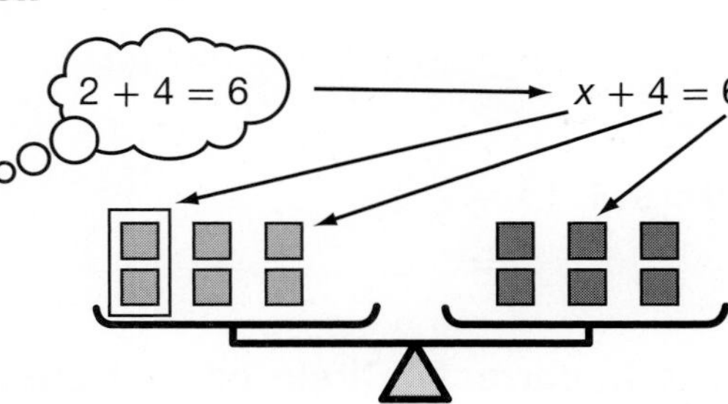

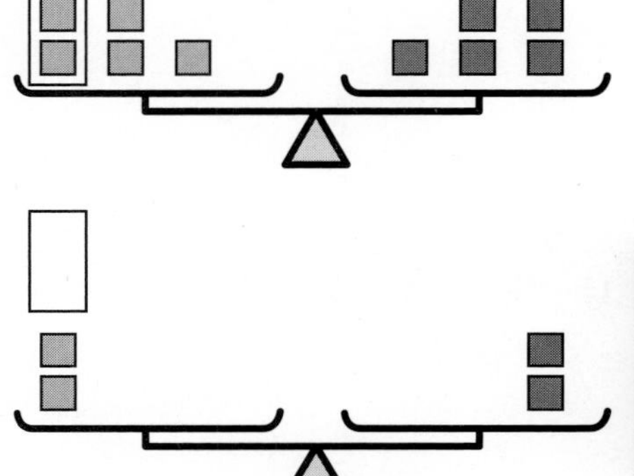

Lesson 10-4

NAME ______________________ DATE ____________

Skills Practice

Solve each equation.

1 $d + 7 = 3$

$d + 7$ ______ $= 3$ ______

$d =$ ______

2 $s - 5 = -1$

$s - 5$ ______ $= -1$ ______

$s =$ ______

3 $a - 12 = 13$

$a - 12$ ______ $= 13$ ______

$a =$ ______

4 $y + 10 = -8$

$y + 10$ ______ $= -8$ ______

$y =$ ______

5 $t - 6 = -15$

$t - 6$ ______ $= -15$ ______

$t =$ ______

6 $n + 16 = 4$

$n + 16$ ______ $= 4$ ______

$n =$ ______

7 $t - 6 = -10$

$t =$ ______

8 $n + 5 = -17$

$n =$ ______

9 $h + 12 = 9$

$h =$ ______

10 $y - 15 = 13$

$y =$ ______

11 $x + 13 = 7$

$x =$ ______

12 $u + 1 = -8$

$u =$ ______

Who Is correct? Circle correct answer(s). Cross out incorrect answer(s).

13 Solve $h - 5 = -6$.

Maria

$h - 5 = -6$
$h - 5 + 5 = -6 + 5$
$h = -11$

Galine

$h - 5 = -6$
$h - 5 + 5 = -6 + 5$
$h = -1$

Elle

$h - 5 = -6$
$h - 5 - 5 = -6 - 5$
$h = -11$

14 Solve $x + 7 = 2$.

Peyton

$x + 7 = 2$
$x + 7 - 7 = 2 - 7$
$x = -5$

Hunter

$x + 7 = 2$
$x + 7 - 7 = 2 - 7$
$x = -9$

Shiro

$x + 7 = 2$
$x + 7 + (-7) = 2 + (-7)$
$x = -5$

Lesson 10-4 NAME ________________________ DATE ____________

Problem-Solving Practice

Solve.

1 **TELEVISION** Ken is choosing between 2 packages for cable television. Write and solve an equation to find c, the number of additional channels Ken will receive, if he gets the premium package instead of the basic package. ____________

SAT-COM
YOUR cable company!

Package	Channels
Basic Cable Package	165 channels
Premium Cable Package	240 channels
Ultimate Cable Package	305 channels

2 **MOVIES** A theater has 105 seats. On Thursday night, there were 28 vacant seats. Write and solve an equation to find t, the number of tickets sold that night. ____________

3 **FASHION** Kiri has a red shirt and a black shirt. The red shirt has sleeves 18 inches long, which is 6 inches shorter than the sleeves of her black shirt. Write and solve an equation to find l, the length of the sleeves on her black shirt. ____________

4 **TELEVISION** Edgar bought a new, larger television set for his house. His new set has a 31-inch screen, which is 6 inches longer than his old set. Write and solve an equation to find d, the size of his old screen. ____________

5 **SALT** Kendra is comparing the salt in two packages of cereal. The oat cereal has 190 mg of salt, which is 130 mg less than that in the rice cereal. Write and solve an equation to find s, the amount of salt in the rice cereal. ____________

6 **DIVING** A diver is 25 feet below the surface of the water. After rising some, he is only 3 feet below the surface. Write and solve an equation to find r, the amount he rose. ____________

NAME ______________________ DATE ______________

Lesson 10-4

Homework Practice

Who Is correct? Circle corerct answer(s). Cross out incorrect answer(s).

1. Solve $f - 7 = -12$.

Samantha	Xavier	Haji
$f - 7 = -12$ $f - 7 + 7 = -12 + 7$ $f = -5$	$f - 7 = -12$ $f - 7 - 7 = -12 - 7$ $f = -19$	$f - 7 = -12$ $f - 7 + 7 = -12 + 7$ $f = 5$

2. Solve $g + 3 = 2$.

Sandra	Steve	Phong
$g + 3 = 2$ $g + 3 - 3 = 2 - 3$ $g = 1$	$g + 3 = 2$ $g + 3 - 3 = 2 - 3$ $g = -1$	$g + 3 = 2$ $g + 3 + (-3) = 2 + (-3)$ $g = -1$

Solve each equation.

3. $w + 7 \quad = 4$
   $w + 7$ ______ $= 4$ ______
   $w =$ ______

4. $r - 8 \quad = -11$
   $r - 8$ ______ $= -11$ ______
   $r =$ ______

5. $w + 18 = 12$
   $w =$ ______

6. $h - 9 = 12$
   $h =$ ______

7. $x - 4 = -12$
   $x =$ ______

8. $p + 13 = 5$
   $p =$ ______

9. $c - 2 = -20$
   $c =$ ______

10. $z + 1 = -9$
    $z =$ ______

Solve.

11. **MOVIES** The total length of the movies showing in cinema 1 and cinema 2 is 257 minutes. Write and solve an equation to find m, the length of the movie showing in cinema 2.

NOW SHOWING	
CINEMA	MOVIE LENGTH
1	125 minutes
2	

____

Lesson 10-5

NAME ______________________________ DATE ______________

Vocabulary and English Language Development

Activate Prior Knowledge

Find the missing value for the box or the variable.

1. $2 \times a = 18$

   $a =$ __________

2. $\square \times 7 = 42$

   $\square =$ __________

3. $\frac{\square}{5} = 9$

   $\square =$ __________

4. $\frac{t}{6} = 4$

   $t =$ __________

5. $k \times 3 = 15$

   $k =$ __________

6. $\frac{\square}{8} = 4$

   $\square =$ __________

Definition Review

Fill in the blanks.

7. The ______________________________ states that multiplying each side of an equation by the same amount results in a balanced equation.

8. The ______________________________ states that dividing each side of an equation by the same amount results in a balanced equation.

Write "*M*" if the Multiplication Property of Equality is shown and "*D*" if the Division Property of Equality is shown.

9. $3x = 12$

   $\frac{3x}{3} = \frac{12}{3}$ __________

10. $\frac{x}{3} = 12$

    $3 \times \frac{x}{3} = 12 \times 3$ __________

Application

Make equations.

- Students work in pairs.
- The first student chooses either the Multiplication or the Division Property of Equality. The second student writes an equation that could be solved by using that property.
- The first student solves the equation. The second student checks the answer by substituting the solution back into the original equation.
- Switch roles. Repeat as time permits.

NAME ______________________ DATE ______________

Lesson 10-5

Skills Practice

Solve each equation.

1. $3g = 12$

inverse operation: ______________

Divide each side of the equation by ______________.

$g =$ ______________

2. $\frac{e}{5} = 5$

inverse operation: ______________

Multiply each side of the equation by ______________.

$e =$ ______________

3. $\frac{m}{-9} = -4$

inverse operation: ______________

Multiply each side of the equation by ______________.

$m =$ ______________

4. $6q = 60$

inverse operation: ______________

Divide each side of the equation by ______________.

$q =$ ______________

5. $-7x = 56$

inverse operation: ______________

Divide each side of the equation by ______________.

$x =$ ______________

6. $\frac{b}{2} = 8$

inverse operation: ______________

Multiply each side of the equation by ______________.

$b =$ ______________

7. $\frac{k}{7} = 3$

$k =$ ______________

8. $9w = 54$

$w =$ ______________

9. $8z = 24$

$z =$ ______________

10. $\frac{x}{4} = 8$

$x =$ ______________

11. $\frac{y}{2} = 7$

$y =$ ______________

12. $-3t = 21$

$t =$ ______________

13. $\frac{x}{10} = -3$

$x =$ ______________

14. $5c = 40$

$c =$ ______________

15. $4x = 28$

$x =$ ______________

16. $-6h = -24$

$h =$ ______________

17. $\frac{k}{9} = -5$

$k =$ ______________

18. $\frac{n}{3} = 5$

$n =$ ______________

19. $-7z = 42$

$z =$ ______________

20. $\frac{d}{6} = 1$

$d =$ ______________

NAME ______________________ DATE ____________

Problem-Solving Practice

Solve.

Nutrition Facts	
Serving Size 1 cup	
Servings Per Container 2	
Amount Per Serving	
Calories 110	**Calories from Fat** 6

1. **CALORIES** Read the label for a can of soup. Write and solve an equation to find c, the total Calories in the entire can of soup.

   ____

2. **AGES** Lucia's mom is three times as old as she is. Lucia's mom is 36 years old. Write and solve an equation to find a, Lucia's age.

   ____

3. **CONSTRUCTION** Sophie and her helper can lay 100 bricks in an hour. Write and solve an equation to find b, the number of bricks Sophie and her helper can lay in 5 hours.

   ____

4. **DEBT** Val owes money to his friend, Nigel. Val plans to pay Nigel back $8 every week for 6 weeks. Write and solve an equation to find m, the total amount of money that Val borrowed.

   ____

5. **BUBBLE GUM** Tanner bought 7 pieces of bubble gum for 56¢. Write and solve an equation to find g, the cost of one piece of bubble gum.

   ____

6. **SIT-UPS** Franz set a goal to do 100 sit-ups. He wants to do 25 sit-ups each day. Write and solve an equation to find d, the number of days it will take to meet his goal.

   ____

7. **RUNNING** Alykhan runs 4 miles every day. Write an equation to find the number of miles, m he runs in 5 days.

   ____

Lesson 10-5

NAME ________________ DATE ________________

Homework Practice

Solve each equation.

1. $\frac{y}{8} = 3$

   inverse operation: ________

   Multiply each side of the equation by ________.

   $y =$ ________

2. $-5f = 30$

   inverse operation: ________

   Divide each side of the equation by ________.

   $f =$ ________

3. $4a = 44$

   inverse operation: ________

   Divide each side of the equation by ________.

   $a =$ ________

4. $\frac{u}{7} = -7$

   inverse operation: ________

   Multiply each side of the equation by ________.

   $u =$ ________

5. $\frac{w}{7} = 9$

   $w =$ ________

6. $6f = 30$

   $f =$ ________

7. $3b = -27$

   $b =$ ________

8. $\frac{d}{5} = 10$

   $d =$ ________

9. $-9s = -45$

   $s =$ ________

10. $2r = 16$

    $r =$ ________

11. $\frac{v}{3} = 8$

    $v =$ ________

12. $\frac{t}{-4} = 12$

    $t =$ ________

13. $\frac{a}{-1} = 35$

    $a =$ ________

14. $-2m = -200$

    $m =$ ________

Solve.

15. **PHOTO ALBUM** Dai is putting photos in an album. She wants to divide the pictures so that there are 5 photos on each page. There are 50 pages in the album. Write and solve an equation for p, the total number of photos Dai can put in the album. ________

Answer Key (Lesson 1-1)

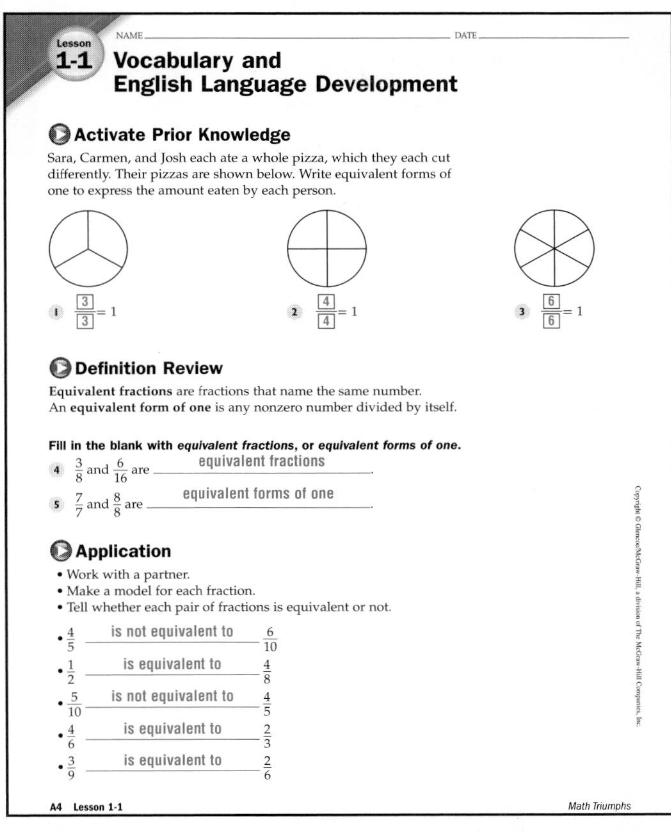

NAME ______________________ DATE ____________

Lesson 1-1 **Vocabulary and English Language Development**

Activate Prior Knowledge

Sara, Carmen, and Josh each ate a whole pizza, which they each cut differently. Their pizzas are shown below. Write equivalent forms of one to express the amount eaten by each person.

1 $\frac{3}{3} = 1$ 2 $\frac{4}{4} = 1$ 3 $\frac{6}{6} = 1$

Definition Review

Equivalent fractions are fractions that name the same number.
An **equivalent form of one** is any nonzero number divided by itself.

Fill in the blank with *equivalent fractions*, or *equivalent forms of one*.

4 $\frac{3}{8}$ and $\frac{6}{16}$ are equivalent fractions.

5 $\frac{7}{7}$ and $\frac{8}{8}$ are equivalent forms of one.

Application

- Work with a partner.
- Make a model for each fraction.
- Tell whether each pair of fractions is equivalent or not.

- $\frac{4}{5}$ is not equivalent to $\frac{6}{10}$
- $\frac{1}{2}$ is equivalent to $\frac{4}{8}$
- $\frac{5}{10}$ is not equivalent to $\frac{4}{5}$
- $\frac{4}{6}$ is equivalent to $\frac{2}{3}$
- $\frac{3}{9}$ is equivalent to $\frac{2}{6}$

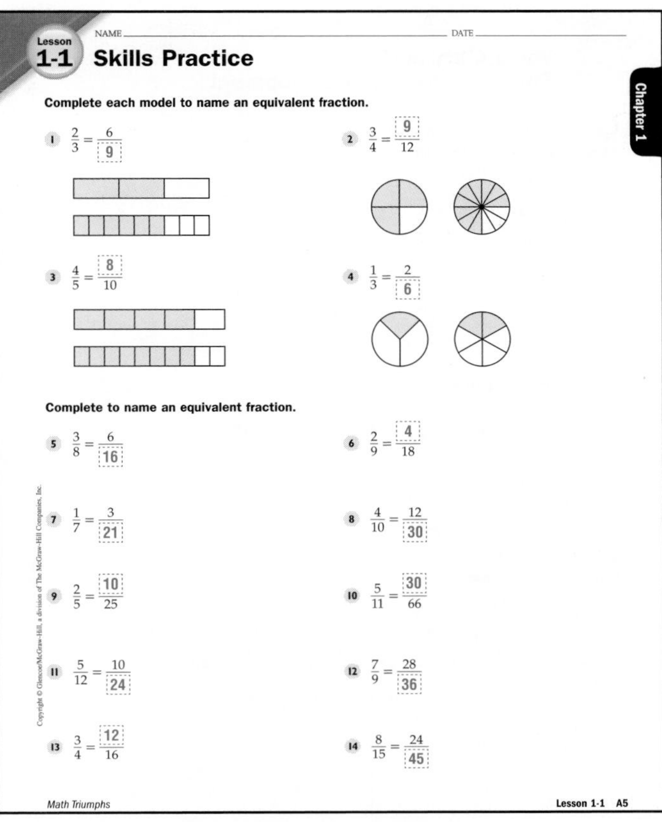

NAME ______________________ DATE ____________

Lesson 1-1 **Skills Practice**

Chapter 1

Complete each model to name an equivalent fraction.

1 $\frac{2}{3} = \frac{6}{9}$ 2 $\frac{3}{4} = \frac{9}{12}$

3 $\frac{4}{5} = \frac{8}{10}$ 4 $\frac{1}{3} = \frac{2}{6}$

Complete to name an equivalent fraction.

5 $\frac{3}{8} = \frac{6}{16}$ 6 $\frac{2}{9} = \frac{4}{18}$

7 $\frac{1}{7} = \frac{3}{21}$ 8 $\frac{4}{10} = \frac{12}{30}$

9 $\frac{2}{5} = \frac{10}{25}$ 10 $\frac{5}{11} = \frac{30}{66}$

11 $\frac{5}{12} = \frac{10}{24}$ 12 $\frac{7}{9} = \frac{28}{36}$

13 $\frac{3}{4} = \frac{12}{16}$ 14 $\frac{8}{15} = \frac{24}{45}$

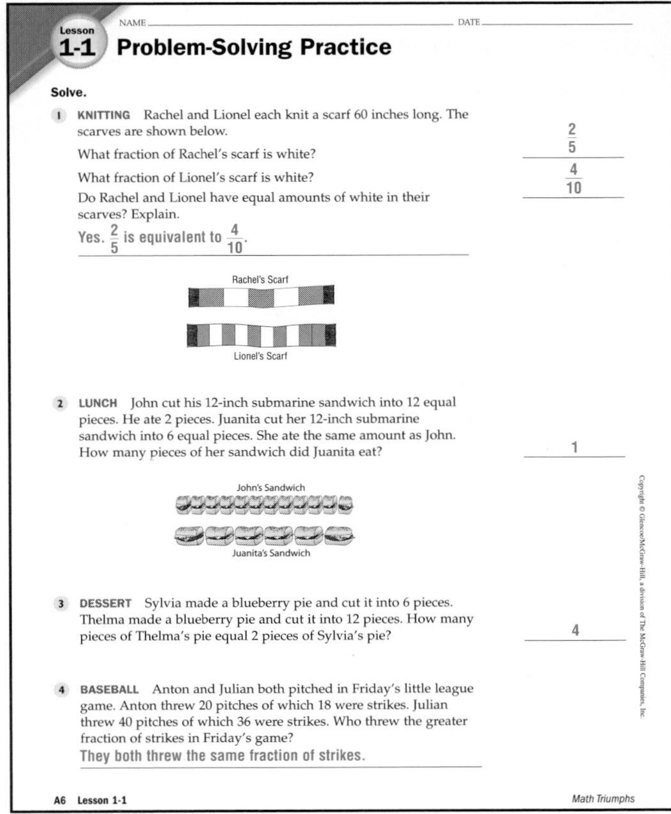

NAME ______________________ DATE ____________

Lesson 1-1 **Problem-Solving Practice**

Solve.

1 **KNITTING** Rachel and Lionel each knit a scarf 60 inches long. The scarves are shown below.
What fraction of Rachel's scarf is white? $\frac{2}{5}$
What fraction of Lionel's scarf is white? $\frac{4}{10}$
Do Rachel and Lionel have equal amounts of white in their scarves? Explain.
Yes. $\frac{2}{5}$ is equivalent to $\frac{4}{10}$.

2 **LUNCH** John cut his 12-inch submarine sandwich into 12 equal pieces. He ate 2 pieces. Juanita cut her 12-inch submarine sandwich into 6 equal pieces. She ate the same amount as John. How many pieces of her sandwich did Juanita eat? 1

3 **DESSERT** Sylvia made a blueberry pie and cut it into 6 pieces. Thelma made a blueberry pie and cut it into 12 pieces. How many pieces of Thelma's pie equal 2 pieces of Sylvia's pie? 4

4 **BASEBALL** Anton and Julian both pitched in Friday's little league game. Anton threw 20 pitches of which 18 were strikes. Julian threw 40 pitches of which 36 were strikes. Who threw the greater fraction of strikes in Friday's game?
They both threw the same fraction of strikes.

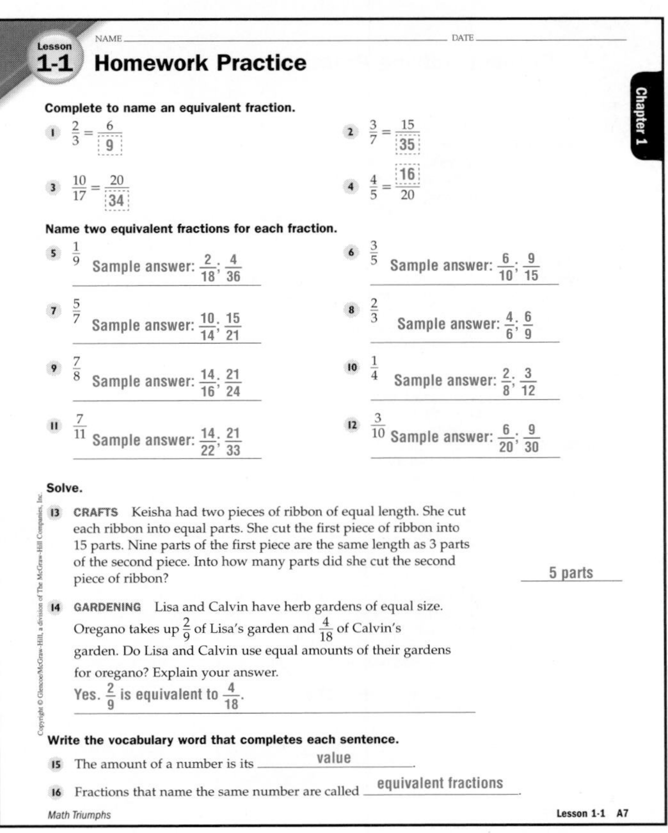

NAME ______________________ DATE ____________

Lesson 1-1 **Homework Practice**

Chapter 1

Complete to name an equivalent fraction.

1 $\frac{2}{3} = \frac{6}{9}$ 2 $\frac{3}{7} = \frac{15}{35}$

3 $\frac{10}{17} = \frac{20}{34}$ 4 $\frac{4}{5} = \frac{16}{20}$

Name two equivalent fractions for each fraction.

5 $\frac{1}{9}$ Sample answer: $\frac{2}{18}, \frac{4}{36}$ 6 $\frac{3}{5}$ Sample answer: $\frac{6}{10}, \frac{9}{15}$

7 $\frac{5}{7}$ Sample answer: $\frac{10}{14}, \frac{15}{21}$ 8 $\frac{2}{3}$ Sample answer: $\frac{4}{6}, \frac{6}{9}$

9 $\frac{7}{8}$ Sample answer: $\frac{14}{16}, \frac{21}{24}$ 10 $\frac{1}{4}$ Sample answer: $\frac{2}{8}, \frac{3}{12}$

11 $\frac{7}{11}$ Sample answer: $\frac{14}{22}, \frac{21}{33}$ 12 $\frac{3}{10}$ Sample answer: $\frac{6}{20}, \frac{9}{30}$

Solve.

13 **CRAFTS** Keisha had two pieces of ribbon of equal length. She cut each ribbon into equal parts. She cut the first piece of ribbon into 15 parts. Nine parts of the first piece are the same length as 3 parts of the second piece. Into how many parts did she cut the second piece of ribbon? 5 parts

14 **GARDENING** Lisa and Calvin have herb gardens of equal size. Oregano takes up $\frac{2}{9}$ of Lisa's garden and $\frac{4}{18}$ of Calvin's garden. Do Lisa and Calvin use equal amounts of their gardens for oregano? Explain your answer.
Yes. $\frac{2}{9}$ is equivalent to $\frac{4}{18}$.

Write the vocabulary word that completes each sentence.

15 The amount of a number is its value.

16 Fractions that name the same number are called equivalent fractions.

Answer Key (Lesson 1-2)

Lesson **1-2** NAME ______ DATE ______

Vocabulary and English Language Development

Activate Prior Knowledge

Name two equivalent fractions for each fraction.

1. $\frac{2}{5}$ Sample answer: $\frac{4}{10}, \frac{6}{15}$
2. $\frac{3}{7}$ Sample answer: $\frac{6}{14}, \frac{9}{21}$
3. $\frac{5}{9}$ Sample answer: $\frac{10}{18}, \frac{15}{27}$
4. $\frac{4}{4}$ Sample answer: $\frac{8}{8}, \frac{12}{12}$

Definition Review

Fill in the blanks.

5. A number greater than 1 with more than two factors is called a composite number.
6. A whole number that has exactly two factors, 1 and the number itself, is called a prime number.

Application

Follow the directions below.

- Students work in pairs.
- Each student rolls a number cube.
- Slide the number cubes together to create a two digit number.
- Decide together whether the number formed is prime or composite.
- If the number is composite, use a factor tree to find the prime factorization of the number.
- Switch the position of the number cubes to make another two digit number.
- Determine if it is prime or composite. Write the prime factorization if it is composite.
- Repeat as time permits.

A8 Lesson 1-2 *Math Triumphs*

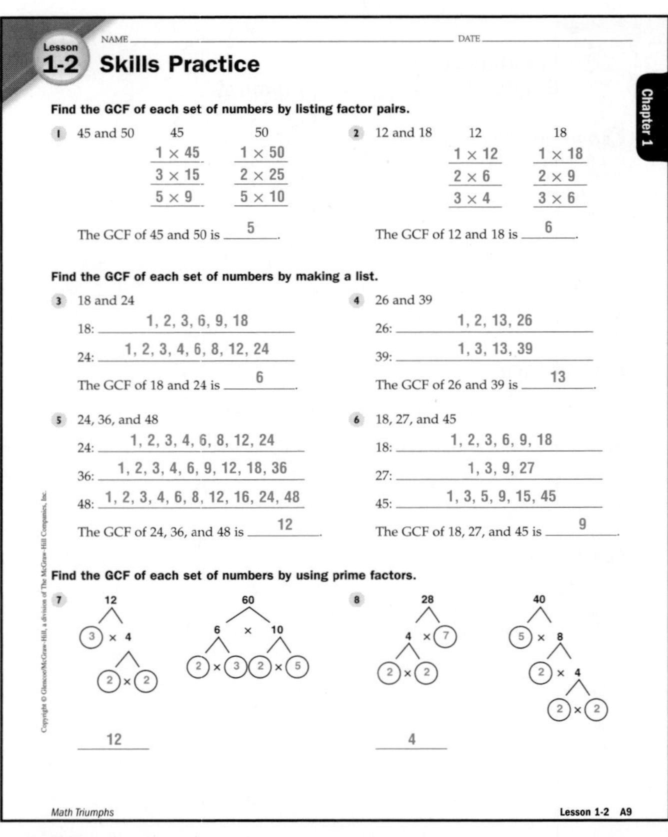
Lesson **1-2** NAME ______ DATE ______

Skills Practice

Chapter 1

Find the GCF of each set of numbers by listing factor pairs.

1. 45 and 50
   45: 1 × 45, 3 × 15, 5 × 9
   50: 1 × 50, 2 × 25, 5 × 10
   The GCF of 45 and 50 is 5.
2. 12 and 18
   12: 1 × 12, 2 × 6, 3 × 4
   18: 1 × 18, 2 × 9, 3 × 6
   The GCF of 12 and 18 is 6.

Find the GCF of each set of numbers by making a list.

3. 18 and 24
   18: 1, 2, 3, 6, 9, 18
   24: 1, 2, 3, 4, 6, 8, 12, 24
   The GCF of 18 and 24 is 6.
4. 26 and 39
   26: 1, 2, 13, 26
   39: 1, 3, 13, 39
   The GCF of 26 and 39 is 13.
5. 24, 36, and 48
   24: 1, 2, 3, 4, 6, 8, 12, 24
   36: 1, 2, 3, 4, 6, 9, 12, 18, 36
   48: 1, 2, 3, 4, 6, 8, 12, 16, 24, 48
   The GCF of 24, 36, and 48 is 12.
6. 18, 27, and 45
   18: 1, 2, 3, 6, 9, 18
   27: 1, 3, 9, 27
   45: 1, 3, 5, 9, 15, 45
   The GCF of 18, 27, and 45 is 9.

Find the GCF of each set of numbers by using prime factors.

7. 12: 3 × 4; 4: 2 × 2 — 60: 6 × 10; 6: 2 × 3; 10: 2 × 5 — 12
8. 28: 4 × 7; 4: 2 × 2 — 40: 5 × 8; 8: 2 × 4; 4: 2 × 2 — 4

Math Triumphs Lesson 1-2 A9

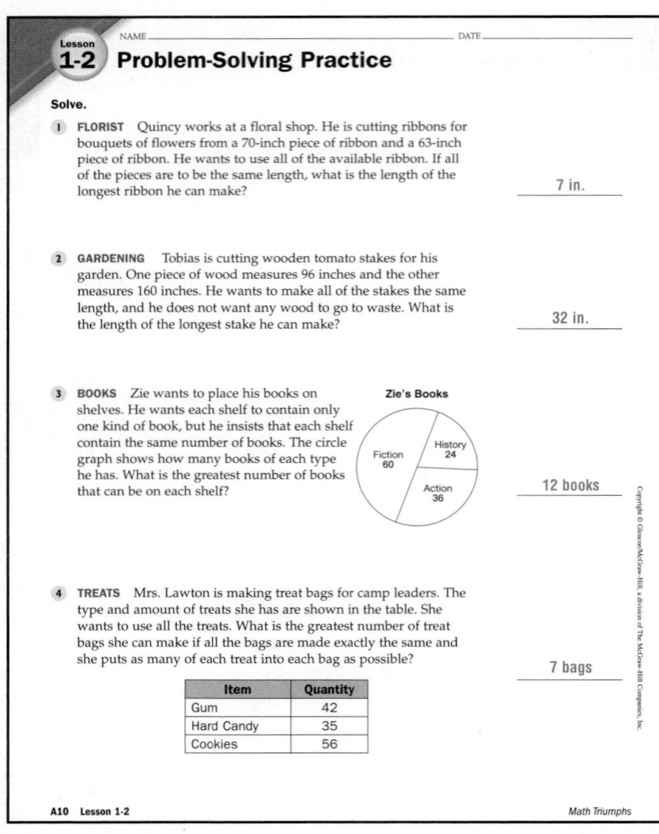
Lesson **1-2** NAME ______ DATE ______

Problem-Solving Practice

Solve.

1. **FLORIST** Quincy works at a floral shop. He is cutting ribbons for bouquets of flowers from a 70-inch piece of ribbon and a 63-inch piece of ribbon. He wants to use all of the available ribbon. If all of the pieces are to be the same length, what is the length of the longest ribbon he can make? 7 in.
2. **GARDENING** Tobias is cutting wooden tomato stakes for his garden. One piece of wood measures 96 inches and the other measures 160 inches. He wants to make all of the stakes the same length, and he does not want any wood to go to waste. What is the length of the longest stake he can make? 32 in.
3. **BOOKS** Zie wants to place his books on shelves. He wants each shelf to contain only one kind of book, but he insists that each shelf contain the same number of books. The circle graph shows how many books of each type he has. What is the greatest number of books that can be on each shelf? 12 books

4. **TREATS** Mrs. Lawton is making treat bags for camp leaders. The type and amount of treats she has are shown in the table. She wants to use all the treats. What is the greatest number of treat bags she can make if all the bags are made exactly the same and she puts as many of each treat into each bag as possible? 7 bags

Item	Quantity
Gum	42
Hard Candy	35
Cookies	56

A10 Lesson 1-2 *Math Triumphs*

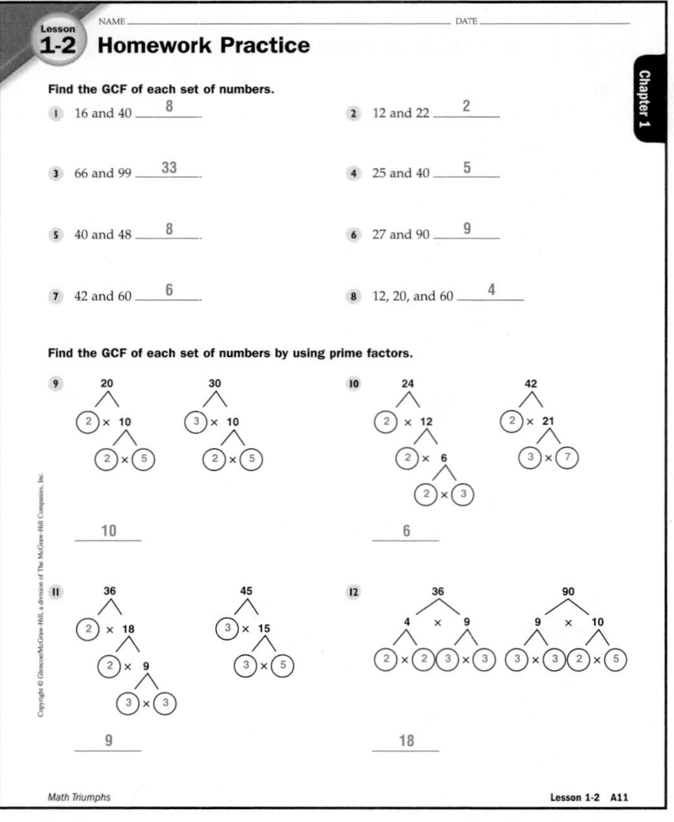
Lesson **1-2** NAME ______ DATE ______

Homework Practice

Chapter 1

Find the GCF of each set of numbers.

1. 16 and 40 8
2. 12 and 22 2
3. 66 and 99 33
4. 25 and 40 5
5. 40 and 48 8
6. 27 and 90 9
7. 42 and 60 6
8. 12, 20, and 60 4

Find the GCF of each set of numbers by using prime factors.

9. 20: 2 × 10; 10: 2 × 5 — 30: 3 × 10; 10: 2 × 5 — 10
10. 24: 2 × 12; 12: 2 × 6; 6: 2 × 3 — 42: 2 × 21; 21: 3 × 7 — 6
11. 36: 2 × 18; 18: 2 × 9; 9: 3 × 3 — 45: 3 × 15; 15: 3 × 5 — 9
12. 36: 4 × 9; 4: 2 × 2; 9: 3 × 3 — 90: 9 × 10; 9: 3 × 3; 10: 2 × 5 — 18

Math Triumphs Lesson 1-2 A11

Answer Key (Lesson 1-3)

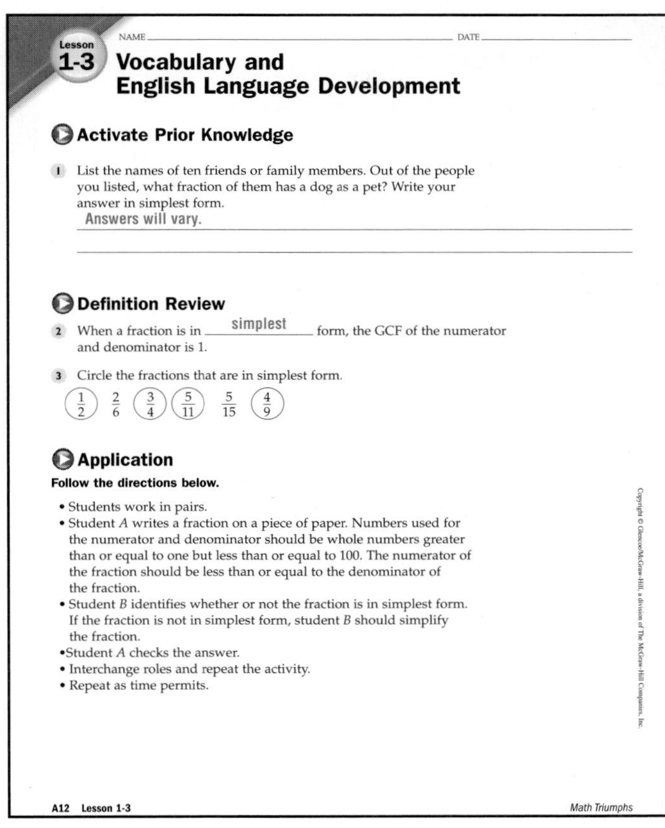

NAME ______ DATE ______

Lesson 1-3 **Vocabulary and English Language Development**

Activate Prior Knowledge

1 List the names of ten friends or family members. Out of the people you listed, what fraction of them has a dog as a pet? Write your answer in simplest form.
Answers will vary.

Definition Review

2 When a fraction is in simplest form, the GCF of the numerator and denominator is 1.

3 Circle the fractions that are in simplest form.
$\frac{1}{2}$ (circled) $\frac{2}{6}$ $\frac{3}{4}$ (circled) $\frac{5}{11}$ (circled) $\frac{5}{15}$ $\frac{4}{9}$ (circled)

Application

Follow the directions below.

- Students work in pairs.
- Student *A* writes a fraction on a piece of paper. Numbers used for the numerator and denominator should be whole numbers greater than or equal to one but less than or equal to 100. The numerator of the fraction should be less than or equal to the denominator of the fraction.
- Student *B* identifies whether or not the fraction is in simplest form. If the fraction is not in simplest form, student *B* should simplify the fraction.
- Student *A* checks the answer.
- Interchange roles and repeat the activity.
- Repeat as time permits.

A12 Lesson 1-3 Math Triumphs

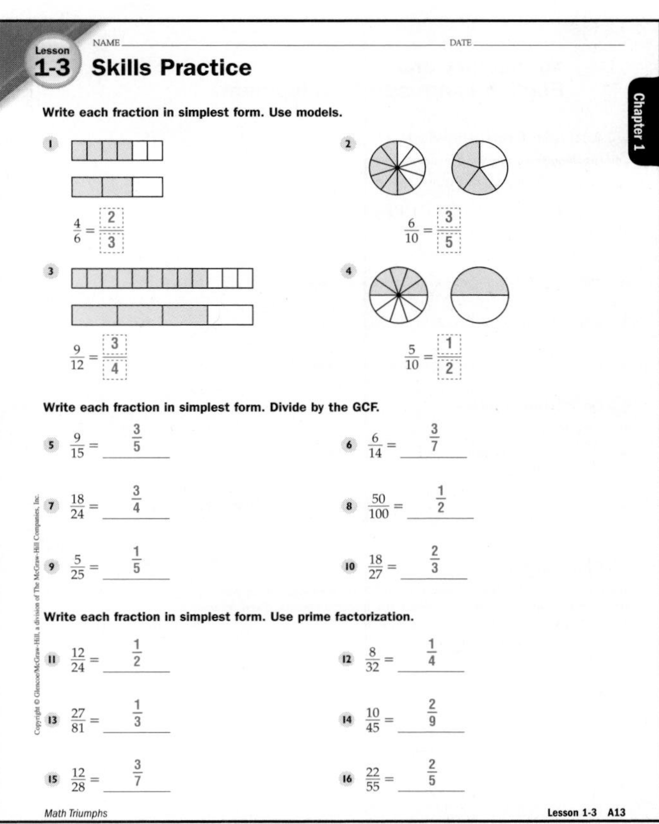

NAME ______ DATE ______

Lesson 1-3 **Skills Practice**

Chapter 1

Write each fraction in simplest form. Use models.

1 $\frac{4}{6} = \frac{2}{3}$

2 $\frac{6}{10} = \frac{3}{5}$

3 $\frac{9}{12} = \frac{3}{4}$

4 $\frac{5}{10} = \frac{1}{2}$

Write each fraction in simplest form. Divide by the GCF.

5 $\frac{9}{15} = \frac{3}{5}$

6 $\frac{6}{14} = \frac{3}{7}$

7 $\frac{18}{24} = \frac{3}{4}$

8 $\frac{50}{100} = \frac{1}{2}$

9 $\frac{5}{25} = \frac{1}{5}$

10 $\frac{18}{27} = \frac{2}{3}$

Write each fraction in simplest form. Use prime factorization.

11 $\frac{12}{24} = \frac{1}{2}$

12 $\frac{8}{32} = \frac{1}{4}$

13 $\frac{27}{81} = \frac{1}{3}$

14 $\frac{10}{45} = \frac{2}{9}$

15 $\frac{12}{28} = \frac{3}{7}$

16 $\frac{22}{55} = \frac{2}{5}$

Math Triumphs Lesson 1-3 A13

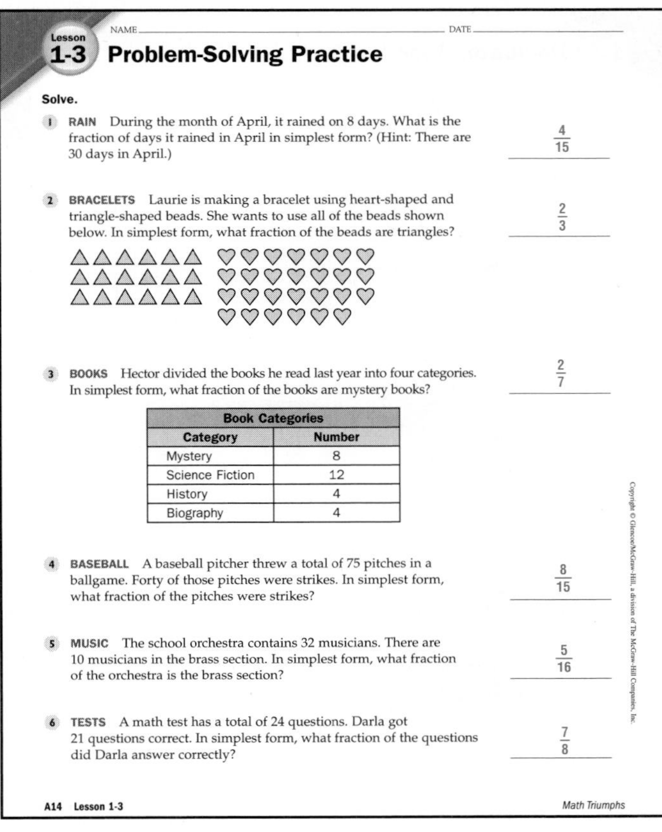

NAME ______ DATE ______

Lesson 1-3 **Problem-Solving Practice**

Solve.

1 **RAIN** During the month of April, it rained on 8 days. What is the fraction of days it rained in April in simplest form? (Hint: There are 30 days in April.) $\frac{4}{15}$

2 **BRACELETS** Laurie is making a bracelet using heart-shaped and triangle-shaped beads. She wants to use all of the beads shown below. In simplest form, what fraction of the beads are triangles? $\frac{2}{3}$

3 **BOOKS** Hector divided the books he read last year into four categories. In simplest form, what fraction of the books are mystery books? $\frac{2}{7}$

Book Categories	
Category	Number
Mystery	8
Science Fiction	12
History	4
Biography	4

4 **BASEBALL** A baseball pitcher threw a total of 75 pitches in a ballgame. Forty of those pitches were strikes. In simplest form, what fraction of the pitches were strikes? $\frac{8}{15}$

5 **MUSIC** The school orchestra contains 32 musicians. There are 10 musicians in the brass section. In simplest form, what fraction of the orchestra is the brass section? $\frac{5}{16}$

6 **TESTS** A math test has a total of 24 questions. Darla got 21 questions correct. In simplest form, what fraction of the questions did Darla answer correctly? $\frac{7}{8}$

A14 Lesson 1-3 Math Triumphs

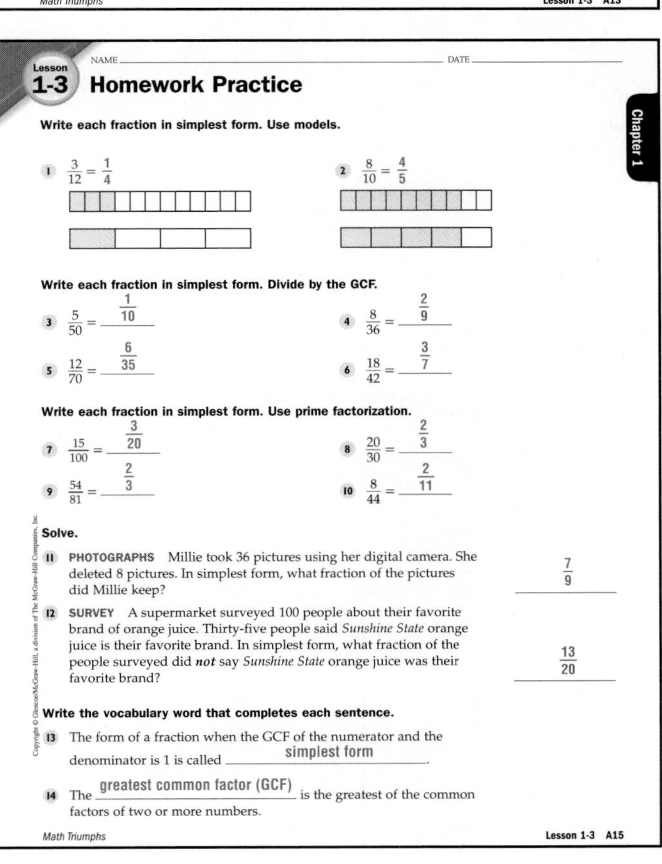

NAME ______ DATE ______

Lesson 1-3 **Homework Practice**

Chapter 1

Write each fraction in simplest form. Use models.

1 $\frac{3}{12} = \frac{1}{4}$

2 $\frac{8}{10} = \frac{4}{5}$

Write each fraction in simplest form. Divide by the GCF.

3 $\frac{5}{50} = \frac{1}{10}$

4 $\frac{8}{36} = \frac{2}{9}$

5 $\frac{12}{70} = \frac{6}{35}$

6 $\frac{18}{42} = \frac{3}{7}$

Write each fraction in simplest form. Use prime factorization.

7 $\frac{15}{100} = \frac{3}{20}$

8 $\frac{20}{30} = \frac{2}{3}$

9 $\frac{54}{81} = \frac{2}{3}$

10 $\frac{8}{44} = \frac{2}{11}$

Solve.

11 **PHOTOGRAPHS** Millie took 36 pictures using her digital camera. She deleted 8 pictures. In simplest form, what fraction of the pictures did Millie keep? $\frac{7}{9}$

12 **SURVEY** A supermarket surveyed 100 people about their favorite brand of orange juice. Thirty-five people said *Sunshine State* orange juice is their favorite brand. In simplest form, what fraction of the people surveyed did ***not*** say *Sunshine State* orange juice was their favorite brand? $\frac{13}{20}$

Write the vocabulary word that completes each sentence.

13 The form of a fraction when the GCF of the numerator and the denominator is 1 is called simplest form.

14 The greatest common factor (GCF) is the greatest of the common factors of two or more numbers.

Math Triumphs Lesson 1-3 A15

Answer Key (Lesson 1-4)

Lesson 1-4 NAME ______ DATE ______

Vocabulary and English Language Development

Activate Prior Knowledge

Use the designs to answer the questions.

★ ○ □ ★ □ □ ★ ○ □ ★ ○ □ ★ Design A

★ ○ □ ★ ○ □ ○ ★ ○ □ ★ ○ Design B

□ ○ ★ ★ ○ □ ○ ★ ★ Design C

1. What fraction of the symbols in Design A is circles? $\frac{3}{13}$
2. What fraction of the symbols in Design B is stars? $\frac{4}{12} = \frac{1}{3}$
3. What fraction of the symbols in Design C is squares? $\frac{2}{9}$

Definition Review

Fill in the blanks.

4. The same denominator used in two or more fractions is the common denominator.
5. The least common denominator is the least common multiple of the denominators of two or more fractions.

Application

Use a ruler to cut 4 strips of paper, each 12 inches long. Divide each strip of paper into equal parts to show the fractions below. Then write the fractions in order from least to greatest.

$\frac{1}{2}$

$\frac{1}{3}$

$\frac{1}{12}$

$\frac{1}{4}$ $\frac{1}{12}, \frac{1}{4}, \frac{1}{3}, \frac{1}{2}$

Lesson 1-4 NAME ______ DATE ______

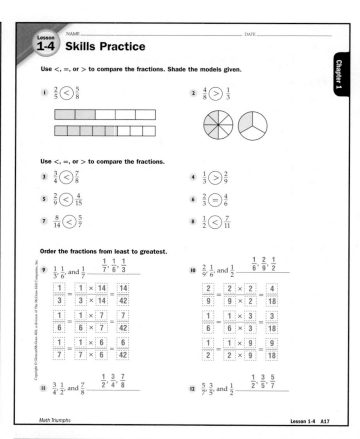

Skills Practice

Use <, =, or > to compare the fractions. Shade the models given.

1. $\frac{2}{5} < \frac{5}{8}$
2. $\frac{4}{8} > \frac{1}{3}$

Use <, =, or > to compare the fractions.

3. $\frac{3}{4} < \frac{7}{8}$
4. $\frac{1}{3} > \frac{2}{9}$
5. $\frac{2}{9} < \frac{4}{15}$
6. $\frac{2}{3} = \frac{4}{6}$
7. $\frac{8}{14} < \frac{5}{7}$
8. $\frac{1}{2} < \frac{7}{11}$

Order the fractions from least to greatest.

9. $\frac{1}{3}, \frac{1}{6}$, and $\frac{1}{7}$ $\frac{1}{7}, \frac{1}{6}, \frac{1}{3}$

$\frac{1}{3} = \frac{1 \times 14}{3 \times 14} = \frac{14}{42}$

$\frac{1}{6} = \frac{1 \times 7}{6 \times 7} = \frac{7}{42}$

$\frac{1}{7} = \frac{1 \times 6}{7 \times 6} = \frac{6}{42}$

10. $\frac{2}{9}, \frac{1}{6}$, and $\frac{1}{2}$ $\frac{1}{6}, \frac{2}{9}, \frac{1}{2}$

$\frac{2}{9} = \frac{2 \times 2}{9 \times 2} = \frac{4}{18}$

$\frac{1}{6} = \frac{1 \times 3}{6 \times 3} = \frac{3}{18}$

$\frac{1}{2} = \frac{1 \times 9}{2 \times 9} = \frac{9}{18}$

11. $\frac{3}{4}, \frac{1}{2}$, and $\frac{7}{8}$ $\frac{1}{2}, \frac{3}{4}, \frac{7}{8}$
12. $\frac{5}{7}, \frac{3}{5}$, and $\frac{1}{2}$ $\frac{1}{2}, \frac{3}{5}, \frac{5}{7}$

Lesson 1-4 NAME ______ DATE ______

Problem-Solving Practice

Solve.

1. **MUSIC** Chris listened to three songs. The lengths of the songs are shown in the table below. Which song has the greatest length? The Long Road

Songs	
Name	Length (min.)
The Long Road	$3\frac{5}{6}$
Skateboard	$3\frac{3}{4}$
Climb High	$3\frac{1}{2}$

2. **SHOPPING** Maria bought $\frac{1}{2}$ pound of white potatoes, $\frac{3}{4}$ pound of red potatoes, and $\frac{7}{8}$ pounds of sweet potatoes. Which kind of potato weighed the least? The white potatoes
3. **HARVEST** Three friends went to a farm to pick strawberries. The table shows the amount each person picked. Who picked the greatest amount of strawberries? Lionel

Strawberries Picked	
Name	Weight (lbs.)
Lionel	$1\frac{7}{8}$
Duncan	$1\frac{5}{6}$
Jorge	$1\frac{3}{4}$

4. **PIZZA** Three friends each ordered a small cheese pizza for lunch. Carolina ate $\frac{4}{9}$ of her pizza. Sharona ate $\frac{3}{4}$ of her pizza. Leona ate $\frac{1}{3}$ of her pizza. Who ate the least amount of pizza? Leona
5. **GARDENING** Manuel plants a vegetable garden every spring. Tomato plants use $\frac{1}{3}$ of the garden space. Pepper plants use $\frac{1}{6}$ of the garden space. Squash plants use $\frac{1}{2}$ of the garden space. Which vegetable takes up the greatest amount of space in the garden? Squash plants
6. **BASKETBALL** Melanie and Alicia both played in last week's basketball game. Melanie threw 10 foul shots and made 6 of them. Alicia threw 8 foul shots and made 6 of them. Who made the greater fraction of foul shots? Alicia

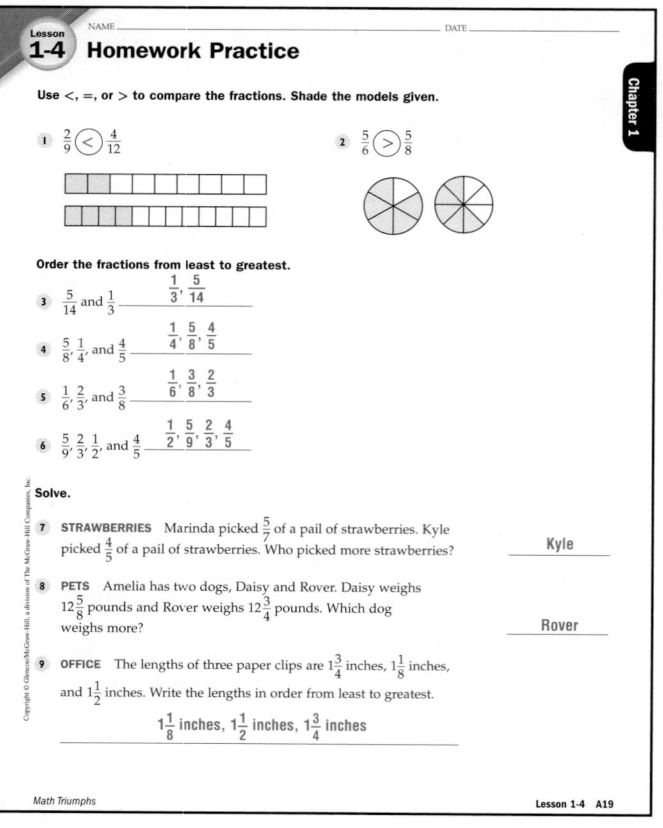

Lesson 1-4 NAME ______ DATE ______

Homework Practice

Use <, =, or > to compare the fractions. Shade the models given.

1. $\frac{2}{9} < \frac{4}{12}$
2. $\frac{5}{6} > \frac{5}{8}$

Order the fractions from least to greatest.

3. $\frac{5}{14}$ and $\frac{1}{3}$ $\frac{1}{3}, \frac{5}{14}$
4. $\frac{5}{8}, \frac{1}{4}$, and $\frac{4}{5}$ $\frac{1}{4}, \frac{5}{8}, \frac{4}{5}$
5. $\frac{1}{6}, \frac{2}{3}$, and $\frac{3}{8}$ $\frac{1}{6}, \frac{3}{8}, \frac{2}{3}$
6. $\frac{5}{9}, \frac{2}{3}, \frac{1}{2}$, and $\frac{4}{5}$ $\frac{1}{2}, \frac{5}{9}, \frac{2}{3}, \frac{4}{5}$

Solve.

7. **STRAWBERRIES** Marinda picked $\frac{5}{7}$ of a pail of strawberries. Kyle picked $\frac{4}{5}$ of a pail of strawberries. Who picked more strawberries? Kyle
8. **PETS** Amelia has two dogs, Daisy and Rover. Daisy weighs $12\frac{5}{8}$ pounds and Rover weighs $12\frac{3}{4}$ pounds. Which dog weighs more? Rover
9. **OFFICE** The lengths of three paper clips are $1\frac{3}{4}$ inches, $1\frac{1}{8}$ inches, and $1\frac{1}{2}$ inches. Write the lengths in order from least to greatest. $1\frac{1}{8}$ inches, $1\frac{1}{2}$ inches, $1\frac{3}{4}$ inches

Answer Key (Lesson 2-1)

Lesson 2-1 Vocabulary and English Language Development

NAME ______ DATE ______

Chapter 2

Activate Prior Knowledge — Check students' work

1. How many members are in your family? ______
2. How many are males? ______
3. How many are females? ______
4. Write the fractions $\frac{\text{males}}{\text{females}}$, $\frac{\text{males}}{\text{total}}$, $\frac{\text{females}}{\text{total}}$. ______

Definition Review

A **ratio** is a comparison of two quantities by division.

Match each group with the correct ratio.

5.  → The ratio of ladybugs to butterflies is 2 to 3.

6. 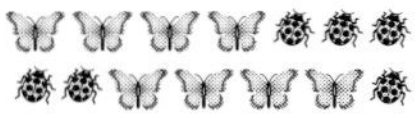 → The ratio of ladybugs to butterflies is 3 to 4.

7. 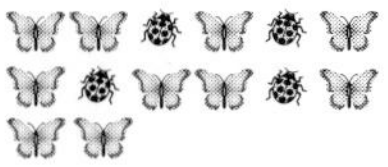 → The ratio of ladybugs to butterflies is 2 to 5.

Application

Finding Ratios

- Students initially work individually.
- Students observe their classmates to find the following ratios:
  - The ratio of girls to boys in the class.
  - The ratio of boys to the total number of students in the class.
  - The ratio of students wearing red to students wearing blue.
  - The ratio of students with blond hair to students with black hair.
  - The ratio of students who do not have brown hair to the total number of students in the class.
- When everyone is done, the students compare their results and discuss any inconsistencies.

Lesson 2-1 Skills Practice

NAME ______ DATE ______

Use the diagram to write each ratio as a fraction in simplest form.

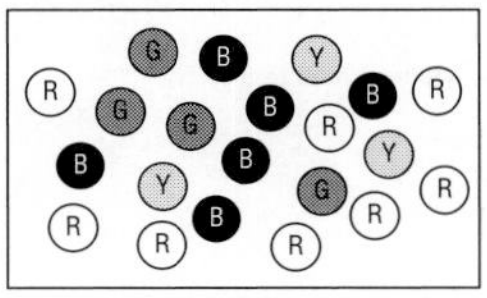

1. The number of yellow marbles to the number of red marbles is $\frac{3}{8}$.
2. The number of black marbles to the number of red marbles is $\frac{3}{4}$.
3. The number of green marbles to the number of yellow marbles is $\frac{4}{3}$.
4. The number of yellow marbles to the number of black marbles is $\frac{1}{2}$.

Write each ratio as a fraction in simplest form.

5. A computer lab has 5 printers and 20 computers. Write the ratio of printers to computers.
$\frac{5}{20} = \frac{5 \div 5}{20 \div 5} = \frac{1}{4}$

6. In 22 minutes, Margo ran 4 miles. Write the ratio of minutes to miles. $\frac{11}{2}$

Write the ratio of length to width for each rectangle as a fraction in simplest form.

7. 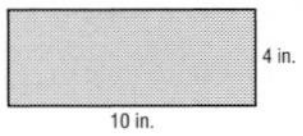

$\frac{5}{2}$

8. 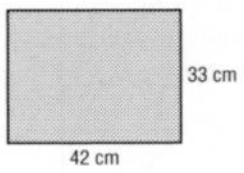

$\frac{14}{11}$

Lesson 2-1 Problem-Solving Practice

NAME ______ DATE ______

Chapter 2

Solve.

1. **GARDENING** The dimensions of a flower garden are 15 feet long by 5 feet wide. Write the ratio of width to length as a fraction in simplest form. $\frac{1}{3}$

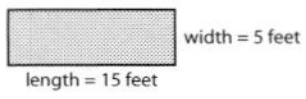

2. **HOBBIES** A jewelry-making kit contains 15 blue beads, 25 red beads, 10 yellow beads, and 30 black beads. Write the ratio of red beads to black beads in simplest form. $\frac{5}{6}$

3. **ELECTIONS** Carlos, Leona, and Kim ran for class president. The table below shows the number of votes each student received. Write the ratio of votes Carlos received to the total number of votes in simplest form. $\frac{11}{28}$

Votes Counted for Class President	
Carlos	𝍸 𝍸 𝍸 𝍸 II
Leona	𝍸 𝍸 𝍸 𝍸 I
Kim	𝍸 𝍸 III

4. **WEATHER** During the first 28 days of April, it rained on 8 days. If it rains the last two days of April, what will be the ratio of the number of rainy days in the month to the total number of days in the month? Write your answer in simplest form. $\frac{1}{3}$

5. **BASEBALL** A baseball team won 40 of the 60 games they played. Write the ratio of games won to the number of games played in simplest form. $\frac{2}{3}$

Lesson 2-1 Homework Practice

NAME ______ DATE ______

Use the diagram to write each ratio as a fraction in simplest form.

1. baseballs and tennis balls to the total number of balls $\frac{3}{5}$
2. footballs and basketballs to tennis balls and baseballs $\frac{2}{3}$
3. baseballs to the total number of balls $\frac{1}{4}$
4. footballs to basketballs $\frac{1}{1}$

Write each ratio as a fraction in simplest form.

5. Michele ran 3 out of 7 days this week. $\frac{3}{7}$
6. A bowl of fruit contains 8 apples and 4 oranges. $\frac{2}{1}$

Solve.

7. **SWIMMING** The dimensions of a rectangular swimming pool are 44 feet long by 20 feet wide. Write the ratio of the pool's width to length as a fraction in simplest form. $\frac{5}{11}$

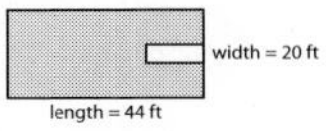

Write the vocabulary word(s) that completes each sentence.

8. A ratio is a comparison of two quantities by division.

Answer Key (Lesson 2-2)

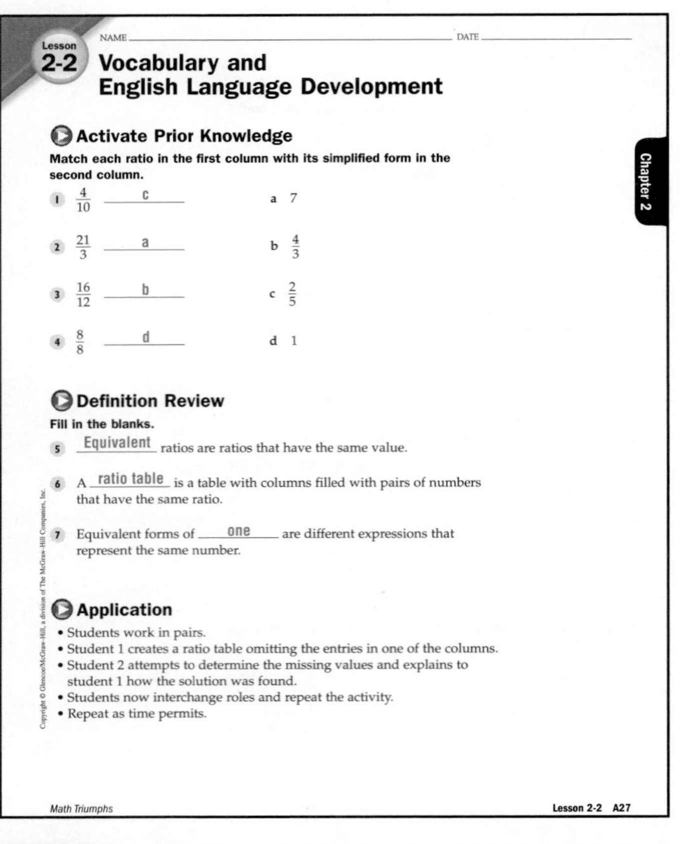

NAME ______ DATE ______

Lesson 2-2

Vocabulary and English Language Development

Chapter 2

Activate Prior Knowledge

Match each ratio in the first column with its simplified form in the second column.

1. $\frac{4}{10}$ ___c___   a 7
2. $\frac{21}{3}$ ___a___   b $\frac{4}{3}$
3. $\frac{16}{12}$ ___b___   c $\frac{2}{5}$
4. $\frac{8}{8}$ ___d___   d 1

Definition Review

Fill in the blanks.

5. ___Equivalent___ ratios are ratios that have the same value.
6. A ___ratio table___ is a table with columns filled with pairs of numbers that have the same ratio.
7. Equivalent forms of ___one___ are different expressions that represent the same number.

Application

- Students work in pairs.
- Student 1 creates a ratio table omitting the entries in one of the columns.
- Student 2 attempts to determine the missing values and explains to student 1 how the solution was found.
- Students now interchange roles and repeat the activity.
- Repeat as time permits.

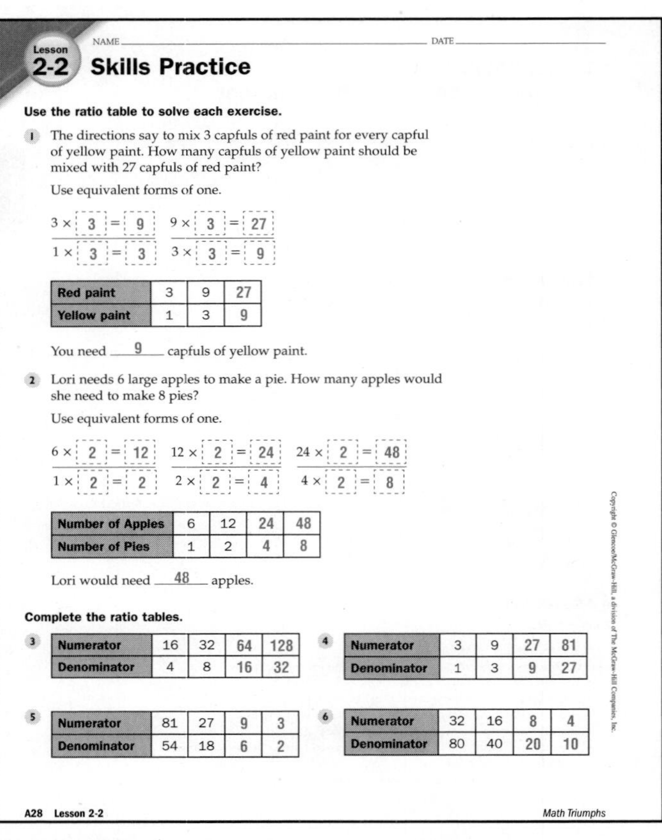

NAME ______ DATE ______

Lesson 2-2

Skills Practice

Use the ratio table to solve each exercise.

1. The directions say to mix 3 capfuls of red paint for every capful of yellow paint. How many capfuls of yellow paint should be mixed with 27 capfuls of red paint?

   Use equivalent forms of one.

   $\frac{3 \times 3 = 9}{1 \times 3 = 3}$ $\frac{9 \times 3 = 27}{3 \times 3 = 9}$

Red paint	3	9	27
Yellow paint	1	3	9

   You need ___9___ capfuls of yellow paint.

2. Lori needs 6 large apples to make a pie. How many apples would she need to make 8 pies?

   Use equivalent forms of one.

   $\frac{6 \times 2 = 12}{1 \times 2 = 2}$ $\frac{12 \times 2 = 24}{2 \times 2 = 4}$ $\frac{24 \times 2 = 48}{4 \times 2 = 8}$

Number of Apples	6	12	24	48
Number of Pies	1	2	4	8

   Lori would need ___48___ apples.

Complete the ratio tables.

3.

Numerator	16	32	64	128
Denominator	4	8	16	32

4.

Numerator	3	9	27	81
Denominator	1	3	9	27

5.

Numerator	81	27	9	3
Denominator	54	18	6	2

6.

Numerator	32	16	8	4
Denominator	80	40	20	10

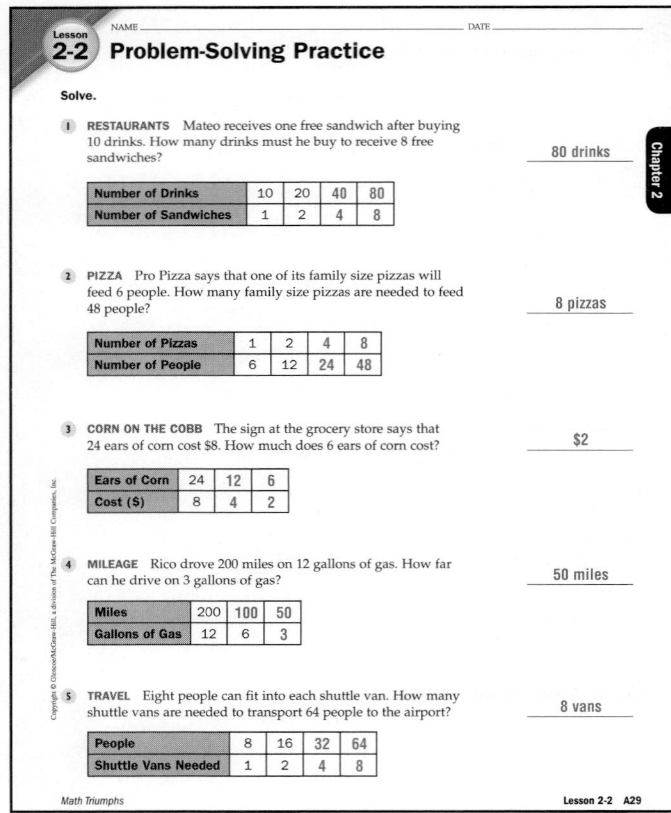

NAME ______ DATE ______

Lesson 2-2

Problem-Solving Practice

Chapter 2

Solve.

1. **RESTAURANTS** Mateo receives one free sandwich after buying 10 drinks. How many drinks must he buy to receive 8 free sandwiches? ___80 drinks___

Number of Drinks	10	20	40	80
Number of Sandwiches	1	2	4	8

2. **PIZZA** Pro Pizza says that one of its family size pizzas will feed 6 people. How many family size pizzas are needed to feed 48 people? ___8 pizzas___

Number of Pizzas	1	2	4	8
Number of People	6	12	24	48

3. **CORN ON THE COBB** The sign at the grocery store says that 24 ears of corn cost \$8. How much does 6 ears of corn cost? ___\$2___

Ears of Corn	24	12	6
Cost (\$)	8	4	2

4. **MILEAGE** Rico drove 200 miles on 12 gallons of gas. How far can he drive on 3 gallons of gas? ___50 miles___

Miles	200	100	50
Gallons of Gas	12	6	3

5. **TRAVEL** Eight people can fit into each shuttle van. How many shuttle vans are needed to transport 64 people to the airport? ___8 vans___

People	8	16	32	64
Shuttle Vans Needed	1	2	4	8

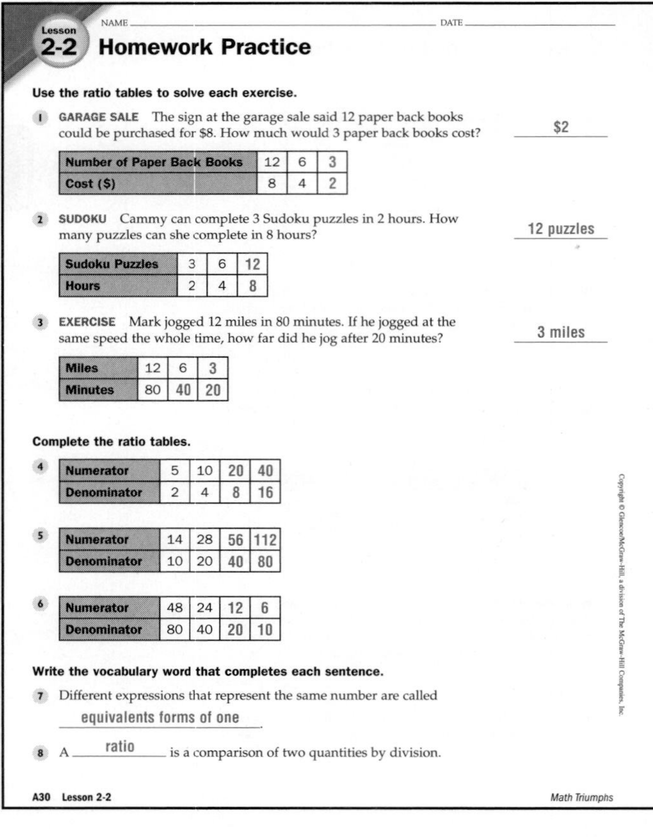

NAME ______ DATE ______

Lesson 2-2

Homework Practice

Use the ratio tables to solve each exercise.

1. **GARAGE SALE** The sign at the garage sale said 12 paper back books could be purchased for \$8. How much would 3 paper back books cost? ___\$2___

Number of Paper Back Books	12	6	3
Cost (\$)	8	4	2

2. **SUDOKU** Cammy can complete 3 Sudoku puzzles in 2 hours. How many puzzles can she complete in 8 hours? ___12 puzzles___

Sudoku Puzzles	3	6	12
Hours	2	4	8

3. **EXERCISE** Mark jogged 12 miles in 80 minutes. If he jogged at the same speed the whole time, how far did he jog after 20 minutes? ___3 miles___

Miles	12	6	3
Minutes	80	40	20

Complete the ratio tables.

4.

Numerator	5	10	20	40
Denominator	2	4	8	16

5.

Numerator	14	28	56	112
Denominator	10	20	40	80

6.

Numerator	48	24	12	6
Denominator	80	40	20	10

Write the vocabulary word that completes each sentence.

7. Different expressions that represent the same number are called ___equivalents forms of one___.
8. A ___ratio___ is a comparison of two quantities by division.

Answer Key (Lesson 2-3)

Lesson 2-3 NAME ______ DATE ______

Vocabulary and English Language Development

Activate Prior Knowledge

You and your friends are playing a board game using the spinner below. Answer the questions about the spinner.

1. How many numbers are there? 12
2. How many of the numbers are even? 6
3. How many of the numbers are greater than 5? 7
4. How many of the numbers are *not* divisible by 4? 9

Definition Review

Fill in the blanks.

5. Probability is the chance that some event will occur.
6. A ratio is a comparison of two quantities by division.
7. Outcomes are the possible results of a probability event.
8. List the outcomes of spinning the spinner above.
   1, 2, 3, 4, 5, 6, 7, 8, 9, 10, 11, 12
9. How many of the outcomes are even numbers? 6

Application

Follow the directions for the activity.

- Work in pairs. Each pair needs one number cube.
- What is the probability of getting a 3 when you roll a 6-sided number cube with the numbers 1–6? $\frac{1}{6}$
- Roll a number cube 36 times and record the result each time.
- What is the ratio of the number of times a 3 was rolled to the total number of times the number cube was rolled? Check students' work.
- Is this ratio equal to the probability you listed above? Is it close? Discuss.

Lesson 2-3 NAME ______ DATE ______

Skills Practice

Use the spinner to find each probability. Write the probability as a fraction in simplest form.

1. P(multiple of 3) $\frac{3}{10}$
2. P(number greater than 8) $\frac{1}{5}$

Use the bag of marbles to find each probability. Write the probability as a fraction in simplest form.

3. P(red) $\frac{1}{8}$
4. P(blue or green) $\frac{1}{2}$
5. P(*not* black) $\frac{11}{16}$
6. P(yellow) $\frac{1}{16}$

Find each probability using a number cube. Write the probability as a fraction in simplest form.

7. P(even number) $\frac{1}{2}$
8. P(not an even number) $\frac{1}{2}$
9. P(number greater than 4) $\frac{1}{3}$
10. P(number less than 2) $\frac{1}{6}$

Find the probability of each event. Write the probability as a fraction in simplest form.

11. You pick a month with only 28 days. $\frac{1}{12}$
12. You pick a month with 6 or fewer letters in its name. $\frac{1}{2}$
13. You pick the letters *A*, *E*, *I*, *O*, or *U* from the alphabet. $\frac{5}{26}$
14. You pick a letter that comes before *Y* in the alphabet. $\frac{12}{13}$

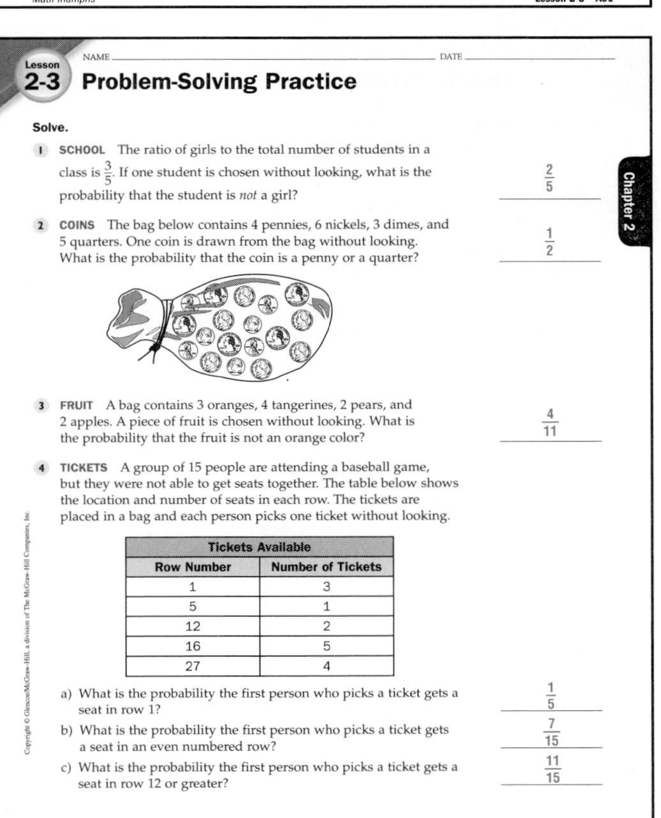

Lesson 2-3 NAME ______ DATE ______

Problem-Solving Practice

Solve.

1. **SCHOOL** The ratio of girls to the total number of students in a class is $\frac{3}{5}$. If one student is chosen without looking, what is the probability that the student is *not* a girl? $\frac{2}{5}$
2. **COINS** The bag below contains 4 pennies, 6 nickels, 3 dimes, and 5 quarters. One coin is drawn from the bag without looking. What is the probability that the coin is a penny or a quarter? $\frac{1}{2}$
3. **FRUIT** A bag contains 3 oranges, 4 tangerines, 2 pears, and 2 apples. A piece of fruit is chosen without looking. What is the probability that the fruit is not an orange color? $\frac{4}{11}$
4. **TICKETS** A group of 15 people are attending a baseball game, but they were not able to get seats together. The table below shows the location and number of seats in each row. The tickets are placed in a bag and each person picks one ticket without looking.

Tickets Available	
Row Number	**Number of Tickets**
1	3
5	1
12	2
16	5
27	4

a) What is the probability the first person who picks a ticket gets a seat in row 1? $\frac{1}{5}$

b) What is the probability the first person who picks a ticket gets a seat in an even numbered row? $\frac{7}{15}$

c) What is the probability the first person who picks a ticket gets a seat in row 12 or greater? $\frac{11}{15}$

Lesson 2-3 NAME ______ DATE ______

Homework Practice

Use the spinner to find each probability. Write the probability as a fraction in simplest form.

1. P(green or black) $\frac{1}{2}$
2. P(not yellow) $\frac{3}{4}$

A cooler contains 6 bottles of water, 3 bottles of tea, 7 bottles of lemonade, and 4 bottles of juice. Write each probability as a fraction in simplest form.

3. What is the probability of choosing one bottle from the cooler without looking and getting a bottle of water? $\frac{3}{10}$
4. What is the probability of choosing one bottle from the cooler without looking and getting a bottle that is *not* juice? $\frac{4}{5}$
5. What is the probability of choosing one bottle from the cooler without looking and getting a bottle of tea or a bottle of lemonade? $\frac{1}{2}$

Find each probability. Write the probability as a fraction in simplest form.

6. 12 red jelly beans, 8 black jelly beans, and 4 yellow jelly beans; P(red jelly bean) $\frac{1}{2}$
7. 4 bags of corn chips, 3 bags of pretzels, and 5 bags of popcorn; P(bag that is *not* popcorn) $\frac{7}{12}$

Solve.

8. **LANGUAGE** Suppose the letters HOLLYWOOD are placed in a bag. A letter is pulled out without looking. What is the probability that the letter is an O? $\frac{1}{3}$

Write the vocabulary word that completes each sentence.

9. An outcome is a possible result of a probability event.
10. A ratio is the comparison of two quantities by division.
11. An event is a set of outcomes.
12. Probability is the chance that some event will occur.

Answer Key (Lesson 2-4)

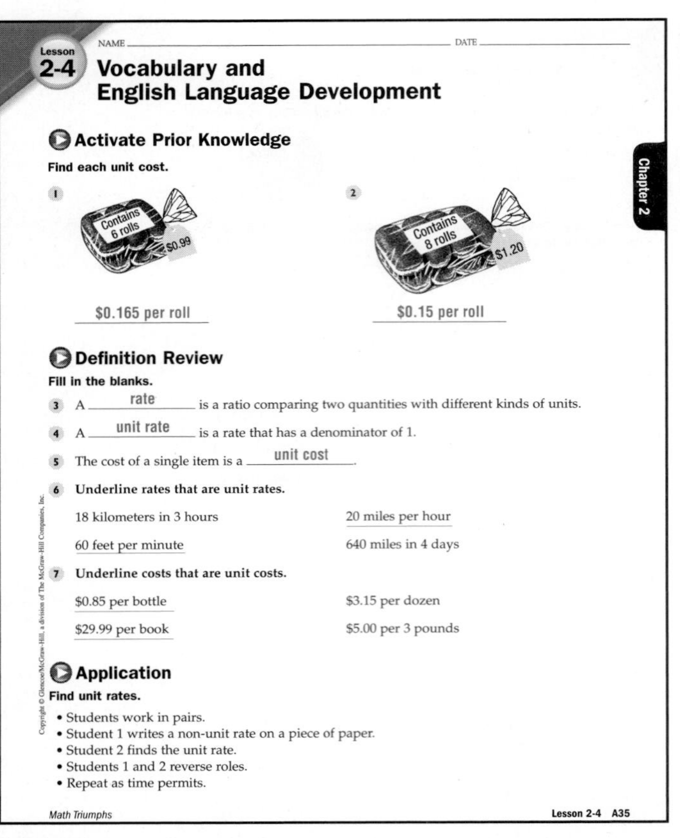

NAME ______ DATE ______

Lesson 2-4

Vocabulary and English Language Development

Activate Prior Knowledge

Find each unit cost.

1. Contains 6 rolls $0.99 — $0.165 per roll

2. Contains 8 rolls $1.20 — $0.15 per roll

Definition Review

Fill in the blanks.

3. A rate is a ratio comparing two quantities with different kinds of units.

4. A unit rate is a rate that has a denominator of 1.

5. The cost of a single item is a unit cost.

6. **Underline rates that are unit rates.**

18 kilometers in 3 hours	20 miles per hour
60 feet per minute	640 miles in 4 days

7. **Underline costs that are unit costs.**

$0.85 per bottle	$3.15 per dozen
$29.99 per book	$5.00 per 3 pounds

Application

Find unit rates.

- Students work in pairs.
- Student 1 writes a non-unit rate on a piece of paper.
- Student 2 finds the unit rate.
- Students 1 and 2 reverse roles.
- Repeat as time permits.

Chapter 2

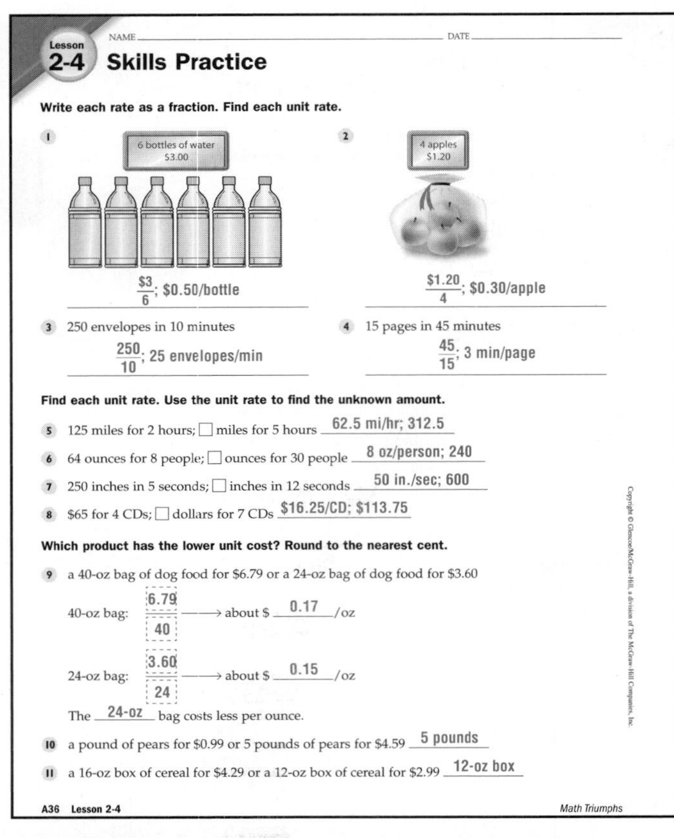

NAME ______ DATE ______

Lesson 2-4

Skills Practice

Write each rate as a fraction. Find each unit rate.

1. 6 bottles of water $3.00 — $\frac{\$3}{6}$; $0.50/bottle

2. 4 apples $1.20 — $\frac{\$1.20}{4}$; $0.30/apple

3. 250 envelopes in 10 minutes — $\frac{250}{10}$; 25 envelopes/min

4. 15 pages in 45 minutes — $\frac{45}{15}$; 3 min/page

Find each unit rate. Use the unit rate to find the unknown amount.

5. 125 miles for 2 hours; ☐ miles for 5 hours 62.5 mi/hr; 312.5

6. 64 ounces for 8 people; ☐ ounces for 30 people 8 oz/person; 240

7. 250 inches in 5 seconds; ☐ inches in 12 seconds 50 in./sec; 600

8. $65 for 4 CDs; ☐ dollars for 7 CDs $16.25/CD; $113.75

Which product has the lower unit cost? Round to the nearest cent.

9. a 40-oz bag of dog food for $6.79 or a 24-oz bag of dog food for $3.60

40-oz bag: $\frac{6.79}{40}$ ⟶ about $ 0.17 /oz

24-oz bag: $\frac{3.60}{24}$ ⟶ about $ 0.15 /oz

The 24-oz bag costs less per ounce.

10. a pound of pears for $0.99 or 5 pounds of pears for $4.59 5 pounds

11. a 16-oz box of cereal for $4.29 or a 12-oz box of cereal for $2.99 12-oz box

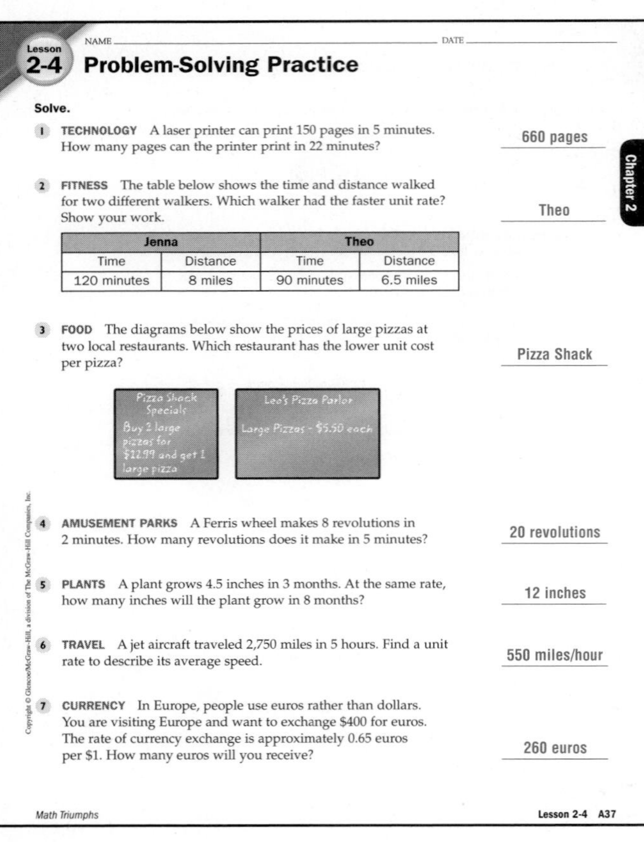

NAME ______ DATE ______

Lesson 2-4

Problem-Solving Practice

Solve.

1. **TECHNOLOGY** A laser printer can print 150 pages in 5 minutes. How many pages can the printer print in 22 minutes? 660 pages

2. **FITNESS** The table below shows the time and distance walked for two different walkers. Which walker had the faster unit rate? Show your work. Theo

Jenna		Theo	
Time	Distance	Time	Distance
120 minutes	8 miles	90 minutes	6.5 miles

3. **FOOD** The diagrams below show the prices of large pizzas at two local restaurants. Which restaurant has the lower unit cost per pizza? Pizza Shack

4. **AMUSEMENT PARKS** A Ferris wheel makes 8 revolutions in 2 minutes. How many revolutions does it make in 5 minutes? 20 revolutions

5. **PLANTS** A plant grows 4.5 inches in 3 months. At the same rate, how many inches will the plant grow in 8 months? 12 inches

6. **TRAVEL** A jet aircraft traveled 2,750 miles in 5 hours. Find a unit rate to describe its average speed. 550 miles/hour

7. **CURRENCY** In Europe, people use euros rather than dollars. You are visiting Europe and want to exchange $400 for euros. The rate of currency exchange is approximately 0.65 euros per $1. How many euros will you receive? 260 euros

Chapter 2

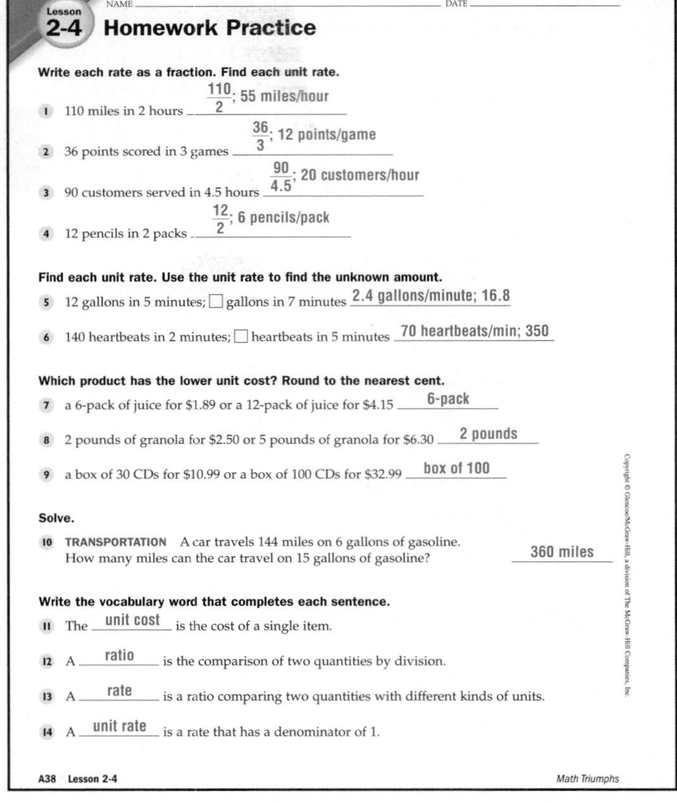

NAME ______ DATE ______

Lesson 2-4

Homework Practice

Write each rate as a fraction. Find each unit rate.

1. 110 miles in 2 hours $\frac{110}{2}$; 55 miles/hour

2. 36 points scored in 3 games $\frac{36}{3}$; 12 points/game

3. 90 customers served in 4.5 hours $\frac{90}{4.5}$; 20 customers/hour

4. 12 pencils in 2 packs $\frac{12}{2}$; 6 pencils/pack

Find each unit rate. Use the unit rate to find the unknown amount.

5. 12 gallons in 5 minutes; ☐ gallons in 7 minutes 2.4 gallons/minute; 16.8

6. 140 heartbeats in 2 minutes; ☐ heartbeats in 5 minutes 70 heartbeats/min; 350

Which product has the lower unit cost? Round to the nearest cent.

7. a 6-pack of juice for $1.89 or a 12-pack of juice for $4.15 6-pack

8. 2 pounds of granola for $2.50 or 5 pounds of granola for $6.30 2 pounds

9. a box of 30 CDs for $10.99 or a box of 100 CDs for $32.99 box of 100

Solve.

10. **TRANSPORTATION** A car travels 144 miles on 6 gallons of gasoline. How many miles can the car travel on 15 gallons of gasoline? 360 miles

Write the vocabulary word that completes each sentence.

11. The unit cost is the cost of a single item.

12. A ratio is the comparison of two quantities by division.

13. A rate is a ratio comparing two quantities with different kinds of units.

14. A unit rate is a rate that has a denominator of 1.

Answer Key (Lesson 2-5)

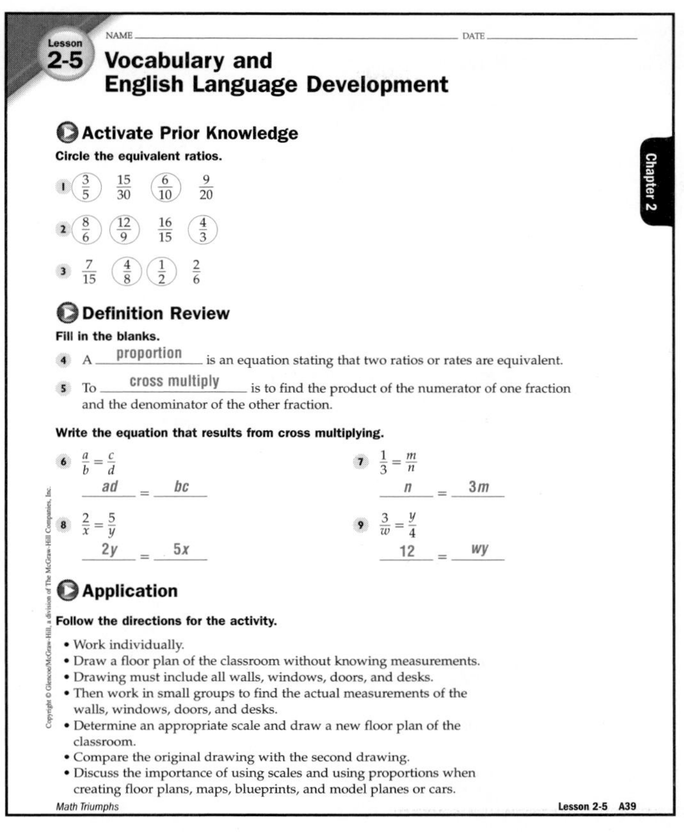

NAME ______ DATE ______

Lesson 2-5

Vocabulary and English Language Development

Chapter 2

Activate Prior Knowledge

Circle the equivalent ratios.

1. $\frac{3}{5}$ (circled) $\frac{15}{30}$ $\frac{6}{10}$ (circled) $\frac{9}{20}$
2. $\frac{8}{6}$ (circled) $\frac{12}{9}$ (circled) $\frac{16}{15}$ $\frac{4}{3}$ (circled)
3. $\frac{7}{15}$ $\frac{4}{8}$ (circled) $\frac{1}{2}$ (circled) $\frac{2}{6}$

Definition Review

Fill in the blanks.

4. A **proportion** is an equation stating that two ratios or rates are equivalent.
5. To **cross multiply** is to find the product of the numerator of one fraction and the denominator of the other fraction.

Write the equation that results from cross multiplying.

6. $\frac{a}{b} = \frac{c}{d}$ — **ad** = **bc**
7. $\frac{1}{3} = \frac{m}{n}$ — **n** = **3m**
8. $\frac{2}{x} = \frac{5}{y}$ — **2y** = **5x**
9. $\frac{3}{w} = \frac{y}{4}$ — **12** = **wy**

Application

Follow the directions for the activity.

- Work individually.
- Draw a floor plan of the classroom without knowing measurements.
- Drawing must include all walls, windows, doors, and desks.
- Then work in small groups to find the actual measurements of the walls, windows, doors, and desks.
- Determine an appropriate scale and draw a new floor plan of the classroom.
- Compare the original drawing with the second drawing.
- Discuss the importance of using scales and using proportions when creating floor plans, maps, blueprints, and model planes or cars.

Math Triumphs Lesson 2-5 A39

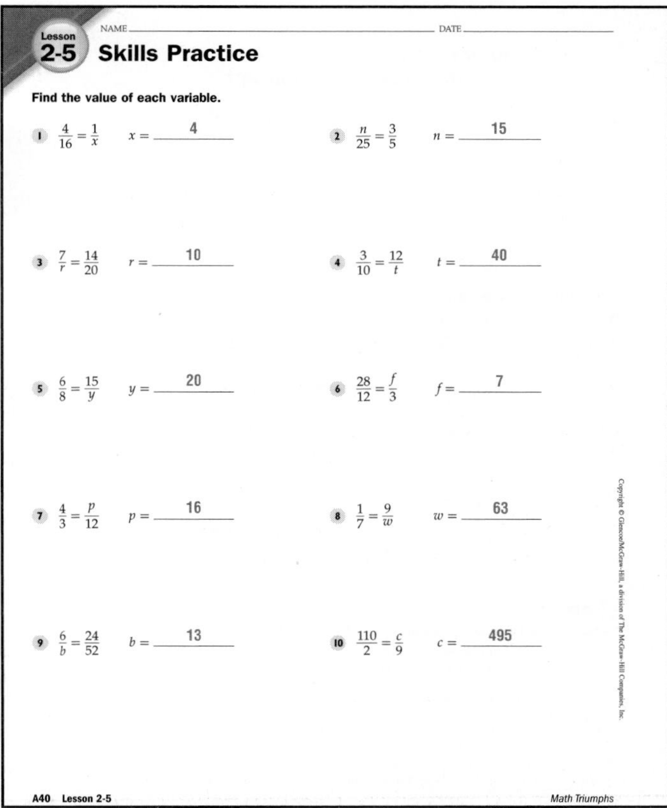

NAME ______ DATE ______

Lesson 2-5

Skills Practice

Find the value of each variable.

1. $\frac{4}{16} = \frac{1}{x}$ $x =$ **4**
2. $\frac{n}{25} = \frac{3}{5}$ $n =$ **15**
3. $\frac{7}{r} = \frac{14}{20}$ $r =$ **10**
4. $\frac{3}{10} = \frac{12}{t}$ $t =$ **40**
5. $\frac{6}{8} = \frac{15}{y}$ $y =$ **20**
6. $\frac{28}{12} = \frac{f}{3}$ $f =$ **7**
7. $\frac{4}{3} = \frac{p}{12}$ $p =$ **16**
8. $\frac{1}{7} = \frac{9}{w}$ $w =$ **63**
9. $\frac{6}{b} = \frac{24}{52}$ $b =$ **13**
10. $\frac{110}{2} = \frac{c}{9}$ $c =$ **495**

A40 Lesson 2-5 Math Triumphs

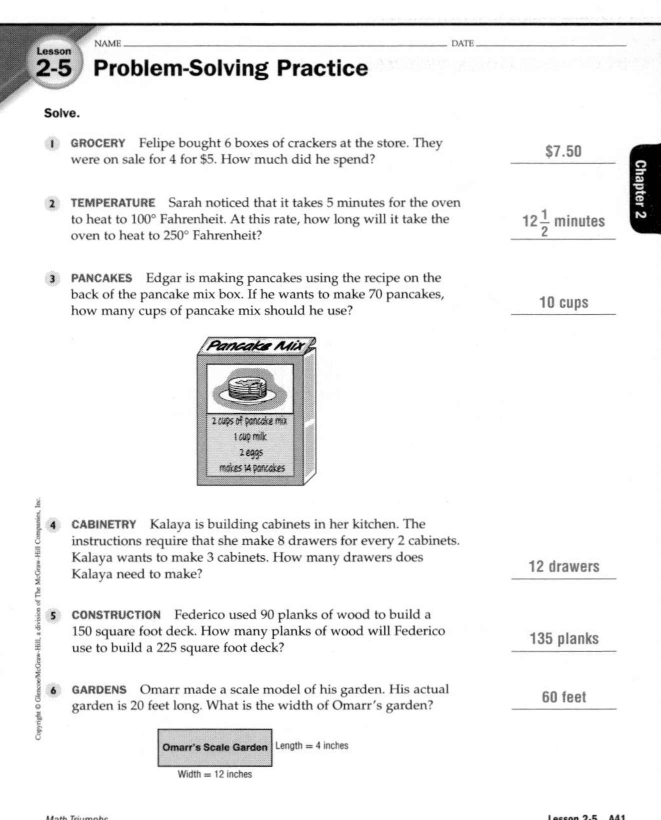

NAME ______ DATE ______

Lesson 2-5

Problem-Solving Practice

Chapter 2

Solve.

1. **GROCERY** Felipe bought 6 boxes of crackers at the store. They were on sale for 4 for $5. How much did he spend? **$7.50**
2. **TEMPERATURE** Sarah noticed that it takes 5 minutes for the oven to heat to 100° Fahrenheit. At this rate, how long will it take the oven to heat to 250° Fahrenheit? **$12\frac{1}{2}$ minutes**
3. **PANCAKES** Edgar is making pancakes using the recipe on the back of the pancake mix box. If he wants to make 70 pancakes, how many cups of pancake mix should he use? **10 cups**

4. **CABINETRY** Kalaya is building cabinets in her kitchen. The instructions require that she make 8 drawers for every 2 cabinets. Kalaya wants to make 3 cabinets. How many drawers does Kalaya need to make? **12 drawers**
5. **CONSTRUCTION** Federico used 90 planks of wood to build a 150 square foot deck. How many planks of wood will Federico use to build a 225 square foot deck? **135 planks**
6. **GARDENS** Omarr made a scale model of his garden. His actual garden is 20 feet long. What is the width of Omarr's garden? **60 feet**

Math Triumphs Lesson 2-5 A41

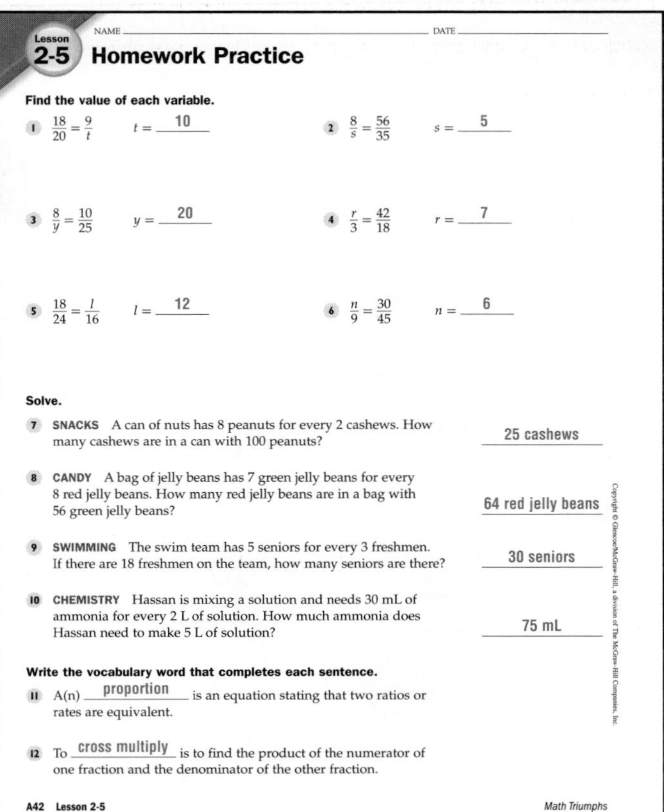

NAME ______ DATE ______

Lesson 2-5

Homework Practice

Find the value of each variable.

1. $\frac{18}{20} = \frac{9}{t}$ $t =$ **10**
2. $\frac{8}{s} = \frac{56}{35}$ $s =$ **5**
3. $\frac{8}{y} = \frac{10}{25}$ $y =$ **20**
4. $\frac{r}{3} = \frac{42}{18}$ $r =$ **7**
5. $\frac{18}{24} = \frac{l}{16}$ $l =$ **12**
6. $\frac{n}{9} = \frac{30}{45}$ $n =$ **6**

Solve.

7. **SNACKS** A can of nuts has 8 peanuts for every 2 cashews. How many cashews are in a can with 100 peanuts? **25 cashews**
8. **CANDY** A bag of jelly beans has 7 green jelly beans for every 8 red jelly beans. How many red jelly beans are in a bag with 56 green jelly beans? **64 red jelly beans**
9. **SWIMMING** The swim team has 5 seniors for every 3 freshmen. If there are 18 freshmen on the team, how many seniors are there? **30 seniors**
10. **CHEMISTRY** Hassan is mixing a solution and needs 30 mL of ammonia for every 2 L of solution. How much ammonia does Hassan need to make 5 L of solution? **75 mL**

Write the vocabulary word that completes each sentence.

11. A(n) **proportion** is an equation stating that two ratios or rates are equivalent.
12. To **cross multiply** is to find the product of the numerator of one fraction and the denominator of the other fraction.

A42 Lesson 2-5 Math Triumphs

Answer Key (Lesson 2-6)

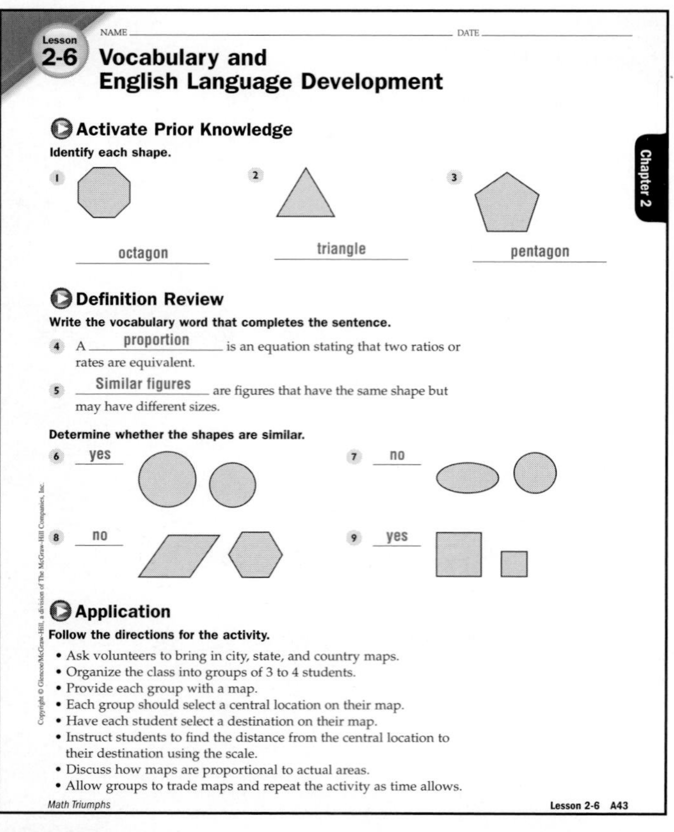

NAME ______ DATE ______

Lesson 2-6 **Vocabulary and English Language Development**

Activate Prior Knowledge

Identify each shape.

1 octagon

2 triangle

3 pentagon

Definition Review

Write the vocabulary word that completes the sentence.

4 A proportion is an equation stating that two ratios or rates are equivalent.

5 Similar figures are figures that have the same shape but may have different sizes.

Determine whether the shapes are similar.

6 yes

7 no

8 no

9 yes

Application

Follow the directions for the activity.

- Ask volunteers to bring in city, state, and country maps.
- Organize the class into groups of 3 to 4 students.
- Provide each group with a map.
- Each group should select a central location on their map.
- Have each student select a destination on their map.
- Instruct students to find the distance from the central location to their destination using the scale.
- Discuss how maps are proportional to actual areas.
- Allow groups to trade maps and repeat the activity as time allows.

Chapter 2

Copyright © Glencoe/McGraw-Hill, a division of The McGraw-Hill Companies, Inc.

Math Triumphs Lesson 2-6 A43

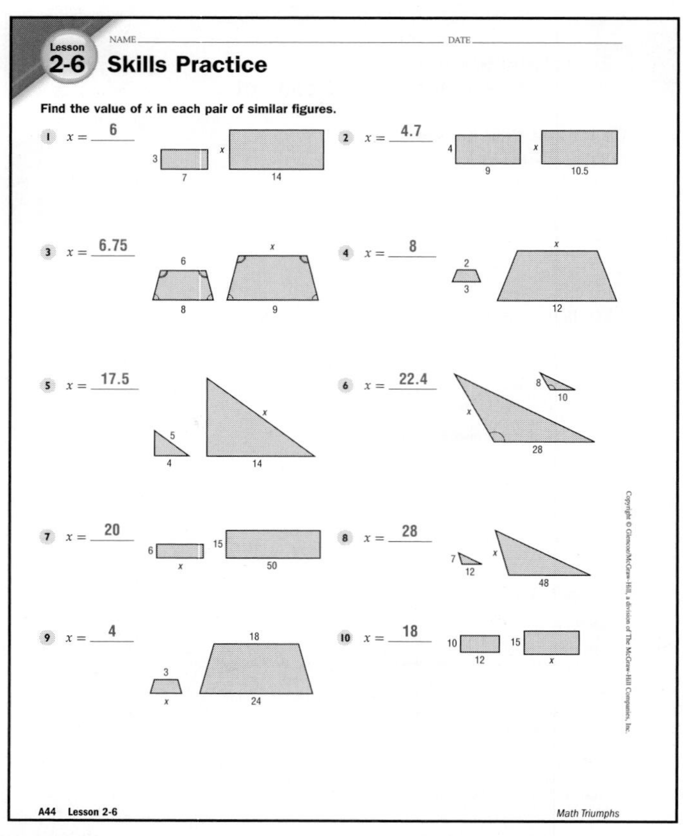

NAME ______ DATE ______

Lesson 2-6 **Skills Practice**

Find the value of *x* in each pair of similar figures.

1 $x =$ 6

2 $x =$ 4.7

3 $x =$ 6.75

4 $x =$ 8

5 $x =$ 17.5

6 $x =$ 22.4

7 $x =$ 20

8 $x =$ 28

9 $x =$ 4

10 $x =$ 18

Copyright © Glencoe/McGraw-Hill, a division of The McGraw-Hill Companies, Inc.

A44 Lesson 2-6 Math Triumphs

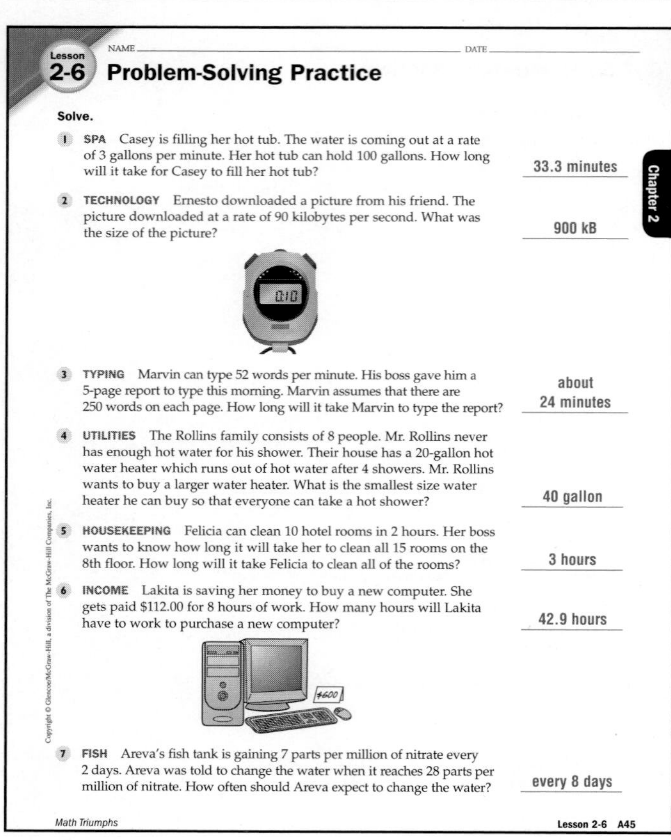

NAME ______ DATE ______

Lesson 2-6 **Problem-Solving Practice**

Solve.

1 **SPA** Casey is filling her hot tub. The water is coming out at a rate of 3 gallons per minute. Her hot tub can hold 100 gallons. How long will it take for Casey to fill her hot tub? 33.3 minutes

2 **TECHNOLOGY** Ernesto downloaded a picture from his friend. The picture downloaded at a rate of 90 kilobytes per second. What was the size of the picture? 900 kB

3 **TYPING** Marvin can type 52 words per minute. His boss gave him a 5-page report to type this morning. Marvin assumes that there are 250 words on each page. How long will it take Marvin to type the report? about 24 minutes

4 **UTILITIES** The Rollins family consists of 8 people. Mr. Rollins never has enough hot water for his shower. Their house has a 20-gallon hot water heater which runs out of hot water after 4 showers. Mr. Rollins wants to buy a larger water heater. What is the smallest size water heater he can buy so that everyone can take a hot shower? 40 gallon

5 **HOUSEKEEPING** Felicia can clean 10 hotel rooms in 2 hours. Her boss wants to know how long it will take her to clean all 15 rooms on the 8th floor. How long will it take Felicia to clean all of the rooms? 3 hours

6 **INCOME** Lakita is saving her money to buy a new computer. She gets paid $112.00 for 8 hours of work. How many hours will Lakita have to work to purchase a new computer? 42.9 hours

7 **FISH** Areva's fish tank is gaining 7 parts per million of nitrate every 2 days. Areva was told to change the water when it reaches 28 parts per million of nitrate. How often should Areva expect to change the water? every 8 days

Chapter 2

Copyright © Glencoe/McGraw-Hill, a division of The McGraw-Hill Companies, Inc.

Math Triumphs Lesson 2-6 A45

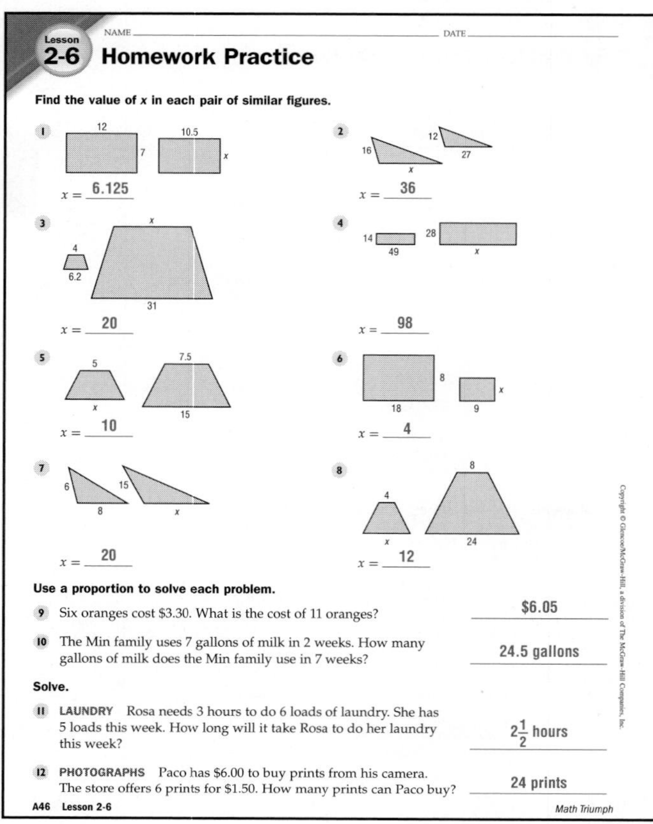

NAME ______ DATE ______

Lesson 2-6 **Homework Practice**

Find the value of *x* in each pair of similar figures.

1 $x =$ 6.125

2 $x =$ 36

3 $x =$ 20

4 $x =$ 98

5 $x =$ 10

6 $x =$ 4

7 $x =$ 20

8 $x =$ 12

Use a proportion to solve each problem.

9 Six oranges cost $3.30. What is the cost of 11 oranges? $6.05

10 The Min family uses 7 gallons of milk in 2 weeks. How many gallons of milk does the Min family use in 7 weeks? 24.5 gallons

Solve.

11 **LAUNDRY** Rosa needs 3 hours to do 6 loads of laundry. She has 5 loads this week. How long will it take Rosa to do her laundry this week? $2\frac{1}{2}$ hours

12 **PHOTOGRAPHS** Paco has $6.00 to buy prints from his camera. The store offers 6 prints for $1.50. How many prints can Paco buy? 24 prints

Copyright © Glencoe/McGraw-Hill, a division of The McGraw-Hill Companies, Inc.

A46 Lesson 2-6 Math Triumph

Answer Key (Lesson 3-1)

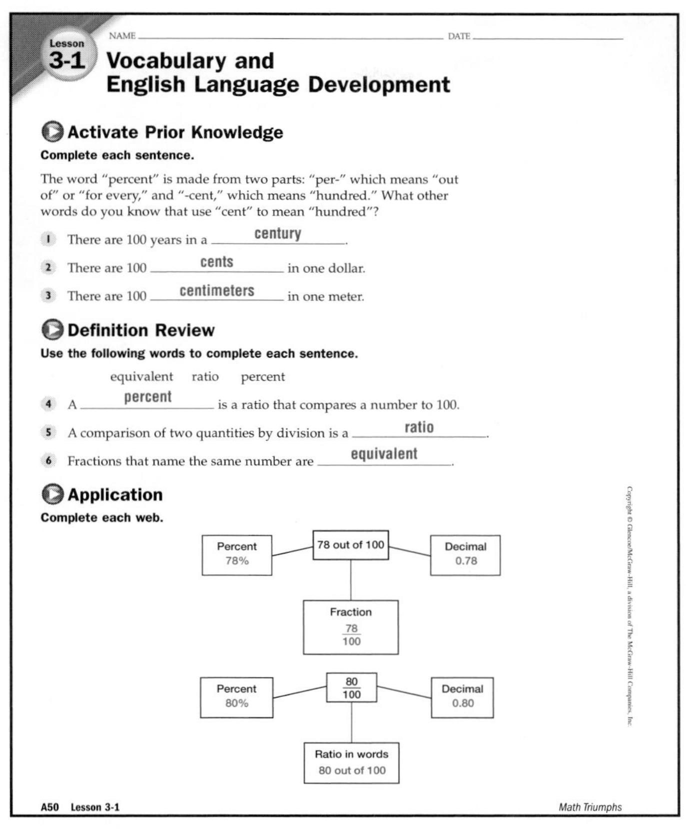

Lesson 3-1 NAME ______ DATE ______

Vocabulary and English Language Development

Activate Prior Knowledge

Complete each sentence.

The word "percent" is made from two parts: "per-" which means "out of" or "for every," and "-cent," which means "hundred." What other words do you know that use "cent" to mean "hundred"?

1 There are 100 years in a **century**.

2 There are 100 **cents** in one dollar.

3 There are 100 **centimeters** in one meter.

Definition Review

Use the following words to complete each sentence.

equivalent ratio percent

4 A **percent** is a ratio that compares a number to 100.

5 A comparison of two quantities by division is a **ratio**.

6 Fractions that name the same number are **equivalent**.

Application

Complete each web.

Percent 78% — 78 out of 100 — Decimal 0.78; Fraction $\frac{78}{100}$

Percent 80% — $\frac{80}{100}$ — Decimal 0.80; Ratio in words 80 out of 100

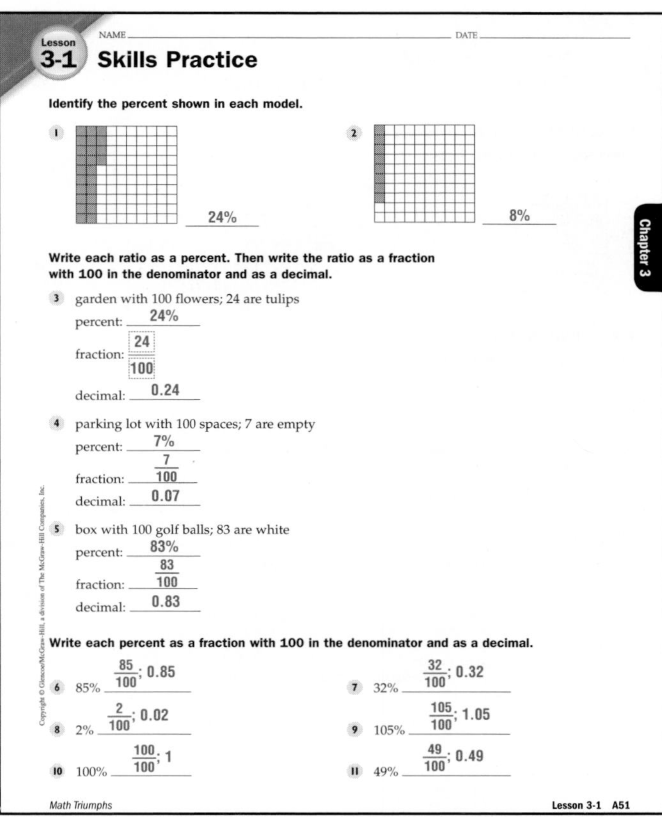

Lesson 3-1 NAME ______ DATE ______

Skills Practice

Chapter 3

Identify the percent shown in each model.

1 **24%**

2 **8%**

Write each ratio as a percent. Then write the ratio as a fraction with 100 in the denominator and as a decimal.

3 garden with 100 flowers; 24 are tulips
percent: **24%**
fraction: $\frac{24}{100}$
decimal: **0.24**

4 parking lot with 100 spaces; 7 are empty
percent: **7%**
fraction: $\frac{7}{100}$
decimal: **0.07**

5 box with 100 golf balls; 83 are white
percent: **83%**
fraction: $\frac{83}{100}$
decimal: **0.83**

Write each percent as a fraction with 100 in the denominator and as a decimal.

6 85% $\frac{85}{100}$; 0.85

7 32% $\frac{32}{100}$; 0.32

8 2% $\frac{2}{100}$; 0.02

9 105% $\frac{105}{100}$; 1.05

10 100% $\frac{100}{100}$; 1

11 49% $\frac{49}{100}$; 0.49

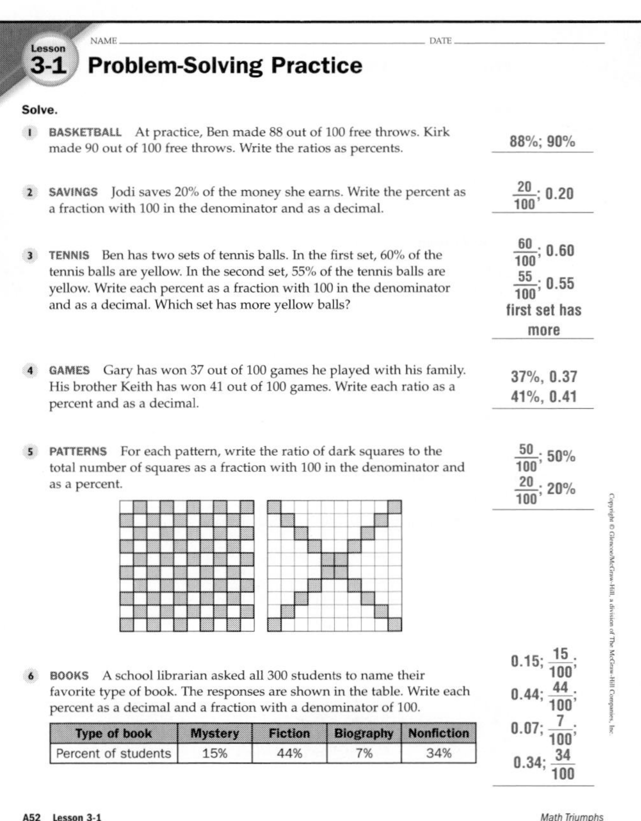

Lesson 3-1 NAME ______ DATE ______

Problem-Solving Practice

Solve.

1 **BASKETBALL** At practice, Ben made 88 out of 100 free throws. Kirk made 90 out of 100 free throws. Write the ratios as percents. **88%; 90%**

2 **SAVINGS** Jodi saves 20% of the money she earns. Write the percent as a fraction with 100 in the denominator and as a decimal. $\frac{20}{100}$; **0.20**

3 **TENNIS** Ben has two sets of tennis balls. In the first set, 60% of the tennis balls are yellow. In the second set, 55% of the tennis balls are yellow. Write each percent as a fraction with 100 in the denominator and as a decimal. Which set has more yellow balls? $\frac{60}{100}$; **0.60**; $\frac{55}{100}$; **0.55**; **first set has more**

4 **GAMES** Gary has won 37 out of 100 games he played with his family. His brother Keith has won 41 out of 100 games. Write each ratio as a percent and as a decimal. **37%, 0.37; 41%, 0.41**

5 **PATTERNS** For each pattern, write the ratio of dark squares to the total number of squares as a fraction with 100 in the denominator and as a percent. $\frac{50}{100}$; **50%**; $\frac{20}{100}$; **20%**

6 **BOOKS** A school librarian asked all 300 students to name their favorite type of book. The responses are shown in the table. Write each percent as a decimal and a fraction with a denominator of 100.

Type of book	Mystery	Fiction	Biography	Nonfiction
Percent of students	15%	44%	7%	34%

0.15; $\frac{15}{100}$, **0.44;** $\frac{44}{100}$, **0.07;** $\frac{7}{100}$, **0.34;** $\frac{34}{100}$

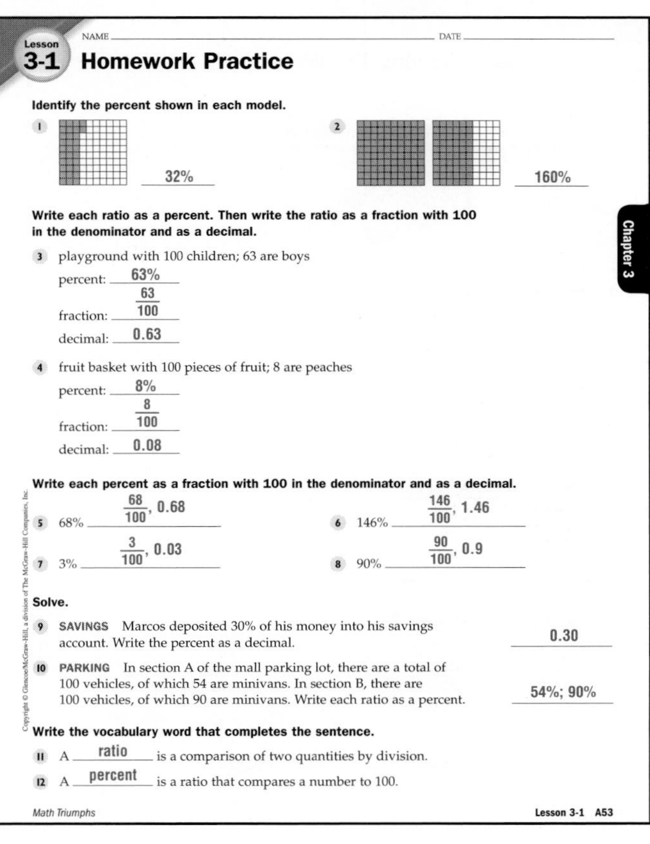

Lesson 3-1 NAME ______ DATE ______

Homework Practice

Chapter 3

Identify the percent shown in each model.

1 **32%**

2 **160%**

Write each ratio as a percent. Then write the ratio as a fraction with 100 in the denominator and as a decimal.

3 playground with 100 children; 63 are boys
percent: **63%**
fraction: $\frac{63}{100}$
decimal: **0.63**

4 fruit basket with 100 pieces of fruit; 8 are peaches
percent: **8%**
fraction: $\frac{8}{100}$
decimal: **0.08**

Write each percent as a fraction with 100 in the denominator and as a decimal.

5 68% $\frac{68}{100}$, 0.68

6 146% $\frac{146}{100}$, 1.46

7 3% $\frac{3}{100}$, 0.03

8 90% $\frac{90}{100}$, 0.9

Solve.

9 **SAVINGS** Marcos deposited 30% of his money into his savings account. Write the percent as a decimal. **0.30**

10 **PARKING** In section A of the mall parking lot, there are a total of 100 vehicles, of which 54 are minivans. In section B, there are 100 vehicles, of which 90 are minivans. Write each ratio as a percent. **54%; 90%**

Write the vocabulary word that completes the sentence.

11 A **ratio** is a comparison of two quantities by division.

12 A **percent** is a ratio that compares a number to 100.

Answer Key (Lesson 3-2)

Lesson 3-2

NAME ____________ DATE ____________

Vocabulary and English Language Development

Activate Prior Knowledge

Shade each model to show the percent.

1. 56%
2. 12%

Definition Review

Percent means *"out of one hundred."*

Fill in the blanks.

3. A **percent** is a ratio that compares a number to 100.
4. A **decimal** is a number that has digits in the tenths place and beyond.
5. **Equivalent fractions** are fractions that name the same number.

Application

- Students work in groups of 4 or 5. Each student answers *yes* or *no* to the following questions.
  - Do you have any pets?
  - Do you walk to school?
  - Do you have any brothers or sisters?
- Students then work together as a group to find the percent of their group that answered yes to each question.
- If time permits, students can make up their own questions and then share the percents with the rest of the class.

Lesson 3-2

NAME ____________ DATE ____________

Skills Practice

Write each percent as a fraction or mixed number in simplest form and as a decimal.

1. 40% $\frac{2}{5}$; 0.4
2. 5% $\frac{1}{20}$; 0.05
3. 15% $\frac{3}{20}$; 0.15
4. 350% $3\frac{1}{2}$; 3.5
5. 166% $1\frac{33}{50}$; 1.66
6. 75% $\frac{3}{4}$; 0.75

Write each fraction as a decimal and as a percent.

7. $\frac{15}{50}$ 0.30, 30%
8. $\frac{1}{4}$ 0.25; 25%
9. $\frac{3}{5}$ 0.60, 60%
10. $\frac{3}{16}$ 0.1875; 18.75%
11. $\frac{11}{25}$ 0.44; 44%
12. $\frac{12}{5}$ 2.4; 240%
13. $\frac{5}{4}$ 1.25; 125%
14. $\frac{13}{50}$ 0.26; 26%
15. $\frac{3}{8}$ 0.375; 37.5%
16. $\frac{37}{10}$ 3.7; 370%

Chapter 3

Lesson 3-2

NAME ____________ DATE ____________

Problem-Solving Practice

Solve.

1. **SHOPPING** A store is having a sale as shown on the sign. Write the percent as a fraction in simplest form and a decimal. $\frac{7}{20}$; 0.35

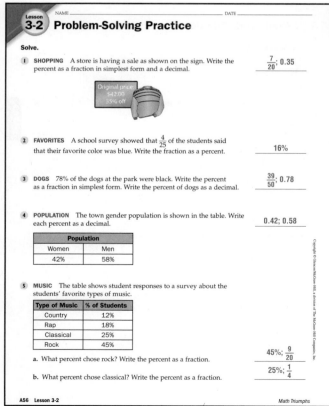

Original price: $42.00 35% off

2. **FAVORITES** A school survey showed that $\frac{4}{25}$ of the students said that their favorite color was blue. Write the fraction as a percent. 16%

3. **DOGS** 78% of the dogs at the park were black. Write the percent as a fraction in simplest form. Write the percent of dogs as a decimal. $\frac{39}{50}$; 0.78

4. **POPULATION** The town gender population is shown in the table. Write each percent as a decimal. 0.42; 0.58

Population	
Women	Men
42%	58%

5. **MUSIC** The table shows student responses to a survey about the students' favorite types of music.

Type of Music	% of Students
Country	12%
Rap	18%
Classical	25%
Rock	45%

a. What percent chose rock? Write the percent as a fraction. 45%; $\frac{9}{20}$

b. What percent chose classical? Write the percent as a fraction. 25%; $\frac{1}{4}$

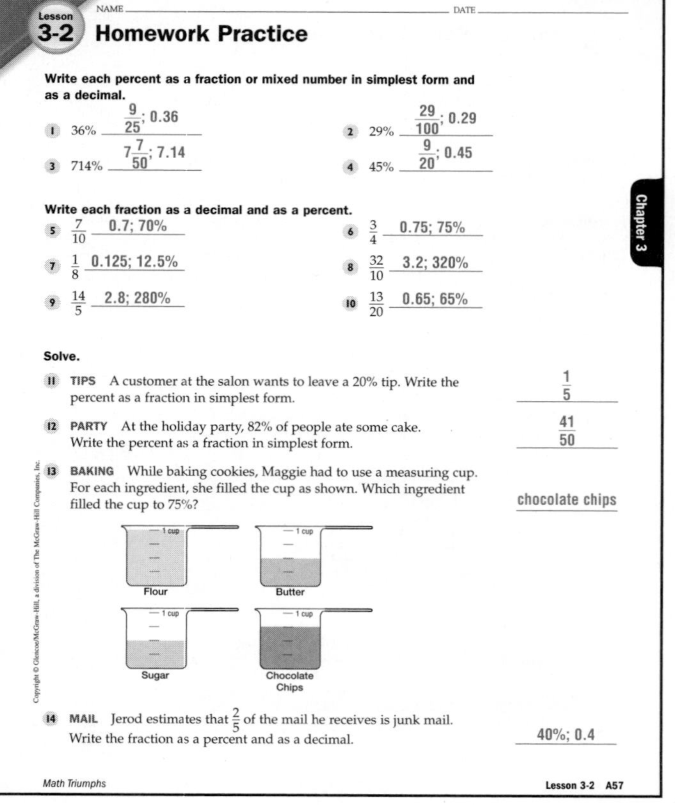

Lesson 3-2

NAME ____________ DATE ____________

Homework Practice

Write each percent as a fraction or mixed number in simplest form and as a decimal.

1. 36% $\frac{9}{25}$; 0.36
2. 29% $\frac{29}{100}$; 0.29
3. 714% $7\frac{7}{50}$; 7.14
4. 45% $\frac{9}{20}$; 0.45

Write each fraction as a decimal and as a percent.

5. $\frac{7}{10}$ 0.7; 70%
6. $\frac{3}{4}$ 0.75; 75%
7. $\frac{1}{8}$ 0.125; 12.5%
8. $\frac{32}{10}$ 3.2; 320%
9. $\frac{14}{5}$ 2.8; 280%
10. $\frac{13}{20}$ 0.65; 65%

Solve.

11. **TIPS** A customer at the salon wants to leave a 20% tip. Write the percent as a fraction in simplest form. $\frac{1}{5}$
12. **PARTY** At the holiday party, 82% of people ate some cake. Write the percent as a fraction in simplest form. $\frac{41}{50}$
13. **BAKING** While baking cookies, Maggie had to use a measuring cup. For each ingredient, she filled the cup as shown. Which ingredient filled the cup to 75%? chocolate chips

14. **MAIL** Jerod estimates that $\frac{2}{5}$ of the mail he receives is junk mail. Write the fraction as a percent and as a decimal. 40%; 0.4

Chapter 3

Answer Key (Lesson 3-3)

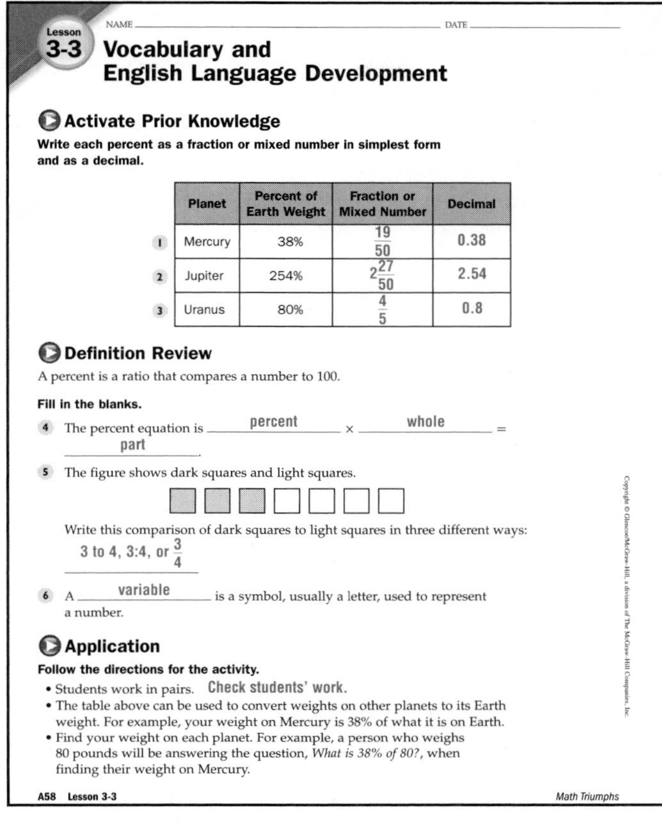

Lesson 3-3 NAME ______ DATE ______

Vocabulary and English Language Development

Activate Prior Knowledge

Write each percent as a fraction or mixed number in simplest form and as a decimal.

	Planet	Percent of Earth Weight	Fraction or Mixed Number	Decimal
1	Mercury	38%	$\frac{19}{50}$	0.38
2	Jupiter	254%	$2\frac{27}{50}$	2.54
3	Uranus	80%	$\frac{4}{5}$	0.8

Definition Review

A percent is a ratio that compares a number to 100.

Fill in the blanks.

4 The percent equation is __percent__ × __whole__ = __part__.

5 The figure shows dark squares and light squares.

Write this comparison of dark squares to light squares in three different ways: 3 to 4, 3:4, or $\frac{3}{4}$

6 A __variable__ is a symbol, usually a letter, used to represent a number.

Application

Follow the directions for the activity.

- Students work in pairs. Check students' work.
- The table above can be used to convert weights on other planets to its Earth weight. For example, your weight on Mercury is 38% of what it is on Earth.
- Find your weight on each planet. For example, a person who weighs 80 pounds will be answering the question, *What is 38% of 80?*, when finding their weight on Mercury.

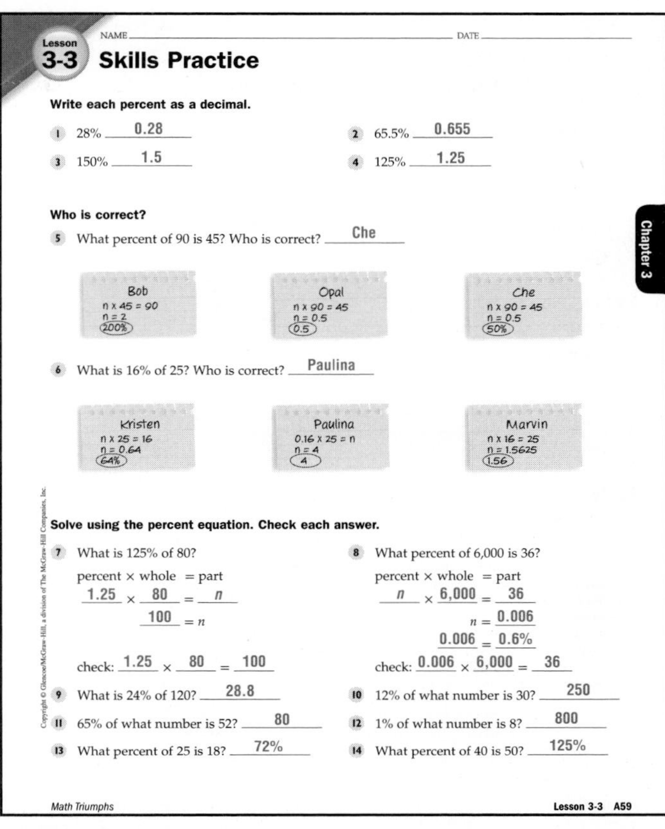

Lesson 3-3 NAME ______ DATE ______

Skills Practice

Write each percent as a decimal.

1 28% __0.28__ 2 65.5% __0.655__

3 150% __1.5__ 4 125% __1.25__

Who is correct?

5 What percent of 90 is 45? Who is correct? __Che__

Bob	Opal	Che
n × 45 = 90	n × 90 = 45	n × 90 = 45
n = 2	n = 0.5	n = 0.5
200%	0.5	50%

6 What is 16% of 25? Who is correct? __Paulina__

Kristen	Paulina	Marvin
n × 25 = 16	0.16 × 25 = n	n × 16 = 25
n = 0.64	n = 4	n = 1.5625
64%	4	1.56

Solve using the percent equation. Check each answer.

7 What is 125% of 80?

percent × whole = part

__1.25__ × __80__ = __n__

__100__ = n

check: __1.25__ × __80__ = __100__

8 What percent of 6,000 is 36?

percent × whole = part

__n__ × __6,000__ = __36__

n = __0.006__

__0.006__ = __0.6%__

check: __0.006__ × __6,000__ = __36__

9 What is 24% of 120? __28.8__ 10 12% of what number is 30? __250__

11 65% of what number is 52? __80__ 12 1% of what number is 8? __800__

13 What percent of 25 is 18? __72%__ 14 What percent of 40 is 50? __125%__

Chapter 3

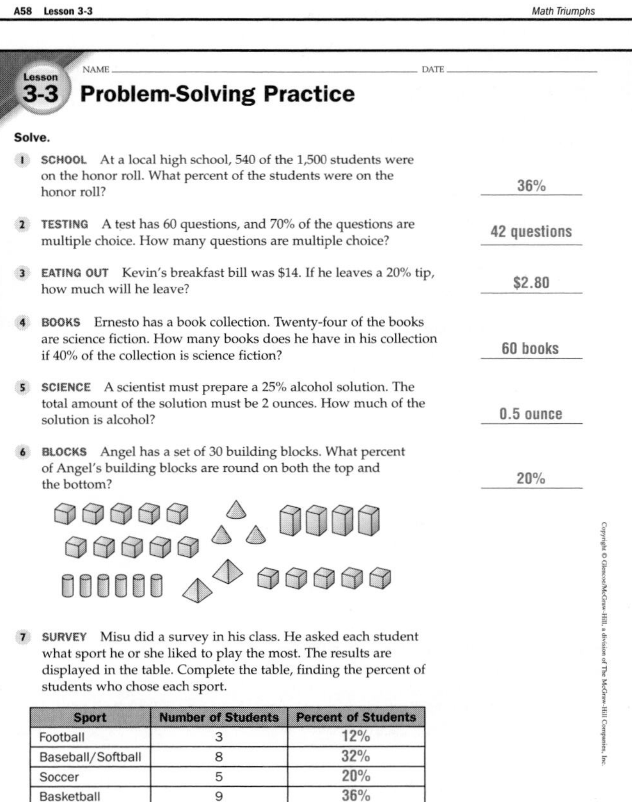

Lesson 3-3 NAME ______ DATE ______

Problem-Solving Practice

Solve.

1 **SCHOOL** At a local high school, 540 of the 1,500 students were on the honor roll. What percent of the students were on the honor roll? __36%__

2 **TESTING** A test has 60 questions, and 70% of the questions are multiple choice. How many questions are multiple choice? __42 questions__

3 **EATING OUT** Kevin's breakfast bill was $14. If he leaves a 20% tip, how much will he leave? __$2.80__

4 **BOOKS** Ernesto has a book collection. Twenty-four of the books are science fiction. How many books does he have in his collection if 40% of the collection is science fiction? __60 books__

5 **SCIENCE** A scientist must prepare a 25% alcohol solution. The total amount of the solution must be 2 ounces. How much of the solution is alcohol? __0.5 ounce__

6 **BLOCKS** Angel has a set of 30 building blocks. What percent of Angel's building blocks are round on both the top and the bottom? __20%__

7 **SURVEY** Misu did a survey in his class. He asked each student what sport he or she liked to play the most. The results are displayed in the table. Complete the table, finding the percent of students who chose each sport.

Sport	Number of Students	Percent of Students
Football	3	12%
Baseball/Softball	8	32%
Soccer	5	20%
Basketball	9	36%

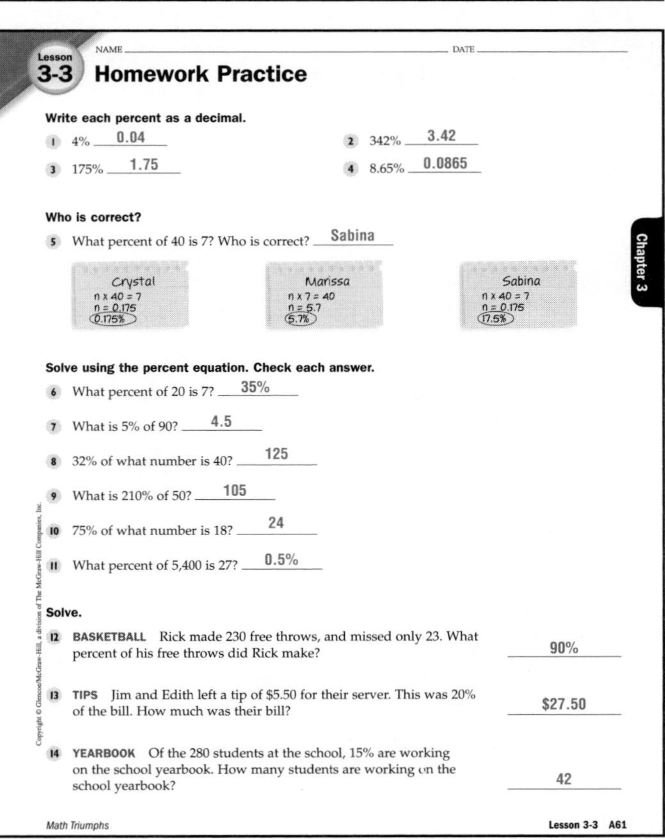

Lesson 3-3 NAME ______ DATE ______

Homework Practice

Write each percent as a decimal.

1 4% __0.04__ 2 342% __3.42__

3 175% __1.75__ 4 8.65% __0.0865__

Who is correct?

5 What percent of 40 is 7? Who is correct? __Sabina__

Crystal	Marissa	Sabina
n × 40 = 7	n × 7 = 40	n × 40 = 7
n = 0.175	n = 5.7	n = 0.175
0.175%	5.7%	17.5%

Solve using the percent equation. Check each answer.

6 What percent of 20 is 7? __35%__

7 What is 5% of 90? __4.5__

8 32% of what number is 40? __125__

9 What is 210% of 50? __105__

10 75% of what number is 18? __24__

11 What percent of 5,400 is 27? __0.5%__

Solve.

12 **BASKETBALL** Rick made 230 free throws, and missed only 23. What percent of his free throws did Rick make? __90%__

13 **TIPS** Jim and Edith left a tip of $5.50 for their server. This was 20% of the bill. How much was their bill? __$27.50__

14 **YEARBOOK** Of the 280 students at the school, 15% are working on the school yearbook. How many students are working on the school yearbook? __42__

Chapter 3

Answer Key (Lesson 3-4)

Lesson 3-4

NAME ______ DATE ______

Vocabulary and English Language Development

Activate Prior Knowledge

1 Draw a line to connect the question on the left with the correct answer on the right.

Question	Answer
What is 10% of 50? ——→	5
What is 25% of 12?	82
What is 100% of 82?	3

Definition Review

A **circle graph** is used to compare parts of a whole.

Fill in the blanks.

2 In a circle graph, the circle represents the **whole** and is separated into parts of a **whole**.

3 A **sector** is a pie-shaped section in a circle graph. The sectors add to **100** %.

Application

- Students divide into 4 groups, Group A, Group B, Group C, or Group D.
- Group A chooses 4 TV shows, then asks all the students which TV show they like best.
  Group B chooses 4 sports, then asks all the students which sport they like best.
  Group C chooses 4 foods, then asks all the students which food they like best.
  Group D chooses 4 pets, then asks all the students which pet they like best.
- Each group finds the percent of students that chose each of their categories. Then they answer the following questions in their group:
  If you put the data in a circle graph…
  …which sector would be the largest? Why?
  …would any of your sectors be the same size? Why?
  …which sector, if any, would take up more than half the circle? Why?
- Each group sketches a circle graph of their data and shares it with the class. The class discusses if the graph looks correct based on the percents shown.

Lesson 3-4

NAME ______ DATE ______

Skills Practice

MUSIC Jenna asked her classmates what color MP3 player they owned. Use the circle graph she created to answer each question.

MP3 Color: Silver 50%, Black 30%, Pink 15%, Blue 5%

1 How many colors are there? **4**

2 What color do most students have? **Silver**

3 What color do the fewest students have? **Blue**

4 What percent of the students have black MP3 players? **30%**

INTERNET Arnie asked his neighbors how many people in their house use the Internet every day. Use the circle graph he created to answer each question.

Daily Internet Use: 40% Four, 32% Three, 18% Two, 3% Five, 7% One

5 Which groups make up 10% of the people Arnie asked? **Houses with either 1 or 5 daily users**

6 What percentage of the neighbors said that 4 people in their house use the Internet everyday? **40%**

VOTING 200 students voted in the Student Council election. The graph shows the percentage of votes each candidate received.

Student Council Votes: 15% Jadan, 17% Allie, 18% Handro, 20% Sayumi, 30% Miguel

7 What is the title of the graph? **Student Council Votes**

8 Who received the most votes? **Miguel**

9 Who received the least votes? **Jadan**

10 Did any two students receive the same number of votes? **no**

11 Miguel received twice as many votes as **Jadan**.

12 Which three students together received 50% of the votes? **Jadan, Allie, and Handro**

Chapter 3

Lesson 3-4

NAME ______ DATE ______

Problem-Solving Practice

Solve. For Exercises 1–4, use the graph at the right.

TRAVEL There are 250 passengers on an airplane. Some of the passengers are on a business trip, some are going on vacation to either the ocean or the mountains, and some are going to visit family or friends. Use the graph to answer the questions.

Reasons for Traveling: 30% Visits, 44% Business, 14% Ocean Vacation, 12% Mountain Vacation

1 What is the title of the graph? **Reasons for Traveling**

2 How many different kinds of trips are there? **4**

3 Why are most of the passengers traveling? **Business**

4 Which two kinds of trips combined equal the percentage traveling for business? **Visits and Ocean Vacation**

Solve. For Exercises 5–10, use the graph at the right.

PASSWORDS The 400 students at Hilltop Middle School use passwords when they use the computer. The circle graph shows what the students use for their passwords. Use the circle graph to answer the questions.

Type of Password: 38% Random numbers, 25% Pet's name, 19% Birthday, 8% Street name, 5% Parent's name, 5% Sport

5 What is the most popular type of password? **Random numbers**

6 Which type of password is more popular than a street name but less popular than a pet's name? **Birthday**

7 How many password categories are there? **6**

8 The **Random numbers** category is twice as popular as the **Birthday** category.

9 Which type of password is less popular than a birthday but more popular than a sport? **Street name**

10 The number of students who used a pet's name is five times the number who used a **Sport** or a **Parent's name**.

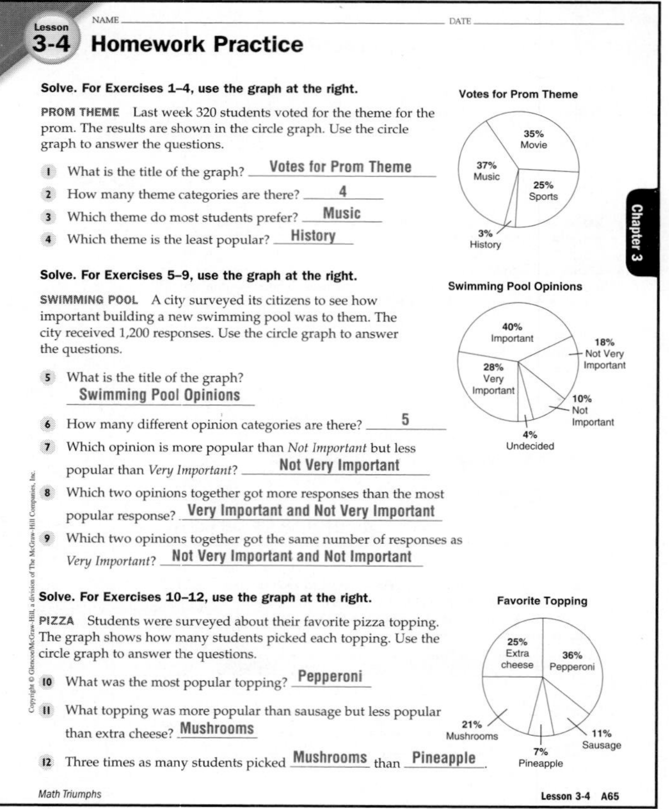

Lesson 3-4

NAME ______ DATE ______

Homework Practice

Solve. For Exercises 1–4, use the graph at the right.

PROM THEME Last week 320 students voted for the theme for the prom. The results are shown in the circle graph. Use the circle graph to answer the questions.

Votes for Prom Theme: 35% Movie, 37% Music, 25% Sports, 3% History

1 What is the title of the graph? **Votes for Prom Theme**

2 How many theme categories are there? **4**

3 Which theme do most students prefer? **Music**

4 Which theme is the least popular? **History**

Solve. For Exercises 5–9, use the graph at the right.

SWIMMING POOL A city surveyed its citizens to see how important building a new swimming pool was to them. The city received 1,200 responses. Use the circle graph to answer the questions.

Swimming Pool Opinions: 40% Important, 18% Not Very Important, 28% Very Important, 10% Not Important, 4% Undecided

5 What is the title of the graph? **Swimming Pool Opinions**

6 How many different opinion categories are there? **5**

7 Which opinion is more popular than *Not Important* but less popular than *Very Important*? **Not Very Important**

8 Which two opinions together got more responses than the most popular response? **Very Important and Not Very Important**

9 Which two opinions together got the same number of responses as *Very Important*? **Not Very Important and Not Important**

Solve. For Exercises 10–12, use the graph at the right.

PIZZA Students were surveyed about their favorite pizza topping. The graph shows how many students picked each topping. Use the circle graph to answer the questions.

Favorite Topping: 25% Extra cheese, 36% Pepperoni, 21% Mushrooms, 11% Sausage, 7% Pineapple

10 What was the most popular topping? **Pepperoni**

11 What topping was more popular than sausage but less popular than extra cheese? **Mushrooms**

12 Three times as many students picked **Mushrooms** than **Pineapple**.

Chapter 3

Answer Key (Lesson 4-1)

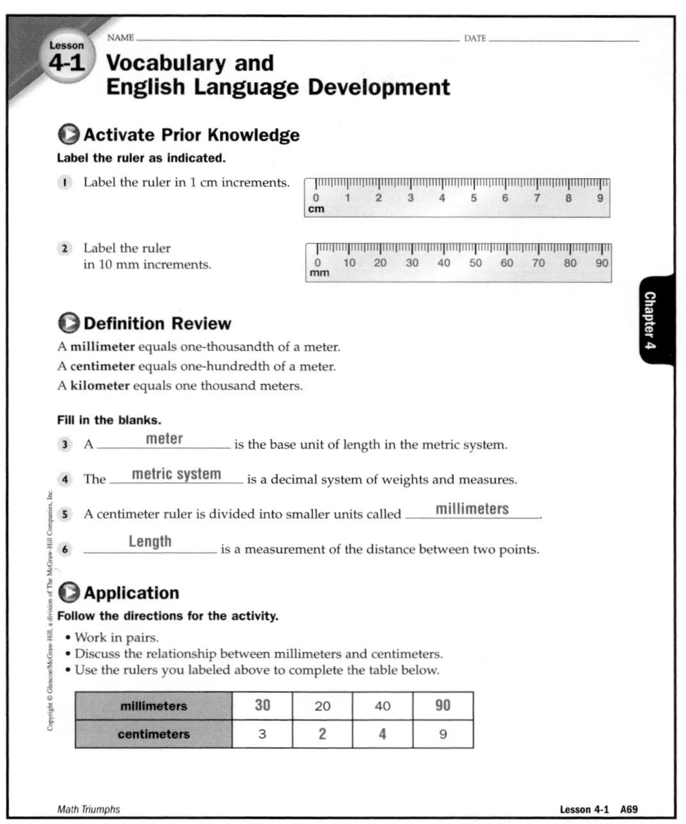
Lesson 4-1

NAME ________ DATE ________

Vocabulary and English Language Development

Activate Prior Knowledge

Label the ruler as indicated.

1. Label the ruler in 1 cm increments. 0 1 2 3 4 5 6 7 8 9 cm
2. Label the ruler in 10 mm increments. 0 10 20 30 40 50 60 70 80 90 mm

Definition Review

A **millimeter** equals one-thousandth of a meter.
A **centimeter** equals one-hundredth of a meter.
A **kilometer** equals one thousand meters.

Fill in the blanks.

3. A **meter** is the base unit of length in the metric system.
4. The **metric system** is a decimal system of weights and measures.
5. A centimeter ruler is divided into smaller units called **millimeters**.
6. **Length** is a measurement of the distance between two points.

Application

Follow the directions for the activity.

- Work in pairs.
- Discuss the relationship between millimeters and centimeters.
- Use the rulers you labeled above to complete the table below.

millimeters	30	20	40	90
centimeters	3	2	4	9

Chapter 4

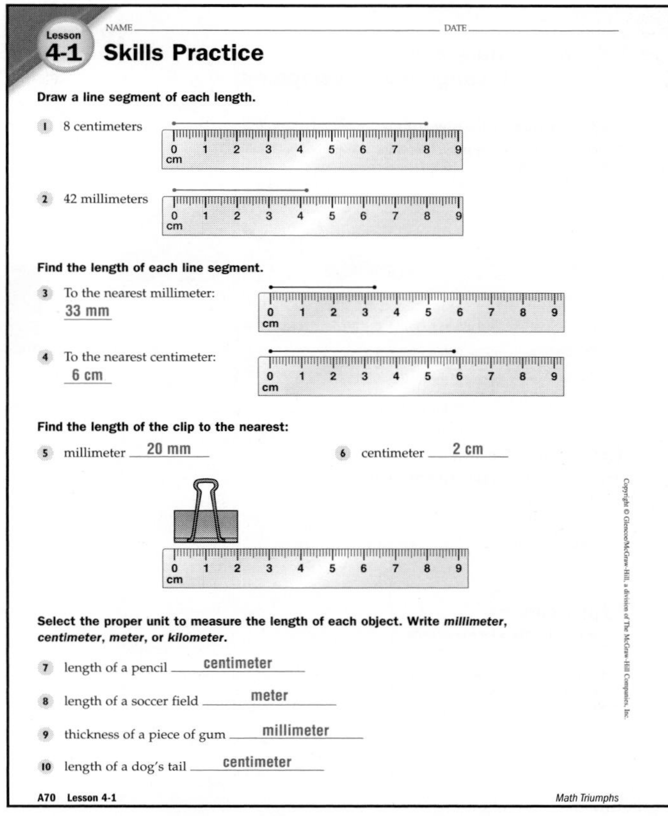
Lesson 4-1

NAME ________ DATE ________

Skills Practice

Draw a line segment of each length.

1. 8 centimeters
2. 42 millimeters

Find the length of each line segment.

3. To the nearest millimeter: **33 mm**
4. To the nearest centimeter: **6 cm**

Find the length of the clip to the nearest:

5. millimeter **20 mm**
6. centimeter **2 cm**

Select the proper unit to measure the length of each object. Write *millimeter*, *centimeter*, *meter*, or *kilometer*.

7. length of a pencil **centimeter**
8. length of a soccer field **meter**
9. thickness of a piece of gum **millimeter**
10. length of a dog's tail **centimeter**

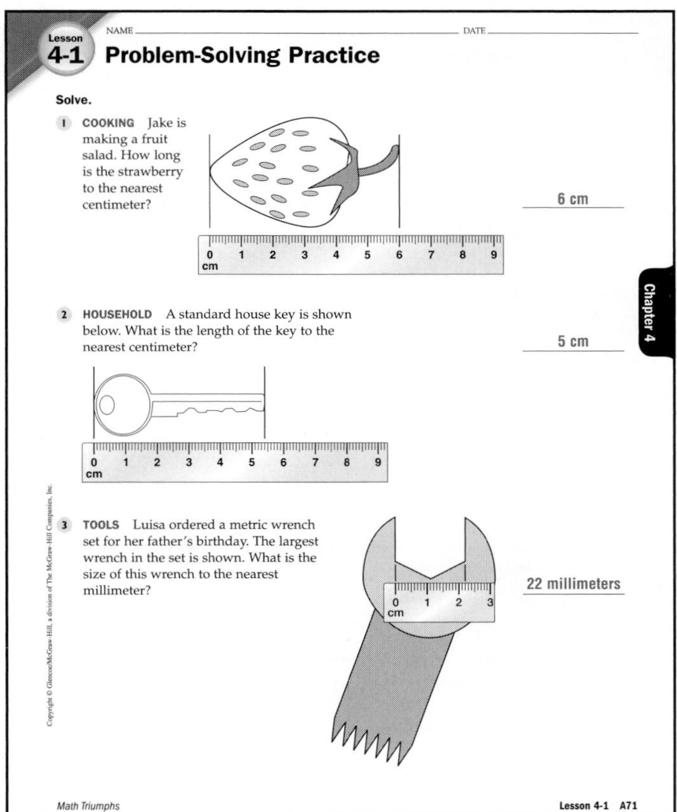
Lesson 4-1

NAME ________ DATE ________

Problem-Solving Practice

Solve.

1. **COOKING** Jake is making a fruit salad. How long is the strawberry to the nearest centimeter? **6 cm**
2. **HOUSEHOLD** A standard house key is shown below. What is the length of the key to the nearest centimeter? **5 cm**
3. **TOOLS** Luisa ordered a metric wrench set for her father's birthday. The largest wrench in the set is shown. What is the size of this wrench to the nearest millimeter? **22 millimeters**

Chapter 4

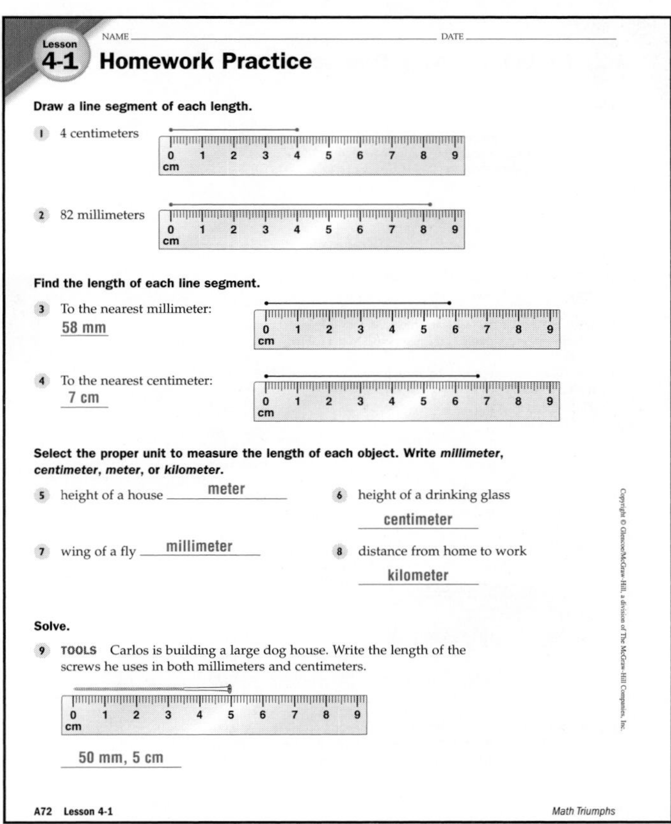
Lesson 4-1

NAME ________ DATE ________

Homework Practice

Draw a line segment of each length.

1. 4 centimeters
2. 82 millimeters

Find the length of each line segment.

3. To the nearest millimeter: **58 mm**
4. To the nearest centimeter: **7 cm**

Select the proper unit to measure the length of each object. Write *millimeter*, *centimeter*, *meter*, or *kilometer*.

5. height of a house **meter**
6. height of a drinking glass **centimeter**
7. wing of a fly **millimeter**
8. distance from home to work **kilometer**

Solve.

9. **TOOLS** Carlos is building a large dog house. Write the length of the screws he uses in both millimeters and centimeters. **50 mm, 5 cm**

Answer Key (Lesson 4-2)

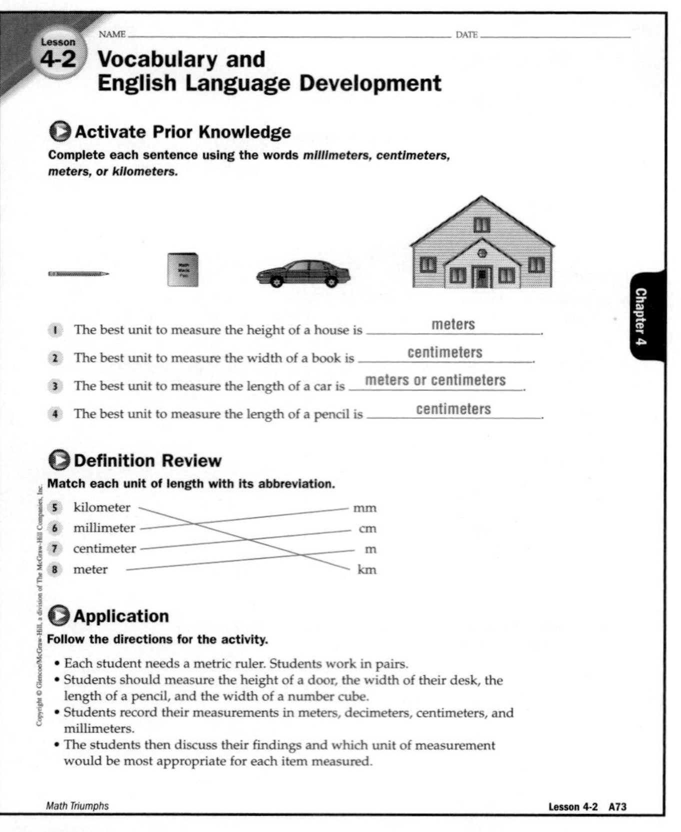
Lesson 4-2 Vocabulary and English Language Development

Activate Prior Knowledge

Complete each sentence using the words *millimeters, centimeters, meters,* or *kilometers.*

1. The best unit to measure the height of a house is meters.
2. The best unit to measure the width of a book is centimeters.
3. The best unit to measure the length of a car is meters or centimeters.
4. The best unit to measure the length of a pencil is centimeters.

Definition Review

Match each unit of length with its abbreviation.

5. kilometer — km
6. millimeter — mm
7. centimeter — cm
8. meter — m

Application

Follow the directions for the activity.

- Each student needs a metric ruler. Students work in pairs.
- Students should measure the height of a door, the width of their desk, the length of a pencil, and the width of a number cube.
- Students record their measurements in meters, decimeters, centimeters, and millimeters.
- The students then discuss their findings and which unit of measurement would be most appropriate for each item measured.

Math Triumphs — Lesson 4-2 A73

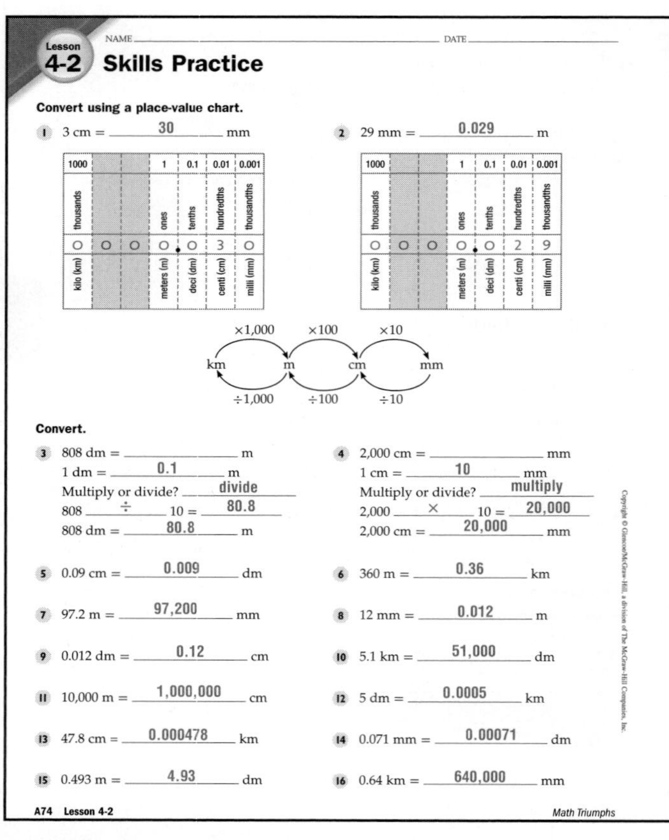
Lesson 4-2 Skills Practice

Convert using a place-value chart.

1. 3 cm = 30 mm
2. 29 mm = 0.029 m

Convert.

3. 808 dm = ___ m; 1 dm = 0.1 m; Multiply or divide? divide; 808 ÷ 10 = 80.8; 808 dm = 80.8 m
4. 2,000 cm = ___ mm; 1 cm = 10 mm; Multiply or divide? multiply; 2,000 × 10 = 20,000; 2,000 cm = 20,000 mm
5. 0.09 cm = 0.009 dm
6. 360 m = 0.36 km
7. 97.2 m = 97,200 mm
8. 12 mm = 0.012 m
9. 0.012 dm = 0.12 cm
10. 5.1 km = 51,000 dm
11. 10,000 m = 1,000,000 cm
12. 5 dm = 0.0005 km
13. 47.8 cm = 0.000478 km
14. 0.071 mm = 0.00071 dm
15. 0.493 m = 4.93 dm
16. 0.64 km = 640,000 mm

A74 Lesson 4-2 — Math Triumphs

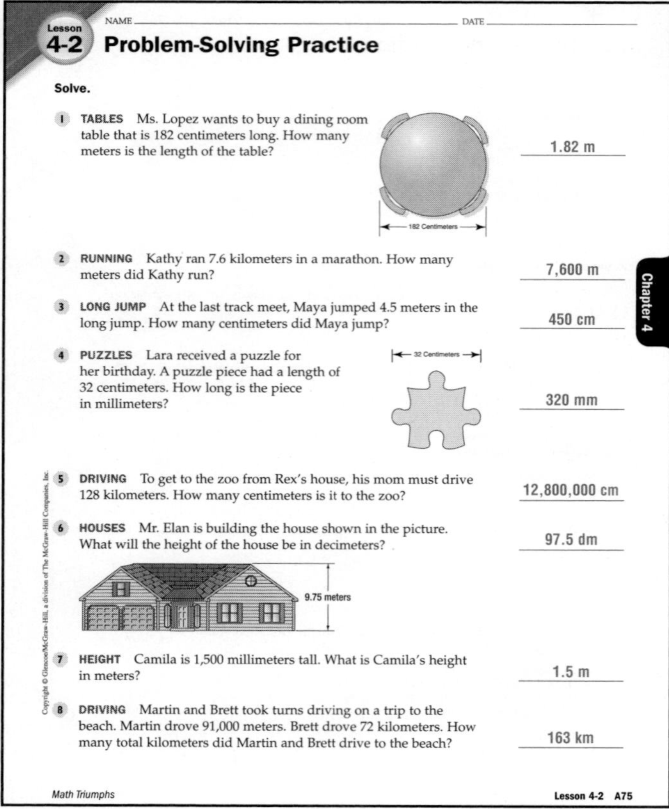
Lesson 4-2 Problem-Solving Practice

Solve.

1. TABLES Ms. Lopez wants to buy a dining room table that is 182 centimeters long. How many meters is the length of the table? 1.82 m
2. RUNNING Kathy ran 7.6 kilometers in a marathon. How many meters did Kathy run? 7,600 m
3. LONG JUMP At the last track meet, Maya jumped 4.5 meters in the long jump. How many centimeters did Maya jump? 450 cm
4. PUZZLES Lara received a puzzle for her birthday. A puzzle piece had a length of 32 centimeters. How long is the piece in millimeters? 320 mm
5. DRIVING To get to the zoo from Rex's house, his mom must drive 128 kilometers. How many centimeters is it to the zoo? 12,800,000 cm
6. HOUSES Mr. Elan is building the house shown in the picture. What will the height of the house be in decimeters? 97.5 dm
7. HEIGHT Camila is 1,500 millimeters tall. What is Camila's height in meters? 1.5 m
8. DRIVING Martin and Brett took turns driving on a trip to the beach. Martin drove 91,000 meters. Brett drove 72 kilometers. How many total kilometers did Martin and Brett drive to the beach? 163 km

Math Triumphs — Lesson 4-2 A75

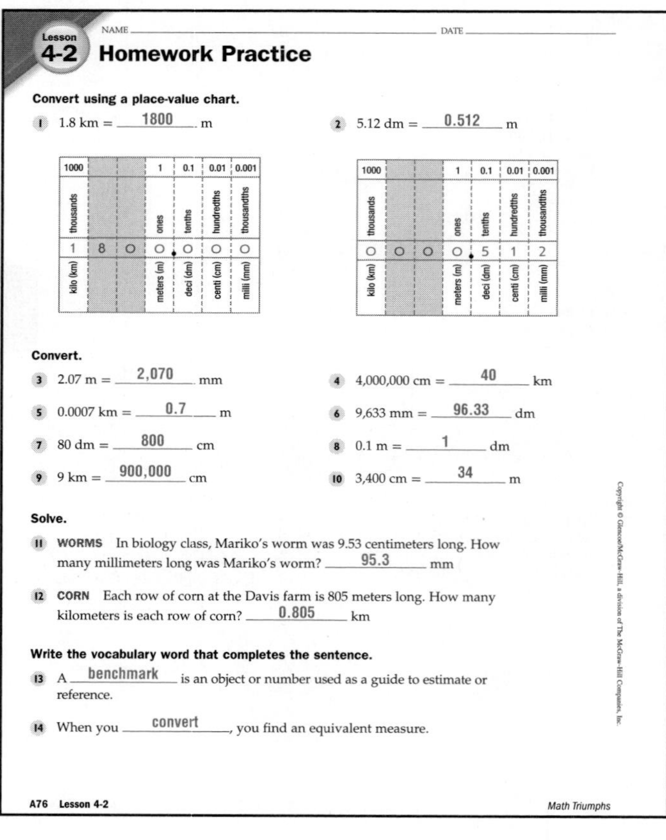
Lesson 4-2 Homework Practice

Convert using a place-value chart.

1. 1.8 km = 1800 m
2. 5.12 dm = 0.512 m

Convert.

3. 2.07 m = 2,070 mm
4. 4,000,000 cm = 40 km
5. 0.0007 km = 0.7 m
6. 9,633 mm = 96.33 dm
7. 80 dm = 800 cm
8. 0.1 m = 1 dm
9. 9 km = 900,000 cm
10. 3,400 cm = 34 m

Solve.

11. WORMS In biology class, Mariko's worm was 9.53 centimeters long. How many millimeters long was Mariko's worm? 95.3 mm
12. CORN Each row of corn at the Davis farm is 805 meters long. How many kilometers is each row of corn? 0.805 km

Write the vocabulary word that completes the sentence.

13. A benchmark is an object or number used as a guide to estimate or reference.
14. When you convert, you find an equivalent measure.

A76 Lesson 4-2 — Math Triumphs

Answer Key (Lesson 4-3)

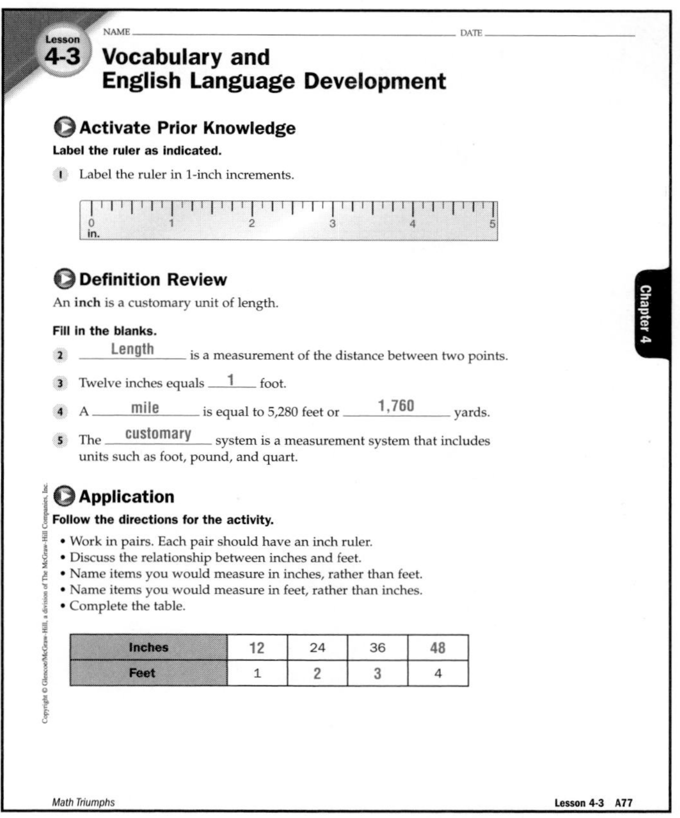

NAME ______ DATE ______

Lesson 4-3

Vocabulary and English Language Development

Activate Prior Knowledge

Label the ruler as indicated.

1 Label the ruler in 1-inch increments.

Definition Review

An **inch** is a customary unit of length.

Fill in the blanks.

2 Length is a measurement of the distance between two points.

3 Twelve inches equals 1 foot.

4 A mile is equal to 5,280 feet or 1,760 yards.

5 The customary system is a measurement system that includes units such as foot, pound, and quart.

Application

Follow the directions for the activity.

- Work in pairs. Each pair should have an inch ruler.
- Discuss the relationship between inches and feet.
- Name items you would measure in inches, rather than feet.
- Name items you would measure in feet, rather than inches.
- Complete the table.

Inches	12	24	36	48
Feet	1	2	3	4

Math Triumphs Lesson 4-3 A77

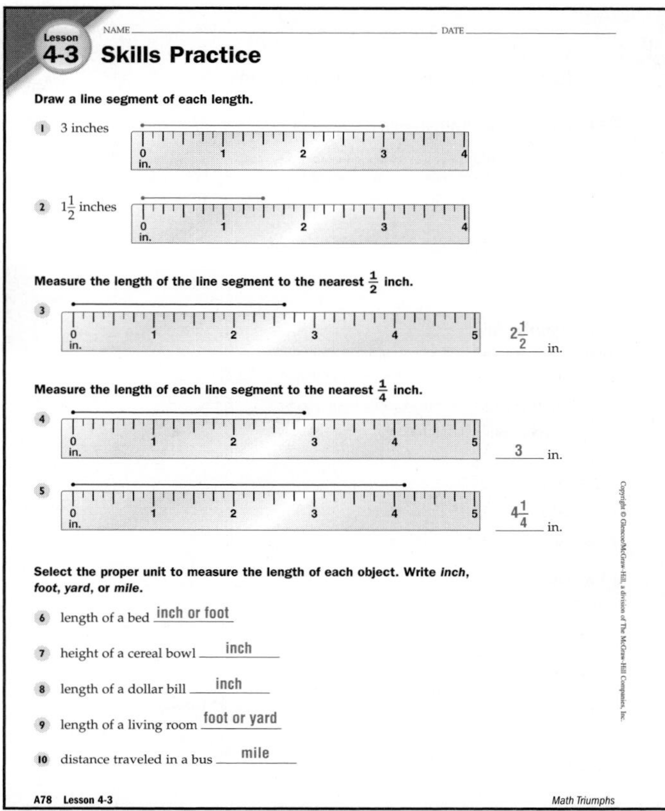

NAME ______ DATE ______

Lesson 4-3

Skills Practice

Draw a line segment of each length.

1 3 inches

2 $1\frac{1}{2}$ inches

Measure the length of the line segment to the nearest $\frac{1}{2}$ inch.

3 $2\frac{1}{2}$ in.

Measure the length of each line segment to the nearest $\frac{1}{4}$ inch.

4 3 in.

5 $4\frac{1}{4}$ in.

Select the proper unit to measure the length of each object. Write *inch, foot, yard,* or *mile*.

6 length of a bed inch or foot

7 height of a cereal bowl inch

8 length of a dollar bill inch

9 length of a living room foot or yard

10 distance traveled in a bus mile

A78 Lesson 4-3 Math Triumphs

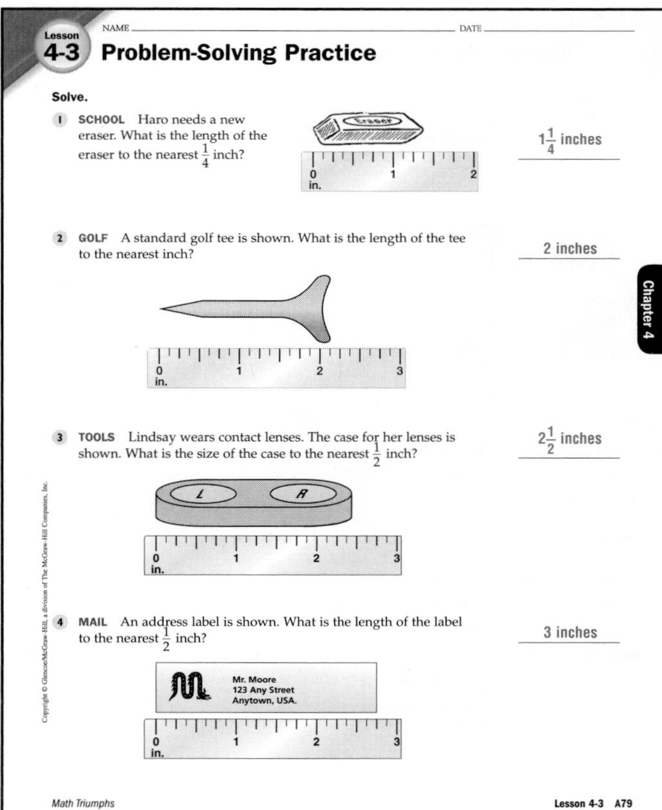

NAME ______ DATE ______

Lesson 4-3

Problem-Solving Practice

Solve.

1 SCHOOL Haro needs a new eraser. What is the length of the eraser to the nearest $\frac{1}{4}$ inch? $1\frac{1}{4}$ inches

2 GOLF A standard golf tee is shown. What is the length of the tee to the nearest inch? 2 inches

3 TOOLS Lindsay wears contact lenses. The case for her lenses is shown. What is the size of the case to the nearest $\frac{1}{2}$ inch? $2\frac{1}{2}$ inches

4 MAIL An address label is shown. What is the length of the label to the nearest $\frac{1}{2}$ inch? 3 inches

Mr. Moore
123 Any Street
Anytown, USA.

Math Triumphs Lesson 4-3 A79

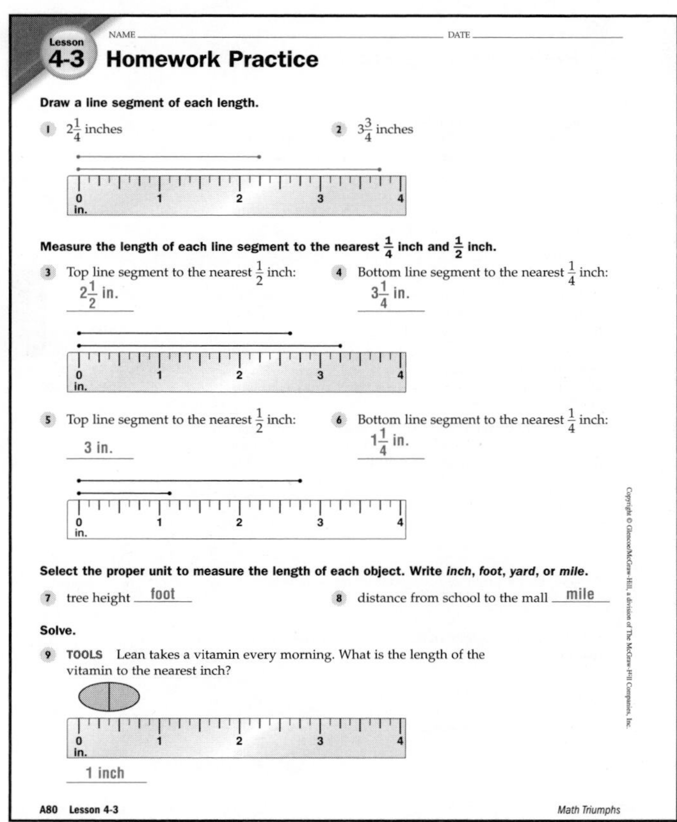

NAME ______ DATE ______

Lesson 4-3

Homework Practice

Draw a line segment of each length.

1 $2\frac{1}{4}$ inches

2 $3\frac{3}{4}$ inches

Measure the length of each line segment to the nearest $\frac{1}{4}$ inch and $\frac{1}{2}$ inch.

3 Top line segment to the nearest $\frac{1}{2}$ inch: $2\frac{1}{2}$ in.

4 Bottom line segment to the nearest $\frac{1}{4}$ inch: $3\frac{1}{4}$ in.

5 Top line segment to the nearest $\frac{1}{2}$ inch: 3 in.

6 Bottom line segment to the nearest $\frac{1}{4}$ inch: $1\frac{1}{4}$ in.

Select the proper unit to measure the length of each object. Write *inch, foot, yard,* or *mile*.

7 tree height foot

8 distance from school to the mall mile

Solve.

9 TOOLS Lean takes a vitamin every morning. What is the length of the vitamin to the nearest inch? 1 inch

A80 Lesson 4-3 Math Triumphs

Answer Key (Lesson 4-4)

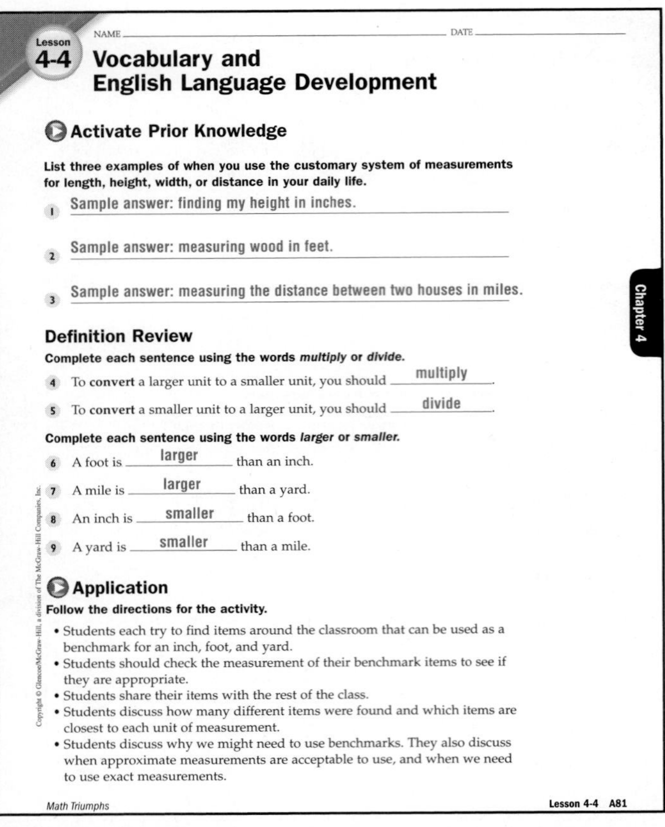

NAME ______ DATE ______

Lesson 4-4

Vocabulary and English Language Development

Activate Prior Knowledge

List three examples of when you use the customary system of measurements for length, height, width, or distance in your daily life.

1. Sample answer: finding my height in inches.
2. Sample answer: measuring wood in feet.
3. Sample answer: measuring the distance between two houses in miles.

Definition Review

Complete each sentence using the words *multiply* or *divide*.

4. To **convert** a larger unit to a smaller unit, you should multiply.
5. To **convert** a smaller unit to a larger unit, you should divide.

Complete each sentence using the words *larger* or *smaller*.

6. A foot is larger than an inch.
7. A mile is larger than a yard.
8. An inch is smaller than a foot.
9. A yard is smaller than a mile.

Application

Follow the directions for the activity.

- Students each try to find items around the classroom that can be used as a benchmark for an inch, foot, and yard.
- Students should check the measurement of their benchmark items to see if they are appropriate.
- Students share their items with the rest of the class.
- Students discuss how many different items were found and which items are closest to each unit of measurement.
- Students discuss why we might need to use benchmarks. They also discuss when approximate measurements are acceptable to use, and when we need to use exact measurements.

Chapter 4

Math Triumphs — Lesson 4-4 A81

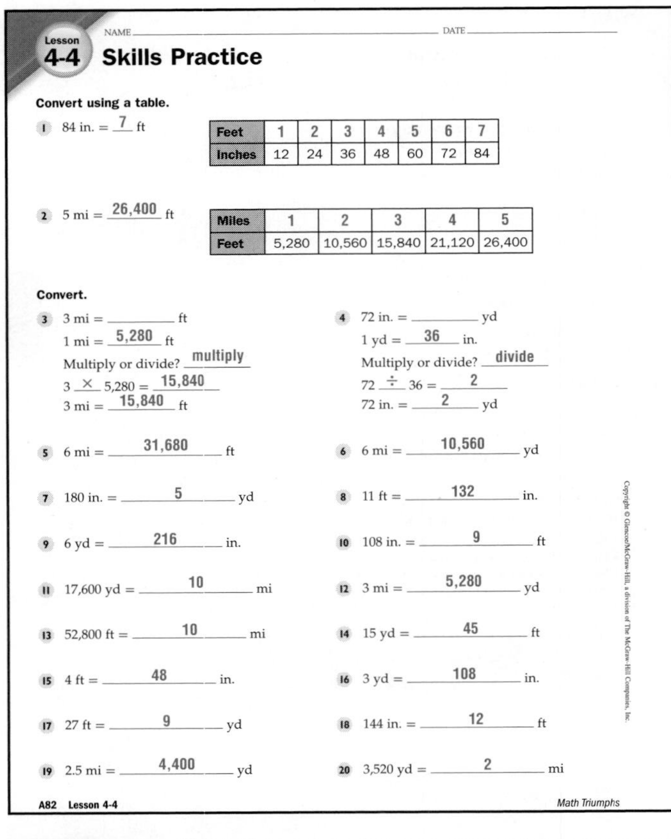

NAME ______ DATE ______

Lesson 4-4

Skills Practice

Convert using a table.

1. 84 in. = 7 ft

Feet	1	2	3	4	5	6	7
Inches	12	24	36	48	60	72	84

2. 5 mi = 26,400 ft

Miles	1	2	3	4	5
Feet	5,280	10,560	15,840	21,120	26,400

Convert.

3. 3 mi = ______ ft
   1 mi = 5,280 ft
   Multiply or divide? multiply
   3 × 5,280 = 15,840
   3 mi = 15,840 ft

4. 72 in. = ______ yd
   1 yd = 36 in.
   Multiply or divide? divide
   72 ÷ 36 = 2
   72 in. = 2 yd

5. 6 mi = 31,680 ft
6. 6 mi = 10,560 yd
7. 180 in. = 5 yd
8. 11 ft = 132 in.
9. 6 yd = 216 in.
10. 108 in. = 9 ft
11. 17,600 yd = 10 mi
12. 3 mi = 5,280 yd
13. 52,800 ft = 10 mi
14. 15 yd = 45 ft
15. 4 ft = 48 in.
16. 3 yd = 108 in.
17. 27 ft = 9 yd
18. 144 in. = 12 ft
19. 2.5 mi = 4,400 yd
20. 3,520 yd = 2 mi

A82 Lesson 4-4 — Math Triumphs

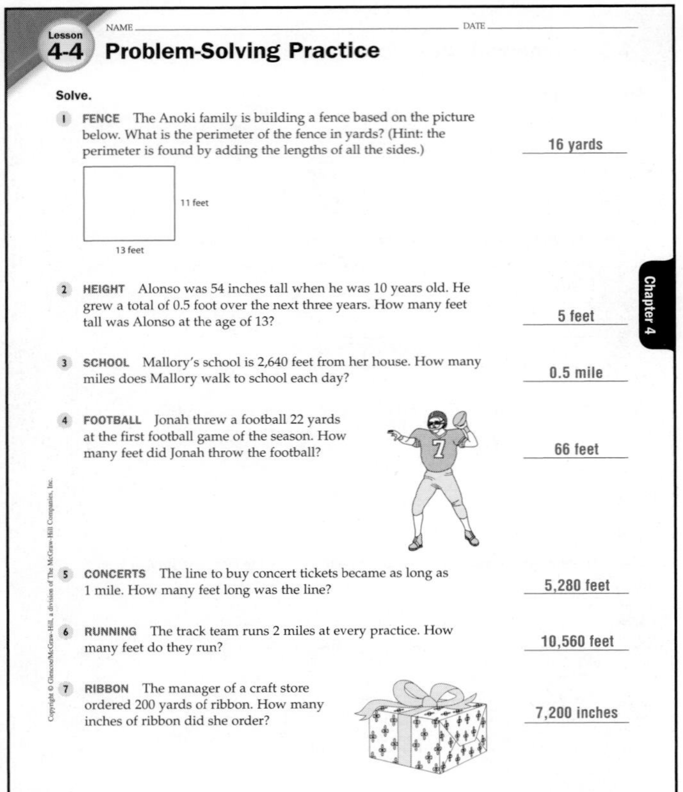

NAME ______ DATE ______

Lesson 4-4

Problem-Solving Practice

Solve.

1. **FENCE** The Anoki family is building a fence based on the picture below. What is the perimeter of the fence in yards? (Hint: the perimeter is found by adding the lengths of all the sides.) — 16 yards

   11 feet
   13 feet

2. **HEIGHT** Alonso was 54 inches tall when he was 10 years old. He grew a total of 0.5 foot over the next three years. How many feet tall was Alonso at the age of 13? — 5 feet

3. **SCHOOL** Mallory's school is 2,640 feet from her house. How many miles does Mallory walk to school each day? — 0.5 mile

4. **FOOTBALL** Jonah threw a football 22 yards at the first football game of the season. How many feet did Jonah throw the football? — 66 feet

5. **CONCERTS** The line to buy concert tickets became as long as 1 mile. How many feet long was the line? — 5,280 feet

6. **RUNNING** The track team runs 2 miles at every practice. How many feet do they run? — 10,560 feet

7. **RIBBON** The manager of a craft store ordered 200 yards of ribbon. How many inches of ribbon did she order? — 7,200 inches

Chapter 4

Math Triumphs — Lesson 4-4 A83

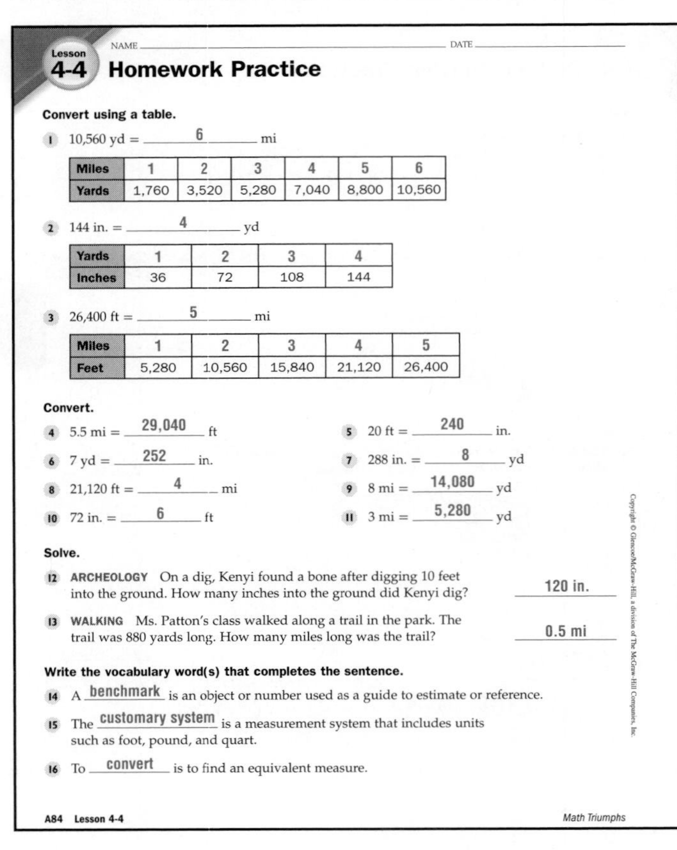

NAME ______ DATE ______

Lesson 4-4

Homework Practice

Convert using a table.

1. 10,560 yd = 6 mi

Miles	1	2	3	4	5	6
Yards	1,760	3,520	5,280	7,040	8,800	10,560

2. 144 in. = 4 yd

Yards	1	2	3	4
Inches	36	72	108	144

3. 26,400 ft = 5 mi

Miles	1	2	3	4	5
Feet	5,280	10,560	15,840	21,120	26,400

Convert.

4. 5.5 mi = 29,040 ft
5. 20 ft = 240 in.
6. 7 yd = 252 in.
7. 288 in. = 8 yd
8. 21,120 ft = 4 mi
9. 8 mi = 14,080 yd
10. 72 in. = 6 ft
11. 3 mi = 5,280 yd

Solve.

12. **ARCHEOLOGY** On a dig, Kenyi found a bone after digging 10 feet into the ground. How many inches into the ground did Kenyi dig? — 120 in.

13. **WALKING** Ms. Patton's class walked along a trail in the park. The trail was 880 yards long. How many miles long was the trail? — 0.5 mi

Write the vocabulary word(s) that completes the sentence.

14. A benchmark is an object or number used as a guide to estimate or reference.
15. The customary system is a measurement system that includes units such as foot, pound, and quart.
16. To convert is to find an equivalent measure.

A84 Lesson 4-4 — Math Triumphs

Answer Key (Lesson 5-1)

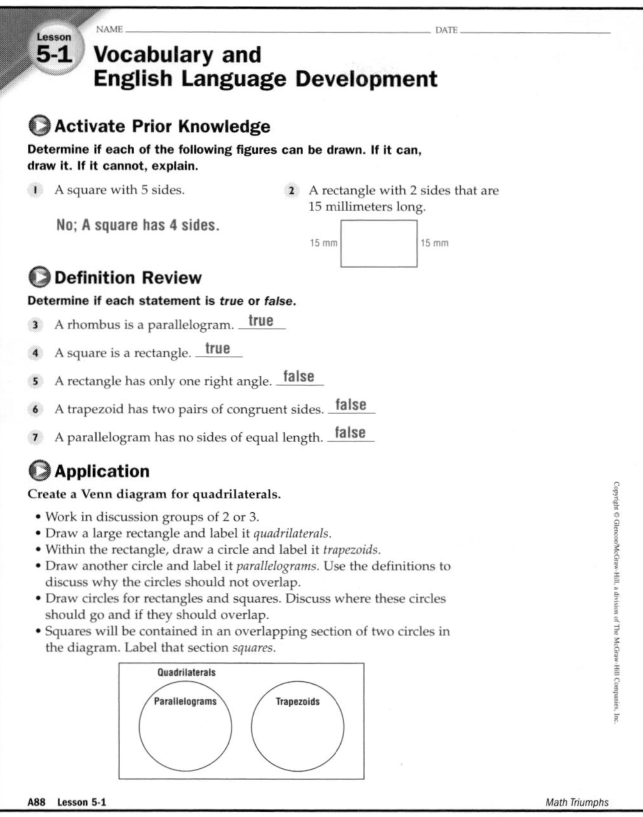

Lesson 5-1 NAME ______ DATE ______

Vocabulary and English Language Development

Activate Prior Knowledge

Determine if each of the following figures can be drawn. If it can, draw it. If it cannot, explain.

1 A square with 5 sides.

No; A square has 4 sides.

2 A rectangle with 2 sides that are 15 millimeters long.

15 mm 15 mm

Definition Review

Determine if each statement is *true* or *false*.

3 A rhombus is a parallelogram. true

4 A square is a rectangle. true

5 A rectangle has only one right angle. false

6 A trapezoid has two pairs of congruent sides. false

7 A parallelogram has no sides of equal length. false

Application

Create a Venn diagram for quadrilaterals.

- Work in discussion groups of 2 or 3.
- Draw a large rectangle and label it *quadrilaterals*.
- Within the rectangle, draw a circle and label it *trapezoids*.
- Draw another circle and label it *parallelograms*. Use the definitions to discuss why the circles should not overlap.
- Draw circles for rectangles and squares. Discuss where these circles should go and if they should overlap.
- Squares will be contained in an overlapping section of two circles in the diagram. Label that section *squares*.

Quadrilaterals
Parallelograms
Trapezoids

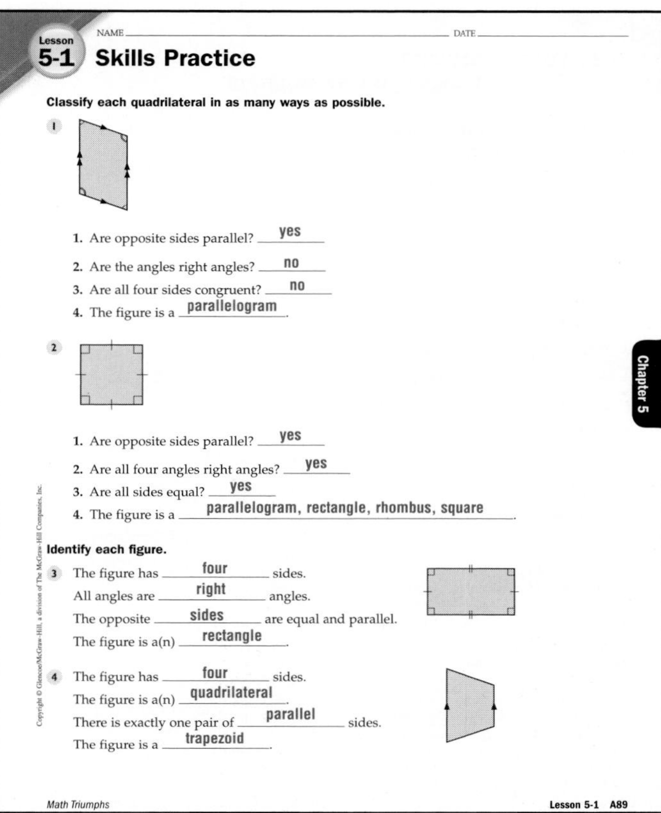

Lesson 5-1 NAME ______ DATE ______

Skills Practice

Classify each quadrilateral in as many ways as possible.

1

1. Are opposite sides parallel? yes
2. Are the angles right angles? no
3. Are all four sides congruent? no
4. The figure is a parallelogram.

2

1. Are opposite sides parallel? yes
2. Are all four angles right angles? yes
3. Are all sides equal? yes
4. The figure is a parallelogram, rectangle, rhombus, square.

Identify each figure.

3 The figure has four sides.
All angles are right angles.
The opposite sides are equal and parallel.
The figure is a(n) rectangle.

4 The figure has four sides.
The figure is a(n) quadrilateral.
There is exactly one pair of parallel sides.
The figure is a trapezoid.

Chapter 5

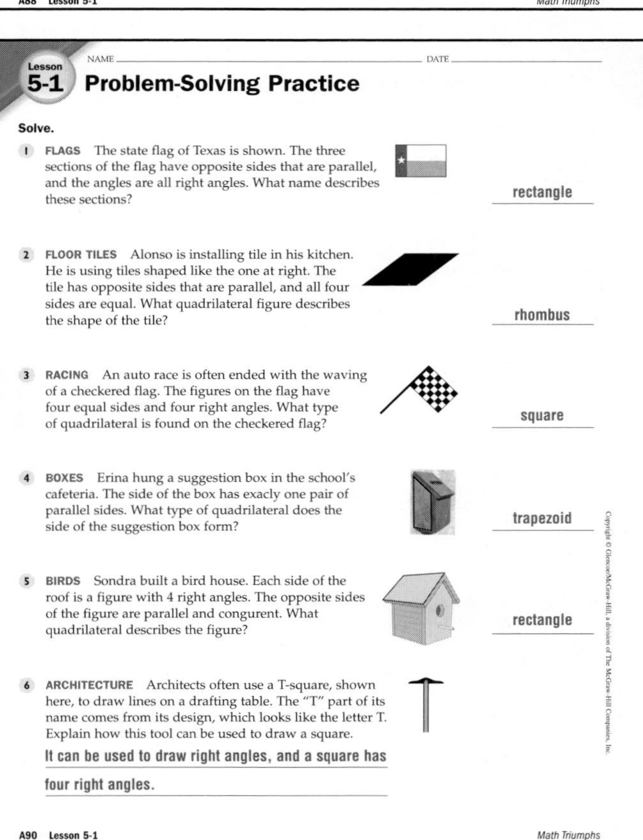

Lesson 5-1 NAME ______ DATE ______

Problem-Solving Practice

Solve.

1 **FLAGS** The state flag of Texas is shown. The three sections of the flag have opposite sides that are parallel, and the angles are all right angles. What name describes these sections? rectangle

2 **FLOOR TILES** Alonso is installing tile in his kitchen. He is using tiles shaped like the one at right. The tile has opposite sides that are parallel, and all four sides are equal. What quadrilateral figure describes the shape of the tile? rhombus

3 **RACING** An auto race is often ended with the waving of a checkered flag. The figures on the flag have four equal sides and four right angles. What type of quadrilateral is found on the checkered flag? square

4 **BOXES** Erina hung a suggestion box in the school's cafeteria. The side of the box has exacly one pair of parallel sides. What type of quadrilateral does the side of the suggestion box form? trapezoid

5 **BIRDS** Sondra built a bird house. Each side of the roof is a figure with 4 right angles. The opposite sides of the figure are parallel and congruent. What quadrilateral describes the figure? rectangle

6 **ARCHITECTURE** Architects often use a T-square, shown here, to draw lines on a drafting table. The "T" part of its name comes from its design, which looks like the letter T. Explain how this tool can be used to draw a square.

It can be used to draw right angles, and a square has four right angles.

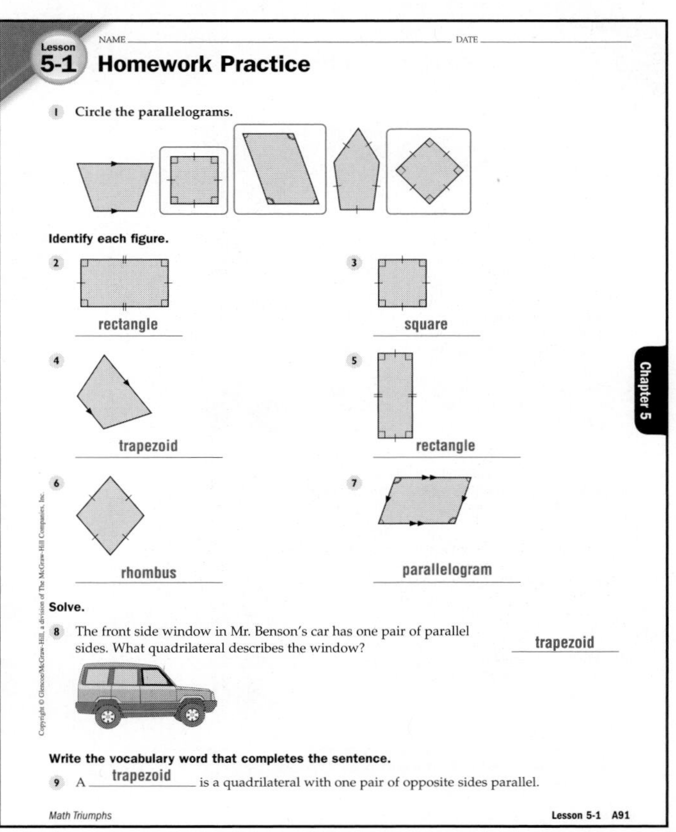

Lesson 5-1 NAME ______ DATE ______

Homework Practice

1 Circle the parallelograms.

Identify each figure.

2 rectangle

3 square

4 trapezoid

5 rectangle

6 rhombus

7 parallelogram

Solve.

8 The front side window in Mr. Benson's car has one pair of parallel sides. What quadrilateral describes the window? trapezoid

Write the vocabulary word that completes the sentence.

9 A trapezoid is a quadrilateral with one pair of opposite sides parallel.

Chapter 5

Answer Key (Lesson 5-2)

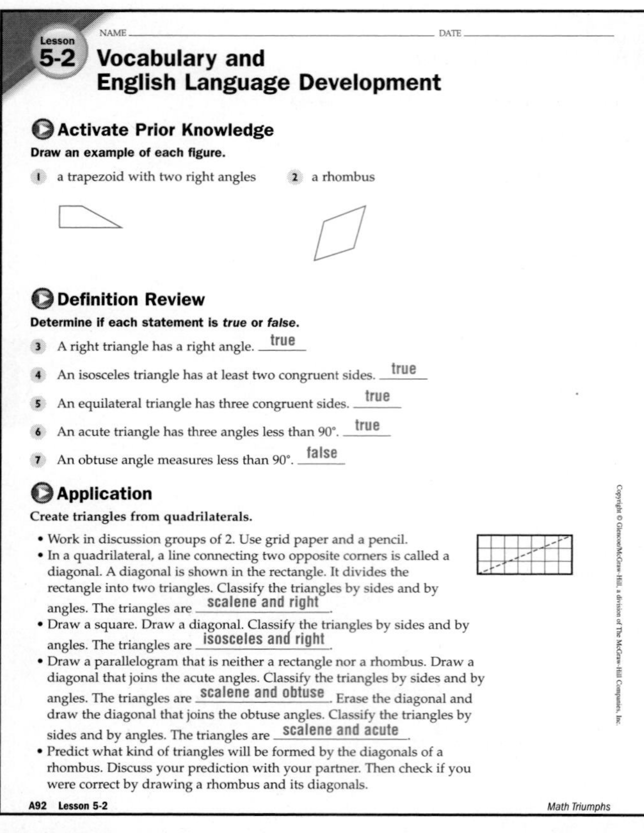

NAME ______ DATE ______

Lesson 5-2

Vocabulary and English Language Development

Activate Prior Knowledge

Draw an example of each figure.

1. a trapezoid with two right angles
2. a rhombus

Definition Review

Determine if each statement is *true* or *false*.

3. A right triangle has a right angle. **true**
4. An isosceles triangle has at least two congruent sides. **true**
5. An equilateral triangle has three congruent sides. **true**
6. An acute triangle has three angles less than 90°. **true**
7. An obtuse angle measures less than 90°. **false**

Application

Create triangles from quadrilaterals.

- Work in discussion groups of 2. Use grid paper and a pencil.
- In a quadrilateral, a line connecting two opposite corners is called a diagonal. A diagonal is shown in the rectangle. It divides the rectangle into two triangles. Classify the triangles by sides and by angles. The triangles are **scalene and right**.
- Draw a square. Draw a diagonal. Classify the triangles by sides and by angles. The triangles are **isosceles and right**.
- Draw a parallelogram that is neither a rectangle nor a rhombus. Draw a diagonal that joins the acute angles. Classify the triangles by sides and by angles. The triangles are **scalene and obtuse**. Erase the diagonal and draw the diagonal that joins the obtuse angles. Classify the triangles by sides and by angles. The triangles are **scalene and acute**.
- Predict what kind of triangles will be formed by the diagonals of a rhombus. Discuss your prediction with your partner. Then check if you were correct by drawing a rhombus and its diagonals.

A92 Lesson 5-2 Math Triumphs

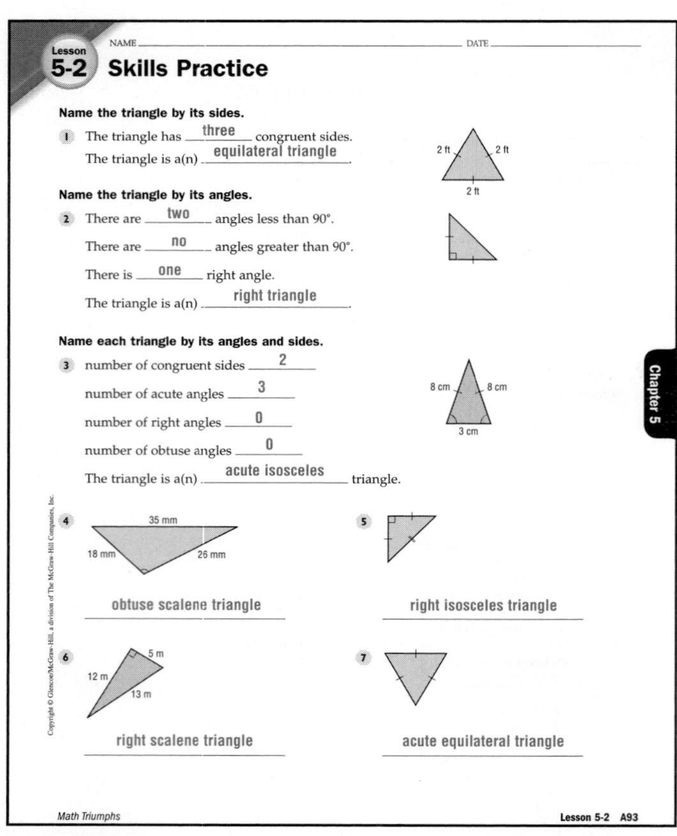

NAME ______ DATE ______

Lesson 5-2

Skills Practice

Name the triangle by its sides.

1. The triangle has **three** congruent sides. The triangle is a(n) **equilateral triangle**.

Name the triangle by its angles.

2. There are **two** angles less than 90°. There are **no** angles greater than 90°. There is **one** right angle. The triangle is a(n) **right triangle**.

Name each triangle by its angles and sides.

3. number of congruent sides **2**
   number of acute angles **3**
   number of right angles **0**
   number of obtuse angles **0**
   The triangle is a(n) **acute isosceles** triangle.

4.
   obtuse scalene triangle
5. **right isosceles triangle**
6.
   right scalene triangle
7. **acute equilateral triangle**

Chapter 5

Math Triumphs Lesson 5-2 A93

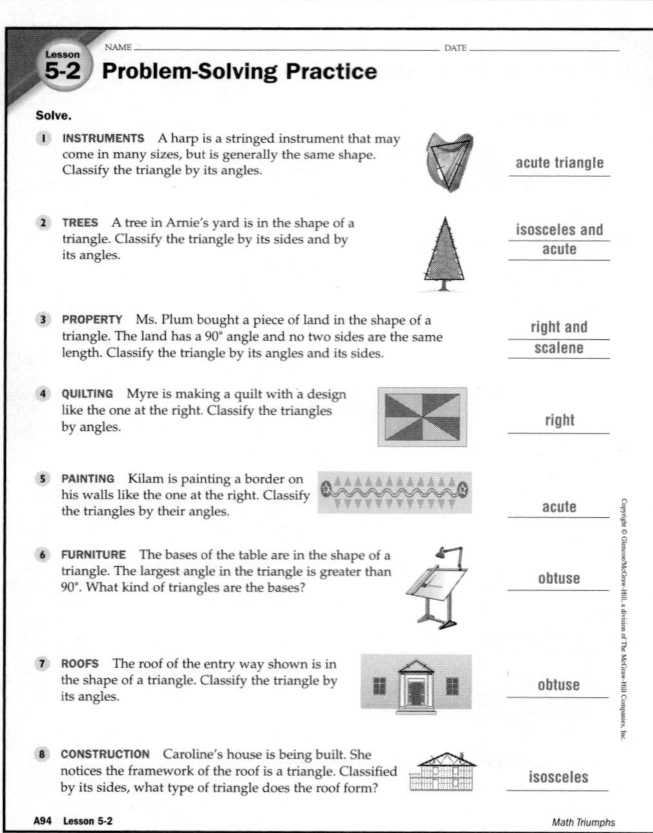

NAME ______ DATE ______

Lesson 5-2

Problem-Solving Practice

Solve.

1. **INSTRUMENTS** A harp is a stringed instrument that may come in many sizes, but is generally the same shape. Classify the triangle by its angles. **acute triangle**
2. **TREES** A tree in Arnie's yard is in the shape of a triangle. Classify the triangle by its sides and by its angles. **isosceles and acute**
3. **PROPERTY** Ms. Plum bought a piece of land in the shape of a triangle. The land has a 90° angle and no two sides are the same length. Classify the triangle by its angles and its sides. **right and scalene**
4. **QUILTING** Myre is making a quilt with a design like the one at the right. Classify the triangles by angles. **right**
5. **PAINTING** Kilam is painting a border on his walls like the one at the right. Classify the triangles by their angles. **acute**
6. **FURNITURE** The bases of the table are in the shape of a triangle. The largest angle in the triangle is greater than 90°. What kind of triangles are the bases? **obtuse**
7. **ROOFS** The roof of the entry way shown is in the shape of a triangle. Classify the triangle by its angles. **obtuse**
8. **CONSTRUCTION** Caroline's house is being built. She notices the framework of the roof is a triangle. Classified by its sides, what type of triangle does the roof form? **isosceles**

A94 Lesson 5-2 Math Triumphs

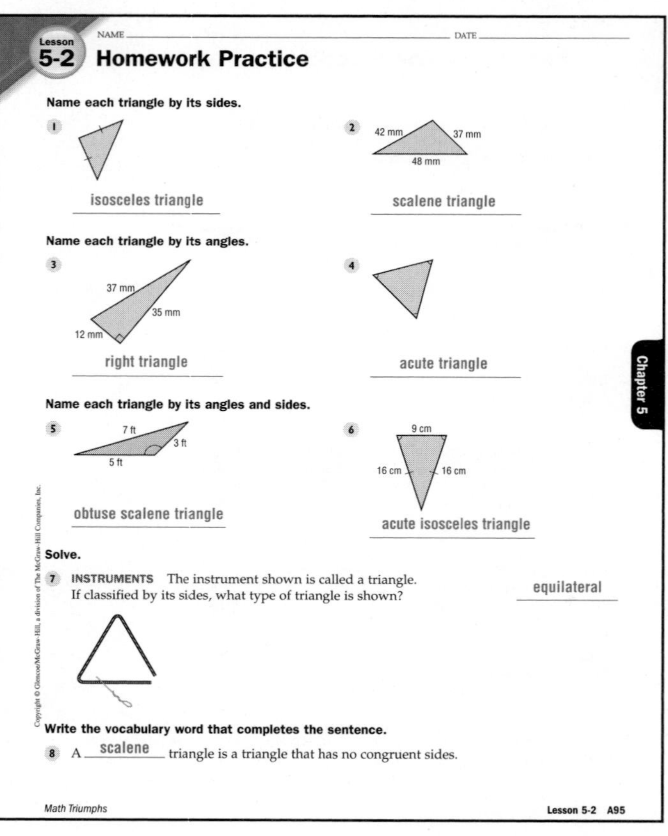

NAME ______ DATE ______

Lesson 5-2

Homework Practice

Name each triangle by its sides.

1. **isosceles triangle**
2.
   scalene triangle

Name each triangle by its angles.

3.
   right triangle
4. **acute triangle**

Name each triangle by its angles and sides.

5.
   obtuse scalene triangle
6.
   acute isosceles triangle

Solve.

7. **INSTRUMENTS** The instrument shown is called a triangle. If classified by its sides, what type of triangle is shown? **equilateral**

Write the vocabulary word that completes the sentence.

8. A **scalene** triangle is a triangle that has no congruent sides.

Chapter 5

Math Triumphs Lesson 5-2 A95

Answer Key (Lesson 5-3)

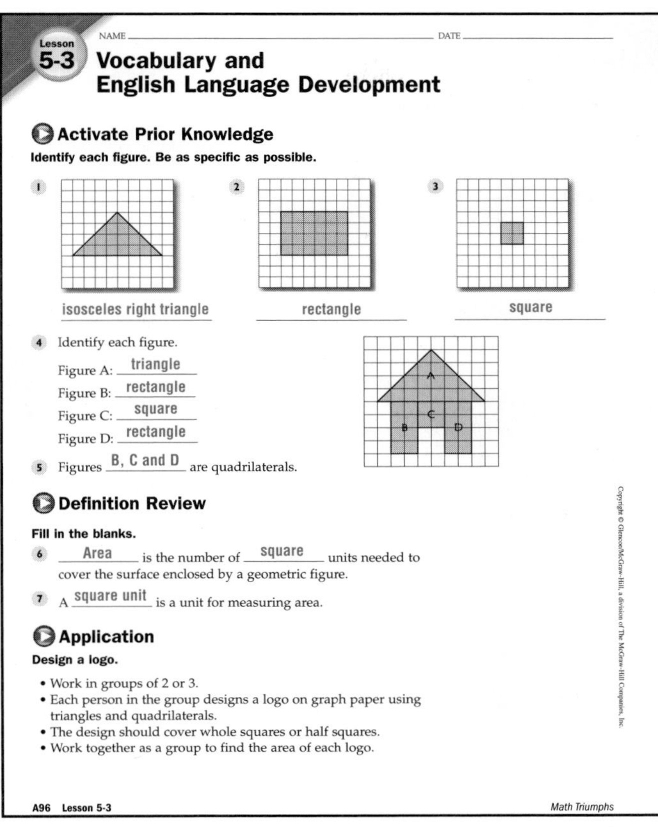

NAME ______ DATE ______

Lesson 5-3

Vocabulary and English Language Development

Activate Prior Knowledge

Identify each figure. Be as specific as possible.

1. isosceles right triangle
2. rectangle
3. square
4. Identify each figure.
   Figure A: triangle
   Figure B: rectangle
   Figure C: square
   Figure D: rectangle
5. Figures B, C and D are quadrilaterals.

Definition Review

Fill in the blanks.

6. Area is the number of square units needed to cover the surface enclosed by a geometric figure.
7. A square unit is a unit for measuring area.

Application

Design a logo.

- Work in groups of 2 or 3.
- Each person in the group designs a logo on graph paper using triangles and quadrilaterals.
- The design should cover whole squares or half squares.
- Work together as a group to find the area of each logo.

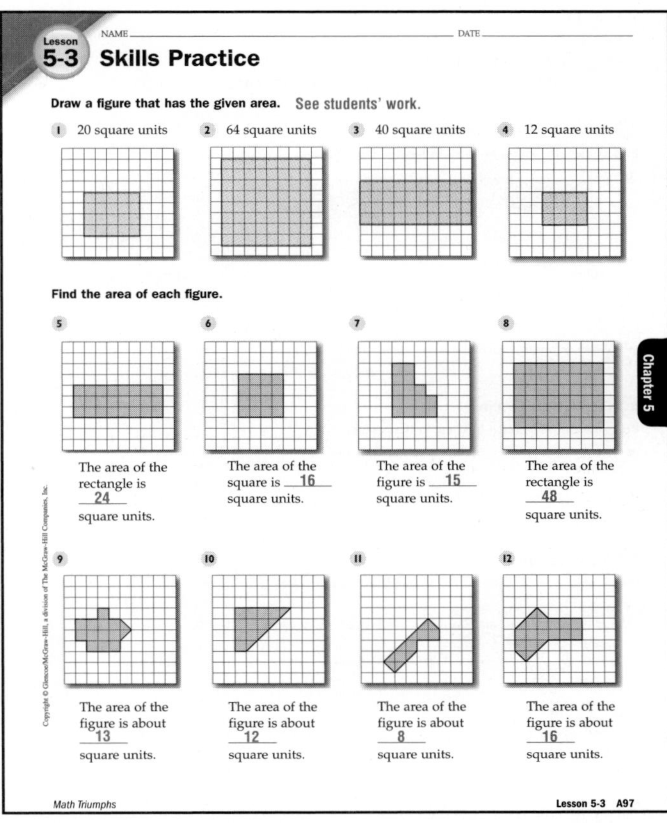

NAME ______ DATE ______

Lesson 5-3

Skills Practice

Draw a figure that has the given area. See students' work.

1. 20 square units
2. 64 square units
3. 40 square units
4. 12 square units

Find the area of each figure.

5. The area of the rectangle is 24 square units.
6. The area of the square is 16 square units.
7. The area of the figure is 15 square units.
8. The area of the rectangle is 48 square units.
9. The area of the figure is about 13 square units.
10. The area of the figure is about 12 square units.
11. The area of the figure is about 8 square units.
12. The area of the figure is about 16 square units.

Chapter 5

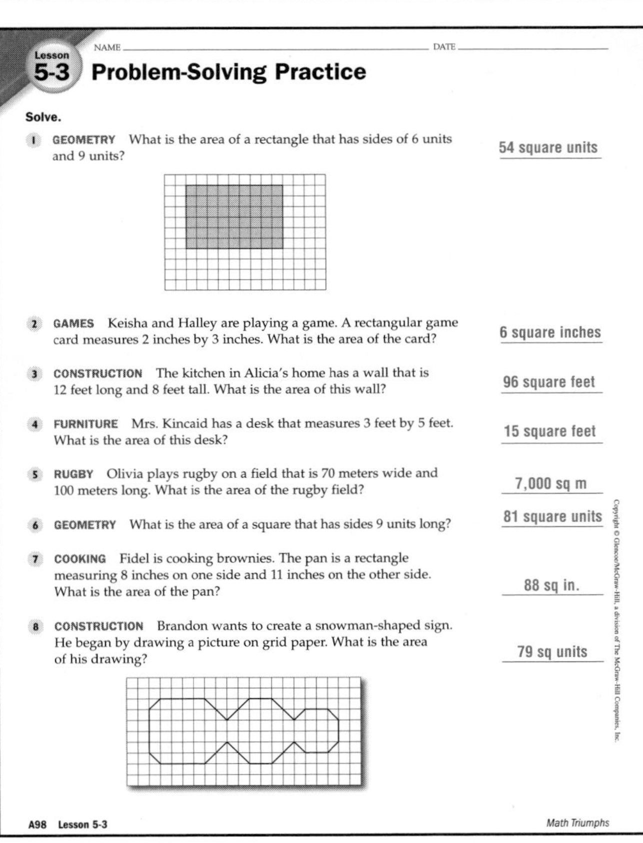

NAME ______ DATE ______

Lesson 5-3

Problem-Solving Practice

Solve.

1. GEOMETRY What is the area of a rectangle that has sides of 6 units and 9 units? 54 square units
2. GAMES Keisha and Halley are playing a game. A rectangular game card measures 2 inches by 3 inches. What is the area of the card? 6 square inches
3. CONSTRUCTION The kitchen in Alicia's home has a wall that is 12 feet long and 8 feet tall. What is the area of this wall? 96 square feet
4. FURNITURE Mrs. Kincaid has a desk that measures 3 feet by 5 feet. What is the area of this desk? 15 square feet
5. RUGBY Olivia plays rugby on a field that is 70 meters wide and 100 meters long. What is the area of the rugby field? 7,000 sq m
6. GEOMETRY What is the area of a square that has sides 9 units long? 81 square units
7. COOKING Fidel is cooking brownies. The pan is a rectangle measuring 8 inches on one side and 11 inches on the other side. What is the area of the pan? 88 sq in.
8. CONSTRUCTION Brandon wants to create a snowman-shaped sign. He began by drawing a picture on grid paper. What is the area of his drawing? 79 sq units

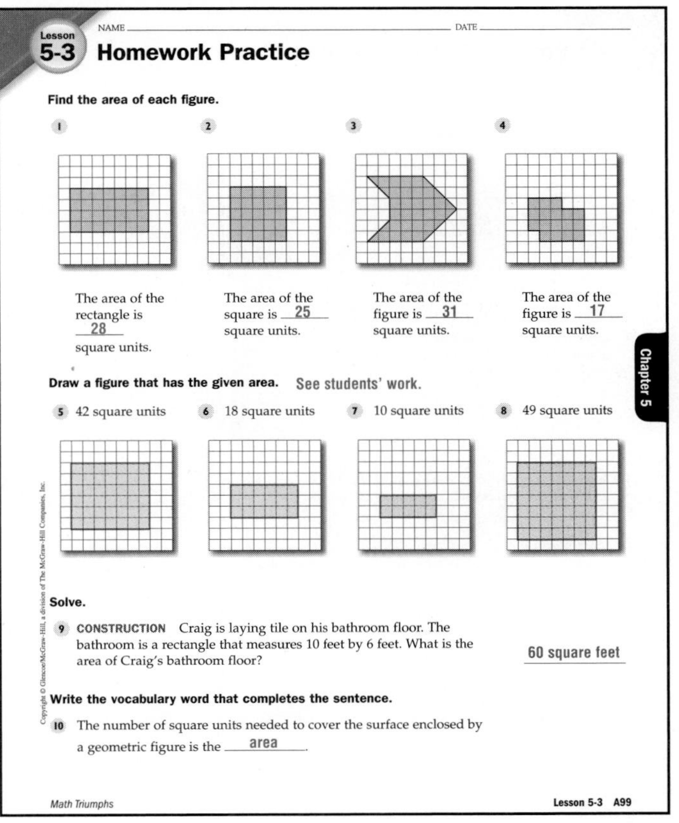

NAME ______ DATE ______

Lesson 5-3

Homework Practice

Find the area of each figure.

1. The area of the rectangle is 28 square units.
2. The area of the square is 25 square units.
3. The area of the figure is 31 square units.
4. The area of the figure is 17 square units.

Draw a figure that has the given area. See students' work.

5. 42 square units
6. 18 square units
7. 10 square units
8. 49 square units

Solve.

9. CONSTRUCTION Craig is laying tile on his bathroom floor. The bathroom is a rectangle that measures 10 feet by 6 feet. What is the area of Craig's bathroom floor? 60 square feet

Write the vocabulary word that completes the sentence.

10. The number of square units needed to cover the surface enclosed by a geometric figure is the area.

Chapter 5

Answer Key (Lesson 5-4)

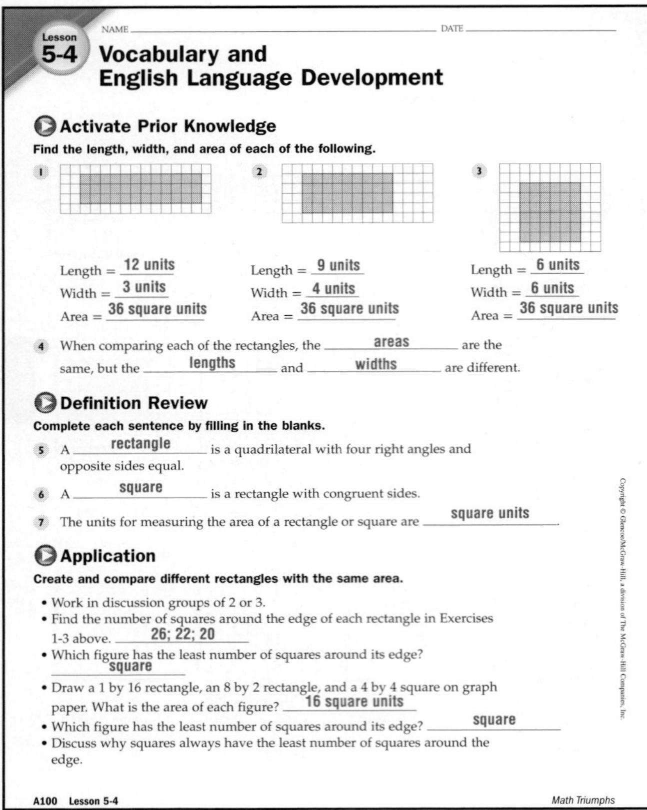

Lesson 5-4 NAME ____ DATE ____

Vocabulary and English Language Development

Activate Prior Knowledge

Find the length, width, and area of each of the following.

1 Length = 12 units
Width = 3 units
Area = 36 square units

2 Length = 9 units
Width = 4 units
Area = 36 square units

3 Length = 6 units
Width = 6 units
Area = 36 square units

4 When comparing each of the rectangles, the areas are the same, but the lengths and widths are different.

Definition Review

Complete each sentence by filling in the blanks.

5 A rectangle is a quadrilateral with four right angles and opposite sides equal.

6 A square is a rectangle with congruent sides.

7 The units for measuring the area of a rectangle or square are square units.

Application

Create and compare different rectangles with the same area.

- Work in discussion groups of 2 or 3.
- Find the number of squares around the edge of each rectangle in Exercises 1-3 above. 26; 22; 20
- Which figure has the least number of squares around its edge? square
- Draw a 1 by 16 rectangle, an 8 by 2 rectangle, and a 4 by 4 square on graph paper. What is the area of each figure? 16 square units
- Which figure has the least number of squares around its edge? square
- Discuss why squares always have the least number of squares around the edge.

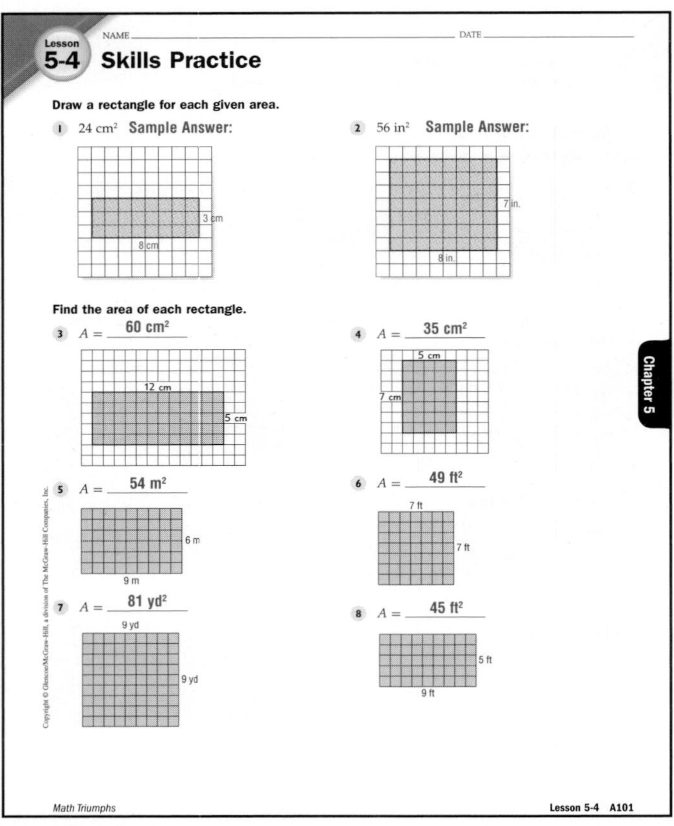

Lesson 5-4 NAME ____ DATE ____

Skills Practice

Draw a rectangle for each given area.

1 24 cm² **Sample Answer:**

2 56 in² **Sample Answer:**

Find the area of each rectangle.

3 $A =$ 60 cm²

4 $A =$ 35 cm²

5 $A =$ 54 m²

6 $A =$ 49 ft²

7 $A =$ 81 yd²

8 $A =$ 45 ft²

Chapter 5

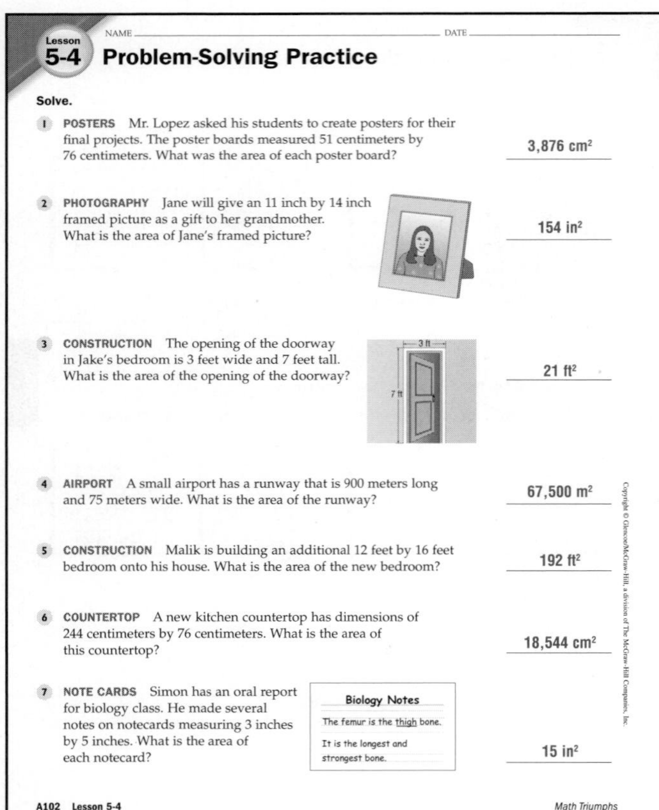

Lesson 5-4 NAME ____ DATE ____

Problem-Solving Practice

Solve.

1 POSTERS Mr. Lopez asked his students to create posters for their final projects. The poster boards measured 51 centimeters by 76 centimeters. What was the area of each poster board? 3,876 cm²

2 PHOTOGRAPHY Jane will give an 11 inch by 14 inch framed picture as a gift to her grandmother. What is the area of Jane's framed picture? 154 in²

3 CONSTRUCTION The opening of the doorway in Jake's bedroom is 3 feet wide and 7 feet tall. What is the area of the opening of the doorway? 21 ft²

4 AIRPORT A small airport has a runway that is 900 meters long and 75 meters wide. What is the area of the runway? 67,500 m²

5 CONSTRUCTION Malik is building an additional 12 feet by 16 feet bedroom onto his house. What is the area of the new bedroom? 192 ft²

6 COUNTERTOP A new kitchen countertop has dimensions of 244 centimeters by 76 centimeters. What is the area of this countertop? 18,544 cm²

7 NOTE CARDS Simon has an oral report for biology class. He made several notes on notecards measuring 3 inches by 5 inches. What is the area of each notecard? 15 in²

Biology Notes
The femur is the thigh bone.
It is the longest and strongest bone.

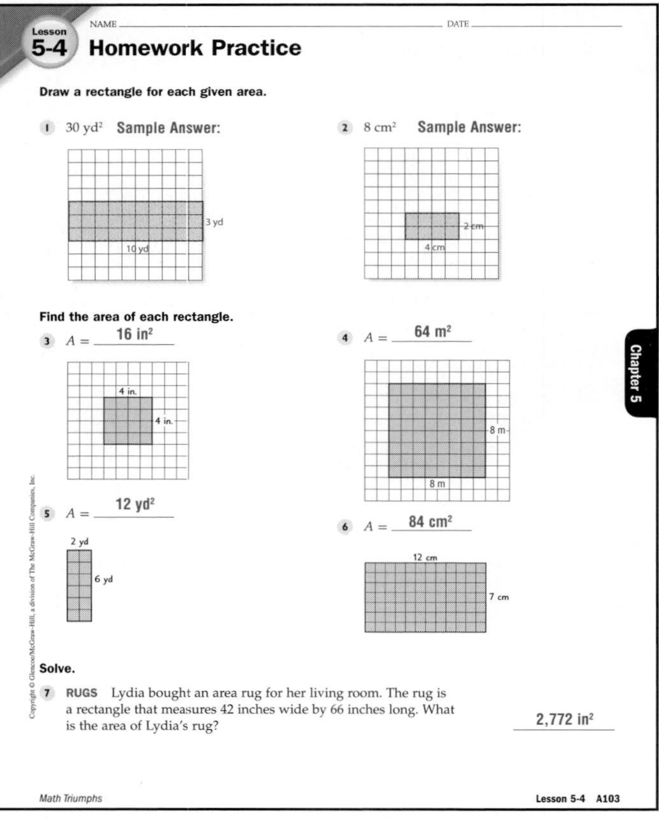

Lesson 5-4 NAME ____ DATE ____

Homework Practice

Draw a rectangle for each given area.

1 30 yd² **Sample Answer:**

2 8 cm² **Sample Answer:**

Find the area of each rectangle.

3 $A =$ 16 in²

4 $A =$ 64 m²

5 $A =$ 12 yd²

6 $A =$ 84 cm²

Solve.

7 RUGS Lydia bought an area rug for her living room. The rug is a rectangle that measures 42 inches wide by 66 inches long. What is the area of Lydia's rug? 2,772 in²

Chapter 5

Answer Key (Lesson 5-5)

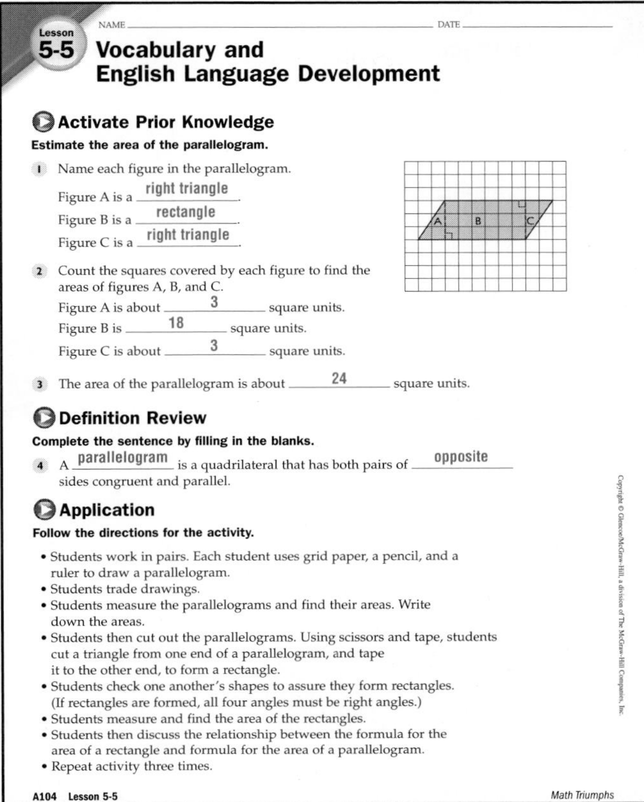

Lesson 5-5 NAME ______ DATE ______

Vocabulary and English Language Development

Activate Prior Knowledge

Estimate the area of the parallelogram.

1. Name each figure in the parallelogram.
   Figure A is a right triangle.
   Figure B is a rectangle.
   Figure C is a right triangle.

2. Count the squares covered by each figure to find the areas of figures A, B, and C.
   Figure A is about 3 square units.
   Figure B is 18 square units.
   Figure C is about 3 square units.

3. The area of the parallelogram is about 24 square units.

Definition Review

Complete the sentence by filling in the blanks.

4. A parallelogram is a quadrilateral that has both pairs of opposite sides congruent and parallel.

Application

Follow the directions for the activity.

- Students work in pairs. Each student uses grid paper, a pencil, and a ruler to draw a parallelogram.
- Students trade drawings.
- Students measure the parallelograms and find their areas. Write down the areas.
- Students then cut out the parallelograms. Using scissors and tape, students cut a triangle from one end of a parallelogram, and tape it to the other end, to form a rectangle.
- Students check one another's shapes to assure they form rectangles. (If rectangles are formed, all four angles must be right angles.)
- Students measure and find the area of the rectangles.
- Students then discuss the relationship between the formula for the area of a rectangle and formula for the area of a parallelogram.
- Repeat activity three times.

A104 Lesson 5-5 *Math Triumphs*

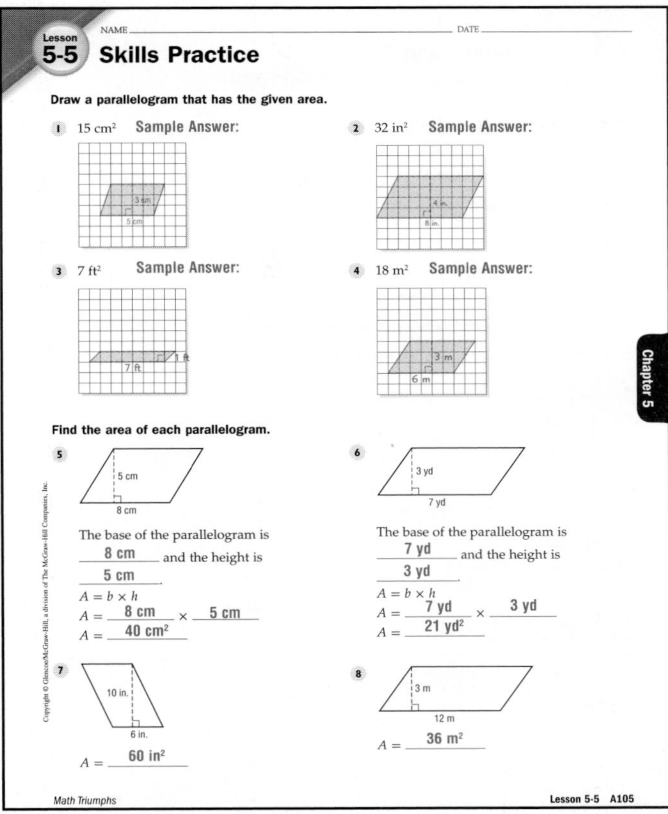

Lesson 5-5 NAME ______ DATE ______

Skills Practice

Draw a parallelogram that has the given area.

1. 15 cm^2 Sample Answer:
2. 32 in^2 Sample Answer:
3. 7 ft^2 Sample Answer:
4. 18 m^2 Sample Answer:

Find the area of each parallelogram.

5. The base of the parallelogram is 8 cm and the height is 5 cm.
   $A = b \times h$
   $A =$ 8 cm × 5 cm
   $A =$ 40 cm^2

6. The base of the parallelogram is 7 yd and the height is 3 yd.
   $A = b \times h$
   $A =$ 7 yd × 3 yd
   $A =$ 21 yd^2

7. (10 in., 6 in.) $A =$ 60 in^2

8. (3 m, 12 m) $A =$ 36 m^2

Math Triumphs Lesson 5-5 A105

Chapter 5

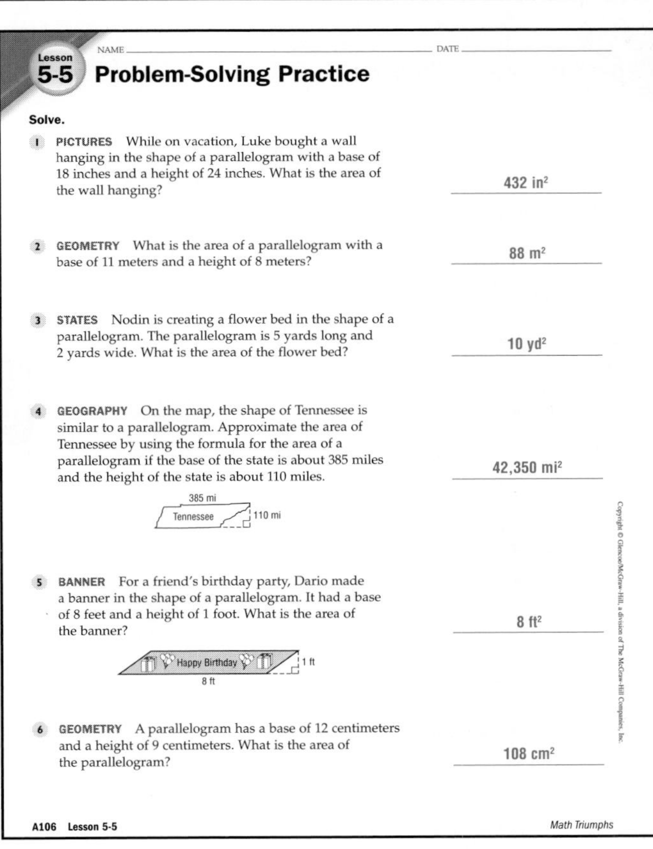

Lesson 5-5 NAME ______ DATE ______

Problem-Solving Practice

Solve.

1. **PICTURES** While on vacation, Luke bought a wall hanging in the shape of a parallelogram with a base of 18 inches and a height of 24 inches. What is the area of the wall hanging? 432 in^2

2. **GEOMETRY** What is the area of a parallelogram with a base of 11 meters and a height of 8 meters? 88 m^2

3. **STATES** Nodin is creating a flower bed in the shape of a parallelogram. The parallelogram is 5 yards long and 2 yards wide. What is the area of the flower bed? 10 yd^2

4. **GEOGRAPHY** On the map, the shape of Tennessee is similar to a parallelogram. Approximate the area of Tennessee by using the formula for the area of a parallelogram if the base of the state is about 385 miles and the height of the state is about 110 miles. 42,350 mi^2

5. **BANNER** For a friend's birthday party, Dario made a banner in the shape of a parallelogram. It had a base of 8 feet and a height of 1 foot. What is the area of the banner? 8 ft^2

6. **GEOMETRY** A parallelogram has a base of 12 centimeters and a height of 9 centimeters. What is the area of the parallelogram? 108 cm^2

A106 Lesson 5-5 *Math Triumphs*

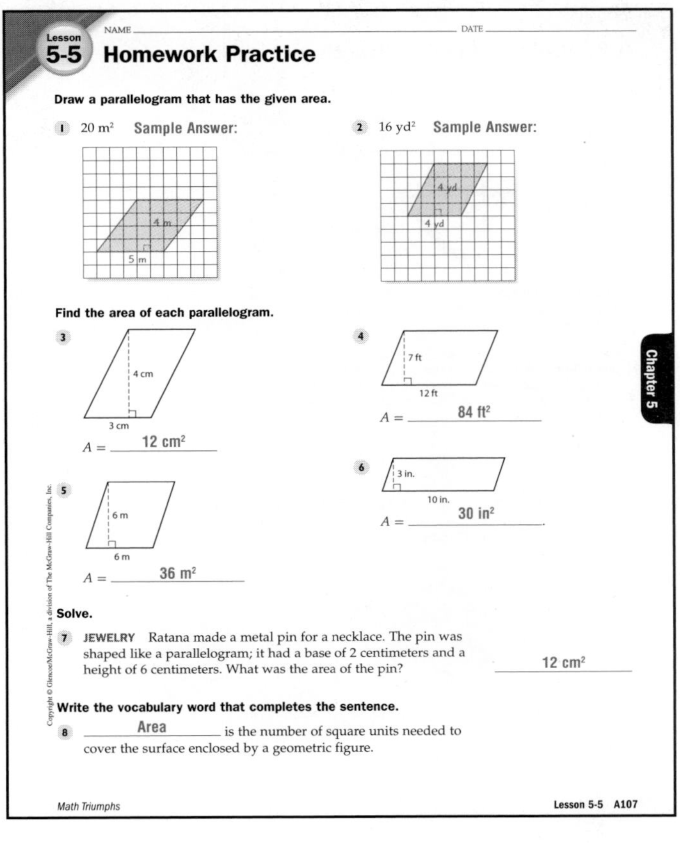

Lesson 5-5 NAME ______ DATE ______

Homework Practice

Draw a parallelogram that has the given area.

1. 20 m^2 Sample Answer:
2. 16 yd^2 Sample Answer:

Find the area of each parallelogram.

3. (4 cm, 3 cm) $A =$ 12 cm^2
4. (7 ft, 12 ft) $A =$ 84 ft^2
5. (6 m, 6 m) $A =$ 36 m^2
6. (3 in., 10 in.) $A =$ 30 in^2

Solve.

7. **JEWELRY** Ratana made a metal pin for a necklace. The pin was shaped like a parallelogram; it had a base of 2 centimeters and a height of 6 centimeters. What was the area of the pin? 12 cm^2

Write the vocabulary word that completes the sentence.

8. Area is the number of square units needed to cover the surface enclosed by a geometric figure.

Math Triumphs Lesson 5-5 A107

Chapter 5

Answer Key (Lesson 5-6)

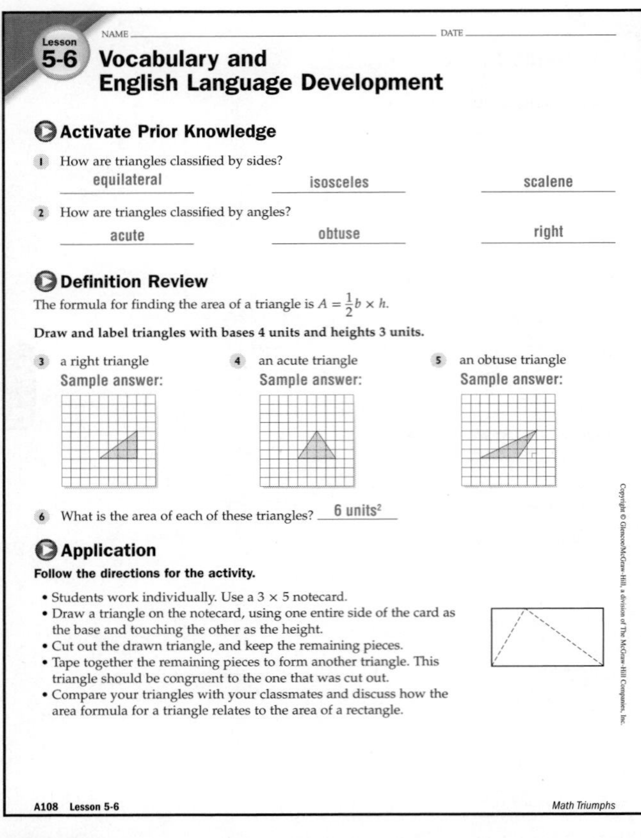

Lesson 5-6
NAME
DATE
Vocabulary and English Language Development
Activate Prior Knowledge
1 How are triangles classified by sides?
equilateral
isosceles
scalene
2 How are triangles classified by angles?
acute
obtuse
right
Definition Review
The formula for finding the area of a triangle is $A = \frac{1}{2}b \times h$.
Draw and label triangles with bases 4 units and heights 3 units.
3 a right triangle
Sample answer:
4 an acute triangle
Sample answer:
5 an obtuse triangle
Sample answer:
6 What is the area of each of these triangles? 6 units²
Application
Follow the directions for the activity.
• Students work individually. Use a 3 × 5 notecard.
• Draw a triangle on the notecard, using one entire side of the card as the base and touching the other as the height.
• Cut out the drawn triangle, and keep the remaining pieces.
• Tape together the remaining pieces to form another triangle. This triangle should be congruent to the one that was cut out.
• Compare your triangles with your classmates and discuss how the area formula for a triangle relates to the area of a rectangle.
A108 Lesson 5-6
Math Triumphs

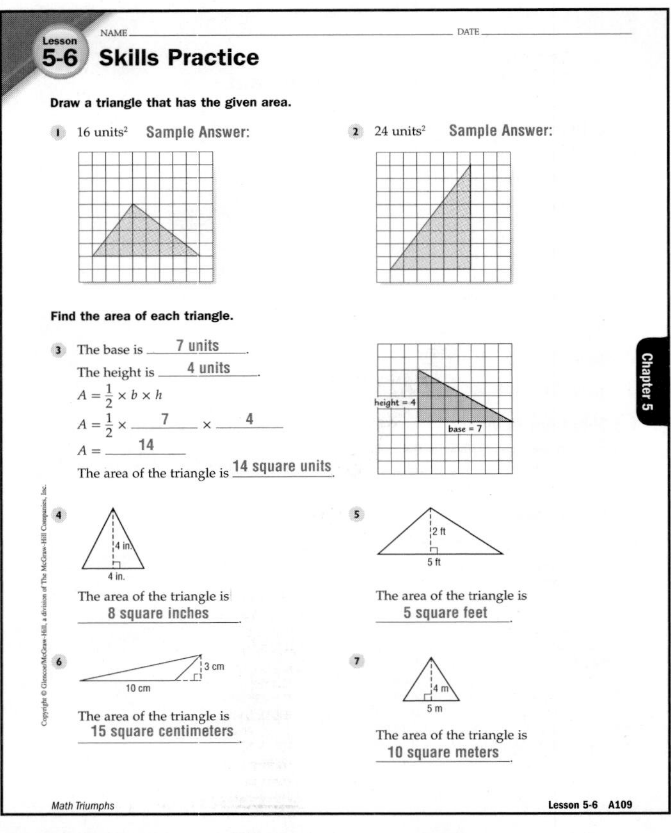

Lesson 5-6
NAME
DATE
Skills Practice
Draw a triangle that has the given area.
1 16 units² Sample Answer:
2 24 units² Sample Answer:
Find the area of each triangle.
3 The base is 7 units.
The height is 4 units.
$A = \frac{1}{2} \times b \times h$
$A = \frac{1}{2} \times$ 7 × 4
A = 14
The area of the triangle is 14 square units.
height = 4
base = 7
4
4 in.
4 in.
The area of the triangle is 8 square inches
5
2 ft
5 ft
The area of the triangle is 5 square feet
6
3 cm
10 cm
The area of the triangle is 15 square centimeters
7
4 m
5 m
The area of the triangle is 10 square meters
Chapter 5
Math Triumphs
Lesson 5-6 A109

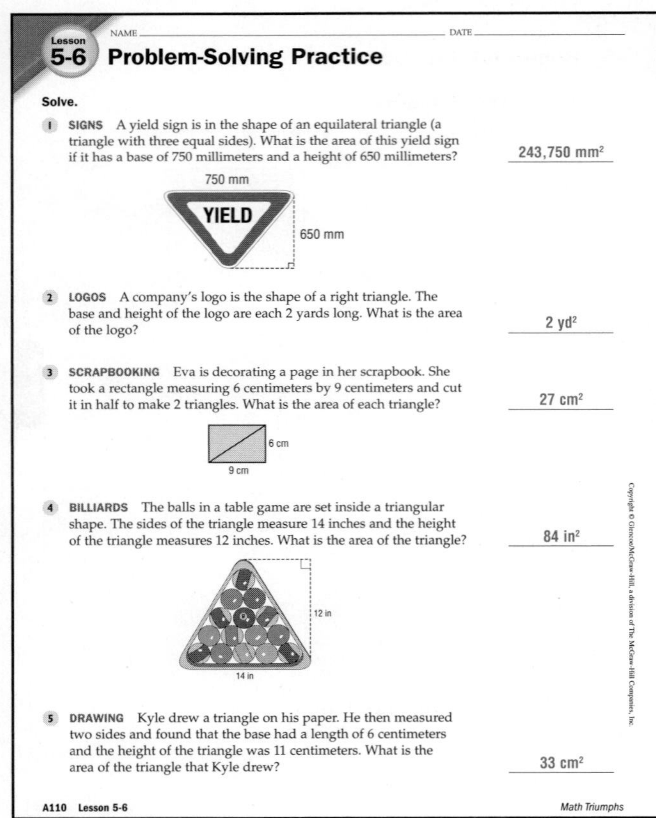

Lesson 5-6
NAME
DATE
Problem-Solving Practice
Solve.
1 SIGNS A yield sign is in the shape of an equilateral triangle (a triangle with three equal sides). What is the area of this yield sign if it has a base of 750 millimeters and a height of 650 millimeters?
243,750 mm²
750 mm
YIELD
650 mm
2 LOGOS A company's logo is the shape of a right triangle. The base and height of the logo are each 2 yards long. What is the area of the logo?
2 yd²
3 SCRAPBOOKING Eva is decorating a page in her scrapbook. She took a rectangle measuring 6 centimeters by 9 centimeters and cut it in half to make 2 triangles. What is the area of each triangle?
27 cm²
6 cm
9 cm
4 BILLIARDS The balls in a table game are set inside a triangular shape. The sides of the triangle measure 14 inches and the height of the triangle measures 12 inches. What is the area of the triangle?
84 in²
12 in
14 in
5 DRAWING Kyle drew a triangle on his paper. He then measured two sides and found that the base had a length of 6 centimeters and the height of the triangle was 11 centimeters. What is the area of the triangle that Kyle drew?
33 cm²
A110 Lesson 5-6
Math Triumphs

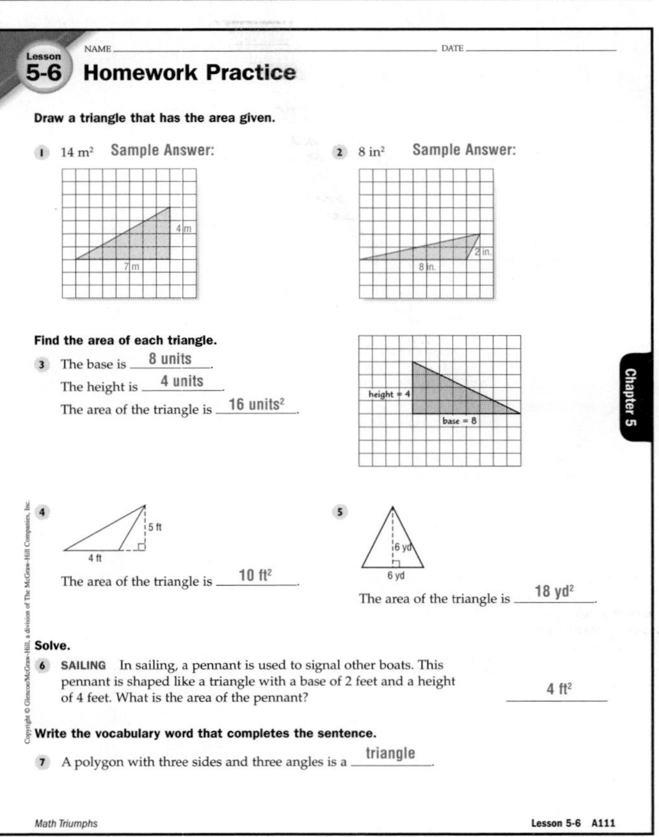

Lesson 5-6
NAME
DATE
Homework Practice
Draw a triangle that has the area given.
1 14 m² Sample Answer:
4 m
7 m
2 8 in² Sample Answer:
2 in.
8 in.
Find the area of each triangle.
3 The base is 8 units.
The height is 4 units.
The area of the triangle is 16 units².
height = 4
base = 8
4
5 ft
4 ft
The area of the triangle is 10 ft².
5
6 yd
6 yd
The area of the triangle is 18 yd².
Solve.
6 SAILING In sailing, a pennant is used to signal other boats. This pennant is shaped like a triangle with a base of 2 feet and a height of 4 feet. What is the area of the pennant?
4 ft²
Write the vocabulary word that completes the sentence.
7 A polygon with three sides and three angles is a triangle.
Chapter 5
Math Triumphs
Lesson 5-6 A111

Answer Key (Lesson 5-7)

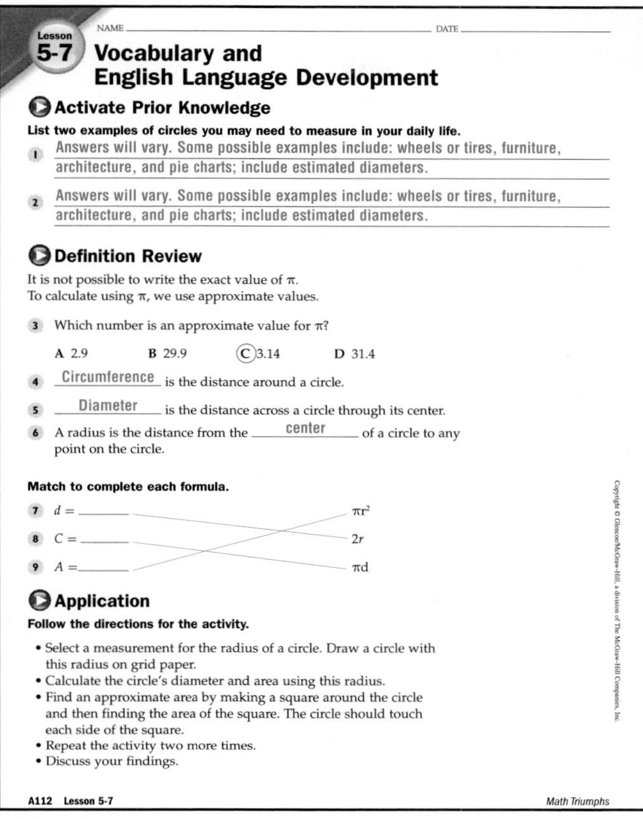

NAME ______ DATE ______

Lesson 5-7

Vocabulary and English Language Development

Activate Prior Knowledge

List two examples of circles you may need to measure in your daily life.

1. Answers will vary. Some possible examples include: wheels or tires, furniture, architecture, and pie charts; include estimated diameters.
2. Answers will vary. Some possible examples include: wheels or tires, furniture, architecture, and pie charts; include estimated diameters.

Definition Review

It is not possible to write the exact value of π.
To calculate using π, we use approximate values.

3. Which number is an approximate value for π?

   A 2.9 B 29.9 (C) 3.14 D 31.4

4. Circumference is the distance around a circle.
5. Diameter is the distance across a circle through its center.
6. A radius is the distance from the center of a circle to any point on the circle.

Match to complete each formula.

7. $d =$ ______ — πr^2
8. $C =$ ______ — $2r$
9. $A =$ ______ — πd

Application

Follow the directions for the activity.

- Select a measurement for the radius of a circle. Draw a circle with this radius on grid paper.
- Calculate the circle's diameter and area using this radius.
- Find an approximate area by making a square around the circle and then finding the area of the square. The circle should touch each side of the square.
- Repeat the activity two more times.
- Discuss your findings.

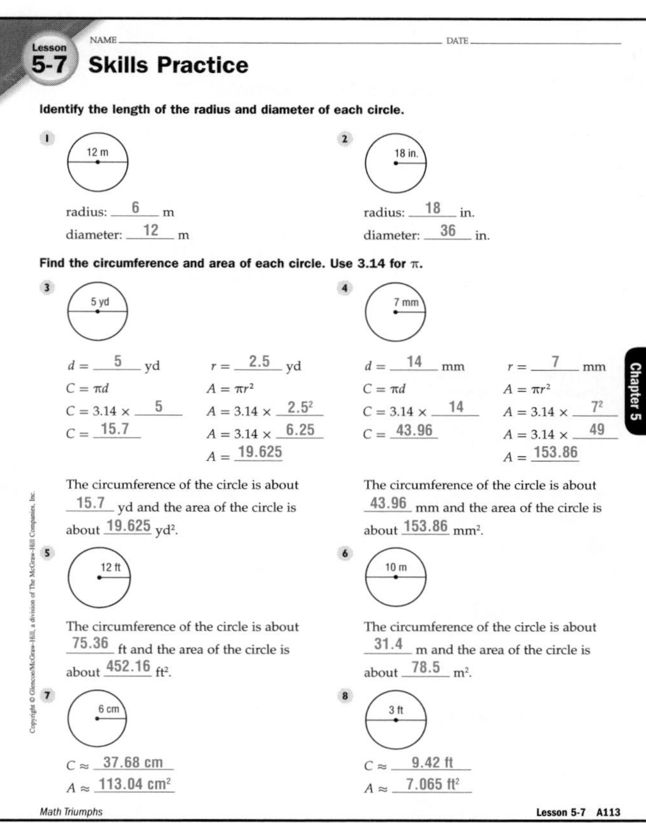

NAME ______ DATE ______

Lesson 5-7

Skills Practice

Identify the length of the radius and diameter of each circle.

1. (12 m) radius: 6 m; diameter: 12 m
2. (18 in.) radius: 18 in.; diameter: 36 in.

Find the circumference and area of each circle. Use 3.14 for π.

3. (5 yd)
   $d =$ 5 yd; $C = \pi d$; $C = 3.14 \times 5$; $C =$ 15.7
   $r =$ 2.5 yd; $A = \pi r^2$; $A = 3.14 \times 2.5^2$; $A = 3.14 \times 6.25$; $A =$ 19.625
   The circumference of the circle is about 15.7 yd and the area of the circle is about 19.625 yd².
4. (7 mm)
   $d =$ 14 mm; $C = \pi d$; $C = 3.14 \times 14$; $C =$ 43.96
   $r =$ 7 mm; $A = \pi r^2$; $A = 3.14 \times 7^2$; $A = 3.14 \times 49$; $A =$ 153.86
   The circumference of the circle is about 43.96 mm and the area of the circle is about 153.86 mm².
5. (12 ft) The circumference of the circle is about 75.36 ft and the area of the circle is about 452.16 ft².
6. (10 m) The circumference of the circle is about 31.4 m and the area of the circle is about 78.5 m².
7. (6 cm) $C \approx$ 37.68 cm; $A \approx$ 113.04 cm²
8. (3 ft) $C \approx$ 9.42 ft; $A \approx$ 7.065 ft²

Chapter 5

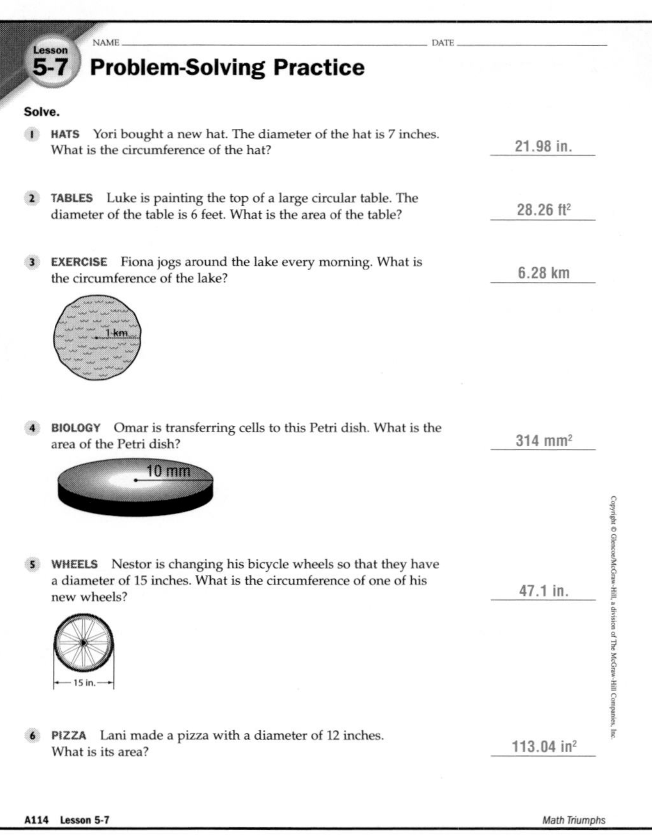

NAME ______ DATE ______

Lesson 5-7

Problem-Solving Practice

Solve.

1. **HATS** Yori bought a new hat. The diameter of the hat is 7 inches. What is the circumference of the hat? — 21.98 in.
2. **TABLES** Luke is painting the top of a large circular table. The diameter of the table is 6 feet. What is the area of the table? — 28.26 ft²
3. **EXERCISE** Fiona jogs around the lake every morning. What is the circumference of the lake? — 6.28 km

4. **BIOLOGY** Omar is transferring cells to this Petri dish. What is the area of the Petri dish? — 314 mm²

5. **WHEELS** Nestor is changing his bicycle wheels so that they have a diameter of 15 inches. What is the circumference of one of his new wheels? — 47.1 in.

6. **PIZZA** Lani made a pizza with a diameter of 12 inches. What is its area? — 113.04 in²

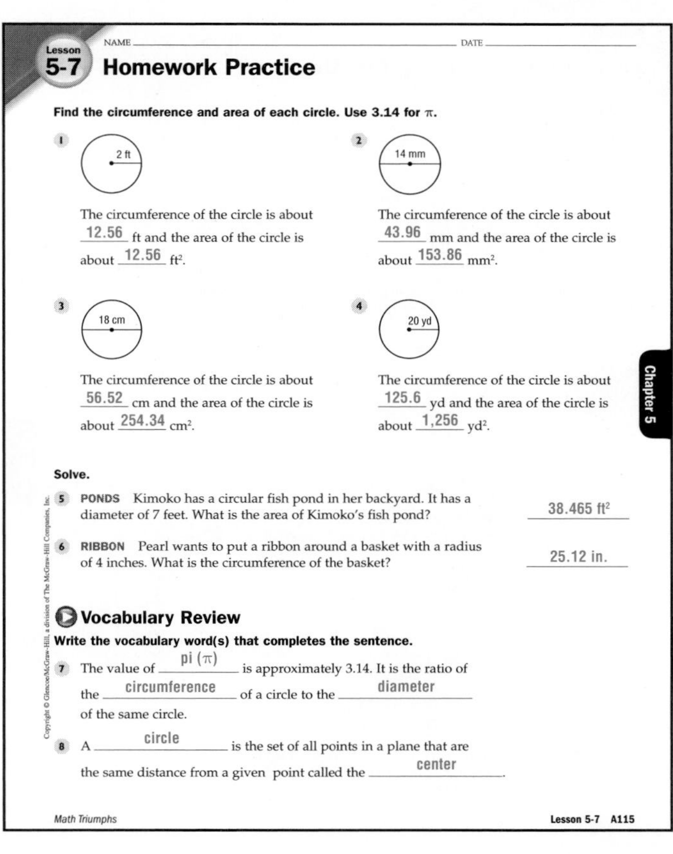

NAME ______ DATE ______

Lesson 5-7

Homework Practice

Find the circumference and area of each circle. Use 3.14 for π.

1. (2 ft) The circumference of the circle is about 12.56 ft and the area of the circle is about 12.56 ft².
2. (14 mm) The circumference of the circle is about 43.96 mm and the area of the circle is about 153.86 mm².
3. (18 cm) The circumference of the circle is about 56.52 cm and the area of the circle is about 254.34 cm².
4. (20 yd) The circumference of the circle is about 125.6 yd and the area of the circle is about 1,256 yd².

Solve.

5. **PONDS** Kimoko has a circular fish pond in her backyard. It has a diameter of 7 feet. What is the area of Kimoko's fish pond? — 38.465 ft²
6. **RIBBON** Pearl wants to put a ribbon around a basket with a radius of 4 inches. What is the circumference of the basket? — 25.12 in.

Vocabulary Review

Write the vocabulary word(s) that completes the sentence.

7. The value of pi (π) is approximately 3.14. It is the ratio of the circumference of a circle to the diameter of the same circle.
8. A circle is the set of all points in a plane that are the same distance from a given point called the center.

Chapter 5

Answer Key (Lesson 6-1)

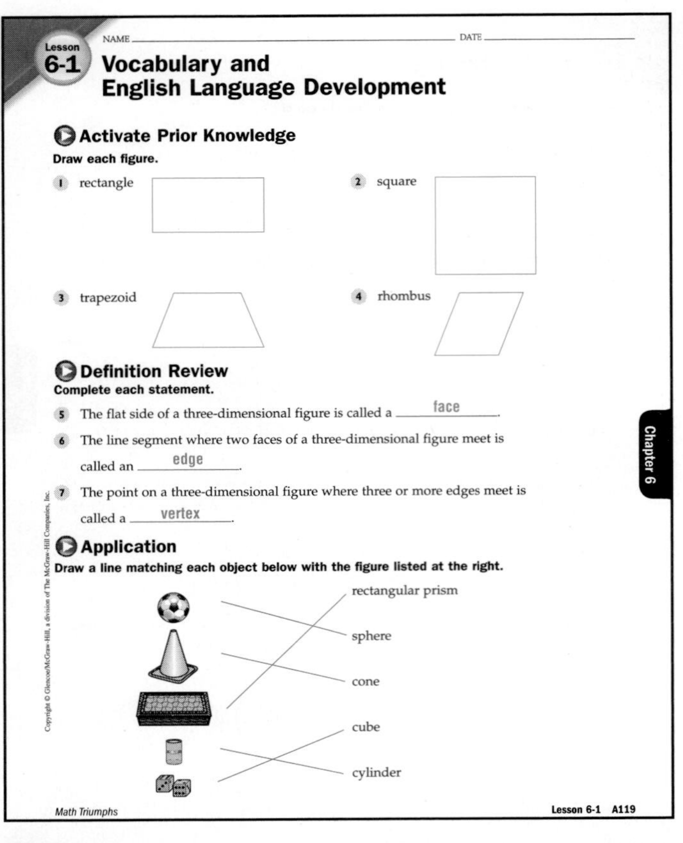

Lesson 6-1 NAME ______ DATE ______

Vocabulary and English Language Development

Activate Prior Knowledge

Draw each figure.

1. rectangle
2. square
3. trapezoid
4. rhombus

Definition Review

Complete each statement.

5. The flat side of a three-dimensional figure is called a face.
6. The line segment where two faces of a three-dimensional figure meet is called an edge.
7. The point on a three-dimensional figure where three or more edges meet is called a vertex.

Application

Draw a line matching each object below with the figure listed at the right.

rectangular prism

sphere

cone

cube

cylinder

Chapter 6

Copyright © Glencoe/McGraw-Hill, a division of The McGraw-Hill Companies, Inc.

Math Triumphs Lesson 6-1 A119

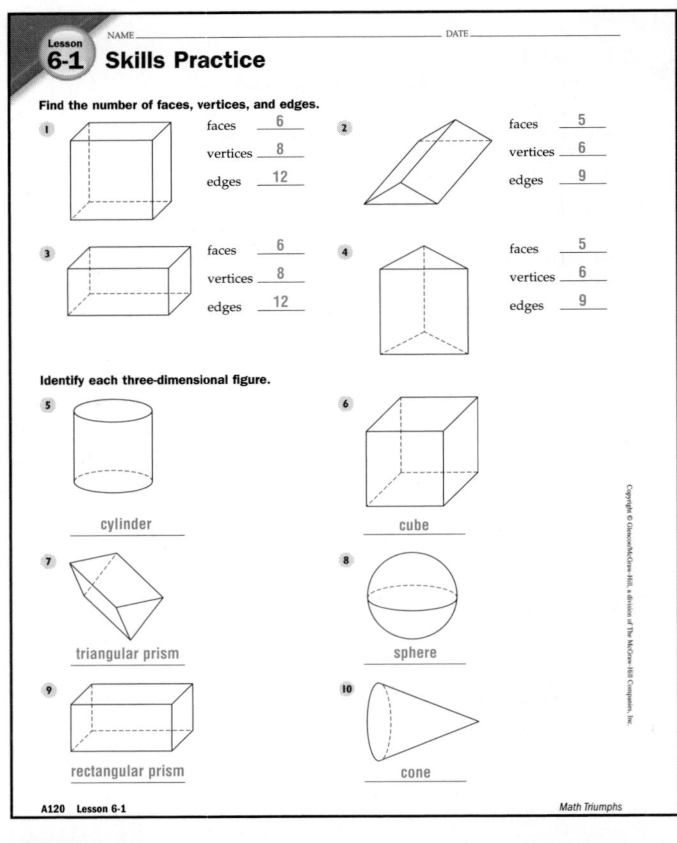

Lesson 6-1 NAME ______ DATE ______

Skills Practice

Find the number of faces, vertices, and edges.

1. faces 6, vertices 8, edges 12
2. faces 5, vertices 6, edges 9
3. faces 6, vertices 8, edges 12
4. faces 5, vertices 6, edges 9

Identify each three-dimensional figure.

5. cylinder
6. cube
7. triangular prism
8. sphere
9. rectangular prism
10. cone

Copyright © Glencoe/McGraw-Hill, a division of The McGraw-Hill Companies, Inc.

A120 Lesson 6-1 Math Triumphs

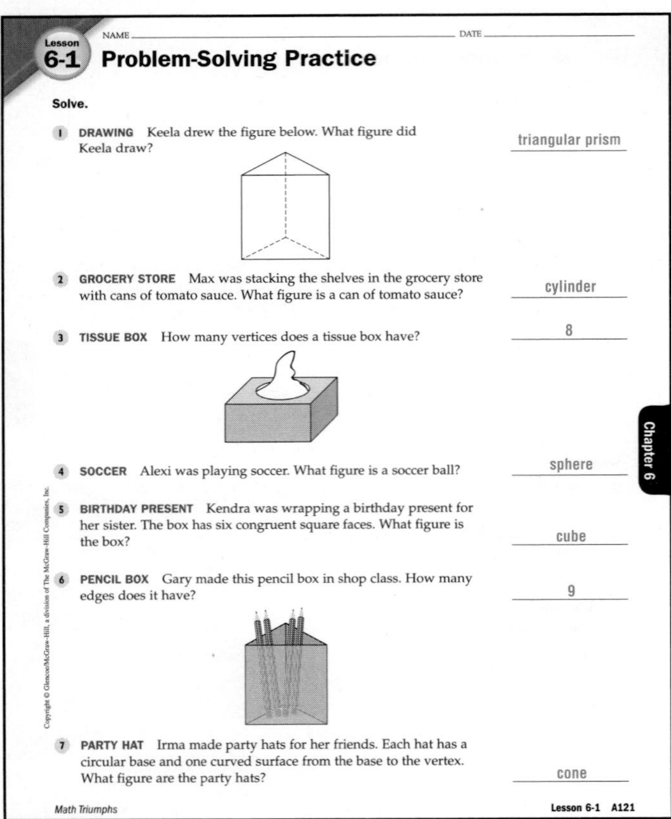

Lesson 6-1 NAME ______ DATE ______

Problem-Solving Practice

Solve.

1. **DRAWING** Keela drew the figure below. What figure did Keela draw? triangular prism
2. **GROCERY STORE** Max was stacking the shelves in the grocery store with cans of tomato sauce. What figure is a can of tomato sauce? cylinder
3. **TISSUE BOX** How many vertices does a tissue box have? 8
4. **SOCCER** Alexi was playing soccer. What figure is a soccer ball? sphere
5. **BIRTHDAY PRESENT** Kendra was wrapping a birthday present for her sister. The box has six congruent square faces. What figure is the box? cube
6. **PENCIL BOX** Gary made this pencil box in shop class. How many edges does it have? 9
7. **PARTY HAT** Irma made party hats for her friends. Each hat has a circular base and one curved surface from the base to the vertex. What figure are the party hats? cone

Chapter 6

Copyright © Glencoe/McGraw-Hill, a division of The McGraw-Hill Companies, Inc.

Math Triumphs Lesson 6-1 A121

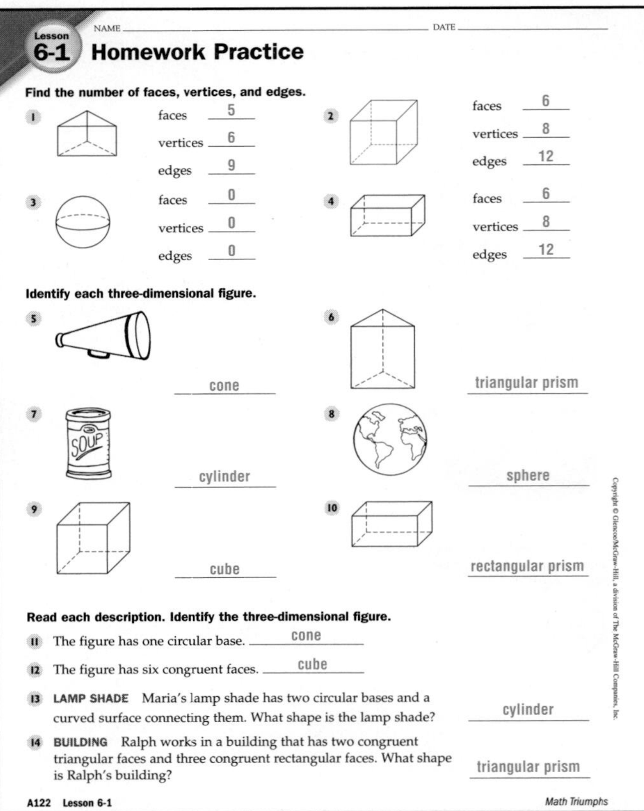

Lesson 6-1 NAME ______ DATE ______

Homework Practice

Find the number of faces, vertices, and edges.

1. faces 5, vertices 6, edges 9
2. faces 6, vertices 8, edges 12
3. faces 0, vertices 0, edges 0
4. faces 6, vertices 8, edges 12

Identify each three-dimensional figure.

5. cone
6. triangular prism
7. cylinder
8. sphere
9. cube
10. rectangular prism

Read each description. Identify the three-dimensional figure.

11. The figure has one circular base. cone
12. The figure has six congruent faces. cube
13. **LAMP SHADE** Maria's lamp shade has two circular bases and a curved surface connecting them. What shape is the lamp shade? cylinder
14. **BUILDING** Ralph works in a building that has two congruent triangular faces and three congruent rectangular faces. What shape is Ralph's building? triangular prism

Copyright © Glencoe/McGraw-Hill, a division of The McGraw-Hill Companies, Inc.

A122 Lesson 6-1 Math Triumphs

Answer Key (Lesson 6-2)

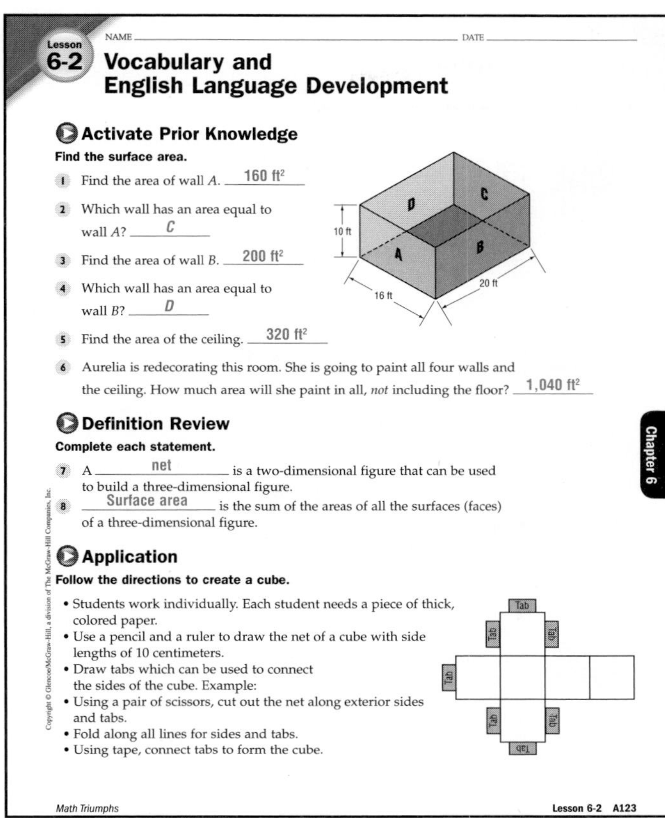

Lesson 6-2

NAME ______ DATE ______

Vocabulary and English Language Development

Activate Prior Knowledge

Find the surface area.

1. Find the area of wall *A*. 160 ft²
2. Which wall has an area equal to wall *A*? C
3. Find the area of wall *B*. 200 ft²
4. Which wall has an area equal to wall *B*? D
5. Find the area of the ceiling. 320 ft²
6. Aurelia is redecorating this room. She is going to paint all four walls and the ceiling. How much area will she paint in all, *not* including the floor? 1,040 ft²

Definition Review

Complete each statement.

7. A net is a two-dimensional figure that can be used to build a three-dimensional figure.
8. Surface area is the sum of the areas of all the surfaces (faces) of a three-dimensional figure.

Application

Follow the directions to create a cube.

- Students work individually. Each student needs a piece of thick, colored paper.
- Use a pencil and a ruler to draw the net of a cube with side lengths of 10 centimeters.
- Draw tabs which can be used to connect the sides of the cube. Example:
- Using a pair of scissors, cut out the net along exterior sides and tabs.
- Fold along all lines for sides and tabs.
- Using tape, connect tabs to form the cube.

Chapter 6

Math Triumphs Lesson 6-2 A123

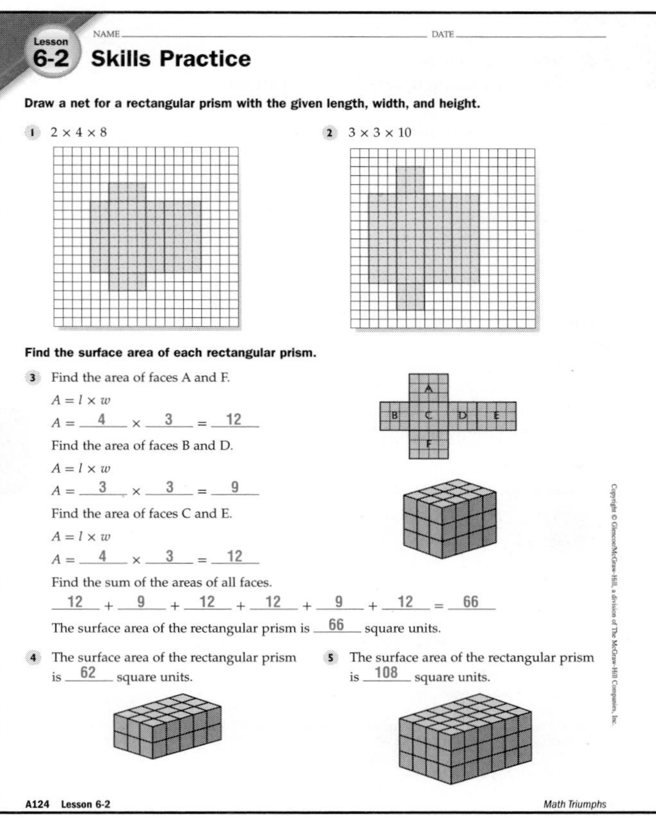

Lesson 6-2

NAME ______ DATE ______

Skills Practice

Draw a net for a rectangular prism with the given length, width, and height.

1. $2 \times 4 \times 8$
2. $3 \times 3 \times 10$

Find the surface area of each rectangular prism.

3. Find the area of faces A and F.
   $A = l \times w$
   $A =$ 4 $\times$ 3 $=$ 12
   Find the area of faces B and D.
   $A = l \times w$
   $A =$ 3 $\times$ 3 $=$ 9
   Find the area of faces C and E.
   $A = l \times w$
   $A =$ 4 $\times$ 3 $=$ 12
   Find the sum of the areas of all faces.
   12 + 9 + 12 + 12 + 9 + 12 = 66
   The surface area of the rectangular prism is 66 square units.

4. The surface area of the rectangular prism is 62 square units.
5. The surface area of the rectangular prism is 108 square units.

A124 Lesson 6-2 Math Triumphs

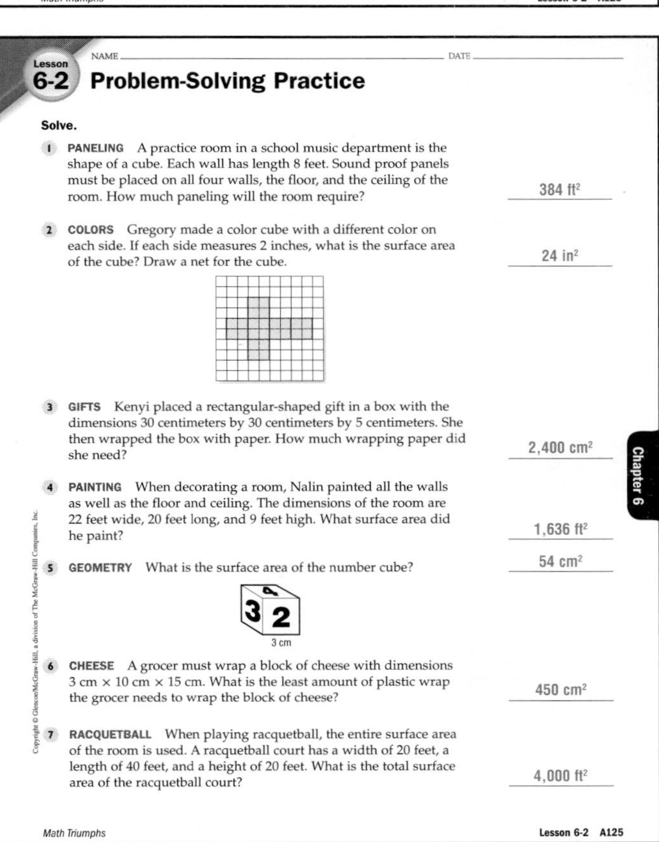

Lesson 6-2

NAME ______ DATE ______

Problem-Solving Practice

Solve.

1. **PANELING** A practice room in a school music department is the shape of a cube. Each wall has length 8 feet. Sound proof panels must be placed on all four walls, the floor, and the ceiling of the room. How much paneling will the room require? 384 ft²
2. **COLORS** Gregory made a color cube with a different color on each side. If each side measures 2 inches, what is the surface area of the cube? Draw a net for the cube. 24 in²
3. **GIFTS** Kenyi placed a rectangular-shaped gift in a box with the dimensions 30 centimeters by 30 centimeters by 5 centimeters. She then wrapped the box with paper. How much wrapping paper did she need? 2,400 cm²
4. **PAINTING** When decorating a room, Nalin painted all the walls as well as the floor and ceiling. The dimensions of the room are 22 feet wide, 20 feet long, and 9 feet high. What surface area did he paint? 1,636 ft²
5. **GEOMETRY** What is the surface area of the number cube? 54 cm²

6. **CHEESE** A grocer must wrap a block of cheese with dimensions 3 cm × 10 cm × 15 cm. What is the least amount of plastic wrap the grocer needs to wrap the block of cheese? 450 cm²
7. **RACQUETBALL** When playing racquetball, the entire surface area of the room is used. A racquetball court has a width of 20 feet, a length of 40 feet, and a height of 20 feet. What is the total surface area of the racquetball court? 4,000 ft²

Chapter 6

Math Triumphs Lesson 6-2 A125

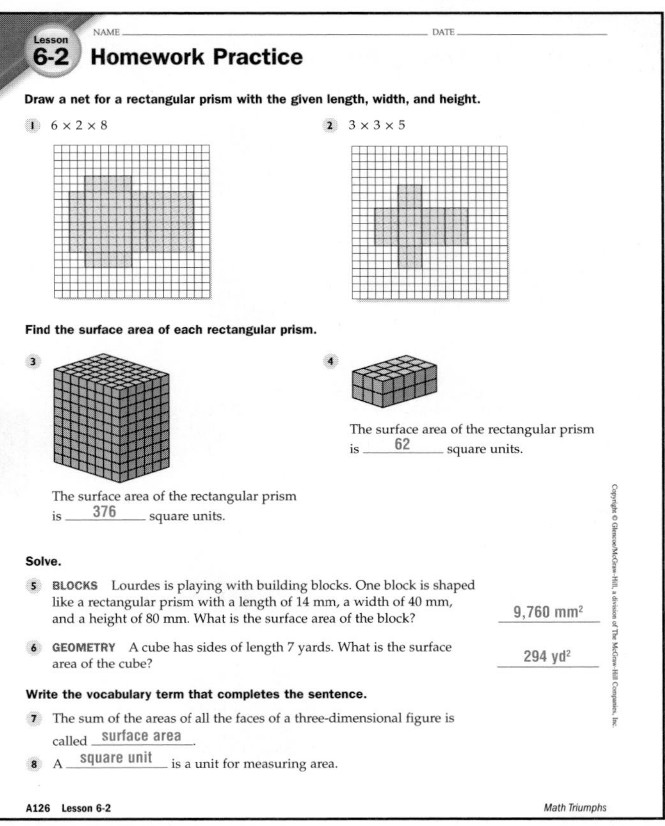

Lesson 6-2

NAME ______ DATE ______

Homework Practice

Draw a net for a rectangular prism with the given length, width, and height.

1. $6 \times 2 \times 8$
2. $3 \times 3 \times 5$

Find the surface area of each rectangular prism.

3. The surface area of the rectangular prism is 376 square units.
4. The surface area of the rectangular prism is 62 square units.

Solve.

5. **BLOCKS** Lourdes is playing with building blocks. One block is shaped like a rectangular prism with a length of 14 mm, a width of 40 mm, and a height of 80 mm. What is the surface area of the block? 9,760 mm²
6. **GEOMETRY** A cube has sides of length 7 yards. What is the surface area of the cube? 294 yd²

Write the vocabulary term that completes the sentence.

7. The sum of the areas of all the faces of a three-dimensional figure is called surface area.
8. A square unit is a unit for measuring area.

A126 Lesson 6-2 Math Triumphs

Answer Key (Lesson 6-3)

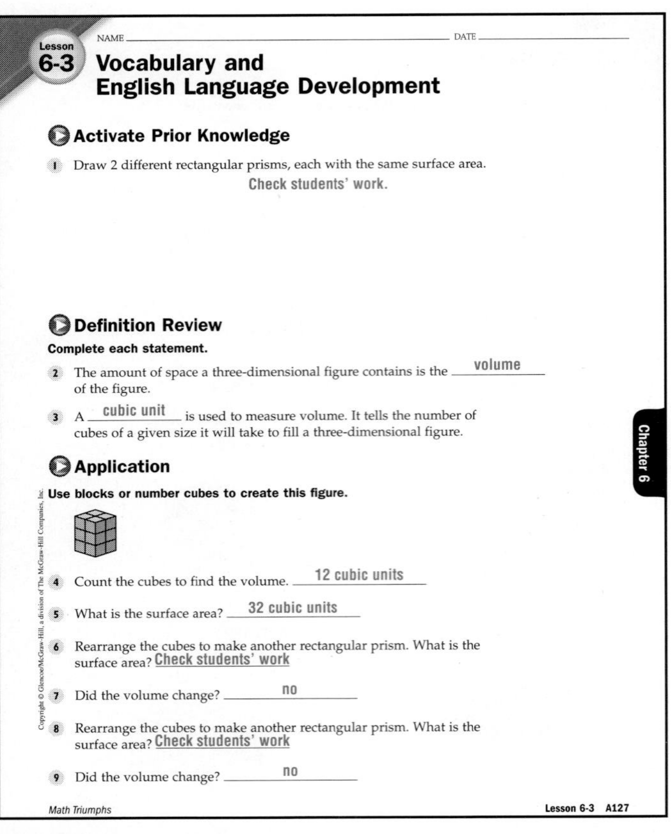

NAME ______ DATE ______

Lesson 6-3

Vocabulary and English Language Development

Activate Prior Knowledge

1 Draw 2 different rectangular prisms, each with the same surface area.
Check students' work.

Definition Review

Complete each statement.

2 The amount of space a three-dimensional figure contains is the volume of the figure.

3 A cubic unit is used to measure volume. It tells the number of cubes of a given size it will take to fill a three-dimensional figure.

Application

Use blocks or number cubes to create this figure.

4 Count the cubes to find the volume. 12 cubic units

5 What is the surface area? 32 cubic units

6 Rearrange the cubes to make another rectangular prism. What is the surface area? Check students' work

7 Did the volume change? no

8 Rearrange the cubes to make another rectangular prism. What is the surface area? Check students' work

9 Did the volume change? no

Chapter 6

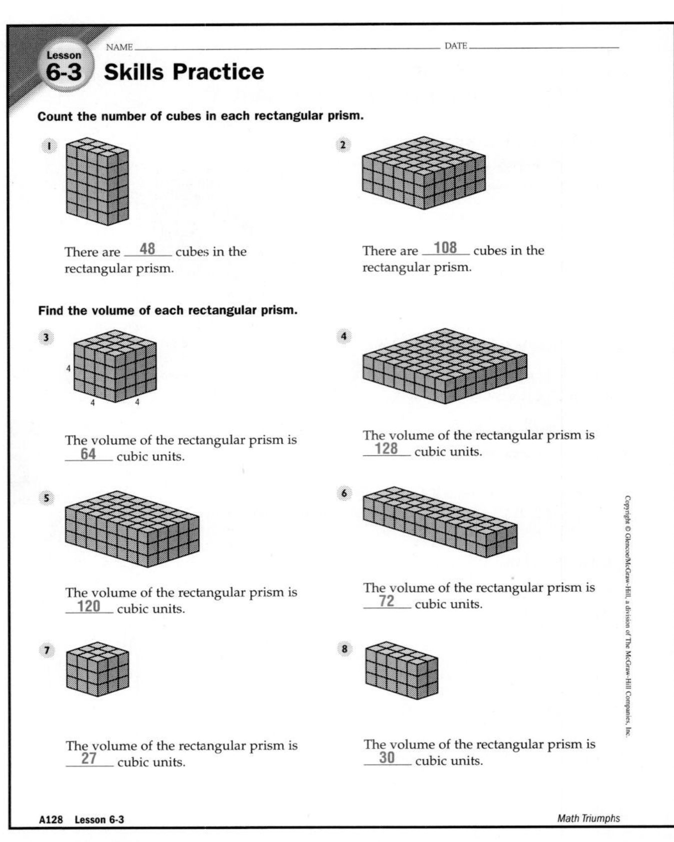

NAME ______ DATE ______

Lesson 6-3

Skills Practice

Count the number of cubes in each rectangular prism.

1 There are 48 cubes in the rectangular prism.

2 There are 108 cubes in the rectangular prism.

Find the volume of each rectangular prism.

3 The volume of the rectangular prism is 64 cubic units.

4 The volume of the rectangular prism is 128 cubic units.

5 The volume of the rectangular prism is 120 cubic units.

6 The volume of the rectangular prism is 72 cubic units.

7 The volume of the rectangular prism is 27 cubic units.

8 The volume of the rectangular prism is 30 cubic units.

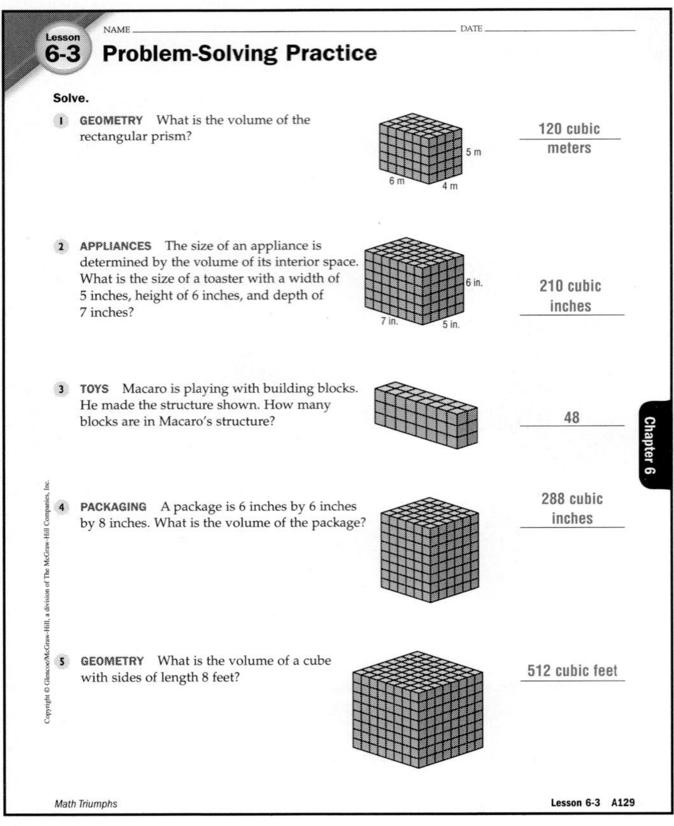

NAME ______ DATE ______

Lesson 6-3

Problem-Solving Practice

Solve.

1 **GEOMETRY** What is the volume of the rectangular prism? 120 cubic meters

2 **APPLIANCES** The size of an appliance is determined by the volume of its interior space. What is the size of a toaster with a width of 5 inches, height of 6 inches, and depth of 7 inches? 210 cubic inches

3 **TOYS** Macaro is playing with building blocks. He made the structure shown. How many blocks are in Macaro's structure? 48

4 **PACKAGING** A package is 6 inches by 6 inches by 8 inches. What is the volume of the package? 288 cubic inches

5 **GEOMETRY** What is the volume of a cube with sides of length 8 feet? 512 cubic feet

Chapter 6

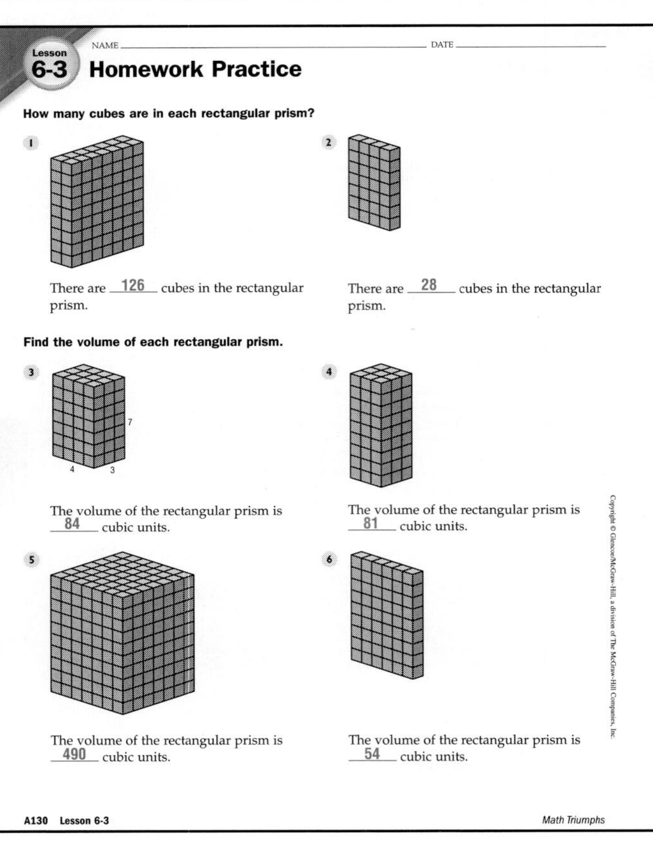

NAME ______ DATE ______

Lesson 6-3

Homework Practice

How many cubes are in each rectangular prism?

1 There are 126 cubes in the rectangular prism.

2 There are 28 cubes in the rectangular prism.

Find the volume of each rectangular prism.

3 The volume of the rectangular prism is 84 cubic units.

4 The volume of the rectangular prism is 81 cubic units.

5 The volume of the rectangular prism is 490 cubic units.

6 The volume of the rectangular prism is 54 cubic units.

Answer Key (Lesson 6-4)

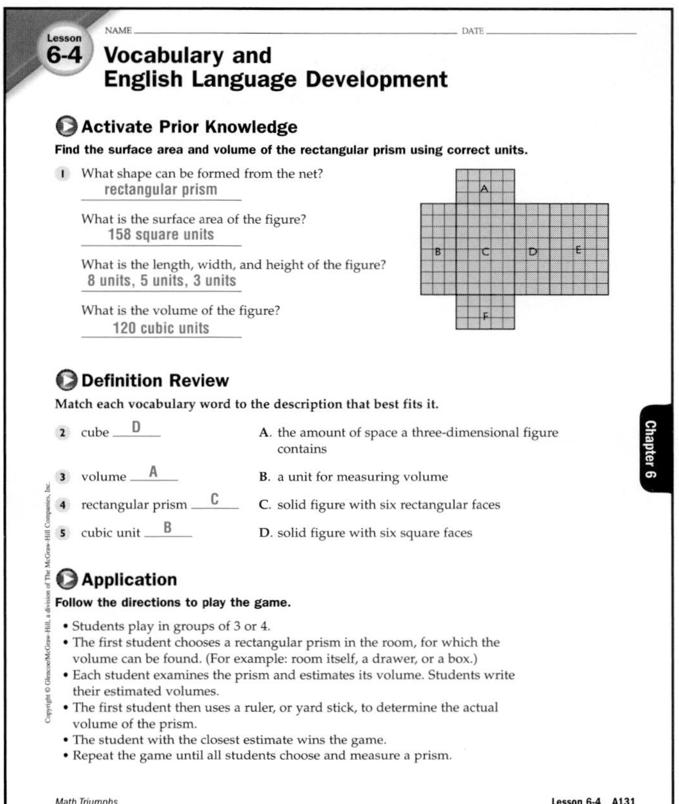

NAME ______ DATE ______

Lesson 6-4 **Vocabulary and English Language Development**

Activate Prior Knowledge

Find the surface area and volume of the rectangular prism using correct units.

1 What shape can be formed from the net? rectangular prism

What is the surface area of the figure? 158 square units

What is the length, width, and height of the figure? 8 units, 5 units, 3 units

What is the volume of the figure? 120 cubic units

Definition Review

Match each vocabulary word to the description that best fits it.

2 cube D

3 volume A

4 rectangular prism C

5 cubic unit B

A. the amount of space a three-dimensional figure contains

B. a unit for measuring volume

C. solid figure with six rectangular faces

D. solid figure with six square faces

Application

Follow the directions to play the game.

- Students play in groups of 3 or 4.
- The first student chooses a rectangular prism in the room, for which the volume can be found. (For example: room itself, a drawer, or a box.)
- Each student examines the prism and estimates its volume. Students write their estimated volumes.
- The first student then uses a ruler, or yard stick, to determine the actual volume of the prism.
- The student with the closest estimate wins the game.
- Repeat the game until all students choose and measure a prism.

Chapter 6

Math Triumphs   Lesson 6-4 A131

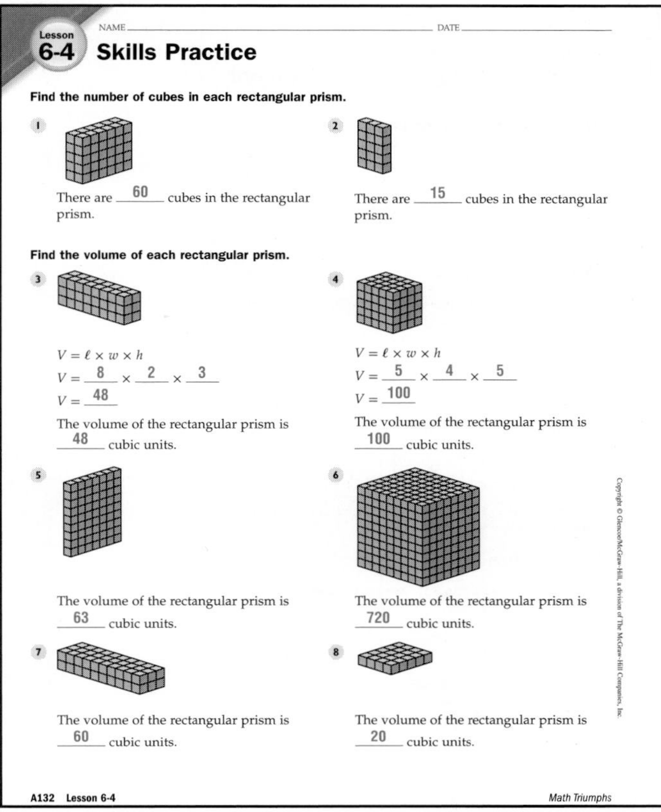

NAME ______ DATE ______

Lesson 6-4 **Skills Practice**

Find the number of cubes in each rectangular prism.

1 There are 60 cubes in the rectangular prism.

2 There are 15 cubes in the rectangular prism.

Find the volume of each rectangular prism.

3 $V = \ell \times w \times h$

$V = 8 \times 2 \times 3$

$V = 48$

The volume of the rectangular prism is 48 cubic units.

4 $V = \ell \times w \times h$

$V = 5 \times 4 \times 5$

$V = 100$

The volume of the rectangular prism is 100 cubic units.

5 The volume of the rectangular prism is 63 cubic units.

6 The volume of the rectangular prism is 720 cubic units.

7 The volume of the rectangular prism is 60 cubic units.

8 The volume of the rectangular prism is 20 cubic units.

A132 Lesson 6-4   Math Triumphs

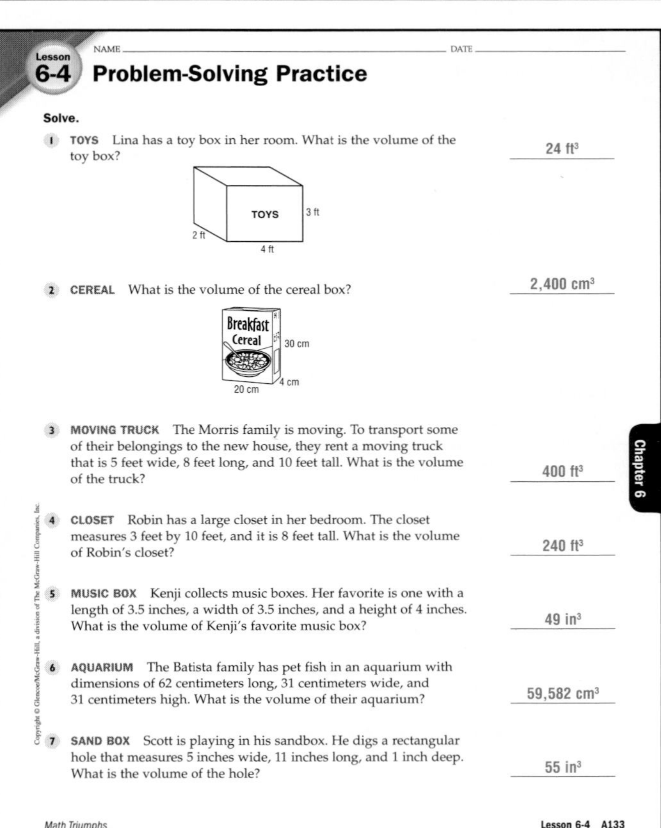

NAME ______ DATE ______

Lesson 6-4 **Problem-Solving Practice**

Solve.

1 **TOYS** Lina has a toy box in her room. What is the volume of the toy box? 24 ft^3

2 **CEREAL** What is the volume of the cereal box? $2{,}400 \text{ cm}^3$

3 **MOVING TRUCK** The Morris family is moving. To transport some of their belongings to the new house, they rent a moving truck that is 5 feet wide, 8 feet long, and 10 feet tall. What is the volume of the truck? 400 ft^3

4 **CLOSET** Robin has a large closet in her bedroom. The closet measures 3 feet by 10 feet, and it is 8 feet tall. What is the volume of Robin's closet? 240 ft^3

5 **MUSIC BOX** Kenji collects music boxes. Her favorite is one with a length of 3.5 inches, a width of 3.5 inches, and a height of 4 inches. What is the volume of Kenji's favorite music box? 49 in^3

6 **AQUARIUM** The Batista family has pet fish in an aquarium with dimensions of 62 centimeters long, 31 centimeters wide, and 31 centimeters high. What is the volume of their aquarium? $59{,}582 \text{ cm}^3$

7 **SAND BOX** Scott is playing in his sandbox. He digs a rectangular hole that measures 5 inches wide, 11 inches long, and 1 inch deep. What is the volume of the hole? 55 in^3

Chapter 6

Math Triumphs   Lesson 6-4 A133

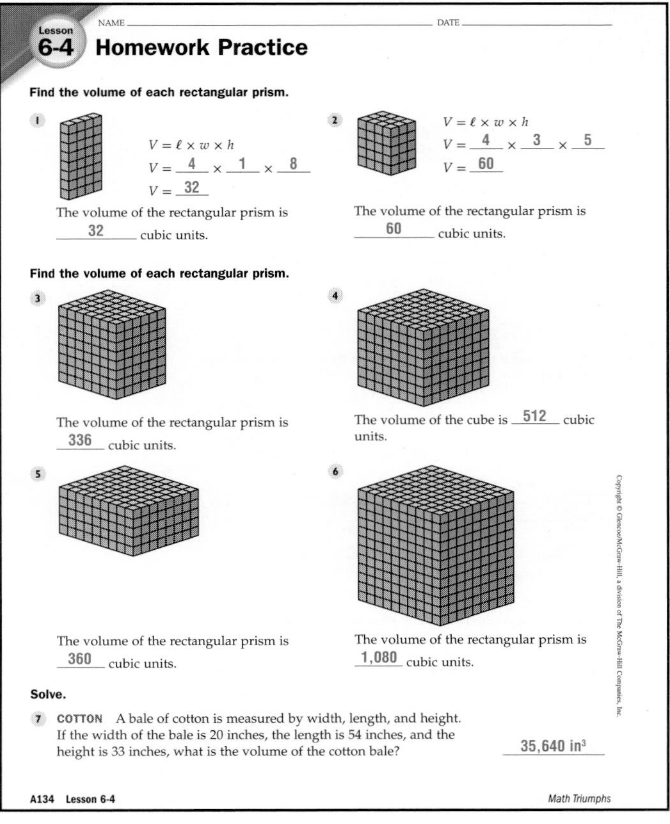

NAME ______ DATE ______

Lesson 6-4 **Homework Practice**

Find the volume of each rectangular prism.

1 $V = \ell \times w \times h$

$V = 4 \times 1 \times 8$

$V = 32$

The volume of the rectangular prism is 32 cubic units.

2 $V = \ell \times w \times h$

$V = 4 \times 3 \times 5$

$V = 60$

The volume of the rectangular prism is 60 cubic units.

Find the volume of each rectangular prism.

3 The volume of the rectangular prism is 336 cubic units.

4 The volume of the cube is 512 cubic units.

5 The volume of the rectangular prism is 360 cubic units.

6 The volume of the rectangular prism is 1,080 cubic units.

Solve.

7 **COTTON** A bale of cotton is measured by width, length, and height. If the width of the bale is 20 inches, the length is 54 inches, and the height is 33 inches, what is the volume of the cotton bale? $35{,}640 \text{ in}^3$

A134 Lesson 6-4   Math Triumphs

Answer Key (Lesson 7-1)

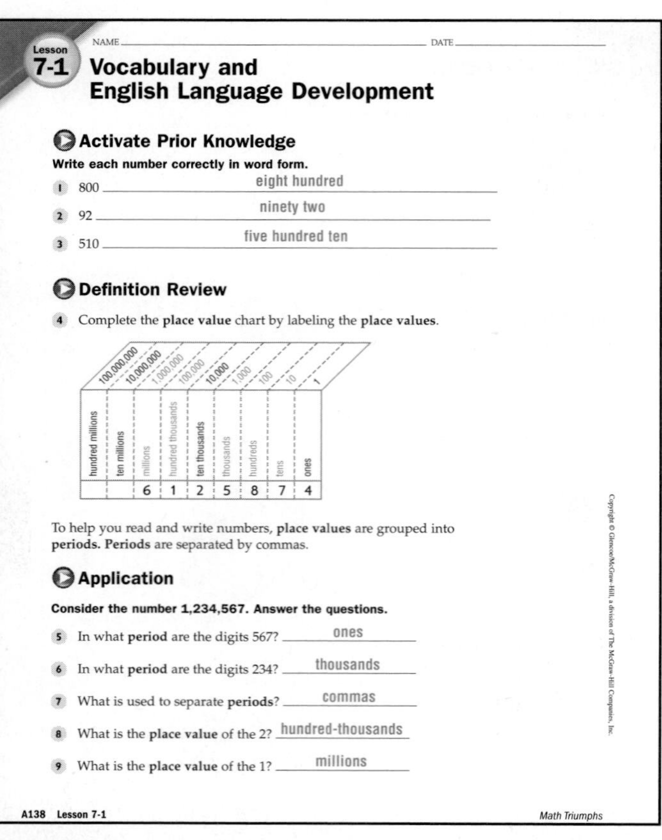

NAME ______ DATE ______

Lesson 7-1 Vocabulary and English Language Development

Activate Prior Knowledge

Write each number correctly in word form.

1. 800 eight hundred
2. 92 ninety two
3. 510 five hundred ten

Definition Review

4. Complete the **place value** chart by labeling the **place values**.

100,000,000	10,000,000	1,000,000	100,000	10,000	1,000	100	10	1
hundred millions	ten millions	millions	hundred thousands	ten thousands	thousands	hundreds	tens	ones
		6	1	2	5	8	7	4

To help you read and write numbers, **place values** are grouped into **periods. Periods** are separated by commas.

Application

Consider the number 1,234,567. Answer the questions.

5. In what **period** are the digits 567? ones
6. In what **period** are the digits 234? thousands
7. What is used to separate **periods**? commas
8. What is the **place value** of the 2? hundred-thousands
9. What is the **place value** of the 1? millions

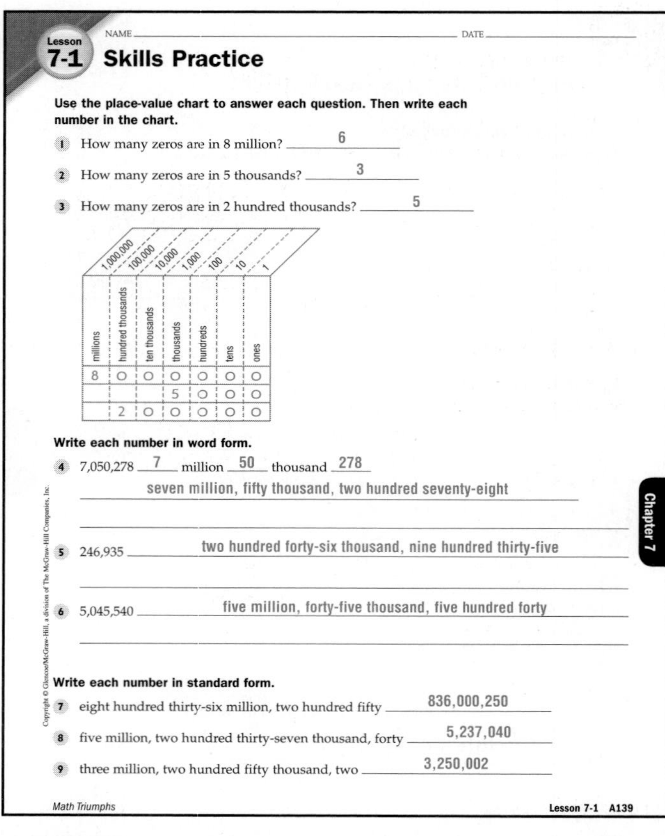

NAME ______ DATE ______

Lesson 7-1 Skills Practice

Use the place-value chart to answer each question. Then write each number in the chart.

1. How many zeros are in 8 million? 6
2. How many zeros are in 5 thousands? 3
3. How many zeros are in 2 hundred thousands? 5

1,000,000	100,000	10,000	1,000	100	10	1
millions	hundred thousands	ten thousands	thousands	hundreds	tens	ones
8	0	0	0	0	0	0
			5	0	0	0
	2	0	0	0	0	0

Write each number in word form.

4. 7,050,278 7 million 50 thousand 278
seven million, fifty thousand, two hundred seventy-eight
5. 246,935 two hundred forty-six thousand, nine hundred thirty-five
6. 5,045,540 five million, forty-five thousand, five hundred forty

Write each number in standard form.

7. eight hundred thirty-six million, two hundred fifty 836,000,250
8. five million, two hundred thirty-seven thousand, forty 5,237,040
9. three million, two hundred fifty thousand, two 3,250,002

Chapter 7

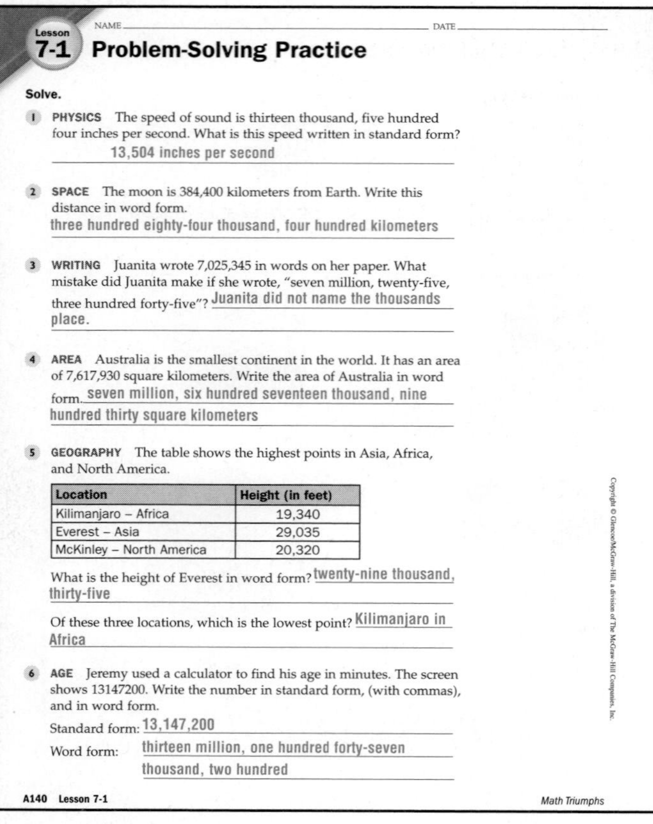

NAME ______ DATE ______

Lesson 7-1 Problem-Solving Practice

Solve.

1. **PHYSICS** The speed of sound is thirteen thousand, five hundred four inches per second. What is this speed written in standard form?
13,504 inches per second
2. **SPACE** The moon is 384,400 kilometers from Earth. Write this distance in word form.
three hundred eighty-four thousand, four hundred kilometers
3. **WRITING** Juanita wrote 7,025,345 in words on her paper. What mistake did Juanita make if she wrote, "seven million, twenty-five, three hundred forty-five"? Juanita did not name the thousands place.
4. **AREA** Australia is the smallest continent in the world. It has an area of 7,617,930 square kilometers. Write the area of Australia in word form. seven million, six hundred seventeen thousand, nine hundred thirty square kilometers
5. **GEOGRAPHY** The table shows the highest points in Asia, Africa, and North America.

Location	Height (in feet)
Kilimanjaro – Africa	19,340
Everest – Asia	29,035
McKinley – North America	20,320

What is the height of Everest in word form? twenty-nine thousand, thirty-five

Of these three locations, which is the lowest point? Kilimanjaro in Africa

6. **AGE** Jeremy used a calculator to find his age in minutes. The screen shows 13147200. Write the number in standard form, (with commas), and in word form.
Standard form: 13,147,200
Word form: thirteen million, one hundred forty-seven thousand, two hundred

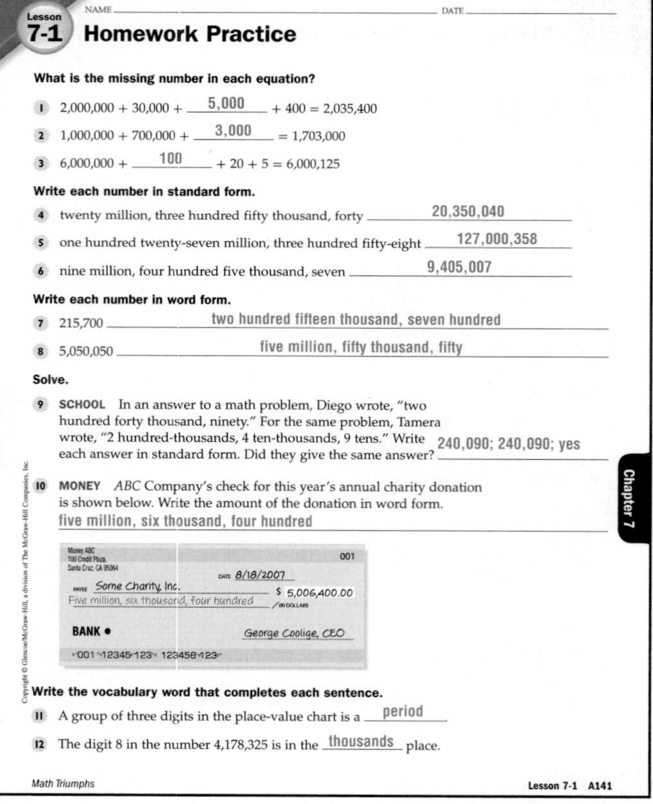

NAME ______ DATE ______

Lesson 7-1 Homework Practice

What is the missing number in each equation?

1. 2,000,000 + 30,000 + 5,000 + 400 = 2,035,400
2. 1,000,000 + 700,000 + 3,000 = 1,703,000
3. 6,000,000 + 100 + 20 + 5 = 6,000,125

Write each number in standard form.

4. twenty million, three hundred fifty thousand, forty 20,350,040
5. one hundred twenty-seven million, three hundred fifty-eight 127,000,358
6. nine million, four hundred five thousand, seven 9,405,007

Write each number in word form.

7. 215,700 two hundred fifteen thousand, seven hundred
8. 5,050,050 five million, fifty thousand, fifty

Solve.

9. **SCHOOL** In an answer to a math problem, Diego wrote, "two hundred forty thousand, ninety." For the same problem, Tamera wrote, "2 hundred-thousands, 4 ten-thousands, 9 tens." Write each answer in standard form. Did they give the same answer? 240,090; 240,090; yes
10. **MONEY** *ABC* Company's check for this year's annual charity donation is shown below. Write the amount of the donation in word form.
five million, six thousand, four hundred

Money ABC 001
DATE 8/18/2007
PAYEE Some Charity, Inc. $ 5,006,400.00
Five million, six thousand, four hundred /00 DOLLARS
BANK ● George Coolige, CEO
⑈001⑈12345⑆123⑈ 123456⑆123⑈

Write the vocabulary word that completes each sentence.

11. A group of three digits in the place-value chart is a period.
12. The digit 8 in the number 4,178,325 is in the thousands place.

Chapter 7

Answer Key (Lesson 7-2)

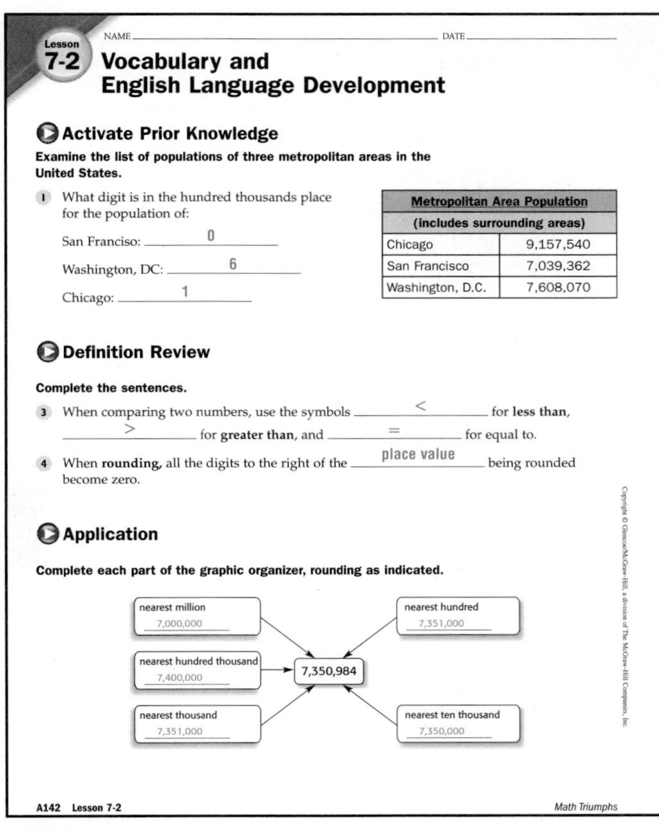

NAME ______ DATE ______

Lesson 7-2 **Vocabulary and English Language Development**

Activate Prior Knowledge

Examine the list of populations of three metropolitan areas in the United States.

1 What digit is in the hundred thousands place for the population of:

San Francisco: 0

Washington, DC: 6

Chicago: 1

Metropolitan Area Population (includes surrounding areas)	
Chicago	9,157,540
San Francisco	7,039,362
Washington, D.C.	7,608,070

Definition Review

Complete the sentences.

3 When comparing two numbers, use the symbols < for **less than**, > for **greater than**, and = for equal to.

4 When **rounding**, all the digits to the right of the place value being rounded become zero.

Application

Complete each part of the graphic organizer, rounding as indicated.

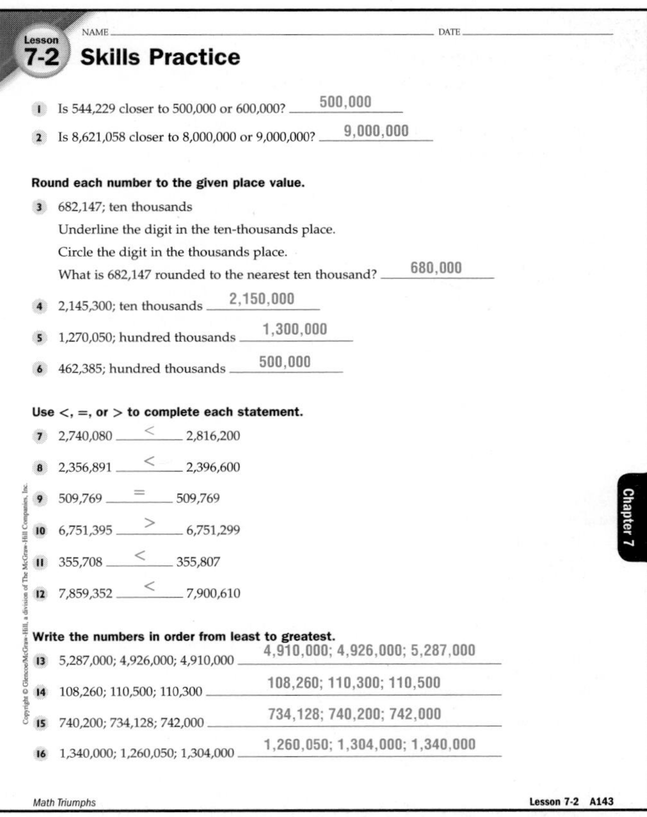

NAME ______ DATE ______

Lesson 7-2 **Skills Practice**

1 Is 544,229 closer to 500,000 or 600,000? 500,000

2 Is 8,621,058 closer to 8,000,000 or 9,000,000? 9,000,000

Round each number to the given place value.

3 682,147; ten thousands

Underline the digit in the ten-thousands place.

Circle the digit in the thousands place.

What is 682,147 rounded to the nearest ten thousand? 680,000

4 2,145,300; ten thousands 2,150,000

5 1,270,050; hundred thousands 1,300,000

6 462,385; hundred thousands 500,000

Use <, =, or > to complete each statement.

7 2,740,080 < 2,816,200

8 2,356,891 < 2,396,600

9 509,769 = 509,769

10 6,751,395 > 6,751,299

11 355,708 < 355,807

12 7,859,352 < 7,900,610

Write the numbers in order from least to greatest.

13 5,287,000; 4,926,000; 4,910,000 4,910,000; 4,926,000; 5,287,000

14 108,260; 110,500; 110,300 108,260; 110,300; 110,500

15 740,200; 734,128; 742,000 734,128; 740,200; 742,000

16 1,340,000; 1,260,050; 1,304,000 1,260,050; 1,304,000; 1,340,000

Chapter 7

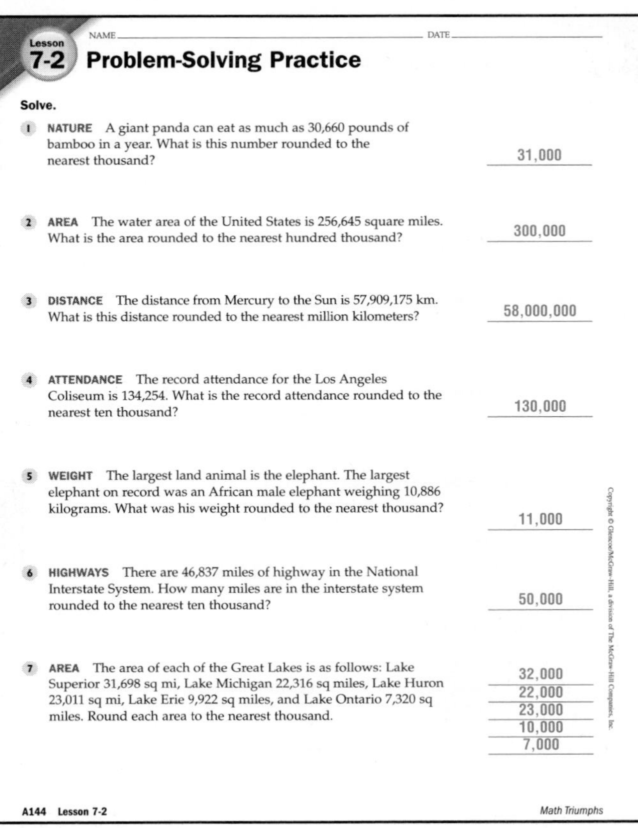

NAME ______ DATE ______

Lesson 7-2 **Problem-Solving Practice**

Solve.

1 **NATURE** A giant panda can eat as much as 30,660 pounds of bamboo in a year. What is this number rounded to the nearest thousand? 31,000

2 **AREA** The water area of the United States is 256,645 square miles. What is the area rounded to the nearest hundred thousand? 300,000

3 **DISTANCE** The distance from Mercury to the Sun is 57,909,175 km. What is this distance rounded to the nearest million kilometers? 58,000,000

4 **ATTENDANCE** The record attendance for the Los Angeles Coliseum is 134,254. What is the record attendance rounded to the nearest ten thousand? 130,000

5 **WEIGHT** The largest land animal is the elephant. The largest elephant on record was an African male elephant weighing 10,886 kilograms. What was his weight rounded to the nearest thousand? 11,000

6 **HIGHWAYS** There are 46,837 miles of highway in the National Interstate System. How many miles are in the interstate system rounded to the nearest ten thousand? 50,000

7 **AREA** The area of each of the Great Lakes is as follows: Lake Superior 31,698 sq mi, Lake Michigan 22,316 sq miles, Lake Huron 23,011 sq mi, Lake Erie 9,922 sq miles, and Lake Ontario 7,320 sq miles. Round each area to the nearest thousand. 32,000; 22,000; 23,000; 10,000; 7,000

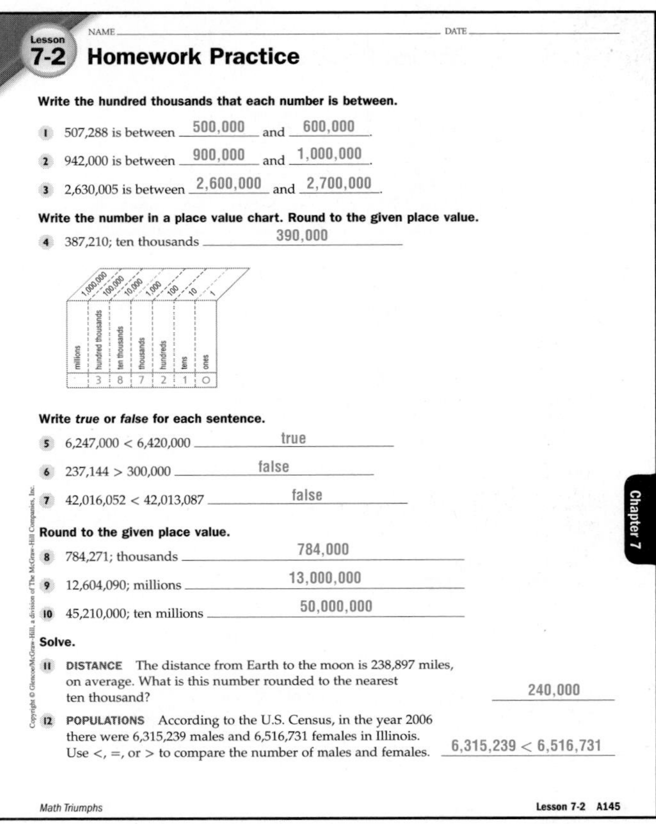

NAME ______ DATE ______

Lesson 7-2 **Homework Practice**

Write the hundred thousands that each number is between.

1 507,288 is between 500,000 and 600,000.

2 942,000 is between 900,000 and 1,000,000.

3 2,630,005 is between 2,600,000 and 2,700,000.

Write the number in a place value chart. Round to the given place value.

4 387,210; ten thousands 390,000

1,000,000	100,000	10,000	1,000	100	10	1
millions	hundred thousands	ten thousands	thousands	hundreds	tens	ones
	3	8	7	2	1	0

Write *true* or *false* for each sentence.

5 6,247,000 < 6,420,000 true

6 237,144 > 300,000 false

7 42,016,052 < 42,013,087 false

Round to the given place value.

8 784,271; thousands 784,000

9 12,604,090; millions 13,000,000

10 45,210,000; ten millions 50,000,000

Solve.

11 **DISTANCE** The distance from Earth to the moon is 238,897 miles, on average. What is this number rounded to the nearest ten thousand? 240,000

12 **POPULATIONS** According to the U.S. Census, in the year 2006 there were 6,315,239 males and 6,516,731 females in Illinois. Use <, =, or > to compare the number of males and females. 6,315,239 < 6,516,731

Chapter 7

Answer Key (Lesson 7-3)

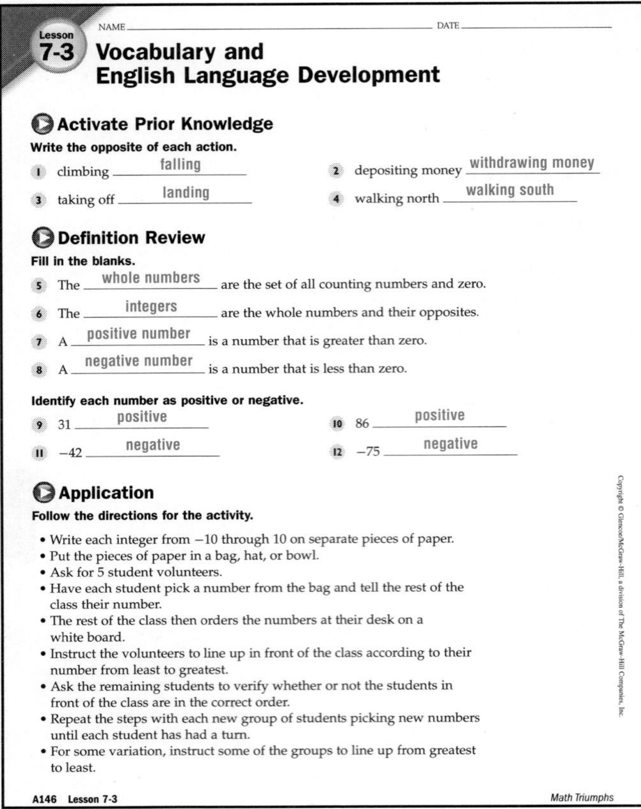

Lesson 7-3 NAME ______ DATE ______

Vocabulary and English Language Development

Activate Prior Knowledge

Write the opposite of each action.

1. climbing falling
2. depositing money withdrawing money
3. taking off landing
4. walking north walking south

Definition Review

Fill in the blanks.

5. The whole numbers are the set of all counting numbers and zero.
6. The integers are the whole numbers and their opposites.
7. A positive number is a number that is greater than zero.
8. A negative number is a number that is less than zero.

Identify each number as positive or negative.

9. 31 positive
10. 86 positive
11. −42 negative
12. −75 negative

Application

Follow the directions for the activity.

- Write each integer from −10 through 10 on separate pieces of paper.
- Put the pieces of paper in a bag, hat, or bowl.
- Ask for 5 student volunteers.
- Have each student pick a number from the bag and tell the rest of the class their number.
- The rest of the class then orders the numbers at their desk on a white board.
- Instruct the volunteers to line up in front of the class according to their number from least to greatest.
- Ask the remaining students to verify whether or not the students in front of the class are in the correct order.
- Repeat the steps with each new group of students picking new numbers until each student has had a turn.
- For some variation, instruct some of the groups to line up from greatest to least.

A146 Lesson 7-3 Math Triumphs

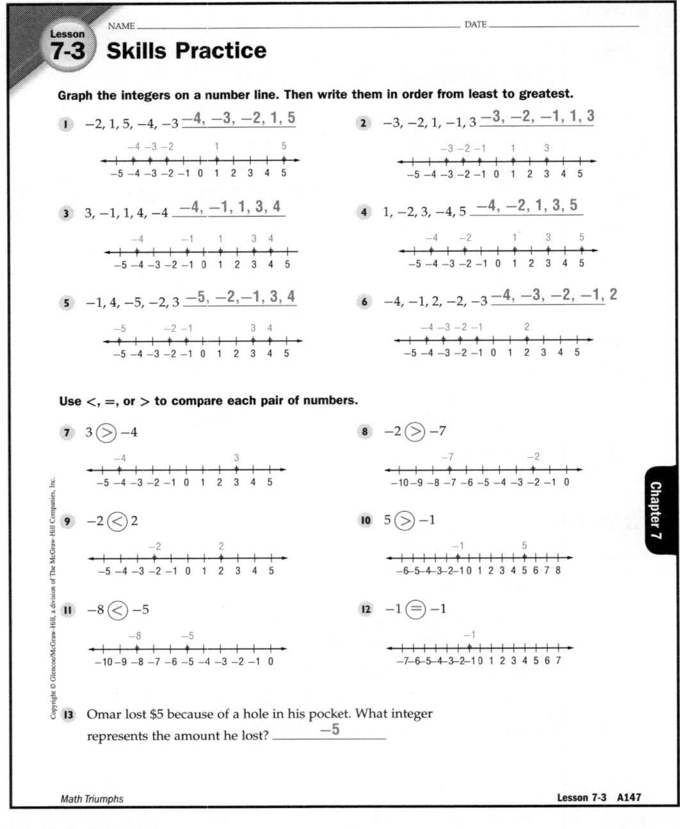

Lesson 7-3 NAME ______ DATE ______

Skills Practice

Graph the integers on a number line. Then write them in order from least to greatest.

1. −2, 1, 5, −4, −3 −4, −3, −2, 1, 5
2. −3, −2, 1, −1, 3 −3, −2, −1, 1, 3
3. 3, −1, 1, 4, −4 −4, −1, 1, 3, 4
4. 1, −2, 3, −4, 5 −4, −2, 1, 3, 5
5. −1, 4, −5, −2, 3 −5, −2, −1, 3, 4
6. −4, −1, 2, −2, −3 −4, −3, −2, −1, 2

Use <, =, or > to compare each pair of numbers.

7. 3 (>) −4
8. −2 (>) −7
9. −2 (<) 2
10. 5 (>) −1
11. −8 (<) −5
12. −1 (=) −1
13. Omar lost $5 because of a hole in his pocket. What integer represents the amount he lost? −5

Chapter 7

Math Triumphs Lesson 7-3 A147

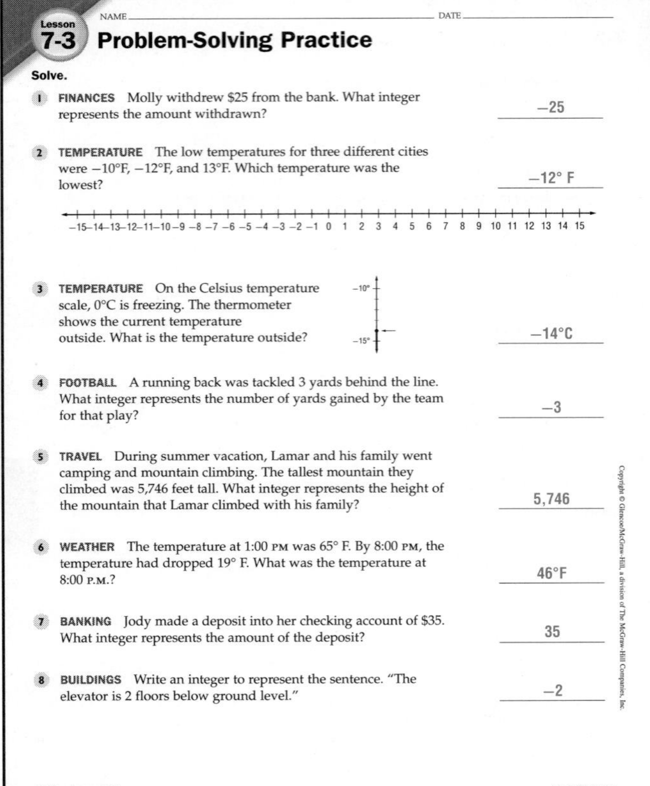

Lesson 7-3 NAME ______ DATE ______

Problem-Solving Practice

Solve.

1. **FINANCES** Molly withdrew $25 from the bank. What integer represents the amount withdrawn? −25
2. **TEMPERATURE** The low temperatures for three different cities were −10°F, −12°F, and 13°F. Which temperature was the lowest? −12° F
3. **TEMPERATURE** On the Celsius temperature scale, 0°C is freezing. The thermometer shows the current temperature outside. What is the temperature outside? −14°C
4. **FOOTBALL** A running back was tackled 3 yards behind the line. What integer represents the number of yards gained by the team for that play? −3
5. **TRAVEL** During summer vacation, Lamar and his family went camping and mountain climbing. The tallest mountain they climbed was 5,746 feet tall. What integer represents the height of the mountain that Lamar climbed with his family? 5,746
6. **WEATHER** The temperature at 1:00 PM was 65° F. By 8:00 PM, the temperature had dropped 19° F. What was the temperature at 8:00 P.M.? 46°F
7. **BANKING** Jody made a deposit into her checking account of $35. What integer represents the amount of the deposit? 35
8. **BUILDINGS** Write an integer to represent the sentence. "The elevator is 2 floors below ground level." −2

A148 Lesson 7-3 Math Triumphs

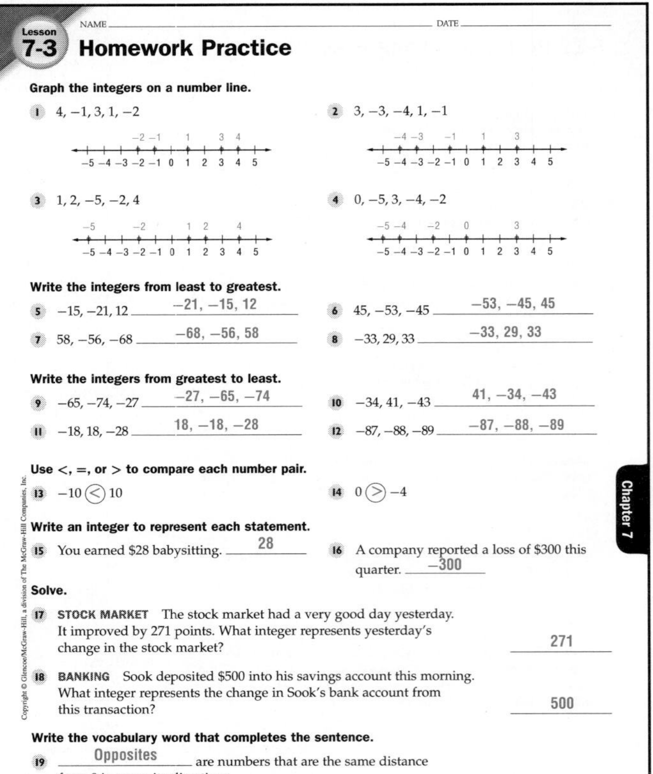

Lesson 7-3 NAME ______ DATE ______

Homework Practice

Graph the integers on a number line.

1. 4, −1, 3, 1, −2
2. 3, −3, −4, 1, −1
3. 1, 2, −5, −2, 4
4. 0, −5, 3, −4, −2

Write the integers from least to greatest.

5. −15, −21, 12 −21, −15, 12
6. 45, −53, −45 −53, −45, 45
7. 58, −56, −68 −68, −56, 58
8. −33, 29, 33 −33, 29, 33

Write the integers from greatest to least.

9. −65, −74, −27 −27, −65, −74
10. −34, 41, −43 41, −34, −43
11. −18, 18, −28 18, −18, −28
12. −87, −88, −89 −87, −88, −89

Use <, =, or > to compare each number pair.

13. −10 (<) 10
14. 0 (>) −4

Write an integer to represent each statement.

15. You earned $28 babysitting. 28
16. A company reported a loss of $300 this quarter. −300

Solve.

17. **STOCK MARKET** The stock market had a very good day yesterday. It improved by 271 points. What integer represents yesterday's change in the stock market? 271
18. **BANKING** Sook deposited $500 into his savings account this morning. What integer represents the change in Sook's bank account from this transaction? 500

Write the vocabulary word that completes the sentence.

19. Opposites are numbers that are the same distance from 0 in opposite directions.

Chapter 7

Math Triumphs Lesson 7-3 A149

Answer Key (Lesson 7-4)

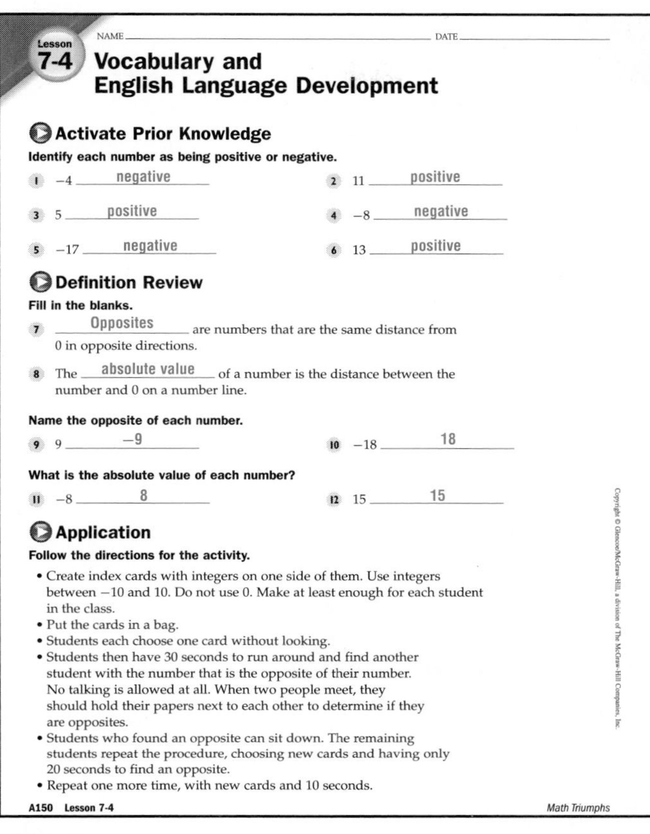

NAME ________ DATE ________

Lesson 7-4 **Vocabulary and English Language Development**

Activate Prior Knowledge

Identify each number as being positive or negative.

1. −4 negative
2. 11 positive
3. 5 positive
4. −8 negative
5. −17 negative
6. 13 positive

Definition Review

Fill in the blanks.

7. Opposites are numbers that are the same distance from 0 in opposite directions.
8. The absolute value of a number is the distance between the number and 0 on a number line.

Name the opposite of each number.

9. 9 −9
10. −18 18

What is the absolute value of each number?

11. −8 8
12. 15 15

Application

Follow the directions for the activity.

- Create index cards with integers on one side of them. Use integers between −10 and 10. Do not use 0. Make at least enough for each student in the class.
- Put the cards in a bag.
- Students each choose one card without looking.
- Students then have 30 seconds to run around and find another student with the number that is the opposite of their number. No talking is allowed at all. When two people meet, they should hold their papers next to each other to determine if they are opposites.
- Students who found an opposite can sit down. The remaining students repeat the procedure, choosing new cards and having only 20 seconds to find an opposite.
- Repeat one more time, with new cards and 10 seconds.

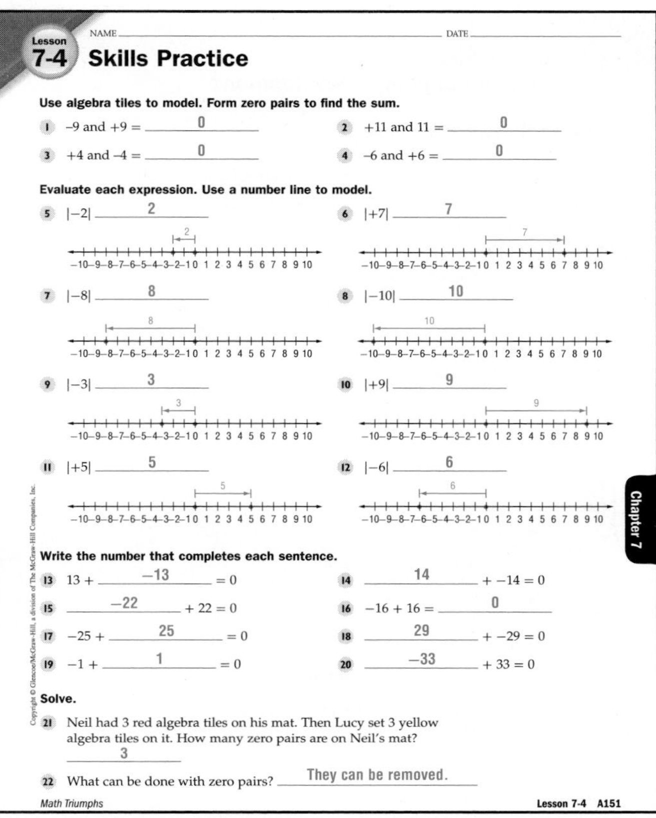

NAME ________ DATE ________

Lesson 7-4 **Skills Practice**

Use algebra tiles to model. Form zero pairs to find the sum.

1. −9 and +9 = 0
2. +11 and 11 = 0
3. +4 and −4 = 0
4. −6 and +6 = 0

Evaluate each expression. Use a number line to model.

5. |−2| 2
6. |+7| 7
7. |−8| 8
8. |−10| 10
9. |−3| 3
10. |+9| 9
11. |+5| 5
12. |−6| 6

Write the number that completes each sentence.

13. 13 + −13 = 0
14. 14 + −14 = 0
15. −22 + 22 = 0
16. −16 + 16 = 0
17. −25 + 25 = 0
18. 29 + −29 = 0
19. −1 + 1 = 0
20. −33 + 33 = 0

Solve.

21. Neil had 3 red algebra tiles on his mat. Then Lucy set 3 yellow algebra tiles on it. How many zero pairs are on Neil's mat? 3
22. What can be done with zero pairs? They can be removed.

Chapter 7

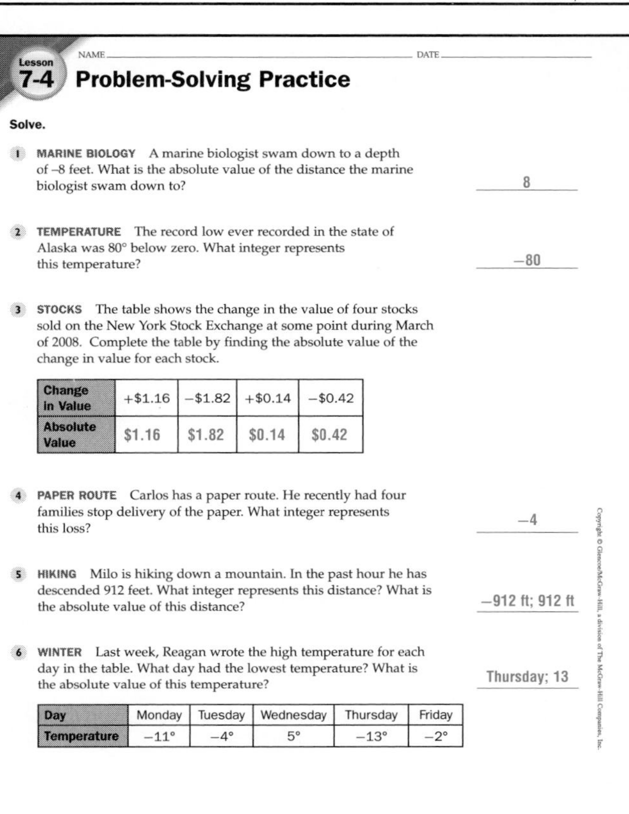

NAME ________ DATE ________

Lesson 7-4 **Problem-Solving Practice**

Solve.

1. **MARINE BIOLOGY** A marine biologist swam down to a depth of −8 feet. What is the absolute value of the distance the marine biologist swam down to? 8
2. **TEMPERATURE** The record low ever recorded in the state of Alaska was 80° below zero. What integer represents this temperature? −80
3. **STOCKS** The table shows the change in the value of four stocks sold on the New York Stock Exchange at some point during March of 2008. Complete the table by finding the absolute value of the change in value for each stock.

Change in Value	+$1.16	−$1.82	+$0.14	−$0.42
Absolute Value	$1.16	$1.82	$0.14	$0.42

4. **PAPER ROUTE** Carlos has a paper route. He recently had four families stop delivery of the paper. What integer represents this loss? −4
5. **HIKING** Milo is hiking down a mountain. In the past hour he has descended 912 feet. What integer represents this distance? What is the absolute value of this distance? −912 ft; 912 ft
6. **WINTER** Last week, Reagan wrote the high temperature for each day in the table. What day had the lowest temperature? What is the absolute value of this temperature? Thursday; 13

Day	Monday	Tuesday	Wednesday	Thursday	Friday
Temperature	−11°	−4°	5°	−13°	−2°

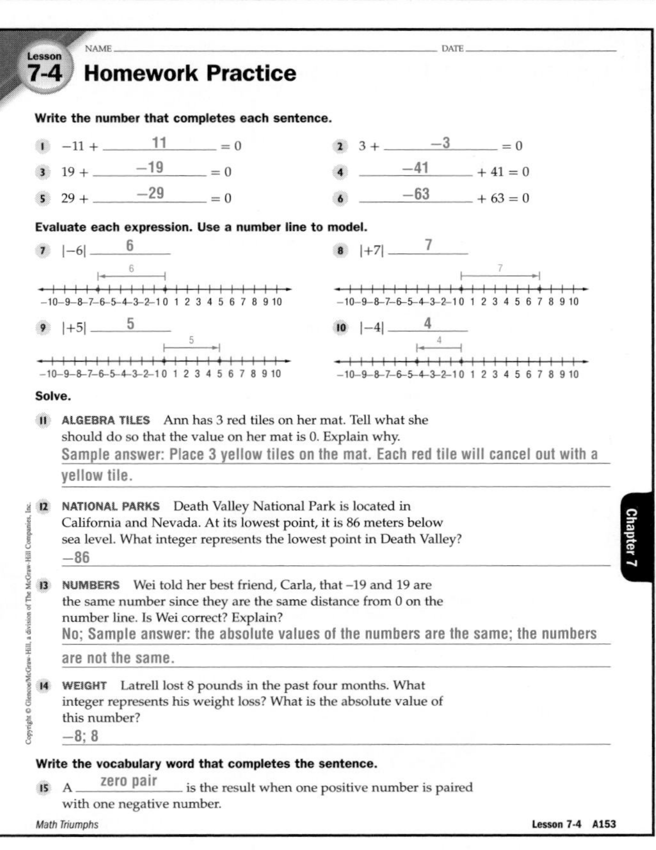

NAME ________ DATE ________

Lesson 7-4 **Homework Practice**

Write the number that completes each sentence.

1. −11 + 11 = 0
2. 3 + −3 = 0
3. 19 + −19 = 0
4. −41 + 41 = 0
5. 29 + −29 = 0
6. −63 + 63 = 0

Evaluate each expression. Use a number line to model.

7. |−6| 6
8. |+7| 7
9. |+5| 5
10. |−4| 4

Solve.

11. **ALGEBRA TILES** Ann has 3 red tiles on her mat. Tell what she should do so that the value on her mat is 0. Explain why. Sample answer: Place 3 yellow tiles on the mat. Each red tile will cancel out with a yellow tile.
12. **NATIONAL PARKS** Death Valley National Park is located in California and Nevada. At its lowest point, it is 86 meters below sea level. What integer represents the lowest point in Death Valley? −86
13. **NUMBERS** Wei told her best friend, Carla, that −19 and 19 are the same number since they are the same distance from 0 on the number line. Is Wei correct? Explain? No; Sample answer: the absolute values of the numbers are the same; the numbers are not the same.
14. **WEIGHT** Latrell lost 8 pounds in the past four months. What integer represents his weight loss? What is the absolute value of this number? −8; 8

Write the vocabulary word that completes the sentence.

15. A zero pair is the result when one positive number is paired with one negative number.

Chapter 7

Answer Key (Lesson 8-1)

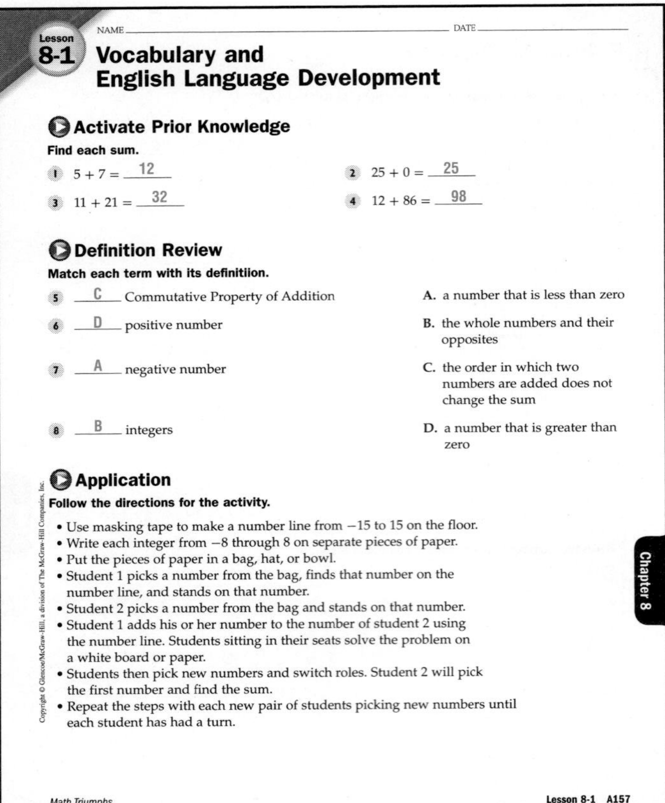

Lesson 8-1 NAME ______ DATE ______

Vocabulary and English Language Development

Activate Prior Knowledge

Find each sum.

1. 5 + 7 = 12
2. 25 + 0 = 25
3. 11 + 21 = 32
4. 12 + 86 = 98

Definition Review

Match each term with its definitiion.

5. C Commutative Property of Addition
6. D positive number
7. A negative number
8. B integers

A. a number that is less than zero
B. the whole numbers and their opposites
C. the order in which two numbers are added does not change the sum
D. a number that is greater than zero

Application

Follow the directions for the activity.

- Use masking tape to make a number line from –15 to 15 on the floor.
- Write each integer from –8 through 8 on separate pieces of paper.
- Put the pieces of paper in a bag, hat, or bowl.
- Student 1 picks a number from the bag, finds that number on the number line, and stands on that number.
- Student 2 picks a number from the bag and stands on that number.
- Student 1 adds his or her number to the number of student 2 using the number line. Students sitting in their seats solve the problem on a white board or paper.
- Students then pick new numbers and switch roles. Student 2 will pick the first number and find the sum.
- Repeat the steps with each new pair of students picking new numbers until each student has had a turn.

Chapter 8

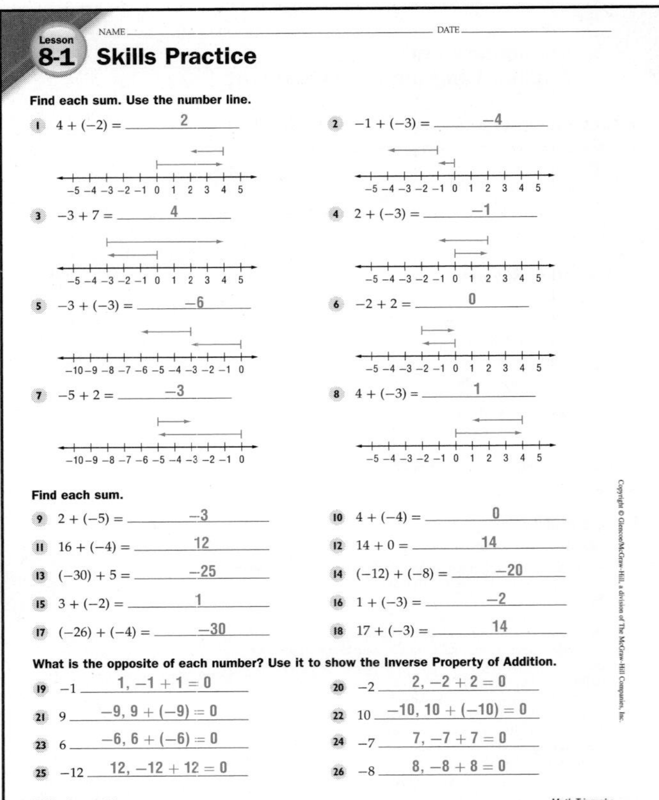

Lesson 8-1 NAME ______ DATE ______

Skills Practice

Find each sum. Use the number line.

1. 4 + (–2) = 2
2. –1 + (–3) = –4
3. –3 + 7 = 4
4. 2 + (–3) = –1
5. –3 + (–3) = –6
6. –2 + 2 = 0
7. –5 + 2 = –3
8. 4 + (–3) = 1

Find each sum.

9. 2 + (–5) = –3
10. 4 + (–4) = 0
11. 16 + (–4) = 12
12. 14 + 0 = 14
13. (–30) + 5 = –25
14. (–12) + (–8) = –20
15. 3 + (–2) = 1
16. 1 + (–3) = –2
17. (–26) + (–4) = –30
18. 17 + (–3) = 14

What is the opposite of each number? Use it to show the Inverse Property of Addition.

19. –1 1, –1 + 1 = 0
20. –2 2, –2 + 2 = 0
21. 9 –9, 9 + (–9) = 0
22. 10 –10, 10 + (–10) = 0
23. 6 –6, 6 + (–6) = 0
24. –7 7, –7 + 7 = 0
25. –12 12, –12 + 12 = 0
26. –8 8, –8 + 8 = 0

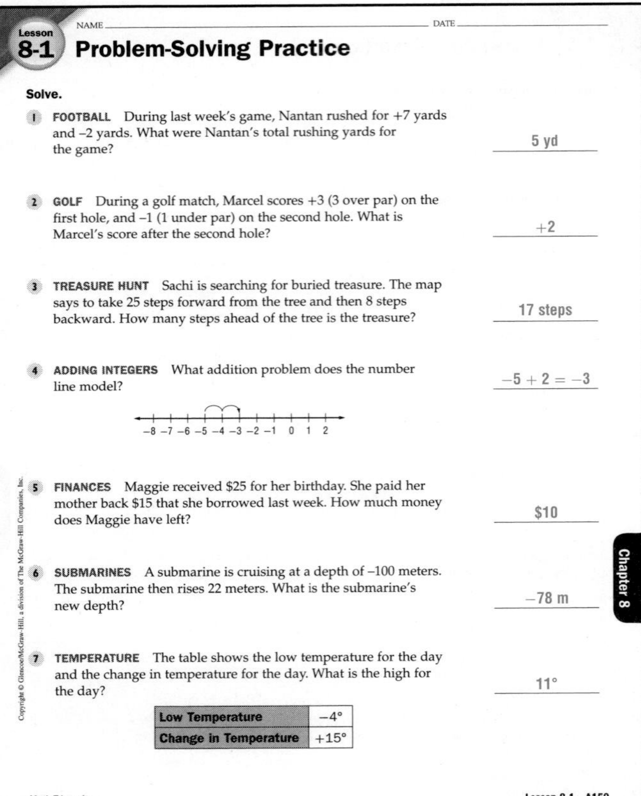

Lesson 8-1 NAME ______ DATE ______

Problem-Solving Practice

Solve.

1. **FOOTBALL** During last week's game, Nantan rushed for +7 yards and –2 yards. What were Nantan's total rushing yards for the game? 5 yd
2. **GOLF** During a golf match, Marcel scores +3 (3 over par) on the first hole, and –1 (1 under par) on the second hole. What is Marcel's score after the second hole? +2
3. **TREASURE HUNT** Sachi is searching for buried treasure. The map says to take 25 steps forward from the tree and then 8 steps backward. How many steps ahead of the tree is the treasure? 17 steps
4. **ADDING INTEGERS** What addition problem does the number line model? –5 + 2 = –3
5. **FINANCES** Maggie received $25 for her birthday. She paid her mother back $15 that she borrowed last week. How much money does Maggie have left? $10
6. **SUBMARINES** A submarine is cruising at a depth of –100 meters. The submarine then rises 22 meters. What is the submarine's new depth? –78 m
7. **TEMPERATURE** The table shows the low temperature for the day and the change in temperature for the day. What is the high for the day? 11°

Low Temperature	–4°
Change in Temperature	+15°

Chapter 8

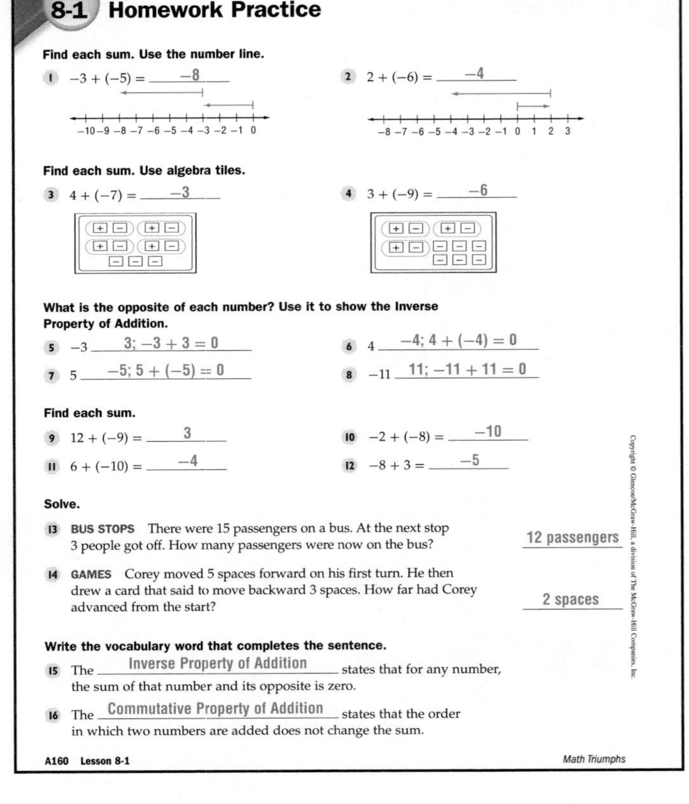

Lesson 8-1 NAME ______ DATE ______

Homework Practice

Find each sum. Use the number line.

1. –3 + (–5) = –8
2. 2 + (–6) = –4

Find each sum. Use algebra tiles.

3. 4 + (–7) = –3
4. 3 + (–9) = –6

What is the opposite of each number? Use it to show the Inverse Property of Addition.

5. –3 3; –3 + 3 = 0
6. 4 –4; 4 + (–4) = 0
7. 5 –5; 5 + (–5) = 0
8. –11 11; –11 + 11 = 0

Find each sum.

9. 12 + (–9) = 3
10. –2 + (–8) = –10
11. 6 + (–10) = –4
12. –8 + 3 = –5

Solve.

13. **BUS STOPS** There were 15 passengers on a bus. At the next stop 3 people got off. How many passengers were now on the bus? 12 passengers
14. **GAMES** Corey moved 5 spaces forward on his first turn. He then drew a card that said to move backward 3 spaces. How far had Corey advanced from the start? 2 spaces

Write the vocabulary word that completes the sentence.

15. The Inverse Property of Addition states that for any number, the sum of that number and its opposite is zero.
16. The Commutative Property of Addition states that the order in which two numbers are added does not change the sum.

Answer Key (Lesson 8-2)

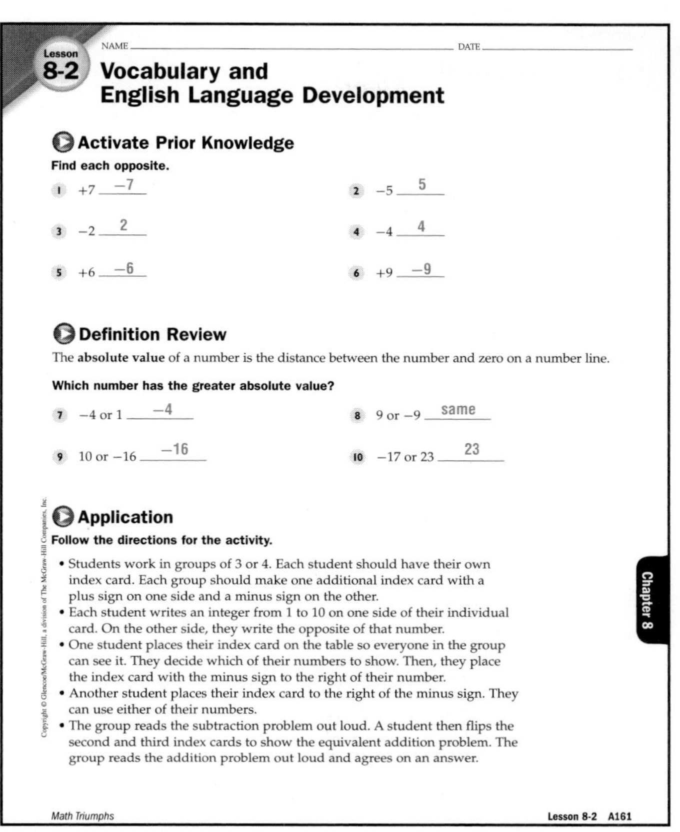

NAME ______ DATE ______

Lesson 8-2 **Vocabulary and English Language Development**

Activate Prior Knowledge

Find each opposite.

1. +7 ___−7___
2. −5 ___5___
3. −2 ___2___
4. −4 ___4___
5. +6 ___−6___
6. +9 ___−9___

Definition Review

The **absolute value** of a number is the distance between the number and zero on a number line.

Which number has the greater absolute value?

7. −4 or 1 ___−4___
8. 9 or −9 ___same___
9. 10 or −16 ___−16___
10. −17 or 23 ___23___

Application

Follow the directions for the activity.

- Students work in groups of 3 or 4. Each student should have their own index card. Each group should make one additional index card with a plus sign on one side and a minus sign on the other.
- Each student writes an integer from 1 to 10 on one side of their individual card. On the other side, they write the opposite of that number.
- One student places their index card on the table so everyone in the group can see it. They decide which of their numbers to show. Then, they place the index card with the minus sign to the right of their number.
- Another student places their index card to the right of the minus sign. They can use either of their numbers.
- The group reads the subtraction problem out loud. A student then flips the second and third index cards to show the equivalent addition problem. The group reads the addition problem out loud and agrees on an answer.

Chapter 8

Math Triumphs Lesson 8-2 A161

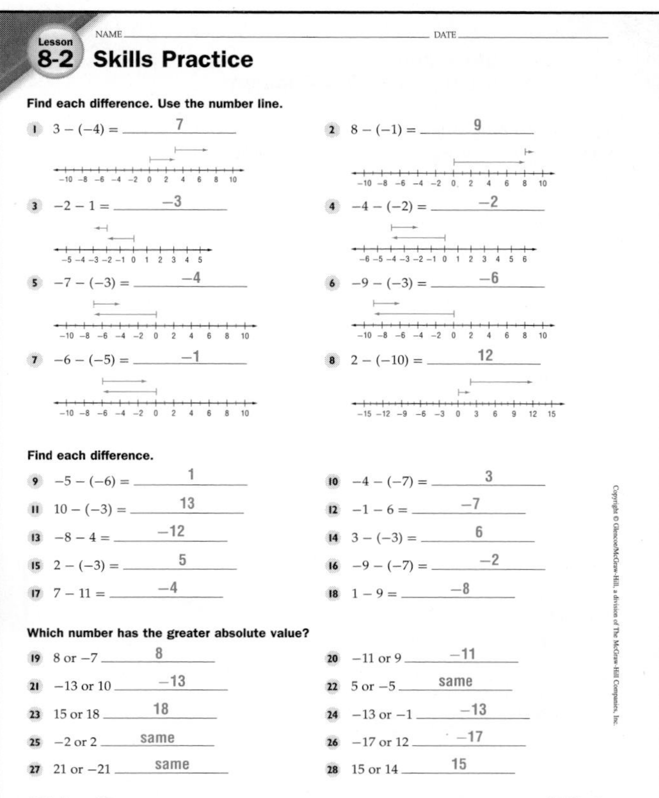

NAME ______ DATE ______

Lesson 8-2 **Skills Practice**

Find each difference. Use the number line.

1. 3 − (−4) = ___7___
2. 8 − (−1) = ___9___
3. −2 − 1 = ___−3___
4. −4 − (−2) = ___−2___
5. −7 − (−3) = ___−4___
6. −9 − (−3) = ___−6___
7. −6 − (−5) = ___−1___
8. 2 − (−10) = ___12___

Find each difference.

9. −5 − (−6) = ___1___
10. −4 − (−7) = ___3___
11. 10 − (−3) = ___13___
12. −1 − 6 = ___−7___
13. −8 − 4 = ___−12___
14. 3 − (−3) = ___6___
15. 2 − (−3) = ___5___
16. −9 − (−7) = ___−2___
17. 7 − 11 = ___−4___
18. 1 − 9 = ___−8___

Which number has the greater absolute value?

19. 8 or −7 ___8___
20. −11 or 9 ___−11___
21. −13 or 10 ___−13___
22. 5 or −5 ___same___
23. 15 or 18 ___18___
24. −13 or −1 ___−13___
25. −2 or 2 ___same___
26. −17 or 12 ___−17___
27. 21 or −21 ___same___
28. 15 or 14 ___15___

A162 Lesson 8-2 Math Triumphs

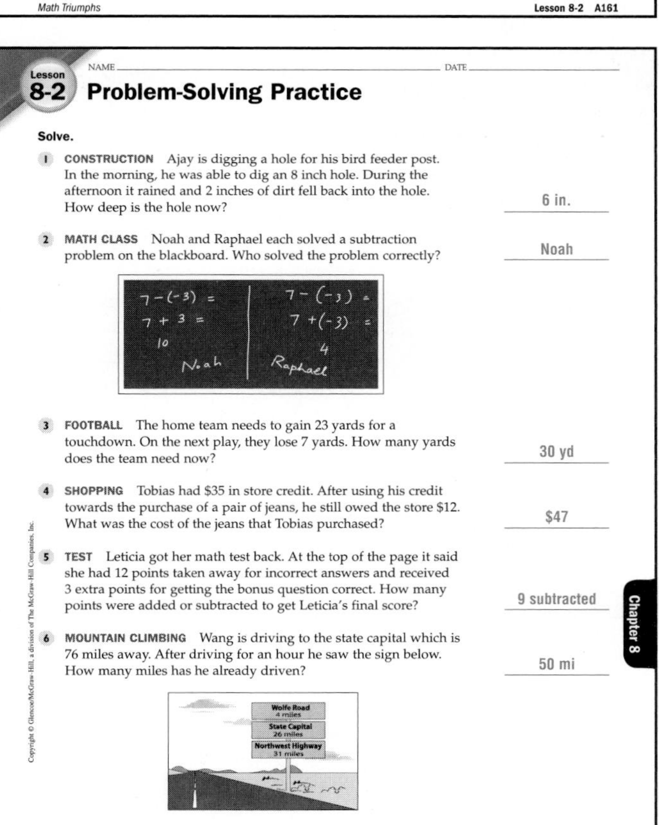

NAME ______ DATE ______

Lesson 8-2 **Problem-Solving Practice**

Solve.

1. **CONSTRUCTION** Ajay is digging a hole for his bird feeder post. In the morning, he was able to dig an 8 inch hole. During the afternoon it rained and 2 inches of dirt fell back into the hole. How deep is the hole now? ___6 in.___
2. **MATH CLASS** Noah and Raphael each solved a subtraction problem on the blackboard. Who solved the problem correctly? ___Noah___

   7 − (−3) = 7 + 3 = 10 Noah | 7 − (−3) = 7 + (−3) = 4 Raphael

3. **FOOTBALL** The home team needs to gain 23 yards for a touchdown. On the next play, they lose 7 yards. How many yards does the team need now? ___30 yd___
4. **SHOPPING** Tobias had $35 in store credit. After using his credit towards the purchase of a pair of jeans, he still owed the store $12. What was the cost of the jeans that Tobias purchased? ___$47___
5. **TEST** Leticia got her math test back. At the top of the page it said she had 12 points taken away for incorrect answers and received 3 extra points for getting the bonus question correct. How many points were added or subtracted to get Leticia's final score? ___9 subtracted___
6. **MOUNTAIN CLIMBING** Wang is driving to the state capital which is 76 miles away. After driving for an hour he saw the sign below. How many miles has he already driven? ___50 mi___

   Wolfe Road 4 miles / State Capital 26 miles / Northwest Highway 31 miles

Chapter 8

Math Triumphs Lesson 8-2 A163

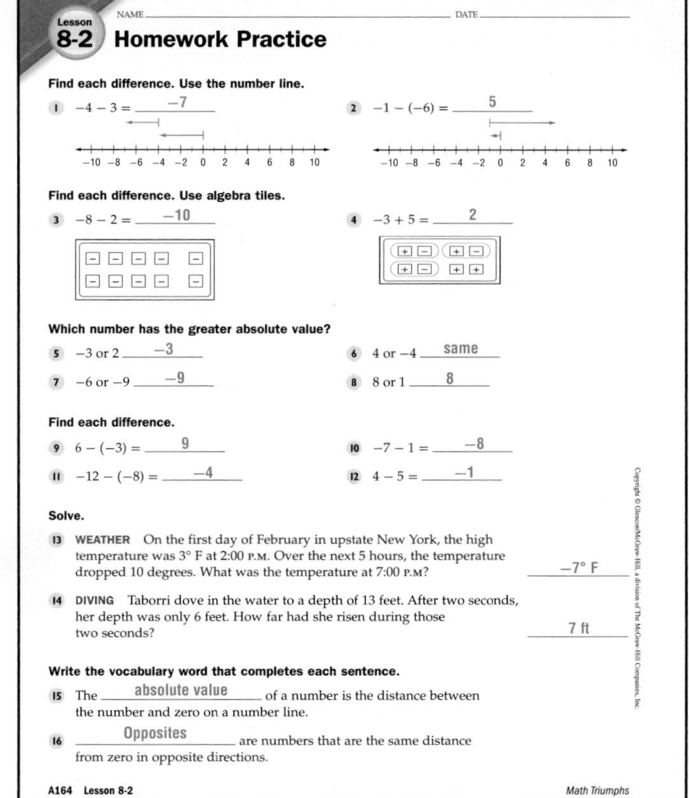

NAME ______ DATE ______

Lesson 8-2 **Homework Practice**

Find each difference. Use the number line.

1. −4 − 3 = ___−7___
2. −1 − (−6) = ___5___

Find each difference. Use algebra tiles.

3. −8 − 2 = ___−10___
4. −3 + 5 = ___2___

Which number has the greater absolute value?

5. −3 or 2 ___−3___
6. 4 or −4 ___same___
7. −6 or −9 ___−9___
8. 8 or 1 ___8___

Find each difference.

9. 6 − (−3) = ___9___
10. −7 − 1 = ___−8___
11. −12 − (−8) = ___−4___
12. 4 − 5 = ___−1___

Solve.

13. **WEATHER** On the first day of February in upstate New York, the high temperature was 3° F at 2:00 P.M. Over the next 5 hours, the temperature dropped 10 degrees. What was the temperature at 7:00 P.M.? ___−7° F___
14. **DIVING** Taborri dove in the water to a depth of 13 feet. After two seconds, her depth was only 6 feet. How far had she risen during those two seconds? ___7 ft___

Write the vocabulary word that completes each sentence.

15. The ___absolute value___ of a number is the distance between the number and zero on a number line.
16. ___Opposites___ are numbers that are the same distance from zero in opposite directions.

A164 Lesson 8-2 Math Triumphs

Answer Key (Lesson 8-3)

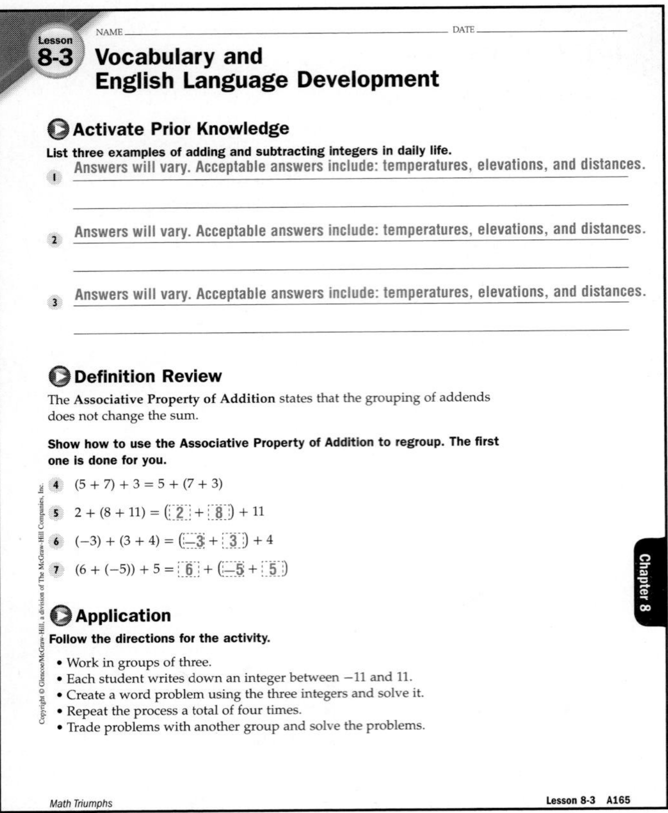

Lesson 8-3

NAME ______________ DATE ______________

Vocabulary and English Language Development

Activate Prior Knowledge

List three examples of adding and subtracting integers in daily life.

1. Answers will vary. Acceptable answers include: temperatures, elevations, and distances.
2. Answers will vary. Acceptable answers include: temperatures, elevations, and distances.
3. Answers will vary. Acceptable answers include: temperatures, elevations, and distances.

Definition Review

The **Associative Property of Addition** states that the grouping of addends does not change the sum.

Show how to use the Associative Property of Addition to regroup. The first one is done for you.

4. $(5 + 7) + 3 = 5 + (7 + 3)$
5. $2 + (8 + 11) = (2 + 8) + 11$
6. $(-3) + (3 + 4) = (-3 + 3) + 4$
7. $(6 + (-5)) + 5 = 6 + (-5 + 5)$

Application

Follow the directions for the activity.

- Work in groups of three.
- Each student writes down an integer between −11 and 11.
- Create a word problem using the three integers and solve it.
- Repeat the process a total of four times.
- Trade problems with another group and solve the problems.

Chapter 8

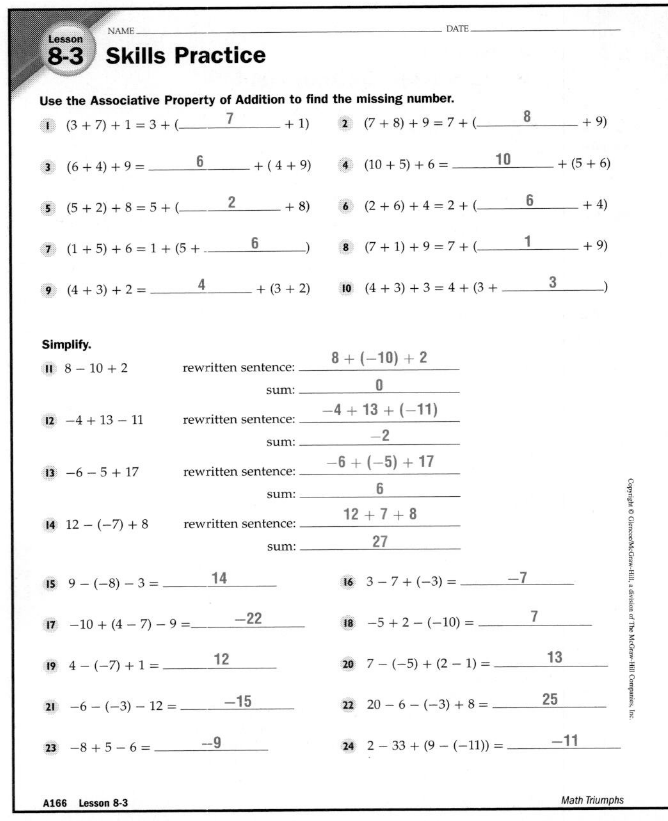

Lesson 8-3

NAME ______________ DATE ______________

Skills Practice

Use the Associative Property of Addition to find the missing number.

1. $(3 + 7) + 1 = 3 + (\underline{7} + 1)$
2. $(7 + 8) + 9 = 7 + (\underline{8} + 9)$
3. $(6 + 4) + 9 = \underline{6} + (4 + 9)$
4. $(10 + 5) + 6 = \underline{10} + (5 + 6)$
5. $(5 + 2) + 8 = 5 + (\underline{2} + 8)$
6. $(2 + 6) + 4 = 2 + (\underline{6} + 4)$
7. $(1 + 5) + 6 = 1 + (5 + \underline{6})$
8. $(7 + 1) + 9 = 7 + (\underline{1} + 9)$
9. $(4 + 3) + 2 = \underline{4} + (3 + 2)$
10. $(4 + 3) + 3 = 4 + (3 + \underline{3})$

Simplify.

11. $8 - 10 + 2$ rewritten sentence: $8 + (-10) + 2$ sum: 0
12. $-4 + 13 - 11$ rewritten sentence: $-4 + 13 + (-11)$ sum: −2
13. $-6 - 5 + 17$ rewritten sentence: $-6 + (-5) + 17$ sum: 6
14. $12 - (-7) + 8$ rewritten sentence: $12 + 7 + 8$ sum: 27
15. $9 - (-8) - 3 = \underline{14}$
16. $3 - 7 + (-3) = \underline{-7}$
17. $-10 + (4 - 7) - 9 = \underline{-22}$
18. $-5 + 2 - (-10) = \underline{7}$
19. $4 - (-7) + 1 = \underline{12}$
20. $7 - (-5) + (2 - 1) = \underline{13}$
21. $-6 - (-3) - 12 = \underline{-15}$
22. $20 - 6 - (-3) + 8 = \underline{25}$
23. $-8 + 5 - 6 = \underline{-9}$
24. $2 - 33 + (9 - (-11)) = \underline{-11}$

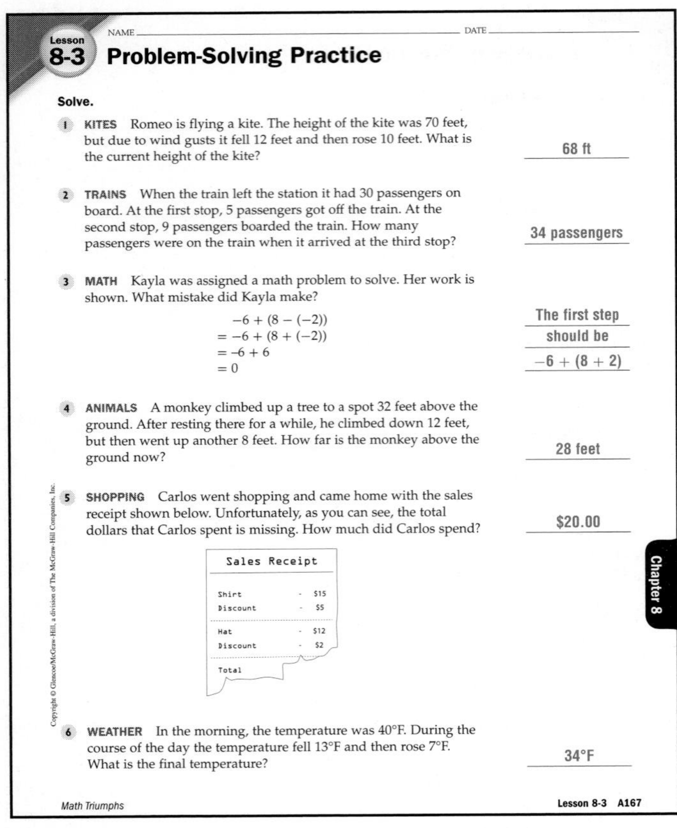

Lesson 8-3

NAME ______________ DATE ______________

Problem-Solving Practice

Solve.

1. **KITES** Romeo is flying a kite. The height of the kite was 70 feet, but due to wind gusts it fell 12 feet and then rose 10 feet. What is the current height of the kite? **68 ft**
2. **TRAINS** When the train left the station it had 30 passengers on board. At the first stop, 5 passengers got off the train. At the second stop, 9 passengers boarded the train. How many passengers were on the train when it arrived at the third stop? **34 passengers**
3. **MATH** Kayla was assigned a math problem to solve. Her work is shown. What mistake did Kayla make?

   $-6 + (8 - (-2))$
   $= -6 + (8 + (-2))$
   $= -6 + 6$
   $= 0$

   The first step should be $-6 + (8 + 2)$
4. **ANIMALS** A monkey climbed up a tree to a spot 32 feet above the ground. After resting there for a while, he climbed down 12 feet, but then went up another 8 feet. How far is the monkey above the ground now? **28 feet**
5. **SHOPPING** Carlos went shopping and came home with the sales receipt shown below. Unfortunately, as you can see, the total dollars that Carlos spent is missing. How much did Carlos spend? **$20.00**

Sales Receipt	
Shirt	$15
Discount	$5
Hat	$12
Discount	$2
Total	

6. **WEATHER** In the morning, the temperature was 40°F. During the course of the day the temperature fell 13°F and then rose 7°F. What is the final temperature? **34°F**

Chapter 8

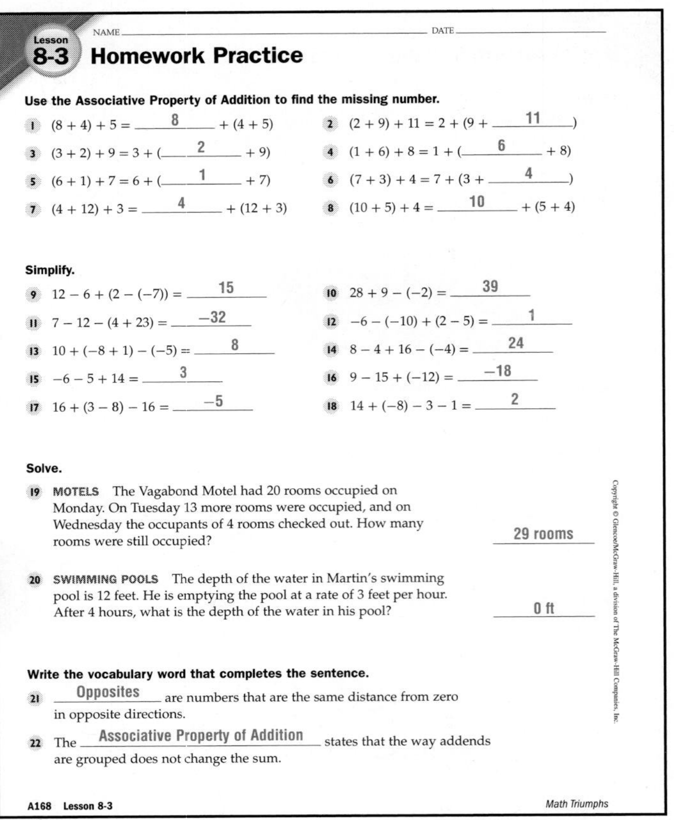

Lesson 8-3

NAME ______________ DATE ______________

Homework Practice

Use the Associative Property of Addition to find the missing number.

1. $(8 + 4) + 5 = \underline{8} + (4 + 5)$
2. $(2 + 9) + 11 = 2 + (9 + \underline{11})$
3. $(3 + 2) + 9 = 3 + (\underline{2} + 9)$
4. $(1 + 6) + 8 = 1 + (\underline{6} + 8)$
5. $(6 + 1) + 7 = 6 + (\underline{1} + 7)$
6. $(7 + 3) + 4 = 7 + (3 + \underline{4})$
7. $(4 + 12) + 3 = \underline{4} + (12 + 3)$
8. $(10 + 5) + 4 = \underline{10} + (5 + 4)$

Simplify.

9. $12 - 6 + (2 - (-7)) = \underline{15}$
10. $28 + 9 - (-2) = \underline{39}$
11. $7 - 12 - (4 + 23) = \underline{-32}$
12. $-6 - (-10) + (2 - 5) = \underline{1}$
13. $10 + (-8 + 1) - (-5) = \underline{8}$
14. $8 - 4 + 16 - (-4) = \underline{24}$
15. $-6 - 5 + 14 = \underline{3}$
16. $9 - 15 + (-12) = \underline{-18}$
17. $16 + (3 - 8) - 16 = \underline{-5}$
18. $14 + (-8) - 3 - 1 = \underline{2}$

Solve.

19. **MOTELS** The Vagabond Motel had 20 rooms occupied on Monday. On Tuesday 13 more rooms were occupied, and on Wednesday the occupants of 4 rooms checked out. How many rooms were still occupied? **29 rooms**
20. **SWIMMING POOLS** The depth of the water in Martin's swimming pool is 12 feet. He is emptying the pool at a rate of 3 feet per hour. After 4 hours, what is the depth of the water in his pool? **0 ft**

Write the vocabulary word that completes the sentence.

21. **Opposites** are numbers that are the same distance from zero in opposite directions.
22. The **Associative Property of Addition** states that the way addends are grouped does not change the sum.

Answer Key (Lesson 8-4)

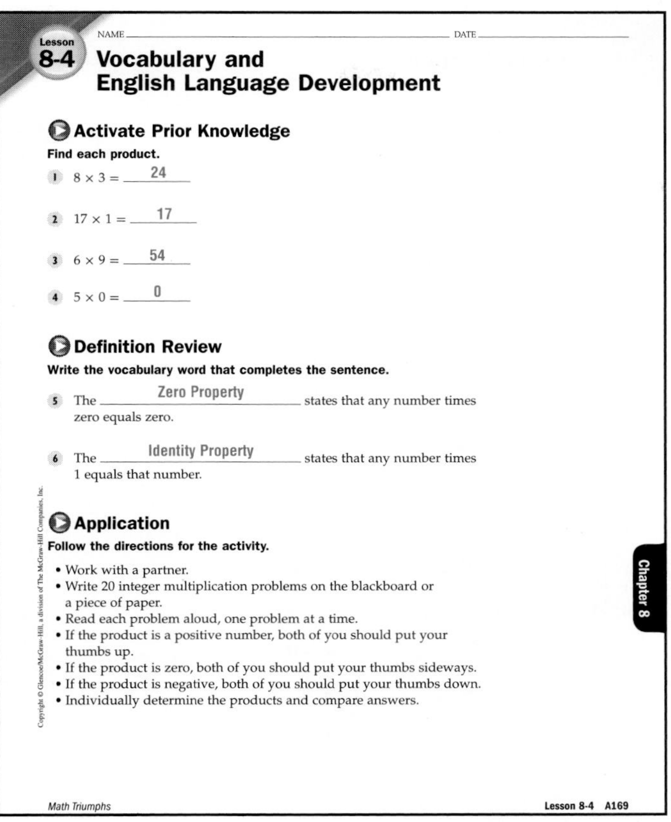

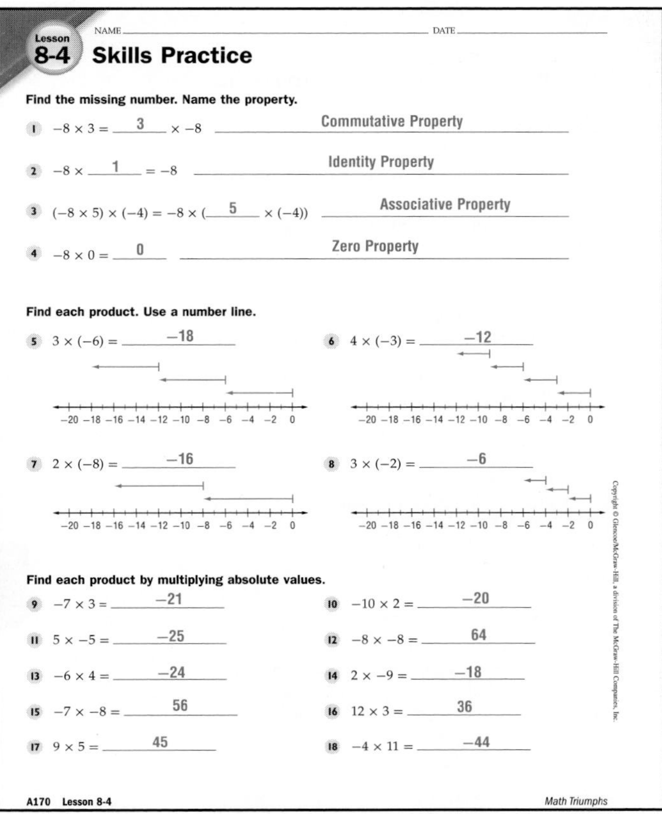

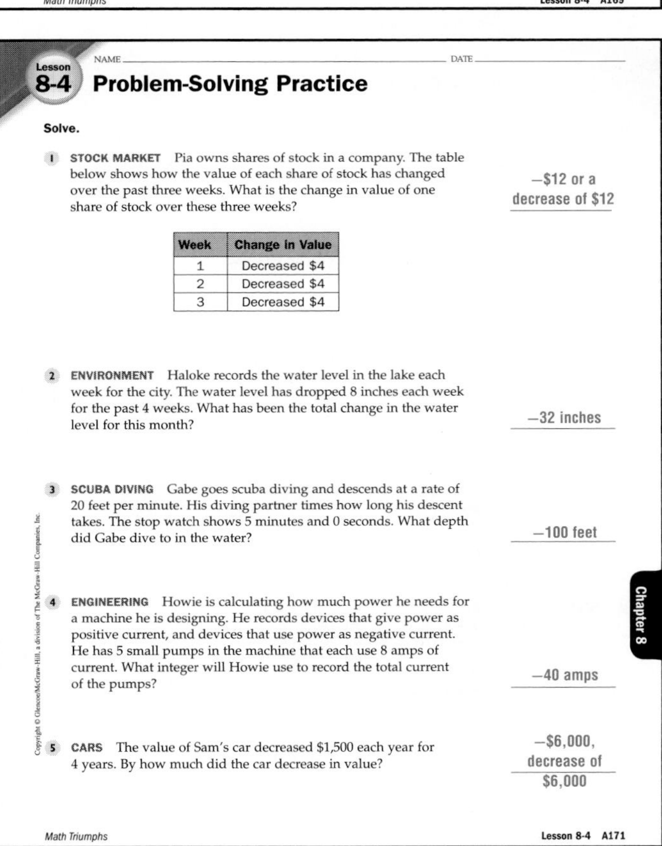

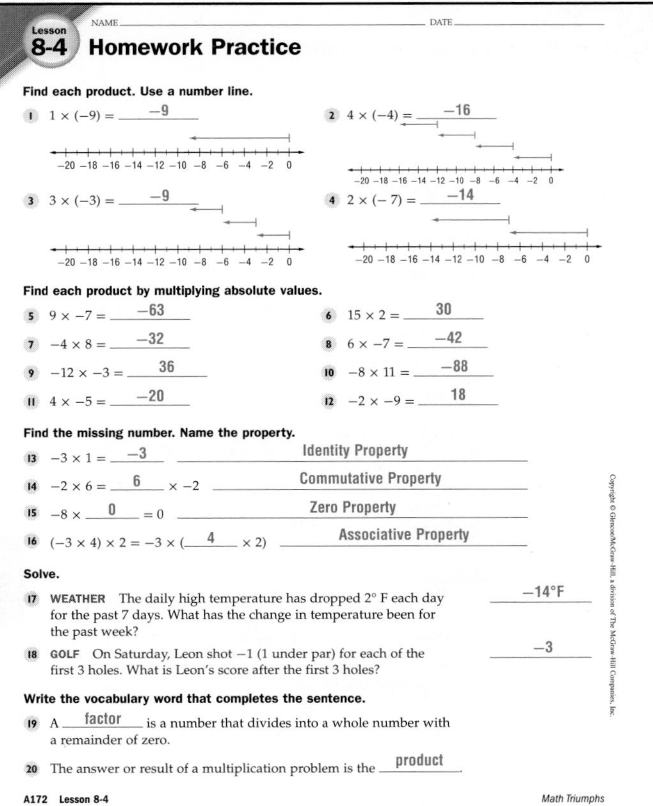

Answer Key (Lesson 8-5)

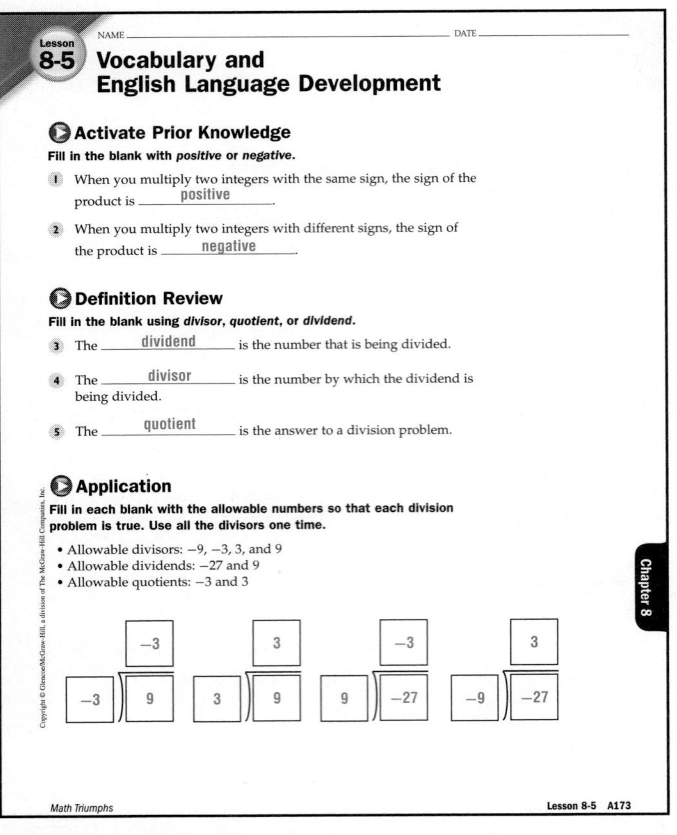

NAME ______ DATE ______

Lesson 8-5 **Vocabulary and English Language Development**

Activate Prior Knowledge

Fill in the blank with *positive* or *negative*.

1. When you multiply two integers with the same sign, the sign of the product is positive.
2. When you multiply two integers with different signs, the sign of the product is negative.

Definition Review

Fill in the blank using *divisor*, *quotient*, or *dividend*.

3. The dividend is the number that is being divided.
4. The divisor is the number by which the dividend is being divided.
5. The quotient is the answer to a division problem.

Application

Fill in each blank with the allowable numbers so that each division problem is true. Use all the divisors one time.

- Allowable divisors: –9, –3, 3, and 9
- Allowable dividends: –27 and 9
- Allowable quotients: –3 and 3

Divisor	Dividend	Quotient
–3	9	–3
3	9	3
9	–27	–3
–9	–27	3

Chapter 8

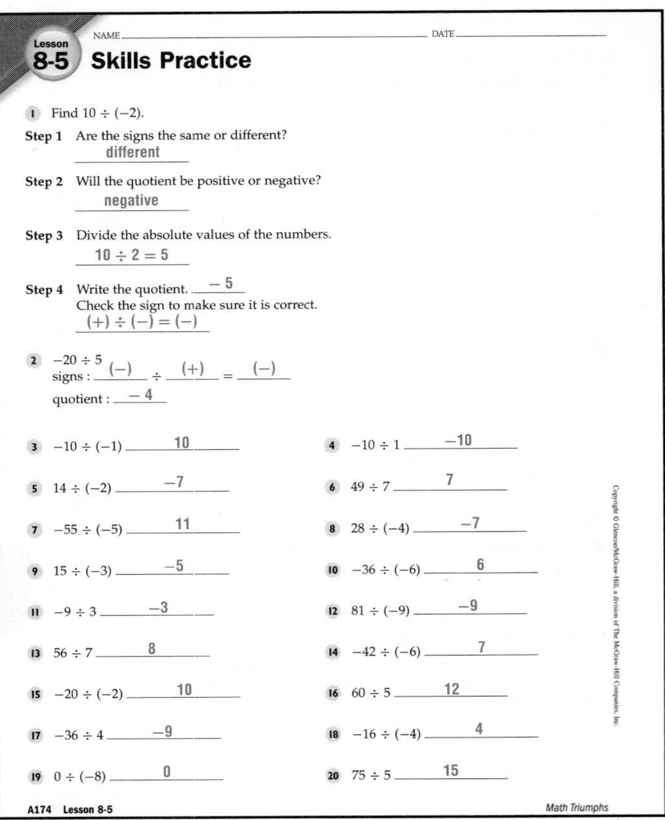

NAME ______ DATE ______

Lesson 8-5 **Skills Practice**

1. Find $10 \div (-2)$.

Step 1 Are the signs the same or different? different

Step 2 Will the quotient be positive or negative? negative

Step 3 Divide the absolute values of the numbers. $10 \div 2 = 5$

Step 4 Write the quotient. -5
Check the sign to make sure it is correct. $(+) \div (-) = (-)$

2. $-20 \div 5$
signs: $(-) \div (+) = (-)$
quotient: -4

3. $-10 \div (-1)$ 10
4. $-10 \div 1$ –10
5. $14 \div (-2)$ –7
6. $49 \div 7$ 7
7. $-55 \div (-5)$ 11
8. $28 \div (-4)$ –7
9. $15 \div (-3)$ –5
10. $-36 \div (-6)$ 6
11. $-9 \div 3$ –3
12. $81 \div (-9)$ –9
13. $56 \div 7$ 8
14. $-42 \div (-6)$ 7
15. $-20 \div (-2)$ 10
16. $60 \div 5$ 12
17. $-36 \div 4$ –9
18. $-16 \div (-4)$ 4
19. $0 \div (-8)$ 0
20. $75 \div 5$ 15

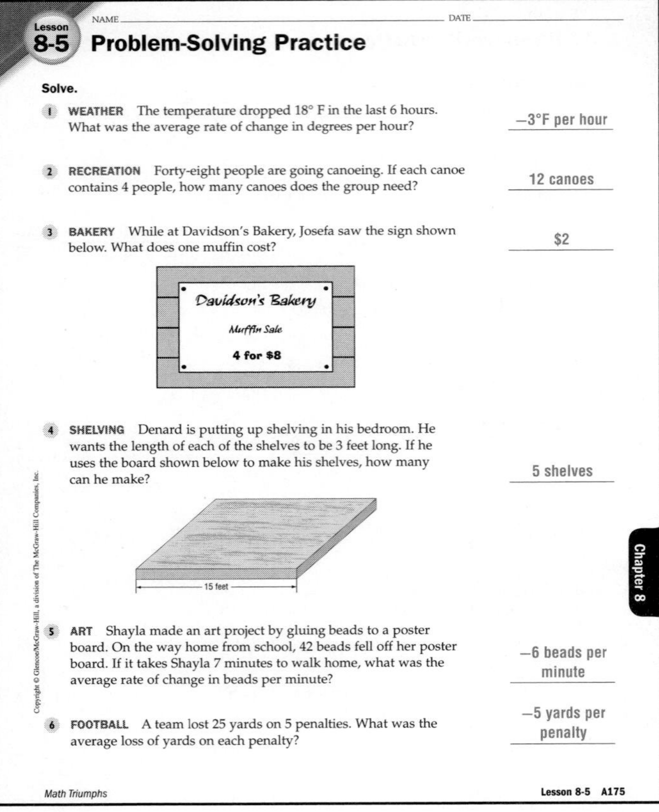

NAME ______ DATE ______

Lesson 8-5 **Problem-Solving Practice**

Solve.

1. **WEATHER** The temperature dropped 18° F in the last 6 hours. What was the average rate of change in degrees per hour? –3°F per hour
2. **RECREATION** Forty-eight people are going canoeing. If each canoe contains 4 people, how many canoes does the group need? 12 canoes
3. **BAKERY** While at Davidson's Bakery, Josefa saw the sign shown below. What does one muffin cost? $2

4. **SHELVING** Denard is putting up shelving in his bedroom. He wants the length of each of the shelves to be 3 feet long. If he uses the board shown below to make his shelves, how many can he make? 5 shelves

5. **ART** Shayla made an art project by gluing beads to a poster board. On the way home from school, 42 beads fell off her poster board. If it takes Shayla 7 minutes to walk home, what was the average rate of change in beads per minute? –6 beads per minute
6. **FOOTBALL** A team lost 25 yards on 5 penalties. What was the average loss of yards on each penalty? –5 yards per penalty

Chapter 8

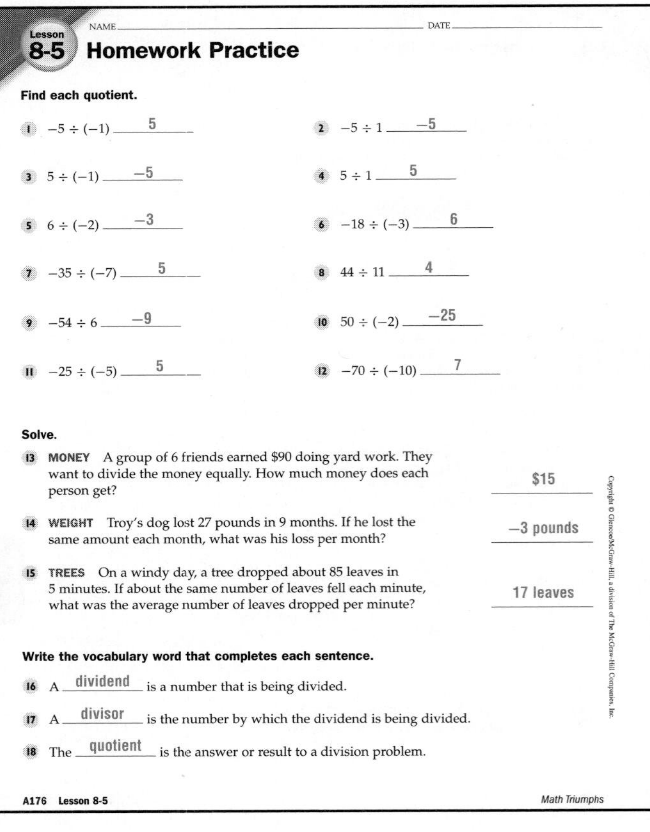

NAME ______ DATE ______

Lesson 8-5 **Homework Practice**

Find each quotient.

1. $-5 \div (-1)$ 5
2. $-5 \div 1$ –5
3. $5 \div (-1)$ –5
4. $5 \div 1$ 5
5. $6 \div (-2)$ –3
6. $-18 \div (-3)$ 6
7. $-35 \div (-7)$ 5
8. $44 \div 11$ 4
9. $-54 \div 6$ –9
10. $50 \div (-2)$ –25
11. $-25 \div (-5)$ 5
12. $-70 \div (-10)$ 7

Solve.

13. **MONEY** A group of 6 friends earned $90 doing yard work. They want to divide the money equally. How much money does each person get? $15
14. **WEIGHT** Troy's dog lost 27 pounds in 9 months. If he lost the same amount each month, what was his loss per month? –3 pounds
15. **TREES** On a windy day, a tree dropped about 85 leaves in 5 minutes. If about the same number of leaves fell each minute, what was the average number of leaves dropped per minute? 17 leaves

Write the vocabulary word that completes each sentence.

16. A dividend is a number that is being divided.
17. A divisor is the number by which the dividend is being divided.
18. The quotient is the answer or result to a division problem.

Answer Key (Lesson 8-6)

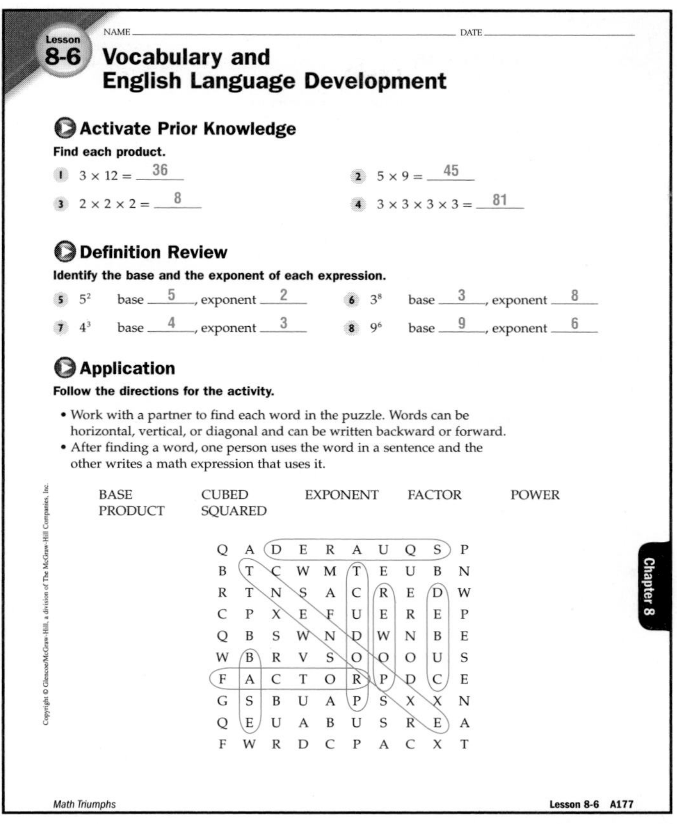

Lesson 8-6

NAME ______ DATE ______

Vocabulary and English Language Development

Activate Prior Knowledge

Find each product.

1. $3 \times 12 =$ 36
2. $5 \times 9 =$ 45
3. $2 \times 2 \times 2 =$ 8
4. $3 \times 3 \times 3 \times 3 =$ 81

Definition Review

Identify the base and the exponent of each expression.

5. 5^2 base 5, exponent 2
6. 3^8 base 3, exponent 8
7. 4^3 base 4, exponent 3
8. 9^6 base 9, exponent 6

Application

Follow the directions for the activity.

- Work with a partner to find each word in the puzzle. Words can be horizontal, vertical, or diagonal and can be written backward or forward.
- After finding a word, one person uses the word in a sentence and the other writes a math expression that uses it.

BASE CUBED EXPONENT FACTOR POWER
PRODUCT SQUARED

Q	A	D	E	R	A	U	Q	S	P
B	T	C	W	M	T	E	U	B	N
R	T	N	S	A	C	R	E	D	W
C	P	X	E	F	U	E	R	E	P
Q	B	S	W	N	D	W	N	B	E
W	B	R	V	S	O	O	O	U	S
F	A	C	T	O	R	P	D	C	E
G	S	B	U	A	P	S	X	X	N
Q	E	U	A	B	U	S	R	E	A
F	W	R	D	C	P	A	C	X	T

Chapter 8

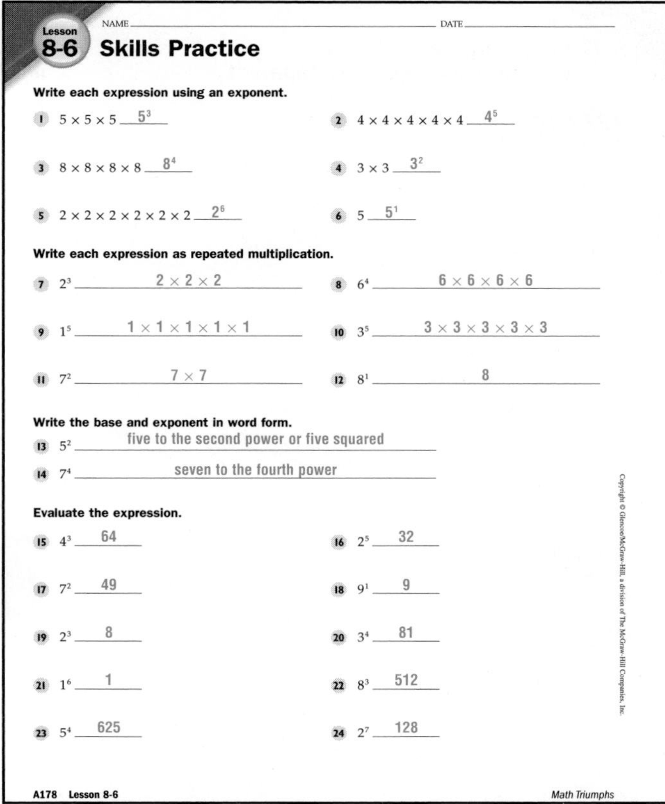

Lesson 8-6

NAME ______ DATE ______

Skills Practice

Write each expression using an exponent.

1. $5 \times 5 \times 5$ 5^3
2. $4 \times 4 \times 4 \times 4 \times 4$ 4^5
3. $8 \times 8 \times 8 \times 8$ 8^4
4. 3×3 3^2
5. $2 \times 2 \times 2 \times 2 \times 2 \times 2$ 2^6
6. 5 5^1

Write each expression as repeated multiplication.

7. 2^3 $2 \times 2 \times 2$
8. 6^4 $6 \times 6 \times 6 \times 6$
9. 1^5 $1 \times 1 \times 1 \times 1 \times 1$
10. 3^5 $3 \times 3 \times 3 \times 3 \times 3$
11. 7^2 7×7
12. 8^1 8

Write the base and exponent in word form.

13. 5^2 five to the second power or five squared
14. 7^4 seven to the fourth power

Evaluate the expression.

15. 4^3 64
16. 2^5 32
17. 7^2 49
18. 9^1 9
19. 2^3 8
20. 3^4 81
21. 1^6 1
22. 8^3 512
23. 5^4 625
24. 2^7 128

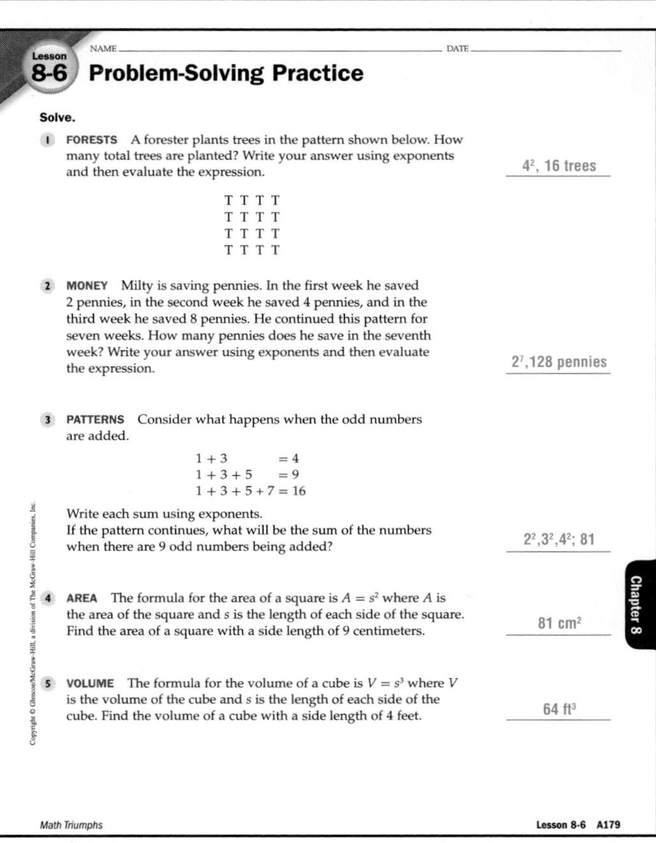

Lesson 8-6

NAME ______ DATE ______

Problem-Solving Practice

Solve.

1. **FORESTS** A forester plants trees in the pattern shown below. How many total trees are planted? Write your answer using exponents and then evaluate the expression. 4^2, 16 trees

T T T T
T T T T
T T T T
T T T T

2. **MONEY** Milty is saving pennies. In the first week he saved 2 pennies, in the second week he saved 4 pennies, and in the third week he saved 8 pennies. He continued this pattern for seven weeks. How many pennies does he save in the seventh week? Write your answer using exponents and then evaluate the expression. 2^7,128 pennies

3. **PATTERNS** Consider what happens when the odd numbers are added.

$1 + 3 = 4$
$1 + 3 + 5 = 9$
$1 + 3 + 5 + 7 = 16$

Write each sum using exponents.
If the pattern continues, what will be the sum of the numbers when there are 9 odd numbers being added? $2^2, 3^2, 4^2$; 81

4. **AREA** The formula for the area of a square is $A = s^2$ where A is the area of the square and s is the length of each side of the square. Find the area of a square with a side length of 9 centimeters. 81 cm^2

5. **VOLUME** The formula for the volume of a cube is $V = s^3$ where V is the volume of the cube and s is the length of each side of the cube. Find the volume of a cube with a side length of 4 feet. 64 ft^3

Chapter 8

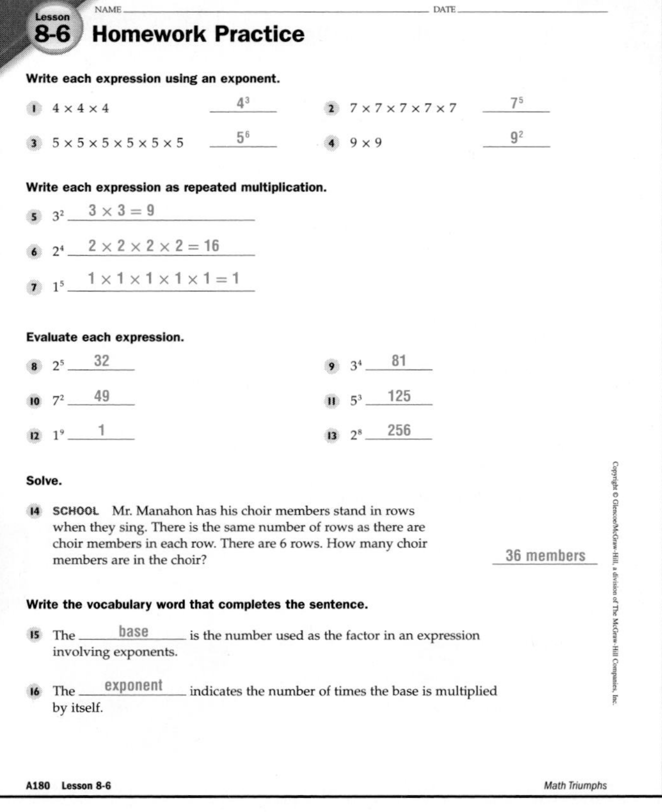

Lesson 8-6

NAME ______ DATE ______

Homework Practice

Write each expression using an exponent.

1. $4 \times 4 \times 4$ 4^3
2. $7 \times 7 \times 7 \times 7 \times 7$ 7^5
3. $5 \times 5 \times 5 \times 5 \times 5 \times 5$ 5^6
4. 9×9 9^2

Write each expression as repeated multiplication.

5. 3^2 $3 \times 3 = 9$
6. 2^4 $2 \times 2 \times 2 \times 2 = 16$
7. 1^5 $1 \times 1 \times 1 \times 1 \times 1 = 1$

Evaluate each expression.

8. 2^5 32
9. 3^4 81
10. 7^2 49
11. 5^3 125
12. 1^9 1
13. 2^8 256

Solve.

14. **SCHOOL** Mr. Manahon has his choir members stand in rows when they sing. There is the same number of rows as there are choir members in each row. There are 6 rows. How many choir members are in the choir? 36 members

Write the vocabulary word that completes the sentence.

15. The base is the number used as the factor in an expression involving exponents.
16. The exponent indicates the number of times the base is multiplied by itself.

Answer Key (Lesson 8-7)

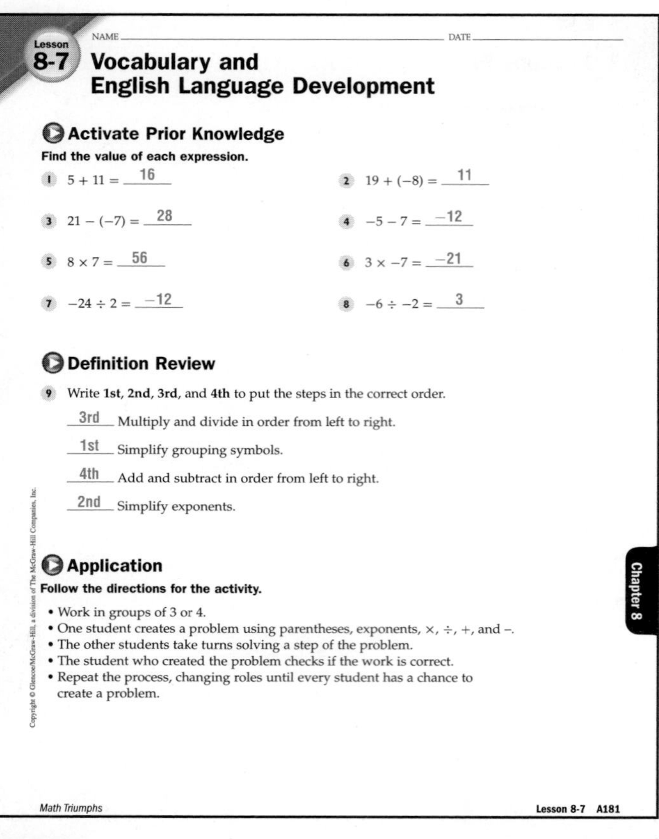

Lesson 8-7 NAME ____ DATE ____

Vocabulary and English Language Development

Activate Prior Knowledge

Find the value of each expression.

1. $5 + 11 =$ 16
2. $19 + (-8) =$ 11
3. $21 - (-7) =$ 28
4. $-5 - 7 =$ −12
5. $8 \times 7 =$ 56
6. $3 \times -7 =$ −21
7. $-24 \div 2 =$ −12
8. $-6 \div -2 =$ 3

Definition Review

9. Write **1st**, **2nd**, **3rd**, and **4th** to put the steps in the correct order.

3rd Multiply and divide in order from left to right.

1st Simplify grouping symbols.

4th Add and subtract in order from left to right.

2nd Simplify exponents.

Application

Follow the directions for the activity.

- Work in groups of 3 or 4.
- One student creates a problem using parentheses, exponents, ×, ÷, +, and −.
- The other students take turns solving a step of the problem.
- The student who created the problem checks if the work is correct.
- Repeat the process, changing roles until every student has a chance to create a problem.

Chapter 8

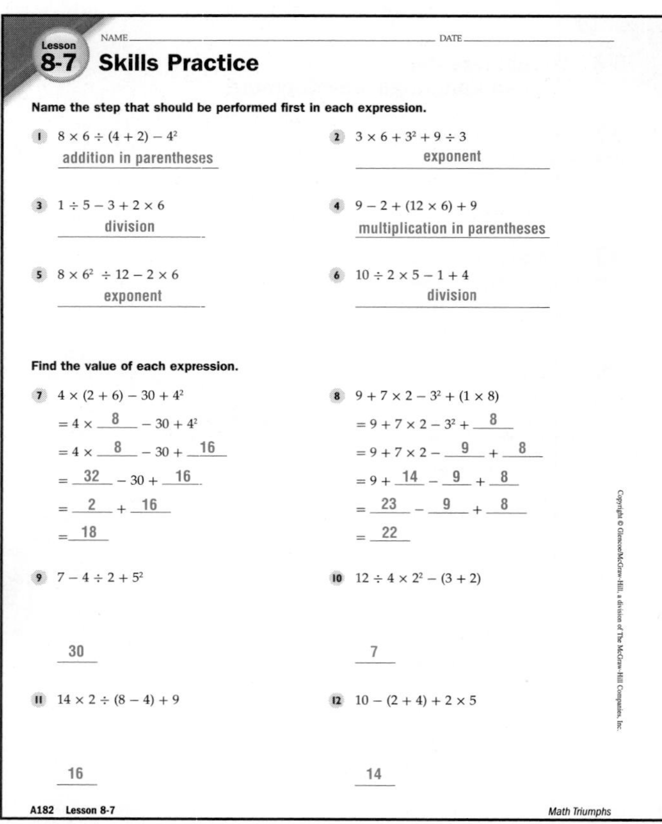

Lesson 8-7 NAME ____ DATE ____

Skills Practice

Name the step that should be performed first in each expression.

1. $8 \times 6 \div (4 + 2) - 4^2$ addition in parentheses
2. $3 \times 6 + 3^2 + 9 \div 3$ exponent
3. $1 \div 5 - 3 + 2 \times 6$ division
4. $9 - 2 + (12 \times 6) + 9$ multiplication in parentheses
5. $8 \times 6^2 \div 12 - 2 \times 6$ exponent
6. $10 \div 2 \times 5 - 1 + 4$ division

Find the value of each expression.

7. $4 \times (2 + 6) - 30 + 4^2$
$= 4 \times 8 - 30 + 4^2$
$= 4 \times 8 - 30 + 16$
$= 32 - 30 + 16$
$= 2 + 16$
$= 18$

8. $9 + 7 \times 2 - 3^2 + (1 \times 8)$
$= 9 + 7 \times 2 - 3^2 + 8$
$= 9 + 7 \times 2 - 9 + 8$
$= 9 + 14 - 9 + 8$
$= 23 - 9 + 8$
$= 22$

9. $7 - 4 \div 2 + 5^2$ 30
10. $12 \div 4 \times 2^2 - (3 + 2)$ 7
11. $14 \times 2 \div (8 - 4) + 9$ 16
12. $10 - (2 + 4) + 2 \times 5$ 14

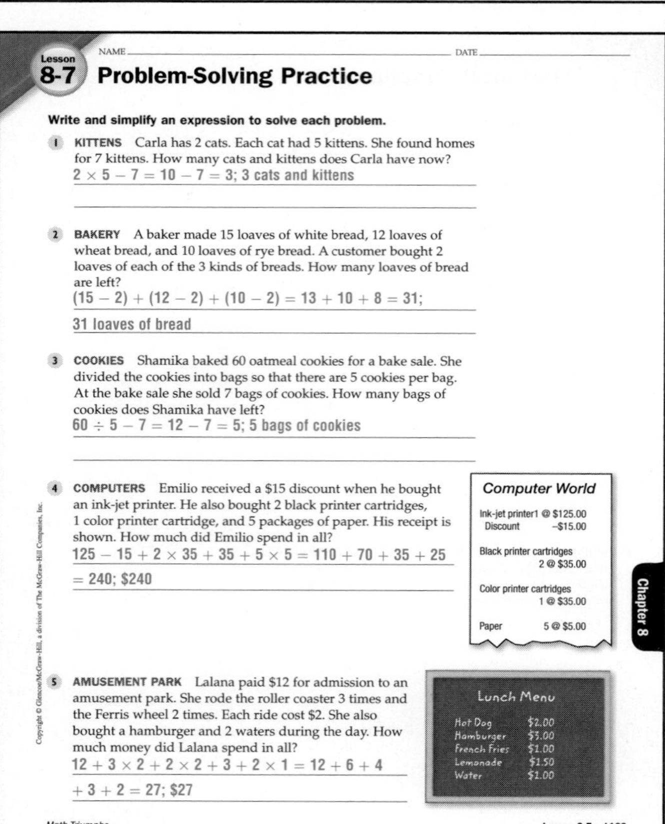

Lesson 8-7 NAME ____ DATE ____

Problem-Solving Practice

Write and simplify an expression to solve each problem.

1. **KITTENS** Carla has 2 cats. Each cat had 5 kittens. She found homes for 7 kittens. How many cats and kittens does Carla have now?
$2 \times 5 - 7 = 10 - 7 = 3$; 3 cats and kittens

2. **BAKERY** A baker made 15 loaves of white bread, 12 loaves of wheat bread, and 10 loaves of rye bread. A customer bought 2 loaves of each of the 3 kinds of breads. How many loaves of bread are left?
$(15 - 2) + (12 - 2) + (10 - 2) = 13 + 10 + 8 = 31$; 31 loaves of bread

3. **COOKIES** Shamika baked 60 oatmeal cookies for a bake sale. She divided the cookies into bags so that there are 5 cookies per bag. At the bake sale she sold 7 bags of cookies. How many bags of cookies does Shamika have left?
$60 \div 5 - 7 = 12 - 7 = 5$; 5 bags of cookies

4. **COMPUTERS** Emilio received a \$15 discount when he bought an ink-jet printer. He also bought 2 black printer cartridges, 1 color printer cartridge, and 5 packages of paper. His receipt is shown. How much did Emilio spend in all?
$125 - 15 + 2 \times 35 + 35 + 5 \times 5 = 110 + 70 + 35 + 25 = 240$; \$240

Computer World
Ink-jet printer1 @ \$125.00
Discount −\$15.00
Black printer cartridges 2 @ \$35.00
Color printer cartridges 1 @ \$35.00
Paper 5 @ \$5.00

5. **AMUSEMENT PARK** Lalana paid \$12 for admission to an amusement park. She rode the roller coaster 3 times and the Ferris wheel 2 times. Each ride cost \$2. She also bought a hamburger and 2 waters during the day. How much money did Lalana spend in all?
$12 + 3 \times 2 + 2 \times 2 + 3 + 2 \times 1 = 12 + 6 + 4 + 3 + 2 = 27$; \$27

Lunch Menu
Hot Dog \$2.00
Hamburger \$3.00
French Fries \$1.00
Lemonade \$1.50
Water \$1.00

Chapter 8

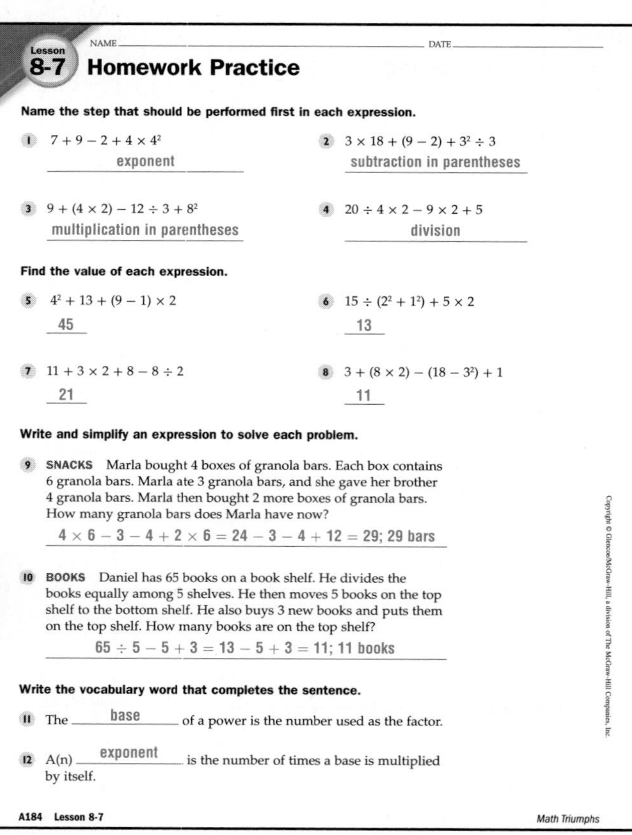

Lesson 8-7 NAME ____ DATE ____

Homework Practice

Name the step that should be performed first in each expression.

1. $7 + 9 - 2 + 4 \times 4^2$ exponent
2. $3 \times 18 + (9 - 2) + 3^2 \div 3$ subtraction in parentheses
3. $9 + (4 \times 2) - 12 \div 3 + 8^2$ multiplication in parentheses
4. $20 \div 4 \times 2 - 9 \times 2 + 5$ division

Find the value of each expression.

5. $4^2 + 13 + (9 - 1) \times 2$ 45
6. $15 \div (2^2 + 1^2) + 5 \times 2$ 13
7. $11 + 3 \times 2 + 8 - 8 \div 2$ 21
8. $3 + (8 \times 2) - (18 - 3^2) + 1$ 11

Write and simplify an expression to solve each problem.

9. **SNACKS** Marla bought 4 boxes of granola bars. Each box contains 6 granola bars. Marla ate 3 granola bars, and she gave her brother 4 granola bars. Marla then bought 2 more boxes of granola bars. How many granola bars does Marla have now?
$4 \times 6 - 3 - 4 + 2 \times 6 = 24 - 3 - 4 + 12 = 29$; 29 bars

10. **BOOKS** Daniel has 65 books on a book shelf. He divides the books equally among 5 shelves. He then moves 5 books on the top shelf to the bottom shelf. He also buys 3 new books and puts them on the top shelf. How many books are on the top shelf?
$65 \div 5 - 5 + 3 = 13 - 5 + 3 = 11$; 11 books

Write the vocabulary word that completes the sentence.

11. The base of a power is the number used as the factor.

12. A(n) exponent is the number of times a base is multiplied by itself.

Answer Key (Lesson 9-1)

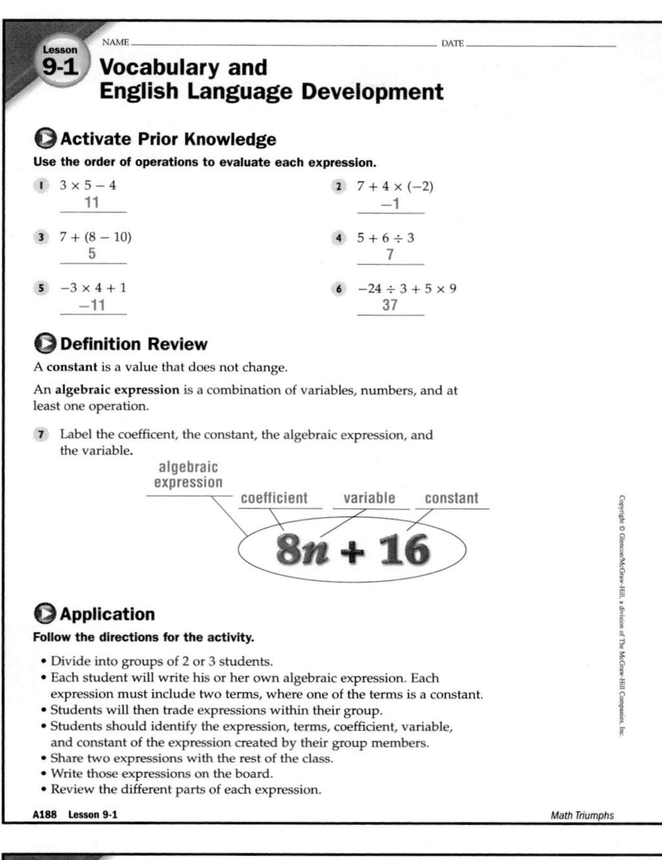

NAME ______ DATE ______

Lesson **9-1**

Vocabulary and English Language Development

Activate Prior Knowledge

Use the order of operations to evaluate each expression.

1. $3 \times 5 - 4$ 11
2. $7 + 4 \times (-2)$ -1
3. $7 + (8 - 10)$ 5
4. $5 + 6 \div 3$ 7
5. $-3 \times 4 + 1$ -11
6. $-24 \div 3 + 5 \times 9$ 37

Definition Review

A **constant** is a value that does not change.

An **algebraic expression** is a combination of variables, numbers, and at least one operation.

7. Label the coefficent, the constant, the algebraic expression, and the variable.

Application

Follow the directions for the activity.

- Divide into groups of 2 or 3 students.
- Each student will write his or her own algebraic expression. Each expression must include two terms, where one of the terms is a constant.
- Students will then trade expressions within their group.
- Students should identify the expression, terms, coefficient, variable, and constant of the expression created by their group members.
- Share two expressions with the rest of the class.
- Write those expressions on the board.
- Review the different parts of each expression.

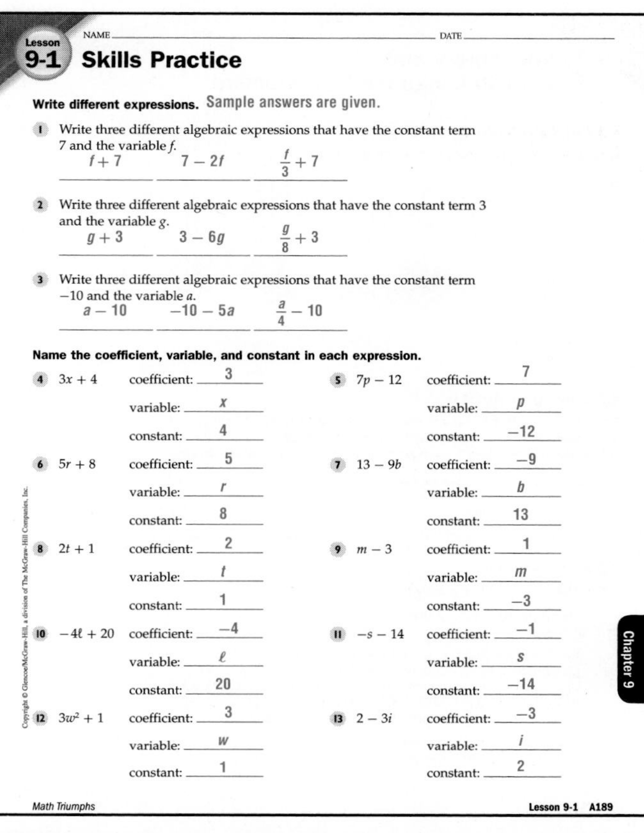

NAME ______ DATE ______

Lesson **9-1**

Skills Practice

Write different expressions. Sample answers are given.

1. Write three different algebraic expressions that have the constant term 7 and the variable *f*.
   $f + 7$ $7 - 2f$ $\frac{f}{3} + 7$
2. Write three different algebraic expressions that have the constant term 3 and the variable *g*.
   $g + 3$ $3 - 6g$ $\frac{g}{8} + 3$
3. Write three different algebraic expressions that have the constant term -10 and the variable *a*.
   $a - 10$ $-10 - 5a$ $\frac{a}{4} - 10$

Name the coefficient, variable, and constant in each expression.

		coefficient	variable	constant
4	$3x + 4$	3	x	4
5	$7p - 12$	7	p	-12
6	$5r + 8$	5	r	8
7	$13 - 9b$	-9	b	13
8	$2t + 1$	2	t	1
9	$m - 3$	1	m	-3
10	$-4\ell + 20$	-4	ℓ	20
11	$-s - 14$	-1	s	-14
12	$3w^2 + 1$	3	w	1
13	$2 - 3i$	-3	i	2

Chapter 9

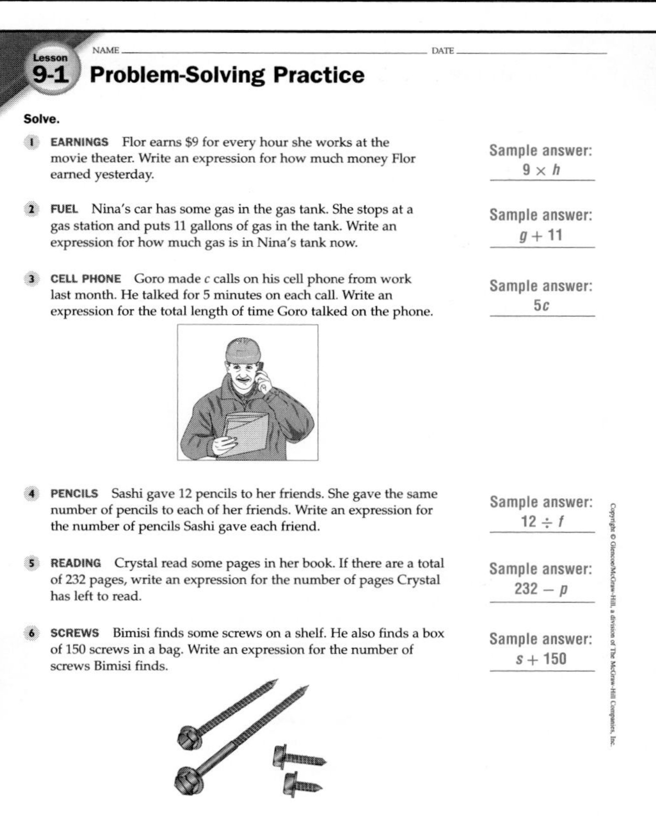

NAME ______ DATE ______

Lesson **9-1**

Problem-Solving Practice

Solve.

1. **EARNINGS** Flor earns $9 for every hour she works at the movie theater. Write an expression for how much money Flor earned yesterday.
   Sample answer: $9 \times h$
2. **FUEL** Nina's car has some gas in the gas tank. She stops at a gas station and puts 11 gallons of gas in the tank. Write an expression for how much gas is in Nina's tank now.
   Sample answer: $g + 11$
3. **CELL PHONE** Goro made *c* calls on his cell phone from work last month. He talked for 5 minutes on each call. Write an expression for the total length of time Goro talked on the phone.
   Sample answer: $5c$
4. **PENCILS** Sashi gave 12 pencils to her friends. She gave the same number of pencils to each of her friends. Write an expression for the number of pencils Sashi gave each friend.
   Sample answer: $12 \div f$
5. **READING** Crystal read some pages in her book. If there are a total of 232 pages, write an expression for the number of pages Crystal has left to read.
   Sample answer: $232 - p$
6. **SCREWS** Bimisi finds some screws on a shelf. He also finds a box of 150 screws in a bag. Write an expression for the number of screws Bimisi finds.
   Sample answer: $s + 150$

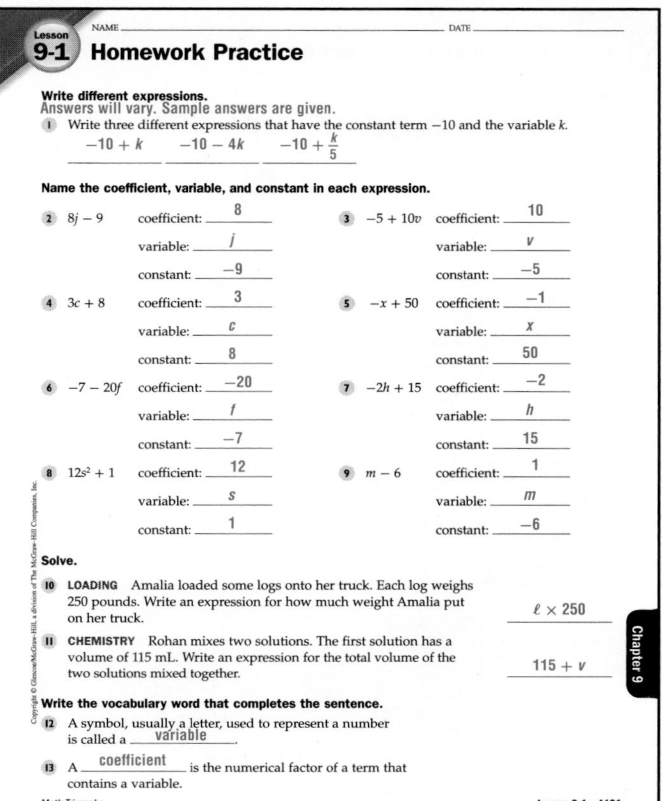

NAME ______ DATE ______

Lesson **9-1**

Homework Practice

Write different expressions.
Answers will vary. Sample answers are given.

1. Write three different expressions that have the constant term -10 and the variable *k*.
   $-10 + k$ $-10 - 4k$ $-10 + \frac{k}{5}$

Name the coefficient, variable, and constant in each expression.

		coefficient	variable	constant
2	$8j - 9$	8	j	-9
3	$-5 + 10v$	10	v	-5
4	$3c + 8$	3	c	8
5	$-x + 50$	-1	x	50
6	$-7 - 20f$	-20	f	-7
7	$-2h + 15$	-2	h	15
8	$12s^2 + 1$	12	s	1
9	$m - 6$	1	m	-6

Solve.

10. **LOADING** Amalia loaded some logs onto her truck. Each log weighs 250 pounds. Write an expression for how much weight Amalia put on her truck.
    $\ell \times 250$
11. **CHEMISTRY** Rohan mixes two solutions. The first solution has a volume of 115 mL. Write an expression for the total volume of the two solutions mixed together.
    $115 + v$

Write the vocabulary word that completes the sentence.

12. A symbol, usually a letter, used to represent a number is called a variable.
13. A coefficient is the numerical factor of a term that contains a variable.

Chapter 9

Answer Key (Lesson 9-2)

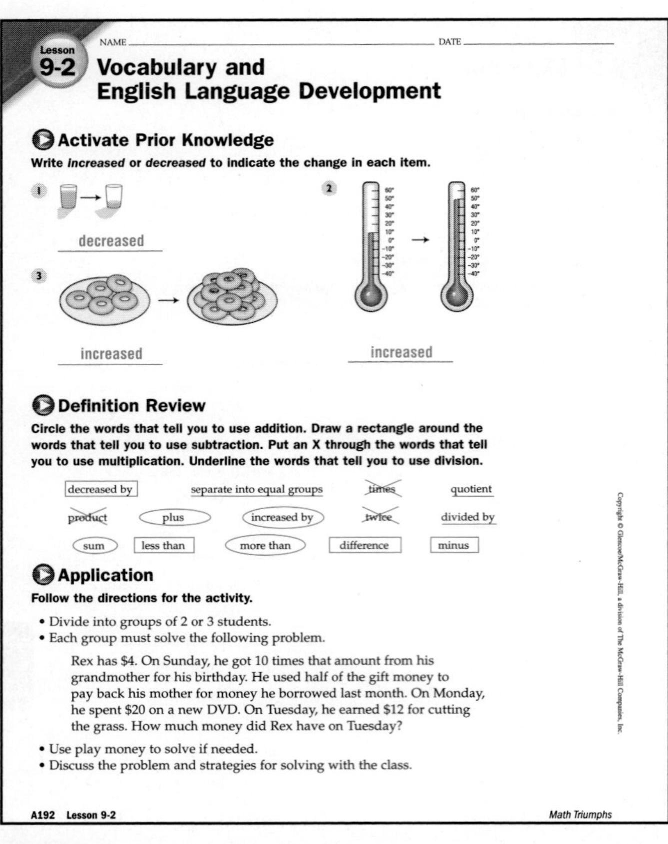

NAME ______ DATE ______

Lesson 9-2 **Vocabulary and English Language Development**

Activate Prior Knowledge

Write *increased* or *decreased* to indicate the change in each item.

1 decreased

2 increased

3 increased

Definition Review

Circle the words that tell you to use addition. Draw a rectangle around the words that tell you to use subtraction. Put an X through the words that tell you to use multiplication. Underline the words that tell you to use division.

decreased by | separate into equal groups | times | quotient
product | plus | increased by | twice | divided by
sum | less than | more than | difference | minus

Application

Follow the directions for the activity.

- Divide into groups of 2 or 3 students.
- Each group must solve the following problem.

Rex has $4. On Sunday, he got 10 times that amount from his grandmother for his birthday. He used half of the gift money to pay back his mother for money he borrowed last month. On Monday, he spent $20 on a new DVD. On Tuesday, he earned $12 for cutting the grass. How much money did Rex have on Tuesday?

- Use play money to solve if needed.
- Discuss the problem and strategies for solving with the class.

A192 Lesson 9-2 *Math Triumphs*

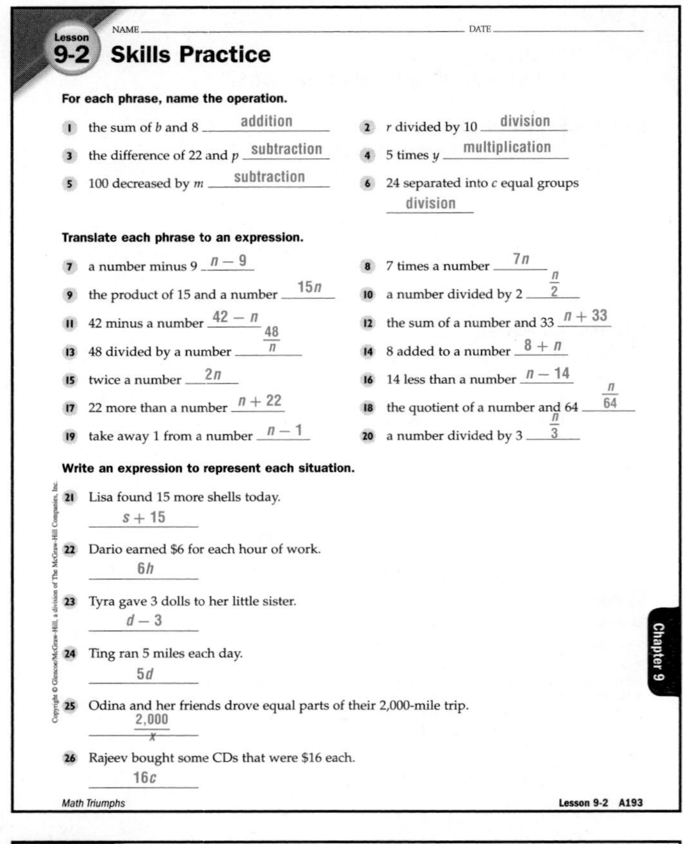

NAME ______ DATE ______

Lesson 9-2 **Skills Practice**

For each phrase, name the operation.

1 the sum of b and 8 addition

2 r divided by 10 division

3 the difference of 22 and p subtraction

4 5 times y multiplication

5 100 decreased by m subtraction

6 24 separated into c equal groups division

Translate each phrase to an expression.

7 a number minus 9 $n - 9$

8 7 times a number $7n$

9 the product of 15 and a number $15n$

10 a number divided by 2 $\frac{n}{2}$

11 42 minus a number $42 - n$

12 the sum of a number and 33 $n + 33$

13 48 divided by a number $\frac{48}{n}$

14 8 added to a number $8 + n$

15 twice a number $2n$

16 14 less than a number $n - 14$

17 22 more than a number $n + 22$

18 the quotient of a number and 64 $\frac{n}{64}$

19 take away 1 from a number $n - 1$

20 a number divided by 3 $\frac{n}{3}$

Write an expression to represent each situation.

21 Lisa found 15 more shells today. $s + 15$

22 Dario earned $6 for each hour of work. $6h$

23 Tyra gave 3 dolls to her little sister. $d - 3$

24 Ting ran 5 miles each day. $5d$

25 Odina and her friends drove equal parts of their 2,000-mile trip. $\frac{2{,}000}{x}$

26 Rajeev bought some CDs that were $16 each. $16c$

Chapter 9

Math Triumphs Lesson 9-2 A193

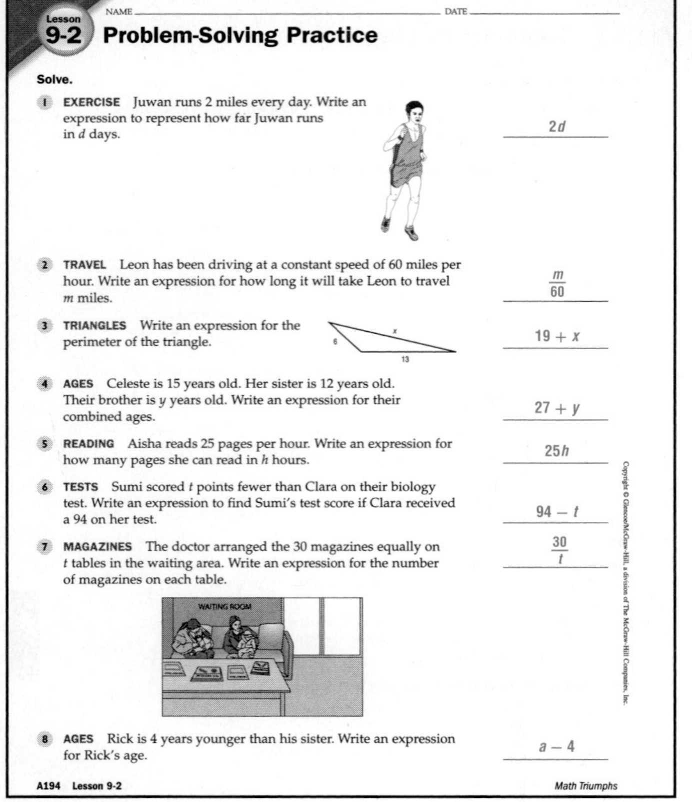

NAME ______ DATE ______

Lesson 9-2 **Problem-Solving Practice**

Solve.

1 **EXERCISE** Juwan runs 2 miles every day. Write an expression to represent how far Juwan runs in d days. $2d$

2 **TRAVEL** Leon has been driving at a constant speed of 60 miles per hour. Write an expression for how long it will take Leon to travel m miles. $\frac{m}{60}$

3 **TRIANGLES** Write an expression for the perimeter of the triangle. (sides 6, x, 13) $19 + x$

4 **AGES** Celeste is 15 years old. Her sister is 12 years old. Their brother is y years old. Write an expression for their combined ages. $27 + y$

5 **READING** Aisha reads 25 pages per hour. Write an expression for how many pages she can read in h hours. $25h$

6 **TESTS** Sumi scored t points fewer than Clara on their biology test. Write an expression to find Sumi's test score if Clara received a 94 on her test. $94 - t$

7 **MAGAZINES** The doctor arranged the 30 magazines equally on t tables in the waiting area. Write an expression for the number of magazines on each table. $\frac{30}{t}$

WAITING ROOM

8 **AGES** Rick is 4 years younger than his sister. Write an expression for Rick's age. $a - 4$

A194 Lesson 9-2 *Math Triumphs*

NAME ______ DATE ______

Lesson 9-2 **Homework Practice**

For each phrase, name the operation.

1 the quotient of t and 3 division

2 the number 2 plus q addition

3 5 times f multiplication

4 1 increased by m addition

5 the difference between k and 4 subtraction

6 the product of v and 10 multiplication

7 80 divided by r division

8 a decreased by 9 subtraction

Translate each phrase to an expression.

9 a number times 18 $18n$

10 46 plus a number $46 + n$

11 13 less than a number $n - 13$

12 a number divided by 11 $\frac{n}{11}$

13 a number minus 20 $n - 20$

14 53 more than a number $53 + n$

15 the quotient of a number and 4 $\frac{n}{4}$

16 1,000 decreased by a number $1{,}000 - n$

17 67 added to a number $n + 67$

18 the product of 3 and a number $3n$

Solve.

19 **PIZZA** An extra large pizza feeds 6 students. Write an expression to find the number of extra large pizzas needed for s students. $\frac{s}{6}$

20 **DRILLS** A factory produces 4 electric drills every minute. Write an expression for how many drills are made in m minutes. $4m$

Write the vocabulary word that completes the sentence.

21 A constant is a value that does not change.

22 A(n) algebraic expression is a combination of variables, numbers, and at least one operation.

Chapter 9

Math Triumphs Lesson 9-2 A195

Answer Key (Lesson 9-3)

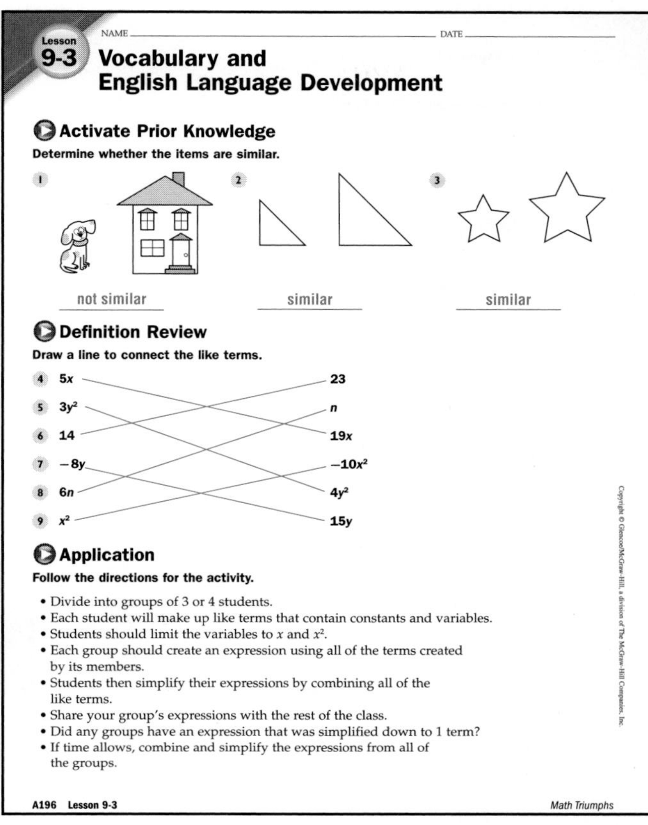

NAME ______ DATE ______

Lesson 9-3 Vocabulary and English Language Development

Activate Prior Knowledge

Determine whether the items are similar.

1 not similar

2 similar

3 similar

Definition Review

Draw a line to connect the like terms.

4 $5x$	23
5 $3y^2$	n
6 14	$19x$
7 $-8y$	$-10x^2$
8 $6n$	$4y^2$
9 x^2	$15y$

Application

Follow the directions for the activity.

- Divide into groups of 3 or 4 students.
- Each student will make up like terms that contain constants and variables.
- Students should limit the variables to x and x^2.
- Each group should create an expression using all of the terms created by its members.
- Students then simplify their expressions by combining all of the like terms.
- Share your group's expressions with the rest of the class.
- Did any groups have an expression that was simplified down to 1 term?
- If time allows, combine and simplify the expressions from all of the groups.

Copyright © Glencoe/McGraw-Hill, a division of The McGraw-Hill Companies, Inc.

A196 Lesson 9-3 Math Triumphs

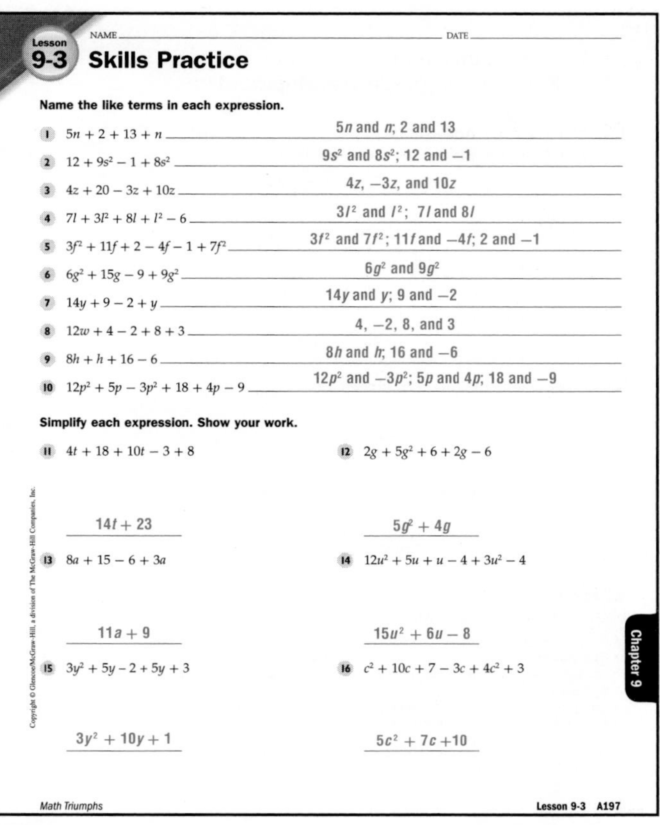

NAME ______ DATE ______

Lesson 9-3 Skills Practice

Name the like terms in each expression.

1 $5n + 2 + 13 + n$ — $5n$ and n; 2 and 13

2 $12 + 9s^2 - 1 + 8s^2$ — $9s^2$ and $8s^2$; 12 and -1

3 $4z + 20 - 3z + 10z$ — $4z$, $-3z$, and $10z$

4 $7l + 3l^2 + 8l + l^2 - 6$ — $3l^2$ and l^2; $7l$ and $8l$

5 $3f^2 + 11f + 2 - 4f - 1 + 7f^2$ — $3f^2$ and $7f^2$; $11f$ and $-4f$; 2 and -1

6 $6g^2 + 15g - 9 + 9g^2$ — $6g^2$ and $9g^2$

7 $14y + 9 - 2 + y$ — $14y$ and y; 9 and -2

8 $12w + 4 - 2 + 8 + 3$ — 4, -2, 8, and 3

9 $8h + h + 16 - 6$ — $8h$ and h; 16 and -6

10 $12p^2 + 5p - 3p^2 + 18 + 4p - 9$ — $12p^2$ and $-3p^2$; $5p$ and $4p$; 18 and -9

Simplify each expression. Show your work.

11 $4t + 18 + 10t - 3 + 8$ — $14t + 23$

12 $2g + 5g^2 + 6 + 2g - 6$ — $5g^2 + 4g$

13 $8a + 15 - 6 + 3a$ — $11a + 9$

14 $12u^2 + 5u + u - 4 + 3u^2 - 4$ — $15u^2 + 6u - 8$

15 $3y^2 + 5y - 2 + 5y + 3$ — $3y^2 + 10y + 1$

16 $c^2 + 10c + 7 - 3c + 4c^2 + 3$ — $5c^2 + 7c + 10$

Chapter 9

Copyright © Glencoe/McGraw-Hill, a division of The McGraw-Hill Companies, Inc.

Math Triumphs Lesson 9-3 A197

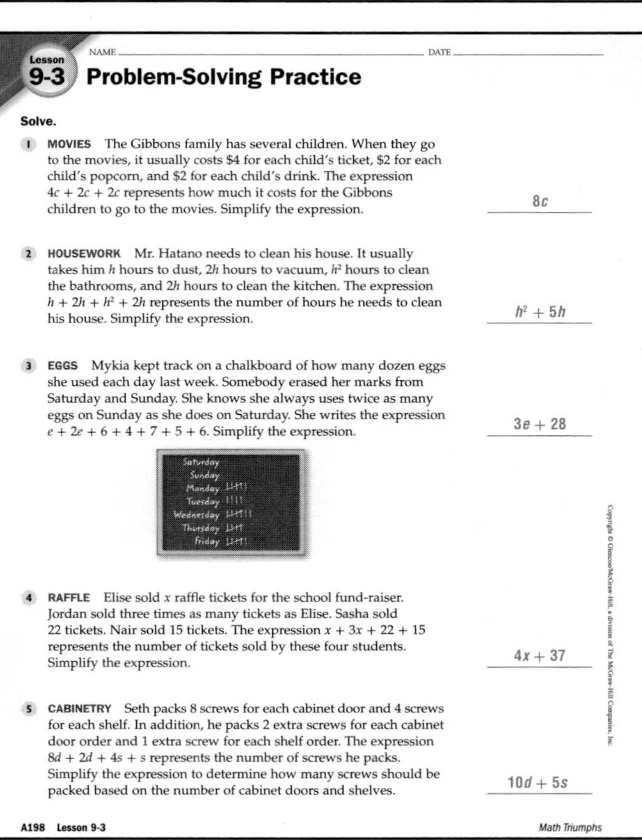

NAME ______ DATE ______

Lesson 9-3 Problem-Solving Practice

Solve.

1 **MOVIES** The Gibbons family has several children. When they go to the movies, it usually costs \$4 for each child's ticket, \$2 for each child's popcorn, and \$2 for each child's drink. The expression $4c + 2c + 2c$ represents how much it costs for the Gibbons children to go to the movies. Simplify the expression. $8c$

2 **HOUSEWORK** Mr. Hatano needs to clean his house. It usually takes him h hours to dust, $2h$ hours to vacuum, h^2 hours to clean the bathrooms, and $2h$ hours to clean the kitchen. The expression $h + 2h + h^2 + 2h$ represents the number of hours he needs to clean his house. Simplify the expression. $h^2 + 5h$

3 **EGGS** Mykia kept track on a chalkboard of how many dozen eggs she used each day last week. Somebody erased her marks from Saturday and Sunday. She knows she always uses twice as many eggs on Sunday as she does on Saturday. She writes the expression $e + 2e + 6 + 4 + 7 + 5 + 6$. Simplify the expression. $3e + 28$

Saturday
Sunday
Monday
Tuesday
Wednesday
Thursday
Friday

4 **RAFFLE** Elise sold x raffle tickets for the school fund-raiser. Jordan sold three times as many tickets as Elise. Sasha sold 22 tickets. Nair sold 15 tickets. The expression $x + 3x + 22 + 15$ represents the number of tickets sold by these four students. Simplify the expression. $4x + 37$

5 **CABINETRY** Seth packs 8 screws for each cabinet door and 4 screws for each shelf. In addition, he packs 2 extra screws for each cabinet door order and 1 extra screw for each shelf order. The expression $8d + 2d + 4s + s$ represents the number of screws he packs. Simplify the expression to determine how many screws should be packed based on the number of cabinet doors and shelves. $10d + 5s$

Copyright © Glencoe/McGraw-Hill, a division of The McGraw-Hill Companies, Inc.

A198 Lesson 9-3 Math Triumphs

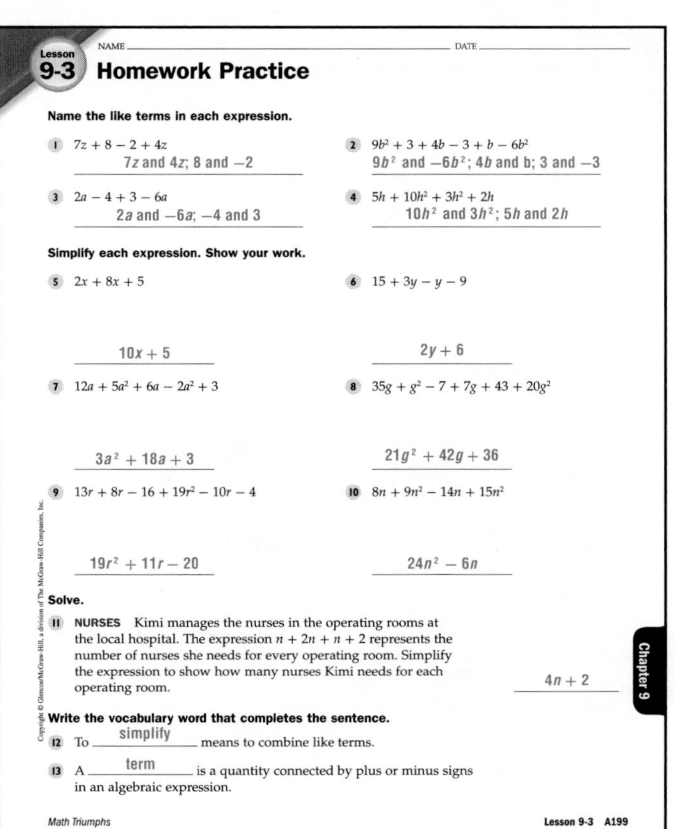

NAME ______ DATE ______

Lesson 9-3 Homework Practice

Name the like terms in each expression.

1 $7z + 8 - 2 + 4z$ — $7z$ and $4z$; 8 and -2

2 $9b^2 + 3 + 4b - 3 + b - 6b^2$ — $9b^2$ and $-6b^2$; $4b$ and b; 3 and -3

3 $2a - 4 + 3 - 6a$ — $2a$ and $-6a$; -4 and 3

4 $5h + 10h^2 + 3h^2 + 2h$ — $10h^2$ and $3h^2$; $5h$ and $2h$

Simplify each expression. Show your work.

5 $2x + 8x + 5$ — $10x + 5$

6 $15 + 3y - y - 9$ — $2y + 6$

7 $12a + 5a^2 + 6a - 2a^2 + 3$ — $3a^2 + 18a + 3$

8 $35g + g^2 - 7 + 7g + 43 + 20g^2$ — $21g^2 + 42g + 36$

9 $13r + 8r - 16 + 19r^2 - 10r - 4$ — $19r^2 + 11r - 20$

10 $8n + 9n^2 - 14n + 15n^2$ — $24n^2 - 6n$

Solve.

11 **NURSES** Kimi manages the nurses in the operating rooms at the local hospital. The expression $n + 2n + n + 2$ represents the number of nurses she needs for every operating room. Simplify the expression to show how many nurses Kimi needs for each operating room. $4n + 2$

Write the vocabulary word that completes the sentence.

12 To simplify means to combine like terms.

13 A term is a quantity connected by plus or minus signs in an algebraic expression.

Chapter 9

Copyright © Glencoe/McGraw-Hill, a division of The McGraw-Hill Companies, Inc.

Math Triumphs Lesson 9-3 A199

Answer Key (Lesson 9-4)

NAME ____ DATE ____

Lesson 9-4 Vocabulary and English Language Development

Activate Prior Knowledge

Simplify the expressions following the order of operations.

1. $12 + 8 \div 2$ 16
2. $5 \times 8 + 3$ 43
3. $2 + 7 \times 4$ 30
4. $9 \div 3 - 1 + 6$ 8

Definition Review

When you **evaluate** an **algebraic expression** you find the **value** of the expression by replacing the variables with numerals.

Write the words that explain the order of operations.

To use the order of operations

1. Simplify grouping symbols.
2. Simplify exponents.
3. Multiply and divide in order from left to right.
4. Add and subtract in order from left to right.

Application

Follow the directions for the activity.

- Divide into groups of 5 or 6 students.
- Each student will make up a term using either a, a^2, b, or b^2.
- Each group should create an expression using all of the terms created by its members.
- Groups exchange and simplify each other's expressions.
- They then choose a value for each variable in the expression and evaluate the expression.
- Groups review and share the expression they simplified and evaluated with the rest of the class.

NAME ____ DATE ____

Lesson 9-4 Skills Practice

Evaluate each expression when $x = 2$ and $y = 7$.

1. $x + 5 + y$ — $2 + 5 + 7 = 14$
2. $3y - 8 + x$ — $3(7) - 8 + 2 = 15$
3. $y^2 - x + 20$ — $7^2 - 2 + 20 = 67$
4. $5x + 3y - x^2$ — $5(2) + 3(7) - 2^2 = 27$
5. $xy - 1$ — $2(7) - 1 = 13$
6. $19 + x \div 2 - 2y$ — $19 + 2 \div 2 - 2(7) = 6$
7. $6 + 8y \div 4$ — $6 + 8(7) \div 4 = 20$
8. $y^2 - 4y + 2x$ — $7^2 - 4(7) + 2(2) = 25$
9. $2x \div 4 + 6y$ — $2(2) \div 4 + 6(7) = 43$
10. $10y - x^2$ — $10(7) - 2^2 = 66$
11. $18 + 12x \div 6$ — $18 + 12(2) \div 6 = 22$
12. $5y - 10 + x^2$ — $5(7) - 10 + 2^2 = 29$

Evaluate each expression when $a = 3$, $b = 4$, and $c = 5$.

13. $8a + b^2 - 55 \div c$ — $8(3) + 4^2 - 55 \div 5 = 29$
14. $3a - b + 6 - a^2$ — $3(3) - 4 + 6 - 3^2 = 2$
15. $18 + c + 2a - b$ — $18 + 5 + 2(3) - 4 = 25$
16. $10b + c^2 - (16 - 7)$ — $10(4) + 5^2 - (16 - 7) = 56$
17. $12 - b \div 2 + (b + c)^2$ — $12 - 4 \div 2 + (4 + 5)^2 = 91$
18. $9b \div 6 + 15 + b^2$ — $9(4) \div 6 + 15 + 4^2 = 37$
19. $(11c - 10a) \div c + 42$ — $(11(5) - 10(3)) \div 5 + 42 = 47$
20. $b + 6c + a^2$ — $4 + 6(5) + 3^2 = 43$
21. $10 - c + 12 - b + 9a$ — $10 - 5 + 12 - 4 + 9(3) = 40$
22. $14 + a^2 - 6 + b \div 2 - 8$ — $14 + 3^2 - 6 + 4 \div 2 - 8 = 11$

Chapter 9

NAME ____ DATE ____

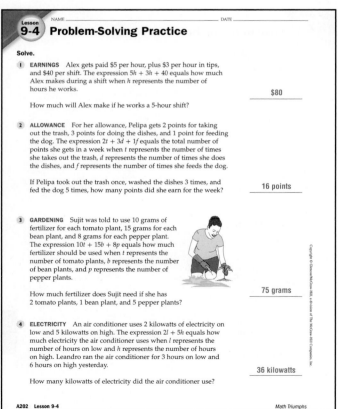

Lesson 9-4 Problem-Solving Practice

Solve.

1. **EARNINGS** Alex gets paid \$5 per hour, plus \$3 per hour in tips, and \$40 per shift. The expression $5h + 3h + 40$ equals how much Alex makes during a shift when h represents the number of hours he works.

   How much will Alex make if he works a 5-hour shift? \$80

2. **ALLOWANCE** For her allowance, Pelipa gets 2 points for taking out the trash, 3 points for doing the dishes, and 1 point for feeding the dog. The expression $2t + 3d + 1f$ equals the total number of points she gets in a week when t represents the number of times she takes out the trash, d represents the number of times she does the dishes, and f represents the number of times she feeds the dog.

   If Pelipa took out the trash once, washed the dishes 3 times, and fed the dog 5 times, how many points did she earn for the week? 16 points

3. **GARDENING** Sujit was told to use 10 grams of fertilizer for each tomato plant, 15 grams for each bean plant, and 8 grams for each pepper plant. The expression $10t + 15b + 8p$ equals how much fertilizer should be used when t represents the number of tomato plants, b represents the number of bean plants, and p represents the number of pepper plants.

   How much fertilizer does Sujit need if she has 2 tomato plants, 1 bean plant, and 5 pepper plants? 75 grams

4. **ELECTRICITY** An air conditioner uses 2 kilowatts of electricity on low and 5 kilowatts on high. The expression $2l + 5h$ equals how much electricity the air conditioner uses when l represents the number of hours on low and h represents the number of hours on high. Leandro ran the air conditioner for 3 hours on low and 6 hours on high yesterday.

   How many kilowatts of electricity did the air conditioner use? 36 kilowatts

NAME ____ DATE ____

Lesson 9-4 Homework Practice

Evaluate each expression when $x = 2$ and $y = 10$.

1. $17 + x$ 19
2. $x - 1 + y^2$ 101
3. $74 \div x$ 37
4. $y \div x + 3x$ 11
5. $7y + 6 - 3x$ 70
6. $x^2 + 139$ 143
7. $3y \div 5 + 4y \div 5$ 14
8. $11 - y + 6x$ 13

Evaluate each expression when $x = 8$, $y = 9$, and $z = 0$.

9. $x^2 + 3 - 10 + z^2$ 57
10. $5y - 2x + 15 - z$ 44
11. $7z - 4 + 3y$ 23
12. $20 - y + 5x + 6z$ 51
13. $6 + y^2 + 12 - x$ 91
14. $15 + x + y + z + 10y$ 122
15. $4x - z + x \div 2$ 36
16. $4y \div 6 + 7z + x$ 14

Solve.

17. Maria's cat is fed 2 scoops of dry food in the morning, and 1 cup of dry food at night. The expression $2s + c$ equals the number of dry food pieces the cat is fed per day, where s equals the number of pieces in a scoop and c equals the number of pieces in a cup. How many pieces of food does the cat eat per day if a scoop has 30 pieces and a cup has 75 pieces? 135 pieces

18. **BAKING** Oya needs 10 minutes to set up, 40 minutes to bake, and 20 minutes to clean up for each loaf of bread. The expression $10b + 40b + 20b$ equals the time it takes for b batches of bread. Oya wants to make 5 batches of bread tomorrow. How many minutes will it take him? 350 minutes

Write the vocabulary word that completes the sentence.

19. A(n) algebraic expression is a combination of variables, numbers, and at least one operation.

20. The order of operations are rules that tell which operation to perform first when more than one operation is used.

Chapter 9

Answer Key (Lesson 10-1)

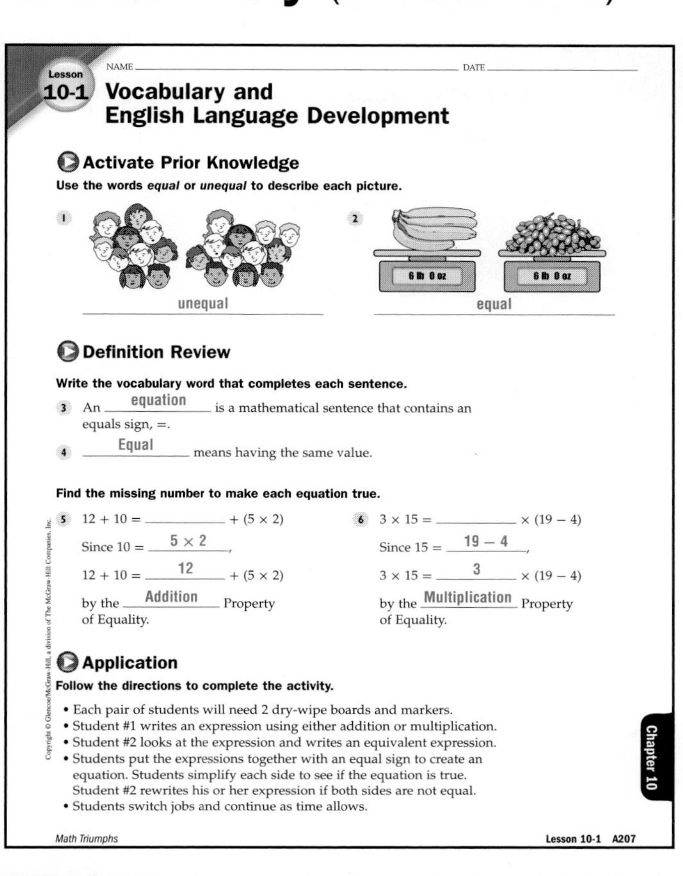

Lesson 10-1 NAME ______ DATE ______

Vocabulary and English Language Development

Activate Prior Knowledge

Use the words *equal* or *unequal* to describe each picture.

1 unequal

2 equal

Definition Review

Write the vocabulary word that completes each sentence.

3 An equation is a mathematical sentence that contains an equals sign, =.

4 Equal means having the same value.

Find the missing number to make each equation true.

5 $12 + 10 =$ ______ $+ (5 \times 2)$
Since $10 =$ 5×2,
$12 + 10 =$ 12 $+ (5 \times 2)$
by the Addition Property of Equality.

6 $3 \times 15 =$ ______ $\times (19 - 4)$
Since $15 =$ $19 - 4$,
$3 \times 15 =$ 3 $\times (19 - 4)$
by the Multiplication Property of Equality.

Application

Follow the directions to complete the activity.

- Each pair of students will need 2 dry-wipe boards and markers.
- Student #1 writes an expression using either addition or multiplication.
- Student #2 looks at the expression and writes an equivalent expression.
- Students put the expressions together with an equal sign to create an equation. Students simplify each side to see if the equation is true. Student #2 rewrites his or her expression if both sides are not equal.
- Students switch jobs and continue as time allows.

Chapter 10

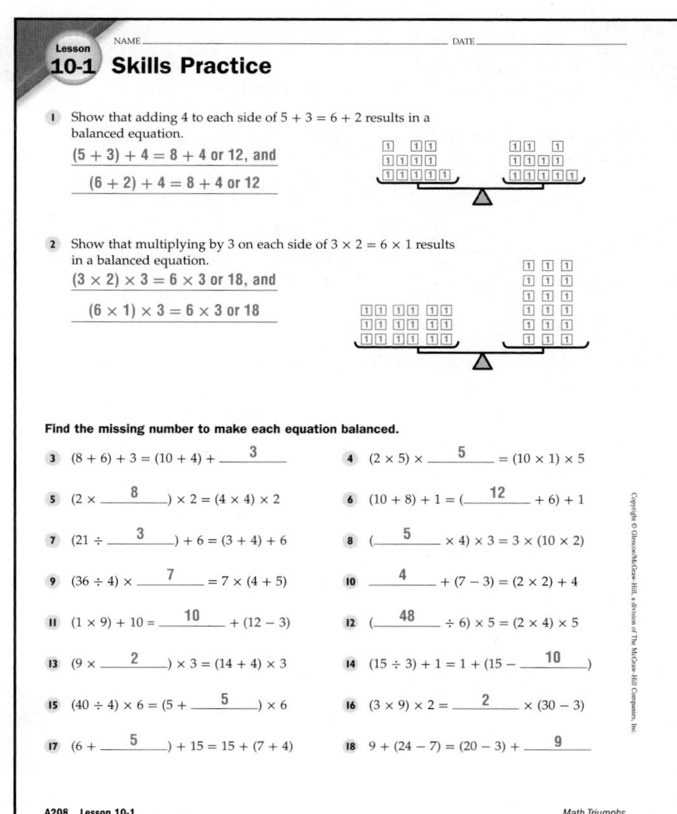

Lesson 10-1 NAME ______ DATE ______

Skills Practice

1 Show that adding 4 to each side of $5 + 3 = 6 + 2$ results in a balanced equation.
$(5 + 3) + 4 = 8 + 4$ or 12, and
$(6 + 2) + 4 = 8 + 4$ or 12

2 Show that multiplying by 3 on each side of $3 \times 2 = 6 \times 1$ results in a balanced equation.
$(3 \times 2) \times 3 = 6 \times 3$ or 18, and
$(6 \times 1) \times 3 = 6 \times 3$ or 18

Find the missing number to make each equation balanced.

3 $(8 + 6) + 3 = (10 + 4) +$ 3

4 $(2 \times 5) \times$ 5 $= (10 \times 1) \times 5$

5 $(2 \times$ 8 $) \times 2 = (4 \times 4) \times 2$

6 $(10 + 8) + 1 = ($ 12 $+ 6) + 1$

7 $(21 \div$ 3 $) + 6 = (3 + 4) + 6$

8 $($ 5 $\times 4) \times 3 = 3 \times (10 \times 2)$

9 $(36 \div 4) \times$ 7 $= 7 \times (4 + 5)$

10 4 $+ (7 - 3) = (2 \times 2) + 4$

11 $(1 \times 9) + 10 =$ 10 $+ (12 - 3)$

12 $($ 48 $\div 6) \times 5 = (2 \times 4) \times 5$

13 $(9 \times$ 2 $) \times 3 = (14 + 4) \times 3$

14 $(15 \div 3) + 1 = 1 + (15 -$ 10 $)$

15 $(40 \div 4) \times 6 = (5 +$ 5 $) \times 6$

16 $(3 \times 9) \times 2 =$ 2 $\times (30 - 3)$

17 $(6 +$ 5 $) + 15 = 15 + (7 + 4)$

18 $9 + (24 - 7) = (20 - 3) +$ 9

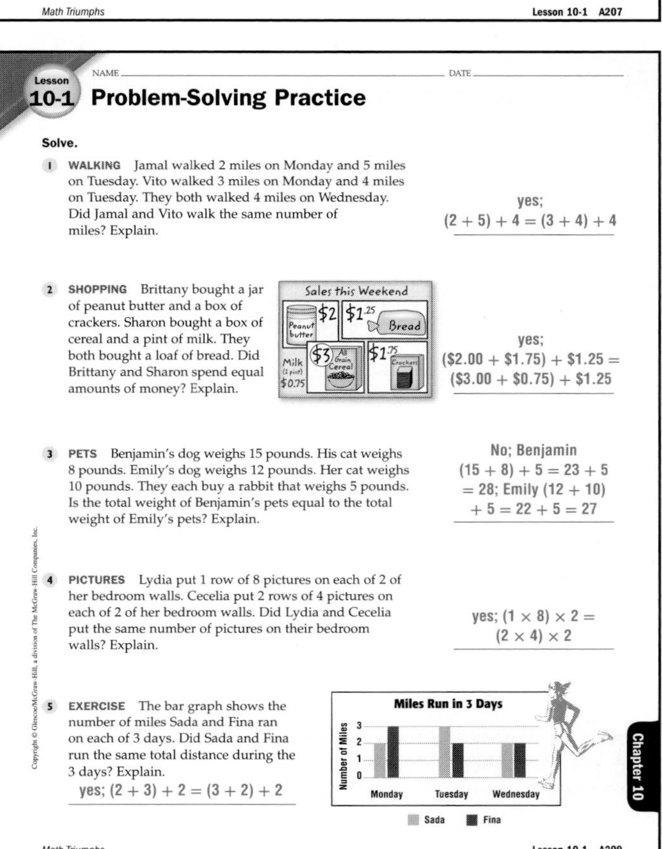

Lesson 10-1 NAME ______ DATE ______

Problem-Solving Practice

Solve.

1 **WALKING** Jamal walked 2 miles on Monday and 5 miles on Tuesday. Vito walked 3 miles on Monday and 4 miles on Tuesday. They both walked 4 miles on Wednesday. Did Jamal and Vito walk the same number of miles? Explain.
yes; $(2 + 5) + 4 = (3 + 4) + 4$

2 **SHOPPING** Brittany bought a jar of peanut butter and a box of crackers. Sharon bought a box of cereal and a pint of milk. They both bought a loaf of bread. Did Brittany and Sharon spend equal amounts of money? Explain.
yes; $(\$2.00 + \$1.75) + \$1.25 = (\$3.00 + \$0.75) + \$1.25$

3 **PETS** Benjamin's dog weighs 15 pounds. His cat weighs 8 pounds. Emily's dog weighs 12 pounds. Her cat weighs 10 pounds. They each buy a rabbit that weighs 5 pounds. Is the total weight of Benjamin's pets equal to the total weight of Emily's pets? Explain.
No; Benjamin $(15 + 8) + 5 = 23 + 5 = 28$; Emily $(12 + 10) + 5 = 22 + 5 = 27$

4 **PICTURES** Lydia put 1 row of 8 pictures on each of 2 of her bedroom walls. Cecelia put 2 rows of 4 pictures on each of 2 of her bedroom walls. Did Lydia and Cecelia put the same number of pictures on their bedroom walls? Explain.
yes; $(1 \times 8) \times 2 = (2 \times 4) \times 2$

5 **EXERCISE** The bar graph shows the number of miles Sada and Fina ran on each of 3 days. Did Sada and Fina run the same total distance during the 3 days? Explain.
yes; $(2 + 3) + 2 = (3 + 2) + 2$

Chapter 10

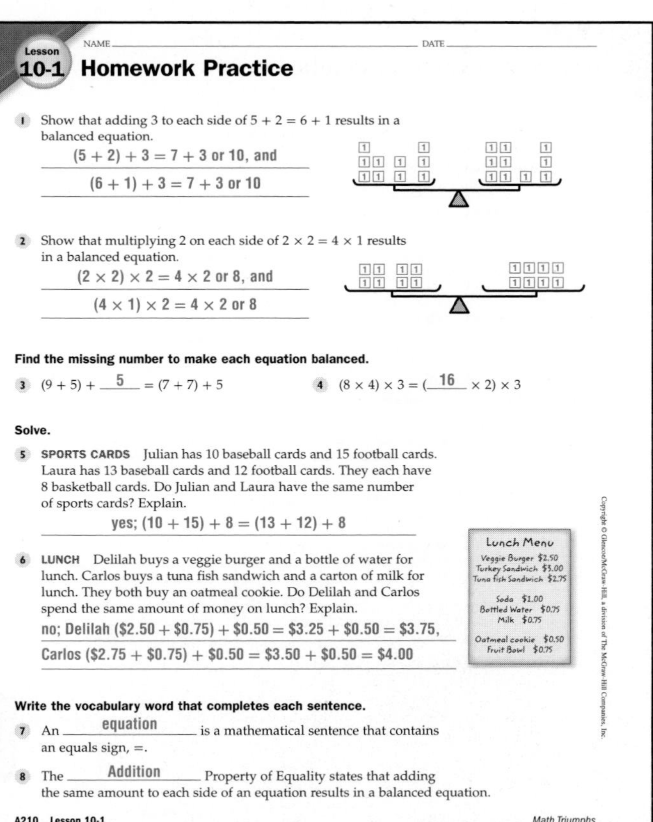

Lesson 10-1 NAME ______ DATE ______

Homework Practice

1 Show that adding 3 to each side of $5 + 2 = 6 + 1$ results in a balanced equation.
$(5 + 2) + 3 = 7 + 3$ or 10, and
$(6 + 1) + 3 = 7 + 3$ or 10

2 Show that multiplying 2 on each side of $2 \times 2 = 4 \times 1$ results in a balanced equation.
$(2 \times 2) \times 2 = 4 \times 2$ or 8, and
$(4 \times 1) \times 2 = 4 \times 2$ or 8

Find the missing number to make each equation balanced.

3 $(9 + 5) +$ 5 $= (7 + 7) + 5$

4 $(8 \times 4) \times 3 = ($ 16 $\times 2) \times 3$

Solve.

5 **SPORTS CARDS** Julian has 10 baseball cards and 15 football cards. Laura has 13 baseball cards and 12 football cards. They each have 8 basketball cards. Do Julian and Laura have the same number of sports cards? Explain.
yes; $(10 + 15) + 8 = (13 + 12) + 8$

6 **LUNCH** Delilah buys a veggie burger and a bottle of water for lunch. Carlos buys a tuna fish sandwich and a carton of milk for lunch. They both buy an oatmeal cookie. Do Delilah and Carlos spend the same amount of money on lunch? Explain.
no; Delilah $(\$2.50 + \$0.75) + \$0.50 = \$3.25 + \$0.50 = \$3.75$,
Carlos $(\$2.75 + \$0.75) + \$0.50 = \$3.50 + \$0.50 = \$4.00$

Write the vocabulary word that completes each sentence.

7 An equation is a mathematical sentence that contains an equals sign, =.

8 The Addition Property of Equality states that adding the same amount to each side of an equation results in a balanced equation.

Answer Key (Lesson 10-2)

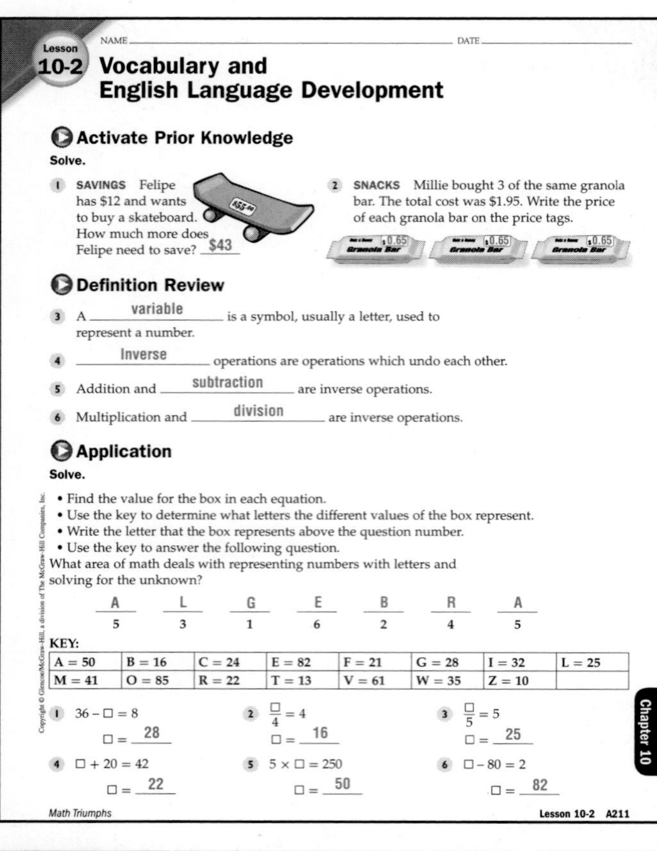

Lesson 10-2 NAME ________ DATE ________

Vocabulary and English Language Development

Activate Prior Knowledge

Solve.

1. **SAVINGS** Felipe has $12 and wants to buy a skateboard. How much more does Felipe need to save? $43

2. **SNACKS** Millie bought 3 of the same granola bar. The total cost was $1.95. Write the price of each granola bar on the price tags. $0.65 $0.65 $0.65

Definition Review

3. A variable is a symbol, usually a letter, used to represent a number.
4. Inverse operations are operations which undo each other.
5. Addition and subtraction are inverse operations.
6. Multiplication and division are inverse operations.

Application

Solve.

- Find the value for the box in each equation.
- Use the key to determine what letters the different values of the box represent.
- Write the letter that the box represents above the question number.
- Use the key to answer the following question.

What area of math deals with representing numbers with letters and solving for the unknown?

A	L	G	E	B	R	A
5	3	1	6	2	4	5

KEY:

A = 50	B = 16	C = 24	E = 82	F = 21	G = 28	I = 32	L = 25
M = 41	O = 85	R = 22	T = 13	V = 61	W = 35	Z = 10	

1. $36 - \square = 8$ $\square =$ 28
2. $\frac{\square}{4} = 4$ $\square =$ 16
3. $\frac{\square}{5} = 5$ $\square =$ 25
4. $\square + 20 = 42$ $\square =$ 22
5. $5 \times \square = 250$ $\square =$ 50
6. $\square - 80 = 2$ $\square =$ 82

Chapter 10

Math Triumphs Lesson 10-2 A211

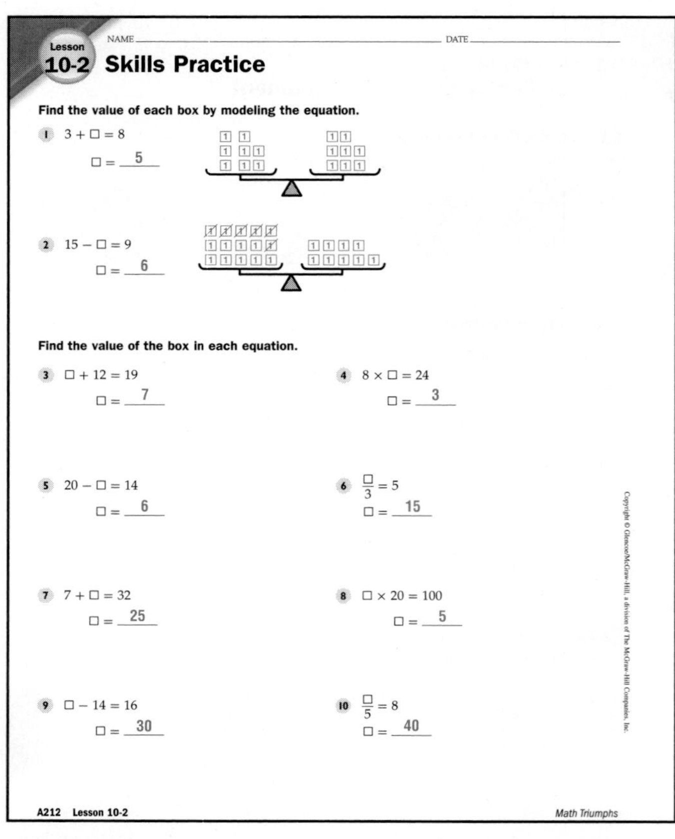

Lesson 10-2 NAME ________ DATE ________

Skills Practice

Find the value of each box by modeling the equation.

1. $3 + \square = 8$ $\square =$ 5
2. $15 - \square = 9$ $\square =$ 6

Find the value of the box in each equation.

3. $\square + 12 = 19$ $\square =$ 7
4. $8 \times \square = 24$ $\square =$ 3
5. $20 - \square = 14$ $\square =$ 6
6. $\frac{\square}{3} = 5$ $\square =$ 15
7. $7 + \square = 32$ $\square =$ 25
8. $\square \times 20 = 100$ $\square =$ 5
9. $\square - 14 = 16$ $\square =$ 30
10. $\frac{\square}{5} = 8$ $\square =$ 40

A212 Lesson 10-2 Math Triumphs

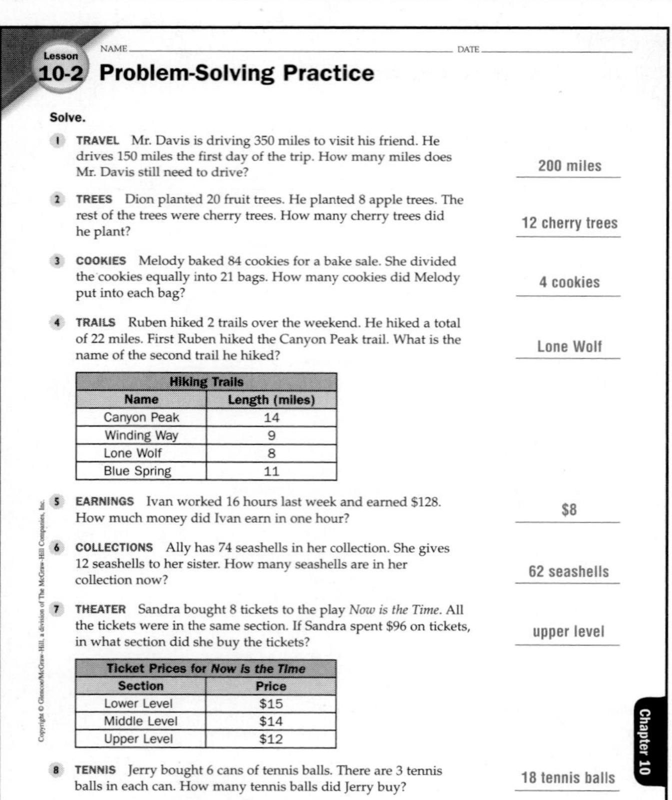

Lesson 10-2 NAME ________ DATE ________

Problem-Solving Practice

Solve.

1. **TRAVEL** Mr. Davis is driving 350 miles to visit his friend. He drives 150 miles the first day of the trip. How many miles does Mr. Davis still need to drive? 200 miles
2. **TREES** Dion planted 20 fruit trees. He planted 8 apple trees. The rest of the trees were cherry trees. How many cherry trees did he plant? 12 cherry trees
3. **COOKIES** Melody baked 84 cookies for a bake sale. She divided the cookies equally into 21 bags. How many cookies did Melody put into each bag? 4 cookies
4. **TRAILS** Ruben hiked 2 trails over the weekend. He hiked a total of 22 miles. First Ruben hiked the Canyon Peak trail. What is the name of the second trail he hiked? Lone Wolf

Hiking Trails	
Name	**Length (miles)**
Canyon Peak	14
Winding Way	9
Lone Wolf	8
Blue Spring	11

5. **EARNINGS** Ivan worked 16 hours last week and earned $128. How much money did Ivan earn in one hour? $8
6. **COLLECTIONS** Ally has 74 seashells in her collection. She gives 12 seashells to her sister. How many seashells are in her collection now? 62 seashells
7. **THEATER** Sandra bought 8 tickets to the play *Now is the Time*. All the tickets were in the same section. If Sandra spent $96 on tickets, in what section did she buy the tickets? upper level

Ticket Prices for *Now Is the Time*	
Section	**Price**
Lower Level	$15
Middle Level	$14
Upper Level	$12

8. **TENNIS** Jerry bought 6 cans of tennis balls. There are 3 tennis balls in each can. How many tennis balls did Jerry buy? 18 tennis balls

Chapter 10

Math Triumphs Lesson 10-2 A213

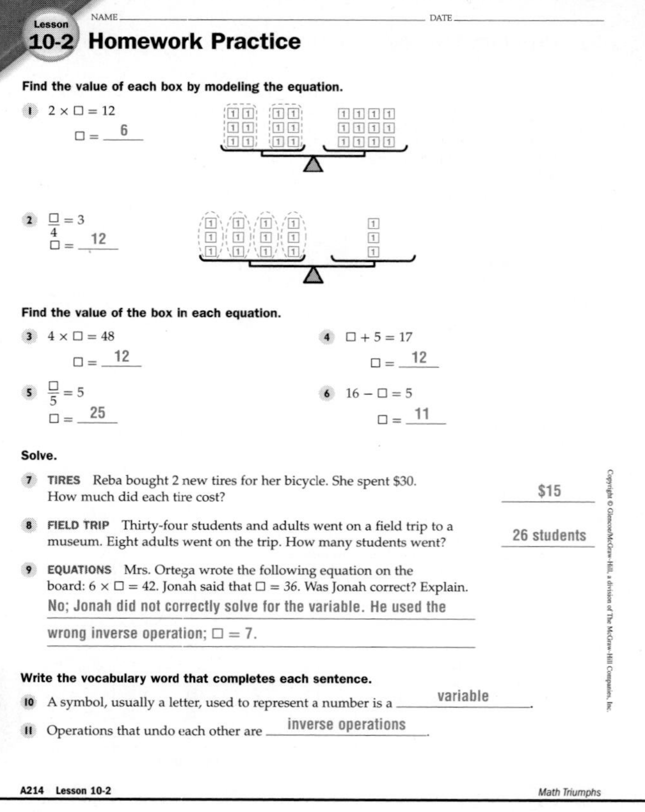

Lesson 10-2 NAME ________ DATE ________

Homework Practice

Find the value of each box by modeling the equation.

1. $2 \times \square = 12$ $\square =$ 6
2. $\frac{\square}{4} = 3$ $\square =$ 12

Find the value of the box in each equation.

3. $4 \times \square = 48$ $\square =$ 12
4. $\square + 5 = 17$ $\square =$ 12
5. $\frac{\square}{5} = 5$ $\square =$ 25
6. $16 - \square = 5$ $\square =$ 11

Solve.

7. **TIRES** Reba bought 2 new tires for her bicycle. She spent $30. How much did each tire cost? $15
8. **FIELD TRIP** Thirty-four students and adults went on a field trip to a museum. Eight adults went on the trip. How many students went? 26 students
9. **EQUATIONS** Mrs. Ortega wrote the following equation on the board: $6 \times \square = 42$. Jonah said that $\square = 36$. Was Jonah correct? Explain. No; Jonah did not correctly solve for the variable. He used the wrong inverse operation; $\square = 7$.

Write the vocabulary word that completes each sentence.

10. A symbol, usually a letter, used to represent a number is a variable.
11. Operations that undo each other are inverse operations.

A214 Lesson 10-2 Math Triumphs

Answer Key (Lesson 10-3)

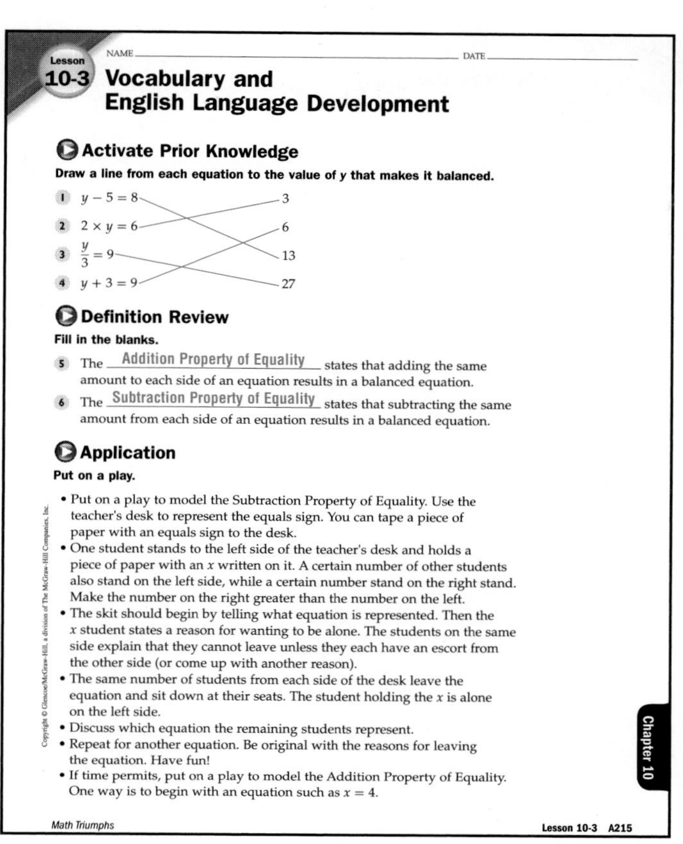

Lesson 10-3 NAME ______ DATE ______

Vocabulary and English Language Development

Activate Prior Knowledge

Draw a line from each equation to the value of y that makes it balanced.

1. $y - 5 = 8$ — 13
2. $2 \times y = 6$ — 3
3. $\frac{y}{3} = 9$ — 27
4. $y + 3 = 9$ — 6

Definition Review

Fill in the blanks.

5. The Addition Property of Equality states that adding the same amount to each side of an equation results in a balanced equation.
6. The Subtraction Property of Equality states that subtracting the same amount from each side of an equation results in a balanced equation.

Application

Put on a play.

- Put on a play to model the Subtraction Property of Equality. Use the teacher's desk to represent the equals sign. You can tape a piece of paper with an equals sign to the desk.
- One student stands to the left side of the teacher's desk and holds a piece of paper with an x written on it. A certain number of other students also stand on the left side, while a certain number stand on the right stand. Make the number on the right greater than the number on the left.
- The skit should begin by telling what equation is represented. Then the x student states a reason for wanting to be alone. The students on the same side explain that they cannot leave unless they each have an escort from the other side (or come up with another reason).
- The same number of students from each side of the desk leave the equation and sit down at their seats. The student holding the x is alone on the left side.
- Discuss which equation the remaining students represent.
- Repeat for another equation. Be original with the reasons for leaving the equation. Have fun!
- If time permits, put on a play to model the Addition Property of Equality. One way is to begin with an equation such as $x = 4$.

Chapter 10

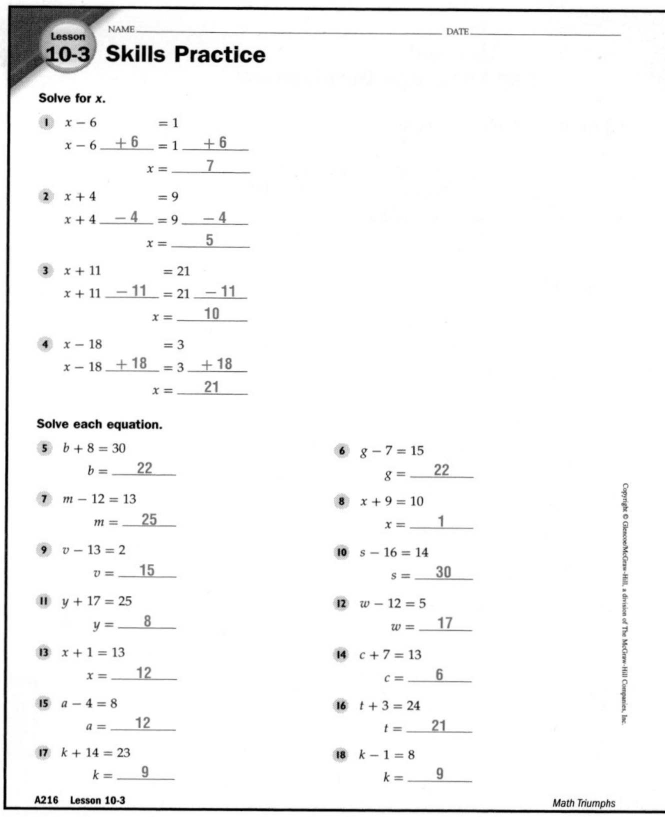

Lesson 10-3 NAME ______ DATE ______

Skills Practice

Solve for x.

1. $x - 6 = 1$; $x - 6 \underline{+6} = 1 \underline{+6}$; $x = \underline{7}$
2. $x + 4 = 9$; $x + 4 \underline{-4} = 9 \underline{-4}$; $x = \underline{5}$
3. $x + 11 = 21$; $x + 11 \underline{-11} = 21 \underline{-11}$; $x = \underline{10}$
4. $x - 18 = 3$; $x - 18 \underline{+18} = 3 \underline{+18}$; $x = \underline{21}$

Solve each equation.

5. $b + 8 = 30$; $b = \underline{22}$
6. $g - 7 = 15$; $g = \underline{22}$
7. $m - 12 = 13$; $m = \underline{25}$
8. $x + 9 = 10$; $x = \underline{1}$
9. $v - 13 = 2$; $v = \underline{15}$
10. $s - 16 = 14$; $s = \underline{30}$
11. $y + 17 = 25$; $y = \underline{8}$
12. $w - 12 = 5$; $w = \underline{17}$
13. $x + 1 = 13$; $x = \underline{12}$
14. $c + 7 = 13$; $c = \underline{6}$
15. $a - 4 = 8$; $a = \underline{12}$
16. $t + 3 = 24$; $t = \underline{21}$
17. $k + 14 = 23$; $k = \underline{9}$
18. $k - 1 = 8$; $k = \underline{9}$

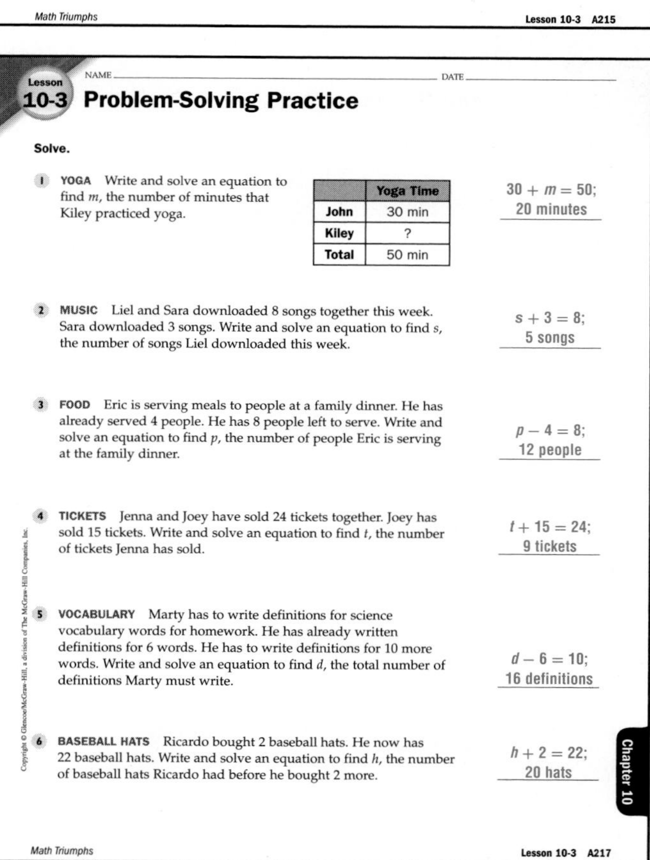

Lesson 10-3 NAME ______ DATE ______

Problem-Solving Practice

Solve.

1. **YOGA** Write and solve an equation to find m, the number of minutes that Kiley practiced yoga.

	Yoga Time
John	30 min
Kiley	?
Total	50 min

$30 + m = 50$; 20 minutes

2. **MUSIC** Liel and Sara downloaded 8 songs together this week. Sara downloaded 3 songs. Write and solve an equation to find s, the number of songs Liel downloaded this week. $s + 3 = 8$; 5 songs

3. **FOOD** Eric is serving meals to people at a family dinner. He has already served 4 people. He has 8 people left to serve. Write and solve an equation to find p, the number of people Eric is serving at the family dinner. $p - 4 = 8$; 12 people

4. **TICKETS** Jenna and Joey have sold 24 tickets together. Joey has sold 15 tickets. Write and solve an equation to find t, the number of tickets Jenna has sold. $t + 15 = 24$; 9 tickets

5. **VOCABULARY** Marty has to write definitions for science vocabulary words for homework. He has already written definitions for 6 words. He has to write definitions for 10 more words. Write and solve an equation to find d, the total number of definitions Marty must write. $d - 6 = 10$; 16 definitions

6. **BASEBALL HATS** Ricardo bought 2 baseball hats. He now has 22 baseball hats. Write and solve an equation to find h, the number of baseball hats Ricardo had before he bought 2 more. $h + 2 = 22$; 20 hats

Chapter 10

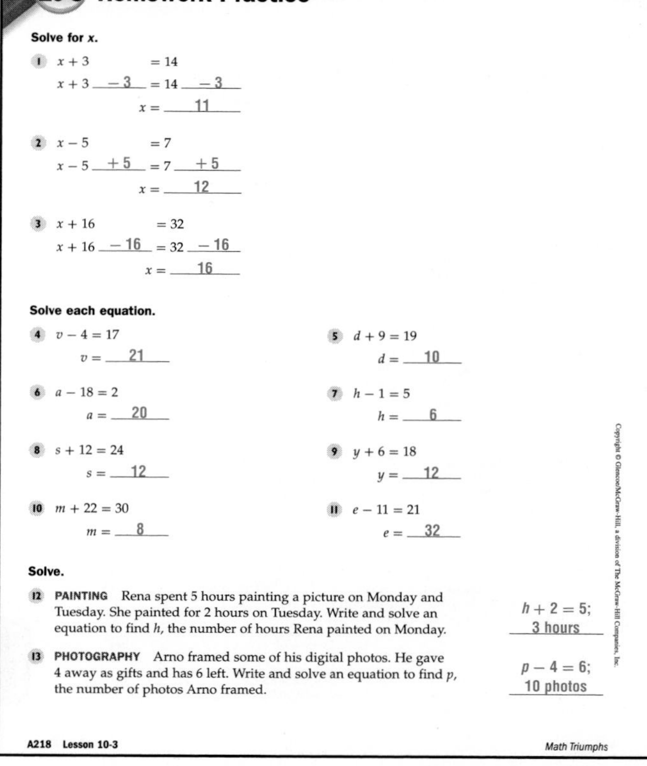

Lesson 10-3 NAME ______ DATE ______

Homework Practice

Solve for x.

1. $x + 3 = 14$; $x + 3 \underline{-3} = 14 \underline{-3}$; $x = \underline{11}$
2. $x - 5 = 7$; $x - 5 \underline{+5} = 7 \underline{+5}$; $x = \underline{12}$
3. $x + 16 = 32$; $x + 16 \underline{-16} = 32 \underline{-16}$; $x = \underline{16}$

Solve each equation.

4. $v - 4 = 17$; $v = \underline{21}$
5. $d + 9 = 19$; $d = \underline{10}$
6. $a - 18 = 2$; $a = \underline{20}$
7. $h - 1 = 5$; $h = \underline{6}$
8. $s + 12 = 24$; $s = \underline{12}$
9. $y + 6 = 18$; $y = \underline{12}$
10. $m + 22 = 30$; $m = \underline{8}$
11. $e - 11 = 21$; $e = \underline{32}$

Solve.

12. **PAINTING** Rena spent 5 hours painting a picture on Monday and Tuesday. She painted for 2 hours on Tuesday. Write and solve an equation to find h, the number of hours Rena painted on Monday. $h + 2 = 5$; 3 hours

13. **PHOTOGRAPHY** Arno framed some of his digital photos. He gave 4 away as gifts and has 6 left. Write and solve an equation to find p, the number of photos Arno framed. $p - 4 = 6$; 10 photos

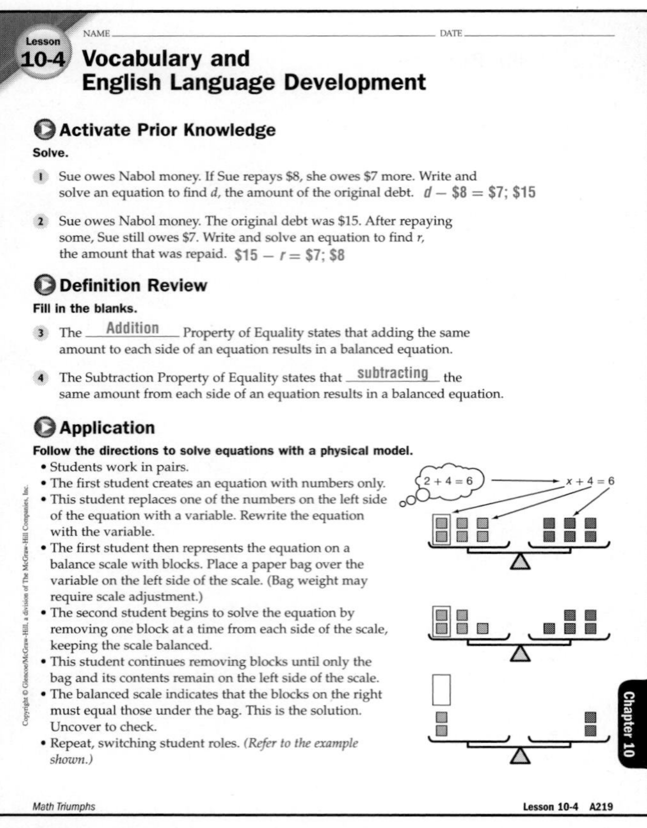

Lesson 10-4 NAME ________ DATE ________

Vocabulary and English Language Development

Activate Prior Knowledge

Solve.

1. Sue owes Nabol money. If Sue repays \$8, she owes \$7 more. Write and solve an equation to find d, the amount of the original debt. $d - \$8 = \$7$; \$15
2. Sue owes Nabol money. The original debt was \$15. After repaying some, Sue still owes \$7. Write and solve an equation to find r, the amount that was repaid. $\$15 - r = \$7$; \$8

Definition Review

Fill in the blanks.

3. The __Addition__ Property of Equality states that adding the same amount to each side of an equation results in a balanced equation.
4. The Subtraction Property of Equality states that __subtracting__ the same amount from each side of an equation results in a balanced equation.

Application

Follow the directions to solve equations with a physical model.

- Students work in pairs.
- The first student creates an equation with numbers only.
- This student replaces one of the numbers on the left side of the equation with a variable. Rewrite the equation with the variable.
- The first student then represents the equation on a balance scale with blocks. Place a paper bag over the variable on the left side of the scale. (Bag weight may require scale adjustment.)
- The second student begins to solve the equation by removing one block at a time from each side of the scale, keeping the scale balanced.
- This student continues removing blocks until only the bag and its contents remain on the left side of the scale.
- The balanced scale indicates that the blocks on the right must equal those under the bag. This is the solution. Uncover to check.
- Repeat, switching student roles. *(Refer to the example shown.)*

$2 + 4 = 6$ → $x + 4 = 6$

Chapter 10

Math Triumphs — Lesson 10-4 A219

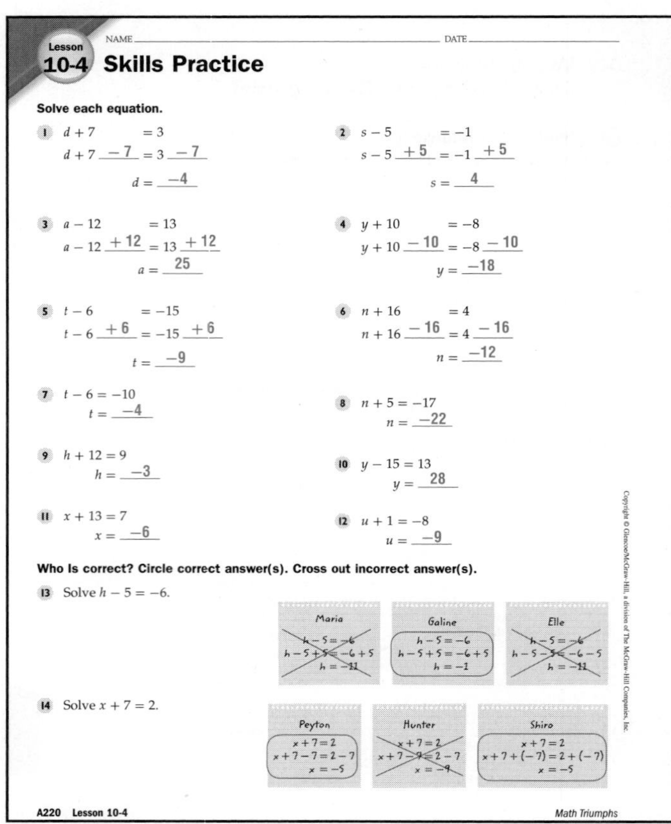

Lesson 10-4 NAME ________ DATE ________

Skills Practice

Solve each equation.

1. $d + 7 = 3$; $d + 7 \underline{-7} = 3 \underline{-7}$; $d = \underline{-4}$
2. $s - 5 = -1$; $s - 5 \underline{+5} = -1 \underline{+5}$; $s = \underline{4}$
3. $a - 12 = 13$; $a - 12 \underline{+12} = 13 \underline{+12}$; $a = \underline{25}$
4. $y + 10 = -8$; $y + 10 \underline{-10} = -8 \underline{-10}$; $y = \underline{-18}$
5. $t - 6 = -15$; $t - 6 \underline{+6} = -15 \underline{+6}$; $t = \underline{-9}$
6. $n + 16 = 4$; $n + 16 \underline{-16} = 4 \underline{-16}$; $n = \underline{-12}$
7. $t - 6 = -10$; $t = \underline{-4}$
8. $n + 5 = -17$; $n = \underline{-22}$
9. $h + 12 = 9$; $h = \underline{-3}$
10. $y - 15 = 13$; $y = \underline{28}$
11. $x + 13 = 7$; $x = \underline{-6}$
12. $u + 1 = -8$; $u = \underline{-9}$

Who Is correct? Circle correct answer(s). Cross out incorrect answer(s).

13. Solve $h - 5 = -6$.
    - Maria (crossed out): $h-5=-6$; $h-5+5=-6+5$; $h=-11$
    - Galine (circled): $h-5=-6$; $h-5+5=-6+5$; $h=-1$
    - Elle (crossed out): $h-5=-6$; $h-5-5=-6-5$; $h=-11$
14. Solve $x + 7 = 2$.
    - Peyton (circled): $x+7=2$; $x+7-7=2-7$; $x=-5$
    - Hunter (crossed out): $x+7=2$; $x+7-9=2-7$; $x=-4$
    - Shiro (circled): $x+7=2$; $x+7+(-7)=2+(-7)$; $x=-5$

A220 Lesson 10-4 — Math Triumphs

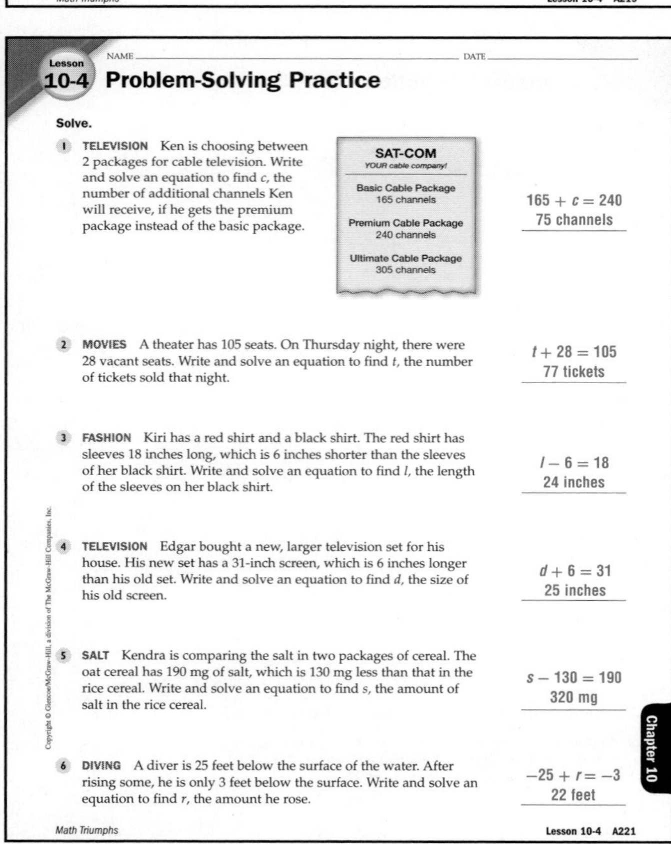

Lesson 10-4 NAME ________ DATE ________

Problem-Solving Practice

Solve.

1. **TELEVISION** Ken is choosing between 2 packages for cable television. Write and solve an equation to find c, the number of additional channels Ken will receive, if he gets the premium package instead of the basic package. $165 + c = 240$; 75 channels

   SAT-COM — YOUR cable company! Basic Cable Package: 165 channels. Premium Cable Package: 240 channels. Ultimate Cable Package: 305 channels.

2. **MOVIES** A theater has 105 seats. On Thursday night, there were 28 vacant seats. Write and solve an equation to find t, the number of tickets sold that night. $t + 28 = 105$; 77 tickets
3. **FASHION** Kiri has a red shirt and a black shirt. The red shirt has sleeves 18 inches long, which is 6 inches shorter than the sleeves of her black shirt. Write and solve an equation to find l, the length of the sleeves on her black shirt. $l - 6 = 18$; 24 inches
4. **TELEVISION** Edgar bought a new, larger television set for his house. His new set has a 31-inch screen, which is 6 inches longer than his old set. Write and solve an equation to find d, the size of his old screen. $d + 6 = 31$; 25 inches
5. **SALT** Kendra is comparing the salt in two packages of cereal. The oat cereal has 190 mg of salt, which is 130 mg less than that in the rice cereal. Write and solve an equation to find s, the amount of salt in the rice cereal. $s - 130 = 190$; 320 mg
6. **DIVING** A diver is 25 feet below the surface of the water. After rising some, he is only 3 feet below the surface. Write and solve an equation to find r, the amount he rose. $-25 + r = -3$; 22 feet

Chapter 10

Math Triumphs — Lesson 10-4 A221

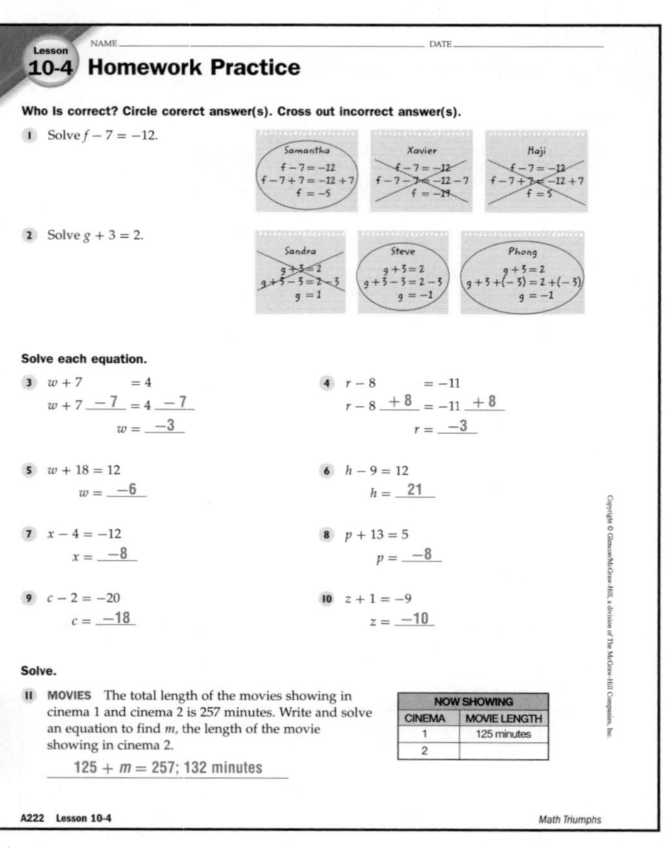

Lesson 10-4 NAME ________ DATE ________

Homework Practice

Who Is correct? Circle corerct answer(s). Cross out incorrect answer(s).

1. Solve $f - 7 = -12$.
    - Samantha (circled): $f-7=-12$; $f-7+7=-12+7$; $f=-5$
    - Xavier (crossed out): $f-7=-12$; $f-7-7=-12-7$; $f=-19$
    - Haji (crossed out): $f-7=-12$; $f-7+7=-12+7$; $f=5$
2. Solve $g + 3 = 2$.
    - Sandra (crossed out): $g+3=2$; $g+3-3=2-3$; $g=1$
    - Steve (circled): $g+3=2$; $g+3-3=2-3$; $g=-1$
    - Phong (circled): $g+3=2$; $g+3+(-3)=2+(-3)$; $g=-1$

Solve each equation.

3. $w + 7 = 4$; $w + 7 \underline{-7} = 4 \underline{-7}$; $w = \underline{-3}$
4. $r - 8 = -11$; $r - 8 \underline{+8} = -11 \underline{+8}$; $r = \underline{-3}$
5. $w + 18 = 12$; $w = \underline{-6}$
6. $h - 9 = 12$; $h = \underline{21}$
7. $x - 4 = -12$; $x = \underline{-8}$
8. $p + 13 = 5$; $p = \underline{-8}$
9. $c - 2 = -20$; $c = \underline{-18}$
10. $z + 1 = -9$; $z = \underline{-10}$

Solve.

11. **MOVIES** The total length of the movies showing in cinema 1 and cinema 2 is 257 minutes. Write and solve an equation to find m, the length of the movie showing in cinema 2. $125 + m = 257$; 132 minutes

NOW SHOWING	
CINEMA	MOVIE LENGTH
1	125 minutes
2	

A222 Lesson 10-4 — Math Triumphs

Answer Key (Lesson 10-5)

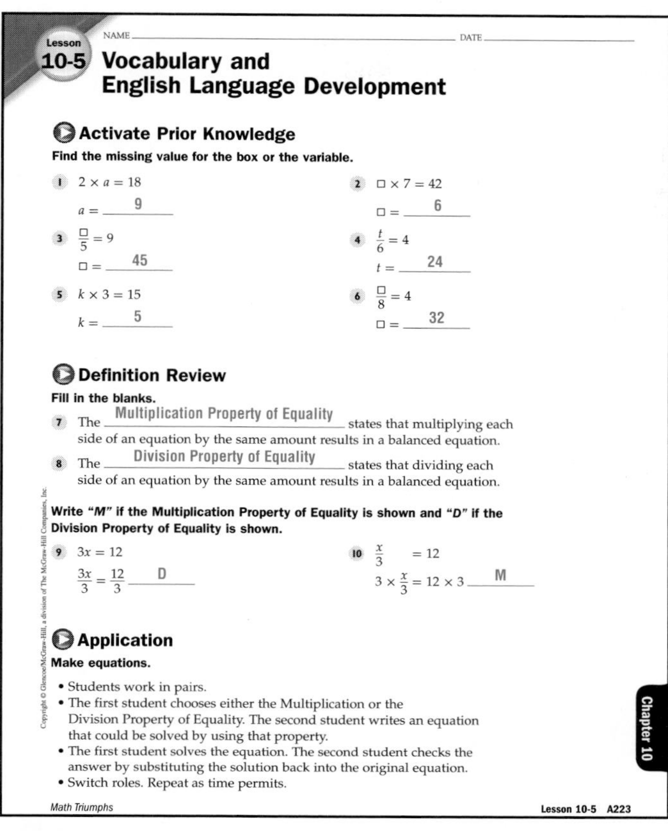
NAME ________ DATE ________

Lesson 10-5 **Vocabulary and English Language Development**

Activate Prior Knowledge

Find the missing value for the box or the variable.

1. $2 \times a = 18$ — $a =$ 9
2. $\square \times 7 = 42$ — $\square =$ 6
3. $\frac{\square}{5} = 9$ — $\square =$ 45
4. $\frac{t}{6} = 4$ — $t =$ 24
5. $k \times 3 = 15$ — $k =$ 5
6. $\frac{\square}{8} = 4$ — $\square =$ 32

Definition Review

Fill in the blanks.

7. The Multiplication Property of Equality states that multiplying each side of an equation by the same amount results in a balanced equation.
8. The Division Property of Equality states that dividing each side of an equation by the same amount results in a balanced equation.

Write "M" if the Multiplication Property of Equality is shown and "D" if the Division Property of Equality is shown.

9. $3x = 12$; $\frac{3x}{3} = \frac{12}{3}$ D
10. $\frac{x}{3} = 12$; $3 \times \frac{x}{3} = 12 \times 3$ M

Application

Make equations.

- Students work in pairs.
- The first student chooses either the Multiplication or the Division Property of Equality. The second student writes an equation that could be solved by using that property.
- The first student solves the equation. The second student checks the answer by substituting the solution back into the original equation.
- Switch roles. Repeat as time permits.

Chapter 10

Math Triumphs — Lesson 10-5 A223

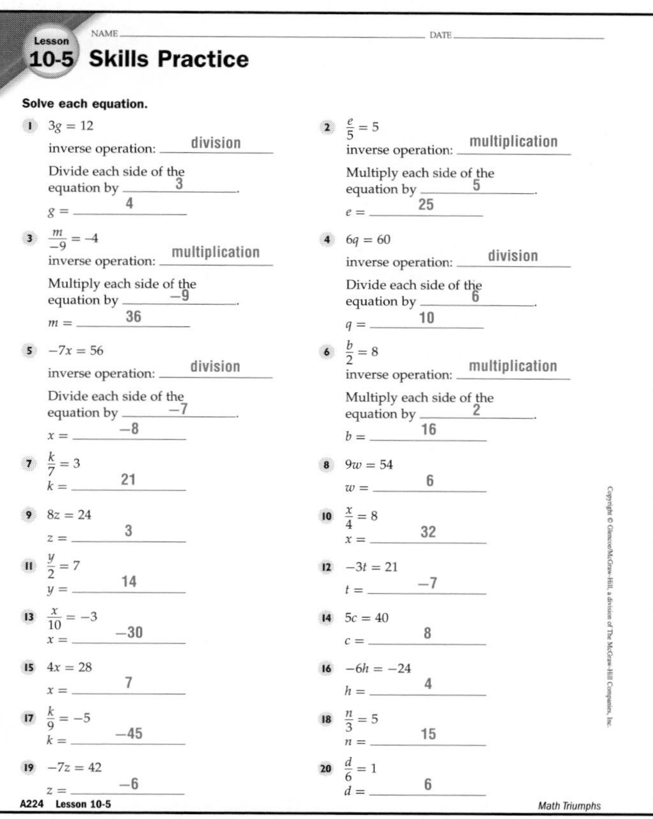
NAME ________ DATE ________

Lesson 10-5 **Skills Practice**

Solve each equation.

1. $3g = 12$; inverse operation: division; Divide each side of the equation by 3. $g =$ 4
2. $\frac{e}{5} = 5$; inverse operation: multiplication; Multiply each side of the equation by 5. $e =$ 25
3. $\frac{m}{-9} = -4$; inverse operation: multiplication; Multiply each side of the equation by −9. $m =$ 36
4. $6q = 60$; inverse operation: division; Divide each side of the equation by 6. $q =$ 10
5. $-7x = 56$; inverse operation: division; Divide each side of the equation by −7. $x =$ −8
6. $\frac{b}{2} = 8$; inverse operation: multiplication; Multiply each side of the equation by 2. $b =$ 16
7. $\frac{k}{7} = 3$; $k =$ 21
8. $9w = 54$; $w =$ 6
9. $8z = 24$; $z =$ 3
10. $\frac{x}{4} = 8$; $x =$ 32
11. $\frac{y}{2} = 7$; $y =$ 14
12. $-3t = 21$; $t =$ −7
13. $\frac{x}{10} = -3$; $x =$ −30
14. $5c = 40$; $c =$ 8
15. $4x = 28$; $x =$ 7
16. $-6h = -24$; $h =$ 4
17. $\frac{k}{9} = -5$; $k =$ −45
18. $\frac{n}{3} = 5$; $n =$ 15
19. $-7z = 42$; $z =$ −6
20. $\frac{d}{6} = 1$; $d =$ 6

A224 Lesson 10-5 — Math Triumphs

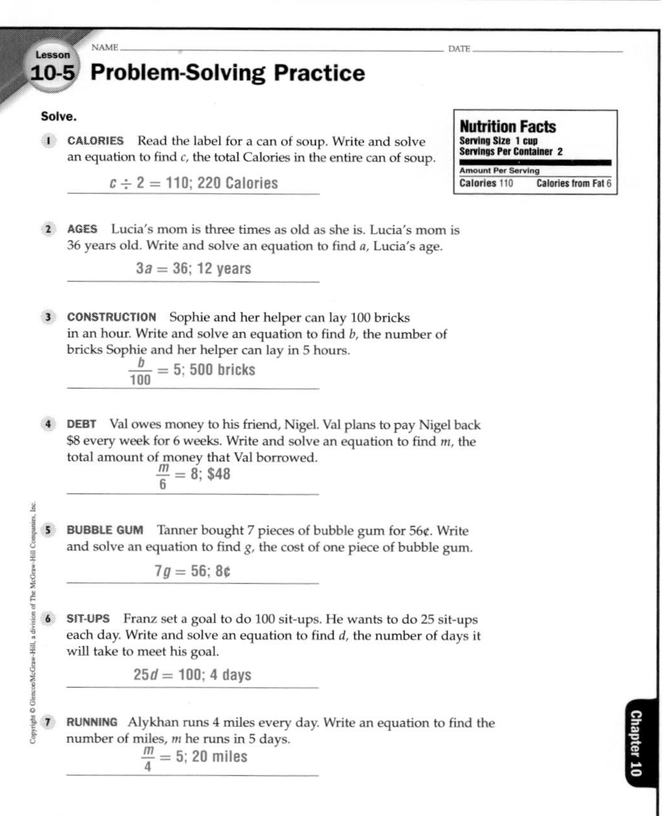
NAME ________ DATE ________

Lesson 10-5 **Problem-Solving Practice**

Solve.

Nutrition Facts	
Serving Size 1 cup	
Servings Per Container 2	
Amount Per Serving	
Calories 110	Calories from Fat 6

1. CALORIES Read the label for a can of soup. Write and solve an equation to find c, the total Calories in the entire can of soup. $c \div 2 = 110$; 220 Calories
2. AGES Lucia's mom is three times as old as she is. Lucia's mom is 36 years old. Write and solve an equation to find a, Lucia's age. $3a = 36$; 12 years
3. CONSTRUCTION Sophie and her helper can lay 100 bricks in an hour. Write and solve an equation to find b, the number of bricks Sophie and her helper can lay in 5 hours. $\frac{b}{100} = 5$; 500 bricks
4. DEBT Val owes money to his friend, Nigel. Val plans to pay Nigel back \$8 every week for 6 weeks. Write and solve an equation to find m, the total amount of money that Val borrowed. $\frac{m}{6} = 8$; \$48
5. BUBBLE GUM Tanner bought 7 pieces of bubble gum for 56¢. Write and solve an equation to find g, the cost of one piece of bubble gum. $7g = 56$; 8¢
6. SIT-UPS Franz set a goal to do 100 sit-ups. He wants to do 25 sit-ups each day. Write and solve an equation to find d, the number of days it will take to meet his goal. $25d = 100$; 4 days
7. RUNNING Alykhan runs 4 miles every day. Write an equation to find the number of miles, m he runs in 5 days. $\frac{m}{4} = 5$; 20 miles

Chapter 10

Math Triumphs — Lesson 10-5 A225

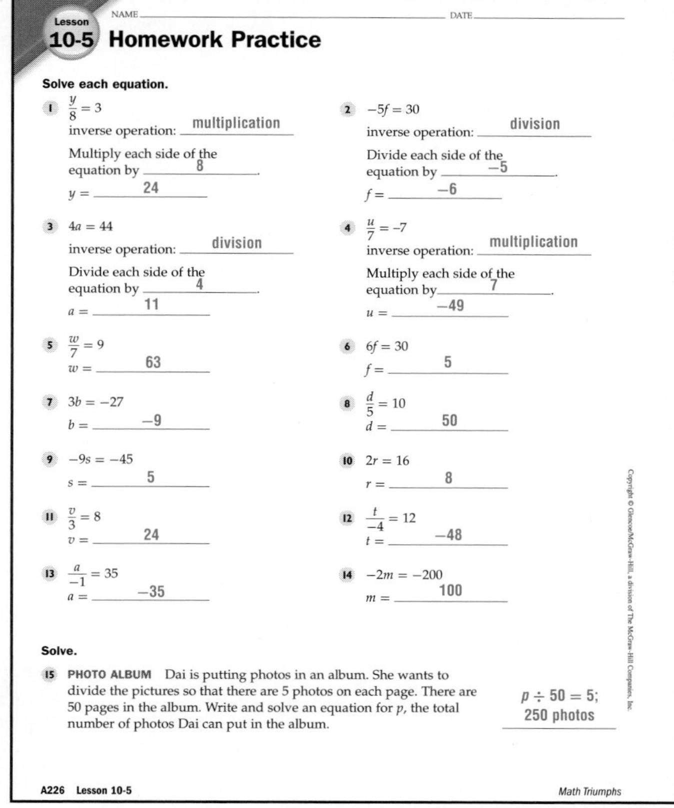
NAME ________ DATE ________

Lesson 10-5 **Homework Practice**

Solve each equation.

1. $\frac{y}{8} = 3$; inverse operation: multiplication; Multiply each side of the equation by 8. $y =$ 24
2. $-5f = 30$; inverse operation: division; Divide each side of the equation by −5. $f =$ −6
3. $4a = 44$; inverse operation: division; Divide each side of the equation by 4. $a =$ 11
4. $\frac{u}{7} = -7$; inverse operation: multiplication; Multiply each side of the equation by 7. $u =$ −49
5. $\frac{w}{7} = 9$; $w =$ 63
6. $6f = 30$; $f =$ 5
7. $3b = -27$; $b =$ −9
8. $\frac{d}{5} = 10$; $d =$ 50
9. $-9s = -45$; $s =$ 5
10. $2r = 16$; $r =$ 8
11. $\frac{v}{3} = 8$; $v =$ 24
12. $\frac{t}{-4} = 12$; $t =$ −48
13. $\frac{a}{-1} = 35$; $a =$ −35
14. $-2m = -200$; $m =$ 100

Solve.

15. PHOTO ALBUM Dai is putting photos in an album. She wants to divide the pictures so that there are 5 photos on each page. There are 50 pages in the album. Write and solve an equation for p, the total number of photos Dai can put in the album. $p \div 50 = 5$; 250 photos

A226 Lesson 10-5 — Math Triumphs